Safety Symbols

These symbols appear in laboratory activities. They warn of possible dangers in the laboratory and remind you to work carefully.

 Safety Goggles Wear safety goggles to protect your eyes in any activity involving chemicals, flames or heating, or glassware.

 Lab Apron Wear a laboratory apron to protect your skin and clothing from damage.

 Breakage Handle breakable materials, such as glassware, with care. Do not touch broken glassware.

 Heat-Resistant Gloves Use an oven mitt or other hand protection when handling hot materials such as hot plates or hot glassware.

 Plastic Gloves Wear disposable plastic gloves when working with harmful chemicals and organisms. Keep your hands away from your face, and dispose of the gloves according to your teacher's instructions.

 Heating Use a clamp or tongs to pick up hot glassware. Do not touch hot objects with your bare hands.

 Flames Before you work with flames, tie back loose hair and clothing. Follow instructions from your teacher about lighting and extinguishing flames.

 No Flames When using flammable materials, make sure there are no flames, sparks, or other exposed heat sources present.

 Corrosive Chemical Avoid getting acid or other corrosive chemicals on your skin or clothing or in your eyes. Do not inhale the vapors. Wash your hands after the activity.

 Poison Do not let any poisonous chemical come into contact with your skin, and do not inhale its vapors. Wash your hands when you are finished with the activity.

 Fumes Work in a ventilated area when harmful vapors may be involved. Avoid inhaling vapors directly. Only test an odor when directed to do so by your teacher, and use a wafting motion to direct the vapor toward your nose.

 Sharp Object Scissors, scalpels, knives, needles, pins, and tacks can cut your skin. Always direct a sharp edge or point away from yourself and others.

 Animal Safety Treat live or preserved animals or animal parts with care to avoid harming the animals or yourself. Wash your hands when you are finished with the activity.

 Plant Safety Handle plants only as directed by your teacher. If you are allergic to certain plants, tell your teacher; do not do an activity involving those plants. Avoid touching harmful plants such as poison ivy. Wash your hands when you are finished with the activity.

 Electric Shock To avoid electric shock, never use electrical equipment around water, or when the equipment is wet or your hands are wet. Be sure cords are untangled and cannot trip anyone. Unplug equipment not in use.

 Physical Safety When an experiment involves physical activity, avoid injuring yourself or others. Alert your teacher if there is any reason you should not participate.

 Disposal Dispose of chemicals and other laboratory materials safely. Follow the instructions from your teacher.

 Hand Washing Wash your hands thoroughly when finished with the activity. Use antibacterial soap and warm water. Rinse well.

 General Safety Awareness When this symbol appears, follow the instructions provided. When you are asked to develop your own procedure in a lab, have your teacher approve your plan before you go further.

Master Teacher Board

This North Carolina Master Teacher Board provided Prentice Hall with valuable feedback during the development of *Science Explorer*. Your teacher's colleagues are listed below along with some of their quotes about how they think the *Science Explorer* program will help you succeed.

Here's what North Carolina Teachers had to say about Prentice Hall *Science Explorer*:

"Appropriately addresses the NC Course of Study Standards."

"All students can get information from this text."

"Great pictures and good lead-ins."

"Great math integration."

"Labs: easy to understand, use accessible materials."

"Test prep is great."

9-12-06

NORTH CAROLINA

Program Authors

Michael J. Padilla, Ph.D.
Professor of Science Education
University of Georgia
Athens, Georgia

Michael Padilla is a leader in middle school science education. He has served as an author and elected officer for the National Science Teachers Association and as a writer of the National Science Education Standards. As lead author of Science Explorer, Mike has inspired the team in developing a program that meets the needs of middle grades students, promotes science inquiry, and is aligned with the National Science Education Standards.

Ioannis Miaoulis, Ph.D.
President
Museum of Science
Boston, Massachusetts

Originally trained as a mechanical engineer, Ioannis Miaoulis is in the forefront of the national movement to increase technological literacy. As dean of the Tufts University School of Engineering, Dr. Miaoulis spearheaded the introduction of engineering into the Massachusetts curriculum. Currently he is working with school systems across the country to engage students in engineering activities and to foster discussions on the impact of science and technology on society.

Martha Cyr, Ph.D.
Director of K–12 Outreach
Worcester Polytechnic Institute
Worcester, Massachusetts

Martha Cyr is a noted expert in engineering outreach. She has over nine years of experience with programs and activities that emphasize the use of engineering principles, through hands-on projects, to excite and motivate students and teachers of mathematics and science in grades K–12. Her goal is to stimulate a continued interest in science and mathematics through engineering.

Book Authors

Linda Cronin Jones, Ph.D.
Associate Professor of Science and
    Environmental Education
University of Florida
Gainesville, Florida

Elizabeth Coolidge-Stolz, Ph.D.
Medical Writer
North Reading, Massachusetts

Donald Cronkite, Ph.D.
Professor of Biology
Hope College
Holland, Michigan

Jan Jenner, Ph.D.
Science Writer
Talladega, Alabama

T. Griffith Jones, Ph.D.
P.K. Wonge Developmental Research
    School
College of Education—University of
    Florida
Gainesville, Florida

Andrew C. Kemp, Ph.D.
Assistant Professor of Education
University of Louisville
Louisville, Kentucky

Marylin Lisowski, Ph.D.
Professor of Science and Environmental
    Education
Eastern Illinois University
Charleston, Illinois

Beth Miaoulis
Technology Writer
Sherborn, Massachusetts

Barbara Brooks Simmons
Science Writer
Boston, Massachusetts

Thomas R. Wellnitz
Science Instructor
The Paideia School
Atlanta, Georgia

Consultants

Reading Consultant

Nancy Romance, Ph.D.
Professor of Science
    Education
Florida Atlantic University
Fort Lauderdale, Florida

Mathematics Consultant

William Tate, Ph.D.
Professor of Education and
    American Culture Studies
Washington University
St. Louis, Missouri

Safety Consultant

Regina M. Barrier
Western Regional
    Outreach Coordinator
The Science House
North Carolina State
    University
Lenoir, North Carolina

Tufts University Content Reviewers

Faculty from Tufts University in Medford, Massachusetts, developed *Science Explorer* chapter projects and reviewed the student books.

Astier M. Almedom, Ph.D.
Department of Biology

Wayne Chudyk, Ph.D.
Department of Civil and Environmental Engineering

John L. Durant, Ph.D.
Department of Civil and Environmental Engineering

George S. Ellmore, Ph.D.
Department of Biology

David Kaplan, Ph.D.
Department of Biomedical Engineering

Samuel Kounaves, Ph.D.
Department of Chemistry

David H. Lee, Ph.D.
Department of Chemistry

Douglas Matson, Ph.D.
Department of Mechanical Engineering

Karen Panetta, Ph.D.
Department of Electrical Engineering and Computer Science

Jan A. Pechenik, Ph.D.
Department of Biology

John C. Ridge, Ph.D.
Department of Geology

William Waller, Ph.D.
Department of Astronomy

Content Reviewers

Paul Beale, Ph.D.
Department of Physics
University of Colorado
Boulder, Colorado

Jeff Bodart, Ph.D.
Chipola Junior College
Marianna, Florida

Michael Castellani, Ph.D.
Department of Chemistry
Marshall University
Huntington, West Virginia

Eugene Chiang, Ph.D.
Department of Astronomy
University of California – Berkeley
Berkeley, California

Charles C. Curtis, Ph.D.
Department of Physics
University of Arizona
Tucson, Arizona

Daniel Kirk-Davidoff, Ph.D.
Department of Meteorology
University of Maryland
College Park, Maryland

Diane T. Doser, Ph.D.
Department of Geological Sciences
University of Texas at El Paso
El Paso, Texas

R. E. Duhrkopf, Ph.D.
Department of Biology
Baylor University
Waco, Texas

Michael Hacker
Co-director, Center for Technological Literacy
Hofstra University
Hempstead, New York

Michael W. Hamburger, Ph.D.
Department of Geological Sciences
Indiana University
Bloomington, Indiana

Alice K. Hankla, Ph.D.
The Galloway School
Atlanta, Georgia

Donald C. Jackson, Ph.D.
Department of Molecular Pharmacology, Physiology, & Biotechnology
Brown University
Providence, Rhode Island

Jeremiah N. Jarrett, Ph.D.
Department of Biological Sciences
Central Connecticut State University
New Britain, Connecticut

David Lederman, Ph.D.
Department of Physics
West Virginia University
Morgantown, West Virginia

Becky Mansfield, Ph.D.
Department of Geography
Ohio State University
Columbus, Ohio

Elizabeth M. Martin, M.S.
Department of Chemistry and Biochemistry
College of Charleston
Charleston, South Carolina

Joe McCullough, Ph.D.
Department of Natural and Applied Sciences
Cabrillo College
Aptos, California

Robert J. Mellors, Ph.D.
Department of Geological Sciences
San Diego State University
San Diego, California

Joseph M. Moran, Ph.D.
American Meteorological Society
Washington, D.C.

David J. Morrissey, Ph.D.
Department of Chemistry
Michigan State University
East Lansing, Michigan

Philip A. Reed, Ph.D.
Department of Occupational & Technical Studies
Old Dominion University
Norfolk, Virginia

Scott M. Rochette, Ph.D.
Department of the Earth Sciences
State University of New York, College at Brockport
Brockport, New York

Laurence D. Rosenhein, Ph.D.
Department of Chemistry
Indiana State University
Terre Haute, Indiana

Ronald Sass, Ph.D.
Department of Biology and Chemistry
Rice University
Houston, Texas

George Schatz, Ph.D.
Department of Chemistry
Northwestern University
Evanston, Illinois

Sara Seager, Ph.D.
Carnegie Institution of Washington
Washington, D.C.

Robert M. Thornton, Ph.D.
Section of Plant Biology
University of California
Davis, California

John R. Villarreal, Ph.D.
College of Science and Engineering
The University of Texas – Pan American
Edinburg, Texas

Kenneth Welty, Ph.D.
School of Education
University of Wisconsin–Stout
Menomonie, Wisconsin

Edward J. Zalisko, Ph.D.
Department of Biology
Blackburn College
Carlinville, Illinois

Teacher Reviewers

David R. Blakely
Arlington High School
Arlington, Massachusetts

Jane E. Callery
Two Rivers Magnet Middle
School
East Hartford, Connecticut

Melissa Lynn Cook
Oakland Mills High School
Columbia, Maryland

James Fattic
Southside Middle School
Anderson, Indiana

Dan Gabel
Hoover Middle School
Rockville, Maryland

Wayne Goates
Eisenhower Middle School
Goddard, Kansas

Katherine Bobay Graser
Mint Hill Middle School
Charlotte, North Carolina

Darcy Hampton
Deal Junior High School
Washington, D.C.

Karen Kelly
Pierce Middle School
Waterford, Michigan

David Kelso
Manchester High School Central
Manchester, New Hampshire

Benigno Lopez, Jr.
Sleepy Hill Middle School
Lakeland, Florida

Angie L. Matamoros, Ph.D.
ALM Consulting, INC.
Weston, Florida

Tim McCollum
Charleston Middle School
Charleston, Illinois

Bruce A. Mellin
Brooks School
North Andover, Massachusetts

Ella Jay Parfitt
Southeast Middle School
Baltimore, Maryland

Evelyn A. Pizzarello
Louis M. Klein Middle School
Harrison, New York

Kathleen M. Poe
Fletcher Middle School
Jacksonville, Florida

Shirley Rose
Lewis and Clark Middle School
Tulsa, Oklahoma

Linda Sandersen
Greenfield Middle School
Greenfield, Wisconsin

Mary E. Solan
Southwest Middle School
Charlotte, North Carolina

Mary Stewart
University of Tulsa
Tulsa, Oklahoma

Paul Swenson
Billings West High School
Billings, Montana

Thomas Vaughn
Arlington High School
Arlington, Massachusetts

Susan C. Zibell
Central Elementary
Simsbury, Connecticut

Safety Reviewers

W. H. Breazeale, Ph.D.
Department of Chemistry
College of Charleston
Charleston, South Carolina

Ruth Hathaway, Ph.D.
Hathaway Consulting
Cape Girardeau, Missouri

Douglas Mandt, M.S.
Science Education Consultant
Edgewood, Washington

Activity Field Testers

Nicki Bibbo
Witchcraft Heights School
Salem, Massachusetts

Rose-Marie Botting
Broward County Schools
Fort Lauderdale, Florida

Colleen Campos
Laredo Middle School
Aurora, Colorado

Elizabeth Chait
W. L. Chenery Middle School
Belmont, Massachusetts

Holly Estes
Hale Middle School
Stow, Massachusetts

Laura Hapgood
Plymouth Community
Intermediate School
Plymouth, Massachusetts

Mary F. Lavin
Plymouth Community
Intermediate School
Plymouth, Massachusetts

James MacNeil, Ph.D.
Cambridge, Massachusetts

Lauren Magruder
St. Michael's Country
Day School
Newport, Rhode Island

Jeanne Maurand
Austin Preparatory School
Reading, Massachusetts

Joanne Jackson-Pelletier
Winman Junior High School
Warwick, Rhode Island

Warren Phillips
Plymouth Public Schools
Plymouth, Massachusetts

Carol Pirtle
Hale Middle School
Stow, Massachusetts

Kathleen M. Poe
Fletcher Middle School
Jacksonville, Florida

Cynthia B. Pope
Norfolk Public Schools
Norfolk, Virginia

Anne Scammell
Geneva Middle School
Geneva, New York

Karen Riley Sievers
Callanan Middle School
Des Moines, Iowa

David M. Smith
Eyer Middle School
Allentown, Pennsylvania

Gene Vitale
Parkland School
McHenry, Illinois

Contents

Contents

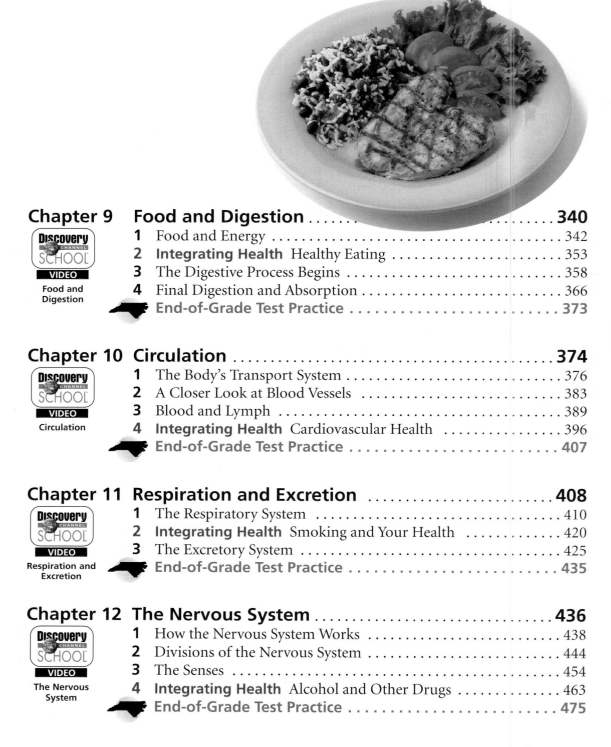

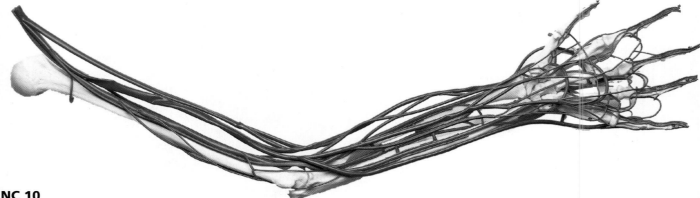

Reference Section

Contents

VIDEO

Enhance understanding through dynamic video.

Preview Get motivated with this introduction to the chapter content.

Field Trip Explore a real-world story related to the chapter content.

Assessment Review content and take an assessment.

Web Links

Get connected to exciting Web resources in every lesson.

SC*LINKS* **NSTA** Find Web links on topics relating to every section.

Active Art Interact with selected visuals from every chapter online.

Planet Diary® Explore news and natural phenomena through weekly reports.

Science News® Keep up to date with the latest science discoveries.

Experience the complete text-book online and on CD-ROM.

Activities Practice skills and learn content.

Videos Explore content and learn important lab skills.

Audio Support Hear key terms spoken and defined.

Self-Assessment Use instant feedback to help you track your progress.

Activities

Lab zone™ Chapter **Project** NC Strand: Science in Personal and Social Perspectives

Lab zone Discover **Activity** NC Strand: Science as Inquiry

Lab zone | Try This **Activity** | NC Strand: Nature of Science

Lab zone | Skills **Activity** | NC Strand: Science as Inquiry

Activities

NORTH CAROLINA

Lab zone — At-Home **Activity** — NC Strand: Science in Personal and Social Perspectives

Activities

active art ► NC Strand: Nature of Science

Standard Course of Study

North Carolina's Standard Course of Study for Science tells you what content and processes you are expected to master. The Standard Course of Study is organized by Competency Goals, with each goal divided into Objectives. When you see these Objectives at the beginning of each chapter, you'll notice that they have been shortened to a brief phrase.

Competency Goal 1:

The learner will design and conduct investigations to demonstrate an understanding of scientific inquiry.

Objectives

1.01 Identify and create questions and hypotheses that can be answered through scientific investigations.

1.02 Develop appropriate experimental procedures for:
- Given questions.
- Student generated questions.

1.03 Apply safety procedures in the laboratory and in field studies:
- Recognize potential hazards.
- Manipulate materials and equipment.
- Conduct appropriate procedures.

What It Means to You
You will learn how to conduct a scientific inquiry. You will also learn how to stay safe while you conduct scientific experiments.

Where You Will Learn This
Chapters 1 through 19

SAMPLE QUESTION 1
Which of the following is a question that can be investigated through scientific inquiry?
A Which roller coaster is the most fun?
B Which amusement park is the best?
C When does a roller coaster travel fastest?
D What part of a roller coaster ride is best?

Objective

1.04 Analyze variables in scientific investigations:
- Identify dependent and independent.
- Use of a control.
- Manipulate.
- Describe relationships between.
- Define operationally.

What It Means to You
You will be learning all about the role that different variables play in a controlled experiment. You will also be learning how to define operationally.

Where You Will Learn This
Chapters 1, 2, 5, 6, 7, 9, 10, 12, 13, 14, and 16 through 19

SAMPLE QUESTION 2
Researchers gathered data about how the temperature of a person's environment affects body temperature. In this investigation, the temperature of the environment is the
A responding variable.
B manipulated variable.
C operational definition.
D dependent variable.

Objectives

1.05 Analyze evidence to:
- Explain observations.
- Make inferences and predictions.
- Develop the relationship between evidence and explanation.

1.06 Use mathematics to gather, organize, and present quantitative data resulting from scientific investigations.
- Measurement.
- Analysis of data.
- Graphing.
- Prediction models.

What It Means to You
You will find out the important roles observation and mathematics play in science. You'll also learn how to measure, make predictions, and analyze data.

Where You Will Learn This
Chapters 1 through 19

SAMPLE QUESTION 3

During which months was precipitation greatest?
- **A** January through March
- **B** April through June
- **C** July through September
- **D** October through December

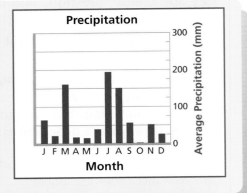

Objectives

1.07 Prepare models and/or computer simulations to:
- Test hypotheses.
- Evaluate how data fit.

1.08 Use oral and written language to:
- Communicate findings.
- Defend conclusions of scientific investigations.

1.09 Use technologies and information systems to:
- Research.
- Gather and analyze data.
- Visualize data.
- Disseminate findings to others.

1.10 Analyze and evaluate information from a scientifically literate viewpoint by reading, hearing, and/or viewing:
- Scientific text.
- Articles.
- Events in the popular press.

What It Means to You
You'll learn about models and simulations. You will also learn how to communicate scientific information and conduct research.

Where You Will Learn This
Chapters 1 through 19

SAMPLE QUESTION 4

Which part of the scientific inquiry process takes place when scientists publish articles in scientific journals?
- **A** communicating
- **B** drawing conclusions
- **C** graphing data
- **D** developing a hypothesis

The learner will demonstrate an understanding of technological design.

Objectives

2.01 Explore evidence that "technology" has many definitions.
- Artifact or hardware.
- Methodology or technique.
- System of production.
- Social-technical system.

2.02 Use information systems to:
- Identify scientific needs, human needs, or problems that are subject to technological solution.
- Locate resources to obtain and test ideas.

What It Means to You
You will learn the many forms that technology takes. You will also find out what a system is and how scientists use computers.

Where You Will Learn This
Chapters 1, 2, 4, 6, 14, 15, 16, 18, and 19

SAMPLE QUESTION 5
Which of the following is an example of communication technology?
A jet plane
B television
C electric lamp
D plastic

Objectives

2.03 Evaluate technological designs for:
- Application of scientific principles.
- Risks and benefits.
- Constraints of design.
- Consistent testing protocol.

2.04 Apply tenets of technological design to make informed consumer decisions about:
- Products.
- Processes.
- Systems.

What It Means to You
You will be learning how technology impacts society. You will also be learning how scientific principles are applied to technological design, and how to analyze the pros and cons of advances in technology.

Where You Will Learn This
Chapters 1 through 6, 8, 9, 12, 14, 17, 18, and 19

SAMPLE QUESTION 6
A new high-speed bike is being sold. In deciding whether or not to buy one, what should consumers do?
A Analyze the bike's risks and benefits.
B State a hypothesis about the bike.
C Design a controlled experiment.
D Graph and interpret data about the bike's speed.

Standard Course of Study

Competency Goal 3:

The learner will conduct investigations and utilize appropriate technologies and information systems to build an understanding of the atmosphere.

Objective

3.01 Explain the composition, properties and structure of the atmosphere:
- Mixture of gases.
- Stratified layers.
- Each layer has distinct properties.
- As altitude increases, air pressure decreases.
- Equilibrium.

What It Means to You

You will be learning what makes up the air you breathe. You will also find out how air changes as you move upward through the atmosphere.

Where You Will Learn This

Chapter 2

SAMPLE QUESTION 7

According to the diagram, what is the depth of the stratosphere?

A 50 km

B 40 km

C 20 km

D 30 km

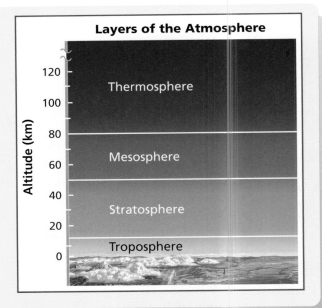

Layers of the Atmosphere

Objective

3.02 Describe properties that can be observed and measured to predict air quality:
- Particulate matter.
- Ozone.

What It Means to You

You will be learning all about the quality of air and how it affects people. You will also learn about air pollutants and solid particles in air.

Where You Will Learn This

Chapters 2 and 5

SAMPLE QUESTION 8

Which of the following are solid particles found in the air that come from natural sources?

A smog

B pollen

C oxygen molecules

D ozone

Objective

3.03 Conclude that the good health of environments and organisms requires:
- The monitoring of air quality.
- Taking steps to maintain healthy air quality.
- Stewardship.

What It Means to You
You'll be learning how legislation and technology can help improve the quality of air.

Where You Will Learn This
Chapters 2 and 5

SAMPLE QUESTION 9

One reason air quality in the United States has improved over the past 30 years is that
- **A** fewer temperature inversions occur today.
- **B** fewer power plants are burning fossil fuels than in the past.
- **C** cars are required to be equipped with pollution-control devices.
- **D** more cars are on the road than ever before.

Objective

3.04 Evaluate how humans impact air quality including:
- Air quality standards.
- Point and non-point sources of air pollution in North Carolina.
- Financial and economic trade-offs.
- Local air quality issues.

What It Means to You
You will learn what causes air pollution and what you can do about it. You will also find out what affects the quality of air in North Carolina.

Where You Will Learn This
Chapters 2 and 5

SAMPLE QUESTION 10

One way people can positively impact air quality is to
- **A** burn more fossil fuels.
- **B** reduce emissions.
- **C** ban smokestack scrubbers.
- **D** stop using pesticides.

Objective

3.05 Examine evidence that atmospheric properties can be studied to predict atmospheric conditions and weather hazards:

- Humidity.
- Temperature.
- Wind speed and direction.
- Air pressure.
- Precipitation.
- Tornadoes.
- Hurricanes.
- Floods.
- Storms.

What It Means to You

You will find out what properties of the atmosphere scientists observe and measure. You will use these properties to predict the weather.

Where You Will Learn This

Chapters 2 and 5

SAMPLE QUESTION 11

Based on the graph, during what month are tornadoes least likely to occur?

A January

B June

C August

D December

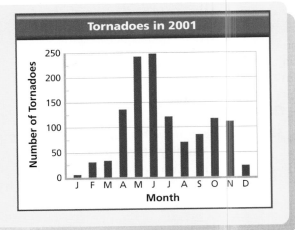

Tornadoes in 2001

Objective

3.06 Assess the use of technology in studying atmospheric phenomena and weather hazards:

- Satellites.
- Weather maps.
- Predicting.
- Recording.
- Communicating information about conditions.

What It Means to You

You will find out how meteorologists use technology to record weather conditions, analyze weather data, and make predictions about the weather.

Where You Will Learn This

Chapters 3 and 4

SAMPLE QUESTION 12

Cameras on which of the following in the exosphere record images of Earth's clouds and storms?

A balloons

B computers

C satellites

D barometers

The learner will conduct investigations, use models, simulations, and appropriate technologies and information systems to build an understanding of the complementary nature of the human body system.

Objective

4.01 Analyze how human body systems interact to provide for the needs of the human organism:
- Musculoskeletal.
- Cardiovascular.
- Endocrine and Nervous.
- Digestive and Circulatory.
- Excretory.
- Reproductive.
- Respiratory.
- Immune.
- Nervous system.

What It Means to You
You will be learning all about the parts of the human body. You will also learn how these parts form systems and how these systems cooperate to keep the body functioning.

Where You Will Learn This
Chapters 8 through 13

SAMPLE QUESTION 13

As food material moves through the large intestine, water is absorbed into the bloodstream. This process is an example of interaction between what two systems of the human body?

A skeletal and circulatory
B muscular and digestive
C endocrine and nervous
D digestive and circulatory

Objectives

4.02 Describe how systems within the human body are defined by the functions it performs.

4.03 Explain how the structure of an organ is adapted to perform specific functions within one or more systems.
- Liver.
- Heart.
- Lung.
- Brain.
- Stomach.
- Kidney.

What It Means to You
You will find out about the many organs in your body and what system they are part of. You will also learn what each system and organ in your body does.

Where You Will Learn This
Chapters 8 through 13

SAMPLE QUESTION 14

What system in the human body moves oxygen into and carbon dioxide out of the body?

A nervous system
B endocrine system
C respiratory system
D excretory system

Objectives

4.04 Evaluate how systems in the human body help regulate the internal environment.

4.05 Analyze how an imbalance in homeostasis may result from a disruption in any human system.

What It Means to You
You will be learning that your body and its organs are internal environments. You will also find out how, despite external influences, these environments are kept stable.

Where You Will Learn This
Chapters 8 and 10 through 13

SAMPLE QUESTION 15
According to the diagram, what will most likely occur if an illness causes blood sugar to become too low?
- **A** Homeostasis will be not be maintained.
- **B** Blood sugar will continue to decrease.
- **C** Glucagon will be released.
- **D** Insulin will be released.

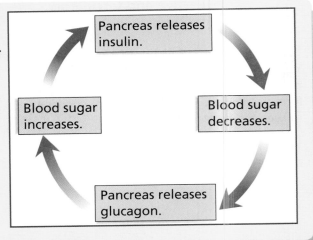

Pancreas releases insulin.

Blood sugar decreases.

Pancreas releases glucagon.

Blood sugar increases.

Objectives

4.06 Describe growth and development of the human organism.

4.07 Explain the effects of environmental influences on human embryo development and human health including:
- Smoking.
- Alcohol.
- Drugs.
- Diet.

4.08 Explain how understanding human body systems can help make informed decisions regarding health.

What It Means to You
You will be learning how humans grow and develop during different stages of life. You will also find out how to make wise health choices based on an understanding of how your body works.

Where You Will Learn This
Chapters 8 through 13

SAMPLE QUESTION 16
To keep the digestive system functioning properly, a person's diet should include plenty of
- **A** fiber.
- **B** saturated fats.
- **C** cholesterol.
- **D** glucose.

The learner will conduct investigations and utilize appropriate technologies and information systems to build an understanding of heredity and genetics.

Objective

5.01 Explain the significance of genes to inherited characteristics:
- Genes are the units of information.
- Parents transmit genes to their offspring.
- Some medical conditions and diseases are genetic.

What It Means to You
You will learn how parents pass along traits to their children through heredity. You will also learn about medical problems that can be inherited.

Where You Will Learn This
Chapters 14 and 15

SAMPLE QUESTION 17
Which of the following is a disorder that can be inherited?
A hemophilia
B lung cancer
C poor nutrition
D heart attack

Objectives

5.02 Explain the significance of reproduction:
- Sorting and recombination of parents' genetic material.
- Potential variation among offspring.

5.03 Identify examples and patterns of human genetic traits:
- Dominant and recessive.
- Incomplete dominance.

What It Means to You
You will be learning how the combination of genes children inherit determines their traits. You will also find out why some traits tend to occur more than others.

Where You Will Learn This
Chapters 14 and 15

SAMPLE QUESTION 18
In pea plants, the allele for tall stems is dominant over the allele for short stems. You can infer that a short pea plant has which of the following?
A no alleles
B 2 recessive alleles
C 2 dominant alleles
D 1 dominant and 1 recessive allele

Standard Course of Study

Objective

5.04 Analyze the role of probability in the study of heredity:
- Role of each parent in transfer of genetic traits.
- Analysis of pedigrees.

What It Means to You

You will be learning how to determine the probability of inheriting certain traits. You will also find out what a pedigree is and how to use it to track traits.

Where You Will Learn This

Chapters 14 and 15

SAMPLE QUESTION 19

The allele for cystic fibrosis is recessive. According to the pedigree, which family member has cystic fibrosis?

A Joe
B Sarah
C Emily
D Father

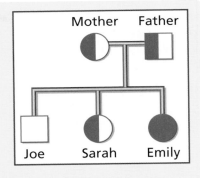

Objectives

5.05 Summarize the genetic transmittance of disease.

5.06 Evaluate evidence that human characteristics are a product of:
- Inheritance.
- Environmental factors.
- Lifestyle choices.

What It Means to You

You will be learning how disease is passed on by genes. You will also learn how a person's behavior and surroundings can alter the effects of genes.

Where You Will Learn This

Chapter 15

SAMPLE QUESTION 20

Bob and Bill are identical twins raised apart. Bob ate a balanced diet and Bill ate a diet low in protein and vitamins. Bob is 15 cm taller than Bill. Which of the following is most likely responsible for their height difference?

A bacterial disease
B genetic disorder
C environment
D birth order

Competency Goal 6:

The learner will conduct investigations, use models, simulations, and appropriate technologies and information systems to build an understanding of motion and forces.

Objectives

6.01 Demonstrate ways that simple machines can change force.

6.02 Analyze simple machines for mechanical advantage and efficiency.

What It Means to You

You'll be learning what force is and how you use it to do work. You'll also learn how machines such as levers and pulleys can be used to make work easier to do.

Where You Will Learn This
Chapter 19

SAMPLE QUESTION 21

What is the ideal mechanical advantage of the lever shown?

A 3

B 2

C 1

D 0.3

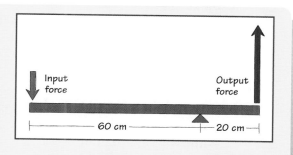

Objectives

6.03 Evaluate motion in terms of Newton's Laws:
- The force of friction retards motion.
- For every action there is an equal and opposite reaction.
- The greater the force, the greater the change in motion.
- An object's motion is the result of the combined effect of all forces acting on the object.
- A moving object that is not subjected to a force will continue to move at a constant speed in a straight line.
- An object at rest will remain at rest.

6.04 Analyze that an object's motion is always judged relative to some other object or point.

What It Means to You

You will be learning Newton's Laws of motion. You will also learn about friction and gravity and how these forces affect how an object moves.

Where You Will Learn This
Chapters 16 and 17

SAMPLE QUESTION 22

You place a toy car on the floor and give it a push. What effect will friction have on the car's motion?

A It will make the car move in the opposite direction.

B It will make the car stop.

C It will make the car move faster in the same direction.

D It will not have an effect.

Standard Course of Study

Objective

6.05 Describe and measure quantities that characterize moving objects and their interactions within a system:

- Time.
- Distance.
- Mass.
- Force.
- Velocity.
- Center of mass.
- Acceleration.

What It Means to You

You will be learning how moving objects interact. You will be able to describe these objects in terms of their mass, velocity, and momentum.

Where You Will Learn This

Chapters 16 through 19

SAMPLE QUESTION 23

The diagram shows a collision between two balls of equal mass. How does the velocity of the balls change after the collision?

A The velocity of both balls increases.

B The velocity of both balls decreases.

C The velocity of the left ball decreases, while the right ball increases.

D The velocity of the left ball increases, while the right ball decreases.

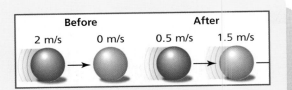

Objective

6.06 Investigate and analyze the real world interactions of balanced and unbalanced forces.

- **Sports and recreation.**
- **Transportation.**
- **The human body.**

What It Means to You

You will learn to recognize how forces act in your everyday life. You will find out how forces relate to the motion that occurs when you play sports or watch a rocket take off.

Where You Will Learn This

Chapters 16, 18, and 19

SAMPLE QUESTION 24

In a game of tug-of-war, Team A with five members pulls on the left end of the rope and Team B with four members pulls on the right end of the rope. Neither team moves. What can you infer about the net force acting on the rope?

A It is acting to the left on the rope.

B It is acting to the right on the rope.

C It is acting downward on the rope.

D It is balanced.

Laboratory Safety

North Carolina's *Total Science Safety System* helps your teacher ensure your safety while working in the science lab. However, safety is not only your teacher's responsibility but yours, too, as stated in Objective 1.03 of the Standard Course of Study.

1. Safety Symbols

Safety symbols alert you to possible dangers in the laboratory that remind you to work carefully.

- **Look inside the front cover for a complete list of the symbols and what they stand for.**
- **Find symbols that apply to your tasks on every lab or activity.**
- **Review all the symbols again in Appendix A.**

Lab zone **Skills Lab**

A Look Beneath the Skin

Problem
What are some characteristics of skeletal muscles? How do skeletal muscles work?

Skills Focus
observing, drawing conclusions

Materials
- apron • goggles • water • paper towels
- scissors • protective gloves • dissecting tray
- uncooked chicken wing, treated with bleach

Procedure
1. Put on protective gloves, apron, and goggles. **CAUTION:** *Wear gloves whenever you handle the chicken.*
2. Your teacher will give you a chicken wing. Rinse it well with water, dry it with paper towels, and place it in a dissecting tray.
3. Carefully extend the wing to find out how many major parts it has. Draw a diagram of the external structure. Label the upper arm, elbow, lower arm, and hand (wing tip).
4. Use scissors to remove the skin. Cut only through the skin. **CAUTION:** *Cut away from your body and your classmates.*
5. Examine the muscles, which are the bundles of pink tissue around the bones. Find the two groups of muscles in the upper arm. Hold the arm down at the shoulder, and alternately pull on each muscle group. Observe what happens.
6. Find the two groups of muscles in the lower arm. Hold down the arm at the elbow, and alternately pull on each muscle group. Then, make a diagram of the wing's muscles.
7. Find the tendons—shiny white tissue at the ends of the muscles. Notice what parts the tendons connect. Add the tendons to your diagram.

move the muscles and tendons. Find the ligaments, which are the whitish ribbon-shaped structures between. Add them to your diagram.
9. Dispose of the chicken parts according to your teacher's instructions. Wash your hands.

Analyze and Conclude
1. Observing How does a chicken wing move at the elbow? How does the motion compare to how your elbow moves? What type of joint is involved?
2. Drawing Conclusions What happened when you pulled on one of the arm muscles? What muscle action does the pulling represent?
3. Classifying Categorize the muscles you observed as smooth, cardiac, or skeletal.
4. Communicating Why is it valuable to record your observations with accurate diagrams? Write a paragraph in which you describe what your diagrams show.

Design an Experiment
Use the procedures from this lab to develop a way to examine an uncooked chicken thigh and leg. Compare how the chicken leg and a human leg move. *Obtain your teacher's permission before carrying out your investigation.*

Chapter 8 ♦ 327

se scissors to remove the skin. Cut only through the skin. **CAUTION:** *Cut away from your body and your classmates.*
mine the muscles, which are the hu

> *"Experimentation allows you to 'discover' science concepts and teaches you to conduct investigations safely. You should be aware of the hazards present during the lab and the actions of nearby students. Read instructions carefully before each lab and practice safety plans. Everyone in the lab has a duty to act responsibly!"*
>
> Regina M. Barrier
> NC Science Safety Consultant

2. CAUTION Statements

Sometimes you'll find CAUTION statements built into the procedure steps on the labs and activities. They alert you to specific actions that will help you stay safe.

3. Appendix A: Laboratory Safety

This appendix reviews the safety symbols and gives you general instructions on how to stay safe when working with science materials.

In Your Textbook

Look at pages 92–93, 174–175, 297, 352, 364–365, 388, and 620–621 for more examples on how your textbook helps you to apply Objective 1.03 of the Standard Course of Study.

Laboratory Safety

Marshall Shepherd tracks powerful thunderstorms at the Goddard Visualization Studio (left). Marshall looks at satellite images like this one of Florida (above).

Eyes in the Sky

At the Kennedy Space Center on the east coast of Florida, a crew prepares to launch a satellite into space. The Kennedy Space Center is about 100 kilometers east of the center of the state. The crew knows that a thunderstorm may be moving toward them. Should they launch the mission or delay it? Before deciding, the crew consults with meteorologists for the latest weather forecast.

More summer thunderstorms occur in central Florida than in any other area in the United States. Predicting when severe storms will develop and where they will move is one of the most demanding jobs for a meteorologist. One of the best people at this job is J. Marshall Shepherd.

Talking With
Dr. J. Marshall Shepherd

Starting Out in Science

Marshall Shepherd is an "old hand" at predicting the weather. He's been at it since sixth grade, when his teacher suggested that he enter a science fair. He constructed a weather station for his science project. The weather station contained an anemometer to measure wind speed, a wind vane to measure wind direction, a barometer to measure air pressure, a hair hygrometer to measure humidity, and a rain gauge. "From these basic instruments, I took weather observations around my neighborhood," he explains. Marshall won prizes for his instruments and scientific work on this project at local, district, and state science fairs.

By the time he graduated from high school, he had a definite goal. "One day, I planned to be a research scientist at NASA (National Aeronautics and Space Administration)," he stated.

Predicting Severe Storms

In graduate school, Marshall investigated the way powerful thunderstorms form and move, especially those in central Florida. The long, narrow shape of Florida is part of the reason that so many storms form there. "When you have land heating faster than water, you get something called sea-breeze circulation," he explains. "On a typical summer day, a sea-breeze forms on both the west coast and the east coast of Florida. They tend to move toward the center. When they collide, you get intense thunderstorm development."

Career Path

Marshall Shepherd, the son of two school principals, grew up in the small town of Canton, Georgia. He graduated from Florida State University, where he later received his Ph.D. in meteorology. Today he works for NASA as a research meteorologist at the Goddard Space Flight Center in Maryland. Below, Marshall acts as a NASA spokesperson to TV and radio reporters.

Lightning flashes in a thunderstorm over Tuscon, Arizona.

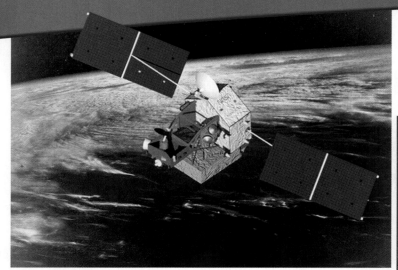

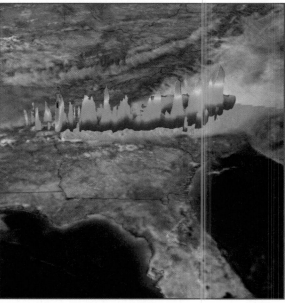

This TRMM satellite image shows an area of severe thunderstorms north of Florida.

TRMM, a satellite that records weather conditions from space, contains two solar panels and instruments to collect weather data (above). TRMM orbits Earth at an altitude of 350 kilometers. It flies over each position on Earth at a different time each day (right).

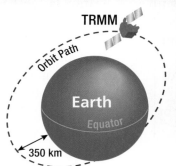

TRMM

Orbit Path

Earth

Equator

350 km

NASA's Earth Science Enterprise

In 1993, Marshall started working at NASA. His research there contributes to NASA's Earth Science Enterprise. This long-term program uses information from satellites, aircraft, and ground stations to understand Earth as a single system. NASA scientists track changes in the atmosphere, land, ocean, and ice. They investigate how those changes affect weather and climate.

Marshall's knowledge of hurricanes and thunderstorms is especially valuable in interpreting data from the Tropical Rainfall Measuring Mission (TRMM). The TRMM is a satellite with instruments that measure tropical and subtropical rainfall. Rainfall cycles located in tropical regions affect weather throughout the world.

Marshall's work involves both observation and calculation. As he did in sixth grade, he designs and builds instruments. But now his devices are some of the most advanced in the world. Marshall specializes in "remote sensing"—making observations of weather conditions, such as rainfall, from a distance. After collecting data, he uses a computer to analyze it.

Studying Global Rainfall

Recently, rain radar helped Marshall identify a relatively new factor in global climate—big cities. Modern cities have cars, roads, buildings, and large areas of concrete and asphalt surfaces. These surfaces hold heat, creating "urban heat islands." As a result, temperatures inside a city can be up to 5.6°C warmer than temperatures in the nearby suburbs.

But satellite pictures showed something more—"urban heat islands" may actually create local weather. Heated air rises over the city, producing clouds. As a result, summer rainfall is heavier over some cities. It is also heavier downwind, in the direction in which the wind is blowing, from the cities. Marshall and his colleagues mapped rainfall around several cities worldwide. Data showed a clear link between rainfall patterns and urban areas. This connection matters because world cities are growing quickly. As they grow, urban areas could have greater effects on the weather.

Looking Ahead

TRMM's mission will end in a few years. Meanwhile, Marshall is already working on a new project, the Global Precipitation Measurement mission. It is scheduled to launch sometime after 2010. Its satellites will carry the next generation of space-based instruments. In planning for this next project, Marshall meets with engineers to talk about the project's scientific goals and how to design spacecraft to meet those goals.

Marshall wears other hats at NASA, too. Sometimes he acts as spokesperson to TV, radio, and magazine reporters. He also talks to government policymakers.

What is it like to fulfill his dream of working at NASA? "I am like a kid in a candy store," Dr. Shepherd says. "I got into the field by doing a science project. Now I make a living doing 'really big' science projects. . . . The biggest difference is that I no longer have to make my own instruments. I can use the satellite, aircraft, and computer model technology at NASA."

Writing in Science

Career Link Marshall Shepherd credits his career success to having detailed goals. "I always write down goals, and check them off as they happen," he says. Think of an important task that you would like to accomplish over the next year. In a paragraph, write the steps and the target dates you will need to meet in order to reach your goal. Explain how those steps help bring you closer to achieving your goal.

Go Online
PHSchool.com

For: More on this career
Visit: PHSchool.com
Web Code: cfb-4000

Urban Heat Islands
Modern cities, like Houston, Texas, help make their own weather.

Cold Air

Wind Direction

4 Rain is heaviest over the city and downwind of the city.

1 A large city absorbs heat.

3 The warm air hits colder air above. The warm air cools and condenses, creating clouds and rain.

2 The warm air from the city and the warm, moist air from coastal waters meet and rise.

The Nature of Science and Technology

Standard Course of Study

This scientist studies young bearded seals that live in subzero waters near Norway. ▶

Lab zone Chapter **Project**

Design and Build a Scale Model

How do scientists study something as large as the solar system or as tiny as an atom? One tool they use is a model. Models help scientists picture things that are difficult to see or understand. In this chapter project, you will create a three-dimensional model of a building or room.

Your Goal To create a three-dimensional model that shows the size relationships among the different parts of the model

To complete this project, you must
- measure or find the actual dimensions of the structure to be modeled
- sketch your model on graph paper and calculate the size of each part you will include
- construct your three-dimensional model
- follow the safety guidelines in Appendix A

Plan It! Choose a room in your house or school, or a familiar building to model. Think about how you could construct a smaller replica of that room or building. Preview the chapter to find out how scientists make measurements. Then write a brief plan detailing how you will proceed with this project. Make sure your plan includes a sketch and a list of the materials you will use. After your teacher approves your plan, start working on your model.

Reading Preview

Key Concepts
- What is scientific inquiry?
- What makes a hypothesis testable?
- How do scientific theories differ from scientific laws?
- What is scientific literacy and how is it important?

Key Terms
- scientific inquiry
- hypothesis • variable
- controlled experiment
- manipulated variable
- responding variable
- operational definition • data
- communicating
- scientific theory • scientific law
- scientific literacy

Target Reading Skill

Building Vocabulary A definition states the meaning of a word or phrase by telling about its most important feature or function. After you read this section, reread the paragraphs that contain definitions of Key Terms. Use all the information you have learned to write a definition of each Key Term in your own words.

▼ A snowy tree cricket

Lab zone Discover **Activity**

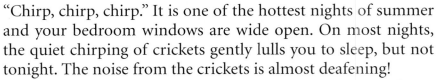

What's Happening?

1. 🧪 🥚 Your teacher will give you two eggs and two beakers filled with water.
2. Put one egg in each beaker. Observe what happens.

Think It Over
Posing Questions Write down three questions you have about your observations. How could you find out the answer?

"Chirp, chirp, chirp." It is one of the hottest nights of summer and your bedroom windows are wide open. On most nights, the quiet chirping of crickets gently lulls you to sleep, but not tonight. The noise from the crickets is almost deafening!

Why do all the crickets in your neighborhood seem determined to keep you awake tonight? Could the crickets be chirping more because of the heat? How could you find out?

As you lie awake, you are probably not thinking much about science. But, in fact, you are thinking just as a scientist would. You made observations—you heard the loud chirping of the crickets and felt the heat of the summer night. Your observations led you to infer that heat might cause increased chirping. You might even make a prediction: "If it's cooler tomorrow night, the crickets will be quieter."

The Scientific Process

Although you might not know it, your thinking and questioning is the start of the **scientific inquiry** process. **Scientific inquiry refers to the diverse ways in which scientists study the natural world and propose explanations based on the evidence they gather.** If you have ever tried to figure out why your CD player has stopped working, then you have used scientific inquiry. Similarly, you could use scientific inquiry to find out whether there is a relationship between the air temperature and crickets' chirping.

Posing Questions Scientific inquiry often begins with a problem or question about an observation. In the case of the crickets, your question might be: Does the air temperature affect the chirping of crickets? Of course, questions don't just come to you from nowhere. Instead, questions come from experiences that you have and from observations and inferences that you make. Curiosity plays a large role as well. Think of a time that you observed something unusual or unexpected. Chances are good that your curiosity sparked a number of questions.

Some questions cannot be investigated by scientific inquiry. Think about the difference between the two questions below.

• Why has my CD player stopped working?

• What kind of music should I listen to on my CD player?

The first question is a scientific question because it can be answered by making observations and gathering evidence. For example, you could change the batteries in your CD player and observe whether it begins to work. In contrast, the second question has to do with personal opinions or values. Scientific inquiry cannot answer questions about personal tastes or judgments.

Developing a Hypothesis How could you explain your observation of noisy crickets on that summer night? "Perhaps crickets chirp more when the temperature is higher," you think. In trying to answer the question, you are in fact developing a hypothesis. A **hypothesis** (plural: *hypotheses*) is a possible explanation for a set of observations or answer to a scientific question. In this case, your hypothesis would be that cricket chirping increases at higher air temperatures.

In science, a hypothesis must be testable. This means that researchers must be able to carry out investigations and gather evidence that will either support or disprove the hypothesis. Many trials will be needed before a hypothesis can be accepted as true.

Reading Checkpoint What is a hypothesis?

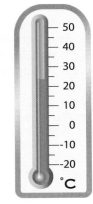

Perhaps crickets chirp more when the temperature is higher.

FIGURE 1
Developing Hypotheses
A hypothesis is one possible way to explain a set of observations. A hypothesis must be testable—scientists must be able to carry out investigations to test the hypothesis.
Developing Hypotheses *Propose another hypothesis that could account for this boy's observations.*

Controlling Variables

Suppose you are designing an experiment to determine whether sugar or salt dissolves more quickly in water. What is your manipulated variable? What is your responding variable? What other variables would you need to control?

FIGURE 2
A Controlled Experiment
In their controlled experiment, these students are using the same kind of containers, thermometers, leaves, and crickets. The manipulated variable in this experiment is temperature. The responding variable is the number of cricket chirps per minute at each temperature.
Controlling Variables What other variables must the students keep constant in this experiment?

Designing an Experiment To test your hypothesis, you will need to observe crickets at different air temperatures. All other **variables,** or factors that can change in an experiment, must be exactly the same. Other variables include the kind of crickets, the type of container you test them in, and the type of thermometer you use. By keeping all of these variables the same, you will know that any difference in cricket chirping must be due to temperature alone.

An experiment in which only one variable is manipulated at a time is called a **controlled experiment.** The one variable that is purposely changed to test a hypothesis is called the **manipulated variable** (also called the independent variable). In your cricket experiment, the manipulated variable is the air temperature. The factor that may change in response to the manipulated variable is called the **responding variable** (also called the dependent variable). The responding variable here is the number of cricket chirps.

One other important aspect of a well-designed experiment is having clear operational definitions. An **operational definition** is a statement that describes how to measure a particular variable or define a particular term. For example, in this experiment you would need to determine what sounds will count as a single "chirp."

Collecting and Interpreting Data Before you begin your experiment, you should create a data table in which to record your data. **Data** are the facts, figures, and other evidence gathered through observations. A data table provides you with an organized way to collect and record your observations.

Graphing Your Results After all the data have been collected, they need to be interpreted. One useful tool that can help you interpret data is a graph. Graphs can reveal patterns or trends in data. You will learn more about graphs in Section 3.

Drawing Conclusions A conclusion is a summary of what you have learned from an experiment. In drawing your conclusion, you should ask yourself whether the data supports the hypothesis. You also need to consider whether you collected enough data and whether anything happened during the experiment that might have affected the results. After reviewing the data, you decide that the evidence supports your original hypothesis. You conclude that cricket chirping does increase with temperature. It's no wonder that you have trouble sleeping on those warm summer nights!

Scientific inquiry usually doesn't end once a set of experiments is done. Often, a scientific inquiry raises new questions. These new questions can lead to new hypotheses and new experiments.

In this cricket experiment, you decided to test your hypothesis in one particular way. Your friend may do it another way. Furthermore, different questions may require different approaches to finding answers. For example, a scientist studying the moon may rely more on observations rather than controlled experiments to test a hypothesis.

Scientific inquiry is a process with many paths, not a rigid sequence of steps. Often, a surprising observation or accidental discovery leads into inquiry. New information springs up, then a scientist's path takes a different turn. Work may go forward—or even backward—when testing a hunch or fitting a new idea with existing ones.

Pose Questions

Form a Hypothesis

Communicate

Design an Experiment

Draw Conclusions

Collect and Interpret Data

FIGURE 3
The Nature of Inquiry
There is no set path that a scientific inquiry must follow. Observations at each stage of the process may lead you to modify your hypothesis or experiment. Conclusions from one experiment often lead to new questions and experiments.

 Reading Checkpoint   **Why doesn't the scientific inquiry process follow a rigid set of steps?**

Go Online
active art

For: The Nature of Inquiry activity
Visit: PHSchool.com
Web Code: cgp-6012

Communicating An important part of the scientific inquiry process is communicating your results. **Communicating** is the sharing of ideas and experimental findings with others through writing and speaking. Scientists share their ideas in many ways. For example, they give talks at scientific meetings, exchange information on the Internet, or publish articles in scientific journals. When scientists communicate their research, they describe their procedures in full detail so that others can repeat their experiments.

 Why is communicating important to scientists?

Scientific Theories and Laws

As a body of knowledge, science is built up cautiously. Scientists do not accept a new hypothesis after just one successful experiment. Rather, a hypothesis is tested repeatedly as many different scientists try to apply it to their own work.

Scientific Theories Sometimes, a large set of related observations can be connected by a single explanation. This can lead to the development of a scientific theory. A **scientific theory** is a well-tested explanation for a wide range of observations or experimental results.

Scientists accept a theory only when there is a large body of evidence that supports it. However, future testing can still prove an accepted theory to be incorrect. If that happens, scientists may modify the theory, or discard it altogether.

Scientific Laws When scientists repeatedly observe the same result in specific circumstances, they may arrive at a scientific law. A **scientific law** is a statement that describes what scientists expect to happen every time under a particular set of conditions. **Unlike a theory, a scientific law describes an observed pattern in nature without attempting to explain it.** You can think of a scientific law as a rule of nature.

 What does a scientific law describe?

FIGURE 4
A Scientific Theory
Based on observations of sunsets and sunrises, ancient people theorized that the sun revolved around Earth. New evidence led scientists to abandon that ancient theory. Today, scientists know that Earth, along with the other planets in the solar system, revolves around the sun.

Scientific Literacy

You may be wondering how the methods used by scientists apply to you. Not everyone is going to be a scientist. Why should you study science? How could anyone possibly learn everything there is to know about science?

Of course, it is not possible to become an expert in every field of science. Nor is it possible to test everything scientifically by yourself. Instead, you need to have scientific literacy. Having **scientific literacy** means that you understand basic scientific terms and principles well enough that you can evaluate information, make personal decisions, and take part in public affairs. **By having scientific literacy, you will be able to identify good sources of scientific information, evaluate them for accuracy, and apply the knowledge to questions or problems in your life.** You will also be able to keep up with the latest scientific trends and be well qualified for jobs.

So, why should you study science? The real question is, why wouldn't you?

FIGURE 5
Sources of Scientific Information
Scientists often give lectures to other scientists and to members of the general public.

 **Reading Checkpoint** Why is a good understanding of scientific terms and principles important?

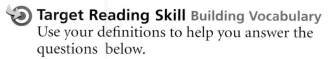

Section 1 Assessment

Target Reading Skill Building Vocabulary Use your definitions to help you answer the questions below.

Reviewing Key Concepts

1. a. Defining Define the term *scientific inquiry*.
   b. Explaining A friend claims that ceiling fans are better than air conditioning because they cool the air faster than air conditioners do. Could you investigate this through scientific inquiry? Explain.
   c. Problem Solving What kind of data would you need to collect to carry out this experiment?

2. a. Reviewing What is meant by saying that a hypothesis must be testable?
   b. Developing Hypotheses Every time you and your friend study for an exam while listening to classical music, both of you do well on the exam. What testable hypothesis can you develop from your observations?

3. a. Defining What is a scientific theory? What is a scientific law?
   b. Comparing and Contrasting How do scientific theories differ from scientific laws?
   c. Classifying The students who conducted the cricket experiment concluded that their results supported their hypothesis. Can their supported hypothesis be called a theory? Why or why not?

4. a. Defining What is scientific literacy?

Writing in Science

Summary Suppose you will be traveling to a convention of cricket scientists from around the world. Write a paragraph describing the results of your cricket experiment. Include questions you'd like to ask other cricket scientists while at the conference.

Piecing Information Together

Problem

How do the skills of observing and inferring help scientists piece together information?

Skills Focus

observing, inferring, predicting

Materials

• paperback book, cut into sections and stapled together
• paper
• pencil

Procedure

1. Examine the small section of the book your teacher gives you. Use your observation skills to list any facts you can state confidently about the book, including its characters, setting, or events.

2. Based on your observations, what can you infer the book is about? Write one or two sentences describing the book's storyline.

3. Get together with a partner and share your book sections, observations, inferences, and story descriptions.

4. Together, write a new one- or two-sentence story description based on your shared observations and information.

5. Get together with another pair of students. Repeat Steps 3 and 4.

6. After you have written your description of the story as a group of four, look back over all your story descriptions. Note how they have changed over time.

Analyze and Conclude

1. **Observing** Look over the list of observations you made in Step 1. Were any of the observations really inferences? If so, explain why.

2. **Inferring** How confident did you feel about the inference you made about the storyline in Step 2? How did your confidence level change when your observations included additional sections of the book?

3. **Predicting** How do you think your level of confidence would change if you observed more and more sections of the book? Explain your reasoning.

4. **Communicating** Write a paragraph explaining how this activity resembles the work of scientists. How do the observations and inferences you made relate to those that scientists make? What do your story descriptions represent?

More to Explore

Choose a scientific article from a newspaper or magazine. Read the article and identify three observations and three inferences that the scientists made.

Measurement—A Common Language

Reading Preview

Key Concepts
- Why do scientists use a standard measurement system?
- What are the SI units of measure for length, mass, volume, density, time, and temperature?
- How are conversion factors useful?

Key Terms
- metric system • SI • mass
- weight • volume • meniscus
- density

🔄 Target Reading Skill

Comparing and Contrasting As you read, compare and contrast different types of measurement by completing a table like the one below.

Measurement

Characteristic	Length	Mass
Definition		
SI unit		
Measuring tool		

Lab zone Discover **Activity**

How Many Shoes?

1. Trace an outline of your shoe onto a piece of paper. Cut out your pattern.
2. Use your pattern to measure the length of your classroom in "shoes."
3. Compare your measurement to those of three classmates. Did you all measure the same number of "shoes"?

Think It Over

Inferring Why do you think it is important that people use standard units of measurement?

Did you ever ask a relative for an old family recipe? If so, the answer might have been, "Use just the right amount of flour and water. Add a spoonful of oil and a pinch of salt. Bake it for awhile until it looks just right."

Instructions like these would be difficult to follow. How much flour is "just the right amount"? How big is a spoonful or a pinch? It would be impossible for you to know what your relative had in mind. You could end up with disastrous results.

◀ In tasks such as cooking, measurements can be critical!

FIGURE 6
Knowing SI units, based on multiples of 10, are easy to use. Understanding what the prefixes mean can help you judge how big or small a measurement is.
Calculating How much larger is a kilo- than a deka-?

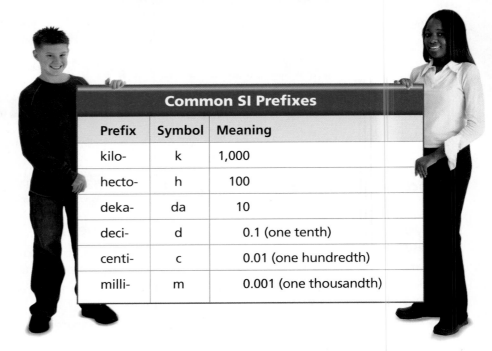

Common SI Prefixes		
Prefix	**Symbol**	**Meaning**
kilo-	k	1,000
hecto-	h	100
deka-	da	10
deci-	d	0.1 (one tenth)
centi-	c	0.01 (one hundredth)
milli-	m	0.001 (one thousandth)

A Standard Measurement System

The recipe example illustrates the importance of using a standard system of measurement. This is especially true in science. Using the same system of measurement minimizes confusion among scientists all over the world.

The Metric System More than 200 years ago, most countries used their own measurement systems. Sometimes two or more different systems were used in the same country. In the 1790s, scientists in France developed a universal system of measurement called the metric system. The **metric system** is a system of measurement based on the number 10.

The International System of Units (SI) Modern scientists use a version of the metric system called the International System of Units, abbreviated as **SI** (for the French, *Système International d'Unités*). Scientists all over the world use SI units to measure length, volume, mass, density, temperature, and time. **Using SI as the standard system of measurement allows scientists to compare data and communicate with each other about their results.** In this book and others in the *Science Explorer* program, you will use both SI and other metric units.

Figure 6 lists the prefixes used to name the most common SI units. Because they are based on multiples of 10, SI units are easy to use. Each unit is ten times larger than the next smallest unit and one tenth the size of the next largest unit. This is similar to our money system, in which a dime is worth ten times more than a penny, but one tenth as much as a dollar.

Discovery CHANNEL SCHOOL™

The Work of Scientists

Video Preview
▶ Video Field Trip
Video Assessment

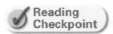 Reading Checkpoint **SI units are based on multiples of what number?**

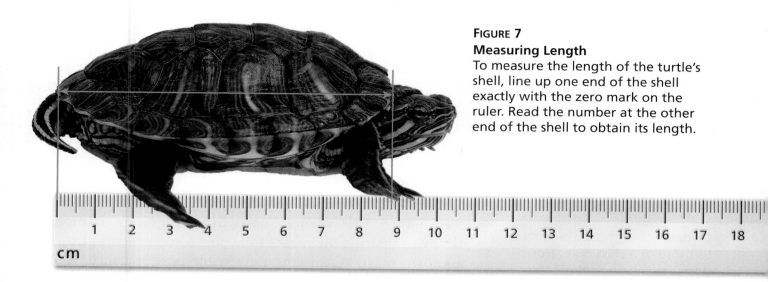

FIGURE 7
Measuring Length
To measure the length of the turtle's shell, line up one end of the shell exactly with the zero mark on the ruler. Read the number at the other end of the shell to obtain its length.

Units of Measurement

Suppose your friend says, "I can throw a softball 15!" That doesn't tell you much. You need to know what unit was used to measure the throw. A throw of 15 centimeters isn't very impressive. A throw of 15 kilometers is impossible.

Length The distance from one point to another is length. **The basic unit of length in the SI system is the meter (m).** One meter is about the distance from the floor to a doorknob. A softball throw would be measured in meters. So would your height. Most students your age are between 1.5 and 2 meters tall.

To measure a long distance, scientists use a unit known as the kilometer (km). The prefix *kilo-* means one thousand. There are 1,000 meters in a kilometer.

To measure objects smaller than a meter, scientists use units called the centimeter (cm) or the millimeter (mm). The prefix *centi-* means "one-hundredth," while the prefix *milli-* means one-thousandth. One meter, then, is equal to 100 centimeters or 1,000 millimeters.

A very common tool used to measure length is the metric ruler. As you can see in Figure 7, a metric ruler is divided into centimeters. The centimeter markings are the longer lines numbered 1, 2, 3, and so on. Each centimeter is then divided into 10 millimeters, which are marked by the shorter lines.

To use a metric ruler, line one end of the object up exactly with the zero mark. Then read the number at the other end of the object. The shell of the turtle in Figure 7 is 8.8 centimeters, or 88 millimeters, long.

Common Conversions for Length	
1 km	= 1,000 m
1 m	= 100 cm
1 m	= 1,000 mm
1 cm	= 10 mm

Reading Checkpoint One centimeter is divided into how many millimeters?

Mass A measure of the amount of matter an object contains is the **mass** of the object. **The basic unit of mass in the SI system is the kilogram (kg).** The mass of a wooden baseball bat is about 1 kilogram.

To measure the mass of smaller objects, you will use a unit known as the gram (g). As you can guess, there are 1,000 grams in a kilogram. A large paper clip has a mass of about 1 gram. Even smaller masses are measured in milligrams (mg). There are 1,000 milligrams in one gram.

To find the mass of an object, you may use a balance like the one in Figure 8. This balance, known as a triple-beam balance, works by comparing the mass of the object you are measuring to a known mass. When you use a triple-beam balance, you first place the object on the pan. You then shift the riders on the beams until they balance the mass of the object. You can find step-by-step instructions for using a triple-beam balance in Appendix C.

Mass is often confused with weight. But weight is not the same thing as mass. **Weight** is a measure of the force of gravity acting on an object. This force can change from place to place. For example, you would weigh less on the moon because the force of gravity is much weaker on the moon than on Earth. But how would your mass compare? Because mass measures the amount of matter an object contains, it remains constant wherever an object may be. Your mass on the moon is the same as your mass on Earth.

Volume The amount of space an object takes up is its **volume.** To measure the volume of a liquid, scientists use a unit known as the liter (L). You can measure smaller liquid volumes using milliliters (mL). There are 1,000 milliliters in a liter.

FIGURE 8
Measuring Mass
You can use a triple-beam balance to find the mass of small objects. To measure mass, place the object on the pan and shift the riders on each beam until the pointer stops at zero. **Observing** *What is the mass of this turtle?*

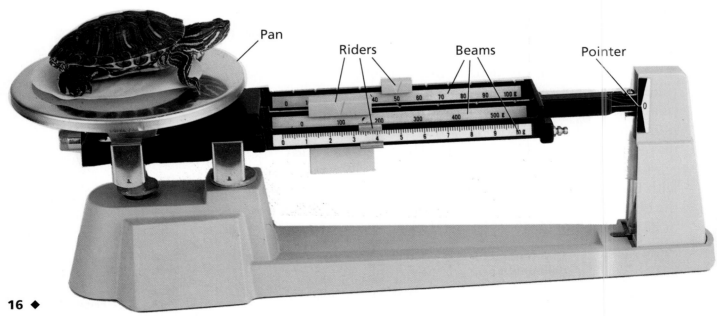

Pan   Riders   Beams   Pointer

To measure the volume of a liquid, scientists commonly use a graduated cylinder. The graduated cylinder in Figure 9 is marked off in 1-milliliter segments. Notice that the top surface of the water in the graduated cylinder is curved. This curve is called the **meniscus.** To determine the volume of water, you should read the milliliter marking at the bottom of the curve.

Density Two objects of the same size can have very different masses. This is because different materials have different densities. **Density** is a measure of how much mass is contained in a given volume. To calculate the density of an object, divide its mass by its volume.

$$\text{Density} = \frac{\text{Mass}}{\text{Volume}}$$

Because density is actually made up of two other measurements—mass and volume—an object's density is expressed as a combination of two units. Two common units of density are grams per cubic centimeter (g/cm^3) and grams per milliliter (g/mL). In each case, the numerator is a measure of mass while the denominator is a measure of volume.

Time **The second (s) is the SI unit used to measure time.** Your heart beats about once per second—when you are not running, that is! The second can easily be divided by multiples of 10, like the other SI units. For example, a millisecond (ms) is one-thousandth of a second. Longer periods of time are expressed in minutes or hours. There are 60 seconds in a minute, and 60 minutes in an hour.

Clocks and watches are used to measure time. Some clocks are more accurate than others. Some digital stopwatches, which are used to time races, can measure time accurately to one hundredth of a second.

Reading Checkpoint How many milliseconds are in one second?

FIGURE 9
Measuring Volume
To measure the volume of a regular solid use the formula: Volume = Length × Width × Height. To measure the volume of an irregular solid, immerse the solid in water, and measure how much the water level rises.
Observing *What is the proper way to read a meniscus?*

25 cm

6 cm

20 cm

FIGURE 10
Measuring Time
A stopwatch can be used to measure time.

Common Conversions for Time	
1 s	= 1,000 ms
1 min	= 60 s
1 h	= 60 min

Common Conversions for Temperature		
0°C	=	273 K
100°C	=	373 K

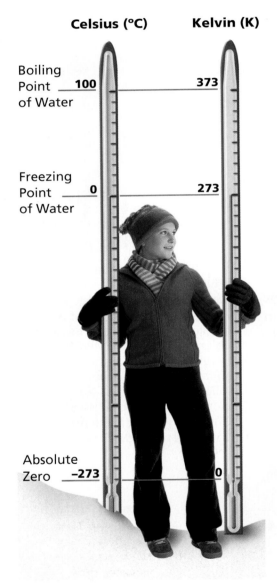

Celsius (°C)   **Kelvin (K)**

Boiling Point of Water — 100   373

Freezing Point of Water — 0   273

Absolute Zero — −273   0

FIGURE 11
Measuring Temperature
Scientists use the Celsius and Kelvin scales to measure temperature. Units on both scales are the same size. *Observing At what temperature on the Kelvin scale does water boil?*

Temperature As you head out the door each morning, one of the first things you might notice is the temperature. Is it cold out this morning? How high will the temperature rise?

Scientists commonly use the Celsius temperature scale. On the Celsius scale, water freezes at 0°C and boils at 100°C. There are exactly 100 degrees between the freezing point and boiling point of water. Normal human body temperature is about 37°C.

In addition to the Celsius scale, scientists sometimes use another temperature scale, called the Kelvin scale. In fact, the kelvin (K) is the official SI unit for temperature. Units on the Kelvin scale are the same size as those on the Celsius scale. Figure 11 compares these two temperature scales.

Zero on the Kelvin scale (0 K) is the temperature that scientists consider to be the coldest possible temperature. Nothing can get colder than this temperature, called absolute zero. Absolute zero is equal to −273°C on the Celsius scale. The Kelvin scale is useful because it does not have negative numbers to complicate calculations.

You can measure temperature using a thermometer. When you first place the thermometer in a substance, the liquid inside the thermometer will begin to move up or down. Wait until the level of the liquid stops changing. Then read the number next to the top of the liquid in the thermometer.

 **Reading Checkpoint**   **What is the official SI unit for temperature?**

Converting Between Units

Do you have a jar where you keep all your pennies? Suppose you counted your penny collection and discovered that you had 236 pennies. How many dollars does that equal? With only a little thought, you could probably answer, "$2.36."

Just like converting between dollars and cents, it is often necessary to convert from one unit of measurement to another. **To convert one measurement to another, you need to know the appropriate conversion factor. A conversion factor is an equation that shows how two units of measurement are related.** For conversion factors, refer to the conversion tables included throughout this section.

Suppose you walk 1.5 kilometers to a friend's house. How many meters have you walked? To convert 1.5 kilometers to meters, follow these steps:

❶ Begin by writing down the measurement you want to convert.

❷ Find a conversion factor that relates the two units you are converting.

❸ Write the conversion factor as a fraction. Make sure to place the units you are converting from in the denominator.

❹ Multiply the measurement you are converting from by the fraction. When you do this, the units in the measurement will cancel out with the units in the denominator of the fraction. Your answer will then be in the units you are converting to.

By converting between units, you now know that you walked 1,500 meters to your friend's house.

 **Reading Checkpoint** What is a conversion factor?

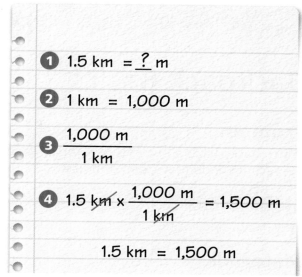

FIGURE 12
Converting Between Units
Using the appropriate conversion factor, you can easily convert one unit of measurement to another. This example shows how to convert 1.5 kilometers to meters.

Section 2 Assessment

Target Reading Skill

Comparing and Contrasting Use the information in your table about the different types of measurement to answer Question 2.

Reviewing Key Concepts

1. a. Identifying What is the standard measurement system used by scientists around the world?

  b. Predicting Suppose that two scientists use different measurement systems in their work. What problems might arise if they shared their data?

2. a. Listing What SI unit would you use to measure the length of a baseball bat? What SI unit would you use to measure the mass of a baseball?

  b. Estimating Estimate the length of a baseball bat and mass of a baseball. Be sure to use the appropriate SI units in your predictions. How could you determine how close your estimates are?

3. a. Reviewing What is a conversion factor?

  b. Identifying What conversion factor would you use to convert between liters and milliliters?

  c. Calculating Your cat's bowl holds 0.25 liters of liquid. How many milliliters of water can you pour into the bowl?

Math Practice

4. Volume How many mililiters of water are there in a 1.2 liter bottle of water?

5. Converting Units The temperature is 293 K. What is the temperature in degrees Celsius?

Consumer **Lab**

Backpack Basics

Problem

Which backpack is a better choice for carrying the recommended safe load of books?

Skills Focus

measuring, calculating, drawing conclusions

Materials

- balance • 5–6 textbooks • meter stick
- 2 backpacks (one large and one small)

Procedure

PART 1 Determining Your Maximum Safe Load

1. To prevent back problems, experts recommend that the mass of the backpack you carry should be no greater than 15 percent of your body mass. Use the table below to find your "maximum safe load."

Determining Maximum Safe Load	
Body Mass kg (lbs)	Maximum Safe Load (kg)
30 (66)	4.5
35 (77)	5.3
40 (88)	6.0
45 (99)	6.8
50 (110)	7.5
55 (121)	8.3
60 (132)	9.0
65 (143)	9.8
70 (154)	10.5
75 (165)	11.3
80 (176)	12.0
85 (187)	12.8

2. To determine how many textbooks equal your maximum safe load, use a balance to find the mass of one textbook. Next, divide your maximum safe load by the mass of the textbook. Your answer is the number of textbooks (of that size) you can safely carry in a backpack. Note that the maximum safe load is given in kilograms.

PART 2 Comparing Backpacks

3. Your teacher will give you two backpacks—one large and one small. Load each backpack with the number of textbooks you calculated in Step 2. Carry each backpack on your back for one minute and note how it feels. Also, observe how empty or full each backpack is.

4. Using a meter stick, measure the length, width, and height in centimeters of each backpack. Your partner should stretch out the backpacks fully as you measure them. Record the dimensions in a data table like the one at the top of the next page.

5. Calculate the volume of each backpack using this formula:

   Volume = Length × Width × Height

   Record the volumes in your data table.

6. Calculate the approximate volume of the textbook you used in Part 1. Measure its length, width, and height in centimeters, and then multiply these measurements together.

Data Table						
Backpack	Length (cm)	Width (cm)	Height (cm)	Volume (cm³)	Total Number of Textbooks	Total Mass of Textbooks (kg)
1						
2						

7. Calculate the total number of textbooks of that size that could fit into each backpack, by dividing the volume of each backpack (from Step 5) by the volume of one textbook (from Step 6). Record the results for each backpack in your data table.

8. Calculate the total mass of textbooks that could fit into each backpack by multiplying the mass of one textbook (from Step 2) by the total number of textbooks that fit into each (from Step 7). Record the results in your data table.

Analyze and Conclude

1. **Observing** Is each backpack large enough to carry your maximum safe load? What differences did you notice between the two backpacks when carrying this load of books?

2. **Measuring** How do the two backpacks compare in volume? What is the total mass of books that each backpack could carry?

3. **Calculating** Calculate how many times your maximum safe load each backpack could carry. (*Hint:* Divide the total mass of books from Step 8 by your maximum safe load in Step 1.)

4. **Drawing Conclusions** Based on the calculations and observations you made in this lab, what are some of the pros and cons of each backpack?

5. **Communicating** Choose one of the backpacks and write an advertisement for it. In your advertisement, be sure to explain why it would be the best choice for students.

More to Explore

For a week, record the actual mass of the backpack you carry to school each day. Then calculate the average (mean) mass of your backpack. How does this compare to your recommended maximum safe load?

Graphs in Science

Reading Preview

Key Concepts
- What type of data can line graphs display?
- How do you determine a line of best fit or the slope of a graph?
- Why are line graphs powerful tools in science?

Key Terms
- graph • horizontal axis
- vertical axis • origin
- coordinate • data point
- line of best fit • linear graph
- slope • nonlinear graph

Target Reading Skill
Building Vocabulary A definition states the meaning of a word or phrase by telling about its most important feature or function. After you read this section, reread the paragraphs that contain definitions of Key Terms. Use all the information you have learned to write a definition of each Key Term in your own words.

Lab zone Discover **Activity**

What's in a Picture?

1. Read over the information written below.
2. At 4 months, Jay's dog Kuma was was 17 cm tall at the shoulders. By the time he turned 8 months, Kuma had grown 9 cm. By 12 months, he was 34 cm tall.
3. Look at the "picture" below.

Think It Over

Inferring What are the advantages of showing information in a visual way, rather than with words in paragraph form?

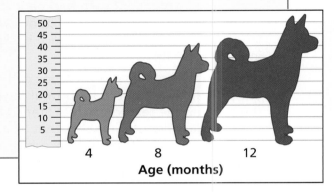

Age (months)

It's another hot summer evening and you're listening to the crickets again. The sound reminds you of the experiment you did to discover whether the rate of the crickets' chirping was related to temperature. You collected a lot of data during that experiment. Then you organized the data into a data table like the one in Figure 13 and studied it to figure out the results.

Now you're ready to write up your experiment and communicate the results with other students. Is there a better way to show the relationship of chirping and temperature than a data table? You'd like to present the results so that the relationship can been seen right away.

The Importance of Graphs

Creating a data table is one way to organize experimental data. Another way to show data is in the form of a graph. You can think of a **graph** as a "picture" of your data. This section focuses specifically on line graphs—what they are used for and how to interpret the patterns they reveal.

Using Line Graphs The data table in Figure 13 shows how many chirps were counted for five crickets at three temperatures. From the data table, you can tell that as the temperature increases, the number of chirps increases as well. But a line graph could reveal more clearly how these variables are related.

Line graphs are used to display data to show how one variable (the responding variable) changes in response to another variable (the manipulated variable). In the cricket experiment, the responding variable is the number of chirps per minute. The manipulated variable is the temperature of the air.

Plotting a Line Graph A line graph has several parts, which are shown in Figure 14.

- **A horizontal axis (or *x*-axis) and a vertical axis (or *y*-axis)** The **horizontal axis** or x-axis, is the graph line that runs left to right. The **vertical axis,** or y-axis, is the graph line that runs up and down. The point where they cross is the **origin.**

- **Labels for the axes** The horizontal axis shows the manipulated variable. The vertical axis shows the responding variable. The scale of each axis is designed to span from the smallest value to the largest that will be shown.

- **A point on the graph for each piece of data** A **coordinate** is a pair of numbers used to determine the position of a **data point** on a graph.

- **A line connecting the data points** The line shows the trend of the data.

- **A title** The title explains what the graph shows.

Reading Checkpoint What is a data point?

Number of Chirps per Minute			
Cricket	15°C	20°C	25°C
1	91	135	180
2	80	124	169
3	89	130	176
4	78	125	158
5	77	121	157
Average	83	127	168

FIGURE 13
Collecting Data
The results of the cricket chirping experiment were collected in this data table.
Interpreting Data *Did each cricket chirp more as the temperature rose? Did you have to examine the data in the table closely to answer the question?*

FIGURE 14
Displaying Data in a Line Graph
The line graph shows how the average number of chirps rises as the temperature rises.
Inferring *Why might a line graph be more useful than a data table?*

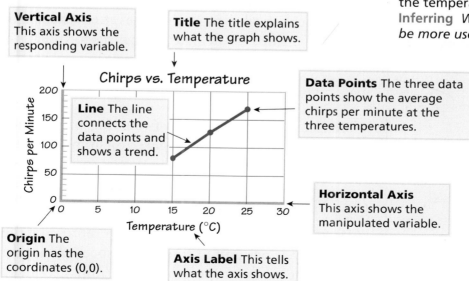

Vertical Axis This axis shows the responding variable.

Title The title explains what the graph shows.

Line The line connects the data points and shows a trend.

Data Points The three data points show the average chirps per minute at the three temperatures.

Horizontal Axis This axis shows the manipulated variable.

Origin The origin has the coordinates (0,0).

Axis Label This tells what the axis shows.

FIGURE 15

Drawing a Line of Best Fit
For this graph, a line going upwards from left to right reflects the data more accuratly than a zig-zag line does. *Relating Cause and Effect What factors might explain why the data points don't fall perfectly along a straight line?*

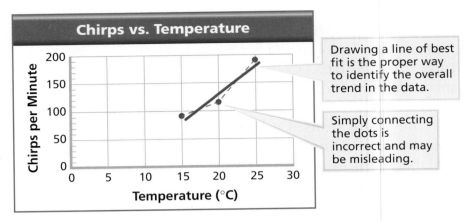

Chirps vs. Temperature

Drawing a line of best fit is the proper way to identify the overall trend in the data.

Simply connecting the dots is incorrect and may be misleading.

Line of Best Fit Sometimes the data points from experimental results don't line up in a straight line. That's because whenever data is collected, small measurement errors and inaccuracies can be introduced. Suppose your friend does the same cricket experiment as you did and plots the graph shown in Figure 15.

Your friend's graph shows the points going upwards from left to right. However, if your friend simply connects the dots, the line would be zigzag, rather than straight. Instead, she draws a straight line between the data points to reflect the general pattern. This graph line, called the **line of best fit,** may touch very few or none of the points. **A line of best fit emphasizes the overall trend shown by all the data taken as a whole.** Notice that the resulting line of best fit for this graph is a straight line. A line graph in which the data points yield a straight line is called a **linear graph.**

Slope

When a line graph is linear, you can determine a value called slope. One way to define **slope** is the steepness of the graph line. **The slope of a graph line tells you how much *y* changes for every change in *x*.** Thus, another definition of slope is the ratio of the vertical change (the "rise") to the horizontal change (the "run"). Slope is calculated using this formula:

$$\text{Slope} = \frac{\text{Rise}}{\text{Run}} = \frac{Y_2 - Y_1}{X_2 - X_1}$$

To calculate slope, pick any two points on the line and write down the coordinates. In Figure 16, suppose you chose the points (20, 10) and (50, 25).

$$\text{Slope} = \frac{25\ \text{km} - 10\ \text{km}}{50\ \text{min} - 20\ \text{min}} = \frac{15\ \text{km}}{30\ \text{min}} = 0.5\ \text{km/min}$$

In the case of Figure 16, the slope represents the distance the car travels per unit of time, or its speed. A slope of 0.5 tells you that the car has a speed of 0.5 km/min.

FIGURE 16

Slope
The slope of a line indicates how much *y* changes for every change in *x*. *Calculating What is the slope of this line?*

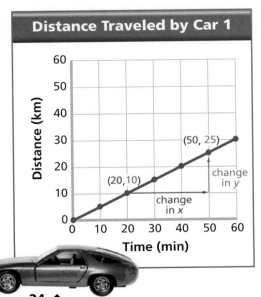

Distance Traveled by Car 1

(50, 25)

change in y

(20,10)

change in x

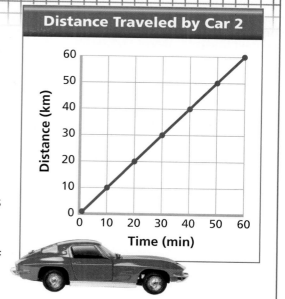

Math Analyzing Data

Car Travel

The graph shows the distance a car travels in a one-hour period. Use the graph to answer the questions below.

1. **Reading Graphs** What variable is plotted on the horizontal axis? What variable is plotted on the vertical axis?

2. **Interpreting Data** How far does the car travel in the first 10 minutes? In 40 minutes?

3. **Predicting** Use the graph to predict how far the car would travel in 120 minutes. Assume the car continues to travel at the same speed.

4. **Calculating** Calculate the slope of the graph. What information does the slope provide about the speed of Car 2?

5. **Drawing Conclusions** Compare this graph to the one for Car 1 in Figure 16. What is the relationship between the steepness of the graph lines and the speed of the cars?

Using Graphs to Identify Trends

Your data won't always give you a graph with a straight line. A line graph in which the data points do not fall along a straight line is called a **nonlinear graph**.

Whether a graph is linear or nonlinear, the information it contains is very useful. **Line graphs are powerful tools in science because they allow you to identify trends and make predictions.** Line graphs show several types of trends.

Linear Trends When a graph is linear, you can easily see how two variables are related. The graphs in Figure 14 on page 23, Figure 15, and Figure 16 all show linear trends. You can use linear graphs to make predictions or estimate values between data points. Look back at Figure 14. How many chirps per minute would you expect to count at 17°C?

Nonlinear Trends In some nonlinear graphs, the trend rises and then levels off. In other nonlinear graphs, data points fall along a curve. Figure 17 shows such a graph. In each time interval, the truck moves a greater distance. This trend shows that the truck's speed is increasing.

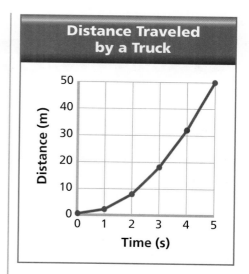

FIGURE 17

Nonlinear Graph

In this nonlinear graph, the data points fall along a curve. Instead of moving at a steady rate, the truck is increasing its speed.

FIGURE 18
Looking for Trends
In many places, temperature varies with the seasons. The graph on the left shows a repeating, or cyclical, pattern. In the graph on the right, there is no relationship between the number of hits these players get and their masses. The data points are scattered, and the graph shows no recognizable pattern.

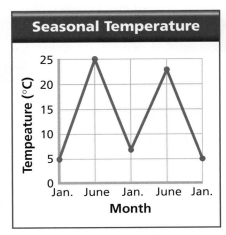

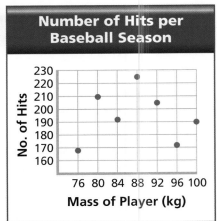

In some nonlinear graphs, the data points show a changing trend. In the graph on the left in Figure 18, there is a repeating pattern. From this graph you can infer that the location where the data were collected has very warm summers and cool winters.

No Trend Sometimes when you plot data points you cannot find a trend. In the graph on the right in Figure 18, the data points are scattered in no recognizable pattern. This tells you that the mass of a baseball player has no effect on the number of hits recorded in a season.

Reading Checkpoint What is a nonlinear graph?

Section 3 Assessment

Target Reading Skill Building Vocabulary Use your definitions to help answer the questions below.

Reviewing Key Concepts

1. a. Reviewing What can graphs reveal that data tables cannot?
   b. Describing What can a line graph tell you about the relationship between the variables in an experiment?
   c. Interpreting Data Could you use a line graph to show data about how the population of mice (the responding variable) changes with the food supply (the manipulated variable)? Explain.

2. a. Defining What is a line of best fit?
   b. Explaining Why is a line of best fit more appropriate for graphing experimental results than simply connecting the data points?

   c. Comparing and Contrasting How does a graph line with a steeper slope compare to one with a shallower slope?

3. a. Listing List two things that line graphs allow scientists to do.
   b. Reading Graphs Describe how the graph on the left in Figure 18 allows scientists to do these two things.

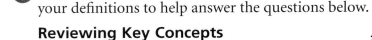

Graphs and Weather Look for local weather data in your newspaper or on the Internet. What types of graphs, if any, do you find? If there are no graphs, what data on the page might be made into a graph?

Technology and Society

Reading Preview

Key Concepts
- What is the goal of technology?
- What are the components of a technological system?
- How does technology have both a good and a bad impact on society?
- Why is it important to analyze both the risks and benefits of a technology?

Key Terms
- technology • obsolete
- system • goal • input
- process • output • feedback
- risk-benefit analysis

Target Reading Skill
Relating Cause and Effect As you read, identify one positive and one negative effect of each technology discussed in this section. Write the information in a graphic organizer like the one below.

Effects

Cause

Invention of air bags → Positive effect: saves lives

→

Lab zone Discover **Activity**

What Are Some Examples of Technology?
1. Look at the objects in the photographs.
2. With a partner, discuss whether or not each object is an example of technology. Write your reasons for each decision.

Think It Over
Forming Operational Definitions On what basis did you and your partner decide whether an object was an example of technology? What is your definition of *technology?*

The year is 1900, and you are going to visit your aunt and uncle in a distant city. You awaken before dawn and get dressed by the flickering light of an oil lamp. Then you and your family hurry to the train station. The train ride is quite an experience. You never imagined anything could move so fast.

Your aunt and uncle greet you with hot soup prepared on their shiny, black, coal-burning stove. After the meal, you help with the cleanup. As you wash the bowls and spoons, you are amazed by the water faucet. To get water at home, you must go outside and pump it by hand.

FIGURE 19
Technology in the Early 1900s
The products shown in these ads are examples of technology. Although they may seem outdated, they were sensations in their time!

Classifying

Look around you. Write down one example of each of the six areas of technology. Compare your list with a classmate's. Discuss any items on your lists that you classified differently.

What Is Technology?

Trains, coal-burning stoves, and oil lamps all made life easier for people living in 1900. All of these items are examples of technology. Modern devices such as computers and CD players are examples of technology, too. In addition to things that people make, technology can also refer to the knowledge and processes needed to produce those objects. **Technology** is how people change the world around them to meet their needs or to solve practical problems.

The goal of technology is to improve the way people live. Medicines help you recover from sickness. Eyeglasses and binoculars extend your ability to see. The Internet makes it easier for you to obtain information.

Technology changes over time. A product may become **obsolete**, or no longer used. Oil lamps became obsolete when electric lighting was invented. Electric lighting is an example of current technology, which means it is in use at this time. Incandescent, fluorescent, and halogen bulbs are commonly used today. Technologies that are in use at the same time are called coexisting technologies.

New, or emerging, technologies may lead to improvements in products. Perhaps in the future, light bulbs will be as small and bright as halogen bulbs and use as little energy as fluorescent bulbs.

The products of technology can be classified into six major areas shown in Figure 20. Think about all the technologies involved in bringing a box of cereal to your breakfast table. Trains (transportation) carry grain from farms to factories (construction). There, vitamins and minerals (biological and chemical) are added to the grain. The cereal is baked in an oven (energy and power) and then packaged (manufacturing). The cereal company advertises the product on TV (communication).

Reading Checkpoint What is an example of transportation technology?

FIGURE 20
Areas of Technology
Technology can be classified into six major areas. Almost everything you do involves products from the different areas of technology.

The Six Areas of Technology	
Area of Technology	**Examples**
Communication	Cellphones, Televisions
Transportation	Automobiles, Airplanes, Bicycles, Trains
Manufacturing	Clothing, Furniture
Energy and power	Heating, Lighting
Biological and chemical	Fertilizers, Detergents
Construction	Houses, Schools, Roads

Technology as a System

When you hear the word *system*, what comes to mind? Maybe you think of your school system or the circulatory system in your body. All **systems** have one thing in common: They are made of parts that work together. The parts of your school system include buildings, books, and teachers. All of these parts are involved in educating the students in your community.

Technology products can be thought of as systems, too. **A technological system includes a goal, inputs, processes, outputs, and, in some cases, feedback.** Figure 21 describes these components in one familiar technological system—an oven.

Technological systems are designed to achieve a particular **goal**, or purpose. An **input** is something that is put into a system in order to reach that goal. The **process** is a sequence of actions that the system undergoes. An **output** is a result or product. If the system works correctly, the output should match the goal. Some technological systems have an additional component, called feedback. **Feedback** is information a system uses to monitor the input, process, and output so that the system can adjust itself to meet the goal.

 **Reading Checkpoint** What do all systems have in common?

FIGURE 21
The Oven as a System
An oven is a technological system. Input, process, output, and feedback are all involved in achieving the goal of cooking food—such as tasty cookies!

Goal

Bake a tray of chocolate chip cookies.

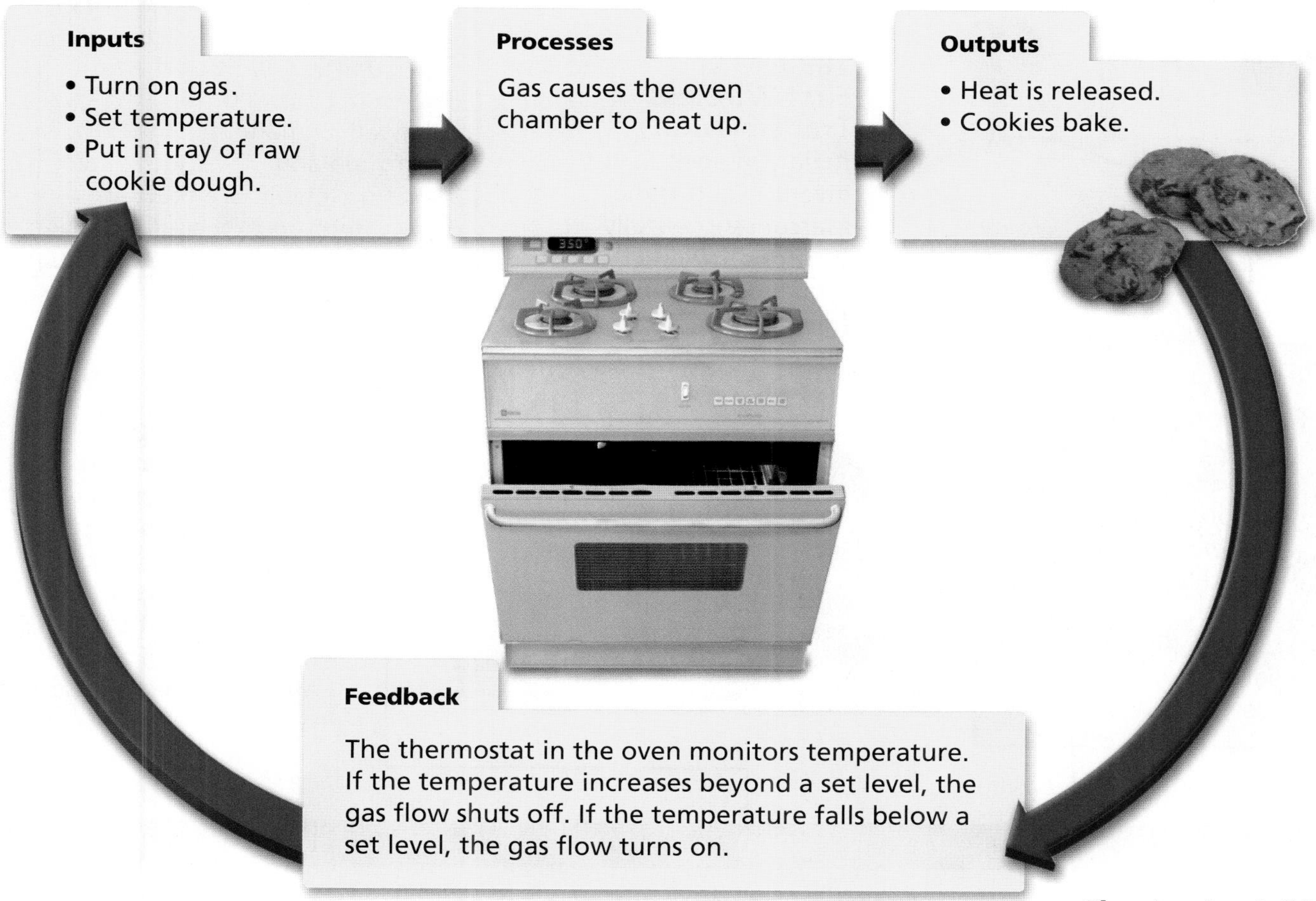

Inputs
- Turn on gas.
- Set temperature.
- Put in tray of raw cookie dough.

Processes

Gas causes the oven chamber to heat up.

Outputs
- Heat is released.
- Cookies bake.

Feedback

The thermostat in the oven monitors temperature. If the temperature increases beyond a set level, the gas flow shuts off. If the temperature falls below a set level, the gas flow turns on.

Technology's Impact on Society

In the early 1800s, many skilled weavers in England worked at home, weaving cloth by hand on looms. Then the steam-powered loom was invented, and weaving could be done by unskilled workers in factories. Some weavers rebelled against the power looms. They invaded factories and smashed the machinery.

The situation of the English weavers is an example of how technology can affect society. The term *society* refers to a group of people who live together in an area and have certain things in common, such as a form of government. In every age of history, technology has had a large impact on society. During the Stone Age, for example, people could communicate only by speaking directly to each other. Today, in the Information Age, computers allow people to share information quickly around the world.

Science and History

Wireless Communication

Since the late 1800s, many developments in communication have turned our world into a global village.

1901
First Transatlantic Signals
On December 12, the first transatlantic radio signal was sent from Poldhu Cove, Cornwall, England, to Signal Hill, Newfoundland. The coded radio waves traveled more than 3,000 km through the air.

1895
First Wireless Transmission
Italian engineer and inventor Guglielmo Marconi successfully used radio waves to send a coded wireless signal a distance of more than 2 km.

1888
Electromagnetic Waves
German scientist Heinrich Hertz proved that radio waves exist. Hertz demonstrated that the waves could be reflected, refracted, diffracted, and polarized just like light waves.

1923
Ship-to-Ship Communication
For the first time, people on one ship could talk to people on another. The signals were sent as electromagnetic waves, received by an antenna, and converted into sound.

1880	1900	1920

Technological advances like plumbing, cars, telephones, and computers have done much to move societies forward through the centuries. **However, it is important to keep in mind that technology has both good and bad impacts on society.** Often, many of the bad consequences are unintentional and are not recognized until after the technology has been put to use.

Many technological products are designed to improve people's safety. For example, chemicals called pesticides protect crops from insects, so farmers can produce more food. However, pesticides also can harm people and animals that eat foods containing these chemicals.

 Reading Checkpoint   **What is a society?**

Writing in Science

Research and Write Use library or Internet resources to find out more about Guglielmo Marconi. Imagine that you were hired as his assistant. Write a short letter to a friend that describes your new job.

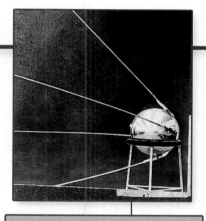

1957
Sputnik I
On October 4, the Soviet Union became the first country to successfully launch an artificial satellite into orbit. This development led to a new era in communications. Since then, more than 5,000 artificial satellites have been placed in orbit.

1963
Geosynchronous Orbit
Communications satellites are launched into orbits at altitudes of about 35,000 km. At this altitude, a satellite orbits Earth at the same rate as Earth rotates.

1979
Cellular Phone Network
In Japan, the world's first cellular phone network allowed people to make wireless phone calls. Today, cellular phone towers like the one above are common.

| 1960 | 1980 | 2000 |

Analyzing Risks and Benefits

If technology can create problems, how then can people decide whether or not to use a new technology? And how do governments determine whether a new technology should be regulated, or limited by laws?

In deciding whether to use a particular technology—or how to use it—people must analyze its possible risks and benefits. The process of **risk-benefit analysis** involves evaluating the possible problems, or risks, of a technology compared to the expected advantages, or benefits. This analysis requires logical thinking and common sense. Different people may make different decisions about whether—and how—a technology should be used.

Identifying the Risks and Benefits Look at Figure 22 to see how risk-benefit analysis can help you make a personal decision, such as whether or not to use headphones. Risk-benefit analysis also helps governments establish regulations about new technology products. For example, suppose a company has developed a new bicycle helmet made of a lightweight material. The helmet provides less protection than older, heavier helmets, but it is much more comfortable and stylish.

FIGURE 22
The Risks and Benefits of Using Headphones
Should you use headphones? Evaluating the risks and benefits can help you decide.
Problem Solving *What decision would you makes, and why?*

Benefit
Able to listen to your own music without disturbing others

Benefit
Can tune out loud noises and other distractions in environment

Benefit
Can be easily carried

Risk
Can damage hearing at high volumes

Risk
Can prevent you from hearing oncoming traffic, horns, and sirens

Risk
Can be easily lost

Identifying the Risks and Benefits In determining whether the new helmet is acceptable safety gear, a government agency first identifies both its risks and its benefits. The main risk of the new helmet is the greater possibility of injury than with heavier helmets. But since the new helmet is more comfortable and looks better, more people may wear it. The benefit of the new helmet, then, is that more people would have some form of head protection, rather than no protection at all.

Often, in evaluating a technology's risks and benefits, individuals and societies must consider human values. A value is something that a person or society regards as important, such as health, honesty, convenience, and personal freedom.

Difficulties can arise when different values conflict—when one value favors a technology while another value cautions against it. In the case of the new helmets, the conflicting values could be safety versus people's freedom of choice. When values conflict, a decision involves trade-offs—exchanging one benefit for another. For example, by choosing the lightweight helmet, people trade safety for style.

 **Reading Checkpoint** **What is meant by a value?**

Go Online
SciLINKS NSTA

For: Links on technology and society
Visit: www.SciLinks.org
Web Code: scn-1633

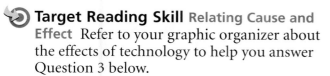
Section 4 Assessment

🎯 **Target Reading Skill** Relating Cause and Effect Refer to your graphic organizer about the effects of technology to help you answer Question 3 below.

Reviewing Key Concepts

1. a. **Reviewing** What is technology?
   b. **Applying Concepts** How does a telephone fulfill the definition of technology?
2. a. **Reviewing** What four components do all technological systems include? What fifth component do some systems also have?
   b. **Applying Concepts** An alarm clock is a technological system. Identify each component in this system.
3. a. **Explaining** Explain this statement: Technology does not provide perfect solutions to the problems it helps solve.
   b. **Applying Concepts** Suppose a robot that cooks meals in minutes has been invented. What positive impacts might it have?

   c. **Relating Cause and Effect** What negative impacts might the robot have over time on jobs, the pace of life, and other things?
4. a. **Defining** What is a risk-benefit analysis?
   b. **Problem Solving** What risks and benefits should be considered when deciding whether or not to buy an insect repellent?
   c. **Making Judgments** Do you think that government agencies should perform risk-benefit analyses on all insect repellents? Explain your reasoning.

Writing in Science

Summary Suppose you are a curator of a history museum. You are organizing an exhibit featuring inventions that have had dramatic impacts on society. Choose one invention that changed people's lives after it was invented. Write a summary about the invention to be posted at the exhibit.

Technology Design Skills

Reading Preview

Key Concepts
- What are the steps in the technology design process, and what is involved in each step?
- What are patents?

Key Terms
- engineer • brainstorming
- constraint • trade-off
- prototype • troubleshooting
- patent

Target Reading Skill
Sequencing A sequence is the order in which a series of events occurs. As you read, make a flowchart that shows the steps in the technology design process. Put the steps of the process in separate boxes in the flowchart in the order in which they typically occur.

The Technology Design Process

Identify the need.

↓

Research the problem.

↓

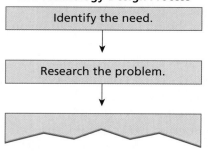

Lab zone ▶ Discover **Activity**

Identifying a Need

1. With a team of three or four classmates, make a list of foods that people commonly heat in a microwave oven.
2. Discuss with your group the quality of these foods. Could any of them be improved? Think about convenience, cooking time, and packaging as well as the taste and texture of the actual food.
3. As a group, decide which improvement is most important.

Think It Over
Communicating You work for a company that produces foods for microwave ovens. Write a memo to the design team, explaining the improvement you want made in the product.

You watch the timer count down as you wait for the sound. Pop! It's starting. Pop, pop, pop! It's getting faster. You watch the bag inflate as the popping gets more intense. Now you can smell it. Just a few seconds to go, and the popping slows down. Beep! Your popcorn is ready. Be careful as you take it out of the microwave oven—the bag is hot!

Have you ever wondered about the microwave oven—what it is made of and how its parts function together? The design of the microwave oven is the key to its success as a technology.

A microwave oven cooks food by exposing it to high-energy waves called microwaves. Inside the oven, a device called a magnetron shown in Figure 23 produces microwaves. The water in food absorbs the microwaves. Any microwaves that "miss" the food hit the inside of the oven and bounce around until they hit the food and are absorbed.

When the water in food absorbs the microwaves, the energy raises the temperature of the food. When the water inside a kernel of popcorn gets hot enough, it expands and the kernel pops.

How a Microwave Oven Works

A microwave oven produces microwaves and scatters them throughout the oven to reach the food to be cooked.

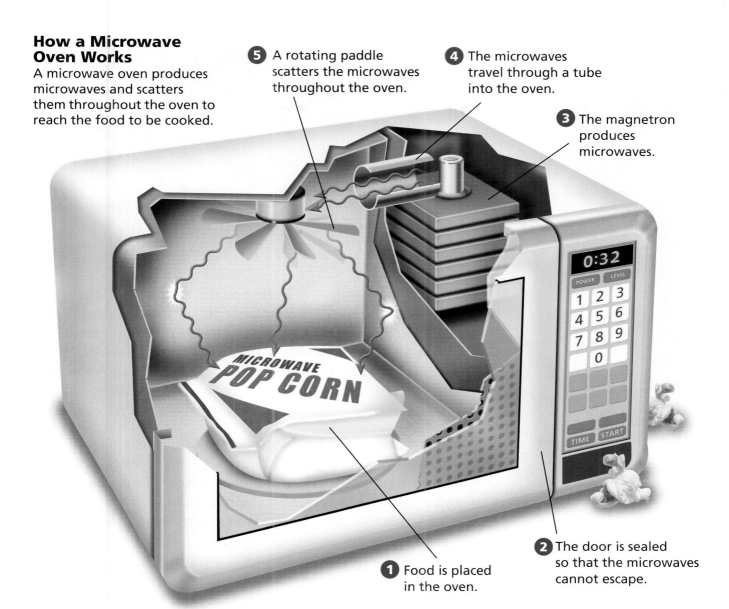

5 A rotating paddle scatters the microwaves throughout the oven.

4 The microwaves travel through a tube into the oven.

3 The magnetron produces microwaves.

1 Food is placed in the oven.

2 The door is sealed so that the microwaves cannot escape.

FIGURE 23
Microwave Oven
A microwave oven produces microwaves and scatters them throughout the oven to reach the food to be cooked.

The Technology Design Process

The microwave oven was the result of a technology design process. The technology design process is a method by which an idea for a new technology is developed into a final product. This process is sometimes called the engineering design process because it often involves the work of engineers. An **engineer** is a person who is trained to use both technological and scientific knowledge to solve practical problems.

Identifying a Need Microwaves were used for radar long before they were used for cooking. The ability of microwave energy to heat matter was noticed in the 1940s. However, the main focus of research at the time was on radar technology. It took more than 20 years to go from the discovery that microwaves could heat matter to a countertop microwave oven.

Go Online
PHSchool.com

For: More on microwave ovens
Visit: PHSchool.com
Web Code: cgh-5030

FIGURE 24
Identifying a Need
The first microwave oven was very large. It stood about 1.7 meters tall and had a mass of more than 340 kilograms!
Comparing and Contrasting *How is the modern microwave oven shown here different from the first model?*

The first microwave ovens, produced in 1947, were large, expensive, and complicated to install. They would not fit easily into someone's kitchen. **When engineers identify a need, they clearly define the problem they are trying to solve.** In this case, the need that was identified was for a microwave oven that would not take up too much space in a kitchen and not cost too much. In addition, it should be safe and easy to use.

Researching the Problem What is the next stage for the engineering team? **After defining a problem, engineers need to research it fully. When engineers research a problem, they gather information that will help them in their tasks.**

There are many ways that engineers obtain information related to the product they are designing. The engineers may read books and articles about the topic. They may also attend conferences, where they can share ideas with other researchers. Engineers usually perform experiments related to the technology they are designing. In addition, engineers often talk to people like you to find out what customers want.

Engineers have to think about details that the people who use the product may take for granted. For example, when engineers work on designs for microwave ovens, one of the considerations is the size. The microwave oven must fit into a reasonable amount of space on a kitchen counter or under a cabinet. But it has to have enough space inside to hold a plate or bowl of food.

Designing a Solution Once a team has a clear understanding of the problem, it is time to start thinking about solutions. **The solution stage involves coming up with ideas, or thinking about different ways to solve the problem. Engineers weigh many possible solutions and choose the best one.** The best design is the one that meets the needs and has the fewest negative characteristics.

An important activity that helps generate ideas is called brainstorming. **Brainstorming** is a process in which group members freely suggest any creative solutions that come to mind. After brainstorming, engineers may refine their ideas by making sketches or constructing models.

Engineers must evaluate the constraints of each possible design. A **constraint** is any factor that limits or restricts a design. For example, the microwave oven must have metal walls so that the microwaves bounce around inside instead of escaping.

Another physical constraint that engineers must consider is the strength of the materials they use. Additional constraints might relate to how much money the finished product can cost and the overall size and appearance of the product. The amount of time needed to manufacture a product can be an additional constraint that engineers must consider.

A team must sometimes make trade-offs on some features of the design. A **trade-off** is an exchange in which one benefit is given up in order to obtain another. For example, people want to be able to see inside the microwave oven. A microwave oven cannot have a light bulb within the oven because the microwaves would overheat the bulb's filament, causing the light bulb to burn out. The light in a microwave oven is behind a metal grid. This design protects the light bulb, but it does reduce the amount of light inside the oven.

 **What is brainstorming?**

FIGURE 25
Design Features
The circular object at the top of this microwave oven rotates to distribute the microwaves evenly throughout the oven. The light is behind a metal grid so that the microwaves cannot overheat the bulb.

Building a Prototype A **prototype** is a working model used to test a design. Prototypes are generally full size and made of the materials proposed for the final product. Many prototypes today, however, are completely "virtual," or computer generated.

Prototypes are used to test the operation of a product, including how well it works, how long it lasts, and how safe it is to use. One of the important tests for a microwave oven is the fit of the door. If the door does not seal correctly, microwaves will leak out. A microwave detector held near the door will indicate if there is leakage. In addition to wasting energy, leakage is a safety hazard.

Troubleshooting and Redesigning The next stage in the design process is to identify the causes of any problems and to redesign the product to address the problems. The process of analyzing a design problem and finding a way to fix it is called **troubleshooting**.

If the leakage test shows that the door becomes loose over time, the engineers have to change the design. Then the new door has to be tested to make sure that the change has solved the problem.

Communicating the Solution Engineers must communicate to consumers how a product meets their needs. They must also communicate with those involved in bringing the product to consumers. For example, engineers need to explain the design to manufacturers who will produce the product. The engineers must also describe their ideas to marketing people, who will advertise the product.

Reading Checkpoint What is a prototype?

FIGURE 26

Communicating With Consumers Companies use advertisements to tell customers about their products. This ad is for the first countertop microwave oven.

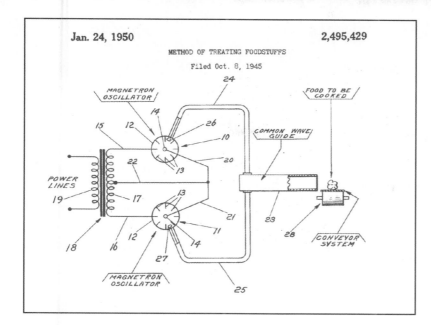

FIGURE 27
Patent
The application for a patent must include diagrams that show how the device works. This diagram is from the first patent issued for a microwave oven.

Patents

Because new products may bring fame or wealth to an inventor or company, **patents** are usually obtained to protect the inventions. **A patent is a legal document issued by a government that gives the inventor exclusive rights to make, use, or sell the invention for a limited time.** If others want to use the invention, they must obtain the patent owner's permission. After the patent's time runs out, however, anyone can make or sell the invention. An inventor may begin a patent application while the design is still in progress.

Section 5 Assessment

Target Reading Skill Sequencing Refer to your flowchart about the technology design process as you answer Question 1.

Reviewing Key Concepts

1. a. Listing List the stages in the technology design process. Describe each stage in a sentence.
   b. Explaining What are design constraints? Give two examples of constraints that should be considered when designing a bicycle frame.
   c. Making Judgments A team working on new packaging for microwaveable french toast has developed a design that will make the french toast crisper. It will also add to the cost of the product and make the package larger. Which trade-off would you make? Explain.

2. a. Defining What is a patent?
   b. Explaining Creativity is a key part of the design process. Explain how patents help reward creativity.
   c. Inferring Why do you think patents remain in effect only for a limited time, rather than forever?

Lab zone At-Home **Activity**

Instructional Manual With a family member, review the instruction manual for a device in your home. Possibilities include kitchen appliances, DVD players, cameras, and hair dryers. Think about the importance of communication between the manufacturer and the user. What would you do to make the manual clearer or easier to use?

1 Scientific Inquiry

Key Concepts

- Scientific inquiry refers to the ways in which scientists study the natural world and propose explanations based on the evidence they gather.

- In science, a hypothesis must be testable. Researchers carry out investigations that will either support or disprove the hypothesis.

- Unlike a theory, a scientific law describes an observed pattern in nature without explaining it.

- By having scientific literacy, you will be able to evaluate scientific information for accuracy.

Key Terms

- scientific inquiry • hypothesis • variable
- controlled experiment • manipulated variable
- responding variable • operational definition
- data • communicating • scientific theory
- scientific law • scientific literacy

2 Measurement—A Common Language

Key Concepts

- Using SI as the standard system of measurement allows scientists to compare data and communicate with each other about their results.

- The basic unit of length in the SI system is the meter (m) and the basic unit of mass is the kilogram (kg).

- Because density is actually made up of two other measurements—mass and volume—an object's density is expressed as a combination of two units.

- The second (s) is the SI unit used to measure time and the kelvin (K) is the unit for temperature.

- A conversion factor is an equation that shows how two units of measurement are related.

Key Terms

- metric system • SI • mass • weight
- volume • meniscus • density

3 Graphs in Science

Key Concepts

- Line graphs are used to show how one variable changes in response to another variable.

- A line of best fit emphasizes the overall trend shown by all the data taken as a whole.

- Line graphs allow you to identify trends and make predictions.

Key Terms

- graph • horizontal axis • vertical axis • origin
- coordinate • data point • line of best fit
- linear graph • slope • nonlinear graph

4 Technology and Society

Key Concepts

- The goal of technology is to improve the way people live.

- A technological system includes a goal, inputs, processes, outputs, and feedback.

- In addition to positive effects, technology can have negative consequences.

- In deciding whether to use a particular technology people analyze its risks and benefits.

Key Terms

- technology • obsolete • system • goal
- input • process • output • feedback
- risk-benefit analysis

5 Technology Design Skills

Key Concepts

- When engineers identify a need, they define the problem they are trying to solve. They gather information and find ways to solve the problem.

- Prototypes are used to test the operation of a product. Then engineers identify the causes of any problems and to redesign the product.

- A patent is issued by a government and gives the inventor exclusive rights to make, use, or sell the invention for a limited time.

Key Terms

- engineer • brainstorming • constraint
- trade-off • prototype • troubleshooting • patent

Review and Assessment

Organizing Information

Identifying Main Ideas Copy the graphic organizer about technological systems onto a separate sheet of paper. Then complete it and add a title. (For more on Identifying Main Ideas, see the Skills Handbook.)

Main Idea

A technological system includes a goal, inputs, processes, outputs, and in some cases, feedback.

Detail	Detail	Detail	Detail	Detail
a. ___?___	b. ___?___	c. ___?___	d. ___?___	e. ___?___

Reviewing Key Terms

Choose the letter of the best answer.

1. The facts, figures, and other evidence gathered through observations are called
   a. predictions.
   b. hypotheses.
   c. conclusions.
   d. data.

2. Being able to understand basic scientific terms and principles well enough to apply them to your life is called
   a. classifying.
   b. scientific inquiry.
   c. scientific literacy.
   d. controlling variables.

3. The curved surface of the water in a graduated cylinder is called a
   a. slope.   b. prototype.
   c. meniscus.   d. variable.

4. To emphasize the overall trend shown by the data in a line graph, you should draw a
   a. line of best fit.   b. slope.
   c. y-axis.   d. data point.

5. The process of evaluating the possible problems of a technology compared to its expected advantages is called
   a. feedback.
   b. risk-benefit analysis.
   c. brainstorming.
   d. prototyping.

If the statement is true, write *true*. If it is false, change the underlined word or words to make the statement true.

6. A <u>hypothesis</u> is a factor that can change in an experiment.

7. A <u>scientific theory</u> is a well-tested explanation for a wide range of observations.

8. A common unit of <u>volume</u> is g/cm^3.

9. The horizontal axis on a graph is also known as the <u>x-axis</u>.

10. A <u>constraint</u> is any factor that limits or restricts a technological design.

Writing in Science

Interview You are a sports reporter interviewing an Olympic swimmer who lost the silver medal by a few hundreths of a second. Write a one page interview in which you discuss the meaning of time and the advanced instruments used to measure time.

DISCOVERY CHANNEL **SCHOOL**™

The Work of Scientists

Video Preview
Video Field Trip
▶ Video Assessment

Review and Assessment

Checking Concepts

11. What are some ways scientists communicate with one another?

12. Why is it important to have clear operational definitions in an experiment?

13. In your own words, describe the difference between mass and weight.

14. Give an example of an obsolete technology and an emerging technology.

15. Do you think that technology affected the lives of people living in your great-grandparents' generation? Explain.

16. What steps might engineers take to research a design problem fully?

Thinking Critically

17. Making Judgments You read an ad claiming that scientific studies prove that frozen fruit is more nutritious than canned vegetables. What questions would you want answered before you accept this claim?

18. Inferring Suppose you are doing an experiment and recording your results. When would a line graph be more useful than a data table? When would a data table be more useful than a line graph?

19. Relating Cause and Effect The keyboard is the most common input device in a computer system. What might cause keyboards to become obsolete?

20. Problem Solving Suppose you came home to the scene below. How might you change the tank's design so that the cat couldn't get into it and air could circulate?

Math Practice

21. Calculating Density An ice cube with a volume of 9 cm³ has a mass of 8.1 g. What is its density?

22. Converting Units You just agreed to take part in a 2,500-m race to raise money for a good cause. How many kilometers will you be running?

Applying Skills

Use the data table below to answer Questions 23–24.

Three students conducted a controlled experiment to find out how walking and running affected their heart rates.

Effect of Activity on Heart Rate (in beats per minute)			
Student	Heart Rate (at rest)	Heart Rate (walking)	Heart Rate (running)
1	70	90	115
2	72	80	100
3	80	100	120

23. Controlling Variables What is the manipulated variable in this experiment? What is the responding variable?

24. Designing Experiments Design a controlled experiment to determine which activity has more of an effect on a person's heart rate—jumping rope or doing push-ups.

Lab zone Chapter **Project**

Performance Assessment Display your model and explain how you chose its scale. What was the most difficult thing about creating your model to scale? How could you improve your model?

🦅 End-of-Grade Test Practice

Choose the letter of the best answer.

1. What would be the best way to measure the mass of a small object like a rock?
   A using a graduated cylinder
   B using a bathroom scale
   C using a triple-beam balance
   D using a meter stick

2. Engineers have designed a car with a new engine and body design. Which of the following trade-offs would have a negative impact on public safety?
   A choosing lower-cost materials over good results in crash tests
   B choosing the appearance of the car seats over their comfort
   C choosing to install a more powerful music system over a better air conditioning system
   D choosing a more powerful engine over better gas mileage

3. A new sunscreen that has to be applied only once a week has been developed. The sunscreen is an example of
   A energy and power technology
   B communication technology
   C construction technology
   D biological and chemical technology

The graph compares how well two different brands of insulated mugs retained heat. Use the graph to answer question 4.

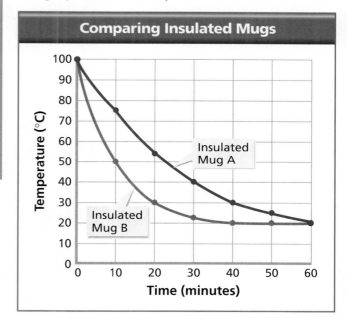

Comparing Insulated Mugs

Insulated Mug A

Insulated Mug B

4. What was the manipulated variable in this experiment?
   A the temperature of the water
   B location of the travel mug
   C brand of travel mug
   D how long the water was allowed to cool

Constructed Response

5. Suppose a newly designed robot automatically scans products at checkout lines in supermarkets. The robot can perform no other function. The cost to install a robot at a cash register is less than the cost of hiring a cashier. Describe some of the positive and negative impacts that this new technology might have on society.

Chapter 2

The Atmosphere

Standard Course of Study

1.01 Identify and create questions and hypotheses.

1.02 Develop appropriate experimental procedures.

1.03 Apply safety procedures.

1.04 Analyze variables.

1.05 Analyze evidence.

1.06 Use mathematics to gather, organize, and present data.

1.07 Prepare models and/or computer simulations.

1.08 Use oral and written language.

1.09 Use technologies and information systems.

2.01 Explore definitions of "technology."

2.02 Use information systems.

3.01 Explain the composition, properties, and structure of the atmosphere.

3.02 Describe observable and measurable properties to predict air quality.

3.03 Conclude that environments and organisms require stewardship.

3.04 Evaluate how humans impact air quality.

3.05 Examine atmospheric properties.

Bubbles are pockets of air surrounded ▶ by a thin film of liquid.

Discovery CHANNEL SCHOOL

The Atmosphere

▶ Video Preview
Video Field Trip
Video Assessment

Lab zone™ Chapter **Project**

Watching the Weather

The weather is always changing. If you pay close attention to weather patterns, you can learn to predict whether a storm is brewing or fair weather will continue. In this project, you will observe weather conditions without using instruments. Then you will look for hints about tomorrow's weather in the weather conditions today.

Your Goal Your project must

● include a plan for observing and describing a variety of weather conditions over a period of two to three weeks
● show your observations in a daily weather log
● display your findings about weather conditions

Plan It! Begin by discussing what weather conditions you can observe. Decide how, when, and where you will make your observations. Organize a notebook to record them. Think of ways to make comparisons from day to day. Then begin your observations. Look for patterns in your data. At the end of the chapter, you will display your weather observations to the class.

Chapter 2 ◆ 45

The Air Around You

Reading Preview

Key Concepts
- What is the composition of Earth's atmosphere?
- How is the atmosphere important to living things?

Key Terms
- weather
- atmosphere
- ozone
- water vapor

Target Reading Skill

Using Prior Knowledge Before you read, look at the section headings and visuals to see what this section is about. Then write what you know about the atmosphere in a graphic organizer like the one below. As you read, write what you learn.

What You Know
1. The atmosphere contains oxygen.
2.

What You Learned
1.
2.

Lab zone Discover **Activity**

How Long Will the Candle Burn?

1. Put on your goggles.
2. Stick a small piece of modeling clay onto an aluminum pie pan. Push a short candle into the clay. Carefully light the candle.
3. Hold a small glass jar by the bottom. Lower the mouth of the jar over the candle until the jar rests on the pie pan. As you do this, start a stopwatch or note where the second hand is on a clock.
4. Watch the candle carefully. How long does the flame burn?
5. Wearing an oven mitt, remove the jar. Relight the candle and then repeat Steps 3 and 4 with a larger jar.

Think It Over
Inferring How would you explain any differences between your results in Steps 4 and 5?

The sky is full of thick, dark clouds. In the distance you see a bright flash. Thirty seconds later, you hear a crack of thunder. You begin to run and reach your home just as the downpour begins. That was close! From your window you look out to watch the storm.

Does the weather where you live change often, or is it fairly constant from day to day? **Weather** is the condition of Earth's atmosphere at a particular time and place. But what is the atmosphere? Earth's **atmosphere** (AT muh sfeer) is the envelope of gases that surrounds the planet. To understand the relative size of the atmosphere, imagine that Earth is the size of an apple. If you breathe on the apple, a thin film of water droplets will form on its surface. Earth's atmosphere is like that water on the apple—a thin layer of gases on Earth's surface.

◀ From space, Earth's atmosphere appears as a thin layer near the horizon.

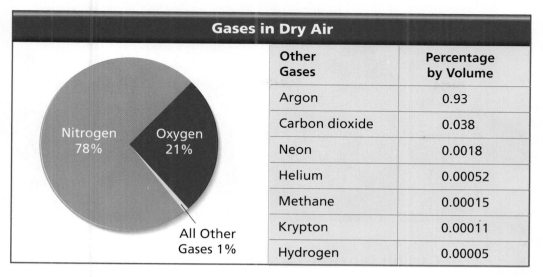

Gases in Dry Air

Other Gases	Percentage by Volume
Argon	0.93
Carbon dioxide	0.038
Neon	0.0018
Helium	0.00052
Methane	0.00015
Krypton	0.00011
Hydrogen	0.00005

Nitrogen 78%

Oxygen 21%

All Other Gases 1%

Composition of the Atmosphere

The atmosphere is made up of a mixture of atoms and molecules of different kinds. An atom is the smallest unit of a chemical element that can exist by itself. Molecules are made up of two or more atoms. **Earth's atmosphere is made up of nitrogen, oxygen, carbon dioxide, water vapor, and many other gases, as well as particles of liquids and solids.**

Nitrogen As you can see in Figure 1, nitrogen is the most abundant gas in the atmosphere. It makes up a little more than three fourths of the air we breathe. Each nitrogen molecule consists of two nitrogen atoms.

Oxygen Even though oxygen is the second most abundant gas in the atmosphere, it makes up less than one fourth of the volume. Plants and animals take oxygen directly from the air and use it to release energy from their food.

Oxygen is also involved in many other important processes. Any fuel you can think of, from the gasoline in a car to the candles on a birthday cake, uses oxygen as it burns. Without oxygen, a fire will go out. Burning uses oxygen rapidly. During other processes, oxygen is used slowly. For example, steel in cars and other objects reacts slowly with oxygen to form iron oxide, or rust.

Most oxygen molecules have two oxygen atoms. **Ozone** is a form of oxygen that has three oxygen atoms in each molecule instead of the usual two. Have you ever noticed a pungent smell in the air after a thunderstorm? This is the odor of ozone, which forms when lightning interacts with oxygen in the air.

 **What is ozone?**

FIGURE 2
Burning Uses Oxygen
Oxygen is necessary in order for the wood to burn.

FIGURE 3
Water Vapor in the Air
There is very little water vapor in the air over the desert where this lizard lives. In the tropical rain forest (right), where the frog lives, as much as four percent of the air may be water vapor.

Breathe In, Breathe Out

How can you detect carbon dioxide in the air you exhale?

1. Put on your goggles.
2. Fill a glass or beaker halfway with limewater.
3.  Using a straw, slowly blow air through the limewater for about a minute. **CAUTION:** *Do not suck on the straw or drink the limewater.*
4. What happens to the limewater?

Developing Hypotheses
What do you think would happen if you did the same experiment after jogging for 10 minutes? What would your results tell you about exercise and carbon dioxide?

Carbon Dioxide Each molecule of carbon dioxide has one atom of carbon and two atoms of oxygen. Carbon dioxide is essential to life. Plants must have carbon dioxide to produce food. When the cells of plants and animals break down food to produce energy, they give off carbon dioxide as a waste product.

When fuels such as coal and gasoline are burned, they release carbon dioxide. Burning these fuels increases the amount of carbon dioxide in the atmosphere.

Other Gases Oxygen and nitrogen together make up 99 percent of dry air. Argon and carbon dioxide make up most of the other one percent. The remaining gases are called trace gases because only small amounts of them are present.

Water Vapor So far, we have discussed the composition of dry air. In reality, air is not dry because it contains water vapor. **Water vapor** is water in the form of a gas. Water vapor is invisible. It is not the same thing as steam, which is made up of tiny droplets of liquid water. Each water molecule contains two atoms of hydrogen and one atom of oxygen.

The amount of water vapor in the air varies greatly from place to place and from time to time. Water vapor plays an important role in Earth's weather. Clouds form when water vapor condenses out of the air to form tiny droplets of liquid water or crystals of ice. If these droplets or crystals become heavy enough, they can fall as rain or snow.

Particles Pure air contains only gases. But pure air exists only in laboratories. In the real world, air also contains tiny solid and liquid particles of dust, smoke, salt, and other chemicals. You can see some of these particles in the air around you, but most of them are too small to see.

✓ **Reading Checkpoint** What is water vapor?

Importance of the Atmosphere

Earth's atmosphere makes conditions on Earth suitable for living things. The atmosphere contains oxygen and other gases that you and other living things need to survive. In turn, living things affect the atmosphere. The atmosphere is constantly changing, with gases moving in and out of living things, the land, and the water.

Living things need warmth and liquid water. By trapping energy from the sun, the atmosphere keeps most of Earth's surface warm enough for water to exist as a liquid. In addition, Earth's atmosphere protects living things from dangerous radiation from the sun. The atmosphere also prevents Earth's surface from being hit by most meteoroids, or rocks from outer space.

Go Online

SciLINKS

For: Links on atmosphere
Visit: www.SciLinks.org
Web Code: scn-0911

Section 1 Assessment

Target Reading Skill Using Prior Knowledge
Review your graphic organizer and revise it based on what you just learned in the section.

Reviewing Key Concepts

1. **a.** **Defining** What is the atmosphere?
   b. **Listing** What are the four most common gases in dry air?
   c. **Explaining** Why are the amounts of gases in the atmosphere usually shown as percentages of dry air?
2. **a.** **Describing** What are three ways in which the atmosphere is important to life on Earth?

   b. **Predicting** How would the amount of carbon dioxide in the atmosphere change if there were no plants?
   c. **Developing Hypotheses** How would Earth be different without the atmosphere?

Writing in Science

Summary Write a paragraph that summarizes in your own words how oxygen from the atmosphere is important. Include its importance to living things and in other processes.

Air Pressure

Reading Preview

Key Concepts
- What are some of the properties of air?
- What instruments are used to measure air pressure?
- How does increasing altitude affect air pressure and density?

Key Terms
- density
- pressure
- air pressure
- barometer
- mercury barometer
- aneroid barometer
- altitude

Target Reading Skill

Identifying Main Ideas As you read the Properties of Air section, write the main idea—the biggest or most important idea—in a graphic organizer like the one below. Then write two supporting details. The supporting details give examples of the main idea.

Main Idea

Because air has mass, it also . . .

Detail   **Detail**

Lab zone Discover Activity

Does Air Have Mass?

1. Use a balance to find the mass of a deflated balloon.
2. Blow up the balloon and tie the neck closed. Predict whether the mass of the balloon plus the air you have compressed into it will differ from the mass of the deflated balloon.
3. Find the mass of the inflated balloon. Compare this to the mass of the deflated balloon. Was your prediction correct?

Think It Over

Drawing Conclusions What can you conclude about whether air has mass? Explain your conclusion.

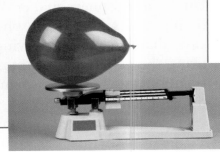

The air is cool and clear—just perfect for an overnight hiking trip. You've stuffed your backpack with your tent, sleeping bag, stove, and food. When you hoist your pack onto your back, its weight presses into your shoulders. That pack sure is heavy! By the end of the day, you'll be glad to take it off and get rid of all that weight.

But here's a surprise: Even when you take off your pack, your shoulders will still have pressure on them. The weight of the atmosphere itself is constantly pressing on your body.

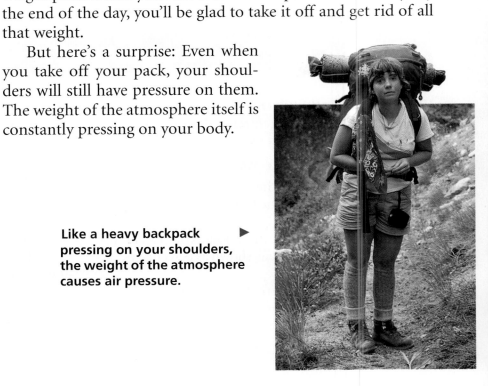

Like a heavy backpack pressing on your shoulders, the weight of the atmosphere causes air pressure.

Properties of Air

It may seem to you that air has no mass. But in fact, air consists of atoms and molecules, which have mass. So air must have mass. **Because air has mass, it also has other properties, including density and pressure.**

Density The amount of mass in a given volume of air is its **density.** You can calculate the density of a substance by dividing its mass by its volume.

$$\text{Density} = \frac{\text{Mass}}{\text{Volume}}$$

If there are more molecules in a given volume, the density is greater. If there are fewer molecules, the density is less.

Pressure The force pushing on an area or surface is known as **pressure.** The weight of the atmosphere exerts a force on surfaces. **Air pressure** is the result of the weight of a column of air pushing down on an area. The column of air extends upward through the entire atmosphere, as shown in Figure 4.

The atmosphere is heavy. The weight of the column of air above your desk is about the same as the weight of a large schoolbus. So why doesn't air pressure crush your desk? The reason is that the molecules in air push in all directions—down, up, and sideways. The air pushing down on top of your desk is balanced by the air pushing up on the bottom of your desk.

Air pressure can change from day to day. A denser substance has more mass per unit volume than a less dense one. So denser air exerts more pressure than less dense air.

 **Reading Checkpoint** How does the density of air affect air pressure?

FIGURE 4
Air Pressure
There is a column of air above you all the time. The weight of the air in the atmosphere causes air pressure.

Soda-Bottle Barometer

Here's how to build a device that shows changes in air pressure.

1. Fill a 2-liter soda bottle one-half full with water.
2. Lower a long straw into the bottle so that the end of the straw is in the water. Seal the mouth of the bottle around the straw with modeling clay.
3. Squeeze the sides of the bottle. What happens to the level of the water in the straw?
4. Let go of the sides of the bottle. Watch the level of the water in the straw.

Inferring Explain your results in terms of air pressure.

Go Online
active.art

For: Measuring Air Pressure activity
Visit: PHSchool.com
Web Code: cfp-4012

Measuring Air Pressure

A **barometer** (buh RAHM uh tur) is an instrument that is used to measure air pressure. **Two common kinds of barometers are mercury barometers and aneroid barometers.**

Mercury Barometers Figure 5 shows the way a mercury barometer works. A **mercury barometer** consists of a glass tube open at the bottom end and partially filled with mercury. The space in the tube above the mercury is almost a vacuum—it contains very little air. The open end of the tube rests in a dish of mercury. The air pressure pushing down on the surface of the mercury in the dish is equal to the pressure exerted by the weight of the column of mercury in the tube. When the air pressure increases, it presses down more on the surface of the mercury. Greater air pressure forces the column of mercury higher. At sea level the mercury column is about 76 centimeters high, on average.

Aneroid Barometers If you have a barometer at home, it is probably an aneroid barometer. The word aneroid means "without liquid." An **aneroid barometer** (AN uh royd) has an airtight metal chamber, as shown in Figure 6. The metal chamber is sensitive to changes in air pressure. When air pressure increases, the thin walls of the chamber are pushed in. When the pressure drops, the walls bulge out. The chamber is connected to a dial by a series of springs and levers. As the shape of the chamber changes, the needle on the dial moves.

FIGURE 5
Mercury Barometer
Air pressure pushes down on the surface of the mercury in the dish, causing the mercury in the tube to rise. The air pressure is greater on the barometer on the right, so the mercury is higher in the tube.
Predicting *What happens to the level of mercury in the tube when the air pressure decreases?*

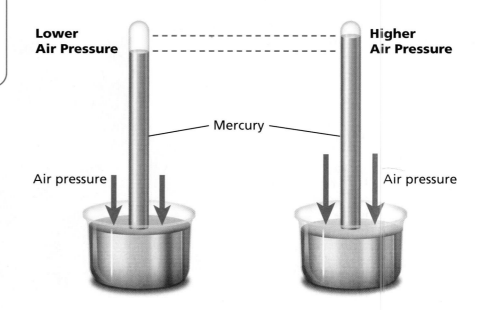

Lower Air Pressure — Higher Air Pressure — Mercury — Air pressure — Air pressure

FIGURE 6
Aneroid Barometer
This diagram shows an aneroid barometer. Changes in air pressure cause the walls of the airtight metal chamber to flex in and out. The needle on the dial indicates the air pressure.

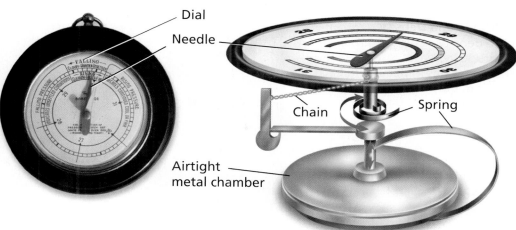

Dial

Needle

Chain

Spring

Airtight
metal chamber

Units of Air Pressure Weather reports use several different units for air pressure. Most weather reports for the general public use inches of mercury. For example, if the column of mercury in a mercury barometer is 30 inches high, the air pressure is "30 inches of mercury" or just "30 inches."

National Weather Service maps indicate air pressure in millibars. One inch of mercury is approximately 33.87 millibars, so 30 inches of mercury is approximately equal to 1,016 millibars.

 **Reading Checkpoint** **What are two common units that are used to measure air pressure?**

Altitude and the Properties of Air

At the top of a mountain, the air pressure is less than the air pressure at sea level. **Altitude,** or elevation, is the distance above sea level, the average level of the surface of the oceans. **Air pressure decreases as altitude increases. As air pressure decreases, so does density.**

Altitude Affects Air Pressure Imagine a stack of books. Which book has more weight on it, the second book from the top or the book at the bottom? The second book from the top has only the weight of one book on top of it. The book at the bottom of the stack has the weight of all the books pressing on it.

Air at sea level is like the bottom book. Sea-level air has the weight of the whole atmosphere pressing on it. So air pressure is greater at sea level. Air near the top of the atmosphere is like the second book from the top. There, the air has less weight pressing on it, and thus has lower air pressure.

FIGURE 7

Air Pressure and Altitude
Air pressure is greater at sea level and decreases as the altitude increases.

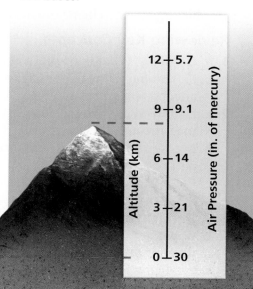

Sea Level

Altitude (km)	Air Pressure (in. of mercury)
12	5.7
9	9.1
6	14
3	21
0	30

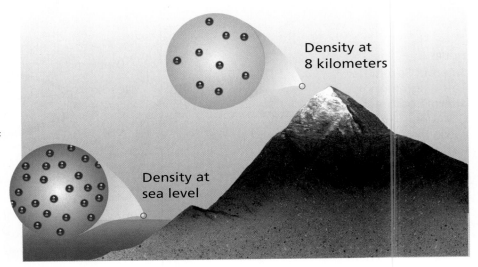

FIGURE 8
Altitude and Density
The density of air decreases as altitude increases. Air at sea level has more gas molecules in each cubic meter than air at the top of a mountain.

Density at 8 kilometers

Density at sea level

The Atmosphere

Video Preview
▶ Video Field Trip
Video Assessment

Altitude Also Affects Density As you go up through the atmosphere, the density of the air decreases. This means the gas molecules that make up the atmosphere are farther apart at high altitudes than they are at sea level. If you were near the top of a tall mountain and tried to run, you would quickly get out of breath. Why? The air contains 21 percent oxygen, whether you are at sea level or on top of a mountain. However, since the air is less dense at a high altitude, there are fewer oxygen molecules to breathe in each cubic meter of air than at sea level. So you would become short of breath quickly at high altitudes.

✓ **Reading Checkpoint** **Why is it hard to breathe at the top of a mountain?**

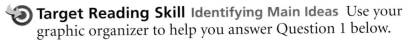

Section 2 Assessment

🎯 **Target Reading Skill** **Identifying Main Ideas** Use your graphic organizer to help you answer Question 1 below.

Reviewing Key Concepts

1. a. **Defining** What is air pressure?
   b. **Explaining** How does increasing the density of a gas affect its pressure?
2. a. **Listing** What two instruments are commonly used to measure air pressure?
   b. **Measuring** What units are commonly used to measure air pressure?
   c. **Calculating** How many millibars are equal to 27.23 inches of mercury?
3. a. **Defining** What is altitude?
   b. **Relating Cause and Effect** As altitude increases, how does air pressure change? How does density change?
   c. **Predicting** What changes in air pressure would you expect if you carried a barometer down a mine shaft?

Lab zone **At-Home Activity**

Model Air Pressure Here's how you can show your family that air has pressure. Fill a glass with water. Place a piece of cardboard over the top of the glass. Hold the cardboard in place with one hand as you turn the glass upside down. **CAUTION:** *Be sure the cardboard does not bend.* Now remove your hand from the cardboard. What happens? Explain to your family that the cardboard doesn't fall because the air pressure pushing up on it is greater than the weight of the water pushing down.

Working Under Pressure

Problem

How can a barometer detect changes in air pressure?

Skills Focus

interpreting data, drawing conclusions

Materials

- modeling clay
- scissors
- white glue
- tape
- pencil
- wide-mouthed glass jar
- metric ruler
- cardboard strip, 10 cm × 25 cm
- rubber band
- large rubber balloon
- drinking straw, 12–15 cm long

Procedure

1. Cut off the narrow opening of the balloon.

2. Fold the edges of the balloon outward. Carefully stretch the balloon over the open end of the glass jar. Use a rubber band to hold the balloon on the rim of the glass jar.

3. Place a small amount of glue on the center of the balloon top. Attach one end of the straw to the glue. Allow the other end to extend several centimeters beyond the edge of the glass jar. This is your pointer.

4. While the glue dries, fold the cardboard strip lengthwise and draw a scale along the edge with marks 0.5 cm apart. Write "High pressure" at the top of your scale and "Low pressure" at the bottom.

5. After the glue dries, add a pea-sized piece of modeling clay to the end of the pointer. Place your barometer and its scale in a location that is as free from temperature changes as possible. Note that the pointer of the straw must just reach the cardboard strip, as shown in the diagram.

6. Tape both the scale and the barometer to a surface so they do not move during your experiment.

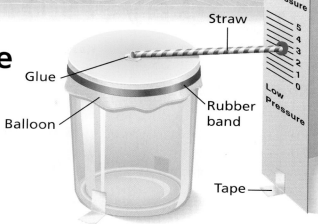

7. Make a data table like the one below in your notebook. Record the date and time. Note the level of the straw on the cardboard strip.

Data Table		
Date and Time	Air Pressure	Weather Conditions

8. Check the barometer twice a day. Record your observations in your data table.

9. Record the weather conditions for at least three days.

Analyze and Conclude

1. **Interpreting Data** What change in atmospheric conditions must occur to cause the free end of the straw to rise? What change must occur for it to fall?

2. **Drawing Conclusions** Based on your observations, what kind of weather is usually associated with high air pressure? With low air pressure?

3. **Communicating** Write a paragraph in which you discuss what effect, if any, a large temperature change might have on the accuracy of your barometer.

More to Explore

Compare your pressure readings with high and low pressure readings shown in newspaper weather maps for the same period. How do your readings compare with those in the newspaper?

Layers of the Atmosphere

Reading Preview

Key Concepts
- What are the four main layers of the atmosphere?
- What are the characteristics of each layer?

Key Terms
- troposphere
- stratosphere
- mesosphere
- thermosphere
- ionosphere
- exosphere

Target Reading Skill

Previewing Visuals Before you read Section 3, preview Figure 9. Then write at least two questions that you have about the diagram in a graphic organizer like the one below. As you read, answer your questions.

Layers of the Atmosphere

Q.	Where is the ozone layer?
A.	
Q.	

Lab zone Discover Activity

Is Air There?

1. Use a heavy rubber band to tightly secure a plastic bag over the top of a wide-mouthed jar.
2. Gently try to push the bag into the jar. What happens? Is the air pressure higher inside or outside the bag?
3. Remove the rubber band and line the inside of the jar with the plastic bag. Use the rubber band to tightly secure the edges of the bag over the rim of the jar.
4. Gently try to pull the bag out of the jar with your fingertips. What happens? Is the air pressure higher inside or outside the bag?

Think It Over

Predicting Explain your observations in terms of air pressure. How do you think differences in air pressure would affect a balloon as it traveled up through the atmosphere?

Imagine taking a trip upward into the atmosphere in a hot-air balloon. You begin on a warm beach near the ocean, at an altitude of 0 kilometers above sea level.

You hear a roar as the balloon's pilot turns up the burner to heat the air in the balloon. The balloon begins to rise, and Earth's surface gets farther and farther away. As the balloon rises to an altitude of 3 kilometers, you realize that the air is getting colder. As you continue to rise, the air gets colder still. At 6 kilometers you begin to have trouble breathing. The air is becoming less dense. It's time to go back down.

What if you could have continued your balloon ride up through the atmosphere? As you rose higher, the air pressure and temperature would change dramatically.

Scientists divide Earth's atmosphere into four main layers classified according to changes in temperature. These layers are the troposphere, the stratosphere, the mesosphere, and the thermosphere. The four main layers of the atmosphere are shown in Figure 9. Read on to learn more about each of these layers.

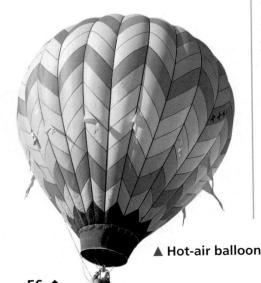

▲ **Hot-air balloon**

FIGURE 9

Layers of the Atmosphere

The atmosphere is divided into four layers: the troposphere, the stratosphere, the mesosphere, and the thermosphere. The thermosphere is further divided into the ionosphere and the exosphere.
Interpreting Diagrams *How deep is the mesosphere?*

Exosphere (Above 400 km)
Phone calls and television pictures are relayed by way of communications satellites that orbit Earth in the exosphere.

500 km

400 km

Ionosphere (80 to 400 km)
Ions in the ionosphere reflect radio waves back to Earth. The aurora borealis occurs in the ionosphere.

300 km

Thermosphere (Above 80 km)
The thermosphere extends from 80 km above Earth's surface outward into space. It has no definite outer limit.

200 km

Mesosphere (50 to 80 km)
Most meteoroids burn up in the mesosphere, producing meteor trails.

100 km

80 km

Stratosphere (12 to 50 km)
The ozone layer in the stratosphere absorbs ultraviolet radiation.

50 km

Troposphere (0 to 12 km)
Rain, snow, storms, and most clouds occur in the troposphere.

12 km

Go Online
PLANET DIARY

For: More on the ozone layer
Visit: PHSchool.com
Web Code: cfd-4013

The Troposphere

You live in the inner, or lowest, layer of Earth's atmosphere, the **troposphere** (TROH puh sfeer). *Tropo-* means "turning" or "changing." Conditions in the troposphere are more variable than in the other layers. **The troposphere is the layer of the atmosphere in which Earth's weather occurs.**

The depth of the troposphere varies from 16 kilometers above the equator to less than 9 kilometers above the North and South poles. Although it is the shallowest layer, the troposphere contains almost all of the mass of the atmosphere.

As altitude increases in the troposphere, the temperature decreases. On average, for every 1-kilometer increase in altitude, the air gets about 6.5 Celsius degrees cooler. At the top of the troposphere, the temperature stops decreasing and stays at about −60°C. Water here forms thin, feathery clouds of ice.

• Tech & Design in History •

Explorers of the Atmosphere
The atmosphere has been explored from the ground and from space.

**1643
Torricelli Invents
the Barometer**
Italian physicist and mathematician Evangelista Torricelli improved existing scientific instruments and invented some new ones. In 1643 he invented the mercury barometer.

**1746
Franklin Experiments
With Electricity**
American statesman and inventor Benjamin Franklin experimented with electricity in the atmosphere. To demonstrate that lightning is a form of electricity, Franklin flew a kite in a thunderstorm. However, Franklin did not hold the kite string in his hand, as this historical print shows.

**1804 Gay-Lussac
Studies the Upper
Troposphere**
French chemist Joseph-Louis Gay-Lussac ascended to a height of about 7 kilometers in a hydrogen balloon to study the upper troposphere. Gay-Lussac studied pressure, temperature, and humidity.

1600	1700	1800

The Stratosphere

The **stratosphere** extends from the top of the troposphere to about 50 kilometers above Earth's surface. *Strato-* means "layer" or "spread out." **The stratosphere is the second layer of the atmosphere and contains the ozone layer.**

The lower stratosphere is cold, about −60°C. Surprisingly, the upper stratosphere is warmer than the lower stratosphere. Why is this? The middle portion of the stratosphere contains a layer of air where there is much more ozone than in the rest of the atmosphere. (Recall that ozone is the three-atom form of oxygen.) When the ozone absorbs energy from the sun, the energy is converted into heat, warming the air. The ozone layer is also important because it protects Earth's living things from dangerous ultraviolet radiation from the sun.

 **Reading Checkpoint** **Why is the upper stratosphere warmer than the lower stratosphere?**

1931 Piccard Explores the Stratosphere
Swiss-Belgian physicist Auguste Piccard made the first ascent into the stratosphere. He reached a height of about 16 kilometers in an airtight cabin attached to a huge hydrogen balloon. Piccard is shown here with the cabin.

1960 First Weather Satellite Launched
TIROS-1, the first weather satellite equipped with a camera to send data back to Earth, was put into orbit by the United States. As later weather satellites circled Earth, they observed cloud cover and recorded temperatures and air pressures in the atmosphere.

1999 *Terra* Satellite Launched
The *Terra* satellite is equipped to study Earth's surface, atmosphere, and oceans from orbit. The data it gathers are used to help understand changes in Earth's climate.

1900   **2000**   **2100**

Math ▶ Analyzing Data

Changing Temperatures

The graph shows how temperatures in the atmosphere change with altitude. Use it to answer the questions below.

1. **Reading Graphs** What two variables are being graphed? In what unit is each measured?

2. **Reading Graphs** What is the temperature at the bottom of the stratosphere?

3. **Interpreting Data** Which layer of the atmosphere has the lowest temperature?

4. **Making Generalizations** Describe how temperature changes as altitude increases in the troposphere.

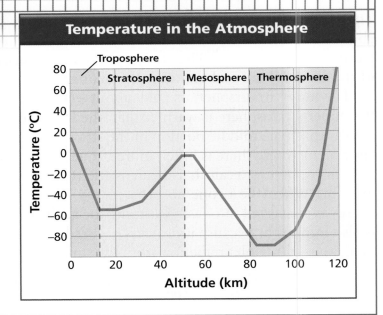

Temperature in the Atmosphere

The Mesosphere

Above the stratosphere, a drop in temperature marks the beginning of the next layer, the **mesosphere.** *Meso-* means "middle," so the mesosphere is the middle layer of the atmosphere. The mesosphere begins 50 kilometers above Earth's surface and ends at an altitude of 80 kilometers. In the outer mesosphere, temperatures approach −90°C.

The mesosphere is the layer of the atmosphere that protects Earth's surface from being hit by most meteoroids. Meteoroids are chunks of stone and metal from space. What you see as a shooting star, or meteor, is the trail of hot, glowing gases the meteoroid leaves behind in the mesosphere.

The Thermosphere

Near the top of the atmosphere, the air is very thin. At 80 kilometers above Earth's surface, the air is only about 0.001 percent as dense as the air at sea level. It's as though you took a cubic meter of air at sea level and expanded it into 100,000 cubic meters at the top of the mesosphere. **The outermost layer of Earth's atmosphere is the thermosphere.** The **thermosphere** extends from 80 kilometers above Earth's surface outward into space. It has no definite outer limit, but blends gradually with outer space.

The *thermo-* in thermosphere means "heat." Even though the air in the thermosphere is thin, it is very hot, up to 1,800°C. This is because sunlight strikes the thermosphere first. Nitrogen and oxygen molecules convert this energy into heat.

Despite the high temperature, you would not feel warm in the thermosphere. An ordinary thermometer would show a temperature well below 0°C. Why is that? Temperature is the average amount of energy of motion of each molecule of a substance. The gas molecules in the thermosphere move very rapidly, so the temperature is very high. However, the molecules are spaced far apart in the thin air. There are not enough of them to collide with a thermometer and warm it very much.

The thermosphere is divided into two layers. The lower layer, called the **ionosphere** (eye AHN uh sfeer), begins about 80 kilometers above the surface and extends to about 400 kilometers. Energy from the sun causes gas molecules in the ionosphere to become electrically charged particles called ions. Radio waves bounce off ions in the ionosphere back to Earth's surface. Brilliant light displays, such as those shown in Figure 10, also occur in the ionosphere. In the Northern Hemisphere, these displays are called the Northern Lights, or the aurora borealis. Auroras are caused by particles from the sun that enter the ionosphere near the poles. These particles strike atoms in the ionosphere, causing them to glow.

Exo- means "outer," so the **exosphere** is the outer portion of the thermosphere. The exosphere extends from about 400 kilometers outward for thousands of kilometers.

FIGURE 10
Aurora Borealis
The aurora borealis, seen from Fairbanks, Alaska, creates a spectacular display in the night sky.

 Reading Checkpoint) **What is the ionosphere?**

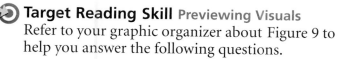

Section 3 Assessment

Target Reading Skill Previewing Visuals
Refer to your graphic organizer about Figure 9 to help you answer the following questions.

Reviewing Key Concepts

1. a. Listing List the four main layers of the atmosphere, beginning with the layer closest to Earth's surface.
  b. Classifying What properties are used to distinguish the layers of the atmosphere?
  c. Interpreting Diagrams According to Figure 9, in which layer of the atmosphere do communications satellites orbit?
2. a. Identifying Give at least one important characteristic of each of the four main layers of Earth's atmosphere.

  b. Comparing and Contrasting How does temperature change as height increases in the troposphere? Compare this to how temperature changes with height in the stratosphere.
  c. Applying Concepts Why would you not feel warm in the thermosphere, even though temperatures can be up to 1,800°C?

Writing in Science

Cause and Effect Paragraph How do you think Earth's surface might be different if it had no atmosphere? Write a paragraph explaining your ideas.

Air Quality

Reading Preview

Key Concepts
- What are the major sources of air pollution?
- What causes smog and acid rain?
- What can be done to improve air quality?

Key Terms
- pollutants
- photochemical smog
- acid rain

Target Reading Skill

Outlining As you read, make an outline about air quality that you can use for review. Use the red headings for the main topics and the blue headings for the subtopics.

Air Quality
I. Sources of air pollution
A. Natural sources
B.
C.
II. Smog and acid rain
A.

Discover **Activity**

What's on the Jar?
1. Put on your goggles.
2.  Put a small piece of modeling clay on a piece of aluminum foil. Push a candle into the clay. Light the candle.
3. Wearing an oven mitt, hold a glass jar by the rim so that the bottom of the jar is just above the flame.

Think It Over
Observing What do you see on the jar? Where did it come from?

As you are reading this page, you are breathing without even thinking about it. Breathing brings air into your lungs, where the oxygen you need is taken into your body. But not everything in the air is healthful. You may also breathe in tiny particles or even a small amount of harmful gases.

If you live in a large city, you may have noticed a brown haze in the air. Even if you live far from a city, the air around you may contain pollutants. **Pollutants** are harmful substances in the air, water, or soil. Air that contains harmful particles and gases is said to be polluted.

Air pollution can affect the health of humans and other living things. Figure 12 identifies the effects of some pollutants.

FIGURE 11
Air Pollution
Air pollution in large cities, such as Mexico City, can cause serious health problems.

Effects of Air Pollution on Human Health		
Pollutant	**Source**	**Health Effect**
Carbon monoxide	Burning of fossil fuels	Reduced ability of blood to deliver oxygen to cells
Nitrogen dioxide	Burning of fossil fuels	Breathing problems, lung damage
Ozone	Chemical reaction of certain carbon compounds	Breathing problems, asthma, eye irritation
Particles of dust, smoke, or soot	Burning of wood and fossil fuels, volcanic eruptions	Respiratory illnesses, nose and throat irritation
Sulfur dioxide	Burning of fossil fuels, volcanic eruptions	Breathing problems, lung damage

Dizziness and headaches

Eye, nose and throat irritation

Allergies

Cough

Lung diseases

Chest pains

FIGURE 12
Air pollution can cause many different problems. The table shows the health effects of air pollution. Pollen also can cause difficulties for people with allergies.

Sources of Pollution

Some air pollution occurs naturally. But many types of air pollution are the result of human activities.

Natural Sources Many natural processes add particles to the atmosphere. Forest fires, soil erosion, and dust storms release a great deal of smoke and dust into the air. The wind carries particles of molds and pollen. Erupting volcanoes spew out clouds of dust and ash along with poisonous gases.

Human Activities Human activities, such as farming and construction, can send soil and dust into the air. But most air pollution is the result of burning fossil fuels, such as coal, oil, gasoline, and diesel fuel. Almost half of this pollution comes from cars and other motor vehicles. Factories and power plants that burn coal and oil also release pollution.

When fossil fuels burn, they release both particles and gases. When people burn wood or coal, particles of soot enter the air. Soot gives smoke its dark color. All fossil fuels contain hydrocarbons, compounds made of hydrogen and carbon. As fossil fuels burn, some hydrocarbons do not burn completely and escape into the air. Burning fossil fuels produces a variety of pollutants, including carbon monoxide, nitrogen oxides, and sulfur oxides.

 **Reading Checkpoint** What are some air pollutants produced by burning fossil fuels?

Go Online
PHSchool.com

For: More on air pollution
Visit: PHSchool.com
Web Code: cfd-4014

Smog and Acid Rain

High levels of air pollution decrease the quality of the air. **The burning of fossil fuels can cause smog and acid rain.**

London-Type Smog One hundred years ago, the city of London, England, was dark and dirty. Factories burned coal, and most houses were heated by coal. The air was full of soot. In 1905, the term *smog* was created by combining the words *smoke* and *fog* to describe this type of air pollution. Typically, London-type smog forms when particles in coal smoke combine with water droplets in humid air. Today, people in London burn much less coal. As a result, the air in London now is much cleaner than it was 100 years ago.

Photochemical Smog Fortunately, London-type smog is no longer common in the United States. Instead, many cities today have another type of smog. The brown haze that develops in sunny cities is called **photochemical smog** (foh toh KEM ih kul). The *photo-* in photochemical means "light." Photochemical smog is formed by the action of sunlight on pollutants such as hydrocarbons and nitrogen oxides. These chemicals react to form a brownish mixture of ozone and other pollutants.

Recall that ozone in the stratosphere blocks ultraviolet radiation, thus protecting living things on Earth. But in the troposphere, ozone is a pollutant that can irritate the eyes, throat, and lungs. It can also harm plants and other living things and damage many materials.

FIGURE 13
Results of Acid Rain
This scientist is studying trees damaged by acid rain. Needle-leafed trees such as pines and spruce are especially sensitive to acid rain. Acid rain may make tree needles turn brown or fall off.

Acid Rain Another result of air pollution is acid rain. Rain is naturally slightly acidic, but rain that contains more acid than normal is known as **acid rain.**

How does acid rain form? The burning of coal that contains a lot of sulfur produces sulfur oxides, substances composed of oxygen and sulfur. Acid rain forms when nitrogen oxides and sulfur oxides combine with water in the air to form nitric acid and sulfuric acid. Rain, sleet, snow, fog, and even dry particles carry these two acids to trees and lakes.

Acid rain is sometimes strong enough to damage the surfaces of buildings and statues. It also harms lakes and ponds. Acid rain can make water so acidic that plants, amphibians, fish, and insects can no longer survive in it.

 **Reading Checkpoint** What is the main pollutant in photochemical smog?

Improving Air Quality

In the United States, the federal and state governments have passed a number of laws and regulations to reduce air pollution. The Environmental Protection Agency (EPA) monitors air pollutants in the United States. Air quality in this country has generally improved over the past 30 years. The amounts of most major air pollutants have decreased. Many newer cars cause less pollution than older models. Recently-built power plants are less polluting than power plants that have been in operation for many years.

However, there are now more cars on the road and more power plants burning fossil fuels than in the past. Unfortunately, the air in many American cities is still polluted. Voluntary measures, such as greater use of public transportation in place of driving, could reduce the total amount of air polllution produced. Many people think that stricter regulations are needed to control air pollution. Others argue that reducing air pollution can be very expensive and that the benefits of stricter regulations may not be worth the costs.

FIGURE 14
Public Tranportation
Public transportation, like the light rail system above, can reduce air pollution.

 **Reading Checkpoint** Explain one way that air quality could be improved.

Section 4 Assessment

Target Reading Skill

Outlining Use the information in your outline about air quality to help you answer the questions below.

Reviewing Key Concepts

1. a. Defining What is a pollutant?
   b. Identifying Name three natural processes and three human activities that cause air pollution.
   c. Summarizing What is the major source of air pollution today?
2. a. Identifying What human activity is responsible for the formation of smog and acid rain?
   b. Explaining What kinds of harm does photochemical smog cause?
   c. Inferring Do you think that photochemical smog levels are higher during the winter or during the summer? Explain.

3. a. Identifying What government agency monitors air quality?
   b. Summarizing How and why has the air quality changed in the United States over the last 30 years?

Lab zone At-Home **Activity**

Dust in the Air It's easy to see particles in the air. Gather your family members in a dark room. Open a window shade or blind slightly, or turn on a flashlight. Can they see tiny particles suspended in the beam of light? Discuss where the particles came from. What might be some natural sources? What might be some human sources?

Design Your Own Lab

How Clean Is the Air?

Problem

How do weather and location affect the number of particles in the air?

Skills Focus

measuring, interpreting data

Materials

- rubber band
- coffee filters
- thermometer
- low-power microscope
- vacuum cleaner with intake hose (1 per class)

Procedure

PART 1   Particles and Weather

1. Predict what factors will affect the number of particles you collect. How might different weather conditions affect your results?

2. In your notebook, make a data table like the one on the next page.

3. Place a coffee filter over the nozzle of the vacuum cleaner hose. Fasten the coffee filter securely to the hose with a rubber band. Make sure the air passes through the coffee filter as it enters the vacuum cleaner.

4. You will take air samples in the same outdoor location for five days. If necessary, you can run the vacuum cleaner cord out of a classroom window. **CAUTION:** *Do not use the vacuum cleaner outdoors on wet or rainy days.* If it is wet or rainy, collect the sample on the next clear day.

5. Hold the vacuum nozzle at least one meter above the ground each time you use the vacuum. Turn on the vacuum. Run the vacuum for 30 minutes.

6. While the vacuum is running, observe the weather conditions. Measure the outdoor temperature. Estimate the amount of precipitation, if any, since the previous observation. Note the direction from which the wind, if any, is blowing. Also note whether the wind is strong, light, or calm. Record your observations.

7. Shut off the vacuum. Remove the coffee filter from the nozzle. Label the filter with the place, time, and date. Draw a circle on the filter to show the area that was over the vacuum nozzle.

8. Place the coffee filter on the stage of a microscope (40 power). Be sure that the part of the filter that was over the vacuum nozzle is directly under the microscope lens. Without moving the coffee filter, count all the particles you see. Record the number in your data table.

9. Repeat Steps 3–8 each clear day.

PART 2   Particles and Locations

10. Based on what you learned in Part 1, write a hypothesis for how the number of particles you collect can vary between two locations. The locations you choose should differ in some factor that might influence particle numbers.

Data Table

Date and Time	Temperature	Amount of Precipitation	Wind Direction	Wind Speed	Number of Particles

11. Design an experiment to test your hypothesis. As you design your plan, consider the following:
    - What factors might affect the number of particles collected?
    - Which locations will you choose?
    - What procedure will you follow?
    - How will you control the variables in your experiment?
    - How will you record your new data?

12. Obtain your teacher's approval before carrying out your experiment. Be sure to record all your observations.

Analyze and Conclude

1. **Measuring** In Part 1, was there a day of the week when you collected more particles?

2. **Interpreting Data** What factors changed during the week that could have caused changes in the particle count recorded in Part 1?

3. **Inferring** Did the weather have any effect on your day-to-day results? If so, which weather factor do you think was most important?

4. **Interpreting Data** Did your experiment in Part 2 prove or disprove your hypothesis?

5. **Controlling Variables** In your experiment in Part 2, which variables did you control? What was the manipulated variable? The responding variable?

6. **Classifying** Make a list of some possible sources of the particles you collected. Are these sources natural, or did the particles come from manufactured products?

7. **Designing Experiments** How could you improve your method to obtain more particles out of the air?

8. **Communicating** Identify areas in or around your school where there may be high levels of dust and other airborne particles. Write a brochure that suggests what people should do to protect themselves in these areas. Include suggestions for improvements that might lower the levels of particles in the identified areas.

More to Explore

Do you think time of day will affect the number of particles you collect? Develop a hypothesis and a plan for testing it. Could you work with other classes to get data at different times of the day? Before carrying out your plan, get your teacher's approval.

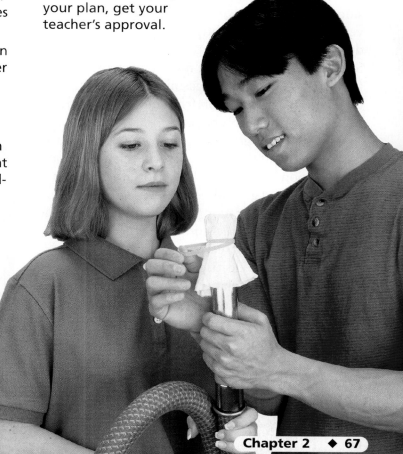

For: Data sharing
Visit: PHSchool.com
Web Code: cfd-4010

Cars and Clean Air

New technology and strict laws have brought cleaner air to many American cities. But in some places the air is still polluted. Cars and trucks cause about half the air pollution in cities. And there are more motor vehicles on the road every year!

Worldwide, there are nearly 600 million cars. More cars will mean more traffic jams and more air pollution. What can people do to reduce air pollution by cars?

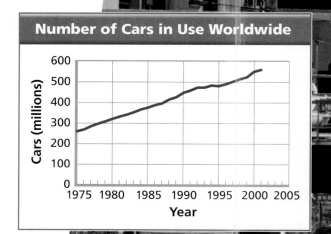

Number of Cars in Use Worldwide

The Issues

Can Cars Be Made to Pollute Less?

From 1975 until 1987, the fuel economy of new cars and light trucks improved significantly. However, since 1987, the average fuel economy of such vehicles has gotten slightly worse. Why? People are driving larger vehicles, such as trucks, vans, and SUVs. These vehicles have more power, but get fewer miles per gallon of gasoline. As a result, the total amount of pollution from motor vehicles has been increasing in recent years.

New technologies offer the promise of improved fuel economy in the future. Hybrid vehicles use a combination of gasoline and electricity to obtain much improved gas mileage. A few vehicles use fuels such as hydrogen or natural gas in place of gasoline. Vehicles using such fuels produce little pollution.

Battery-powered electric cars produce no air pollution. But the electricity to charge the batteries comes from power plants that may burn oil or coal. So electric cars produce some pollution indirectly.

A futuristic hybrid car ▼

U.S. Motor Vehicle Fuel Economy

Average Fuel Economy (miles per gallon)

— Cars and Light Trucks

Model Year
1975 1980 1985 1990 1995 2000 2005

Should People Drive Less?

Many car trips are shorter than a mile—an easy distance for most people to walk. People might also consider riding a bicycle sometimes instead of driving. Many cars on the road are occupied by just one person. People might consider riding with others in car pools or taking buses or trains instead of driving.

Are Stricter Standards or Taxes the Answer?

Some state governments have led efforts to reduce pollution. The state of California, for example, has strict anti-pollution laws. These laws set standards for gradually reducing pollutants released by cars. Stricter pollution laws might make new cars more expensive and old cars more costly to maintain.

Another approach is to make driving more expensive so that people use their cars less. That might mean higher gasoline taxes or fees for using the highways at busy times.

You Decide

1. Identify the Problem
In your own words, explain how trends in automobile use make it hard to improve air quality. What kinds of pollution are caused by automobiles?

2. Analyze the Options
What are some ways to reduce the pollution caused by cars? Should these actions be voluntary, or should governments require them?

3. Find a Solution
How would you encourage people to try to reduce the pollution from cars? Create a visual essay from newspaper and magazine clippings. Write captions to explain your solution.

Go Online
PHSchool.com

For: More on cars and clean air
Visit: PHSchool.com
Web Code: cfh-4010

Environmental Issues

Reading Preview

Key Concepts
- What are the general categories of environmental issues?
- How do decision makers balance different needs and concerns?

Key Terms
- natural resource
- renewable resource
- nonrenewable resource
- pollution
- environmental science

Target Reading Skill

Identifying Main Ideas As you read the Types of Environmental Issues section, write the main idea in a graphic organizer like the one below. Then write three supporting details that give examples of the main idea.

Main Idea

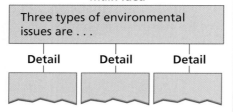

| Three types of environmental issues are . . . |
| Detail | Detail | Detail |

Lab zone Discover **Activity**

How Do You Decide?

1. On a sheet of paper, list the three environmental issues you think are most important today.
2. Next to each issue you have listed, write the reason you think it is important.
3. Form a group with three other classmates. Share your lists. Decide as a group which one of the issues on your lists is the most important.

Think It Over

Forming Operational Definitions Based on your group's discussion, how would you define *environmental issue?*

Here's a riddle for you: What is bigger than the United States and Mexico combined; is covered with more than two kilometers of ice; is a unique habitat for many animals; and is a source of oil, coal, and iron? The answer is Antarctica. Some people think of Antarctica as a useless, icy wasteland. But there are unique wildlife habitats in Antarctica. There are also valuable minerals beneath its thick ice.

Now the question is, What is the best use of Antarctica? Many people want access to its rich deposits of minerals and oil. Others worry that mining will harm its delicate ecosystems. Some people propose building hotels, parks, and ski resorts. But others feel that Antarctica should remain undeveloped. It is not even clear who should decide Antarctica's fate.

In 1998, 26 nations agreed to ban mining and oil exploration in Antarctica for at least 50 years. As resources become more scarce elsewhere in the world, the debate will surely continue.

| **1000** B.C.
About 50 million | **A.D. 1**
About 285 million |

Types of Environmental Issues

The debate about Antarctica's future is just one environmental issue that people face today. **Environmental issues fall into three general categories: resource use, population growth, and pollution.** Because these three types of issues are interconnected, they are very difficult to study and solve.

Resource Use Anything in the environment that is used by people is called a **natural resource.** Some natural resources are renewable. **Renewable resources** are either always available or are naturally replaced in a relatively short time. Renewable resources include sunlight, wind, fresh water, and trees. Some people think that renewable resources can never be used up. This is not true for some renewable resources. For example, if people cut down trees faster than they can grow back, the supply of this resource will decrease and could possibly run out.

Natural resources that are not replaced in a useful time frame are called **nonrenewable resources.** As nonrenewable resources such as coal or oil are used, the supply decreases.

Population Growth Figure 15 shows how the human population has changed in the last 3,000 years. You can see that the population grew very slowly until about A.D. 1650. Around that time, improvements in medicine, agriculture, and waste disposal began to enable people to live longer. The human population has been growing faster and faster since then. However, scientists do not expect the population to grow as rapidly in the future.

When a population grows, the demand for resources also grows. Has your town ever experienced a water shortage? If so, you might have noticed that people have been asked to restrict their water use. This sometimes happens in areas with fast-growing populations. The water supplies in such areas were designed to serve fewer people than they now do, so shortages sometimes occur during unusually warm or dry weather.

A.D. **2000**
About 6 billion

FIGURE 15
Human Population Growth
More than 6 billion people now live on Earth.
Making Generalizations
How has the human population changed over the past 1,000 years?

A.D. **1000**
About 300 million

Go Online
SciLINKS NSTA

For: Links on the environment
Visit: www.SciLinks.org
Web Code: scn-0531

Pollution The contamination of Earth's land, water, or air is called **pollution.** Pollution can be caused by a variety of factors, including chemicals, wastes, noise, heat, and light. Pollution can destroy wildlife and cause human health problems.

Pollution can be related to resource use. As you probably know, the burning of gasoline releases pollutants into the air. With more cars on the road, more gasoline is used, so more pollutants are released into the air.

Pollution can also be related to population growth. For example, as populations grow, and more people need to be fed, more fertilizers and other chemicals may be used to produce that food. As these chemicals run off the land, they can pollute bodies of water.

✓ **Reading Checkpoint** **What are three factors that can cause pollution?**

Science and **History**

Making a Difference
Can one individual change the way people think? The leaders featured in this timeline have influenced the way that many people think about environmental issues.

1890 John Muir
The actions of John Muir, a nature writer from California, lead to the establishment of Yosemite National Park.

1905 Gifford Pinchot
Forestry scientist Gifford Pinchot is appointed the first director of the United States Forest Service. His goal is to manage forests scientifically to meet current and future lumber needs.

1903 Theodore Roosevelt
President Theodore Roosevelt establishes the first National Wildlife Refuge on Pelican Island, Florida, to protect the brown pelican.

| 1880 | 1900 | 1920 |

Making Environmental Decisions

Dealing with environmental issues means making decisions. These decisions can be made at personal, local, national, or global levels. Your decision to walk to your friend's house rather than ride in a car is made at a personal level. A town's decision about how to dispose of its trash is made at a local level. A decision about whether the United States should allow oil drilling in a wildlife refuge is a decision made on a national level. Decisions about how to protect Earth's atmosphere are made on a global level.

Every decision has some impact on the environment. Your personal decisions of what to eat or how to travel have a small impact. But when the personal decisions of millions of people are combined, they have a huge impact on the environment.

Writing in Science

Research and Write Find out more about one of the people featured in this timeline. Write a short biography of the person's life that explains how he or she became involved in environmental issues. What obstacles did the person overcome to accomplish his or her goal?

1962 Rachel Carson
Biologist Rachel Carson writes *Silent Spring*, which describes the harmful effects of pesticides on the environment. The book raises awareness of how human activities can affect the environment.

1969 Marjory Stoneman Douglas
At the age of 79, journalist Marjory Stoneman Douglas founds Friends of the Everglades. This grassroots organization is dedicated to preserving the unique Florida ecosystem. She continued to work for the Everglades until her death in 1998.

1949 Aldo Leopold
A Sand County Almanac is published shortly after the death of its author, Aldo Leopold. This classic book links wildlife management to the science of ecology.

1977 Wangari Maathai
Biologist Wangari Maathai founds the Green Belt Movement. This organization encourages restoring forests in Kenya and in other African nations.

1940	1960	1980

FIGURE 16
Resource Use

Decisions about undeveloped land must weigh the costs and benefits. Some benefits of parks are shown here.

Scenic Benefit The park is a beautiful and peaceful place where we can hike and bird watch.

Economic Benefit The trees and other resources of the park provide jobs for loggers and builders.

Balancing Different Needs Lawmakers work with many groups to make environmental decisions. One such group is environmental scientists. **Environmental science** is the study of natural processes in the environment and how humans can affect them. But the data provided by environmental scientists are only part of the decision-making process.

Environmental decision making requires a delicate balance between the needs of the environment and the needs of people. **To help balance the different opinions on an environmental issue, decision makers weigh the costs and benefits of a proposal.**

Types of Costs and Benefits Costs and benefits are often economic. Will a proposal provide jobs? Will it cost too much money? But costs and benefits are not only measured in terms of money. For example, suppose a state must decide whether to allow logging in a park. Removing trees changes the ecosystem, which is an ecological cost. However, by providing jobs and needed wood, logging has an economic benefit.

It is also important to consider the short-term and long-term costs and benefits of an environmental decision. A plan's short-term costs might be outweighed by its long-term benefits.

Weighing Costs and Benefits Once you have identified the potential costs and benefits of a decision, you must analyze them. Consider the costs and benefits of drilling for oil in Antarctica. There would be many costs. It would be very expensive to set up a drilling operation in such a cold and distant place. Transporting the oil would also be difficult and costly. An oil spill in the seas around Antarctica could harm the fish, penguins, and seals there.

Valley View Trail

Eagle Lake

Mt. Peak Trail

• Bald Peak
1,530 ft
466 m

Recreational Benefit The park rivers are great places for us to fish in.

Ecological Benefit The park contains habitats for many animals, plants, and other organisms.

On the other hand, there would be benefits to drilling for oil in Antarctica. Oil drilling would provide a new supply of oil for heat, electricity, and transportation. If the worldwide supply of oil were larger, the price might drop, making oil available to more people. The plan would also create many new jobs. Would the benefits of drilling for oil in Antarctica outweigh the costs? This is the kind of question lawmakers must ask before they make environmental decisions.

 **Reading Checkpoint** **What are two types of costs and benefits?**

Section 5 Assessment

🔄 **Target Reading Skill** Identifying Main Ideas Use your graphic organizer about types of environmental issues to help you answer Question 1 below.

Reviewing Key Concepts

1. a. Identifying What are the three main types of environmental issues?
  b. Explaining Why is population growth an environmental issue?
  c. Relating Cause and Effect How might a growing population affect the supply of trees, a renewable resource? Explain your answer.
2. a. Reviewing Why is weighing costs and benefits useful for decision makers?

  b. Classifying Name one economic cost and one noneconomic cost of drilling for oil in Antarctica. List one benefit of drilling in Antarctica.
  c. Making Judgments Suppose you were a world leader faced with the question of drilling in Antarctica. What decision would you make? Give reasons for your decision.

Writing in Science

Persuasive Letter Write a letter to the editor expressing your viewpoint on whether people should be allowed to use powerboats on a lake in your town. Your letter should clearly show how you weighed the costs and benefits to arrive at your viewpoint.

Global Changes in the Atmosphere

Reading Preview

Key Concepts
- How have human activities damaged the ozone layer?
- How might human activities be linked to global climate changes?

Key Terms
- ozone layer
- chlorofluorocarbon
- greenhouse effect
- global warming

 Target Reading Skill

Outlining As you read, make an outline about global atmospheric changes that you can use for review. Use the red headings for the main ideas and the blue headings for the supporting ideas.

Global Changes in the Atmosphere
I. The thinning of the ozone layer
A. The source of ozone
B.
C.
II. Global climate change
A.
B.

Lab zone Discover **Activity**

What Happens to the Beads?

1. Your teacher will give you beads that change color under certain conditions, along with two pipe cleaners and a small piece of T-shirt material.
2. Thread half of the beads on one pipe cleaner, twisting the ends together.
3. Repeat Step 2 with the remaining beads. Cover the beads on this pipe cleaner with the T-shirt fabric.
4. Take both sets of beads outdoors. After two minutes, go inside. Then remove the fabric covering. Immediately observe the two sets of beads and compare their colors.

Think It Over
Developing Hypotheses Was there any difference in color between the two sets of beads? Form a hypothesis to explain your observations.

It's the first day of vacation, and it's a perfect day for the beach. It's hot, and there's not a cloud in the sky. You've found the perfect spot to read your new book. But as you begin to read, the heat and the sound of the ocean start to make you sleepy. The next thing you know, you're waking up with your head in your book! You've been asleep for two hours! And the redness on your arms reminds you that you forgot to apply sunscreen. Ouch!

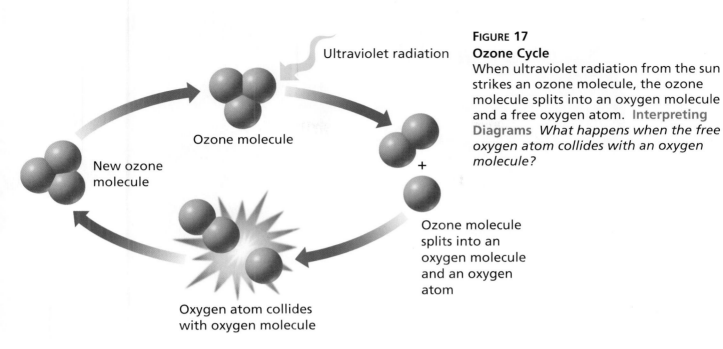

FIGURE 17
Ozone Cycle
When ultraviolet radiation from the sun strikes an ozone molecule, the ozone molecule splits into an oxygen molecule and a free oxygen atom. **Interpreting Diagrams** *What happens when the free oxygen atom collides with an oxygen molecule?*

Ultraviolet radiation

Ozone molecule

New ozone molecule

+

Ozone molecule splits into an oxygen molecule and an oxygen atom

Oxygen atom collides with oxygen molecule

The Thinning of the Ozone Layer

If you have ever had a sunburn, you have experienced the painful effects of the sun's ultraviolet radiation. But did you know that such burns would be even worse without the protection of the ozone layer? The **ozone layer** is a layer of the upper atmosphere about 30 kilometers above Earth's surface. Actually, the concentration of ozone in this layer is very low—only a few parts per million. Yet even the small amount of ozone in the ozone layer protects people from the effects of too much ultraviolet radiation. These effects include sunburn, eye diseases, and skin cancer.

Since you read earlier that ozone is a pollutant, the fact that ozone can be helpful may sound confusing. The difference between ozone as a pollutant and ozone as a helpful gas is its location. Ozone close to Earth's surface in the form of smog is harmful. Higher in the atmosphere, where people cannot breathe it, ozone protects us.

The Source of Ozone Ozone is constantly being made and destroyed. When sunlight strikes an ozone molecule, the energy of the ultraviolet radiation is partly absorbed. This energy causes the ozone molecule to break apart into an oxygen molecule and an oxygen atom, as shown in Figure 17. The oxygen atom soon collides with another oxygen molecule. They react to form a new ozone molecule. Each time this cycle occurs, some ultraviolet energy is absorbed. That energy does not reach Earth's surface.

Math Skills

Calculating a Concentration

Levels of pollutants are often written as concentrations. A concentration is a ratio that compares the amount of one substance to the amount of another substance. For example, suppose that the concentration of ozone in part of the atmosphere is 3 parts per million. This means that there are 3 molecules of ozone in 1,000,000 molecules of air. This ratio can also be written in three other ways:

3 : 1,000,000

3 to 1,000,000

$$\frac{3}{1,000,000}$$

Practice Problems Express each of these concentrations in three different ways.

1. 7 parts per hundred
2. 25 parts per billion

▲ 1979
Scientists detect a hole in the ozone layer over Antarctica. (The bluish area represents the extent of the ozone hole.)

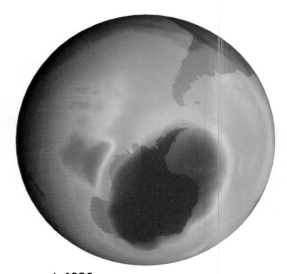

▲ 1986
The ozone hole has grown to cover much of Antarctica.

FIGURE 18
Ozone Hole

The ozone hole was first detected over Antarctica in the 1970s. The hole has generally grown since then, though it varies a bit from year to year. In each of the globes, the blue area indicates the extent of the ozone hole in the spring of that year. **Observing** *How would you describe the change in the ozone hole from 1979 to 2000?*

The Ozone Hole In the late 1970s, scientists observed that the ozone layer over Antarctica was growing thinner each spring. The amount of ozone in the ozone layer was decreasing, causing an area of severe ozone depletion, or an ozone hole. In Figure 18, you can see the size of the ozone hole in four selected years. In 2000, the hole was the largest ever, and in 2003, it was the second-largest ever.

What is to blame for the ozone hole? **Scientists determined that the major cause of the ozone hole is a group of gases called CFCs, which were used in many household products.** CFCs, or **chlorofluorocarbons,** are human-made gases that contain chlorine and fluorine. CFCs had been used in air conditioners, aerosol spray cans, and other products. High in the atmosphere, CFCs react with ozone molecules. The CFCs block the cycle in which ozone molecules absorb ultraviolet radiation. As a result, more ultraviolet light reaches Earth's surface.

What's Being Done In 1990, many nations signed an agreement to eventually ban the use of ozone-depleting substances, including CFCs. Most uses of CFCs were banned in 2000. Some uses of CFCs are still allowed, but compared to the 1970s, few CFCs now enter the atmosphere. Unfortunately, CFC molecules remain in the atmosphere for a long time. But scientists predict that if the ban on ozone-depleting substances is maintained, the ozone layer will gradually recover.

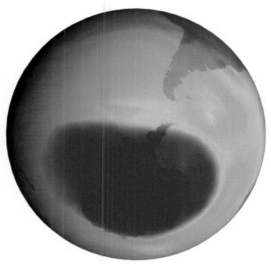

▲ **1993**
The ozone hole covers nearly all of Antarctica.

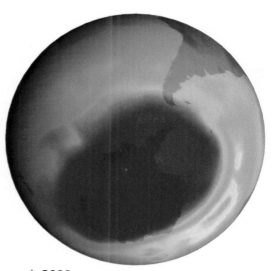

▲ **2000**
The ozone hole covers Antarctica and extends north over the tip of South America.

When scientists discovered that CFCs were harming the atmosphere, they immediately began to search for substitutes. Refrigerators and air conditioners were redesigned to use less harmful substances. Most spray cans were either replaced by pump sprays or redesigned to use other gases. Researchers developed new ways to make products such as plastic foam without using CFCs. As a result of this research and invention, far fewer CFCs now enter the atmosphere.

 **Reading Checkpoint** What do scientists predict will happen if the ban on CFCs is maintained?

Math ▸ Analyzing Data

Chlorine Levels

The line graph shows a scientist's measurements and predictions of how the ban on CFCs might affect chlorine levels in the atmosphere. The red line shows the levels of chlorine without the ban on CFCs. The blue line shows the levels with the ban on CFCs.

1. **Reading Graphs** What variable is plotted on the horizontal axis? What variable is plotted on the vertical axis?

2. **Interpreting Data** Which graphed line shows rising levels of chlorine? What trend does the other line show?

3. **Inferring** Why do the two lines start at the same point?

Chlorine Levels in the Atmosphere, 1970–2010

Graph: vertical axis labeled "Chlorine Level (parts per billion)" ranging 0 to 14; horizontal axis labeled "Year" from 1970 to 2010. One line labeled "Without CFC ban" rises to about 12.5 by 2010. Another line labeled "With CFC ban" levels off around 3.

4. **Drawing Conclusions** How does the relationship between the two lines change?

Global Climate Change

Some changes to the atmosphere could affect the climate of the whole planet. To understand why, you need to know more about the atmosphere.

The Greenhouse Effect Think about the sun shining through a window on a cool day. The window lets light enter the room. The light strikes objects in the room and is converted to heat. The closed windows then trap the warm air inside, and the room becomes warmer.

In the atmosphere, water vapor, carbon dioxide, and certain other gases act like windows. These gases allow sunlight to reach Earth's surface, but they prevent some of the heat from escaping into space. The trapping of heat near Earth's surface is called the **greenhouse effect.** Without the greenhouse effect, Earth would be much colder—about 33 Celsius degrees colder, on average. All of Earth's water would be frozen!

Global Warming Since the 1800s, coal and oil have been the main sources of energy in many parts of the world. As you have read, burning these substances produces carbon dioxide. As a result, the amount of carbon dioxide in the atmosphere has increased from 280 parts per million to 380 parts per million. This amount is increasing more quickly every year.

Human activities that increase carbon dioxide levels may be intensifying the greenhouse effect. One theory, called **global warming,** predicts that the increase in carbon dioxide levels will cause the average temperature to continue to rise. Scientists have estimated that in this century, the average global temperature could rise by as much as 3.5 Celsius degrees.

FIGURE 19
Greenhouse Effect
When energy in the form of sunlight strikes Earth's surface, it changes to heat. Certain gases in the atmosphere trap some of the heat, preventing it from escaping back into space. This trapping of heat is known as the greenhouse effect. *Applying Concepts What gases in the atmosphere trap heat near Earth's surface?*

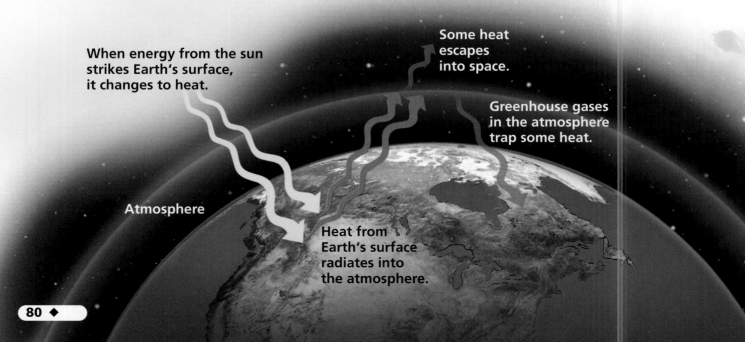

When energy from the sun strikes Earth's surface, it changes to heat.

Some heat escapes into space.

Greenhouse gases in the atmosphere trap some heat.

Atmosphere

Heat from Earth's surface radiates into the atmosphere.

Possible Consequences Although the predicted increase in temperature may not sound like a big change, it could have a huge impact. Parts of the Antarctic ice cap would melt, raising the level of the oceans and causing increased flooding. The temperature change would affect climate patterns all over the world. This change would, in turn, affect where crops could be grown. There might also be more hurricanes and other severe storms.

The Difficulty of Predicting Climate Change

It is difficult to predict how Earth's climate will be affected by changes in the atmosphere. The systems that determine climate are very complex. For example, Earth's oceans, forests, clouds, and volcanoes all affect carbon dioxide levels in the atmosphere. It is difficult to know what impact each of these factors might have on climate change.

Scientists have studied climate systems for less than a century, a very short time to understand processes that can take thousands of years. Most scientists base their global climate predictions on computer models. But only time will tell if their long-range predictions have been accurate.

 **Reading Checkpoint** What might be three consequences of global warming?

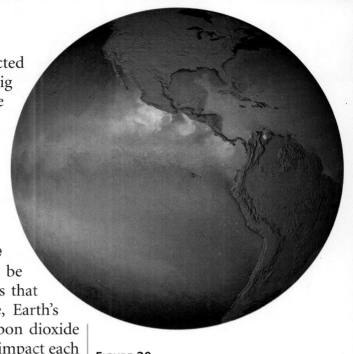

FIGURE 20
Predicting Climate Change
This computer-generated image of Earth shows ocean temperatures near North and South America. The lightest colors indicate the warmest temperatures. The darkest colors indicate the coolest temperatures. Images like this can help scientists predict climate change.

Section 6 Assessment

Target Reading Skill Outlining Use the information in your outline about global atmospheric changes to help you answer the questions below.

Reviewing Key Concepts

1. **a. Reviewing** How have human activities affected the ozone layer?
   b. Relating Cause and Effect What part of the ozone cycle do CFCs interrupt? What effect does this have?
   c. Predicting Exposure to ultraviolet radiation can cause skin cancer. How would you expect the thinning of the ozone layer to affect skin cancer rates? Explain.

2. **a. Identifying** What human activities have led to increased levels of carbon dioxide in the atmosphere?
   b. Explaining Explain how increased carbon dioxide levels could be linked to global climate changes.
   c. Problem Solving What are some steps people could take to reduce the amount of carbon dioxide that enters the atmosphere?

Math Practice

3. **Calculating a Concentration** Draw a picture to show what is meant by each of the following concentrations. Then express each concentration in three different ways.
   a. 4 parts per 10
   b. 19 parts per 100
   c. 7 to 10
   d. 27 : 100

Study Guide

1 The Air Around You

Key Concepts

- Earth's atmosphere is made up of nitrogen, oxygen, carbon dioxide, water vapor, and many other gases, as well as particles of liquids and solids.
- Earth's atmosphere makes conditions on Earth suitable for living things.

Key Terms

weather	ozone
atmosphere	water vapor

2 Air Pressure

Key Concepts

- Because air has mass, it also has other properties, including density and pressure.
- Two common kinds of barometers are mercury barometers and aneroid barometers.
- Air pressure decreases as altitude increases. As air pressure decreases, so does density.

Key Terms

density	mercury barometer
pressure	aneroid barometer
air pressure	altitude
barometer	

3 Layers of the Atmosphere

Key Concept

- Scientists divide Earth's atmosphere into four main layers classified according to changes in temperature. These layers are the troposphere, the stratosphere, the mesosphere, and the thermosphere.
- The troposphere is the layer of the atmosphere in which Earth's weather occurs.
- The stratosphere is the second layer of the atmosphere and contains the ozone layer.
- The mesosphere is the layer of the atmosphere that protects Earth's surface from being hit by most meteoroids.
- The outermost layer of Earth's atmosphere is the thermosphere.

Key Terms

troposphere	thermosphere
stratosphere	ionosphere
mesosphere	exosphere

4 Air Quality

Key Concepts

- Some air pollution occurs naturally. But many types of air pollution are the result of human activities.
- The burning of fossil fuels can cause smog and acid rain.
- The United States government and state governments have passed a number of laws and regulations to reduce air pollution.

Key Terms

pollutants	acid rain
photochemical smog	

5 Environmental Issues

Key Concepts

- Environmental issues fall into three general categories: resource use, population growth, and pollution.
- To help balance the different opinions on an environmental issue, decision makers weigh the costs and benefits of a proposal.

Key Terms

natural resource	pollution
renewable resource	environmental science
nonrenewable resource	

6 Global Changes in the Atmosphere

Key Concepts

- The major cause of the ozone hole is a group of gases called CFCs, or chlorofluorocarbons.
- Human activities that increase carbon dioxide levels may add to the greenhouse effect.

Key Terms

ozone layer	greenhouse effect
chlorofluorocarbon	global warming

Review and Assessment

Organizing Information

Concept Mapping Copy the concept map about air pressure onto a separate sheet of paper. Then complete it and add a title. (For more on concept mapping, see the Skills Handbook.)

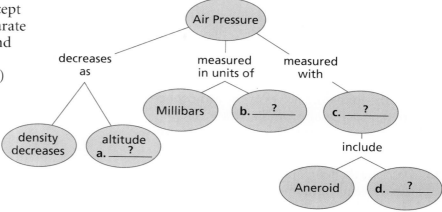

Reviewing Key Terms

Choose the letter of the best answer.

1. The most abundant gas in the atmosphere is
   a. ozone.   **b.** water vapor.
   c. oxygen.   **d.** nitrogen.

2. Air pressure is typically measured with a
   a. thermometer.
   b. satellite.
   c. barometer.
   d. hot-air balloon.

3. The layers of the atmosphere are classified according to changes in
   a. altitude.
   b. temperature.
   c. air pressure.
   d. pollutants.

4. The layer of the atmosphere that reflects radio waves is called the
   a. mesosphere.
   b. troposphere.
   c. ionosphere.
   d. stratosphere.

5. The contamination of Earth's air, land, or water is called
   a. pollution.
   b. extinction.
   c. aquaculture.
   d. habitat destruction.

If the statement is true, write *true*. If it is false, change the underlined word or words to make the statement true.

6. <u>Weather</u> is the condition of Earth's atmosphere at a particular time and place.

7. The force pushing on an area or surface is known as <u>density</u>.

8. Earth's weather occurs in the <u>thermosphere</u>.

9. The ozone layer is found in the <u>exosphere</u>.

10. <u>Carbon dioxide</u> is thought to be one of the causes of global warming.

Writing in Science

Descriptive Paragraph Suppose you are on a hot air balloon flight to the upper levels of the troposphere. Describe how the properties of the atmosphere, such as air pressure and amount of oxygen, would change during your trip.

The Atmosphere

Video Preview
Video Field Trip
▶ Video Assessment

Review and Assessment

Checking Concepts

11. Explain why it is difficult to include water vapor in a graph that shows the percentages of various gases in the atmosphere.

12. Name two ways in which carbon dioxide is added to the atmosphere.

13. List the following layers of the atmosphere in order, moving up from Earth's surface: thermosphere, stratosphere, troposphere, mesosphere.

14. Describe the temperature changes that occur as you move upward through the troposphere.

15. What is a renewable resource? What is a nonrenewable resource?

16. How does acid rain form and what kinds of problems can it cause?

Thinking Critically

17. **Reading Graphs** According to the graph below, what is the air pressure at an altitude of 4 km? In general, how does air pressure change with altitude?

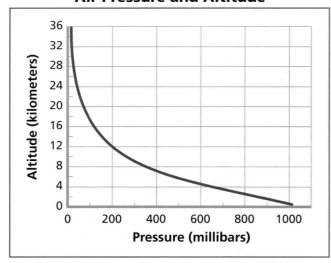

Air Pressure and Altitude

18. **Inferring** Why are clouds at the top of the troposphere made of ice crystals rather than drops of water?

19. **Relating Cause and Effect** Explain how human population growth affects resource use and pollution.

Math Practice

20. **Calculating a Concentration** The concentration of iron in one water sample is 500 parts per million. The iron concentration in a second sample is 300 parts per million. Which sample has the higher iron concentration? Explain.

Applying Skills

Use the graph showing carbon dioxide levels to answer Questions 21–22.

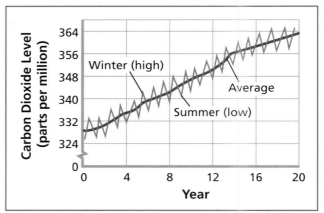

21. **Interpreting Data** What was the average level of carbon dioxide in the atmosphere at the beginning of the study? What was the average level of carbon dioxide in Year 20 of the study?

22. **Calculating** How much did the average level of carbon dioxide increase during the study?

Lab zone Chapter **Project**

Performance Assessment For your class presentation, prepare a display of your weather observations. Include drawings, graphs, and tables that summarize the weather you observed. Practice presenting your project to your group.

🐾 End-of-Grade Test Practice

Layers of the Atmosphere

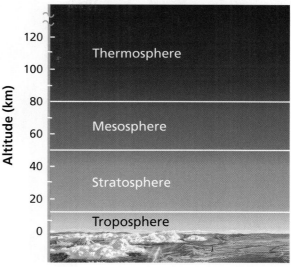

Use the the diagram above and your knowledge of science to answer Questions 3 and 4.

3. Use the diagram to estimate the depth of the stratosphere.
   A about 50 kilometers
   B about 40 kilometers
   C about 30 kilometers
   D about 20 kilometers

4. According to the diagram, where is a meteoroid when it is 75 kilometers above Earth's surface?
   A the mesosphere
   B the stratosphere
   C the thermosphere
   D the troposphere

5. The ozone layer is found in the
   A troposphere.
   B stratosphere.
   C mesosphere.
   D thermosphere.

Choose the letter of the best answer.

1. What two gases make up approximately 99% of Earth's atmosphere?
   A nitrogen and carbon dioxide
   B oxygen and carbon dioxide
   C nitrogen and hydrogen
   D nitrogen and oxygen

2. In the troposphere, as altitude increases
   A air pressure decreases.
   B temperature decreases.
   C air density decreases.
   D all of the above

Constructed Response

6. What is acid rain and why is it considered an environmental problem? Describe how acid rain forms and how it affects living things. Include in your answer the specific substances that combine to form acid rain.

Weather Factors

Standard Course of Study

This chapter addresses the following North Carolina Objectives:

1.01 Identify and create questions and hypotheses.

1.02 Develop appropriate experimental procedures.

1.03 Apply safety procedures.

1.05 Analyze evidence.

1.06 Use mathematics to gather, organize, and present data.

1.07 Prepare models and/or computer simulations.

1.08 Use oral and written language.

1.09 Use technologies and information systems.

2.02 Use information systems.

2.03 Evaluate technological designs.

3.05 Examine atmospheric properties.

3.06 Assess the use of technology in studying atmospheric phenomena and weather hazards.

Rain is an important factor in helping ▶ these black-eyed susans grow.

Lab zone™ Chapter **Project**

Design and Build Your Own Weather Station

In this chapter, you will learn about a variety of weather factors—such as air pressure, precipitation, and wind speed. As you learn about these factors, you will build your own weather station. Your weather station will include simple instruments that you will use to monitor the weather.

Your Goal To design and build a weather station to monitor at least three weather factors and to look for patterns that can be used to predict the next day's weather

You must

- design and build instruments for your weather station
- use your instruments to collect and record data in a daily log
- display your data in a set of graphs
- use your data to try to predict the weather
- follow the safety guidelines in Appendix A

Plan It! Begin your project by deciding where your weather station will be located. Plan which instruments you will build and how you will make your measurements. Prepare a log to record your daily observations. Finally, graph the data and look for any patterns that you can use to predict the next day's weather.

Section

1

Energy in Earth's Atmosphere

Reading Preview

Key Concepts
- In what forms does energy from the sun travel to Earth?
- What happens to the sun's energy when it reaches Earth?

Key Terms
- electromagnetic waves
- radiation
- infrared radiation
- ultraviolet radiation
- scattering
- greenhouse effect

 Target Reading Skill

Sequencing As you read, make a flowchart that shows how the sun's energy reaches Earth's surface. Put each step of the process in a separate box in the order in which it occurs.

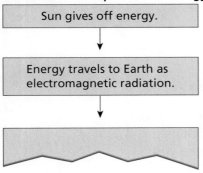

How Earth's Atmosphere Gets Energy

Sun gives off energy.

↓

Energy travels to Earth as electromagnetic radiation.

↓

Lab zone Discover **Activity**

Does a Plastic Bag Trap Heat?

1. Record the initial temperatures on two thermometers. (You should get the same readings.)
2. Place one of the thermometers in a plastic bag. Put a small piece of paper in the bag so that it shades the bulb of the thermometer. Seal the bag.
3. Place both thermometers on a sunny window ledge or near a light bulb. Cover the bulb of the second thermometer with a small piece of paper. Predict what you think will happen.
4. Wait five minutes. Then record the temperatures on the two thermometers.

Think It Over
Measuring Were the two temperatures the same? How could you explain any difference?

In the deserts of Arizona, summer nights can be chilly. In the morning, the sun is low in the sky and the air is cool. As the sun rises, the temperature increases. By noon it is quite hot. As you will learn in this chapter, heat is a major factor in the weather. The movement of heat in the atmosphere causes temperatures to change, winds to blow, and rain to fall.

Energy From the Sun

Where does this heat come from? Nearly all the energy in Earth's atmosphere comes from the sun. This energy travels to Earth as **electromagnetic waves,** a form of energy that can move through the vacuum of space. Electromagnetic waves are classified according to wavelength, or distance between waves. **Radiation** is the direct transfer of energy by electromagnetic waves.

What kinds of energy do we receive from the sun? Is all of the energy the same? **Most of the energy from the sun travels to Earth in the form of visible light and infrared radiation. A small amount arrives as ultraviolet radiation.**

As the sun rises, energy in the form of electromagnetic waves reaches Earth's surface.

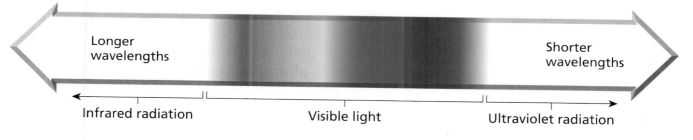

Longer wavelengths

Shorter wavelengths

Infrared radiation   Visible light   Ultraviolet radiation

FIGURE 1

Radiation From the Sun
Energy from the sun travels to Earth as infrared radiation, visible light, and ultraviolet radiation.
Interpreting Diagrams *What type of radiation has wavelengths that are shorter than visible light?*

Visible Light Visible light includes all of the colors that you see in a rainbow: red, orange, yellow, green, blue, and violet. The different colors are the result of different wavelengths. Red and orange light have the longest wavelengths, while blue and violet light have the shortest wavelengths, as shown in Figure 1.

Non-Visible Radiation One form of electromagnetic energy, **infrared radiation,** has wavelengths that are longer than red light. Infrared radiation is not visible, but can be felt as heat. The sun also gives off **ultraviolet radiation,** which is an invisible form of energy with wavelengths that are shorter than violet light. Ultraviolet radiation can cause sunburns. This radiation can also cause skin cancer and eye damage.

 **Reading Checkpoint** Which color of visible light has the longest wavelengths?

◆ **89**

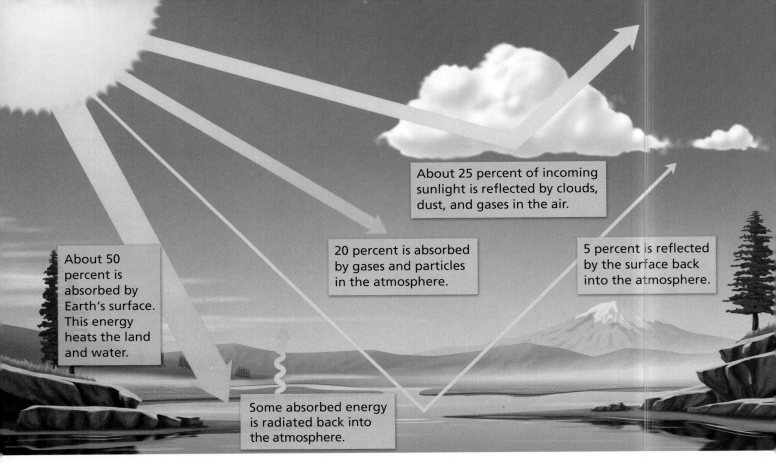

About 25 percent of incoming sunlight is reflected by clouds, dust, and gases in the air.

20 percent is absorbed by gases and particles in the atmosphere.

5 percent is reflected by the surface back into the atmosphere.

About 50 percent is absorbed by Earth's surface. This energy heats the land and water.

Some absorbed energy is radiated back into the atmosphere.

FIGURE 2
Energy in the Atmosphere
The sun's energy interacts with Earth's atmosphere and surface in several ways. About half is either reflected back into space or absorbed by the atmosphere. The rest reaches Earth's surface.

Go Online

SciLINKS **NSTA**

For: Links on energy in Earth's atmosphere
Visit: www.SciLinks.org
Web Code: scn-0921

Energy in the Atmosphere

Before reaching Earth's surface, sunlight must pass through the atmosphere. The path of the sun's rays is shown in Figure 2. **Some sunlight is absorbed or reflected by the atmosphere before it can reach the surface. The rest passes through the atmosphere to the surface.**

Part of the sun's energy is absorbed by the atmosphere. The ozone layer in the stratosphere absorbs most of the ultraviolet radiation. Water vapor and carbon dioxide absorb some infrared radiation. Clouds, dust, and other gases also absorb energy.

Some sunlight is reflected. Clouds act like mirrors, reflecting sunlight back into space. Dust particles and gases in the atmosphere reflect light in all directions, a process called **scattering.** When you look at the sky, the light you see has been scattered by gas molecules in the atmosphere. Gas molecules scatter short wavelengths of visible light (blue and violet) more than long wavelengths (red and orange). Scattered light therefore looks bluer than ordinary sunlight. This is why the daytime sky looks blue.

When the sun is rising or setting, its light passes through a greater thickness of the atmosphere than when the sun is higher in the sky. More light from the blue end of the spectrum is removed by scattering before it reaches your eyes. The remaining light contains mostly red and orange light. The sun looks red, and clouds around it become very colorful.

Energy at Earth's Surface

Some of the sun's energy reaches Earth's surface and is reflected back into the atmosphere. About half of the sun's energy, however, is absorbed by the land and water and changed into heat.

When Earth's surface is heated, it radiates most of the energy back into the atmosphere as infrared radiation. As shown in Figure 3, much of this infrared radiation cannot travel all the way through the atmosphere back into space. Instead, it is absorbed by water vapor, carbon dioxide, methane, and other gases in the air. The energy from the absorbed radiation heats the gases in the air. These gases form a "blanket" around Earth that holds heat in the atmosphere. The process by which gases hold heat in the air is called the **greenhouse effect.**

The greenhouse effect is a natural process that keeps Earth's atmosphere at a temperature that is comfortable for most living things. Over time, the amount of energy absorbed by the atmosphere and Earth's surface is in balance with the amount of energy radiated into space. In this way, Earth's average temperatures remain fairly constant. However, as you will learn later, emissions from human activities may be altering this process.

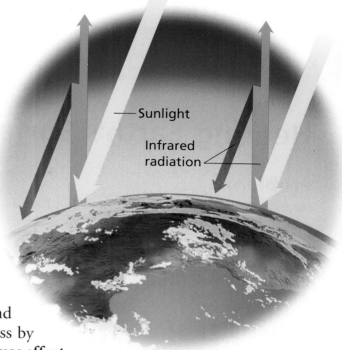

Sunlight

Infrared radiation

FIGURE 3
Greenhouse Effect
Sunlight travels through the atmosphere to Earth's surface. Earth's surface then gives off infrared radiation. Much of this energy is held by the atmosphere, warming it.

 **Reading Checkpoint** What is the greenhouse effect?

Section 1 Assessment

Target Reading Skill
Sequencing Refer to your flowchart about how the sun's energy reaches Earth's surface as you answer Question 2.

Reviewing Key Concepts

1. a. Listing List three forms of radiation from the sun.
   b. Comparing and Contrasting Which form of radiation from the sun has the longest wavelength? The shortest wavelength?
2. a. Summarizing What happens to most of the sunlight that reaches Earth?
   b. Interpreting Diagrams What percentage of incoming sunlight is reflected by clouds, dust, and gases in the atmosphere?
   c. Applying Concepts Why are sunsets red?

3. a. Describing What happens to the energy from the sun that is absorbed by Earth's surface?
   b. Predicting How might conditions on Earth be different without the greenhouse effect?

Lab zone At-Home Activity

Heating Your Home With an adult family member, explore the role radiation from the sun plays in heating your home. Does it make some rooms warmer in the morning? Are other rooms warmer in the afternoon? How does opening and closing curtains or blinds affect the temperature of a room? Explain your observations to your family.

Heating Earth's Surface

Problem

How do the heating and cooling rates of sand and water compare?

Skills Focus

developing hypotheses, graphing, drawing conclusions

Materials

- 2 thermometers or temperature probes
- 2 beakers, 400-mL
- sand, 300 mL
- water, 300 mL
- lamp with 150-W bulb
- metric ruler
- clock or stopwatch
- string
- graph paper
- ring stand and two ring clamps

Procedure

1. Which do you think will heat up faster—sand or water? Record your hypothesis. Then follow these steps to test your hypothesis.

2. Copy the data table into your notebook. Add enough rows to record data for 15 minutes.

3. Fill one beaker with 300 mL of dry sand.

4. Fill the second beaker with 300 mL of water at room temperature.

5. Arrange the beakers side by side beneath the ring stand.

6. Place one thermometer in each beaker. If you are using a temperature probe, see your teacher for instructions.

7. Suspend the thermometers from the ring stand with string. This will hold the thermometers in place so they do not fall.

8. Adjust the height of the clamp so that the bulb of each thermometer is covered by about 0.5 cm of sand or water in a beaker.

9. Position the lamp so that it is about 20 cm above the sand and water. There should be no more than 8 cm between the beakers. **CAUTION:** *Be careful not to splash water onto the hot light bulb.*

10. Record the temperature of the sand and water in your data table.

11. Turn on the lamp. Read the temperature of the sand and water every minute for 15 minutes. Record the temperatures in the *Temperature With Light On* column in the data table.

12. Which material do you think will cool off more quickly? Record your hypothesis. Again, give reasons why you think your hypothesis is correct.

13. Turn the light off. Read the temperature of the sand and water every minute for another 15 minutes. Record the temperatures in the *Temperature With Light Off* column (16–30 minutes).

Data Table					
Temperature With Light On (°C)			Temperature With Light Off (°C)		
Time (min)	Sand	Water	Time (min)	Sand	Water
Start			16		
1			17		
2			18		
3			19		
4			20		
5			21		

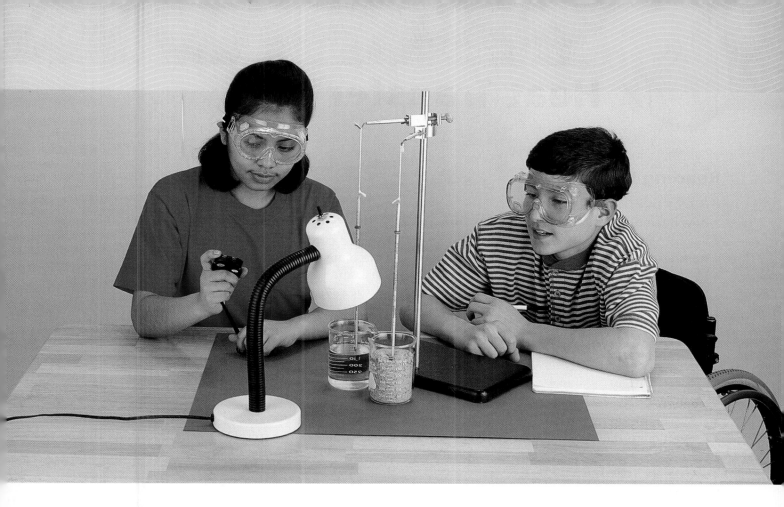

Analyze and Conclude

1. **Graphing** Draw two line graphs to show the data for the temperature change in sand and water over time. Label the horizontal axis from 0 to 30 minutes and the vertical axis in degrees Celsius. Draw both graphs on the same piece of graph paper. Use a dashed line to show the temperature change in water and a solid line to show the temperature change in sand.

2. **Calculating** Calculate the total change in temperature for each material.

3. **Interpreting Data** Based on your data, which material had the greater increase in temperature?

4. **Drawing Conclusions** What can you conclude about which material absorbed heat faster? How do your results compare with your hypothesis?

5. **Interpreting Data** Review your data again. In 15 minutes, which material cooled faster?

6. **Drawing Conclusions** How do these results compare to your second hypothesis?

7. **Developing Hypotheses** Based on your results, which do you think will heat up more quickly on a sunny day: the water in a lake or the sand surrounding it? After dark, which will cool off more quickly?

8. **Communicating** If your results did not support either of your hypotheses, why do you think the results differed from what you expected? Write a paragraph in which you discuss the results and how they compared to your hypotheses.

Design an Experiment

Do you think all solid materials heat up as fast as sand? For example, consider gravel, crushed stone, or different types of soil. Write a hypothesis about their heating rates as an "If ... then...." statement. With the approval and supervision of your teacher, develop a procedure to test your hypothesis. Was your hypothesis correct?

Heat Transfer

Reading Preview

Key Concepts

- How is temperature measured?
- In what three ways is heat transferred?
- How is heat transferred in the troposphere?

Key Terms

- temperature
- thermal energy
- thermometer
- heat
- conduction
- convection
- convection currents

Target Reading Skill

Outlining As you read, make an outline about how heat is transferred. Use the red headings for the main topics and the blue headings for the subtopics.

Heat Transfer

I. Thermal energy and temperature
   A. Measuring temperature
   B.
II. How heat is transferred
   A.

Lab zone Discover Activity

What Happens When Air Is Heated?

1. Use heavy scissors to cut the flat part out of an aluminum pie plate. Use the tip of the scissors to poke a small hole in the middle of the flat part of the plate.
2. Cut the part into a spiral shape, as shown in the photo. Tie a 30-centimeter piece of thread to the middle of the spiral.
3. Hold the spiral over a source of heat, such as a candle, hot plate, or incandescent light bulb.

Think It Over

Inferring What happened to the spiral? Why do you think this happened?

You pour a cup of steaming tea from a teapot. Your teacup is warm to the touch. Somehow, heat was transferred from one object (the cup) to another (your hand) that it was touching. This is an example of conduction, one of three ways that heat can be transferred. As you'll learn in this section, heat transfer in the troposphere plays an important role in influencing Earth's weather.

It takes only a small amount of energy to heat up a cup of tea. ▶

FIGURE 4
Movement of Molecules The iced tea is cold, so its molecules move slowly. The herbal tea is hot, so its molecules move faster than the molecules in the iced tea.
Inferring *Which liquid has a higher temperature?*

Thermal Energy and Temperature

The tea in the cup and in the teapot are at the same temperature but have a different amount of total energy. To understand this, you need to know that all substances are made up of tiny particles that are constantly moving. The faster the particles are moving, the more energy they have. Figure 4 shows how the motion of the particles is related to the amount of energy they hold. **Temperature** is the *average* amount of energy of motion of each particle of a substance. That is, temperature is a measure of how hot or cold a substance is. In contrast, the *total* energy of motion in the particles of a substance is called **thermal energy.** The hot tea in the teapot has more thermal energy than the hot tea in the cup because it has more particles.

Measuring Temperature Temperature is one of the most important factors affecting the weather. **Air temperature is usually measured with a thermometer.** A **thermometer** is a thin glass tube with a bulb on one end that contains a liquid, usually mercury or colored alcohol.

Thermometers work because liquids expand when they are heated and contract when they are cooled. When the air temperature increases, the temperature of the liquid in the bulb also increases. This causes the liquid to expand and rise up the column.

Temperature Scales Temperature is measured in units called degrees. Two temperature scales are commonly used: the Celsius scale and the Fahrenheit scale. Scientists use the Celsius scale. On the Celsius scale, the freezing point of pure water is 0°C (read "zero degrees Celsius"). The boiling point of pure water at sea level is 100°C. Weather reports in the United States use the Fahrenheit scale. On the Fahrenheit scale, the freezing point of water is 32°F and the boiling point is 212°F.

 **Reading Checkpoint** **Which temperature scale do scientists use?**

Math Skills

Converting Units

Temperatures in weather reports use the Fahrenheit scale, but scientists use the Celsius scale. Temperature readings can be converted from the Fahrenheit scale to the Celsius scale using the following equation:

$$°C = \frac{5}{9}(°F - 32)$$

If the temperature is 68°F, what is the temperature in degrees Celsius?

$$°C = \frac{5}{9}(68 - 32)$$

$$°C = 20°C$$

Practice Problem Use the equation to convert the following temperatures from Fahrenheit to Celsius: 35.0°F, 60.0°F, and 72.0°F.

Lab zone **Try This Activity**

Temperature and Height

How much difference is there between air temperatures near the ground and higher up? Give reasons for your prediction.

1. Take all of your measurements outside at a location that is sunny all day.

2. ![] Early in the morning, measure the air temperature 1 cm and 1.25 m above the ground. Record the time and temperature for each height. Repeat your measurements late in the afternoon.

3. Repeat Step 2 for two more days.

4. Graph your data for each height with temperature on the vertical axis and time of day on the horizontal axis. Use the same graph paper and same scale for each graph. Label each graph.

Interpreting Data At which height did the temperature vary the most? How can you explain the difference?

How Heat Is Transferred

Heat is the transfer of thermal energy from a hotter object to a cooler one. **Heat is transferred in three ways: radiation, conduction, and convection.**

Radiation Have you ever felt the warmth of the sun's rays on your face? You were feeling energy coming directly from the sun as radiation. Recall that radiation is the direct transfer of energy by electromagnetic waves. Most of the heat you feel from the sun travels to you as infrared radiation. You cannot see infrared radiation, but you can feel it as heat.

Conduction Have you ever walked barefoot on hot sand? Your feet felt hot because heat moved directly from the sand into your feet. The direct transfer of heat from one substance to another substance that it is touching is called **conduction.** When a fast-moving sand molecule bumps into a slower-moving molecule, the faster molecule transfers some of its energy.

The closer together the atoms or molecules in a substance are, the more effectively they can conduct heat. Conduction works well in some solids, such as metals, but not as well in liquids and gases. Air and water do not conduct heat very well.

Convection In fluids (liquids and gases), particles can move easily from one place to another. As the particles move, their energy goes along with them. The transfer of heat by the movement of a fluid is called **convection.**

Heating the Troposphere Radiation, conduction, and convection work together to heat the troposphere. During the day, the sun's radiation heats Earth's surface. The land becomes warmer than the air. Air near Earth's surface is warmed by both radiation and conduction. However, heat is not easily transferred from one air particle to another by conduction. Only the first few meters of the troposphere are heated by conduction. Thus, the air close to the ground is usually warmer than the air a few meters up.

Within the troposphere, heat is transferred mostly by convection. When the air near the ground is heated, its particles move more rapidly. As a result, they bump into each other and move farther apart. The air becomes less dense. Cooler, denser air sinks toward the surface, forcing the warmer air to rise. The upward movement of warm air and the downward movement of cool air form **convection currents.** Convection currents move heat throughout the troposphere.

 **Reading Checkpoint** How is the air near Earth's surface heated?

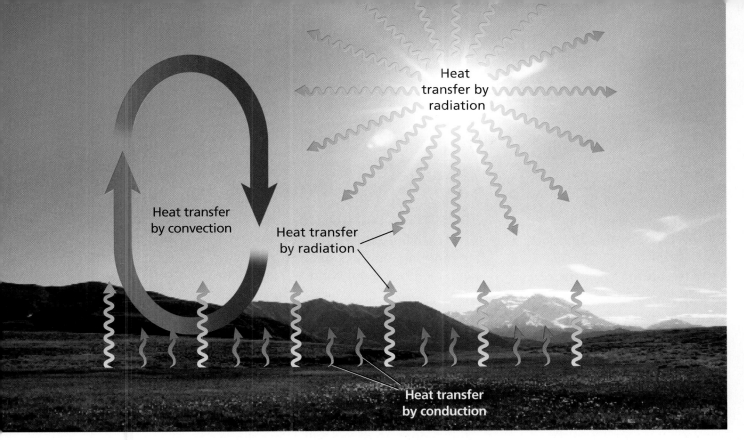

Heat
transfer by
radiation

Heat transfer
by convection

Heat transfer
by radiation

Heat transfer
by conduction

Radiation

Conduction

Convection

FIGURE 5
Heat Transfer
All three types of heat transfer—
radiation, conduction, and
convection—occur near Earth's
surface.

Section 2 Assessment

🎯 **Target Reading Skill** Outlining Use the
information in your outline about heat transfer to
help you answer the questions below.

Reviewing Key Concepts

1. a. **Defining** What is temperature?
   b. **Identifying** What instrument is used to
   measure air temperature?
   c. **Comparing and Contrasting** A pail of water
   is the same temperature as a lake. Compare
   the amount of thermal energy of the water in
   the lake and the water in the pail.

2. a. **Naming** Name three ways that heat can be
   transferred.
   b. **Describing** How do the three types of heat
   transfer work together to heat the troposphere?

c. **Identifying** What is the major way that heat
   is transferred in the troposphere?
d. **Applying Concepts** Explain how a hawk or
   eagle can sometimes soar upward without
   flapping its wings.

Math Practice

3. **Converting Units** Use the equation from
   the Math Skills Activity to convert the
   following temperatures from Fahrenheit to
   Celsius: 52°F, 86°F, 77°F, and 97°F.

3 Winds

Reading Preview

Key Concepts
- What causes winds?
- How do local winds and global winds differ?
- Where are the major global wind belts located?

Key Terms
- wind • anemometer
- wind-chill factor • local winds
- sea breeze • land breeze
- global winds • Coriolis effect
- latitude • jet stream

Target Reading Skill
Relating Cause and Effect As you read, identify how the unequal heating of the atmosphere causes the air to move. Write the information in a graphic organizer like the one below.

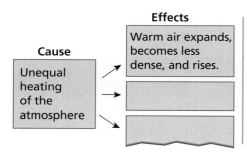

Effects

Cause

Unequal heating of the atmosphere

Warm air expands, becomes less dense, and rises.

Lab zone Discover **Activity**

Does the Wind Turn?
Do this activity with a partner. Let the ball represent a model of Earth and the marker represent wind.

1. Using heavy-duty tape, attach a pencil to a large smooth ball so that you can spin the ball from the top without touching it.
2. One partner should hold the pencil. Slowly turn the ball counterclockwise when seen from above.
3. While the ball is turning, the second partner should use a marker to try to draw a straight line from the "North Pole" to the "equator" of the ball. What shape does the line form?

Think It Over
Making Models If cold air were moving south from Canada into the continental United States, how would its movement be affected by Earth's rotation?

Have you ever flown a kite? Start by unwinding a few meters of string with the kite downwind from you. Have a friend hold the kite high overhead. Then, as your friend releases the kite, run directly into the wind. If you're lucky, the kite will start to rise. Once the kite is stable, you can unwind your string to let the wind lift the kite high into the sky. But what exactly is the wind that lifts the kite, and what causes it to blow?

A kite festival in Capetown, South Africa ▶

What Is Wind?

Because air is a fluid, it can move easily from place to place. Differences in air pressure cause the air to move. A **wind** is the horizontal movement of air from an area of high pressure to an area of lower pressure. **Winds are caused by differences in air pressure.**

Most differences in air pressure are caused by the unequal heating of the atmosphere. Convection currents form when an area of Earth's surface is heated by the sun's rays. Air over the heated surface expands and becomes less dense. As the air becomes less dense, its air pressure decreases. If a nearby area is not heated as much, the air above the less-heated area will be cooler and denser. The cool, dense air with a higher pressure flows underneath the warm, less dense air. This forces the warm air to rise.

Measuring Wind Winds are described by their direction and speed. Wind direction is determined with a wind vane. The wind swings the wind vane so that one end points into the wind. The name of a wind tells you where the wind is coming from. For example, a south wind blows from the south toward the north. A north wind blows to the south.

Wind speed can be measured with an **anemometer** (an uh MAHM uh tur). An anemometer has three or four cups mounted at the ends of spokes that spin on an axle. The force of the wind against the cups turns the axle. A meter on the axle shows the wind speed.

Wind-Chill Factor On a warm day, a cool breeze can be refreshing. But during the winter, the same breeze can make you feel uncomfortably cold. The wind blowing over your skin removes body heat. The stronger the wind, the colder you feel. The increased cooling a wind can cause is called the **wind-chill factor.** Thus a weather report may say, "The temperature outside is 20 degrees Fahrenheit. But with a wind speed of 30 miles per hour, the wind-chill factor makes it feel like 1 degree above zero."

 **Reading Checkpoint** Toward what direction does a west wind blow?

FIGURE 6
Wind Direction and Speed
The wind vane on the left points in the direction the wind is blowing from. The anemometer on the right measures wind speed. The cups catch the wind, turning faster when the wind blows faster.

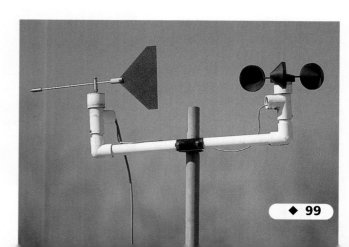

Local Winds

Have you ever noticed a breeze at the beach on a hot summer day? Even if there is no wind inland, there may be a cool breeze blowing in from the water. This breeze is an example of a local wind. **Local winds** are winds that blow over short distances. **Local winds are caused by the unequal heating of Earth's surface within a small area.** Local winds form only when large-scale winds are weak.

Sea Breeze Unequal heating often occurs along the shore of a large body of water. It takes more energy to warm up a body of water than it does to warm up an equal area of land. As the sun heats Earth's surface during the day, the land warms up faster than the water. As a result, the air over the land becomes warmer than the air over the water. The warm air expands and rises, creating a low-pressure area. Cool air blows inland from over the water and moves underneath the warm air, causing a sea breeze. A **sea breeze** or a lake breeze is a local wind that blows from an ocean or lake. Figure 7 shows a sea breeze.

Land Breeze At night, the process is reversed. Land cools more quickly than water, so the air over the land becomes cooler than the air over the water. As the warmer air over the water expands and rises, cooler air from the land moves beneath it. The flow of air from land to a body of water is called a **land breeze.**

Sea Breeze

Warm air rises

Cooler air moves beneath warm air

Land Breeze

Warm air rises

Cooler air moves beneath warm air

FIGURE 7
Local Winds
During the day, cool air moves from the sea to the land, creating a sea breeze. At night, cooler air moves from the land to the sea.
Forming Operational Definitions *What type of breeze occurs at night?*

Global Winds

Global winds are winds that blow steadily from specific directions over long distances. **Like local winds, global winds are created by the unequal heating of Earth's surface. But unlike local winds, global winds occur over a large area.** Recall how the sun's radiation strikes Earth. In the middle of the day near the equator, the sun is almost directly overhead. The direct rays from the sun heat Earth's surface intensely. Near the poles, the sun's rays strike Earth's surface at a lower angle. The sun's energy is spread out over a larger area, so it heats the surface less. As a result, temperatures near the poles are much lower than they are near the equator.

Global Convection Currents How do global winds develop? Temperature differences between the equator and the poles produce giant convection currents in the atmosphere. Warm air rises at the equator, and cold air sinks at the poles. Therefore air pressure tends to be lower near the equator and greater near the poles. This difference in pressure causes winds at Earth's surface to blow from the poles toward the equator. Higher in the atmosphere, however, air flows away from the equator toward the poles. Those air movements produce global winds.

The Coriolis Effect If Earth did not rotate, global winds would blow in a straight line from the poles toward the equator. Because Earth is rotating, however, global winds do not follow a straight path. As the winds blow, Earth rotates from west to east underneath them, making it seem as if the winds have curved. The way Earth's rotation makes winds curve is called the **Coriolis effect** (kawr ee OH lis).

Because of the Coriolis effect, global winds in the Northern Hemisphere gradually turn toward the right. As Figure 9 shows, a wind blowing toward the south gradually turns toward the southwest. In the Southern Hemisphere, winds curve toward the left.

Reading Checkpoint Which way do winds turn in the Southern Hemisphere?

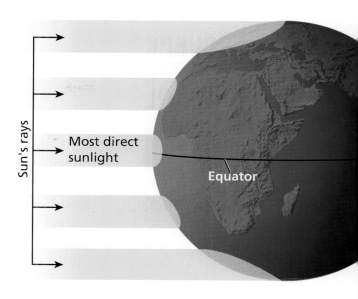

FIGURE 8
Angle of Sun's Rays
Near the equator, energy from the sun strikes Earth almost directly. Near the poles, the same amount of energy is spread out over a larger area.

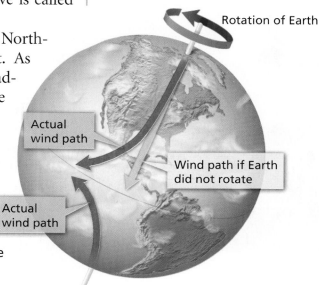

FIGURE 9
Coriolis Effect
As Earth rotates, the Coriolis effect turns winds in the Northern Hemisphere toward the right.

Weather Factors

Video Preview
▶ Video Field Trip
Video Assessment

FIGURE 10
Ocean Sailing
Sailing ships relied on global winds to speed their journeys to various ports around the world. *Applying Concepts How much effect do you think the prevailing winds have on shipping today?*

Global Wind Belts

The Coriolis effect and other factors combine to produce a pattern of calm areas and wind belts around Earth, as shown in Figure 11. The calm areas include the doldrums and the horse latitudes. **The major global wind belts are the trade winds, the polar easterlies, and the prevailing westerlies.**

Doldrums Near the equator, the sun heats the surface strongly. Warm air rises steadily, creating an area of low pressure. Cool air moves into the area, but is warmed rapidly and rises before it moves very far. There is very little horizontal motion, so the winds near the equator are very weak. Regions near the equator with little or no wind are called the doldrums.

Horse Latitudes Warm air that rises at the equator divides and flows both north and south. **Latitude** is distance from the equator, measured in degrees. At about 30° north and south latitudes, the air stops moving toward the poles and sinks. In each of these regions, another belt of calm air forms. Hundreds of years ago, sailors becalmed in these waters ran out of food and water for their horses and had to throw the horses overboard. Because of this, the latitudes 30° north and south of the equator came to be called the horse latitudes.

Trade Winds When the cold air over the horse latitudes sinks, it produces a region of high pressure. This high pressure causes surface winds to blow both toward the equator and away from it. The winds that blow toward the equator are turned west by the Coriolis effect. As a result, winds in the Northern Hemisphere between 30° north latitude and the equator generally blow from the northeast. In the Southern Hemisphere between 30° south latitude and the equator, the winds blow from the southeast. For hundreds of years, sailors relied on these winds to move ships carrying valuable cargoes from Europe to the West Indies and South America. As a result, these steady easterly winds are called the trade winds.

Prevailing Westerlies In the mid-latitudes, between 30° and 60° north and south, winds that blow toward the poles are turned toward the east by the Coriolis effect. Because they blow from the west to the east, they are called prevailing westerlies. The prevailing westerlies blow generally from the southwest in north latitudes and from the northwest in south latitudes. The prevailing westerlies play an important part in the weather of the United States.

FIGURE 11
Global Winds

A series of wind belts circles Earth. Between the wind belts are calm areas where air is rising or falling. **Interpreting Diagrams** *Which global wind belt would a sailor choose to sail from eastern Canada to Europe?*

Go Online
active art

For: Global Winds activity
Visit: PHSchool.com
Web Code: cfp-4023

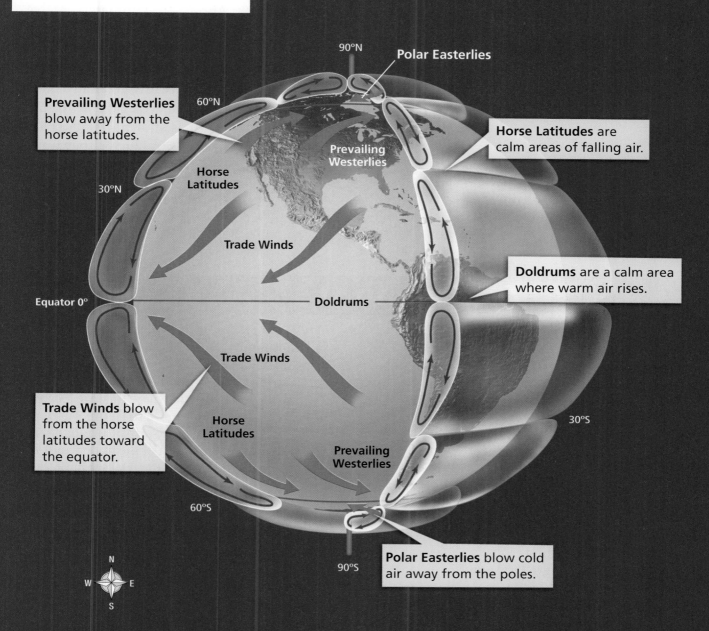

90°N
Polar Easterlies

60°N

Prevailing Westerlies blow away from the horse latitudes.

Prevailing Westerlies

Horse Latitudes are calm areas of falling air.

30°N

Horse Latitudes

Trade Winds

Equator 0°

Doldrums

Doldrums are a calm area where warm air rises.

Trade Winds

Trade Winds blow from the horse latitudes toward the equator.

Horse Latitudes

30°S

Prevailing Westerlies

60°S

N
W   E
S

90°S

Polar Easterlies blow cold air away from the poles.

FIGURE 12
Jet Streams
The jet streams are high-speed bands of winds occurring at the top of the troposphere. By traveling east in a jet stream, pilots can save time and fuel.

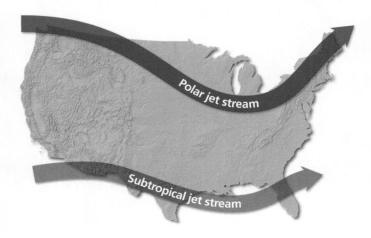

Polar jet stream

Subtropical jet stream

Polar Easterlies Cold air near the poles sinks and flows back toward lower latitudes. The Coriolis effect shifts these polar winds to the west, producing the polar easterlies. The polar easterlies meet the prevailing westerlies at about 60° north and 60° south latitudes, along a region called the polar front. The mixing of warm and cold air along the polar front has a major effect on weather in the United States.

Jet Streams About 10 kilometers above Earth's surface are bands of high-speed winds called **jet streams.** These winds are hundreds of kilometers wide but only a few kilometers deep. Jet streams generally blow from west to east at speeds of 200 to 400 kilometers per hour, as shown in Figure 12. As jet streams travel around Earth, they wander north and south along a wavy path.

 **Reading Checkpoint** **What are the jet streams?**

Section 3 Assessment

Target Reading Skill

Relating Cause and Effect Refer to your graphic organizer about the effects of unequal heating to help you answer Question 1 below.

Reviewing Key Concepts

1. **a. Defining** What is wind?
   b. Relating Cause and Effect How is wind related to air temperature and air pressure?
   c. Applying Concepts It's fairly warm but windy outside. Use the concept of wind-chill factor to explain why it may be a good idea to wear a jacket.

2. **a. Defining** What are local winds?
   b. Summarizing What causes local winds?
   c. Comparing and Contrasting Compare the conditions that cause a sea breeze with those that cause a land breeze.

3. **a. Identifying** Name the three major global wind belts.
   b. Describing Briefly describe the three major global wind belts and where they are located.
   c. Interpreting Diagrams Use Figure 9 and Figure 11 to describe how the Coriolis effect influences the direction of the trade winds in the Northern Hemisphere. Does it have the same effect in the Southern Hemisphere? Explain.

Writing in Science

Explanation Imagine that you are a hot-air balloonist. You want to fly your balloon across the continental United States. To achieve the fastest time, would it make more sense to fly east-to-west or west-to-east? Explain how the prevailing winds influenced your decision.

Technology Lab
• Tech & Design •

Measuring the Wind

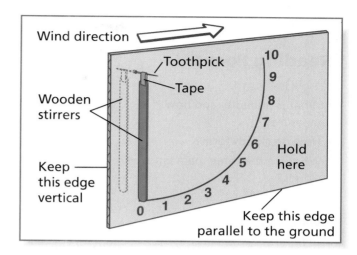

Wind direction

Toothpick
Tape
Wooden stirrers
Keep this edge vertical
Hold here
Keep this edge parallel to the ground

10 9 8 7 6 5 4 3 2 1 0

Problem

Can you design and build an anemometer to measure the wind?

Design Skills

evaluating the design, redesigning

Materials

- pen • round toothpick • masking tape
- 2 wooden coffee stirrers • meter stick
- corrugated cardboard sheet, 15 cm × 20 cm
- wind vane

Procedure

1. Begin by making a simple anemometer that uses wooden coffee stirrers to indicate wind speed. On a piece of cardboard, draw a curved scale like the one shown in the diagram. Mark it in equal intervals from 0 to 10.

2. Carefully use the pen to make a small hole where the toothpick will go. Insert the toothpick through the hole.

3. Tape the wooden coffee stirrers to the toothpick as shown in the diagram, one on each side of the cardboard.

4. Copy the data table into your notebook.

Data Table		
Location	Wind Direction	Wind Speed

5. Take your anemometer outside the school. Stand about 2–3 m away from the building and away from any corners or large plants.

6. Use the wind vane to find out what direction the wind is coming from. Hold your anemometer so that the card is straight, vertical, and parallel to the wind direction.

7. Observe the wooden stirrer on your anemometer for one minute. Record the highest wind speed that occurs during that time.

8. Repeat your measurements on all the other sides of the building. Record your data.

Analyze and Conclude

1. **Interpreting Data** Was the wind stronger on one side of the school than on the other sides? Explain your observations.

2. **Applying Concepts** Based on your data, which side of the building provides the best location for a door?

3. **Evaluating the Design** Do you think your anemometer accurately measured all of the winds you encountered? How could you improve its accuracy?

4. **Redesigning** What was the hardest part of using your anemometer? How could you change your design to make it more useful at very low or at very high wind speeds? Explain.

5. **Working With Design Constraints** How did having to use the materials provided by your teacher affect your anemometer? How would your design have changed if you could have used any materials you wanted to?

Communicate

Write a brochure describing the benefits of your anemometer. Make sure your brochure explains how the anemometer works and its potential uses.

Water in the Atmosphere

Reading Focus

Key Concepts
- What is humidity and how is it measured?
- How do clouds form?
- What are the three main types of clouds?

Key Terms
- water cycle • evaporation
- humidity • relative humidity
- psychrometer • condensation
- dew point • cirrus
- cumulus • stratus

Target Reading Skill

Asking Questions Before you read, preview the red headings. In a graphic organizer like the one below, ask *what* or *how* questions for each heading. As you read, write answers to your questions.

The Water Cycle

Question	Answer
How does the water cycle work?	During the water cycle . . .

Lab zone Discover **Activity**

How Does Fog Form?

1. Fill a narrow-necked plastic bottle with hot tap water. Pour out most of the water, leaving about 3 cm at the bottom. **CAUTION:** *Avoid spilling hot water. Do not use water that is so hot that you cannot safely hold the bottle.*
2. Place an ice cube on the mouth of the bottle. What happens?
3. Repeat Steps 1 and 2 using cold water instead of hot water. What happens?

Think It Over

Developing Hypotheses How can you explain your observations? Why is there a difference between what happens with the hot water and what happens with the cold water?

During a rainstorm, the air feels moist. On a clear, cloudless day, the air may feel dry. As the sun heats the land and oceans, the amount of water in the atmosphere changes. Water is always moving between the atmosphere and Earth's surface.

The movement of water between the atmosphere and Earth's surface is called the **water cycle.** As you can see in Figure 13, water vapor enters the air by evaporation from the oceans and other bodies of water. **Evaporation** is the process by which water molecules in liquid water escape into the air as water vapor. Water vapor is also added to the air by living things. Water enters the roots of plants, rises to the leaves, and is released as water vapor.

As part of the water cycle, some of the water vapor in the atmosphere condenses to form clouds. Rain and snow fall from the clouds toward the surface. The water then runs off the surface or moves through the ground, back into the lakes, streams, and eventually the oceans.

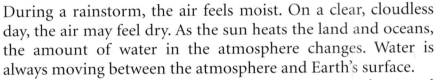

Humidity

How is the quantity of water vapor in the atmosphere measured? **Humidity** is a measure of the amount of water vapor in the air. Air's ability to hold water vapor depends on its temperature. Warm air can hold more water vapor than cool air.

Relative Humidity Weather reports usually refer to the water vapor in the air as relative humidity. **Relative humidity** is the percentage of water vapor that is actually in the air compared to the maximum amount of water vapor the air can hold at a particular temperature. For example, at 10°C, 1 cubic meter of air can hold at most 8 grams of water vapor. If there actually were 8 grams of water vapor in the air, then the relative humidity of the air would be 100 percent. Air with a relative humidity of 100 percent is said to be saturated. If the air had 4 grams of water vapor, the relative humidity would be half, or 50 percent.

FIGURE 13
Water Cycle

In the water cycle, water moves from oceans, lakes, rivers, and plants into the atmosphere and then falls back to Earth.

Go Online
active art

For: Water Cycle activity
Visit: PHSchool.com
Web Code: cfp-4024

Condensation

Precipitation

Evaporation from plants

Evaporation from oceans, lakes, and streams

Surface runoff

FIGURE 14
Sling Psychrometer
A sling psychrometer is used to measure relative humidity.

Measuring Relative Humidity Relative humidity can be measured with an instrument called a psychrometer. A psychrometer (sy KRAHM uh tur) has two thermometers, a wet-bulb thermometer and a dry-bulb thermometer, as shown in Figure 14. The bulb of the wet-bulb thermometer has a cloth covering that is moistened with water. When the psychrometer is "slung," or spun by its handle, air blows over both thermometers. Because the wet-bulb thermometer is cooled by evaporation, its reading drops below that of the dry-bulb thermometer.

If the relative humidity is high, the water on the wet bulb evaporates slowly, and the wet-bulb temperature does not change much. If the relative humidity is low, the water on the wet bulb evaporates rapidly, and the wet-bulb temperature drops. The relative humidity can be found by comparing the temperatures of the wet-bulb and dry-bulb thermometers.

 **Reading Checkpoint** What instrument measures relative humidity?

Math Analyzing Data

Determining Relative Humidity

Relative humidity is affected by temperature. Use the data table to answer the questions below. First, find the dry-bulb temperature in the left column of the table. Then find the difference between the wet- and dry-bulb temperatures across the top of the table. The number in the table where these two readings intersect indicates the relative humidity in percent.

Relative Humidity					
Dry-Bulb Reading (°C)	Difference Between Wet- and Dry-Bulb Readings (°C)				
	1	2	3	4	5
10	88	76	65	54	43
12	88	78	67	57	48
14	89	79	69	60	50
16	90	80	71	62	54
18	91	81	72	64	56
20	91	82	74	66	58
22	92	83	75	68	60

1. **Interpreting Data** At noon, the readings on a sling psychrometer are 18°C for the dry-bulb thermometer and 14°C for the wet-bulb thermometer. What is the relative humidity?

2. **Interpreting Data** At 5 P.M., the psychrometer is used again. The reading on the dry-bulb thermometer is 12°C, and the reading on the wet-bulb thermometer is 11°C. Determine the new relative humidity.

3. **Interpreting Data** How did the temperature change between noon and 5 P.M.?

4. **Interpreting Data** How did relative humidity change during the course of the day?

5. **Drawing Conclusions** How was the relative humidity affected by air temperature? Explain your answer.

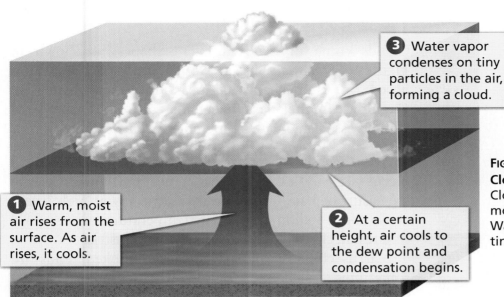

③ Water vapor condenses on tiny particles in the air, forming a cloud.

① Warm, moist air rises from the surface. As air rises, it cools.

② At a certain height, air cools to the dew point and condensation begins.

FIGURE 15
Cloud Formation
Clouds form when warm, moist air rises and cools. Water vapor condenses onto tiny particles in the air.

How Clouds Form

When you look at a cloud, you are seeing millions of tiny water droplets or ice crystals. **Clouds form when water vapor in the air condenses to form liquid water or ice crystals.** Molecules of water vapor in the air become liquid water in the process of **condensation.** How does water in the atmosphere condense? Two conditions are required for condensation: cooling of the air and the presence of particles in the air.

The Role of Cooling As you have learned, cold air holds less water vapor than warm air. As air cools, the amount of water vapor it can hold decreases. The water vapor condenses into tiny droplets of water or ice crystals.

The temperature at which condensation begins is called the **dew point.** If the dew point is above freezing, the water vapor forms water droplets. If the dew point is below freezing, the water vapor may change directly into ice crystals.

The Role of Particles But something else besides a change in temperature is needed for cloud formation. For water vapor to condense, tiny particles must be present so the water has a surface on which to condense. In cloud formation, most of these particles are salt crystals, dust from soil, and smoke. Water vapor also condenses onto solid surfaces, such as blades of grass or window panes. Liquid water that condenses from the air onto a cooler surface is called dew. Ice that has been deposited on a surface that is below freezing is called frost.

 **Reading Checkpoint** What two factors are required for condensation to occur?

FIGURE 16
Condensation
Water vapor condensed on this insect to form dew. **Predicting** *What would happen if the surface were below freezing?*

◆ **109**

Cirrus clouds

Cumulus clouds

Stratus clouds

Types of Clouds

Clouds come in many different shapes, as shown in Figure 17. **Scientists classify clouds into three main types based on their shape: cirrus, cumulus, and stratus. Clouds are further classified by their altitude.** Each type of cloud is associated with a different type of weather.

Cirrus Clouds Wispy, feathery clouds are known as **cirrus** (SEER us) clouds. *Cirrus* comes from a word meaning a curl of hair. Cirrus clouds form only at high levels, above about 6 kilometers, where temperatures are very low. As a result, cirrus clouds are made of ice crystals.

Cirrus clouds that have feathery "hooked" ends are sometimes called mare's tails. Cirrocumulus clouds, which look like rows of cotton balls, often indicate that a storm is on its way. The rows of cirrocumulus clouds look like the scales of a fish. For this reason, the term "mackerel sky" is used to describe a sky full of cirrocumulus clouds.

Cumulus Clouds Clouds that look like fluffy, rounded piles of cotton are called **cumulus** (KYOO myuh lus) clouds. The word *cumulus* means "heap" or "mass" in Latin. Cumulus clouds form less than 2 kilometers above the ground, but they may grow in size and height until they extend upward as much as 18 kilometers. Cumulus clouds that are not very tall usually indicate fair weather. These clouds, which are common on sunny days, are called "fair weather cumulus." Towering clouds with flat tops, called cumulonimbus clouds, often produce thunderstorms. The suffix *-nimbus* means "rain."

Stratus Clouds Clouds that form in flat layers are called **stratus** (STRAT us) clouds. Recall that *strato* means "spread out." Stratus clouds usually cover all or most of the sky and are a uniform dull, gray color. As stratus clouds thicken, they may produce drizzle, rain, or snow. They are then called nimbostratus clouds.

 **Reading Checkpoint** What are stratus clouds?

FIGURE 17
Clouds
The three main types of clouds are cirrus, cumulus, and stratus. A cloud's name contains clues about its height and structure. **Interpreting Diagrams** *What type of cloud is found at the highest altitudes?*

Cirrus

Cirrocumulus

Altocumulus

Cumulonimbus

Altostratus

Cumulus

Nimbostratus

Stratus

Fog

(km)
13
12
11
10
9
8
7
6
5
4
3
2
1

FIGURE 18
Fog Around the Golden Gate Bridge
The cold ocean water of San Francisco Bay is often covered by fog in the early morning.
Predicting *What will happen as the sun rises and warms the air?*

Altocumulus and Altostratus Part of a cloud's name may be based on its height. The names of clouds that form between 2 and 6 kilometers above Earth's surface have the prefix *alto-*, which means "high." The two main types of these clouds are altocumulus and altostratus. These are "middle-level" clouds that are higher than regular cumulus and stratus clouds, but lower than cirrus and other "high" clouds.

Fog Clouds that form at or near the ground are called fog. Fog often forms when the ground cools at night after a warm, humid day. The ground cools the air just above the ground to the air's dew point. The next day the heat of the morning sun "burns" the fog off as its water droplets evaporate. Fog is more common in areas near bodies of water or low-lying marshy areas. In mountainous areas, fog can form as warm, moist air moves up the mountain slopes and cools.

 **Reading Checkpoint** **What is fog?**

Section 4 Assessment

 Target Reading Skill

Asking Questions Use the answers to the questions you wrote about the headings to help answer the questions below.

Reviewing Key Concepts

1. **a. Reviewing** What is humidity?
   b. Comparing and Contrasting How are humidity and relative humidity different?
   c. Calculating Suppose a sample of air can at most hold 10 grams of water vapor. If the sample actually has 2 grams of water vapor, what is its relative humidity?
2. **a. Identifying** What process is involved in cloud formation?
   b. Summarizing What two conditions are needed for clouds to form?
   c. Inferring When are clouds formed by ice crystals instead of drops of liquid water?
3. **a. Listing** What are the three main types of clouds?
   b. Describing Briefly describe each of the three main types of clouds.
   c. Classifying Classify each of the following cloud types as low-level, medium-level, or high-level: altocumulus, altostratus, cirrostratus, cirrus, cumulus, fog, nimbostratus, and stratus.

Lab zone **At-Home Activity**

Water in the Air Fill a large glass half full with cold water. Show your family members what happens as you add ice cubes to the water. Explain to your family that the water that appears on the outside of the glass comes from water vapor in the atmosphere. Also explain why the water on the outside of the glass only appears after you add ice to the water in the glass.

Precipitation

Reading Focus

Key Concepts
- What are the common types of precipitation?
- How is precipitation measured?

Key Terms
- precipitation
- drought
- cloud seeding
- rain gauge

Target Reading Skill

Using Prior Knowledge Before you read, write what you know about precipitation in a graphic organizer like the one below. As you read, write what you learn.

What You Know
1. Precipitation can be rain or snow. 2.

What You Learned
1. 2.

Lab zone **Discover Activity**

How Can You Make Hail?

1. Put on your goggles.
2. Put 15 g of salt into a beaker. Add 50 mL of water. Stir the solution until most of the salt is dissolved.
3. Put 15 mL of cold water in a clean test tube.
4. Place the test tube in the beaker.
5. Fill the beaker almost to the top with crushed ice. Stir the ice mixture every minute for six minutes.
6. Remove the test tube from the beaker and drop an ice chip into the test tube. What happens?

Think It Over
Inferring Based on your observation, what conditions are necessary for hail to form?

In Arica, Chile, the average rainfall is less than 1 millimeter per year. But in Hawaii, the average rainfall on Mount Waialeale is about 12 meters per year. As you can see, rainfall varies greatly around the world.

Water evaporates from every water surface on Earth and from living things. This water eventually returns to the surface as precipitation. **Precipitation** (pree sip uh TAY shun) is any form of water that falls from clouds and reaches Earth's surface.

Not all clouds produce precipitation. For precipitation to occur, cloud droplets or ice crystals must grow heavy enough to fall through the air. One way that cloud droplets grow is by colliding and combining with other droplets. As the droplets grow larger, they move faster and collect more small droplets. Finally, the droplets become heavy enough to fall out of the cloud as raindrops.

Typical Droplet Size
(Diameter)

Cloud droplet
(0.02mm)

Mist droplet
(0.005 – 0.05mm)

Drizzle droplet
(0.05 – 0.5mm)

Raindrop
(0.5 – 5mm)

FIGURE 19
Water Droplets
Droplets come in many sizes. Believe it or not, a raindrop has about one million times as much water in it as a cloud droplet.

Go Online

SCiLINKS™ NSTA

For: Links on precipitation
Visit: www.SciLinks.org
Web Code: scn-0925

Types of Precipitation

In warm parts of the world, precipitation is almost always in the form of rain. In colder regions, precipitation may fall as snow or ice. **Common types of precipitation include rain, sleet, freezing rain, snow, and hail.**

Rain The most common kind of precipitation is rain. Drops of water are called rain if they are at least 0.5 millimeter in diameter. Precipitation made up of smaller drops of water is called drizzle. Precipitation of even smaller drops is called mist. Drizzle and mist usually fall from stratus clouds.

Sleet Sometimes raindrops fall through a layer of air that is below 0°C, the freezing point of water. As they fall, the rain-drops freeze into solid particles of ice. Ice particles smaller than 5 millimeters in diameter are called sleet.

Freezing Rain Sometimes raindrops falling through cold air near the ground do not freeze in the air. Instead, they freeze when they touch a cold surface. This kind of precipitation is called freezing rain. In an ice storm, a smooth, thick layer of ice builds up on every surface. The weight of the ice may break tree branches and cause them to fall onto power lines, causing power failures. Freezing rain and sleet can make sidewalks and roads slippery and dangerous.

 **Reading Checkpoint** **What is sleet?**

FIGURE 20
Rain and Freezing Rain
Rain is the most common form of precipitation. Freezing rain coats objects with a layer of ice.
Relating Cause and Effect *What conditions are necessary for freezing rain to occur?*

Snow Often water vapor in a cloud is converted directly into ice crystals called snowflakes. Snowflakes have an endless number of different shapes and patterns, all with six sides or branches. Snowflakes often join together into larger clumps of snow in which the six-sided crystals are hard to see.

FIGURE 21
Snowflake
Snowflakes are tiny ice crystals. They all have six sides or branches.

Hail Round pellets of ice larger than 5 millimeters in diameter are called hailstones. Hail forms only inside cumulonimbus clouds during thunderstorms. A hailstone starts as an ice pellet inside a cold region of a cloud. Strong updrafts carry the hailstone up through the cold region many times. Each time the hailstone goes through the cold region, a new layer of ice forms around it. Eventually the hailstone becomes heavy enough to fall to the ground. If you cut a hailstone in half, you often see shells of ice, like the layers of an onion, as shown in Figure 22. Because hailstones can grow quite large before finally falling to the ground, hail can cause tremendous damage to crops, buildings, and vehicles.

FIGURE 22
How Hail Forms
Hailstones start as small pellets of ice in cumulonimbus clouds. They grow larger as they are repeatedly tossed up and down, until they become so heavy that they fall to the ground.

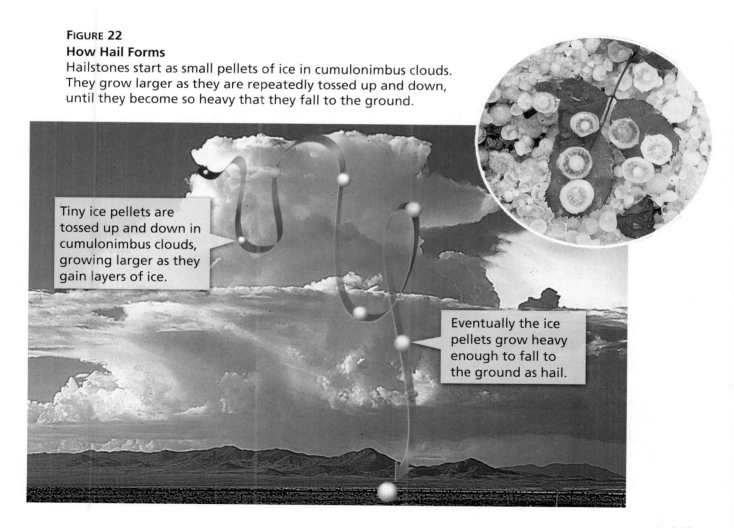

Tiny ice pellets are tossed up and down in cumulonimbus clouds, growing larger as they gain layers of ice.

Eventually the ice pellets grow heavy enough to fall to the ground as hail.

FIGURE 23
Cloud Seeding
Small planes are used to sprinkle chemicals into clouds to try to produce rain.

Lab zone **Skills Activity**

Calculating

Make a rain gauge by putting a funnel into a narrow, straight-sided glass jar. Here's how to calculate how much more rain your funnel collects than the jar alone.

1. First measure the diameter of the top of the funnel and square it.
   Example: $4 \times 4 = 16$

2. Then measure the diameter of the bottom of the jar and square it.
   Example: $2 \times 2 = 4$

3. Divide the first square by the second square.

   Example: $\frac{16}{4} = 4$

4. To find the actual depth of rain that fell, divide the depth of water in the jar by the ratio from Step 3.

   Example: $\frac{8 \text{ cm}}{4} = 2 \text{ cm}$

Modifying Precipitation Sometimes a region goes through a period of weather that is much drier than usual. Long periods of unusually low precipitation are called **droughts.** Droughts can cause great hardship.

Since the 1940s, scientists have been trying to produce rain during droughts. One method used to modify precipitation is called **cloud seeding.** In cloud seeding, tiny crystals of silver iodide and dry ice (solid carbon dioxide) are sprinkled into clouds from airplanes. Many clouds contain droplets of water which are supercooled below 0°C. The droplets don't freeze because there aren't enough solid particles around which ice crystals can form. Water vapor can condense on the particles of silver iodide, forming rain or snow. Dry ice cools the droplets even further, so that they will freeze without particles being present. However, to date cloud seeding has not been very effective in producing precipitation.

 **Reading Checkpoint** What is a drought?

Measuring Precipitation

There are various ways to measure the amount of rain or snow. **Scientists measure precipitation with various instruments, including rain gauges and measuring sticks.**

Snowfall Measurement Snowfall is usually measured in two ways; using a simple measuring stick or by melting collected snow and measuring the depth of water it produces. On average, 10 centimeters of snow contains about the same amount of water as 1 centimeter of rain. However, light, fluffy snow contains far less water than heavy, wet snow.

Collecting funnel

1 cm of rain enters the funnel.

Area of collecting funnel is 10 times larger than the measuring tube.

10 cm of rain is collected in the tube.

Measuring tube

30

20

10

FIGURE 24
Rain Gauge
A rain gauge measures the depth of rain that falls.
Observing *How much rain was collected in the measuring tube of this rain gauge?*

Rain Measurements An open-ended can or tube that collects rainfall is called a **rain gauge.** The amount of rainfall is measured by dipping a ruler into the water or by reading a marked scale. To increase the accuracy of the measurement, the top of a rain gauge may have a funnel that collects ten times as much rain as the tube alone, as shown in Figure 24. The funnel collects a greater depth of water that is easier to measure. To get the actual depth of rain, it is necessary to divide by ten. The narrow opening of the tube helps to minimize evaporation.

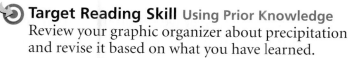

Section 5 Assessment

🔄 **Target Reading Skill** Using Prior Knowledge
Review your graphic organizer about precipitation and revise it based on what you have learned.

Reviewing Key Concepts

1. a. Listing Name the five common types of precipitation.
   b. Comparing and Contrasting Compare and contrast freezing rain and sleet.
   c. Classifying A thunderstorm produces precipitation in the form of ice particles that are about 6 millimeters in diameter. What type of precipitation would this be?
   d. Relating Cause and Effect How do hailstones become so large in cumulonimbus clouds?

2. a. Identifying How can a rain gauge be used to measure precipitation?
   b. Explaining How does the funnel in a rain gauge increase the accuracy of the measurement?

Writing in Science

Firsthand Account Think about the most exciting experience you have had with precipitation. Write a paragraph about that event. Make sure you describe the precipitation itself as well as the effect it had on you.

Droughts and Floods

Reading Preview

Key Concepts
- What is a drought?
- What is a flood, and how can the dangers of floods be reduced?

Key Terms
- drought
- flash flood
- levee

Target Reading Skill
Comparing and Contrasting As you read, compare and contrast droughts and floods by completing a table like the one below.

Droughts and Floods

Feature	Droughts	Floods
Cause	Scarce rainfall	
Possible to predict?		
Preparation		
Major effects		

Discover **Activity**

How Does Dryness Affect Soil?

1. Spread a layer of soil about 3 centimeters thick in a rectangular pan.
2. Add water to the soil and stir so that it forms a thick mud.
3. Place the pan under a lamp for several hours. At the end of the day, check the soil.

Think It Over

Observing What does the soil look like? How does it feel? If the soil in your area looked similar to this soil sample, do you think it could support plants? Explain your answer.

Imagine trying to drink from a tall glass of milk through a straw no longer than a toothpick. When the level of the milk falls below the bottom of the straw, you can no longer reach the milk. In the same way, when the water table falls below the bottom of a well, the well runs dry. A water shortage may occur.

As you read in Chapter 1, water shortages can be triggered by human activities, such as overuse of an aquifer. However, natural processes also can cause areas to receive too little water—or, conversely, too much water. In this section, you'll learn what causes these conditions and how they impact people.

Droughts

A certain area might receive, on average, enough rainfall to meet its water needs. But if the area experiences a long period of scarce rainfall, a condition known as a **drought** (drowt) might occur. A drought reduces the supplies of groundwater and surface water. Without precipitation to recharge the aquifer, the amount of groundwater in the aquifer decreases. A decrease in the amount of water in the aquifer can result in a shortage of water for homes and businesses.

Causes and Effects of Droughts Droughts are weather-related events. **They are usually caused by dry weather systems that remain in one place for weeks or months at a time.**

Long-term droughts can devastate a region. Droughts can cause crop failure or even widespread famine. Streams and ponds dry up, and both people and animals suffer. During the drought that struck Florida in 1998, plants withered and died. The dry conditions set the stage for drought-related fires—more than 475,000 acres burned, causing an estimated $500 million in damage.

Predicting and Preparing for Droughts Droughts are difficult to predict. However, since the 1980s, federal and state governments have begun monitoring soil and water conditions, as well as precipitation levels. This information allows scientists to pinpoint areas that may, in the near future, experience droughts. As soon as the level of rainfall drops below normal, state agricultural officials may contact farmers to warn them of a possible drought.

Little can be done to actually control a drought. However, people can prepare for droughts in several ways. When dry conditions first occur, people can begin conserving water. Washing cars and watering lawns, for example, are two activities that can be curtailed. Farmers can grow drought-resistant plants that have been especially bred to withstand dry conditions. In general, practicing water conservation and soil conservation ensures that when droughts do occur, the effects will be as mild as possible.

 **What is a drought?**

Go Online
PLANET DIARY

For: More on droughts
Visit: PHSchool.com
Web Code: cfd-3024

FIGURE 25
A Drought
Europe experienced a severe drought in the summer of 2003, causing the Rhine River to dry up. The smaller photo shows Düsseldorf, Germany, during a normal summer.

FIGURE 26
Floods
Severe flooding can leave many homes and farms under water.
Inferring *What characteristic of the land along the river allowed floodwaters to spread out over a large area?*

Floods

The spring of 1993 was much wetter than usual in the midwestern United States. Severe rainstorms brought a great deal of rain within a short period. The Missouri and Mississippi rivers and their tributaries could not contain the huge volumes of water. The rivers soon overflowed their banks, causing some of the worst flooding on record. Along the Mississippi River at St. Louis, the flood lasted for six months! At its peak, the flood covered thousands of square kilometers of land. The flood destroyed homes, roads, and city water supplies. It also ruined valuable farmland.

Causes and Effects of Floods Not all floods are as devastating as those that struck in 1993. Some cause relatively little damage. **Small or large, however, all floods occur when the volume of water in a river increases so much that the river overflows its channel.** As rain and melting snow add more and more water, a river gains in speed and strength. When the speed of a river increases, the amount of energy it has increases, too. A flooding river can uproot trees and pluck boulders from the ground. As it overflows its banks, the powerful water can even wash away bridges and buildings.

 **Reading Checkpoint** **What happens to a river's speed and strength during a flood?**

Flash Floods Floods are the most dangerous weather-related events in the United States. Unexpected floods, called flash floods, are the most dangerous of all because the water rises very rapidly—"in a flash"—and people have little time to reach safe ground. A **flash flood** is a sudden, violent flood that occurs within a few hours, or even minutes, of a storm. Figure 27 shows one way in which a flash flood can occur.

Most flash floods are due to large amounts of rain. For example, a line of thunderstorms may remain over an area, dropping heavy rain for several hours or days. Hurricanes or tropical storms bring downpours that quickly fill stream channels. A flash flood can also be caused by a dam breaking, releasing millions of liters of water all at once. Similarly, if ice that has jammed a river breaks free, the sudden rush of water can cause a flash flood.

Some of the most dangerous flash floods occur in the deserts of the southwestern United States. For example, in 1997, a serious flash flood struck Antelope Canyon in the northern Arizona desert. On August 12, a group of 12 hikers entered the dry, narrow canyon. That afternoon, a severe thunderstorm dropped several inches of rain on the Kaibeto Plateau, 24 kilometers away. Dry stream channels that drain into Antelope Canyon quickly filled with rainwater. The water rushed into the canyon, creating a wall of water over 3 meters high. Only one hiker survived.

Lab zone Skills **Activity**

Inferring

1. Fill a cup with water. Hold a funnel above a basin and pour the water very slowly into the funnel.
2. Refill the cup with the same amount of water you used in Step 1. Hold the funnel above the basin and this time pour the water rapidly into the funnel. What happens?

How is a funnel like a river valley? What do you think would happen if a large amount of water entered a river valley in a short period of time?

FIGURE 27
Flash Floods
Flash floods (left) occur when large amounts of rain are funneled into a narrow valley. This process flooded Antelope Canyon in Arizona (right) in 1997.

Heavy rain falls on the plateau.

Instead of soaking into the hard soil, the water runs into the canyon.

The rainwater is funneled into the narrow canyon and floods it.

Flood Precautions

Despite efforts to control flooding, floods have killed millions of people around the world in the last century. In the United States alone, 20 million people live in places where flooding is likely. What can people do to protect themselves and their homes?

Predicting Floods Using different types of technology, scientists can often issue flood warnings. **Advance warnings help reduce flood damage and loss of life.** Weather satellites supply information about snow cover so that scientists can estimate how much water will run into rivers when the snow melts. Radar can track and measure the size of an approaching rainstorm. Scientists check river gauges that measure water levels. With this information, forecasters can predict flood heights at different points along a river. Their goal is to issue warnings in time for people to prepare and evacuate if necessary.

Controlling Floods For as long as people have lived near rivers, they have tried to control floods. **Building dams is one method of flood control.** A dam is a barrier across a river that may redirect the flow of a river to other channels. It can also be used to store water in an artificial lake. Engineers can open the dam's floodgates to release water in dry seasons. Dams work fairly well to control small floods. During severe floods, however, powerful flood waters can wash over the top of a dam or break through it.

FIGURE 28
Trying to Control a Flood
These people are working together to protect their community during a flood.

There is also a natural defense against floods—sediments. Sediments are particles of rock and soil that are picked up and carried along by forces such as flowing water. As a river overflows, it slows down, depositing its heavier sediments alongside the river channel.

Over time, these deposits build up into long ridges called **levees.** Levees that form naturally help keep the river inside its banks. People sometimes strengthen natural levees with sandbags or stone and concrete to provide further protection against floods.

 **Reading Checkpoint** How do sediments help protect against a flood?

1 The car stalls. Moving water pushes against the car.

2 As the water rises, the car begins to float.

3 Sixty centimeters of water can wash a car away.

Flood Safety What should you do in the event of a flood? When the danger becomes too great or the water rises too high, people are usually evacuated. The first rule of flood safety is: Move to higher ground and stay away from flood waters. If your family is in a car, the driver shouldn't try to drive on a flooded road. Sometimes less than 60 centimeters of fast-moving water can sweep a car away.

High water is not the only hazard in a flood. Floods can knock down electrical poles and wires. Downed electrical poles can leave dangerous live wires hanging loose and cause power outages. Flood waters can also saturate soil, causing landslides or mudslides. If roads have been flooded or washed away, emergency vehicles such as fire trucks and ambulances may not be able to get through.

Flood waters can wash into wells and water treatment plants, polluting the water. Therefore, be careful with food and water that flood waters have touched. Boil drinking water after a flood if you are instructed to do so.

FIGURE 29
Dangers of a Flood
Flood waters can wash away cars. It is extremely dangerous to remain in a car during a flood.
Applying Concepts *Why is it dangerous to stay in a car that is caught in a flood?*

Section 6 Assessment

Target Reading Skill Comparing and Contrasting Use your table to quiz a partner about droughts and floods.

Reviewing Key Concepts

1. a. Reviewing What causes droughts?
  b. Summarizing What are some effects of droughts?
  c. Problem Solving What are two ways to reduce the effects of droughts?
2. a. Describing When do floods occur?
  b. Explaining What are two ways to help reduce the dangers of floods?
  c. Making Judgments Your community is considering building a dam and on a nearby river to reduce flooding. Would you support this proposal? Explain.

Writing in Science

Radio Announcement Write a script for a 30-second public service radio announcement in which you tell about the dangers of floods. Include safety steps to follow in case of a flood.

1 Energy in Earth's Atmosphere

Key Concepts

- Most energy from the sun travels to Earth in the form of visible light and infrared radiation. A small amount arrives as ultraviolet radiation.
- Some sunlight is absorbed or reflected by the atmosphere before it can reach the surface. The rest passes through to the surface.
- When the surface is heated, it radiates energy back into the atmosphere as infrared radiation.

Key Terms

electromagnetic waves	ultraviolet radiation
radiation	scattering
infrared radiation	greenhouse effect

2 Heat Transfer

Key Concepts

- Air temperature is usually measured with a thermometer.
- Heat is transferred in three ways: radiation, conduction, and convection.
- Radiation, conduction, and convection work together to heat the troposphere.

Key Terms

temperature	conduction
thermal energy	convection
thermometer	convection currents
heat	

3 Winds

Key Concepts

- Winds are caused by differences in air pressure.
- Local winds are caused by unequal heating of Earth's surface within a small area.
- Like local winds, global winds are created by the unequal heating of Earth's surface. But unlike local winds, global winds occur over a large area.
- The major global wind belts are the trade winds, the polar easterlies, and the prevailing westerlies.

Key Terms

- wind • anemometer • wind-chill factor
- local winds • sea breeze • land breeze
- global winds • Coriolis effect • latitude
- jet stream

4 Water in the Atmosphere

Key Concepts

- Relative humidity can be measured with an instrument called a psychrometer.
- Clouds form when water vapor in the air condenses to form liquid water or ice crystals.
- Scientists classify clouds into three main types based on their shape: cirrus, cumulus, and stratus. Clouds are further classified by altitude.

Key Terms

- water cycle • evaporation • humidity
- relative humidity • psychrometer
- condensation • dew point • cirrus
- cumulus • stratus

5 Precipitation

Key Concepts

- Common types of precipitation include rain, sleet, freezing rain, snow, and hail.
- Scientists measure precipitation with various instruments, including rain gauges and measuring sticks.

Key Terms

precipitation	cloud seeding
drought	rain gauge

6 Droughts and Floods

Key Concepts

- Droughts are usually caused by weather systems that remain in one place for weeks or months.
- Floods occur when the volume of water in a river increases so much that the river overflows its channel.
- Advance warnings help reduce flood damage and loss of life. Building dams is one method of flood control.

Key Terms

- drought • flash flood • levee

Review and Assessment

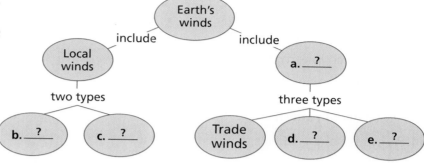

Organizing Information

Concept Mapping Copy the concept map about Earth's winds onto a separate sheet of paper. Then complete it and add a title. (For more on Concept Maps, see the Skills Handbook).

Earth's winds

include · include

Local winds · a. ___?___

two types · three types

b. ___?___ · c. ___?___ · Trade winds · d. ___?___ · e. ___?___

Reviewing Key Terms

Choose the letter of the best answer.

1. Energy from the sun travels to Earth's surface by
   a. radiation.
   b. convection.
   c. evaporation.
   d. conduction.

2. Rising warm air transports thermal energy by
   a. conduction.
   b. convection.
   c. radiation.
   d. condensation.

3. Bands of high-altitude, high-speed winds are called
   a. jet streams.
   b. sea breezes.
   c. land breezes.
   d. local winds.

4. A type of cloud that forms in flat layers and often covers much of the sky is
   a. cirrus.
   b. cumulus.
   c. fog.
   d. stratus.

5. Rain, sleet, and hail are all forms of
   a. evaporation.
   b. condensation.
   c. precipitation.
   d. convection.

If the statement is true, write *true*. If it is false, change the underlined word or words to make the statement true.

6. Infrared radiation and <u>ultraviolet radiation</u> make up most of the energy Earth receives from the sun.

7. The transfer of heat by the movement of a fluid is called <u>conduction</u>.

8. Winds that blow steadily from specific directions for long distances are called <u>sea breezes</u>.

9. <u>Cirrus</u> clouds are made mostly of ice crystals.

10. People sometimes strengthen natural <u>levees</u> with sandbags to protect against floods.

Writing in Science

Descriptive Paragraph Suppose you are preparing for an around-the-world sailing trip. Select a route. Then write a description of the types of winds you would expect to find along different parts of your route.

DISCOVERY CHANNEL SCHOOL™

Weather Factors
Video Preview
Video Field Trip
▶ Video Assessment

Review and Assessment

Checking Concepts

11. What causes the greenhouse effect? How does it affect Earth's atmosphere?

12. Describe examples of radiation, conduction, and convection from your daily life.

13. Describe how the movements of hot air at the equator and cold air at the poles produce global wind patterns.

14. Why are solid particles required for cloud formation?

15. Describe sleet, hail, and snow in terms of how each one forms.

16. How might building a dam affect people living nearby?

Math Practice

17. Converting Units Suppose the outside temperature is 60° F. What is the temperature in degrees Celsius?

18. Converting Units What is 30° C in degrees Fahrenheit?

Thinking Critically

19. Inferring Venus has an atmosphere that is mostly carbon dioxide. How do you think the greenhouse effect has altered Venus?

20. Interpreting Diagrams Describe the journey of a small particle of water through the water cycle, using the terms in the diagram below.

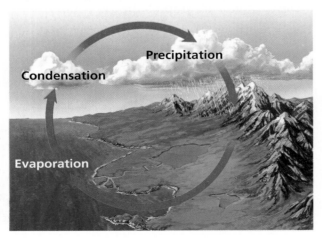

21. Relating Cause and Effect What circumstances could cause a nighttime land breeze in a city near the ocean?

22. Problem Solving A psychrometer gives the same reading on both thermometers. What is the relative humidity?

23. Making Judgments Your neighborhood is located at the end of a narrow canyon. You hear reports of heavy rains several miles away. Is there cause for concern? Explain.

Applying Skills

Use the table to answer questions 24–26.

Average Monthly Rainfall

Month	Rainfall	Month	Rainfall
January	1 cm	July	49 cm
February	1 cm	August	57 cm
March	1 cm	September	40 cm
April	2 cm	October	20 cm
May	25 cm	November	4 cm
June	52 cm	December	1 cm

24. Graphing Use the information in the table to draw a bar graph that shows the rainfall for each month at this location.

25. Calculating What is the total amount of rainfall each year at this location?

26. Classifying Which months of the year would you classify as "dry"? Which months would you classify as "wet"?

Lab zone Chapter **Project**

Performance Assessment Decide how to present the findings from your weather station to the class. For example, you could put your graphs and predictions on a poster or use a computer to make a slide show. Make sure your graphs are neatly drawn and easy to understand.

🌀 End-of-Grade Test Practice

Choose the letter of the best answer.

1. When the temperature equals the dew point, the relative humidity is
   A zero.
   B about 10 percent.
   C about 50 percent.
   D 100 percent.

2. A sudden, violent flood that occurs within a few hours of a storm is called a
   A levee.
   B dam.
   C flash flood.
   D mudslide.

3. What is the temperature in degrees Celsius when a room thermometer reads 77°F?

   A 25°C   B 32°C
   C 45°C   D 77°C

In the table below, the chart shows the actual air temperature when the wind speed is zero. Use the data table and your knowledge of science to answer questions 4–5.

Wind-Chill Temperature Index

Wind Speed	Equivalent Air Temperature (°C)			
0 km/h	5°	0°	−5°	−10°
10 km/h	2.7°	−3.3°	−9.3°	−15.3°
15 km/h	1.7°	−4.4°	−10.6°	−16.7°
20 km/h	1.1°	−5.2°	−11.6°	−17.9°

4. On a windy winter's day, the actual air temperature is −5°C and the wind speed is 15 kilometers per hour. What would the wind-chill factor make the temperature feel like to a person outdoors?
   A 1.7°C   B −5°C
   C −10.6°C   D −16.7°C

5. Use trends shown in the data table to predict how cold the air temperature would feel if the actual temperature was 0°C, and the wind speed was 25 km/hr.
   A about 0°C   B about −6°C
   C about −15°C   D about 25°C

Constructed Response

6. Describe the process by which a cloud forms. What two conditions are necessary for this process to take place? How does this process compare to the process by which dew or frost is formed?

Standard Course of Study

This chapter addresses the following North Carolina Objectives:

1.01 Identify and create questions and hypotheses.

1.05 Analyze evidence.

1.06 Use mathematics to gather, organize, and present data.

1.08 Use oral and written language.

1.09 Use technologies and information systems.

1.10 Analyze and evaluate information from a scientifically literate viewpoint.

2.01 Explore definitions of "technology."

2.03 Evaluate technological designs.

3.05 Examine atmospheric properties.

3.06 Assess the use of technology in studying atmospheric phenomena and weather hazards.

Hurricane Hugo approaches ▶ the Florida coast.

Lab zone™ Chapter **Project**

The Weather Tomorrow

When the sky turns dark and threatening, it's not hard to predict the weather. A storm is likely on its way. But wouldn't you rather know about an approaching storm before it arrives? In this project you will get a chance to make your own weather forecasts and compare them to the forecasts of professionals. Good luck!

Your Goal To predict the weather for your own community and two other locations in the United States

To complete the project you must

● compare weather maps for several days at a time
● look for patterns in the weather
● draw maps to show your weather predictions

Plan It! Begin by previewing the chapter to learn about weather maps and symbols. Start a project folder to store daily national weather maps and a description of the symbols used on the maps. Choose two locations that are at least 1,000 kilometers away from your town and from each other. As you collect weather maps, look for patterns in day-to-day weather changes. Then predict the next day's weather and compare your predictions to professional forecasts and to the actual weather.

Air Masses and Fronts

Reading Preview

Key Concepts
- What are the major types of air masses in North America, and how do they move?
- What are the main types of fronts?
- What type of weather is associated with cyclones and anticyclones?

Key Terms
- air mass • tropical • polar
- maritime • continental
- front • occluded • cyclone
- anticyclone

🎯 Target Reading Skill
Comparing and Contrasting As you read, compare and contrast the four types of fronts by completing a table like the one below.

Types of Fronts

Front	How Forms	Type of Weather
Cold front	A cold air mass overtakes a warm air mass.	
Warm front		
Occluded front		

Lab zone Discover **Activity**

How Do Fluids of Different Densities Behave?

1. Put on your apron. Place a cardboard divider across the middle of a plastic shoe box.
2. Add a few drops of red food coloring to a liter of warm water. Pour the red liquid, which represents low-density warm air, into the shoe box on one side of the divider.

3. Add about 100 mL of table salt and a few drops of blue food coloring to a liter of cold water. Pour the blue liquid, which represents high-density cold air, into the shoe box on the other side of the divider.
4. What do you think will happen if you remove the divider?
5. Now quickly remove the divider. Watch carefully from the side. What happens?

Think It Over

Developing Hypotheses Based on this activity, write a hypothesis stating what would happen if a mass of cold air ran into a mass of warm air.

Listen to the evening news in the winter and you may hear a weather forecast like this: "A huge mass of Arctic air is moving our way, bringing freezing temperatures." Today's weather can be influenced by air from thousands of kilometers away—perhaps from Canada or the Pacific Ocean. A huge body of air that has similar temperature, humidity, and air pressure at any given height is called an **air mass.** A single air mass may spread over millions of square kilometers and be up to 10 kilometers deep.

FIGURE 1
Major Snowstorm
In winter, humid air masses bring heavy snowstorms to areas like New York City.

Types of Air Masses

Scientists classify air masses according to two characteristics: temperature and humidity. **Four major types of air masses influence the weather in North America: maritime tropical, continental tropical, maritime polar, and continental polar.**

The characteristics of an air mass depend on the temperatures and moisture content of the region over which the air mass forms. Remember that temperature affects air pressure. Cold, dense air has a higher pressure, while warm, less dense air has a lower pressure. **Tropical,** or warm, air masses form in the tropics and have low air pressure. **Polar,** or cold, air masses form north of 50° north latitude and south of 50° south latitude. Polar air masses have high air pressure.

Whether an air mass is humid or dry depends on whether it forms over water or land. **Maritime** air masses form over oceans. Water evaporates from the oceans, so the air can become very humid. **Continental** air masses form over land. Continental air masses have less exposure to large amounts of moisture from bodies of water. Therefore, continental air masses are drier than maritime air masses.

Maritime Tropical Warm, humid air masses form over tropical oceans. Maritime tropical air masses that form over the Gulf of Mexico and the Atlantic Ocean move first into the southeastern United States. These air masses then move north and northeast, where they influence weather in the central and eastern United States. In the west, maritime tropical air masses form over the Pacific Ocean. They mainly affect the weather on the West Coast. As they cross the coastal mountain ranges, the Pacific air masses lose moisture.

In summer, maritime tropical air masses usually bring hot, humid weather. Many summer showers and thunderstorms in the eastern United States develop in air masses that have formed over the Gulf of Mexico. In winter, a humid air mass can bring heavy rain or snow.

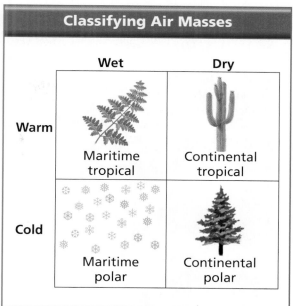

Classifying Air Masses

	Wet	Dry
Warm	Maritime tropical	Continental tropical
Cold	Maritime polar	Continental polar

FIGURE 2
Air masses can be classified according to their temperature and humidity. **Identifying** *What type of air mass consists of warm, moist air?*

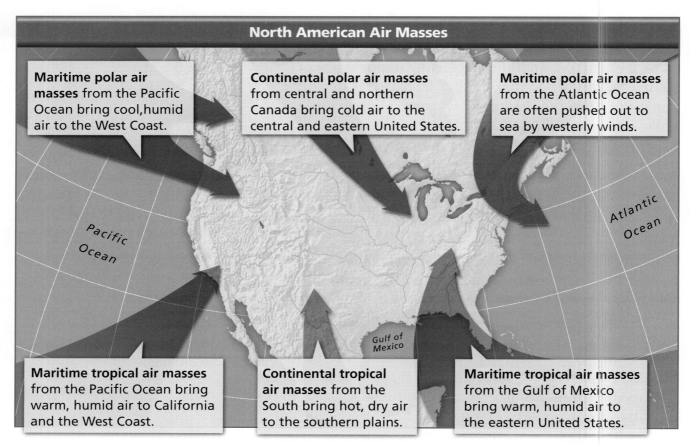

North American Air Masses

Maritime polar air masses from the Pacific Ocean bring cool, humid air to the West Coast.

Continental polar air masses from central and northern Canada bring cold air to the central and eastern United States.

Maritime polar air masses from the Atlantic Ocean are often pushed out to sea by westerly winds.

Pacific Ocean

Atlantic Ocean

Gulf of Mexico

Maritime tropical air masses from the Pacific Ocean bring warm, humid air to California and the West Coast.

Continental tropical air masses from the South bring hot, dry air to the southern plains.

Maritime tropical air masses from the Gulf of Mexico bring warm, humid air to the eastern United States.

FIGURE 3
Air masses can be warm or cold, and humid or dry. As an air mass moves into an area, the weather changes.

Maritime Polar Cool, humid air masses form over the icy cold North Pacific and North Atlantic oceans. Maritime polar air masses affect the West Coast more than the East Coast. Even in summer, these masses of cool, humid air often bring fog, rain, and cool temperatures to the West Coast.

Continental Tropical Hot, dry air masses form mostly in summer over dry areas of the Southwest and northern Mexico. Continental tropical air masses cover a smaller area than other air masses. They occasionally move northeast, bringing hot, dry weather to the southern Great Plains.

Continental Polar Large continental polar air masses form over central and northern Canada and Alaska, as shown in Figure 3. Air masses that form near the Arctic Circle can bring bitterly cold weather with very low humidity. In winter, continental polar air masses bring clear, cold, dry air to much of North America. In summer, the air mass is milder. Storms may occur when continental polar air masses move south and collide with maritime tropical air masses moving north.

 **Reading Checkpoint** Where do continental polar air masses come from?

How Air Masses Move

When an air mass moves into an area and interacts with other air masses, it causes the weather to change. **In the continental United States, air masses are commonly moved by the prevailing westerlies and jet streams.**

Prevailing Westerlies The prevailing westerlies, the major wind belts over the continental United States, generally push air masses from west to east. For example, maritime polar air masses from the Pacific Ocean are blown onto the West Coast, bringing low clouds and showers.

Jet Streams Embedded within the prevailing westerlies are jet streams. Recall that jet streams are bands of high-speed winds about 10 kilometers above Earth's surface. As jet streams blow from west to east, air masses are carried along their tracks.

Fronts As huge masses of air move across the land and the oceans, they collide with each other. But the air masses do not easily mix. Think about a bottle of oil and water. The less dense oil floats on top of the denser water. Something similar happens when two air masses with a different temperature and humidity collide. The air masses do not easily mix. The boundary where the air masses meet becomes a **front.** Storms and changeable weather often develop along fronts, as shown in Figure 4.

Reading Checkpoint In what direction does the jet stream move storms?

Calculating

When planes fly from west to east, they fly with the jet stream, and therefore can fly faster. When traveling from east to west, planes fly against the jet stream, and travel slower. To calculate the rate at which the planes fly, divide the distance traveled by the time it takes.

$$\text{Rate} = \frac{\text{Distance}}{\text{Time}}$$

If a plane flies from Denver, Colorado, to New York City, a distance of about 2,618 kilometers, it takes about 3 hours and 30 minutes. The return flight takes about 4 hours. Calculate the rates of air travel, in km/h, in each direction. How much extra speed does the jet stream add to the west-to-east flight?

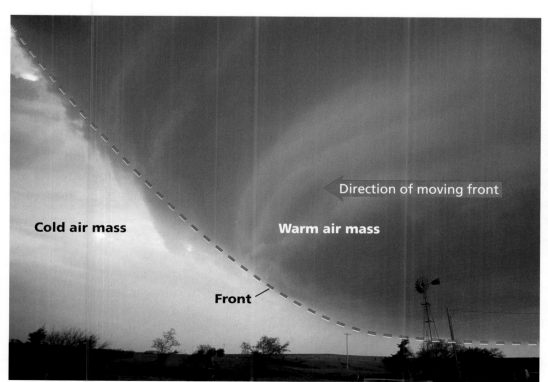

FIGURE 4
How a Front Forms
The boundary where unlike air masses meet is called a front. A front may be 15 to 600 kilometers wide and extend high into the troposphere.

Cold air mass

Direction of moving front

Warm air mass

Front

FIGURE 5

Types of Fronts

There are four types of fronts: cold fronts, warm fronts, stationary fronts, and occluded fronts. **Interpreting Diagrams** *What kind of weather occurs at a warm front?*

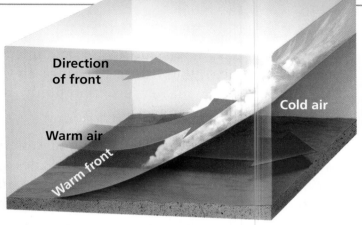

▲ **Warm Front**
A warm air mass overtakes a slow-moving cold air mass.

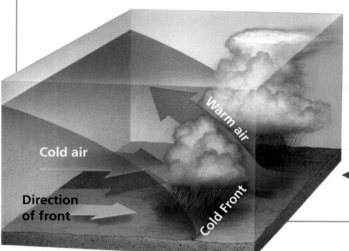

◄ **Cold Front**
A fast-moving cold air mass overtakes a warm air mass.

Types of Fronts

Colliding air masses can form four types of fronts: cold fronts, warm fronts, stationary fronts, and occluded fronts. The kind of front that develops depends on the characteristics of the air masses and how they are moving.

Cold Fronts As you have learned, cold air is dense and tends to sink. Warm air is less dense and tends to rise. When a rapidly moving cold air mass runs into a slowly moving warm air mass, the denser cold air slides under the lighter warm air. The warm air is pushed upward along the leading edge of the colder air, as shown in Figure 5. A cold front forms.

As the warm air rises, it expands and cools. Remember that warm air can hold more water vapor than cool air. The rising air soon reaches the dew point, the temperature at which the water vapor in the air condenses into droplets of liquid water or forms tiny ice crystals. Clouds form. If there is a lot of water vapor in the warm air, heavy rain or snow may fall. If the warm air mass contains only a little water vapor, then the cold front may be accompanied by only cloudy skies.

Since cold fronts tend to move quickly, they can cause abrupt weather changes, including thunderstorms. After a cold front passes through an area, colder, drier air moves in, often bringing clear skies, a shift in wind, and lower temperatures.

Reading Checkpoint **What type of weather do cold fronts bring?**

Lab zone Skills **Activity**

Classifying

At home, watch the weather forecast on television. Make a note of each time the weather reporter mentions a front. Classify the fronts mentioned or shown as cold, warm, stationary, or occluded. What type of weather is predicted to occur when the front arrives? Note the specific weather conditions, such as temperature and air pressure, associated with the front. Is each type of front always associated with the same type of weather?

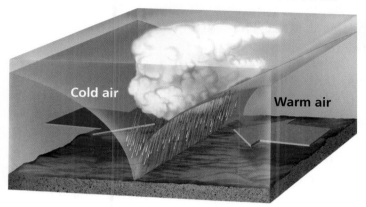

▼ Stationary Front
Cold and warm air masses meet, but neither can move the other.

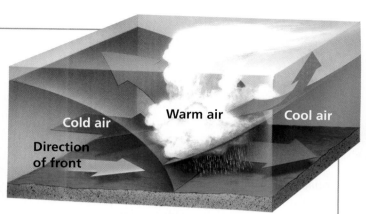

▲ Occluded Front
A warm air mass is caught between two cooler air masses.

Go Online
active art

For: Weather Fronts activity
Visit: PHSchool.com
Web Code: cfp-4031

Warm Fronts Clouds and precipitation also accompany warm fronts. At a warm front, a fast-moving warm air mass overtakes a slowly moving cold air mass. Because cold air is denser than warm air, the warm air moves over the cold air. If the warm air is humid, light rain or snow falls along the front. If the warm air is dry, scattered clouds form. Because warm fronts move slowly, the weather may be rainy or cloudy for several days. After a warm front passes through an area, the weather is likely to be warm and humid.

Stationary Fronts Sometimes cold and warm air masses meet, but neither one can move the other. The two air masses face each other in a "standoff." In this case, the front is called a stationary front. Where the warm and cool air meet, water vapor in the warm air condenses into rain, snow, fog, or clouds. If a stationary front remains stalled over an area, it may bring many days of clouds and precipitation.

Occluded Fronts The most complex weather situation occurs at an occluded front, where a warm air mass is caught between two cooler air masses. The denser cool air masses move underneath the less dense warm air mass and push the warm air upward. The two cooler air masses meet in the middle and may mix. The temperature near the ground becomes cooler. The warm air mass is cut off, or **occluded,** from the ground. As the warm air cools and its water vapor condenses, the weather may turn cloudy and rain or snow may fall.

FIGURE 6

Structure of Cyclones and Anticyclones
Winds spiral inward towards the low-pressure center of a cyclone. Winds spiral outward from the high-pressure center of an anticyclone.
Interpreting Diagrams *Do cyclone winds spin clockwise or counter-clockwise in the Northern Hemisphere?*

Cyclone (Low)

Anticyclone (High)

Cyclones and Anticyclones

As air masses collide to form fronts, the boundary between the fronts sometimes becomes distorted. This distortion can be caused by surface features, such as mountains, or strong winds, such as the jet stream. When this happens, bends can develop along the front. The air begins to swirl. The swirling air can cause a low-pressure center to form.

Cyclones If you look at a weather map, you will see areas marked with an *L*. The L stands for "low," and indicates an area of relatively low air pressure. A swirling center of low air pressure is called a **cyclone,** from a Greek word meaning "wheel."

As warm air at the center of a cyclone rises, the air pressure decreases. Cooler air blows toward this low-pressure area from nearby areas where the air pressure is higher. As shown in Figure 6, winds spiral inward toward the center of the system. Recall that, in the Northern Hemisphere, the Coriolis effect deflects winds to the right. Because of this deflection, winds in a cyclone spin counterclockwise in the Northern Hemisphere when viewed from above.

Cyclones play a large part in the weather of the United States. As air rises in a cyclone, the air cools, forming clouds and precipitation. **Cyclones and decreasing air pressure are associated with clouds, wind, and precipitation.**

Anticyclones As its name suggests, an anticyclone is the opposite of a cyclone. **Anticyclones** are high-pressure centers of dry air. Anticyclones are usually called "highs"—*H* on a weather map. Winds spiral outward from the center of an anticyclone, moving toward areas of lower pressure. Because of the Coriolis effect, winds in an anticyclone spin clockwise in the Northern Hemisphere. Because air moves out from the center of the anticyclone, cool air moves downward from higher in the troposphere. As the cool air falls, it warms up, so its relative humidity drops. **The descending air in an anticyclone generally causes dry, clear weather.**

 **Reading Checkpoint** What is an anticyclone?

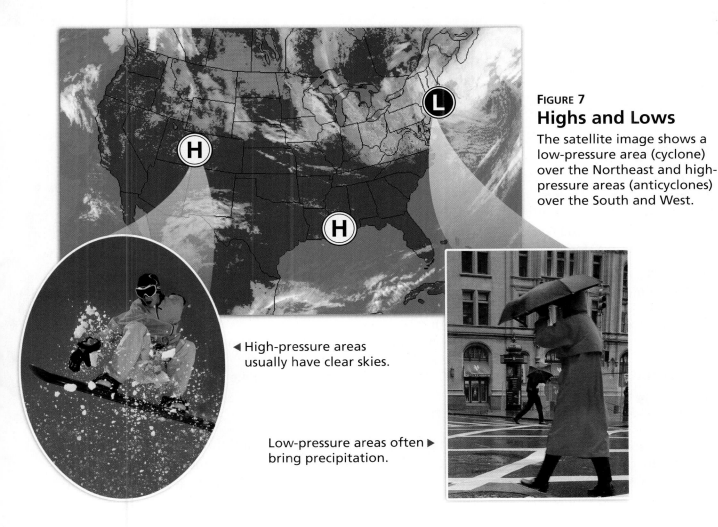

FIGURE 7
Highs and Lows
The satellite image shows a low-pressure area (cyclone) over the Northeast and high-pressure areas (anticyclones) over the South and West.

◄ High-pressure areas usually have clear skies.

Low-pressure areas often ► bring precipitation.

Section 1 Assessment

🔄 **Target Reading Skill** Comparing and Contrasting Use the information in your table about fronts to help you answer Question 2 below.

Reviewing Key Concepts

1. a. **Reviewing** What two characteristics are used to classify air masses?
   b. **Classifying** Classify the four major types of air masses according to whether they are dry or humid.
   c. **Applying Concepts** What type of air mass would form over the northern Atlantic Ocean?
2. a. **Defining** What is a front?
   b. **Describing** Name the four types of fronts and describe the type of weather each brings.
   c. **Classifying** What type of front would most likely be responsible for several days of rain and clouds?

3. a. **Identifying** What is a cyclone?
   b. **Relating Cause and Effect** How does air move in an anticyclone? How does this movement affect the weather?
   c. **Comparing and Contrasting** Compare cyclones and anticyclones. What type of weather is associated with each?

Writing in Science

News Report Suppose you are a television weather reporter covering a severe thunderstorm. Write a brief report to explain to viewers the conditions that caused the thunderstorm.

Storms

Reading Preview

Key Concepts
- What are the main kinds of storms, and how do they form?
- What measures can you take to ensure safety in a storm?

Key Terms
- storm • thunderstorm
- lightning • tornado
- hurricane • storm surge
- evacuate

Target Reading Skill

Sequencing As you read, make a flowchart like the one below that shows how a hurricane forms. Write each step of the process in the flowchart in a separate box in the order in which it occurs.

Hurricane Formation

Begins as a low-pressure area over warm water, or a tropical disturbance.

↓

Warm, humid air rises and begins to spiral.

↓

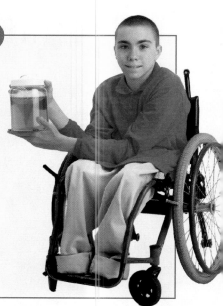

Lab zone Discover Activity

Can You Make a Tornado?

1. Fill a large jar three-quarters full with water. Add a drop of liquid dish detergent and a penny or a marble.
2. Put the lid on the jar tightly. Now move the jar in a circle until the water inside begins to spin.

Think It Over
Observing What happens to the water in the jar? Describe the pattern that forms. How is it like a tornado? Unlike a tornado?

As a storm rages, lightning flashes and thunder rumbles. After the sky clears, dripping trees and numerous puddles are the only evidence of the passing storm. Right? Not always. Scientists search for other evidence—"fossil lightning"! When lightning strikes sand or sandy soil, the sand grains are fused together to form a fulgurite. The shape of the fulgurite reflects the path of the lightning bolt that formed it, as shown in Figure 8. These structures clearly show the tremendous power of storms.

A **storm** is a violent disturbance in the atmosphere. Storms involve sudden changes in air pressure, which in turn cause rapid air movements. Conditions that bring one kind of storm often cause other kinds of storms in the same area. For example, the conditions that cause thunderstorms can also cause tornadoes. There are several types of severe storms.

FIGURE 8
Fulgurites
A fulgurite forms when lightning strikes sand or sandy soil. The temperature of the lightning is so high that it melts the sand and forms a tube.

FIGURE 9
Thunderstorm Formation
A thunderstorm forms when warm, humid air rises rapidly within a cumulonimbus cloud.
Applying Concepts *Why do cumulonimbus clouds often form along cold fronts?*

Labels on figure: Storm movement · Cold air moves downward. · Warm, humid air rises. · Heavy rain

Thunderstorms

Do you find thunderstorms frightening? Exciting? As you watch the brilliant flashes of lightning and listen to long rolls of thunder, you may wonder what caused them.

How Thunderstorms Form A **thunderstorm** is a small storm often accompanied by heavy precipitation and frequent thunder and lightning. **Thunderstorms form in large cumulonimbus clouds, also known as thunderheads.** Most cumulonimbus clouds form on hot, humid afternoons. They also form when warm air is forced upward along a cold front. In both cases, the warm, humid air rises rapidly. The air cools, forming dense thunderheads. Heavy rain falls, sometimes along with hail. Within the thunderhead are strong upward and downward winds—updrafts and downdrafts—as shown in Figure 9. Many thunderstorms form in the spring and summer in southern states or on the Western Plains.

Lightning and Thunder During a thunderstorm, areas of positive and negative electrical charges build up in the storm clouds. **Lightning** is a sudden spark, or electrical discharge, as these charges jump between parts of a cloud, between nearby clouds, or between a cloud and the ground. Lightning is similar to the shocks you sometimes feel when you touch a metal object on a very dry day, but on a much larger scale.

What causes thunder? A lightning bolt can heat the air near it to as much as 30,000°C, much hotter than the sun's surface. The rapidly heated air expands suddenly and explosively. Thunder is the sound of the explosion. Because light travels much faster than sound, you see lightning before you hear thunder.

Lab zone · **Try This Activity**

Lightning Distances
Because light travels faster than sound, you see a lightning flash before you hear the clap of thunder. Here's how to calculate your distance from a thunderstorm. **CAUTION:** *Only do this activity inside a building.*

1. Count the number of seconds between the moment when you see the lightning and when you hear the thunder.

2. Divide the number of seconds you counted by three to get the approximate distance in kilometers. Example:

$$\frac{15 \text{ s}}{3 \text{ s/km}} = 5 \text{ km}$$

Calculating Wait for another lightning flash and calculate the distance again. How can you tell whether a thunderstorm is moving toward you or away from you?

Thunderstorm Damage Thunderstorms can cause severe damage. The heavy rains associated with thunderstorms can flood low-lying areas. Lightning can also cause damage. When lightning strikes the ground, the hot, expanding air can shatter tree trunks or start forest fires. When lightning strikes people or animals, it acts like a powerful electric shock. Lightning can cause unconsciousness, serious burns, or even heart failure.

Floods A major danger during severe thunderstorms is flooding. Floods occur when so much water pours into a stream or river that its banks overflow, covering the surrounding land. In urban areas, floods can occur when the ground is already saturated by heavy rains. The water can't soak into the water-logged ground or the many areas covered with buildings, roads, and parking lots. A flash flood is a sudden, violent flood that occurs shortly after a storm.

Thunderstorm Safety The safest place to be during a thunderstorm is indoors. If you are inside a house, avoid touching telephones, electrical appliances, or plumbing fixtures, all of which can conduct electricity. It is usually safe to stay in a car with a hard top during a thunderstorm. The electricity will move along the metal skin of the car and jump to the ground. However, do not touch any metal inside the car. **During thunderstorms, avoid places where lightning may strike. Also avoid objects that can conduct electricity, such as metal objects and bodies of water.**

How can you remain safe if you are caught outside during a thunderstorm? It is dangerous to seek shelter under a tree, because lightning may strike the tree and you. Instead, find a low area away from trees, fences, and poles. Crouch with your head down. If you are swimming or in a boat, get to shore and find shelter away from the water.

 **How can lightning be dangerous?**

Tornadoes

A tornado is one of the most frightening and destructive types of storms. A **tornado** is a rapidly whirling, funnel-shaped cloud that reaches down from a storm cloud to touch Earth's surface. If a tornado occurs over a lake or ocean, the storm is known as a waterspout. Tornadoes are usually brief, but can be deadly. They may touch the ground for 15 minutes or less and be only a few hundred meters across. But wind speeds in the most intense tornadoes may approach 500 kilometers per hour.

FIGURE 10
Lightning Striking Earth
Lightning occurs when electricity jumps within clouds, between clouds, or between clouds and the ground. Lightning can cause fires or serious injuries.

Go Online
PLANET DIARY

For: More on thunder and lightning
Visit: PHSchool.com
Web Code: cfd-4032

FIGURE 11

Tornado Formation

Tornadoes can form when warm, humid air rises rapidly in a cumulonimbus cloud. Varying winds at different heights can spin the rising air like a top.

2 The warm air begins to rotate as it meets winds blowing in different directions at different altitudes.

Cumulonimbus cloud

1 Warm, moist air flows in at the bottom of a cumulonimbus cloud and moves upward. A low pressure area forms inside the cloud.

3 A tornado forms as part of the cloud descends to earth in a funnel.

Rain

How Tornadoes Form Tornadoes can form in any situation that produces severe weather. **Tornadoes most commonly develop in thick cumulonimbus clouds—the same clouds that bring thunderstorms.** Tornadoes are most likely to occur when thunderstorms are likely—in spring and early summer, often late in the afternoon when the ground is warm. The Great Plains often have the kind of weather pattern that is likely to create tornadoes: A warm, humid air mass moves north from the Gulf of Mexico into the lower Great Plains. A cold, dry air mass moves south from Canada. When the air masses meet, the cold air moves under the warm air, forcing it to rise. A squall line of thunderstorms is likely to form, with storms traveling from southwest to northeast. A single squall line can produce ten or more tornadoes.

Tornado Alley Tornadoes occur more often in the United States than in any other country. About 800 tornadoes occur in the United States every year. Weather patterns on the Great Plains result in a "tornado alley," as shown in Figure 12. However, tornadoes can and do occur in nearly every part of the United States.

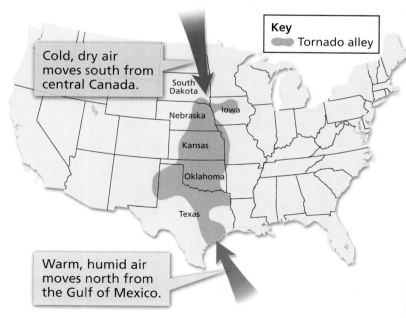

Key
- Tornado alley

Cold, dry air moves south from central Canada.

South Dakota

Nebraska

Iowa

Kansas

Oklahoma

Texas

Warm, humid air moves north from the Gulf of Mexico.

FIGURE 12
Tornado Alley
Tornadoes in the U.S. are most likely to occur in a region known as Tornado Alley. **Interpreting Maps** *Name five states that Tornado Alley crosses.*

Tornado Damage Tornado damage comes from both strong winds and flying debris. The low pressure inside the tornado sucks dust and other objects into the funnel. Tornadoes can move large objects—sheds, trailers, cars—and scatter debris many miles away. One tornado tore off a motel sign in Broken Bow, Oklahoma, and dropped it 30 miles away in Arkansas! One of the reasons that tornadoes are so frightening is that they are unpredictable. A tornado can level houses on one street but leave neighboring houses standing.

Tornadoes are ranked on the Fujita scale by the amount of damage they cause. The Fujita scale was named for the scientist who devised it, Dr. T. Theodore Fujita. The scale goes from light damage (F0) to extreme damage (F5). Luckily, only about one percent of tornadoes are ranked as F4 or F5.

Science and History

Weather That Changed History
Unanticipated storms have caused incredible damage, killed large numbers of people, and even changed the course of history.

1588 England
King Philip II of Spain sent the Spanish Armada, a fleet of 130 ships, to invade England. Strong winds in the English Channel trapped the Armada near shore. Some Spanish ships escaped, but storms wrecked most of them.

1281 Japan
In an attempt to conquer Japan, Kublai Khan, the Mongol emperor of China, sent a fleet of ships carrying a huge army. A hurricane from the Pacific brought high winds and towering waves that sank the ships. The Japanese named the storm *kamikaze*, meaning "divine wind."

1620 Massachusetts
English Pilgrims set sail for the Americas in the *Mayflower*. They had planned to land near the mouth of the Hudson River, but turned back north because of rough seas and storms. When the Pilgrims landed farther north, they decided to stay and so established Plymouth Colony.

| 1200 | 1600 | 1700 |

Tornado Safety What should you do if a tornado is predicted in your area? A "tornado watch" is an announcement that tornadoes are possible in your area. Watch for approaching thunderstorms. A "tornado warning" is an announcement that a tornado has been seen in the sky or on weather radar. If you hear a tornado warning, move to a safe area as soon as you can. Do not wait until you actually see the tornado.

The safest place to be during a tornado is in a storm shelter or the basement of a well-built building. If the building you are in does not have a basement, move to the middle of the ground floor. Stay away from windows and doors to avoid flying debris. Lie on the floor under a sturdy piece of furniture, such as a large table. If you are outdoors, lie flat in a ditch.

✓ **Reading Checkpoint** **What is a tornado warning?**

Writing in Science

Research and Write
Many of these events happened before forecasters had the equipment to predict weather scientifically. Research one of the events in the timeline. Write a paragraph describing the event and how history might have been different if the people involved had had accurate weather predictions.

1900 and 1915 Texas
When a hurricane struck the port city of Galveston in 1900, it killed at least 8,000 people and destroyed much of the city. As a result, a seawall 5 meters high and 16 kilometers long was built. When another hurricane struck in 1915, the seawall greatly reduced the amount of damage.

1837 North Carolina
The steamship *Home* sank during a hurricane off Ocracoke, North Carolina. In one of the worst storm-caused disasters at sea, 90 people died. In response, the U.S. Congress passed a law requiring seagoing ships to carry a life preserver for every passenger.

1870 Great Lakes
Learning that more than 1,900 boats had sunk in storms on the Great Lakes in 1869, Congress set up a national weather service, the Army Signal Corps. In 1891 the job of issuing weather warnings and forecasts went to a new agency, the U.S. Weather Bureau.

1800   1900   2000

Weather Patterns

Video Preview
▶ Video Field Trip
Video Assessment

Hurricanes

A **hurricane** is a tropical cyclone that has winds of 119 kilometers per hour or higher. A typical hurricane is about 600 kilometers across. Hurricanes form in the Atlantic, Pacific, and Indian oceans. In the western Pacific Ocean, hurricanes are called typhoons.

How Hurricanes Form A typical hurricane that strikes the United States forms in the Atlantic Ocean north of the equator in August, September, or October. **A hurricane begins over warm ocean water as a low-pressure area, or tropical disturbance.** If the tropical disturbance grows in size and strength, it becomes a tropical storm, which may then become a hurricane.

A hurricane draws its energy from the warm, humid air at the ocean's surface. As this air rises and forms clouds, more air is drawn into the system. As with other storm systems, winds spiral inward toward the area of low pressure. Inside the storm are bands of very high winds and heavy rains. The lowest air pressure and warmest temperatures are at the center of the hurricane. The lower the air pressure at the center of a storm, the faster the winds blow toward the center. Hurricane winds may be as strong as 320 kilometers per hour.

Look at Figure 13. Hurricane winds are strongest in a narrow band around the center of the storm. At the center is a ring of clouds, called the eyewall, that enclose a quiet "eye." The wind gets stronger as the eye approaches. When the eye arrives, the weather changes suddenly. The air grows calm and the sky may clear. After the eye passes, the storm resumes, but the wind blows from the opposite direction.

FIGURE 13
Structure of a Hurricane
In a hurricane, air moves rapidly around a low-pressure area called the eye.

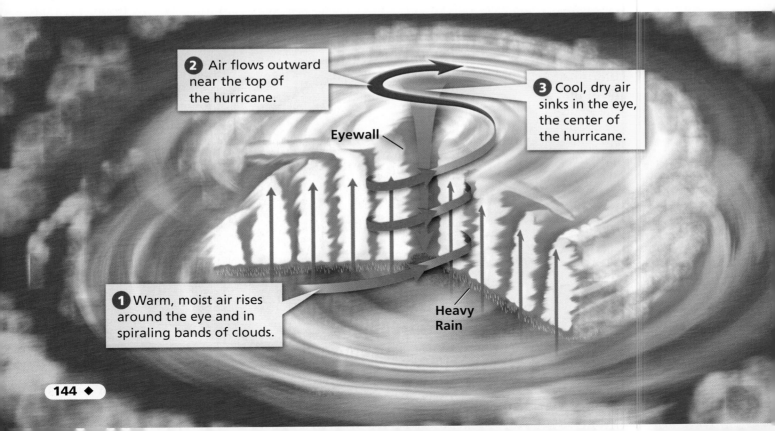

2 Air flows outward near the top of the hurricane.

3 Cool, dry air sinks in the eye, the center of the hurricane.

Eyewall

1 Warm, moist air rises around the eye and in spiraling bands of clouds.

Heavy Rain

How Hurricanes Move Hurricanes last longer than other storms, usually a week or more. During that period, they can travel quite a distance. Hurricanes that form in the Atlantic Ocean are steered by easterly trade winds toward the Caribbean islands and the southeastern United States. After a hurricane passes over land, it no longer has warm, moist air to draw energy from. The hurricane gradually loses strength, although heavy rainfall may continue for several days.

August 25

August 24

August 23

FIGURE 14
Hurricane Andrew
The path of Hurricane Andrew over three consecutive days can be seen in this photo montage.

Hurricane Damage When a hurricane comes ashore, it brings high waves and severe flooding as well as wind damage. The low pressure and high winds of the hurricane over the ocean raise the level of the water up to 6 meters above normal sea level. The result is a **storm surge,** a "dome" of water that sweeps across the coast where the hurricane lands. Storm surges can cause great damage, washing away beaches, destroying buildings along the coast, and eroding the coastlines.

Hurricane Safety Until the 1950s, a fast-moving hurricane could strike with little warning. People now receive information well in advance of an approaching hurricane.

A "hurricane watch" indicates that hurricane conditions are possible in an area within the next 36 hours. You should be prepared to **evacuate** (ee VAK yoo ayt), or move away temporarily. A "hurricane warning" means that hurricane conditions are expected within 24 hours. **If you hear a hurricane warning and are told to evacuate, leave the area immediately.** If you must stay in a house, move away from the windows.

✔ Reading Checkpoint **What is a storm surge?**

FIGURE 15
Hurricane Damage
Residents were forced to flee as Hurricane Georges roared down on the Florida Keys in 1998.

Winter Storms

In the winter in the northern United States, a large amount of precipitation falls as snow. **All year round, most precipitation begins in clouds as snow. If the air is colder than 0°C all the way to the ground, the precipitation falls as snow.** Heavy snowfalls can block roads, trapping people in their homes and making it hard for emergency vehicles to move. Extreme cold can damage crops and cause water pipes to freeze and burst.

Lake-Effect Snow Two of the snowiest cities in the United States are Buffalo and Rochester in upstate New York. On average, nearly three meters of snow falls on each of these cities every winter. Why do Buffalo and Rochester get so much snow?

Study Figure 16. Notice that Buffalo is located east of Lake Erie, and Rochester is located south of Lake Ontario. In the fall and winter, the land near these lakes cools much more rapidly than the water in the lakes. Although the water in these lakes is cold, it is still much warmer than the surrounding land and air.

When a cold, dry air mass from central Canada moves southeast across one of the Great Lakes, it picks up water vapor and heat from the lake. As soon as the air mass reaches the other side of the lake, the air rises and cools again. The water vapor condenses and falls as snow, usually within 40 kilometers of the lake.

FIGURE 16
Lake-Effect Snow
As cold dry air moves across the warmer water, it becomes more humid as water vapor evaporates from the lake surface. When the air reaches land and cools, lake-effect snow falls.
Interpreting Maps *Which two cities on the map receive large amounts of lake-effect snow?*

Great Lakes Snow Belts

FIGURE 17
Winter Storm Damage
Major winter storms can cause a great deal of damage. Here, utility workers in Maine remove a pole snapped by a fierce winter storm.

Snowstorm Safety Imagine being caught in a snowstorm when the wind suddenly picks up. High winds can blow falling snow sideways or pick up snow from the ground and suspend it in the air. This situation can be extremely dangerous because the blowing snow limits your vision and makes it easy to get lost. Also, strong winds cool a person's body rapidly. **If you are caught in a snowstorm, try to find shelter from the wind.** Cover exposed parts of your body and try to stay dry. If you are in a car, the driver should keep the engine running only if the exhaust pipe is clear of snow.

 **Reading Checkpoint** How can snowstorms be dangerous?

Section 2 Assessment

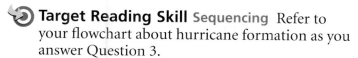 **Target Reading Skill** Sequencing Refer to your flowchart about hurricane formation as you answer Question 3.

Reviewing Key Concepts

1. a. **Defining** What is a thunderstorm?
   b. **Listing** List two dangers associated with thunderstorms.
   c. **Describing** What safety precautions should you follow during a thunderstorm?

2. a. **Identifying** What weather conditions are most likely to produce tornadoes?
   b. **Developing Hypotheses** Why do tornadoes occur most often in the area known as "tornado alley"?

3. a. **Defining** What is a hurricane?
   b. **Relating Cause and Effect** How do hurricanes form?

4. a. **Explaining** What is lake-effect snow?
   b. **Inferring** Why doesn't lake-effect snow fall to the north or west of the Great Lakes?
   c. **Describing** What should you do if you are caught in a snowstorm?

Lab zone At-Home **Activity**

Storm Eyewitness Interview a family member or other adult about a dramatic storm that he or she has experienced. Before the interview, make a list of questions you would like to ask. For example, when and where did the storm occur? Write up your interview in a question-and-answer format, beginning with a short introduction.

Tracking a Hurricane

Problem

How can you predict when and where a hurricane will come ashore?

Skills Focus

interpreting data, predicting, drawing conclusions

Materials

- ruler
- red, blue, green, and brown pencils
- tracing paper

Procedure

1. Look at the plotted path of the hurricane on the map. Each dot represents the location of the eye of the hurricane at six-hour intervals. The last dot shows where the hurricane was located at noon on August 30.

2. Predict the path you think the hurricane will take. Place tracing paper over the map below. Using a red pencil, place an *X* on your tracing paper where you think the hurricane will first reach land. Next to your *X*, write the date and time you think the hurricane will come ashore.

3. Hurricane warnings are issued for an area that is likely to experience a hurricane within 24 hours. On your tracing paper, shade in red the area for which you would issue a hurricane warning.

4. Using the following data table, plot the next five positions for the storm using a blue pencil. Use your ruler to connect the dots to show the hurricane's path.

Data Table		
Date and Time	Latitude	Longitude
August 30, 6:00 P.M.	28.3° N	86.8° W
August 31, midnight	28.4° N	86.0° W
August 31, 6:00 A.M.	28.6° N	85.3° W
August 31, noon	28.8° N	84.4° W
August 31, 6:00 P.M.	28.8° N	84.0° W

5. Based on the new data, decide if you need to change your prediction of where and when the hurricane will come ashore. Mark your new predictions in blue pencil on your tracing paper.

6. During September 1, you obtain four more positions. (Plot these points only after you have completed Step 5.) Based on these new data, use the green pencil to indicate when and where you now think the hurricane will come ashore.

Data Table		
Date and Time	Latitude	Longitude
September 1, midnight	28.8° N	83.8° W
September 1, 6:00 A.M.	28.6° N	83.9° W
September 1, noon	28.6° N	84.2° W
September 1, 6:00 P.M.	28.9° N	84.8° W

7. The next day, September 2, you plot four more positions using a brown pencil. (Plot these points only after you have completed Step 6.)

Data Table		
Date and Time	Latitude	Longitude
September 2, midnight	29.4° N	85.9° W
September 2, 6:00 A.M.	29.7° N	87.3° W
September 2, noon	30.2° N	88.8° W
September 2, 6:00 P.M.	31.0° N	90.4° W

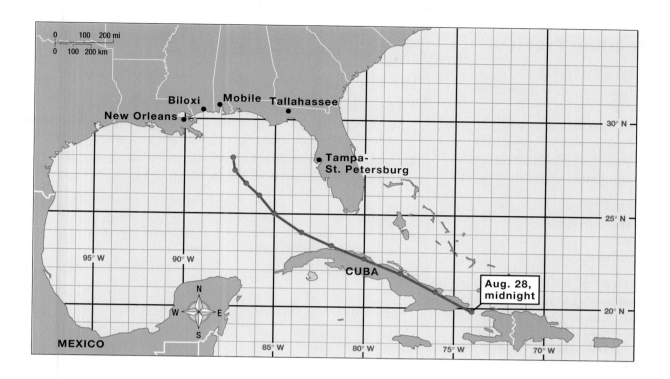

Analyze and Conclude

1. **Interpreting Data** Describe in detail the complete path of the hurricane you tracked. Include where it came ashore and identify any cities that were in the vicinity.

2. **Predicting** How did your predictions in Steps 2, 5, and 6 compare to what actually happened?

3. **Interpreting Data** What was unusual about your hurricane's path?

4. **Inferring** How do you think hurricanes with a path like this one affect the issuing of hurricane warnings?

5. **Drawing Conclusions** Why do you have to be so careful when issuing warnings? What problems might be caused if you issued an unnecessary hurricane warning? What might happen if a hurricane warning were issued too late?

6. **Communicating** In this activity you only had data for the hurricane's position. If you were tracking a hurricane and issuing warnings, what other types of information would help you make decisions about the hurricane's path? Write a paragraph describing the additional information you would need.

More to Explore

With your teacher's help, search the Internet for more hurricane tracking data. Map the data and try to predict where the hurricane will come ashore.

Predicting the Weather

Reading Preview

Key Concepts
- How do weather forecasters predict the weather?
- How has technology helped to improve weather forecasts?
- What can be learned from the information on weather maps?

Key Terms
- meteorologist
- isobar
- isotherm

Target Reading Skill

Previewing Visuals Before you read, look at Figure 21, a weather map. Then write three questions about the map in a graphic organizer like the one below. As you read, answer your questions.

Weather Map

Q.	What type of front is located west of Oklahoma City?
A.	
Q.	

FIGURE 18
Red Sky
The red sky shown in this sunrise may indicate an approaching storm.

Lab zone Discover **Activity**

What's the Weather?
1. Look at the weather report in your local newspaper. Note what weather conditions are predicted for your area today, including temperature, precipitation, and wind speed.
2. Look out the window or think about what it was like the last time you were outside. Write down the actual weather conditions where you are.

Think It Over
Observing Does the weather report match what you observe? What is the same? What is different?

Every culture's folklore includes weather sayings. Many of these sayings are based on long-term observations. Sailors, pilots, farmers, and others who work outdoors are usually careful observers of clouds, winds, and other signs of changes in the weather. Two examples are shown below.

Why do these two weather sayings agree that a red morning sky means bad weather? Recall that in the United States storms usually move from west to east. Clouds in the west may indicate an advancing low-pressure area, bringing stormy weather. If there are high clouds in the west in the morning, the rising sun in the east turns these clouds red. The reverse is true at sunset. As the sun sets in the west, it turns clouds in the east red. Clouds in the east may indicate that a storm is moving away to the east. A red sky is one kind of observation that helps people to predict the weather.

Evening red and morning gray
Will send the traveler on his way;
Evening gray and morning red
Will bring down rain upon his head.

Red sky in the morning,
sailors take warning;
Red sky at night,
sailor's delight.

Weather Forecasting

The first step in forecasting is to collect data, either from simple, direct observations or through the use of instruments. For example, if a barometer shows that the air pressure is falling, you can expect a change in the weather. Falling air pressure usually indicates an approaching low-pressure area, possibly bringing rain or snow.

Making Simple Observations You can read weather signs in the clouds, too. Cumulus clouds often form on warm afternoons when warm air rises. If you see these clouds growing larger and taller, you can expect them to become cumulonimbus clouds, which may produce a thunderstorm. If you can see thin cirrus clouds high in the sky, a warm front may be approaching.

Even careful weather observers often turn to professional meteorologists for weather information. **Meteorologists** (mee tee uh RAHL uh jists) are scientists who study the causes of weather and try to predict it.

Interpreting Complex Data Meteorologists are able to interpret information from a variety of sources, including local weather observers, instruments carried by balloons, satellites, and weather stations around the world. **Meteorologists use maps, charts, and computers to analyze weather data and to prepare weather forecasts.** They often use radar to track areas of rain or snow and to locate severe storms such as tornadoes. Forecasters can also follow the path of a storm system.

Where do weather reporters get their information? Most weather information comes from the National Weather Service. The National Weather Service uses balloons, satellites, radar, and surface instruments to gather weather data.

 **Reading Checkpoint** What is a meteorologist?

Weather Technology

Techniques for predicting weather have changed dramatically in recent years. Short-range forecasts—forecasts for up to five days—are now fairly reliable. Meteorologists can also make somewhat accurate long-range predictions. **Technological improvements in gathering weather data and using computers have improved the accuracy of weather forecasts.**

Weather Balloons Weather balloons carry instruments high into the troposphere and lower stratosphere. Remember that these are the two lowest layers of the atmosphere. The instruments measure temperature, air pressure, and humidity.

Weather Satellites The first weather satellite, *TIROS-1*, was launched in 1960. Satellites orbit Earth in the exosphere, the uppermost layer of the atmosphere. Cameras on weather satellites in the exosphere can make images of Earth's surface, clouds, storms, and snow cover. These images are then transmitted to meteorologists on Earth, who interpret the information. New technologies, such as NASA's *Terra* satellite, shown in Figure 20, provide large amounts of data to meteorologists. Modern satellites collect data on temperature, humidity, solar radiation, wind speed and wind direction, and provide images of clouds and storm systems.

FIGURE 20
Satellite Technology
The large satellite image shows an intense cyclone over Ireland and Great Britain. The *Terra* satellite (right) collects data on weather and environmental conditions.

Automated Weather Stations Data are also gathered from surface locations for temperature, air pressure, relative humidity, rainfall, and wind speed and direction. The National Weather Service has established a network of over 1,700 surface weather observation sites.

Computer Forecasts Computers are widely used to help forecast weather. Instruments can now gather large amounts of data, including temperature, humidity, air pressure, wind speed and direction, and other factors. Computers process such information quickly to help forecasters make predictions. To make a forecast, the computer starts with weather conditions reported from various weather stations over a large area. The computer then works through thousands of calculations using equations from weather models. These data are used to make forecasts for 12 hours, 24 hours, 36 hours, and so on. Each forecast builds on the previous forecast. When new weather data come in, the computer forecasts are revised.

Go Online
PLANET DIARY

For: More on weather maps
Visit: PHSchool.com
Web Code: cfd-4033

Reading Checkpoint How are computers used to produce weather forecasts?

Math — Analyzing Data

Computer Weather Forecasting

Scientists use computers to develop different models of how a front may move. These predictions are then used to make weather forecasts. As more data become available, some models are found to be incorrect, while others are found to closely fit the predicted conditions. The upper graph shows predicted air pressure from two models. The lower graph shows actual data for air pressure.

1. **Reading Graphs** What two variables are being graphed?

2. **Interpreting Data** How is air pressure predicted to change according to each model in the top graph?

3. **Inferring** Which computer model most closely matches the actual air pressure data?

4. **Predicting** What weather would you forecast for Monday and Tuesday? Explain. (*Hint:* Remember that falling air pressure usually means an approaching low-pressure area and possible precipitation.)

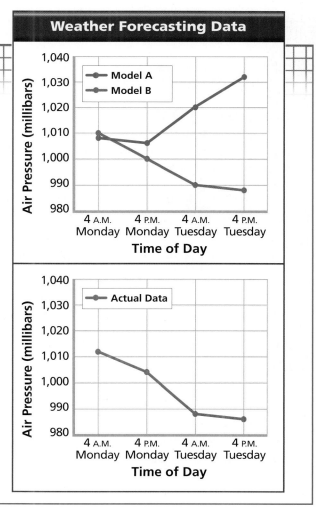

Weather Forecasting Data

FIGURE 21
Reading Weather Map Symbols

The figure below shows what various weather symbols mean. At right, the weather map shows data collected from many weather stations.

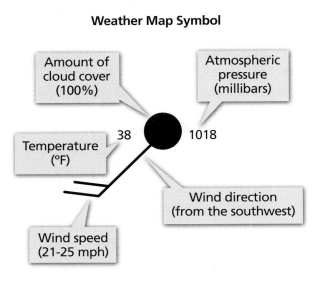

Weather Map Symbol

Wind Speed (mph)	Symbol
1 – 2	
3 – 8	
9 – 14	
15 – 20	
21 – 25	
26 – 31	
32 – 37	
38 – 43	
44 – 49	
50 – 54	
55 – 60	
61 – 66	
67 – 71	
72 – 77	

Cloud Cover (%)	Symbol
0	
10	
20–30	
40	
50	
60	
70–80	
90	
100	

Lab zone Skills Activity

Interpreting Data
Use Figure 21 to help you answer questions about this weather station data.

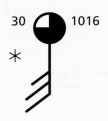

30   1016

1. What is the temperature at this station?
2. What is the wind speed?
3. Which way is the wind blowing?
4. What is the air pressure?
5. What percent of the sky is covered by clouds?
6. What type of precipitation, if any, is falling?

Reading Weather Maps

A weather map is a "snapshot" of conditions at a particular time over a large area. There are many types of weather maps. Weather forecasters often present maps generated by computers from surface data, radar, or satellite information.

Weather Service Maps Data from many local weather stations all over the country are assembled into weather maps at the National Weather Service. The data collected by a typical station is summarized in Figure 21 above. The simplified weather map on the next page includes most of the weather station data shown in the key.

On some weather maps, you see curved lines. These lines connect places where certain conditions—temperature or air pressure—are the same. **Isobars** are lines joining places on the map that have the same air pressure. (*Iso* means "equal" and *bar* means "pressure.") The numbers on the isobars are the pressure readings. Air pressure readings may be given in inches of mercury or in millibars or both. The isobars in Figure 21 are shown in both millbars and inches of mercury.

Isotherms are lines joining places that have the same temperature. The isotherm may be labeled with the temperature in degrees Fahrenheit, degrees Celsius, or both.

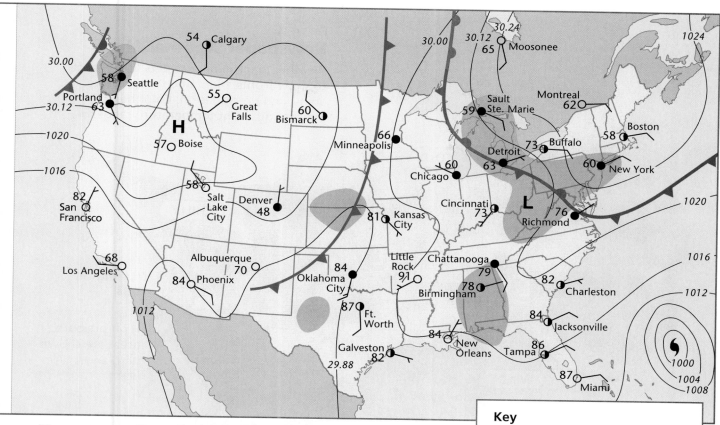

Key

⌐	Drizzle		(gray oval)	Precipitation area
≡	Fog		▲▲▲	Cold front
△	Hail		●●●	Warm front
∞	Haze		●▲●	Stationary front
⌐	Hurricane		▲●▲	Occluded front
–1020–	Isobar			
●	Rain			
▽	Shower			
△	Sleet			
∿	Smoke			
✳	Snow			
⌐	Thunderstorm			

Newspaper Weather Maps Maps in newspapers are simplified versions of maps produced by the National Weather Service. Figure 22 on the next page shows a typical newspaper weather map. From what you have learned in this chapter, you can probably interpret most of the symbols on this map. **Standard symbols on weather maps show fronts, areas of high and low pressure, types of precipitation, and temperatures.** Note that the high and low temperatures are given in degrees Fahrenheit instead of Celsius.

Limits of Weather Forecasts As computers have grown more powerful, and new satellites and radar technologies have been developed, scientists have been able to make better forecasts. But even with extremely fast computers, it is unlikely that forecasters will ever be able to predict the weather a month in advance with great accuracy. This has to do with the so-called "butterfly effect." The atmosphere works in such a way that a small change in the weather today can mean a larger change in the weather a week later! The name refers to a scientist's suggestion that even the flapping of a butterfly's wings causes a tiny disturbance in the atmosphere. This tiny event might cause a larger disturbance that could—eventually—grow into a large storm.

 **Reading Checkpoint** What is the "butterfly effect"?

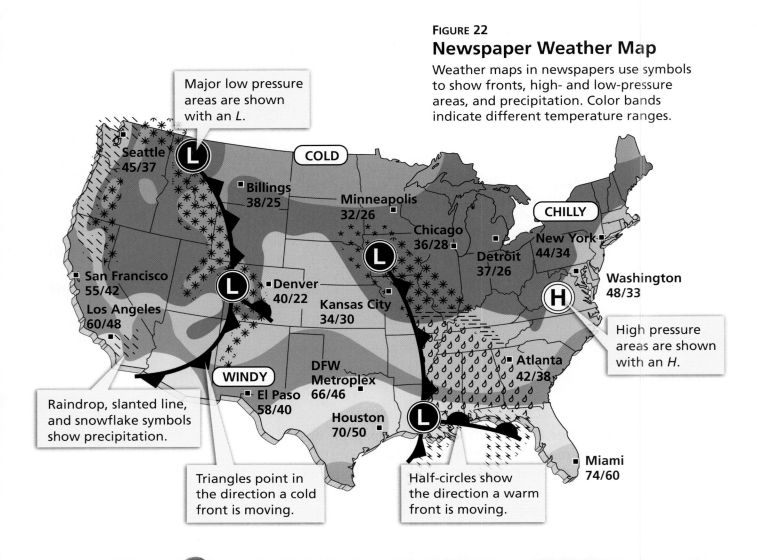

FIGURE 22
Newspaper Weather Map
Weather maps in newspapers use symbols to show fronts, high- and low-pressure areas, and precipitation. Color bands indicate different temperature ranges.

Major low pressure areas are shown with an *L*.

COLD

CHILLY

Seattle 45/37

Billings 38/25

Minneapolis 32/26

Chicago 36/28

New York 44/34

Detroit 37/26

San Francisco 55/42

Denver 40/22

Kansas City 34/30

Washington 48/33

Los Angeles 60/48

High pressure areas are shown with an *H*.

Raindrop, slanted line, and snowflake symbols show precipitation.

WINDY

DFW Metroplex 66/46

El Paso 58/40

Atlanta 42/38

Houston 70/50

Miami 74/60

Triangles point in the direction a cold front is moving.

Half-circles show the direction a warm front is moving.

Section 3 Assessment

Target Reading Skill Previewing Visuals Refer to your questions and answers about weather maps to help you answer Question 3 below.

Reviewing Key Concepts

1. a. **Describing** What is a meteorologist?
   b. **Explaining** What tools do meteorologists rely on to forecast the weather?
2. a. **Listing** List three technologies used to gather weather data.
   b. **Summarizing** Describe the types of weather data gathered by satellites.
   c. **Drawing Conclusions** How does the large amount of weather data gathered by various modern technologies affect the accuracy of weather forecasts?

3. a. **Identifying** What is the symbol for a cold front on a weather map?
   b. **Explaining** How is wind direction indicated on a weather map?
   c. **Interpreting Diagrams** According to Figure 22, what is the weather like in Chicago? How might this change in a few hours?

Writing in Science

Weather Report Find a current weather map from a newspaper. Use the map to write a brief weather report for your region. Include a description of the various weather symbols used on the map.

Reading a Weather Map

Problem

How does a weather map communicate data?

Skills Focus

interpreting maps, observing, drawing conclusions

Procedure

1. Examine the symbols on the weather map below. For more information about the symbols used on the map, refer to Figure 21 and Figure 22 earlier in this section.
2. Observe the different colors on the weather map below.
3. Find the symbols for snow and rain.
4. Locate the warm fronts and cold fronts.
5. Locate the symbols for high and low pressure.

Analyze and Conclude

1. **Interpreting Maps** What color represents the highest temperatures? What color represents the lowest temperatures?

2. **Interpreting Maps** Which city has the highest temperature? Which city has the lowest temperature?

3. **Interpreting Maps** Where on the map is it raining? Where on the map is it snowing?

4. **Interpreting Maps** How many different kinds of fronts are shown on the map?

5. **Observing** How many areas of low pressure are shown on the map? How many areas of high pressure are shown on the map?

6. **Drawing Conclusions** What season does this map represent? How do you know?

7. **Communicating** The triangles and semicircles on the front lines show which way the front is moving. What type of front is moving toward Minneapolis? What kind of weather do you think it will bring?

More to Explore

Compare this weather map to one shown on a television news report. Which symbols on these maps are similar? Which symbols are different?

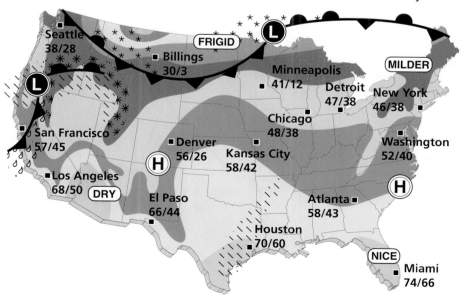

Doppler Radar

"Let's look at our Doppler radar screen," says a TV meteorologist pointing to a weather map with moving color blotches. The colors represent different locations and intensities of precipitation. "The purple area here shows a severe storm moving rapidly into our area." Doppler radar helps meteorologists make more accurate weather forecasts by tracking the speed and direction of precipitation.

What Is Doppler Radar?

Doppler radar gets its name from the "Doppler effect," which describes the changes that occur in radio waves as they bounce off a moving object. Nearly 150 Doppler radar stations throughout the United States continuously send out radio waves. These waves bounce off particles in the air, such as raindrops, snowflakes, hail, and even dust. Some of these radio waves are reflected back to the Doppler radar station where computers process the data.

Transmitter sends out radio waves that bounce off particles, such as raindrops, in the air. Some waves are reflected back to the station.

Antenna picks up the returning radio waves. Data from incoming waves are sent to a computer.

Computer is used to process data and generate a Doppler radar image for meteorologists.

Doppler Radar Station
Rotating continuously inside the protective housing, the station is supported by a tower that may be as tall as 30 meters.

How Effective Is Doppler Radar?

Before Doppler radar, it was hard to track fast-moving storms such as tornadoes. Tornado warnings were issued an average of just five minutes in advance. Today, Doppler radar can give people several extra minutes to prepare. People also use Doppler images to make decisions about everyday activities.

But the technology does have limitations. Doppler radar doesn't "see" everything. Sometimes mountains or buildings block the radio waves. In addition, Doppler radar doesn't always pick up light precipitation such as drizzle. Meteorologists must review the completeness of the data and decide how it might affect the forecast.

Tornado
Doppler radar can detect the air movements in thunderstorms that may lead to tornadoes. A tornado is a rapidly spinning, funnel-shaped cloud formed of condensed water particles.

Weigh the Impact

1. Identify the Need
How is Doppler radar an important technology in weather forecasting?

2. Research
Using the Internet, research Doppler radar reports for your city. Examine a Doppler image and explain each element on the map, including the different colors and the direction of motion.

3. Write
As a TV meteorologist, write the script for a local weather forecast. Describe areas with precipitation, the amount of precipitation, and the direction of weather systems. Use your research and notes.

Go Online
PHSchool.com

For: More on Doppler radar
Visit: PHSchool.com
Web Code: cfh-4030

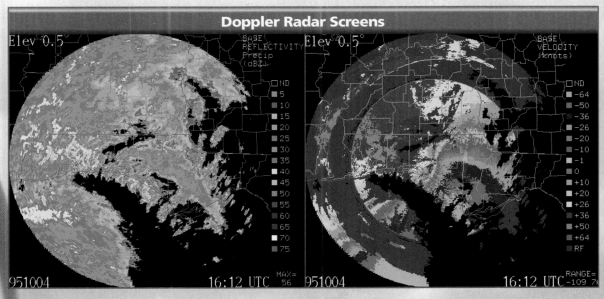

Doppler Radar Screens

The amount of precipitation is shown above by using different colors.

The different colors above show the speed and direction of precipitation.

1 Air Masses and Fronts

Key Concepts

- Four major types of air masses influence the weather in North America: maritime tropical, continental tropical, maritime polar, and continental polar.

- In the continental United States, air masses are commonly moved by the prevailing westerlies and jet streams.

- Colliding air masses can form four types of fronts: cold fronts, warm fronts, stationary fronts, and occluded fronts.

- Cyclones and decreasing air pressure are associated with clouds, wind, and precipitation.

- The descending air in an anticyclone generally causes dry, clear weather.

Key Terms

air mass	front
tropical	occluded
polar	cyclone
maritime	anticyclone
continental	

2 Storms

Key Concepts

- Thunderstorms form in large cumulonimbus clouds, also known as thunderheads.

- During thunderstorms, avoid places where lightning may strike. Also avoid objects that can conduct electricity, such as metal objects and bodies of water.

- Tornadoes most commonly develop in thick cumulonimbus clouds—the same clouds that bring thunderstorms.

- The safest place to be during a tornado is in a storm shelter or the basement of a well-built building.

- A hurricane begins over warm ocean water as a low-pressure area, or tropical disturbance.

- If you hear a hurricane warning and are told to evacuate, leave the area immediately.

- All year round, most precipitation begins in clouds as snow.

- If you are caught in a snowstorm, try to find shelter from the wind.

Key Terms

storm	hurricane
thunderstorm	storm surge
lightning	evacuate
tornado	

3 Predicting the Weather

Key Concepts

- Meteorologists use maps, charts, and computers to analyze weather data and to prepare weather forecasts.

- Technological improvements in gathering weather data and using computers have improved the accuracy of weather forecasts.

- Standard symbols on weather maps show fronts, areas of high and low pressure, types of precipitation, and temperatures.

Key Terms

meteorologist
isobar
isotherm

Review and Assessment

Go Online
PHSchool.com

For: Self-Assessment
Visit: PHSchool.com
Web Code: cfa-4030

Organizing Information

Comparing and Contrasting Copy the table, which compares and contrasts thunderstorms, tornadoes, and hurricanes, onto a separate sheet of paper. Then complete it and add a title. (For more on Comparing and Contrasting, see the Skills Handbook.)

Type of Storm	Where Forms	Typical Time of Year	Safety Rules
Thunderstorm	Within large cumulonimbus clouds	a. ___?___	b. ___?___
Tornado	c. ___?___	Spring, early summer	d. ___?___
Hurricane	e. ___?___	f. ___?___	Evacuate or move inside a well-built building

Reviewing Key Terms

Choose the letter of the best answer.

1. An air mass that forms over an ocean is called
   a. tropical.
   b. continental.
   c. maritime.
   d. polar.

2. Cool, clear weather usually follows a
   a. warm front.
   b. cold front.
   c. stationary front.
   d. occluded front.

3. A rotating funnel-shaped cloud with high winds that extends from a storm cloud to Earth's surface is a
   a. storm surge.
   b. thunderstorm.
   c. hurricane.
   d. tornado.

4. Very large tropical cyclones with high winds are called
   a. hurricanes.
   b. tornadoes.
   c. air masses.
   d. anticyclones.

5. Lines joining places that have the same temperature are
   a. isobars.
   b. isotherms.
   c. fronts.
   d. occluded.

If the statement is true, write *true*. If it is false, change the underlined word or words to make the statement true.

6. Summers in the Southwest are hot and dry because of <u>maritime tropical</u> air masses.

7. A <u>cyclone</u> is a high-pressure center of dry air.

8. Cumulonimbus clouds may produce both thunderstorms and <u>hurricanes.</u>

9. <u>Lightning</u> is a sudden spark or electrical discharge, as electrical charges jump between parts of a cloud, between nearby clouds, or between a cloud and the ground.

10. On a weather map, <u>isotherms</u> join places on the map with the same air pressure.

Writing in Science

Descriptive Paragraph Imagine that you are a hurricane hunter—a scientist who flies into a hurricane to collect data. Describe what it would feel like as you flew through the hurricane's eyewall into its eye.

Discovery CHANNEL SCHOOL™

Weather Patterns
Video Preview
Video Field Trip
▶ Video Assessment

Review and Assessment

Checking Concepts

11. Describe how wind patterns affect the movement of air masses in North America.

12. How does a cold front form?

13. What safety precautions should you take if a tornado is predicted in your area? If a hurricane is predicted?

14. What happens to a hurricane when it moves onto land? Why?

15. Explain how lake-effect snow forms.

16. What are some of the sources of information that meteorologists use to predict the weather?

Thinking Critically

17. **Relating Cause and Effect** How do differences in air density influence the movement of air along cold and warm fronts?

18. **Making Generalizations** What type of weather is most likely to form at the front shown below?

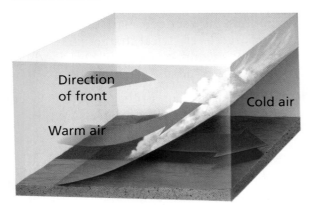

Direction of front

Warm air

Cold air

19. **Comparing and Contrasting** Compare thunderstorms and tornadoes. How are they similar? How are they different?

20. **Predicting** If you observe that air pressure is decreasing, what kind of weather do you think is coming?

21. **Applying Concepts** Would you expect hurricanes to form over the oceans off the northeast or northwest coasts of the United States? Explain.

22. **Making Judgments** What do you think is the most important thing people should do to reduce the dangers of storms?

23. **Applying Concepts** Why can't meteorologists accurately forecast the weather a month in advance?

Applying Skills

Use the map to answer Questions 24–27.

24. **Interpreting Maps** Does the map show a cyclone or an anticyclone? How can you tell?

25. **Interpreting Data** What do the arrows show about the movement of the winds in this pressure center? What else indicates wind direction?

26. **Making Models** Using this diagram as an example, draw a similar diagram to illustrate a high-pressure area. Remember to indicate wind direction in your diagram.

27. **Posing Questions** If you saw a pressure center like the one shown above on a weather map, what could you predict about the weather? What questions would you need to ask in order to make a better prediction?

Lab zone Chapter **Project**

Performance Assessment Present your weather maps and weather forecasts to the class. Discuss how accurate your weather predictions were. Explain why inaccuracies may have occurred in your forecasts.

🌀 End-of-Grade Test Practice

Test-Taking Tip

Interpreting Graphs A bar graph is used to compare quantities of different things. Each bar represents a quantity or amount of something. When answering a question with a bar graph, keep the following tips in mind. Read the title of the graph; the title should help you identify what information is shown on the graph. Then carefully examine the labels for the axes to determine what variables are plotted.

Sample Question
Use the graph at the right to determine how many tornadoes occurred in January.

- **A** 30
- **B** 25
- **C** 5
- **D** 15

Answer
First, find **J** for January on the *x*-axis. Then check the length of the bar and determine on the *y*-axis how many tornadoes occurred. The answer is **C**— five tornadoes occurred in January.

Use the graph below and your knowledge of science to answer Questions 3-4.

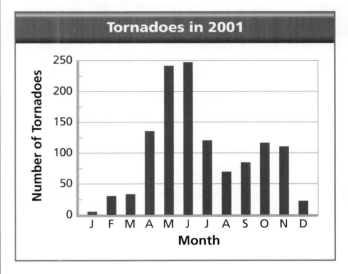

Tornadoes in 2001

Choose the letter of the best answer.

1. How are air masses classified?
   - **A** by temperature and pressure
   - **B** by pressure and humidity
   - **C** by temperature and density
   - **D** by temperature and humidity

2. A rapidly moving cold air mass meets a slowly moving warm air mass and forms a front. What will most likely occur at this front?
   - **A** The two air masses will mix together.
   - **B** The warm air will slide under the cold air. The cold air will rise and get warmer.
   - **C** Cold air will slide under the warm air. Warm air will rise and cool. Clouds will form.
   - **D** The less dense warm air will sink and cool. Clouds will form.

3. According to the graph, which two months in 2001 had the most tornadoes?
   - **A** April and May
   - **B** May and July
   - **C** May and June
   - **D** June and July

4. Which statement best summarizes the trend shown in the graph?
   - **A** Tornadoes always occur most frequently in May and June.
   - **B** Tornadoes occur when the weather is warmest.
   - **C** In 2001, tornadoes were most frequent in April, May, and June.
   - **D** Tornadoes are generally most frequent in the winter.

Constructed Response

5. Sound travels at a speed of about 330 m/s. How could you use this information to determine how far away lightning bolts are from you during a thunderstorm? Use an example to show how you would calculate the distance.

Standard Course of Study

1.01 Identify and create questions and hypotheses.

1.02 Develop appropriate experimental procedures.

1.03 Apply safety procedures.

1.04 Analyze variables.

1.05 Analyze evidence.

1.06 Use mathematics to gather, organize, and present data.

1.07 Prepare models and/or computer simulations.

1.08 Use oral and written language.

1.09 Use technologies and information systems.

2.02 Use information systems.

2.04 Apply tenets of technological design.

3.02 Describe observable and measurable properties to predict air quality.

3.03 Conclude that environments and organisms require stewardship.

3.04 Evaluate how humans impact air quality.

3.05 Examine atmospheric properties.

► These emperor penguins thrive in Antarctica's polar climate.

Labzone™ Chapter **Project**

Investigating Microclimates

A microclimate is a small area with its own climate. As you work through this chapter, you will investigate microclimates in your community.

Your Goal To compare weather conditions from at least three microclimates

To complete your project, you must

- hypothesize how the microclimates in three areas differ from each other
- collect data from your locations at the same time each day
- relate each microclimate to the plants and animals found there

Plan It! Begin by brainstorming a list of nearby places that may have different microclimates. How are the places different? Keep in mind weather factors such as temperature, precipitation, humidity, wind direction, and wind speed. Consider areas that are grassy, sandy, sunny, or shaded. You will need to measure daily weather conditions and record them in a logbook. Collect the instruments you need before you begin your investigation. Once you have collected all the data, construct your graphs and look for patterns. Then plan your presentation.

What Causes Climate?

Reading Preview

Key Concepts
- What factors influence temperature?
- What factors influence precipitation?
- What causes the seasons?

Key Terms
- climate • microclimate
- tropical zone • polar zone
- temperate zone
- marine climate
- continental climate
- windward • leeward
- monsoon

Target Reading Skill
Building Vocabulary After you read the section, reread the paragraphs that contain definitions of Key Terms. Use all the information you have learned to write a meaningful sentence using each Key Term.

An oasis in the Mojave Desert ▼

Lab zone Discover **Activity**

How Does Latitude Affect Climate?

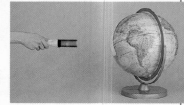

1. On a globe, tape a strip of paper from the equator to the North Pole. Divide the tape into three equal parts. Label the top section *poles,* the bottom section *equator,* and the middle section *mid-latitudes.*

2. Tape the end of an empty toilet paper roll to the end of a flashlight. Hold the flashlight about 30 cm from the equator. Turn on the flashlight to represent the sun. On the paper strip, have a partner draw the area the light shines on.

3. Move the flashlight up slightly to aim at the "mid-latitudes." Keep the flashlight horizontal and at the same distance from the globe. Again, draw the lighted area.

4. Repeat Step 3, but this time aim the light at the "poles."

Think It Over
Observing How does the size of the illuminated area change? Do you think the sun's rays heat Earth's surface evenly?

The weather in an area changes every day. At a given location, the weather may be cloudy and rainy one day and clear and sunny the next. **Climate,** on the other hand, refers to the average, year-after-year conditions of temperature, precipitation, winds, and clouds in an area. For example, California's Mojave Desert, shown below, has a hot, dry climate.

Scientists use two main factors—precipitation and temperature—to describe the climate of a region. A climate region is a large area that has similar climate conditions throughout. For example, the climate in the southwestern United States is dry, with hot summers.

The factors that affect large climate regions also affect smaller areas. Have you ever noticed that it is cooler and more humid in a grove of trees than in an open field? A small area with climate conditions that differ from those around it may have its own **microclimate.**

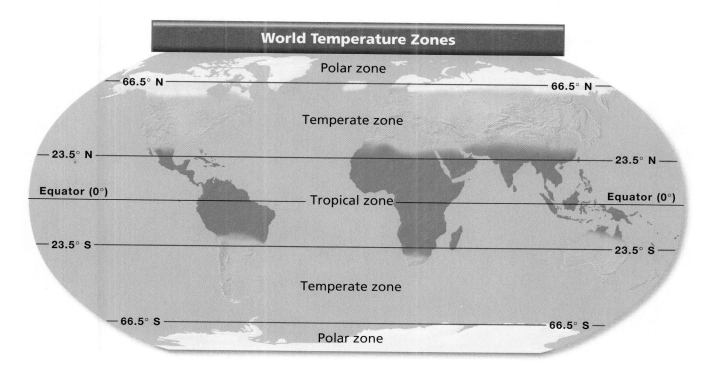

World Temperature Zones

Polar zone

66.5° N — 66.5° N

Temperate zone

23.5° N — 23.5° N

Equator (0°) — Equator (0°)

Tropical zone

23.5° S — 23.5° S

Temperate zone

66.5° S — 66.5° S

Polar zone

Factors Affecting Temperature

Why are some places warm and others cold? **The main factors that influence temperature are latitude, altitude, distance from large bodies of water, and ocean currents.**

Latitude In general, climates of locations near the equator are warmer than climates of areas far from the equator. The reason is that the sun's rays hit Earth's surface most directly at the equator. At the poles, the same amount of solar radiation is spread over a larger area, and therefore brings less warmth.

Recall that latitude is the distance from the equator, measured in degrees. Based on latitude, Earth's surface can be divided into the three temperature zones shown in Figure 1. The **tropical zone** is the area near the equator, between about 23.5° north latitude and 23.5° south latitude. The tropical zone receives direct or nearly direct sunlight all year round, making climates there warm.

In contrast, the sun's rays always strike at a lower angle near the North and South poles. As a result, the areas near both poles have cold climates. These **polar zones** extend from about 66.5° to 90° north and 66.5° to 90° south latitudes.

Between the tropical zones and the polar zones are the **temperate zones**. In summer, the sun's rays strike the temperate zones more directly. In winter, the sun's rays strike at a lower angle. As a result, the weather in the temperate zones ranges from warm or hot in summer to cool or cold in winter.

FIGURE 1
The tropical zone has the warmest climates. Cold climates occur in the polar zone. In between lies the temperate zone, where climates vary from warm to cool.
Interpreting Maps *In which temperature zone is most of the United States located?*

FIGURE 2
Effect of Altitude
Mount Kilimanjaro, in Tanzania, is near the equator.
Relating Cause and Effect What factor is responsible for the difference between the climate at the mountaintop and the climate at the base?

Altitude The peak of Mount Kilimanjaro towers high above the plains of East Africa. Kilimanjaro is covered in snow all year round, as shown in Figure 2. Yet it is located near the equator, at 3° south latitude. Why is Mount Kilimanjaro so cold?

In the case of high mountains, altitude is a more important climate factor than latitude. In the troposphere, temperature decreases about 6.5 Celsius degrees for every 1-kilometer increase in altitude. As a result, highland areas everywhere have cool climates, no matter what their latitude. At nearly 6 kilometers, the air at the top of Kilimanjaro is about 39 Celsius degrees colder than the air at sea level at the same latitude.

Distance From Large Bodies of Water Oceans or large lakes can also affect temperatures. Oceans greatly moderate, or make less extreme, the temperatures of nearby land. Water heats up more slowly than land. It also cools down more slowly. Therefore, winds off the ocean often prevent extremes of hot and cold in coastal regions. Much of the west coasts of North America, South America, and Europe have mild **marine climates,** with relatively mild winters and cool summers.

The centers of North America and Asia are too far inland to be warmed or cooled by the ocean. Most of Canada and of Russia, as well as the central United States, have continental climates. **Continental climates** have more extreme temperatures than marine climates. Winters are cold, while summers are warm or hot.

Ocean Currents Marine climates are influenced by ocean currents, streams of water within the oceans that move in regular patterns. Some warm ocean currents move from the tropics towards the poles. This affects climate as the warm ocean water warms the air above it. The warmed air then moves over nearby land. In the same way, cold currents bring cold water from the polar zones toward the equator. A cold current brings cool air.

As you read about the following currents, trace their paths on the map in Figure 3. The best-known warm-water current is the Gulf Stream. The Gulf Stream begins in the Gulf of Mexico, then flows north along the east coast of the United States. When it crosses the North Atlantic, it becomes the North Atlantic Drift. This warm current brings mild, humid air to Ireland and southern England. As a result, these areas have a mild, wet climate despite their relatively high latitude.

In contrast, the cool California Current flows southward down the West Coast of the United States. The California Current makes climates along the West Coast cooler than you would expect at those latitudes.

 **Reading Checkpoint** What effect do oceans have on the temperatures of nearby land areas?

Lab zone Skills **Activity**

Inferring
Look at the currents in the South Pacific, South Atlantic, and Indian oceans. What pattern can you observe? Now compare currents in the South Atlantic to those in the North Atlantic. What might be responsible for differences in the current patterns?

FIGURE 3
On this map, warm currents are shown in red and cold currents in blue. **Interpreting Maps** *What type of current occurs around Antarctica?*

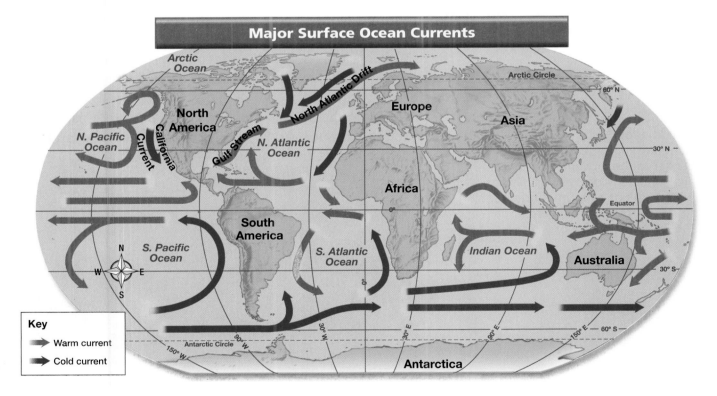

Major Surface Ocean Currents

Key
➡ Warm current
➡ Cold current

Factors Affecting Precipitation

The air masses that pass over an area may bring rain or snow. The amount of precipitation varies from year to year. But over time, total precipitation tends toward a yearly average. What determines the amount of precipitation an area receives? **The main factors that affect precipitation are prevailing winds, the presence of mountains, and seasonal winds.**

Prevailing Winds As you know, weather patterns depend on the movement of huge air masses. Air masses are moved from place to place by prevailing winds, the directional winds that usually blow in a region. Air masses can be warm or cool, dry or humid. The amount of water vapor in the air mass influences how much rain or snow will fall.

The amount of water vapor in prevailing winds also depends on where the winds come from. Winds that blow inland from oceans or large lakes carry more water vapor than winds that blow from over land. For example, winter winds generally blow from west to east across the Great Lakes. The winds pick up moisture that evaporates from the lakes. As a result, areas that are downwind can receive large amounts of snow.

Mountain Ranges A mountain range in the path of prevailing winds can also influence where precipitation falls. When humid winds blow from the ocean toward coastal mountains, they are forced to rise, as shown in Figure 4. The rising air cools and its water vapor condenses, forming clouds. Rain or snow falls on the **windward** side of the mountains, the side the wind hits.

By the time the air has moved over the mountains, it has lost much of its water vapor, so it is cool and dry. The land on the **leeward** side of the mountains—downwind—is in a rain shadow. Little precipitation falls there.

FIGURE 4
Rain Shadow
A mountain range can form a barrier to the movement of humid air. Humid air cools as it is blown up the side of a mountain range.
Applying Concepts *Where does the heaviest rainfall occur?*

Warm, moist air blows in from the ocean and is pushed up by the mountains.

Warm, moist air

As the air rises, it cools and water vapor condenses. Moisture in the air is released as precipitation.

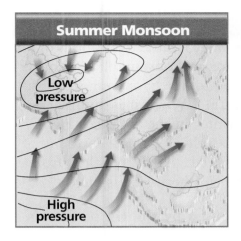

Summer Monsoon

Low pressure

High pressure

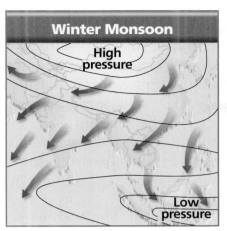

Winter Monsoon

High pressure

Low pressure

FIGURE 5
Monsoons
In a summer monsoon, wind blows from the ocean to the land. In the winter, the monsoon reverses and blows from the land to the ocean. Summer monsoons in Nepal cause heavy rain (above).

Seasonal Winds A seasonal change in wind patterns can affect precipitation. These seasonal winds are similar to land and sea breezes, but occur over a wider area. Sea and land breezes over a large region that change direction with the seasons are called **monsoons.** What produces a monsoon? In the summer in South and Southeast Asia, the land gradually gets warmer than the ocean. A "sea breeze" blows steadily inland from the ocean all summer, even at night. The air blowing from the ocean during this season is very warm and humid. As the humid air rises over the land, the air cools. This causes water vapor to condense into clouds, producing heavy rains.

Thailand and parts of India receive much of their rain from the summer monsoons. These rains supply the water needed by rice and other crops. Monsoon winds also bring rain to coastal areas in West Africa and northeastern South America.

Regions affected by monsoon winds receive very little rain in winter. In the winter, the land cools and becomes colder than the ocean. A "land breeze" blows steadily from the land to the ocean. These winds carry little moisture.

 Reading Checkpoint   **Why does precipitation fall mainly on the windward sides of mountains?**

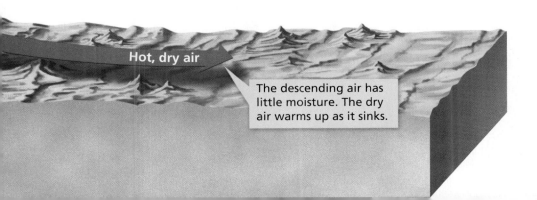

Hot, dry air

The descending air has little moisture. The dry air warms up as it sinks.

Math Skills

Percentage Light from the sun strikes Earth's surface at different angles. An angle is made up of two lines that meet at a point. Angles are measured in degrees. A full circle has 360 degrees.

When the sun is directly overhead near the equator, it is at an angle of 90° to Earth's surface. A 90° angle is called a right angle. What percentage of a circle is it?

$$\frac{90 \text{ degrees}}{360 \text{ degrees}} = \frac{d\%}{100\%}$$

$$90 \times 100 = 360 \times d$$

$$\frac{90 \times 100}{360} = d = 25$$

A 90° angle is 25 percent of a full circle.

Practice Problem Earth's axis is tilted at an angle of 23.5°. About what percentage of a right angle is this?

The Seasons

Although you can describe the average weather conditions of a climate region, these conditions are not constant all year long. Instead, most places outside the tropics have four seasons: winter, spring, summer, and autumn. When it is summer in the Northern Hemisphere it is winter in the Southern Hemisphere. So the seasons are not a result of changes in the distance between Earth and the sun. In fact, Earth is farthest from the sun during the summer in the Northern Hemisphere.

Tilted Axis **The seasons are caused by the tilt of Earth's axis as Earth travels around the sun.** The axis is an imaginary line through Earth's center that passes through both poles. Earth rotates, or turns, around this axis once each day. Earth's axis is not straight up and down, but is tilted at an angle of 23.5°. As Earth travels around the sun, its axis always points in the same direction. So the north end of the axis is pointed away from the sun for one part of the year and toward the sun for another part of the year.

Effect of the Tilted Axis Look at Figure 7. Which way is the north end of Earth's axis tilted in June? Notice that the Northern Hemisphere receives more direct rays from the sun. Also, in June the days in the Northern Hemisphere are longer than the nights. The combination of more direct rays and longer days makes Earth's surface warmer in the Northern Hemisphere than at any other time of the year. It is summer in the Northern Hemisphere. At the same time, the Southern Hemisphere is experiencing winter.

In December, on the other hand, the north end of Earth's axis is tilted away from the sun. It is winter in the Northern Hemisphere and summer in the Southern Hemisphere.

Reading Checkpoint **In June, what season is it in the Southern Hemisphere?**

FIGURE 6
Summer and Winter
There can be a striking difference between summer and winter in the same location. **Inferring** *During which season does the area shown receive more solar energy?*

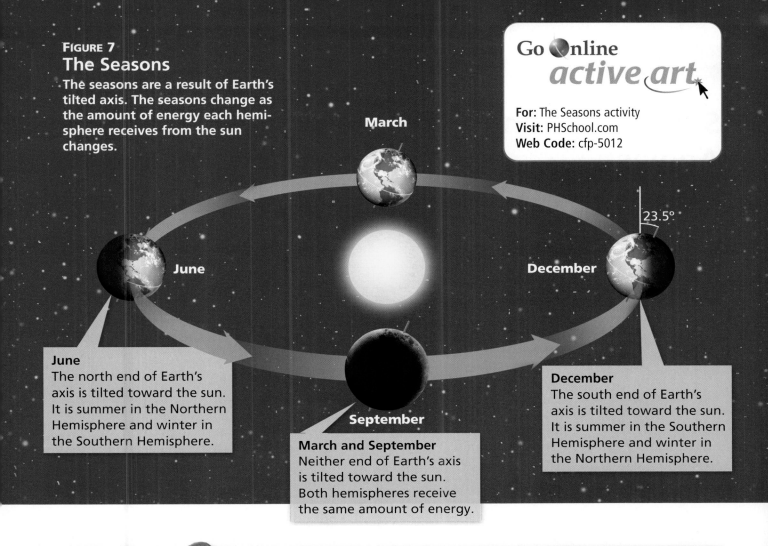

FIGURE 7
The Seasons
The seasons are a result of Earth's tilted axis. The seasons change as the amount of energy each hemisphere receives from the sun changes.

March

Go Online
active art

For: The Seasons activity
Visit: PHSchool.com
Web Code: cfp-5012

23.5°

December

June

September

June
The north end of Earth's axis is tilted toward the sun. It is summer in the Northern Hemisphere and winter in the Southern Hemisphere.

March and September
Neither end of Earth's axis is tilted toward the sun. Both hemispheres receive the same amount of energy.

December
The south end of Earth's axis is tilted toward the sun. It is summer in the Southern Hemisphere and winter in the Northern Hemisphere.

Section 1 Assessment

 **Target Reading Skill** Building Vocabulary
Use your sentences to help answer the questions.

Reviewing Key Concepts

1. a. **Identifying** Name four factors that affect temperature.
   b. **Describing** How does temperature vary in Earth's temperature zones?
   c. **Comparing and Contrasting** Two locations are at the same latitude in the temperate zone. One is in the middle of a continent. The other is on a coast affected by a warm ocean current. How will their climates differ?

2. a. **Listing** List three factors that affect precipitation.
   b. **Summarizing** How do prevailing winds affect the amount of precipitation an area receives?

   c. **Relating Cause and Effect** How does a mountain range in the path of prevailing winds affect precipitation on either side of the mountains?

3. a. **Reviewing** What causes the seasons?
   b. **Describing** Describe the changes in Earth's orbit around the sun that cause the seasons.
   c. **Developing Hypotheses** How might Earth's climates be different if Earth were not tilted on its axis?

Math Practice

4. **Percentage** At noon at a particular location, the sun makes an angle of 66.5° with Earth's surface. What percentage of a full circle is this?

Sunny Rays and Angles

Problem

How does the angle of a light source affect the rate at which the temperature of a surface changes?

Skills Focus

controlling variables, graphing, interpreting data, making models

Materials

- books • graph paper • pencil
- watch or clock • ruler • clear tape
- 3 thermometers or temperature probes
- protractor • 100-W incandescent lamp
- scissors • black construction paper

Procedure

1. Cut a strip of black construction paper 5 cm by 10 cm. Fold the paper in half and tape two sides to form a pocket.

2. Repeat Step 1 to make two more pockets.

Time (min.)	Temperature (°C)		
	0° Angle	45° Angle	90° Angle
Start			
1			
2			
3			
4			
5			

Data Table

3. Place the bulb of a thermometer inside each pocket. If you're using a temperature probe, see your teacher for instructions.

4. Place the pockets with thermometers close together, as shown in the photo. Place one thermometer in a vertical position (90° angle), one at a 45° angle, and the third one in a horizontal position (0° angle). Use a protractor to measure the angles. Support the thermometers with books.

5. Position the lamp so that it is 30 cm from each of the thermometer bulbs. Make sure the lamp will not move during the activity.

6. Copy a data table like the one above into your notebook.

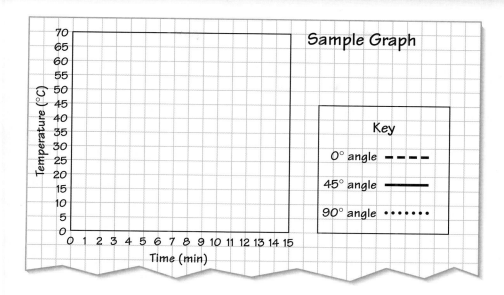

Sample Graph

Temperature (°C): 70 65 60 55 50 45 40 35 30 25 20 15 10 5 0

Time (min): 0 1 2 3 4 5 6 7 8 9 10 11 12 13 14 15

Key

0° angle – – – –

45° angle ——

90° angle ·······

7. In your data table, record the temperature on all three thermometers. (All three temperatures should be the same.)

8. Switch on the lamp. In your data table, record the temperature on each thermometer every minute for 15 minutes. **CAUTION:** *Be careful not to touch the hot lampshade.*

9. After 15 minutes, switch off the lamp.

Analyze and Conclude

1. **Controlling Variables** In this experiment, what was the manipulated variable? What was the responding variable?

2. **Graphing** Graph your data. Label the horizontal axis and vertical axis of your graph as shown on the sample graph. Use solid, dashed, and dotted lines to show the results from each thermometer, as shown in the key.

3. **Interpreting Data** Based on your data, at which angle did the temperature increase the most?

4. **Interpreting Data** At which angle did the temperature increase the least?

5. **Making Models** What part of Earth's surface does each thermometer represent?

6. **Drawing Conclusions** Why is air at the North Pole still very cold in the summer even though the Northern Hemisphere is tilted toward the sun?

7. **Communicating** Write a paragraph explaining what variables were held constant in this experiment.

Design an Experiment

Design an experiment to find out how the results of the investigation would change if the lamp were placed farther from the thermometers. Then, design another experiment to find out what happened if the lamp were placed closer to the thermometers.

Climate Regions

Reading Preview

Key Concepts
- What factors are used to classify climates?
- What are the six main climate regions?

Key Terms
- rain forest • savanna
- desert • steppe
- humid subtropical • subarctic
- tundra • permafrost

Target Reading Skill
Comparing and Contrasting
As you read, compare and contrast the six main climate regions by completing a table like the one below.

Climate Regions

Climate Region	Precipitation	Temperature
Tropical Rainy	Heavy precipitation	
Dry		
Temperate Marine		

Lab zone Discover **Activity**

How Do Climates Differ?
1. Collect pictures from magazines and newspapers of a variety of land areas around the world.
2. Sort the pictures into categories according to common weather characteristics.

Think It Over
Forming Operational Definitions Choose several words that describe the typical weather for each category. What words would you use to describe the typical weather where you live?

Suppose you lived for an entire year near the equator. It would be very different from where you live now. The daily weather, the amount of sunlight, and the pattern of seasons would all be new to you. You would be in another climate region.

Scientists classify climates according to two major factors: temperature and precipitation. They use a system developed around 1900 by Wladimir Köppen (KEP un). Besides temperature and precipitation, Köppen also looked at the distinct vegetation in different areas. This system identifies broad climate regions, each of which has smaller subdivisions.

There are six main climate regions: tropical rainy, dry, temperate marine, temperate continental, polar, and highlands. These climate regions are shown in Figure 10.

Maps can show boundaries between the climate regions. In the real world, of course, no clear boundaries mark where one climate region ends and another begins. Each region blends gradually into the next.

Tropical Rainy Climates

The tropics have two types of rainy climates: tropical wet and tropical wet-and-dry. Tropical wet climates are found in low-lying lands near the equator.

Tropical Wet In areas that have a tropical wet climate, many days are rainy, often with afternoon thunderstorms. These thunderstorms are triggered by midday heating. Another source of precipitation is prevailing winds. In many areas with a tropical wet climate, the trade winds bring moisture from the oceans. With year-round heat and heavy rainfall, vegetation grows lush and green. Dense rain forests grow in these rainy tropical climates. **Rain forests** are forests in which large amounts of rain fall year-round. Tropical rain forests are important because it is thought that at least half of the world's species of land plants and animals are found there.

In the United States, only the windward sides of the Hawaiian islands have a tropical wet climate. Rainfall is very heavy—over 10 meters per year on the windward side of the Hawaiian island of Kauai. The rain forests of Hawaii have a large variety of plants, including ferns, orchids, and many types of vines and trees.

Tropical Wet-and-Dry Areas that have tropical wet-and-dry climates receive slightly less rain than tropical climates and have distinct dry and rainy seasons. Instead of rain forests, there are tropical grasslands called **savannas.** Scattered clumps of trees that can survive the dry season dot the coarse grasses. Only a small part of the United States—the southern tip of Florida—has a tropical wet-and-dry climate. The graphs in Figure 9 show how temperature and precipitation vary in Makindu, Kenya, in East Africa.

Reading Checkpoint What parts of the United States have tropical rainy climates?

FIGURE 8
Tropical Rain Forests
Lush tropical rain forests grow in the tropical wet climate.

FIGURE 9
Climate Graphs
A graph of average temperature (left) can be combined with a graph of average precipitation (middle) to form a climate graph. These graphs show data for a tropical wet-and-dry region.

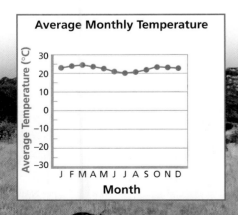

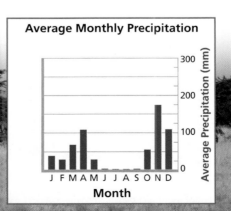

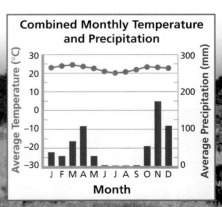

Figure 10
Climate Regions

Climate regions are classified according to a combination of temperature and precipitation. Climates in highland regions change rapidly as altitude changes.

Key

Tropical Rainy
- Tropical wet
- Tropical wet-and-dry

Dry
- Semiarid
- Arid

Temperate Marine
- Mediterranean
- Humid subtropical
- Marine west coast

Temperate Continental
- Humid continental
- Subarctic

Polar
- Tundra
- Ice cap

Highlands

Tropical Rainy

Temperature always 18°C or above

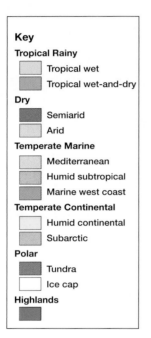

Tropical wet Always hot and humid, with heavy rainfall (at least 6 centimeters per month) all year round

Tropical wet-and-dry Always hot; alternating wet and dry seasons; heavy rainfall in the wet season

Dry

Occurs wherever potential evaporation is greater than precipitation; may be hot or cold

Semiarid Dry but receives about 25 to 50 centimeters of precipitation per year

Arid Desert, with little precipitation, usually less than 25 centimeters per year

Temperate Marine

Averages 10°C or above in warmest month, between −3°C and 18°C in the coldest month

Mediterranean Warm, dry summers and rainy winters

Humid subtropical Hot summers and cool winters

Marine west coast Mild winters and cool summers, with moderate precipitation all year

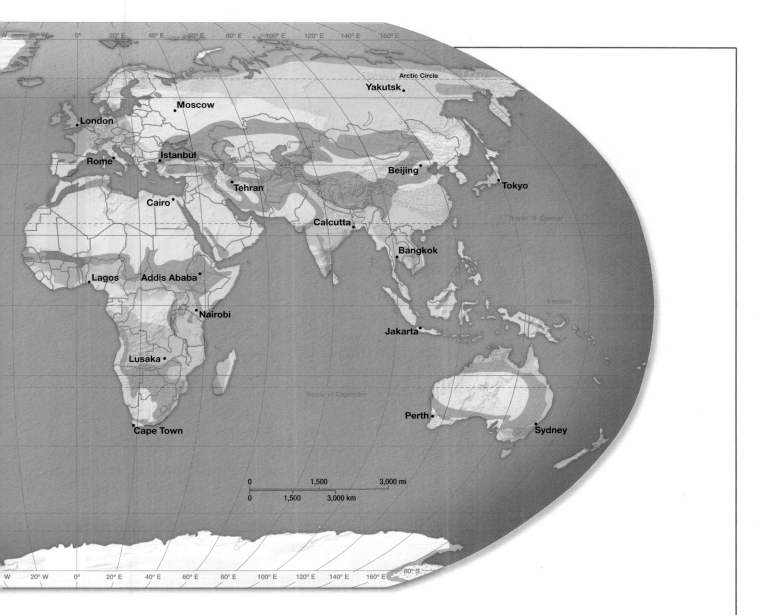

Yakutsk

Moscow

London

Istanbul

Rome

Tehran

Cairo

Calcutta

Bangkok

Beijing

Tokyo

Lagos

Addis Ababa

Nairobi

Jakarta

Lusaka

Perth

Sydney

Cape Town

Arctic Circle

Tropic of Cancer

Equator

Tropic of Capricorn

80° S

| 0 | 1,500 | 3,000 mi |
| 0 | 1,500 | 3,000 km |

Temperate Continental

Average temperature 10°C or above in the warmest month, −3°C or below in the coldest month

Humid continental Hot, humid summers and cold winters, with moderate precipitation year round

Subarctic Short, cool summers and long, cold winters; light precipitation, mainly in summer

Polar

Average temperature below 10°C in the warmest month

Tundra Always cold with a short, cool summer—warmest temperature about 10°C

Ice cap Always cold, average temperature at or below 0°C

Highlands

Generally cooler and wetter than nearby lowlands; temperature decreasing with altitude

Dry Climates

A climate is "dry" if the amount of precipitation that falls is less than the amount of water that could potentially evaporate. Because water evaporates more slowly in cool weather, a cool place with low rainfall may not be as dry as a warmer place that receives the same amount of rain. **Dry climates include arid and semiarid climates.**

Look at the map of world climate regions in Figure 10. What part of the United States is dry? Why is precipitation in this region so low? As you can see, dry regions often lie inland, far from oceans that are the source of humid air masses. In addition, much of the region lies in the rain shadow east of the Sierra Nevada and Rocky Mountains. Humid air masses from the Pacific Ocean lose much of their water as they cross the mountains. Little rain or snow is carried to dry regions.

Arid When you think about **deserts,** or arid regions, you may picture blazing heat and drifting sand dunes. Some deserts are hot and sandy, but others are cold or rocky. On average, arid regions, or deserts, get less than 25 centimeters of rain a year. Some years may bring no rain at all. Only specialized plants such as cactus and yucca can survive the desert's dryness and extremes of hot and cold. In the United States there are arid climates in portions of California, the Great Basin, and the Southwest.

Semiarid Locate the semiarid regions in Figure 10. As you can see, large semiarid areas are usually located on the edges of deserts. These semiarid areas are called steppes. A **steppe** is dry but gets enough rainfall for short grasses and low bushes to grow. For this reason, a steppe may also be called a prairie or grassland. The Great Plains are the steppe region of the United States.

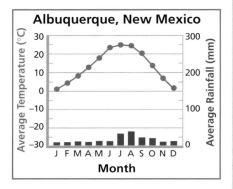

FIGURE 11
Arid Climate
Deserts of the southwestern United States are home to the western patchnose snake.
Interpreting Graphs *Which month has the highest average temperature?*

Albuquerque, New Mexico

 **What is a desert?**

Temperate Marine Climates

Look once again at Figure 10. Along the coasts of continents in the temperate zones, you will find the third main climate region, temperate marine. **There are three kinds of temperate marine climates: marine west coast, humid subtropical, and mediterranean.** Because of the moderating influence of oceans, all three are humid and have mild winters.

Marine West Coast The coolest temperate marine climates are found on the west coasts of continents north of 40° north latitude and south of 40° south latitude. Humid ocean air brings mild, rainy winters. Summer precipitation can vary considerably.

In North America, the marine west coast climate extends from northern California to southern Alaska. In the northwestern United States, humid air from the Pacific Ocean hits the western slopes of the Coastal Ranges. The air rises up the slopes of the mountains, and it cools. As the air cools, large amounts of rain or snow fall on the western slopes. The eastern slopes lie in the rain shadow of the mountains and receive little precipitation.

Because of the heavy precipitation, thick forests of tall trees grow in this region, including coniferous, or cone-bearing, trees such as Sitka spruce, Douglas fir, redwoods, and Western red cedar, as shown in Figure 12. One of the main industries of this region is harvesting and processing wood for lumber, paper, and furniture.

Eugene, Oregon

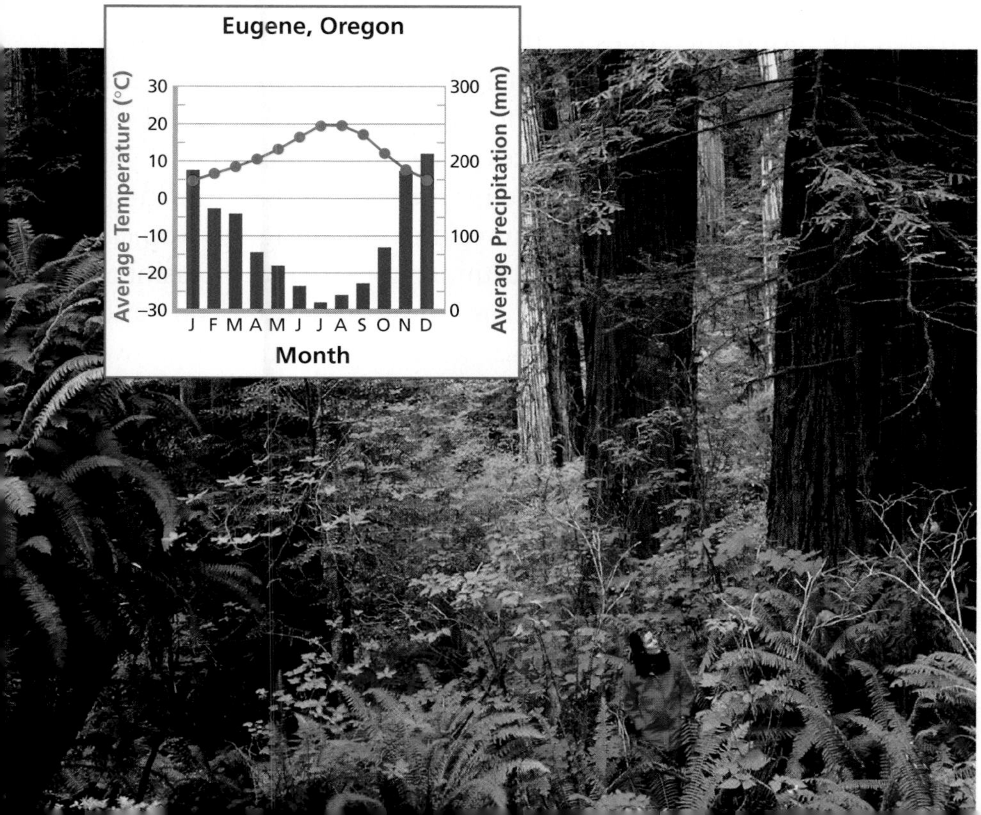

FIGURE 12
Marine West Coast Climate
Redwoods, Douglas firs, and Sitka spruce dominate the lush forests found in marine west coast climates.

Santa Barbara, California

FIGURE 13
Mediterranean Climate
Santa Barbara, on the coast of southern California, has a Mediterranean climate. Mild temperatures throughout the year make the area ideal for growing olives and citrus fruits.
Interpreting Graphs How much precipitation does Santa Barbara receive in July? In January?

Lab zone Skills **Activity**

Classifying
The table shows some climate data for three cities.

	City A	City B	City C
Average Jan. Temp. (°C)	12.8	18.9	−5.6
Average July Temp. (°C)	21.1	27.2	20
Annual Precipitation (cm)	33	152	109

Describe the climate you would expect each city to have. Identify the cities of Miami, Florida; Los Angeles, California; and Portland, Maine. Use Figure 10 to help identify each city's climate.

Mediterranean A coastal climate that is drier and warmer than west coast marine is known as Mediterranean. Most areas with this climate are found around the Mediterranean Sea. In the United States, the southern coast of California has a Mediterranean climate. This climate is mild, with two seasons. In winter, marine air masses bring cool, rainy weather. Summers are somewhat warmer, with little rain.

Mediterranean climates have two main vegetation types. One is made up of dense shrubs and small trees, called chaparral (chap uh RAL). The other vegetation type includes grasses with a few large trees.

Agriculture is important to the economy of California's Mediterranean climate region. Using irrigation, farmers grow many different crops, including rice, many vegetables, fruits, and nuts.

Humid Subtropical The warmest temperate marine climates are along the edges of the tropics. **Humid subtropical** climates are wet and warm, but not as constantly hot as the tropics. Locate the humid subtropical climates in Figure 10.

The southeastern United States has a humid subtropical climate. Summers are hot, with much more rainfall than in winter. Maritime tropical air masses move inland, bringing tropical weather conditions, including thunderstorms and occasional hurricanes, to southern cities such as Houston, New Orleans, and Atlanta. Winters are cool to mild, with more rain than snow. However, polar air masses moving in from the north can bring freezing temperatures and frosts.

Mixed forests of oak, ash, hickory, and pines grow in the humid subtropical region of the United States. Important crops in this region include oranges, peaches, peanuts, sugar cane, and rice.

✓ **Reading Checkpoint** What region of the United States has a humid subtropical climate?

Temperate Continental Climates

Temperate continental climates are not influenced very much by oceans, so they commonly have extremes of temperature. **Temperate continental climates are only found on continents in the Northern Hemisphere, and include humid continental and subarctic.** The parts of continents in the Southern Hemisphere south of 40° south latitude are not far enough from oceans for dry continental air masses to form.

Humid Continental Shifting tropical and polar air masses bring constantly changing weather to humid continental climates. In winter, continental polar air masses move south, bringing bitterly cold weather. In summer, tropical air masses move north, bringing heat and high humidity. Humid continental climates receive moderate amounts of rain in the summer. Smaller amounts of rain or snow fall in winter.

What parts of the United States have a humid continental climate? The eastern part of the region—the Northeast—has a range of forest types, from mixed forests in the south to coniferous forests in the north. Much of the western part of this region—the Midwest—was once tall grasslands, but is now farmland.

Subarctic The **subarctic** climates lie north of the humid continental climates. Summers in the subarctic are short and cool. Winters are long and bitterly cold.

In North America, coniferous trees such as spruce and fir make up a huge northern forest that stretches from Alaska to eastern Canada. Wood products from this forest are an important part of the economy. Many large mammals, including bears and moose, live in the forest. Birds of many species breed in the subarctic.

 **Reading Checkpoint** Which area of the United States has a subarctic climate?

FIGURE 14
Subarctic Climate
Subarctic climates have cool summers and cold winters. The world's largest subarctic regions are in Russia, Canada, and Alaska. This emperor goose is breeding in the subarctic climate region in Alaska.

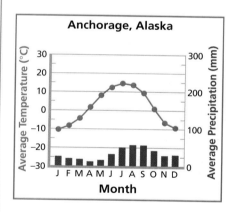

Go Online
SCI LINKS™ NSTA

For: Links on climates of the world
Visit: www.SciLinks.org
Web Code: scn-0942

Polar Climates

The polar climate is the coldest climate region, and includes the ice cap and tundra climates. Ice cap and tundra climates are found only in the far north and south, near the North and South poles. Most polar climates are relatively dry, because the cold air holds little moisture.

Ice Cap As Figure 10 shows, ice cap climates are found mainly on Greenland and in Antarctica. With average temperatures always at or below freezing, the land in ice cap climate regions is covered with ice and snow. Intense cold makes the air dry. Lichens and a few low plants may grow on the rocks.

Tundra The **tundra** climate region stretches across northern Alaska, Canada, and Russia. Short, cool summers follow bitterly cold winters. Because of the cold, some layers of the tundra soil are always frozen. This permanently frozen tundra soil is called **permafrost.** Because of the permafrost, water cannot drain away, so the soil is wet and boggy in summer.

It is too cold on the tundra for trees to grow. Despite the harsh climate, during the short summers the tundra is filled with life. Mosquitoes and other insects hatch in the ponds and marshes above the frozen permafrost. Mosses, grasses, lichens, wildflowers, and shrubs grow quickly during the short summers. In North America, herds of caribou eat the vegetation and are in turn preyed upon by wolves. Some birds, such as the white-tailed ptarmigan, live on the tundra year-round. Others, such as the arctic tern and many waterfowl, spend only their summer breeding seasons there.

 **Reading Checkpoint** **What type of vegetation is found on the tundra?**

FIGURE 15
Tundra Climate
The Nenet people are reindeer herders on the tundra of northern Russia. These reindeer are grazing on some short shrubs typical of tundra plants.

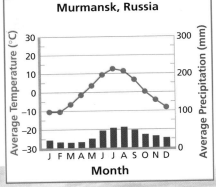

Murmansk, Russia

Highlands

Why are highlands a distinct climate region? **Temperature falls as altitude increases, so highland regions are colder than the regions that surround them.** Increasing altitude produces climate changes similar to the climate changes you would expect with increasing latitude. Precipitation also increases as air masses carrying moisture pass over highland areas.

The climate on the lower slopes of a mountain range is like that of the surrounding countryside. The Rocky Mountain foothills, for instance, share the semi-arid climate of the Great Plains. But as you go higher up into the mountains, temperatures become lower and precipitation increases. Climbing 1,000 meters up in elevation is like traveling 1,200 kilometers toward the poles. The climate higher in the mountains is like that of the subarctic: cool with coniferous trees.

Above a certain elevation—the tree line—temperatures are too low for trees to grow. The climate above the tree line is like that of the tundra. Only low plants, mosses, and lichens can grow there.

FIGURE 16
Highland Climate
Highland climates are generally cooler than surrounding regions. The Mount Rainier area in Washington State has short summers and long, severe winters.
Classifying *What climate zone does the mountaintop resemble?*

Section 2 Assessment

Target Reading Skill Comparing and Contrasting Use the information in your table about climate regions to help you answer Question 1.

Reviewing Key Concepts

1. **a. Listing** What two major factors are used to classify climates?
   b. Reviewing What other factor did Köppen use in classifying climates?
2. **a. Identifying** What are the six main climate regions?
   b. Comparing and Contrasting How is a tropical wet climate similar to a tropical wet-and-dry climate? How are they different?
   c. Inferring In what climate region would you find plains covered with short grasses and small bushes? Explain.
   d. Relating Cause and Effect Why do marine west coast climates have abundant precipitation?
   e. Predicting Which place would have more severe winters—central Russia or the west coast of France? Why?
   f. Sequencing Place the following climates in order from coldest to warmest: tundra, subarctic, humid continental, ice cap.
   g. Relating Cause and Effect How could a forest grow on a mountain that is surrounded by a desert?

Lab zone At-Home Activity

What's Your Climate? Describe to your family the characteristics of the climate region in which you live. What plants and animals live in your climate region? What characteristics do these plants and animals have that make them well-adapted to the region?

Cool Climate Graphs

Problem

Based on climate data, what is the best time of year to visit various cities to enjoy particular recreational activities?

Skills Focus

graphing, interpreting data

Materials

• calculator • ruler • 3 pieces of graph paper
• black, blue, red, and green pencils
• climate map on pages 178–179
• U.S. map with city names and latitude lines

Procedure

1. Work in groups of three. Each person should graph the data for a different city, A, B, or C.

2. On graph paper, use a black pencil to label the axes as on the climate graph below. Title your climate graph City A, City B, or City C.

3. Use your green pencil to make a bar graph of the monthly average amount of precipitation. Place a star below the name of each month that has more than a trace of snow.

4. Use a red pencil to plot the average monthly maximum temperature. Make a dot for the temperature in the middle of each space for the month. When you have plotted data for all 12 months, connect the points into a smooth curved line.

5. Use a blue pencil to plot the average monthly minimum temperature for your city. Use the same procedure as in Step 4.

6. Calculate the total average annual precipitation for this city and include it in your observations. Do this by adding the average precipitation for each month.

Analyze and Conclude

Use all three climate graphs, plus the graph for Washington, D.C., to answer these questions.

1. **Interpreting Data** Which of the four cities has the least change in average temperatures during the year?

2. **Interpreting Maps** Use the map on pages 120–121 to help find the climate region in which each city is located.

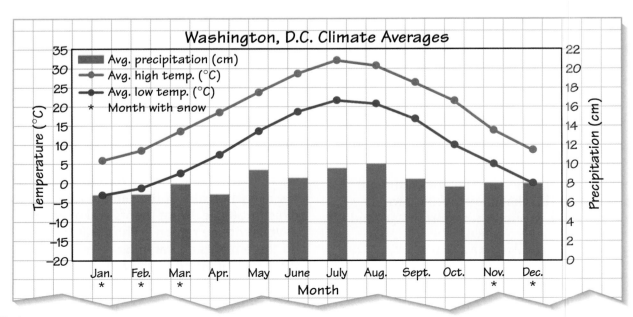

Climate Data

Washington, D.C.	Jan.	Feb.	Mar.	April	May	June	July	Aug.	Sept.	Oct.	Nov.	Dec.
Average High Temp. (°C)	6	8	14	19	24	29	32	31	27	21	14	8
Average Low Temp. (°C)	−3	−2	3	8	14	19	22	21	17	10	5	0
Average Precipitation (cm)	6.9	6.9	8.1	6.9	9.4	8.6	9.7	9.9	8.4	7.6	7.9	7.9
Months With Snow	*	*	*	trace	—	—	—	—	—	trace	*	*
City A	Jan.	Feb.	Mar.	April	May	June	July	Aug.	Sept.	Oct.	Nov.	Dec.
Average High Temp. (°C)	13	16	16	17	17	18	18	19	21	21	17	13
Average Low Temp. (°C)	8	9	9	10	11	12	12	13	13	13	11	8
Average Precipitation (cm)	10.4	7.6	7.9	3.3	0.8	0.5	0.3	0.3	0.8	3.3	8.1	7.9
Months With Snow	trace	trace	trace	—	—	—	—	—	—	—	—	trace
City B	Jan.	Feb.	Mar.	April	May	June	July	Aug.	Sept.	Oct.	Nov.	Dec.
Average High Temp. (°C)	5	7	10	16	21	26	29	27	23	18	11	6
Average Low Temp. (°C)	−9	−7	−4	1	6	11	14	13	8	2	−4	−8
Average Precipitation (cm)	0.8	1.0	2.3	3.0	5.6	5.8	7.4	7.6	3.3	2.0	1.3	1.3
Months With Snow	*	*	*	*	*	—	—	—	trace	*	*	*
City C	Jan.	Feb.	Mar.	April	May	June	July	Aug.	Sept.	Oct.	Nov.	Dec.
Average High Temp. (°C)	7	11	13	18	23	28	33	32	27	21	12	8
Average Low Temp. (°C)	−6	−4	−2	1	4	8	11	10	5	1	−3	−7
Average Precipitation (cm)	2.5	2.3	1.8	1.3	1.8	1	0.8	0.5	0.8	1	2	2.5
Months With Snow	*	*	*	*	*	trace	—	—	trace	trace	*	*

3. **Applying Concepts** Which of the cities below matches each climate graph?
   Colorado Springs, Colorado; latitude 39° N
   San Francisco, California; latitude 38° N
   Reno, Nevada; latitude 40° N

4. **Inferring** The four cities are at approximately the same latitude. Why are their climate graphs so different?

5. **Graphing** What factors do you need to consider when setting up and numbering the left and right *y*-axes of a climate graph so that your data will fit on the graph?

6. **Communicating** Imagine that you are writing a travel brochure for one of the four cities. Write a description of the climate of the city and discuss the best time to visit to do a selected outdoor activity.

More to Explore

What type of climate does the area where you live have? Find out what outdoor recreational opportunities your community has. How is each activity particularly suited to the climate of your area?

Long-Term Changes in Climate

Reading Preview

Key Concepts
- What principle do scientists follow in studying ancient climates?
- What changes occur on Earth's surface during an ice age?
- What factors can cause climate change?

Key Terms
- ice age
- sunspot

Target Reading Skill
Identifying Supporting Evidence As you read, identify the evidence that is used to show that climates change. Write the evidence in a graphic organizer like the one below.

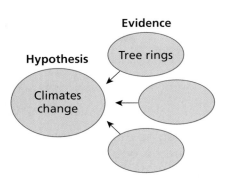

Discover Activity

What Story Can Tree Rings Tell?

1. Look at the photo of tree rings in Figure 18. Tree rings are the layers of new wood that form each year as a tree grows.
2. Look closely at the tree rings. Note whether they are all the same thickness.
3. What weather conditions might cause a tree to form thicker or thinner tree rings?

Think It Over
Inferring How could you use tree rings to tell you about weather in the past?

One of the greatest Native American cultures in the American Southwest was the Ancestral Pueblos. These farming people built great pueblos, or "apartment houses," of stone and sun-baked clay, with hundreds of rooms, as shown in Figure 17. By about the year 1000, the Ancestral Pueblos were flourishing. Evidence from tree rings indicates that several periods of intense drought then occurred. These droughts may have contributed to a breakdown in their society. By the late 1200s, they had abandoned the pueblos and moved to other areas.

Although weather varies from day to day, climates usually change more slowly. But climates do change, both in small areas and throughout the world. Although climate change is usually slow, its consequences are great.

FIGURE 17
Ancient Pueblo Dwellings
The Ancestral Pueblos lived in these buildings, now in Mesa Verde National Park in southwestern Colorado, about 1,000 years ago.

Studying Climate Change

Climate changes have affected many regions in addition to the Southwest. For example, Greenland today is mostly covered by an ice cap. But 80 million years ago, Greenland had a warm, moist climate. Fossils of magnolias and palm trees found in Greenland provide evidence for this climate change. Today magnolia and palm trees grow only in warm, moist climates. Scientists assume that the ancestors of these trees required similar conditions. **In studying ancient climates, scientists follow an important principle: If plants or animals today need certain conditions to live, then similar plants and animals in the past also required those conditions.**

Pollen One source of information about ancient climates is pollen records. Each type of plant has a particular type of pollen. The bottoms of some lakes are covered with thick layers of mud and plant material, including pollen that fell to the bottom of the lake over thousands of years. Scientists can drill down into these layers and bring up cores to examine. By looking at the pollen present in each layer, scientists can tell what types of plants lived in the area. From pollen data, scientists can infer that an ancient climate was similar to the climate where the same plants grow today.

Tree Rings Tree rings can also be used to learn about ancient climates. Every summer, a tree grows a new layer of wood just under its bark. These layers form rings, as shown in Figure 18. In cool climates, the amount the tree grows—the thickness of a ring—depends on the length of the warm growing season. In dry climates, the thickness of each ring depends on the amount of rainfall. Scientists study the pattern of thick or thin tree rings. From these data they can see whether previous years were warm or cool, wet or dry.

 **Reading Checkpoint** What are two ways scientists study ancient climates?

FIGURE 18

Evidence of Climate Change
The width of tree rings provides information on temperature and rainfall. A thin ring indicates that the year was cool or dry. A thick ring indicates that the year was warm or wet. Inferring *Which tree rings would provide information about climate close to the time that the tree was cut down?*

Glaciers in North America

Key
☐ Area covered by glaciers
▓ Mammoth steppe

FIGURE 19
The Last Ice Age
The map shows the parts of North America that were covered by glaciers 18,000 years ago. On the steppe near the glaciers lived many mammals that are now extinct, including woolly mammoths.

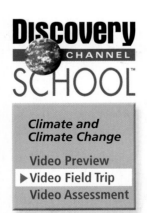

Ice Ages

Throughout Earth's history, climates have gradually changed. Over millions of years, warm periods have alternated with cold periods known as **ice ages,** or glacial episodes. **During each ice age, huge sheets of ice called glaciers covered large parts of Earth's surface.**

Glaciers transform the landscape by carving giant grooves in solid rock, depositing enormous piles of sediment, and moving huge boulders hundreds of kilometers. From this evidence and from fossils, scientists have concluded that in the past two million years there have been many major ice ages. Each one lasted 100,000 years or longer. Long, warmer periods occurred between the ice ages. Some scientists think that we are now in a warm period between ice ages.

The last ice age ended only about 10,500 years ago. Ice sheets covered much of northern Europe and North America, reaching as far south as present-day Iowa and Nebraska, as shown in Figure 19. In some places, the ice was more than 3 kilometers thick. So much water was frozen in the ice sheets that the average sea level was much lower than it is today. When the ice sheets melted, the rising oceans flooded coastal areas. Inland, the Great Lakes formed.

 **Reading Checkpoint** Why were the oceans lower during the ice ages than they are now?

DISCOVERY
CHANNEL
SCHOOL

Climate and Climate Change

Video Preview
▶ Video Field Trip
Video Assessment

Causes of Climate Change

Why do climates change? **Possible explanations for major climate changes include variations in the position of Earth relative to the sun, changes in the sun's energy output, major volcanic eruptions, and the movement of the continents.**

Earth's Position As Earth revolves around the sun, the time of year when Earth is closest to the sun shifts from January to July and back again over a period of about 23,000 years. The angle at which Earth's axis tilts and the shape of Earth's orbit around the sun also change slightly over long periods of time. The combined effects of these changes may be the main cause of ice ages.

Solar Energy Short-term changes in climate have been linked to changes in the number of **sunspots**—dark, cooler regions on the surface of the sun. Sunspots increase and decrease in fairly regular 11-year cycles. Satellite measurements have shown that the amount of energy the sun produces increases slightly when there are more sunspots. This may cause Earth's temperature to warm.

Volcanic Activity Major volcanic eruptions release huge quantities of gases and ash into the atmosphere. These materials can stay in the upper atmosphere for months or years. Scientists think that the gases and ash filter out some of the incoming solar radiation, and may lower temperatures.

Math ▸ Analyzing Data

Ice Ages and Temperature

The graph shows the estimated average worldwide temperature over the last 350,000 years. During this time, cold glacial periods (blue) alternated with warmer interglacial periods (pink).

1. **Reading Graphs** What does the x-axis of the graph represent? What does the y-axis represent?

2. **Interpreting Data** What pattern do you see in these data? How would you explain this pattern?

3. **Predicting** Based on the pattern over the last 350,000 years, predict how global temperature will change in the future.

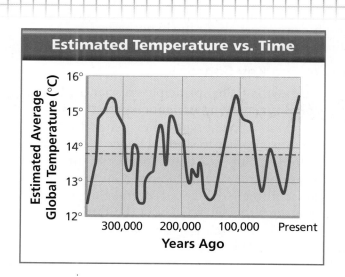

Estimated Temperature vs. Time

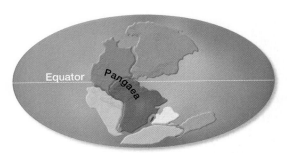

225 Million Years Ago

180—200 Million Years Ago

FIGURE 20
Moving Continents
The continents have moved over millions of years.
Interpreting Maps *Which present-day continents broke away from Gondwanaland? Which broke away from Laurasia?*

For: Continental Drift activity
Visit: PHSchool.com
Web Code: cfp-1015

Movement of Continents The continents have not always been located where they are now. About 225 million years ago, most of the land on Earth was part of a single continent called Pangaea (pan JEE uh), as Figure 20 shows. At that time, most continents were far from their present positions. Continents that are now in the polar zones were once near the equator. This movement explains how tropical plants such as magnolias and palm trees could once have grown in Greenland.

The movements of continents over time changed the locations of land and sea. These changes affected the global patterns of winds and ocean currents, which in turn slowly changed climates. And as the continents continue to move, climates will continue to change.

 **Reading Checkpoint** What was Pangaea?

Section 3 Assessment

Target Reading Skill
Identifying Supporting Evidence Refer to your graphic organizer about the hypothesis that climate changes as you answer Question 1 below.

Reviewing Key Concepts
1. a. **Reviewing** What principle do scientists follow in studying ancient climates?
   b. **Describing** What types of evidence do scientists gather to study changes in climate?
   c. **Inferring** Suppose that you are a scientist studying tree rings in a cross-section of an ancient tree. What could several narrow tree rings in a row tell you about the climate when those rings were formed?
2. a. **Defining** What is a glacier?
   b. **Explaining** What occurs during an ice age?
   c. **Comparing and Contrasting** Compare the climate today with it during an ice age.

3. a. **Listing** What are four factors that could be responsible for changing Earth's climate?
   b. **Summarizing** Select one of the four factors that could cause climate change and summarize how it may cause the climate to change.

Writing in Science

Procedure for Data Collection Suppose that you are a scientist who wants to use pollen data from a lake bed to learn about ancient climates. Write the steps for the procedure that you would follow to collect and analyze your data.

Global Changes in the Atmosphere

Reading Preview

Key Concepts
• What events can cause short-term climate changes?
• How might human activities be affecting the temperature of Earth's atmosphere?
• How have human activities affected the ozone layer?

Key Terms
• El Niño • La Niña
• global warming
• greenhouse gas
• chlorofluorocarbon

Target Reading Skill
Asking Questions Before you read, preview the red headings. Ask a *what* or *how* question for each heading, for example, "How does short-term climate change occur?" As you read, write the answers to your questions.

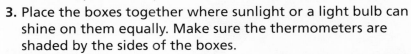

Lab zone | Discover **Activity**

What Is the Greenhouse Effect?
1. ✂ Cut two pieces of black construction paper to fit the bottoms of two shoe boxes.
2. 🔬 Place a thermometer in each box. Record the temperatures on the thermometers. Cover one box with plastic wrap.
3. Place the boxes together where sunlight or a light bulb can shine on them equally. Make sure the thermometers are shaded by the sides of the boxes.
4. Wait 15 minutes and read the thermometers again. Record the temperatures.

Think It Over
Inferring How can you explain any temperature difference between the two boxes?

If you live in one area for several years, you get to know the area's climate. But in some years, the weather is so unusual that you might think the climate has changed. That's what happened in several different parts of the world during 1997–1998. Droughts occurred in parts of Africa, Asia, and Australia. Heavy rains struck parts of South America. In the United States, very heavy rains swept across California and the South.

What produced these global changes? During the droughts and floods of 1998, parts of the Pacific Ocean were much warmer than usual. Even the ocean's winds and currents changed. Scientists have evidence that these changes in the Pacific Ocean led to wild weather in other parts of the world.

◀ In 1998, mudslides from heavy rains caused severe damage in California.

Chapter 5 ◆ 193

▲ In **normal years**, water in the eastern Pacific is kept relatively cool by currents along the coast of North and South America.

▲ When **El Niño** occurs, warm surface water from the western Pacific moves east toward the coast of South America.

▲ **La Niña** occurs when surface waters in the eastern Pacific Ocean are colder than normal.

FIGURE 21
El Niño and La Niña
In these satellite images, warmer water is red and white. Cooler water is blue and purple.

Short-Term Climate Change

Changes in ocean currents and winds can greatly affect climate. **El Niño and La Niña are short-term changes in the tropical Pacific Ocean caused by changes in ocean surface currents and prevailing winds.** El Niño and La Niña both influence weather patterns all over the world.

El Niño The warm-water event known as **El Niño** begins when an unusual pattern of winds forms over the western Pacific. This causes a vast sheet of warm water to move eastward toward the South American coast, as shown in Figure 21. El Niño causes the surface of the ocean in the eastern Pacific to be unusually warm. El Niño typically occurs every two to seven years.

The arrival of El Niño's warm surface water disrupts the cold ocean currents along the western coast of South America and changes weather patterns there. El Niño also affects weather patterns around the world, often bringing severe conditions such as heavy rains or droughts. El Niño conditions can last for one to two years before normal winds and currents return.

La Niña When surface waters in the eastern Pacific are colder than normal, a climate event known as **La Niña** occurs. A La Niña event is the opposite of an El Niño event. La Niña events typically bring colder than normal winters and greater precipitation to the Pacific Northwest and the north central United States. Another major effect of La Niña is greater hurricane activity in the western Atlantic.

 **Reading Checkpoint** How often does El Niño typically occur?

194 ◆

Global Warming

Most changes in world climates are caused by natural factors. But recently scientists have observed climate changes that could be the result of human activities. For example, over the last 120 years, the average temperature of the troposphere has risen by about 0.5 Celsius degree. This gradual increase in the temperature of Earth's atmosphere is called **global warming.**

The Greenhouse Hypothesis Recall that gases in Earth's atmosphere hold in heat from the sun, keeping the atmosphere at a comfortable temperature for living things. The process by which gases in Earth's atmosphere trap this energy is called the greenhouse effect. Look at the greenhouse in Figure 22. Notice that sunlight does not heat the air in the greenhouse directly. Instead, sunlight first heats the soil, benches, and pots. Then infrared radiation from these surfaces heats the air in the greenhouse. The greenhouse effect in Earth's atmosphere is similar in some ways.

Gases in the atmosphere that trap energy are called **greenhouse gases.** Carbon dioxide, water vapor, and methane are some of the greenhouse gases. **Many scientists have hypothesized that human activities that add greenhouse gases to the atmosphere may be warming Earth's atmosphere.**

FIGURE 22
Greenhouse Effect
Sunlight enters a greenhouse and is absorbed. The interior of the greenhouse radiates back energy in the form of infrared radiation, or heat. Much of the heat is trapped and held inside the greenhouse, warming it.
Applying Concepts *What gases in Earth's atmosphere can trap heat like a greenhouse?*

Infrared radiation cannot pass through the greenhouse roof.

Sunlight

Key

Sunlight

Infrared radiation

Changing Levels of Carbon Dioxide Scientists think that an increase in carbon dioxide is a major factor in global warming. Until the late 1800s, the level of carbon dioxide in the atmosphere remained about the same. How did scientists determine this? They measured the amount of carbon dioxide in air bubbles trapped in Antarctic ice. They obtained these samples of ancient air from ice cores, as shown in Figure 23. The glacier that covers Antarctica formed over millions of years. Gas bubbles in the ice cores provide samples of air from the time the ice formed.

Is global warming caused by human activities, or does it have a natural cause? Scientists have done a great deal of research to try to answer this question.

Since the late 1800s, the level of carbon dioxide in the atmosphere has increased steadily, as shown in Figure 23. Many scientists think that this change is a result of increased human activities. For example, the burning of wood, coal, oil, and natural gas adds carbon dioxide to the air. During the last 100 years, these activities have increased greatly in many different countries. Some scientists predict that the level of carbon dioxide could double by the year 2100. If that happens, then global temperature could rise by 1.5 to 3.5 Celsius degrees.

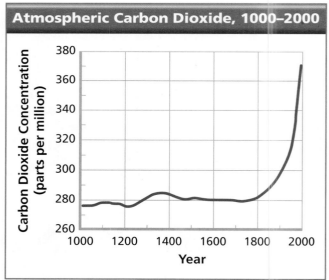

Atmospheric Carbon Dioxide, 1000–2000

FIGURE 23
Carbon Dioxide Levels
These scientists are taking an ice core from the glacier that covers Antarctica (left). Gas bubbles in the ice provide samples of the atmosphere at the time the ice formed. Data from ice cores enables scientists to graph changing levels of carbon dioxide (above).

1960

1990

Climate Variation Hypothesis Not all scientists agree about the causes of global warming. Some scientists think that the 0.5 Celsius degree rise in global temperatures over the past 120 years may be part of natural variations in climate rather than a result of increases in carbon dioxide.

Satellite measurements have shown that the amount of energy the sun produces increases and decreases from year to year. These changes in solar energy could be causing periods of warmer and cooler climates. Or climate change could be a result of changes in both carbon dioxide levels and the amount of solar energy.

Possible Effects Global warming could have some positive effects. Farmers in some cool areas could plant two crops a year. Places that are too cold for farming today could become farmland. However, many effects of global warming are likely to be less positive. Higher temperatures would cause water to evaporate from exposed soil, such as plowed farmland. Dry soil blows away easily. Thus, some fertile fields might become "dust bowls."

A rise in temperatures of even a few degrees could warm up water in the oceans. Some scientists think warmer ocean water could increase the strength of hurricanes.

As the water warmed, it would expand, raising sea level around the world. The melting of glaciers and polar ice caps could also increase sea level. Sea level has already risen by 10 to 20 centimeters over the last 100 years, and could rise another 25 to 80 centimeters by the year 2100. Even such a small rise in sea level would flood low-lying coastal areas.

 **Reading Checkpoint** **What are three possible effects of global warming?**

FIGURE 24
Melting Glaciers
The photos show the Burroughs glacier in Alaska. The photo on the left was taken in 1960. The photo on the right was taken in 1990, and shows the large amount of melting that has taken place.

For: More on the greenhouse effect
Visit: PHSchool.com
Web Code: cfd-4044

Lab zone · Try This **Activity**

It's Your Skin!

Compare how well sunscreens block out ultraviolet rays.

1. Close the blinds or curtains in the room. Place one square of sun-sensitive paper inside each of three plastic sandwich bags.

2. Place three drops of one sunscreen on the outside of one bag. Spread the sunscreen as evenly as possible. Label this bag with the SPF number of the sunscreen.

3. On another bag, repeat Step 2 using a sunscreen with a different SPF. Wash your hands after spreading the sunscreen. Leave the third bag untreated as a control.

4. Place the bags outside in direct sunlight. Bring them back inside after 3 minutes or after one of the squares turns completely white.

Drawing Conclusions Did both of the sunscreens block ultraviolet radiation? Was one better than the other? Explain.

Ozone Depletion

Another global change in the atmosphere involves the ozone layer. Ozone in the stratosphere filters out much of the harmful ultraviolet radiation from the sun, as shown in Figure 25.

In the 1970s, scientists noticed that the ozone layer over Antarctica was growing thinner each spring. A large area of reduced ozone, or ozone hole, was being created. In 2000, the ozone hole reached a record size of over 28.5 million km^2—almost the size of Africa. Satellite data indicates that the ozone hole in 2003 was nearly as large as it was in 2000. What created the ozone hole? **Chemicals produced by humans have been damaging the ozone layer.**

Chlorofluorocarbons A major cause of ozone depletion is a group of compounds called **chlorofluorocarbons,** or CFCs. CFCs were used in air conditioners and refrigerators, as cleaners for electronic parts, and in aerosol sprays, such as deodorants.

Most chemical compounds released into the air eventually break down. CFCs, however, can last for decades and rise all the way to the stratosphere. In the stratosphere, ultraviolet radiation breaks down the CFC molecules into atoms, including chlorine. The chlorine atoms then break ozone down into oxygen atoms.

Results of Ozone Depletion Because ozone blocks ultraviolet radiation, a decrease in ozone means an increase in the amount of ultraviolet radiation that reaches Earth's surface. Ultraviolet radiation can cause eye damage and several kinds of skin cancer.

In the late 1970s, the United States and many other countries banned most uses of CFCs in aerosol sprays. In 1990, many nations agreed to phase out the production and use of CFCs. Because ozone depletion affects the whole world, such agreements must be international to be effective. Worldwide production of the chemicals has greatly decreased. In the United States, at the current rate it will take until 2010 to completely eliminate the use of CFCs.

 **What are CFCs?**

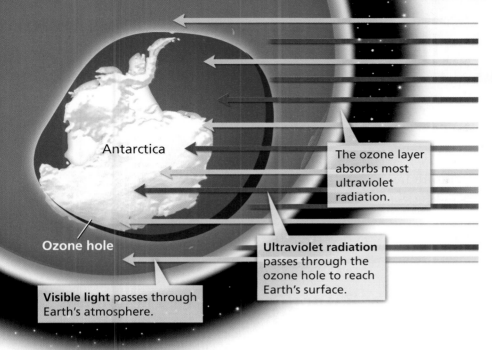

FIGURE 25
The Ozone Hole
The ozone layer blocks much of the ultraviolet radiation (purple) coming from the sun. Visible light (yellow) can pass through the ozone layer. The satellite images below show the concentration of ozone over the South Pole for three years. The dark area shows where the ozone layer is thinnest. **Observing** *How has the size of the ozone layer changed over time?*

Antarctica

Ozone hole

The ozone layer absorbs most ultraviolet radiation.

Ultraviolet radiation passes through the ozone hole to reach Earth's surface.

Visible light passes through Earth's atmosphere.

1979

2000

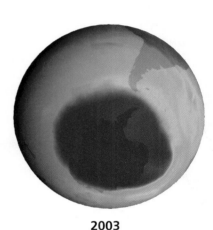

2003

Section 4 Assessment

🎯 **Target Reading Skill**

Asking Questions Use the answers to your *what* and *how* questions to help you answer the questions below.

Reviewing Key Concepts

1. a. Listing What are two events that can cause short-term climate change?
  b. Describing Describe the changes that occur in the Pacific Ocean and the atmosphere above it during El Niño.
  c. Relating Cause and Effect What effects does El Niño have on weather and climate?
2. a. Defining What is global warming?
  b. Relating Cause and Effect How do scientists think that increased carbon dioxide levels contributed to global warming?

3. a. Reviewing What effect have human activities had on the ozone layer?
  b. Summarizing Summarize the cause of ozone depletion and the steps taken to reverse it.

Lab zone **At-Home Activity**

Sun Protection Visit a drugstore with your family. Compare the SPF (sun protection factor) of the various sunscreens for sale. Explain why it is important to protect your skin from ultraviolet radiation. Ask your family members to determine the best value for the money in terms of SPF rating and price.

① What Causes Climate?

Key Concepts

- The main factors that influence temperature are latitude, altitude, distance from large bodies of water, and ocean currents.

- The main factors that influence precipitation are prevailing winds, the presence of mountains, and seasonal winds.

- The seasons are caused by the tilt of Earth's axis as Earth travels around the sun.

Key Terms

climate	marine climate
microclimate	continental climate
tropical zone	windward
polar zone	leeward
temperate zone	monsoon

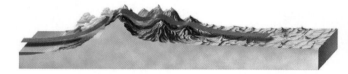

② Climate Regions

Key Concepts

- Scientists classify climates according to two major factors: temperature and precipitation.

- There are six main climate regions: tropical rainy, dry, temperate marine, temperate continental, polar, and highlands.

- The tropics have two types of rainy climates: tropical wet and tropical wet-and-dry.

- Dry climates can be arid and semiarid climates.

- There are three kinds of temperate marine climates: marine west coast, humid subtropical, and mediterranean.

- Temperate continental climates are only found on continents in the Northern Hemisphere, and include humid continental and subarctic.

- The polar climate is the coldest climate region, and includes the ice cap and tundra climates.

- Temperature falls as altitude increases, so highland regions are colder than regions that surround them.

Key Terms

rain forest
savanna
desert
steppe
humid subtropical
subarctic
tundra
permafrost

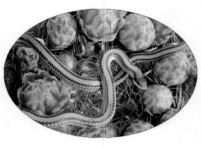

③ Long-Term Changes in Climate

Key Concepts

- In studying ancient climates, scientists follow an important principle: If plants or animals today need certain conditions to live, then similar plants and animals in the past also required those conditions.

- During each ice age, huge sheets of ice called glaciers covered large parts of Earth's surface.

- Possible explanations for major climate changes include variations in the position of Earth relative to the sun, changes in the sun's energy output, major volcanic eruptions, and the movement of continents.

Key Terms

ice age   sunspot

④ Global Changes in the Atmosphere

Key Concepts

- El Niño and La Niña are short-term changes in the tropical Pacific Ocean caused by changes in ocean surface currents and prevailing winds.

- Human activities that add greenhouse gases to the atmosphere may be warming Earth's atmosphere.

- Chemicals produced by humans have been damaging the ozone layer.

Key Terms

El Niño	greenhouse gas
La Niña	chlorofluorocarbon
global warming	

Review and Assessment

Organizing Information

Concept Mapping Copy the graphic organizer about climate onto a separate sheet of paper. Then complete it and add a title. (For more on Concept Mapping, see the Skills Handbook.)

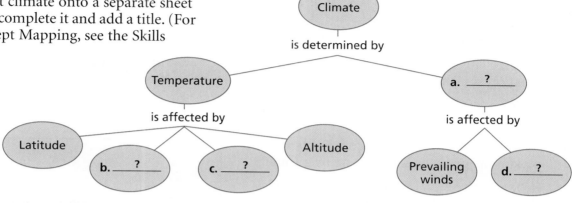

Climate

is determined by

Temperature

a. ___?___

is affected by

is affected by

Latitude

b. ___?___

c. ___?___

Altitude

Prevailing winds

d. ___?___

Reviewing Key Terms

Choose the letter of the best answer.

1. The average conditions of temperature, precipitation, wind, and clouds in an area over a period of years make up its
   a. weather.　　**b.** latitude.
   c. climate.　　**d.** season.

2. Temperatures range from warm or hot in summer to cool or cold in winter in
   a. polar zones.
   b. tropical zone.
   c. tundra climates.
   d. temperate zones.

3. A wet, warm climate zone on the edge of the tropics is
   a. humid subtropical.
   b. tundra.
   c. subarctic.
   d. continental climate.

4. A tropical grassland with scattered clumps of trees is a
   a. steppe.　　**b.** desert.
   c. savanna.　　**d.** rain forest.

5. The main cause of ozone depletion is
   a. global warming.
   b. chlorofluorocarbons.
   c. greenhouse gases.
   d. sunspots.

If the statement is true, write *true*. If it is false, change the underlined word or words to make the statement true.

6. The climate conditions that exist in a small area are its <u>microclimate</u>.

7. Rain or snow usually falls on the <u>leeward</u> side of a mountain range.

8. Permanently frozen soil is called <u>tundra</u>.

9. During <u>ice ages</u> large parts of Earth's surface are covered by glaciers.

10. Carbon dioxide is a <u>chlorofluorocarbon</u> that traps energy in the atmosphere.

Writing in Science

Expedition Plan Suppose that you are preparing to take a trip back in time to the last ice age. Write a list of the equipment you will need to bring with you and describe what the climate will be like.

Discovery CHANNEL SCHOOL™

Climate and Climate Change
Video Preview
Video Field Trip
▶ Video Assessment

Review and Assessment

Checking Concepts

11. Explain how distance from large bodies of water can affect the temperature of nearby land areas.

12. What are monsoons, and how do they affect climate in the regions where they occur?

13. What causes Earth's seasons?

14. How are "dry" climates defined? How do the two types of dry climate differ?

15. How does the movement of continents explain major changes in climate over time?

16. To be effective, why must agreements aimed at preventing or reducing ozone depletion be international?

Thinking Critically

17. Relating Cause and Effect Describe three ways in which water influences climate.

18. Relating Cause and Effect Why do parts of the United States have a semiarid climate while neighboring areas have a humid continental climate?

19. Reading Graphs Which month shown on the graph has the warmest average temperature? Which month is the wettest? What type of climate is indicated by the graph?

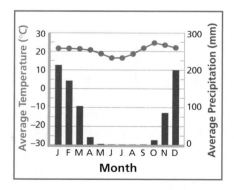

20. Inferring How is Earth's climate affected by major volcanic eruptions?

21. Comparing and Contrasting How is global warming different from earlier changes in Earth's climate?

Math Practice

22. Percentage Suppose a city receives an average of 35 cm of precipitation in November. If an average of 140 cm of precipitation falls there in a year, what percentage falls in November?

Applying Skills

Use the map of world temperature zones to answer Questions 23–26.

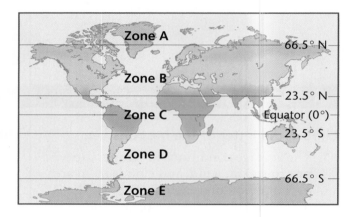

23. Interpreting Maps Name each of the five zones shown on the map.

24. Measuring What is the name of the temperature zone that includes the equator? How many degrees of latitude does this zone cover?

25. Interpreting Data Which of the five zones shown on the map has the greatest amount of land area suitable for people to live?

26. Drawing Conclusions Which zone has the highest average temperatures all year round? Explain why.

Lab zone Chapter **Project**

Performance Assessment Now share your project with your class. In your presentation, describe the patterns you found in your graphs. Then explain what you think causes different microclimates. After your presentation, think about how you could have improved your investigation.

End-of-Grade Test Practice

The graphs below show average monthly precipitation for two locations in Arizona. Use the information and your knowledge of science to answer questions 4–5.

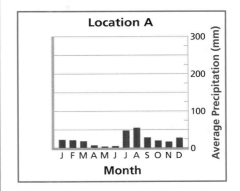

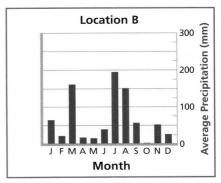

Choose the letter of the best answer.

1. Predict what type of climate would be the most likely in an area located in the interior of a large continent, on the east side of a major mountain range. Winds in the area commonly blow from west to east.

   A dry   **B** polar

   C temperate marine   **D** tropical rainy

2. What type of data would you need to collect to determine the climate of a particular area?

   A daily changes in the weather for the area

   B daily changes in temperature and air pressure for the area

   C long-term averages of temperature and precipitation for the area

   D long-term averages of air pressure and wind direction for the area

3. What is the major result at Earth's surface of ozone depletion in the stratosphere?

   A an increase in the amount of ultraviolet radiation reaching the surface

   B a decrease in the amount of ultraviolet radiation reaching the surface

   C an increase in global temperatures

   D a decrease in global temperatures

4. During which months do these locations receive the most precipitation?

   A January through March

   B April through June

   C July through September

   D October through December

5. Although they are only a few kilometers apart, Location B receives nearly three times as much precipitation as Location A. What is the best explanation for this fact?

   A Location B is in a rain shadow.

   B Location B is near a mountain top.

   C Location A is dried by prevailing winds.

   D Location A is much colder than Location B.

Constructed Response

6. Ice ages have occurred at several times during Earth's history. What is an ice age, and how does an ice age affect the land surface and the oceans?

Take a Deep Breath

Everyone needs clean air because it is important for good health. Clean air keeps organisms and their habitats thriving. Without it, the health of humans, the environment, and an area's economy may be at risk.

Is Air Pollution a Problem in North Carolina?

The federal government sets air quality standards that limit levels of air pollution. The good news is that North Carolina meets the federal standards for four air pollutants: nitrogen dioxide, sulfur dioxide, lead, and carbon monoxide. Unfortunately, there are several areas in North Carolina that do not meet the federal standards for ozone and fine solid particles. Some of the state's pollution problems are local and short-term, such as smoke particles from outdoor fires. Others, like ozone, are more widespread.

What Pollutes North Carolina's Air?

According to the Environmental Protection Agency (EPA), there are three main sources of hazardous air pollutants: mobile sources, point sources, and area sources. Mobile sources include cars, buses, trucks, lawn mowers, farm equipment, boats, trains, and airplanes. Point sources are facilities, such as industrial plants, that must report their emissions to the government. Area sources are sources that are too small to be required to report their emissions. Examples include small industrial facilities, residential wood burning, wildfires, gas stations, and waste disposal facilities. In North Carolina, area sources contribute the greatest percentage of emissions to the air.

Traffic Jam
An increase in traffic results in increasing ozone levels.

How Can People Help Reduce Air Pollution?

Today, most industries use technology to control emissions from factory smokestacks. People also can support strict automobile emission standards and clean-air regulations in order to improve air quality in their cities. Preventing forest fires and avoiding large-scale open burning will help reduce pollution, too.

Compare this vehicle to others in the FREE FUEL ECONOMY GUIDE available at the dealer.

CITY MPG

29

Fuel Economy Information

DOE EPA

HIGHWAY MPG

38

Actual Mileage will vary with options, driving conditions, driving habits and vehicle's condition. Results reprted to EPA indicate that the majority of vehicles with these estimates will achieve between

24 and 34 mpg in the city and between

32 and 44 mpg on the highway.

4-CYL., 1.8 LITER DISP., VVT-I, DOHC, SFI ENGINE. 4-SPEED ECT AUTOMATIC TRANSMISSION.

Estimated Annual Fuel Cost:

$655

For Comparison Shopping, all vehicles classified as

COMPACT have been issued mileage ratings ranging from

13 to 48 mpg city and

19 to 51 mpg highway.

see www.fueleconomy.gov

Fuel Economy
Choosing a car that is energy efficient and has low emissions helps to reduce air pollution.

Car Exhaust
The smoke coming out of this car contains fine solid particles, one of the categories of air pollutants.

What Do You Think?

1. Identify the Problem
Explain why you think North Carolina does or does not have an air quality problem.

2. Analyze the Options
Stewardship involves people taking responsibility for reducing their impact on the environment. What could people do to reduce their impact on air quality and show good stewardship?

3. Find a Solution
Write a letter to a state legislator about reducing air pollution. Tell which air pollution sources you feel future legislation should target and why.

Antarctica

On July 21, 1983, the temperature at the Russian research station Vostok dropped to a world record low of −89°C. Welcome to Antarctica!

Amundsen-Scott Station
This is one of the United States stations at the South Pole.

Because Antarctica is in the Southern Hemisphere, July is midwinter there. But the temperature isn't very warm in summer, either. The average summer temperature at Vostok is −33°C. Antarctica's climate is unusual in other ways. It's the windiest continent as well as the coldest. Even though Antarctica is covered with snow and ice, it's also the driest continent—a snowy desert. Less than five centimeters of precipitation falls in the interior in a year. Antarctic blizzards are terrifying, but they don't bring much new snow. They just blow drifts from one place to another.

Many countries have set up research stations in Antarctica to study climate, temperature, and the atmosphere. Scientists in Antarctica also research wildlife and geology.

Antarctica
The map shows major research stations established in Antarctica by countries around the world.

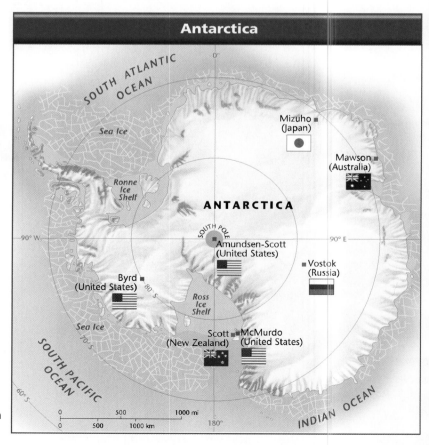

1912
Robert Falcon Scott (below center) and his men reached the South Pole, but lost the race.

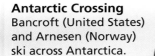

Antarctic Crossing
Bancroft (United States) and Arnesen (Norway) ski across Antarctica.

Race to the South Pole

Would you brave the darkness and cold of Antarctica? In the early 1900s, several famous explorers began a "race to the pole." Their attempts to reach the South Pole produced stories of heroism—and tragedy.

In October 1911, the British explorer Robert Scott traveled to the South Pole. He started overland with dog teams, motorized sleds, and ponies. He and four other explorers reached the South Pole in January 1912—only to find that a Norwegian expedition led by Roald Amundsen had beaten them there by a month! Scott's team had lost the race!

Soon after, Scott and his crew started back. But all of them died in a blizzard. Searchers later found their tent, Scott's diary, and photographs. Scott's team had been only 18 kilometers from a supply camp.

In 1914, Sir Ernest Shackleton was the hero of an incredible Antarctic survival story. On the way to the South Pole, ice trapped and crushed his ship. He and his men escaped to an island. Shackleton and a few others sailed in a small whaleboat to find help. Amazingly, everyone was rescued.

Other expeditions followed. In 1929, American explorer Richard E. Byrd led the first flight over the South Pole. More recently, in 2001, Ann Bancroft and Liv Arnesen became the first women to cross Antarctica.

Social Studies Activity

Create a timeline of important events in Antarctica. Find photos or draw sketches to illustrate the events. Include the following events:

- early expeditions
- "race to the pole" in the early 1900s
- International Geophysical Year
- Antarctic Treaty
- new research stations

Why did it take courage and endurance to try to reach the South Pole in the early 1900s?

Continent of Extremes

Why is Antarctica so cold? Its high latitude and months of darkness are important reasons. In addition, the broad expanses of white snow and icy glaciers reflect back sunlight before much heat is absorbed.

As on every continent, climates vary from place to place. Warmer parts of Antarctica are at lower elevations, at lower latitudes, or near the coast. Coastal areas are warmer because the nearby ocean moderates temperatures. These areas also have bare land, which absorbs heat.

Summer weather patterns in Antarctica are different from winter patterns. The short summer warm-up starts in October. The warmest temperatures are from mid-December to mid-January. Then temperatures drop suddenly. So by mid-March, the beginning of winter, the temperature has fallen to winter levels. Over the next six months Antarctica remains very cold—and dark.

Science Activity

Staying warm is essential for life in the Antarctic. Set up an experiment to test how well different materials keep heat from escaping. Use socks made of nylon, silk, cotton, and wool. You will need a jar for each material plus one jar as a control.

- Fill jars with equal amounts of very hot water. The water in each jar should be the same temperature.

- Record the temperature of each jar and screw each cap on.

- Place each jar, except the control, inside a sock. Refrigerate all the jars for 30 minutes.

- Remove the jars and record the water temperature of each.

Which jar cooled fastest? Which materials retained the heat best?

Cold-Weather Clothing

The secret to staying warm is to wear layers of clothing that keep body heat from escaping.

Inner Layer
An inner layer of long underwear carries moisture away from the skin.

Insulating Layer
A fluffy insulating layer, such as fleece or down, traps pockets of air that are warmed by body heat.

Outer Layer
The outer shell layer protects against wind and water. An insulated hood and a face mask protect against wind. Boots and gloves are layered, too. Fleece in boots may be sealed in by a waterproof rubber layer.

Protective Gear
Goggles, or sunglasses worn by this man in Antarctica, reduce the glare of sunlight and protect eyes from freezing.

Sky Watch

It's March 21—the beginning of winter—and you're watching the sun set very, very slowly. It takes 30 hours—more than a day—for the sun to disappear below the horizon. Once it's gone, you won't see sunshine again until September! April and early May aren't completely dark, but there is hardly enough light to cast a shadow. Then it's dark for two months. In August, light begins again. The sky brightens quickly until the polar sunrise.

The tilt of Earth on its axis affects the hours of daylight and darkness from season to season. At the poles, midsummer brings the "midnight sun," which circles around the sky but does not set. Midwinter brings almost total darkness.

Anvers Island in Antarctica

Math Activity

The table (right) shows hours of daylight on the 15th of each month. It shows readings at two different Antarctic locations—the Amundsen-Scott station and Japan's Mizuho station.

Use the table to make a graph that shows hours of daylight for the Mizuho station and the Amundsen-Scott station.

- On the horizontal axis of the graph, list the months.

- On the vertical axis, mark off spaces for 0 to 24 hours.

- Choose a different color marker for each latitude. Above the month for each location, place a colored dot at the correct hour mark. Connect the dots to show changes in daylight at each place during a year.

- How are the changes in darkness and daylight in Antarctica like those you see at home? How are they different?

Hours of Daylight in Antarctica*

Month	Mizuho Station 70° S	Amundsen-Scott Station 90° S
January	24	24
February	18	24
March	14	24
April	9	0
May	3	0
June	0	0
July	0	0
August	7	0
September	11	0
October	16	24
November	22	24
December	24	24

*Sunrise to sunset, rounded to nearest hour

Alone in Antarctica

Admiral Richard Byrd worked in the Antarctic for nearly 30 years after his flight over the South Pole. He led several expeditions and set up research stations at Little America. Byrd's book *Alone* is based on the journal he kept while spending the winter of 1934 alone at a weather station outpost. During his four-and-a-half-month stay, Byrd nearly gave up mentally and physically. He endured, however, and kept up his weather research until help arrived in August.

In this memoir of his days in early April, 1934, Byrd describes some of the problems of working in the intense cold.

Admiral Byrd
In his small shack at Little America, Byrd tries to keep warm.

At times I felt as if I were the last survivor of an Ice Age, striving to hold on with the flimsy tools bequeathed by an easy-going, temperate world. Cold does queer things. At 50° Fahrenheit below zero a flashlight dies out in your hand. At −55° Fahrenheit kerosene will freeze, and the flame will dry up on the wick.

At −60° Fahrenheit rubber turns brittle. One day, I remember, the antenna wire snapped in my hands when I tried to bend it to make a new connection. Below −60° Fahrenheit cold will find the last microscopic touch of oil in an instrument and stop it dead. If there is the slightest breeze, you can hear your breath freeze as it floats away, making a sound like that of Chinese firecrackers. . . . And if you work too hard and breathe too deeply, your lungs will sometimes feel as if they were on fire.

Cold—even April's relatively moderate cold—gave me plenty to think about. . . . Two cases of tomato juice shattered their bottles. Whenever I brought canned food inside the shack I had to let it stand all day near the stove to thaw. . . . Frost was forever collecting on the electrical contact points of the wind vane and wind cups. Some days I climbed the twelve-foot anemometer pole two and three times to clean them. It was a bitter job, especially on blustery nights. With my legs twined around the slender pole, my arms flung over the cleats, and my free hands trying to scrape the contact point clean with a knife and at the same time hold a flashlight to see, I qualified for the world's coldest flagpole sitter. I seldom came down from that pole without a frozen finger, toe, nose, or cheek.

The shack was always freezingly cold in the morning. I slept with the door open [for ventilation]. When I arose the inside temperature (depending upon the surface weather) might be anywhere from 10° to 40° Fahrenheit below zero. Frost coated the sleeping bag where my breath had condensed during the night; my socks and boots, when I picked them up, were so stiff with frozen sweat that I first had to work them between my hands. A pair of silk gloves hung from a nail over the bunk, where I could grab them the first thing. Yet, even with their protection, my fingers would sting and burn from the touch of the lamp and stove as I lighted them.

From this passage, what can you conclude about Byrd's attitude toward his research? Although you've probably never traveled to Antarctica, you may have had an outdoor adventure—at summer camp or even in a city park.

Use descriptive writing to recapture that experience. Remember to include concrete, sensory details like those in Byrd's journal. If you prefer, write about an imaginary event or adventure in the outdoors.

Port Lockroy in Antarctica

Tie It Together

Plan a Cool Expedition

You're on your way to Antarctica! Good planning is the key to a successful expedition. Work in small groups to plan your expedition. When your group has finished planning, meet with your class to present your program.

Consider these questions and issues in making your plan:

- What research will you do—weather, wildlife, geology, or another topic?
- Where will you work? Will you work near the coast? Will you join an existing research station?
- Will you travel? Plot your travel course and location on a map of Antarctica.
- How long do you plan to stay?

- What equipment will you take— climbing gear to cross glaciers, boats and kayaks, tents for camping?
- What clothing will you need? Check the illustration of protective clothing.
- What supplies will you take? Plan the kinds and amounts of food that you will take.

Cold-Weather Clothing
How are these young people staying warm?

Chapter

6

Plants

Standard Course of Study

This chapter addresses the following North Carolina Objectives:

1.02 Develop appropriate experimental procedures.

1.03 Apply safety procedures.

1.04 Analyze variables.

1.05 Analyze evidence.

1.06 Use mathematics to gather, organize, and present data.

1.08 Use oral and written language.

1.09 Use technologies and information systems.

2.01 Explore definitions of "technology."

2.02 Use information systems.

2.03 Evaluate technological designs.

2.04 Apply tenets of technological design.

Ferns and other plants grow along a woodland stream. ▶

Lab zone™ Chapter **Project**

Design and Build an Interactive Exhibit

Cotton, medicines, and paper are just some of the products that come from plants. Which plants are the sources of these products, and how are the products made? In this project, you will build an exhibit to teach young children how a plant becomes a useful product.

Your Goal To build an interactive exhibit showing how a particular plant is transformed into a useful product

To complete this project successfully, you must

- choose one plant product and research where it comes from
- design an interactive exhibit that shows how the product is made
- build your exhibit and ask some children to critique it
- use the children's feedback to redesign your exhibit
- follow the safety guidelines in Appendix A

Plan It! Think of a creative way to teach children about the plant product you chose. Then sketch out your exhibit design and obtain your teacher's approval to build it. Also, identify a few children who can provide you with useful feedback.

The Plant Kingdom

Reading Preview

Key Concepts
- What characteristics do all plants share?
- What do plants need to live successfully on land?
- How do nonvascular plants and vascular plants differ?
- What are the different stages of a plant's life cycle?

Key Terms
- photosynthesis • tissue
- chloroplast • vacuole
- cuticle • vascular tissue
- fertilization • zygote
- nonvascular plant
- vascular plant • chlorophyll
- sporophyte • gametophyte

Target Reading Skill
Building Vocabulary A definition states the meaning of a word or phrase by telling about its most important feature or function. After you read the section, reread the paragraphs that contain definitions of Key Terms. Use all the information you have learned to write a definition of each Key Term in your own words.

Lab zone Discover Activity

What Do Leaves Reveal About Plants?

1. Your teacher will give you two leaves from plants that grow in two very different environments: a desert and an area with average rainfall.
2. Carefully observe the color, size, shape, and texture of the leaves. Touch the surfaces of each leaf. Examine each leaf with a hand lens. Record your observations in your notebook.
3. When you have finished, wash your hands thoroughly with soap and water.

Think It Over
Inferring Use your observations to determine which plant lives in the desert and which does not. Give at least one reason to support your inference.

There are some very strange plants in the world. There are plants that trap animals, plants that bloom only once every thirty years, and plants with flowers that smell like rotting meat. You probably don't see such unusual plants every day. But you probably do see plants every day. You encounter plants whenever you see moss on a tree trunk, run across a lawn, or pick ripe tomatoes from a garden. And all plants, both the unfamiliar and the familiar, have a lot in common.

What Is a Plant?

Members of the plant kingdom share several characteristics. **Nearly all plants are autotrophs, organisms that produce their own food. All plants are eukaryotes that contain many cells. In addition, all plant cells are surrounded by cell walls.**

Plants Are Autotrophs You can think of a typical plant as a sun-powered, food-making factory. Sunlight provides the energy for this food-making process, called **photosynthesis.** During photosynthesis, a plant uses carbon dioxide gas and water to make food and oxygen. You will learn more about photosynthesis in Section 2.

Plants Are Multicellular You don't need a microscope to see plants because they are multi-cellular. Plants vary greatly in size, of course. Both the tiniest moss and the tallest redwood tree are plants.

No matter how large or small a plant is, its cells are organized into **tissues**—groups of similar cells that perform a specific function in an organism. For example, most plants that live on land have tissues that transport materials throughout their bodies.

Plant Cells If you were to look at a plant's cells under a microscope, you would see that plants are eukaryotes. But unlike the cells of some other eukaryotes, a plant's cells are enclosed by a cell wall. The cell wall surrounds the cell membrane and separates the cell from the environment. Plant cell walls contain cellulose, a material that makes the walls rigid. Cell walls are what makes apples and carrots crunchy. Because their cell walls are rigid, plant cells look like small boxes.

Plant cells also contain many other structures, as shown in Figure 1. **Chloroplasts** (KLAWR uh plasts), which look something like green jelly beans, are the structures in which food is made. The Greek word *chloro* means "green." A **vacuole** is a large storage sac that can expand and shrink like a balloon. The vacuole stores many substances, including water, wastes, and food. A plant wilts when too much water has left its vacuoles.

Chloroplast

Nucleus

Cell wall

Vacuole

Cell membrane

▲ Single plant cell

FIGURE 1
Plant Cell Structures
Like all plants, this maple tree is multicellular. Plants have eukaryotic cells that are enclosed by a cell wall. **Relating Diagrams and Photos** *Which cell structures can you see in the inset photograph of plant cells?*

 **Reading Checkpoint** What is the function of the vacuole in a plant cell?

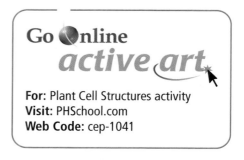

Go Online
active.art

For: Plant Cell Structures activity
Visit: PHSchool.com
Web Code: cep-1041

Adaptations for Living on Land

Most plants live on land. How is living on land different from living in water? Imagine multicellular algae floating in the ocean. The algae obtain water and other materials directly from the water around them. Their bodies are held up toward the sunlight by the water. The water also aids in reproduction, allowing sperm cells to swim to egg cells.

Now imagine plants living on land. What adaptations would help them meet their needs without water all around them? **For plants to survive on land, they must have ways to obtain water and other nutrients from their surroundings, retain water, transport materials in their bodies, support their bodies, and reproduce.**

Obtaining Water and Other Nutrients Recall that all organisms need water to survive. Obtaining water is easy for algae because water surrounds them. To live on land, though, plants need adaptations for obtaining water from the soil. Plants must also have ways of obtaining other nutrients from the soil.

Retaining Water Plants must have ways of holding onto the water they obtain. Otherwise, they could easily dry out due to evaporation. When there is more water in plant cells than in the air, the water leaves the plant and enters the air. One adaptation that helps a plant reduce water loss is a waxy, waterproof layer called the **cuticle** that covers the leaves of most plants.

FIGURE 2
Retaining Water
Plants have adaptations that help them retain water. The shiny, waterproof cuticle on this leaf slows down evaporation.

Math | Analyzing Data

Water Loss in Plants

The graph shows how much water a certain plant loses during the hours shown.

1. **Reading Graphs** What variable is plotted along each axis?

2. **Interpreting Data** According to the graph, during what part of the day did the plant lose the most water? The least water?

3. **Drawing Conclusions** What could account for the pattern of water loss shown?

4. **Predicting** How would you expect the graph to look from 10 P.M. to 8 A.M.? Explain your reasoning.

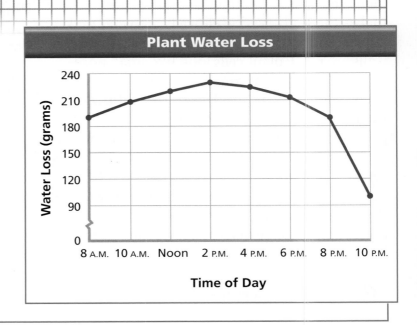

Plant Water Loss
Water Loss (grams) vs. Time of Day

FIGURE 3
Transport and Support
For this tall coconut palm to survive, it must transport water, minerals, and food over long distances. It must also support its body so its leaves are exposed to sunlight.
Relating Cause and Effect *What structures allow plants to transport materials?*

Water and minerals

Food

Transporting Materials A plant needs to transport water, minerals, food, and other materials from one part of its body to another. In general, water and minerals are taken up by the bottom part of the plant, while food is made in the top part. But all of the plant's cells need water, minerals, and food.

In small plants, materials can simply move from one cell to the next. But larger plants need a more efficient way to transport materials farther, from one part of the plant to another. These plants have transporting tissue called vascular tissue. **Vascular tissue** is a system of tubelike structures inside a plant through which water, minerals, and food move.

Support A plant on land must support its own body. Support is not an issue for small plants that grow low to the ground. But for larger plants to survive, the plant's food-making parts must be exposed to as much sunlight as possible. Rigid cell walls and vascular tissue strengthen and support the large bodies of these plants.

Reproduction All plants undergo sexual reproduction that involves fertilization. **Fertilization** occurs when a sperm cell unites with an egg cell. The fertilized egg is called a **zygote.** For algae and some plants, fertilization can only occur if there is water in the environment. This is because the sperm cells of these plants swim through the water to the egg cells. Other plants, however, have an adaptation that makes it possible for fertilization to occur in dry environments. You will learn more about this adaptation in Section 2.

 Reading Checkpoint **Why do plants need adaptations to prevent water loss?**

FIGURE 4
Plant Classification

The hundreds of thousands of plants that exist today can be classified as either nonvascular plants or vascular plants. Nonvascular plants are small and live in moist environments. Vascular plants can grow tall and live in diverse habitats. *Classifying What are the three groups of vascular plants?*

Nonvascular Plants

Nonvascular plants do not have true vascular tissue for support or transport. They grow low to the ground.

◀ Mosses grow in damp, shady places.

Liverworts grow on moist soil and rocks. ▶

DISCOVERY
CHANNEL
SCHOOL™

Introduction to Plants

Video Preview
▶ Video Field Trip
Video Assessment

Classification of Plants

Scientists informally group plants into two major groups—nonvascular plants and vascular plants.

Nonvascular Plants Plants that lack a well-developed system of tubes for transporting water and other materials are known as **nonvascular plants.** Nonvascular plants are low-growing and do not have roots for absorbing water from the ground. Instead, they obtain water and materials directly from their surroundings. The materials then simply pass from one cell to the next. This means that materials do not travel very far or very quickly. This slow method of transport helps explain why most nonvascular plants live in damp, shady places.

Most nonvascular plants have only thin cell walls to provide support. This is one reason why these plants cannot grow more than a few centimeters tall.

Vascular Plants Plants with true vascular tissue are called **vascular plants.** Vascular plants are better suited to life in dry areas than are nonvascular plants. Their well-developed vascular tissue solves the problem of transport, moving materials quickly and efficiently throughout the plant's body.

Vascular tissue also provides strength, stability, and support to a plant. Thus, vascular plants are able to grow quite tall.

Vascular Plants

Seedless Vascular Plants

Seedless vascular plants reproduce by making spores.

◄ The staghorn fern produces spores at the tips of its antler-shaped leaves. This fern clings to the bark of trees in tropical areas.

Gymnosperms

Gymnosperms are vascular plants that reproduce by seeds. They do not form flowers or fruits.

◄ Ginkgo trees produce fleshy seeds that resemble fruits but are not. The seeds smell like vomit!

▲ The bristlecone pine can live for more than 4,000 years.

Angiosperms

Angiosperms are vascular plants that flower, and produce seeds that are surrounded by fruit.

The beavertail cactus produces brilliantly colored flowers. ▼

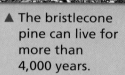

Wheat has been an important food crop for thousands of years. The grains, or fruits, are ground to make flour. ►

Rock containing two plant fossils ▶

Origin of Plants Which organisms were the ancestors of today's plants? In search of answers, biologists studied fossils, the traces of ancient life forms preserved in rock and other substances. The oldest plant fossils are about 400 million years old. The fossils show that even at that early date, plants already had many adaptations for life on land, including vascular tissue.

Better clues to the origin of plants came from comparing the chemicals in modern plants to those in other organisms. In particular, biologists studied a green pigment called **chlorophyll** (KLAWR uh fil), found in the chloroplasts of plants, algae, and some bacteria. Land plants and green algae contain the same forms of chlorophyll. This evidence led biologists to infer that ancient green algae were the ancestors of today's land plants. Further comparisons of genetic material clearly showed that plants and green algae are very closely related. In fact, some scientists think that green algae should be classified in the plant kingdom.

 **Reading Checkpoint** What is chlorophyll?

Complex Life Cycles

Plants have complex life cycles that include two different stages, the sporophyte stage and the gametophyte stage. In the **sporophyte** (SPOH ruh fyt) stage, the plant produces spores, tiny cells that can grow into new organisms. A spore develops into the plant's other stage, called the gametophyte. In the **gametophyte** (guh MEE tuh fyt) stage, the plant produces two kinds of sex cells: sperm cells and egg cells.

Figure 6 shows a typical plant life cycle. A sperm cell and egg cell join to form a zygote. The zygote then develops into a sporophyte. The sporophyte produces spores, which develop into the gametophyte. Then the gametophyte produces sperm cells and egg cells, and the cycle starts again. The sporophyte of a plant usually looks quite different from the gametophyte.

 **Reading Checkpoint** During which stage does a plant produce spores?

FIGURE 5
Ancient and Modern Plants
Fossils of ancient plants help scientists understand the origin of plants. These fossils are of two plants that lived about 300 million years ago. Notice the similarities between the fossils and modern-day ferns and horsetails.

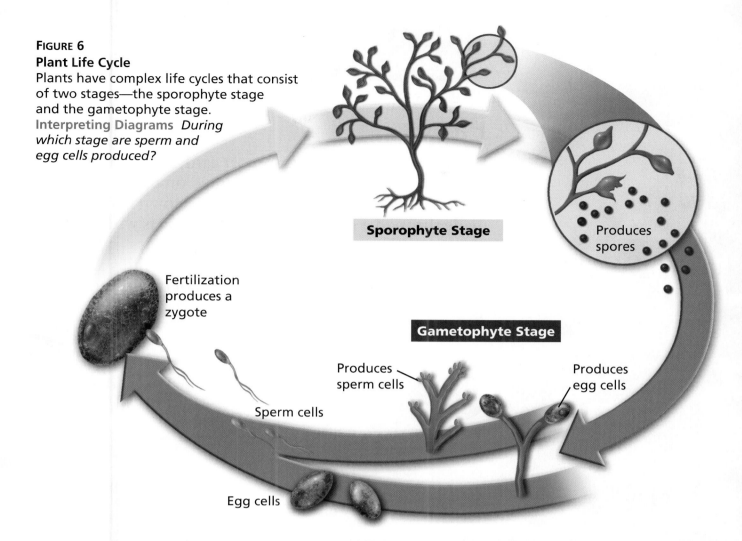

FIGURE 6
Plant Life Cycle
Plants have complex life cycles that consist of two stages—the sporophyte stage and the gametophyte stage.
Interpreting Diagrams During which stage are sperm and egg cells produced?

Sporophyte Stage

Produces spores

Fertilization produces a zygote

Gametophyte Stage

Produces sperm cells

Produces egg cells

Sperm cells

Egg cells

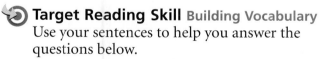

Section 1 Assessment

Target Reading Skill Building Vocabulary
Use your sentences to help you answer the questions below.

Reviewing Key Concepts

1. a. Listing List three characteristics of plants.
  b. Comparing and Contrasting Describe three ways that plant cells differ from the cells of some other eukaryotes.
  c. Predicting How might a plant cell be affected if it lacked chloroplasts?
2. a. Identifying What are five adaptations that plants need to survive on land?
  b. Inferring Why is a cuticle a useful adaptation in plants but not in algae?
3. a. Reviewing How do vascular plants differ from nonvascular plants?

  b. Explaining Explain why vascular plants are better suited to life in dry areas.
  c. Classifying Would you expect a tall desert plant to be a vascular plant? Explain.
4. a. Describing What are the two major stages of a plant's life cycle?
  b. Sequencing Describe in order the major events in the life cycle of a plant, starting with a zygote.

Writing in Science

Video Script You are narrating a video called *Living on Land*, which is written from the perspective of a plant. Write a one-page script for your narration. Be sure to discuss the challenges that life on land poses for plants and how they meet their needs.

Paper

What do a dollar bill, your report card, and a comic book have in common? They are all printed on paper, of course! But where does paper come from? As shown here, paper is made through a process that typically starts with wood from trees. The papermaking process was first invented in China about 2,000 years ago. Today, paper mills around the world rely on powerful machines to produce huge quantities of paper.

1 **Trees are grown and harvested.**
Paper is produced mostly from trees that are grown for this specific purpose.

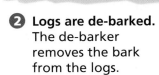

2 **Logs are de-barked.**
The de-barker removes the bark from the logs.

3 **Wood chips are made.**
The chipper chops the wood into small pieces.

4 **Pulp is formed.**
Heat and chemicals break down the chips into fibers called pulp.

The Benefits of Paper

Paper benefits society in so many ways. Many everyday items are made out of paper—tissues, paper cups, and cardboard packaging. Perhaps most important, paper is used as a portable, inexpensive way to print words and images. Throughout time, paper has allowed people to express their thoughts, record history, and share knowledge. In addition, the paper industry employs many people, and generates income for the economy.

Paper and the Environment

Paper has negative impacts on the environment. Each step in the papermaking process requires energy and produces wastes. Some of these wastes, such as dioxins, are toxic. Dioxins form when water is used to flush chemicals from the paper. Paper products also make up a lot of the garbage in landfills. Because of the environmental costs, engineers are working to create a new type of "paper" called electronic paper, or e-paper. Someday soon, you might use flexible, ultra-thin, digital screens instead of paper.

Weigh the Impact

1. Identify the Need
How does society rely on paper? How would your life be different if paper had never been invented?

2. Research
Use the Internet to investigate e-paper, a new technology that may replace traditional paper. List some potential uses of e-paper.

3. Write
Write a paragraph or two comparing e-paper and regular paper. Be sure to include the pros and cons of both technologies based on your research.

Go Online
PHSchool.com

For: More on paper
Visit: PHSchool.com
Web Code: ceh-1040

❺ Water is added.
Water is added to the pulp to form slush. The slush is then sprayed onto wide screens. The water begins to drain off.

❻ Water is removed.
The paper is squeezed through several presses to remove the excess water.

❼ Paper is dried.
Heated rollers dry the paper, making it flat and smooth.

The Characteristics of Seed Plants

Reading Preview

Key Concepts
- What characteristics do seed plants share?
- How do seeds become new plants?
- What are the main functions of roots, stems, and leaves?

Key Terms
- phloem • xylem • pollen
- seed • embryo • cotyledon
- germination • root cap
- cambium • stomata
- transpiration

Target Reading Skill
Outlining As you read, make an outline about seed plants that you can use for review. Use the red headings for the main ideas and the blue headings for the supporting ideas.

The Characteristics of Seed Plants
I. What is a seed plant?
A. Vascular tissue
B.
II. How seeds become new plants
A.
B.

Lab zone Discover **Activity**

Which Plant Part Is It?

1. With a partner, carefully observe the items of food your teacher gives you.
2. Make a list of the food items.
3. For each food item, write the name of the plant part—root, stem, or leaf— from which you think it is obtained.

Think It Over

Classifying Classify the items into groups depending on the plant part from which the food is obtained. Compare your groupings with those of your classmates.

Have you ever planted seeds in a garden? If so, then you may remember how it seemed to take forever before those first green shoots emerged. Shortly afterwards, you saw one set of leaves, and then others. Then a flower may have appeared. Did you wonder where all those plant parts came from? How did they develop from one small seed? Read on to find out.

What Is a Seed Plant?

The plant growing in your garden was a seed plant. So are most of the other plants around you. In fact, seed plants outnumber seedless plants by more than ten to one. You eat many seed plants—rice, peas, and squash, for example. You wear clothes made from seed plants, such as cotton and flax. You may live in a home built from seed plants—oak, pine, or maple trees. In addition, seed plants produce much of the oxygen you breathe.

Seed plants share two important characteristics. They have vascular tissue, and they use pollen and seeds to reproduce. In addition, all seed plants have body plans that include roots, stems, and leaves. Like seedless plants, seed plants have complex life cycles that include the sporophyte and the gametophyte stages. In seed plants, the plants that you see are the sporophytes. The gametophytes are microscopic.

Vascular Tissue Most seed plants live on land. Land plants face many challenges, including standing upright and supplying all their cells with food and water. Like ferns, seed plants meet these two challenges with vascular tissue. The thick walls of the cells in the vascular tissue help support the plants. In addition, food, water, and nutrients are transported throughout the plants in vascular tissue.

There are two types of vascular tissue. **Phloem** (FLOH um) is the vascular tissue through which food moves. When food is made in the leaves, it enters the phloem and travels to other parts of the plant. Water and minerals, on the other hand, travel in the vascular tissue called **xylem** (ZY lum). The roots absorb water and minerals from the soil. These materials enter the root's xylem and move upward into the stems and leaves.

Pollen and Seeds Unlike seedless plants, seed plants can live in a wide variety of environments. Recall that seedless plants need water in their surroundings for fertilization to occur. Seed plants do not need water for sperm to swim to the eggs. Instead, seed plants produce **pollen,** tiny structures that contain the cells that will later become sperm cells. Pollen delivers sperm cells directly near the eggs. After sperm cells fertilize the eggs, seeds develop. A **seed** is a structure that contains a young plant inside a protective covering. Seeds protect the young plant from drying out.

 **Reading Checkpoint** What material travels in phloem? What materials travel in xylem?

FIGURE 7
Harvesting Wild Rice
Like all seed plants, wild rice plants have vascular tissue and use seeds to reproduce. The seeds develop in shallow bodies of water, and the plants grow up above the water's surface. These men are harvesting the mature rice grains.

FIGURE 8
Seed Structure
The structures of three different seeds are shown here.
Inferring How is the stored food used?

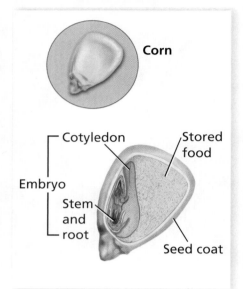

Corn

Cotyledon
Stored food
Embryo
Stem and root
Seed coat

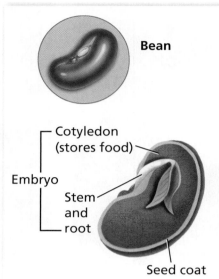

Bean

Cotyledon (stores food)
Embryo
Stem and root
Seed coat

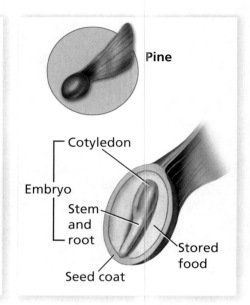

Pine

Cotyledon
Embryo
Stem and root
Seed coat
Stored food

Lab zone Try This Activity

The In-Seed Story

1. Your teacher will give you a hand lens and two different seeds that have been soaked in water.

2. Carefully observe the outside of each seed. Draw what you see.

3. Gently remove the coverings of the seeds. Then carefully separate the parts of each seed. Use a hand lens to examine the inside of each seed. Draw what you see.

Observing Based on your observations, label the parts of each seed. Then describe the function of each part next to its label.

How Seeds Become New Plants

All seeds share important similarities. **Inside a seed is a partially developed plant. If a seed lands in an area where conditions are favorable, the plant sprouts out of the seed and begins to grow.**

Seed Structure A seed has three main parts—an embryo, stored food, and a seed coat. The young plant that develops from the zygote, or fertilized egg, is called the **embryo.** The embryo already has the beginnings of roots, stems, and leaves. In the seeds of most plants, the embryo stops growing when it is quite small. When the embryo begins to grow again, it uses the food stored in the seed until it can make its own food by photosynthesis. In all seeds, the embryo has one or more seed leaves, or **cotyledons** (kaht uh LEED unz). In some seeds, food is stored in the cotyledons. In others, food is stored outside the embryo. Figure 8 compares the structure of corn, bean, and pine seeds.

The outer covering of a seed is called the seed coat. Some familiar seed coats are the "skins" on lima beans and peanuts. The seed coat acts like plastic wrap, protecting the embryo and its food from drying out. This allows a seed to remain inactive for a long time. In many plants, the seeds are surrounded by a structure called a fruit, which you will learn more about in Section 4.

Seed Dispersal After seeds have formed, they are usually scattered, sometimes far from where they were produced. The scattering of seeds is called seed dispersal. Seeds are dispersed in many ways. One method involves other organisms. For example, some animals eat fruits, such as cherries or grapes. The seeds inside the fruits pass through the animal's digestive system and are deposited in new areas. Other seeds are enclosed in barblike structures that hook onto an animal's fur or a person's clothes. The structures then fall off the fur or clothes in a new area.

A second means of dispersal is water. Water can disperse seeds that fall into oceans and rivers. A third dispersal method involves wind. Wind disperses lightweight seeds that often have structures to catch the wind, such as those of dandelions and maple trees. Finally, some plants eject their seeds in a way that might remind you of popping popcorn. The force scatters the seeds in many directions.

FIGURE 9
Seed Dispersal
The seeds of these plants are enclosed in fruits with adaptations that help them disperse.

Dispersal by wind: Dandelion fruits with "parachutes" ▶

◀ **Dispersal by animals:** Barblike fruits

Dispersal by water: Floating coconut palm fruit ▶

Germination After a seed is dispersed, it may remain inactive for a while before it germinates. **Germination** (jur muh NAY shun) occurs when the embryo begins to grow again and pushes out of the seed. Germination begins when the seed absorbs water from the environment. Then the embryo uses its stored food to begin to grow. As shown in Figure 10, the embryo's roots first grow downward; then its stem and leaves grow upward. Once you can see a plant's leaves, the plant is called a seedling.

A seed that is dispersed far from its parent plant has a better chance of survival. When a seed does not have to compete with its parent for light, water, and nutrients, it has a better chance of becoming a seedling.

 **Reading Checkpoint** What must happen in order for germination to begin?

Roots

Have you ever tried to pull a dandelion out of the soil? It's not easy, is it? That is because most roots are good anchors. Roots have three main functions. **Roots anchor a plant in the ground, absorb water and minerals from the soil, and sometimes store food.** The more root area a plant has, the more water and minerals it can absorb.

Types of Roots The two main types of root systems are shown in Figure 11. A fibrous root system consists of many similarly sized roots that form a dense, tangled mass. Plants with fibrous roots take much soil with them when you pull them out of the ground. Lawn grass, corn, and onions have fibrous root systems. In contrast, a taproot system has one long, thick main root. Many smaller roots branch off the main root. A plant with a taproot system is hard to pull out of the ground. Carrots, dandelions, and cacti have taproots.

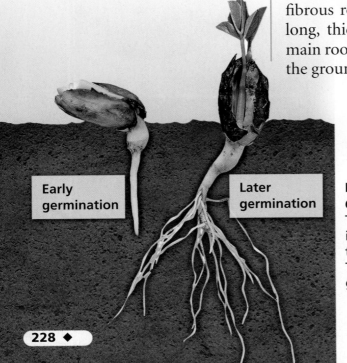

Early germination

Later germination

FIGURE 10
Germination
The embryo in this peanut seed uses its stored food to germinate. First, the embryo's roots grow downward. Then, its stem and leaves begin to grow upward.

The Structure of a Root In Figure 11, you can see the structure of a typical root. Notice that the tip of the root is rounded and is covered by a structure called the root cap. The **root cap** protects the root from injury from rocks as the root grows through the soil. Behind the root cap are the cells that divide to form new root cells.

Root hairs grow out of the root's surface. These tiny hairs can enter the spaces between soil particles, where they absorb water and minerals. By increasing the surface area of the root that touches the soil, root hairs help the plant absorb large amounts of substances. The root hairs also help to anchor the plant in the soil.

Locate the vascular tissue in the center of the root. The water and nutrients that are absorbed from the soil quickly move into the xylem. From there, these substances are transported upward to the plant's stems and leaves.

Phloem transports food manufactured in the leaves to the root. The root tissues may then use the food for growth or store it for future use by the plant.

Reading Checkpoint What is a root cap?

FIGURE 11
Root Structure

Some plants have fibrous roots while others have taproots. A root's structure is adapted for absorbing water and minerals from the soil. *Relating Cause and Effect How do root hairs help absorb water and minerals?*

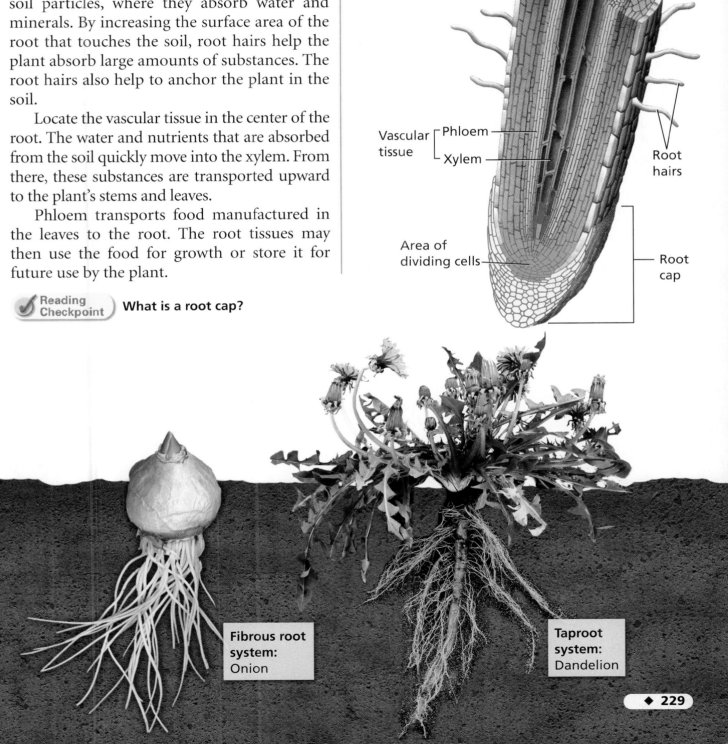

Surface cells

Vascular tissue — Phloem — Xylem

Root hairs

Area of dividing cells

Root cap

Fibrous root system: Onion

Taproot system: Dandelion

Calculating

In this activity, you will calculate the speed at which water moves up a celery stalk.

1. Pour about 1 cm of water into a tall plastic container. Stir in several drops of red food coloring.
2. Place the freshly cut end of a celery stalk in the water. Lean the stalk against the container's side.
3. After 20 minutes, remove the celery. Use a metric ruler to measure the height of the water in the stalk.
4. Use the measurement and the following formula to calculate how fast the water moved up the stalk.

$$\text{Speed} = \frac{\text{Height}}{\text{Time}}$$

Based on your calculation, predict how far the water would move in 2 hours. Then test your prediction.

Stems

The stem of a plant has two main functions. **The stem carries substances between the plant's roots and leaves. The stem also provides support for the plant and holds up the leaves so they are exposed to the sun.** In addition, some stems, such as those of asparagus, store food.

The Structure of a Stem Stems can be either herbaceous (hur BAY shus) or woody. Herbaceous stems contain no wood and are often soft. Coneflowers and pepper plants have herbaceous stems. In contrast, woody stems are hard and rigid. Maple trees and roses have woody stems.

Both herbaceous and woody stems consist of phloem and xylem tissue as well as many other supporting cells. Figure 12 shows the inner structure of one type of herbaceous stem.

As you can see in Figure 13, a woody stem contains several layers of tissue. The outermost layer is bark. Bark includes an outer protective layer and an inner layer of living phloem, which transports food through the stem. Next is a layer of cells called the **cambium** (KAM bee um), which divide to produce new phloem and xylem. It is xylem that makes up most of what you call "wood." Sapwood is active xylem that transports water and minerals through the stem. The older, darker, heartwood is inactive but provides support.

✓ **Reading Checkpoint** What function does the bark of a woody stem perform?

FIGURE 12
A Herbaceous Stem

Herbaceous stems, like those on these coneflowers, are often soft. The inset shows the inner structure of one type of herbaceous stem.

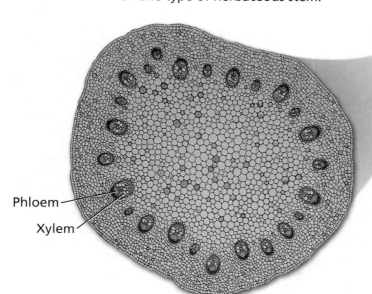

Phloem
Xylem

Annual Rings Have you ever looked at a tree stump and seen a pattern of circles that looks something like a target? These circles are called annual rings because they represent a tree's yearly growth. Annual rings are made of xylem. Xylem cells that form in the spring are large and have thin walls because they grow rapidly. They produce a wide, light brown ring. Xylem cells that form in the summer grow slowly and, therefore, are small and have thick walls. They produce a thin, dark ring. One pair of light and dark rings represents one year's growth. You can estimate a tree's age by counting its annual rings.

The width of a tree's annual rings can provide important clues about past weather conditions, such as rainfall. In rainy years, more xylem is produced, so the tree's annual rings are wide. In dry years, rings are narrow. By examining annual rings from some trees in the southwestern United States, scientists were able to infer that severe droughts occurred in the years 840, 1067, 1379, and 1632.

FIGURE 13
A Woody Stem
Trees like these maples have woody stems. A typical woody stem is made up of many layers. The layers of xylem form annual rings that can reveal the age of the tree and the growing conditions it has experienced.
Interpreting Diagrams *Where is the cambium located?*

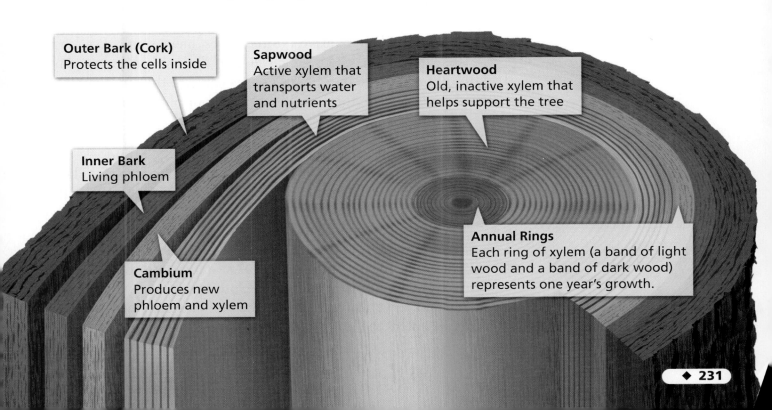

Outer Bark (Cork)
Protects the cells inside

Sapwood
Active xylem that transports water and nutrients

Heartwood
Old, inactive xylem that helps support the tree

Inner Bark
Living phloem

Cambium
Produces new phloem and xylem

Annual Rings
Each ring of xylem (a band of light wood and a band of dark wood) represents one year's growth.

FIGURE 14
The Structure of a Leaf

A leaf is a well-adapted food factory. Each structure helps the leaf produce food.

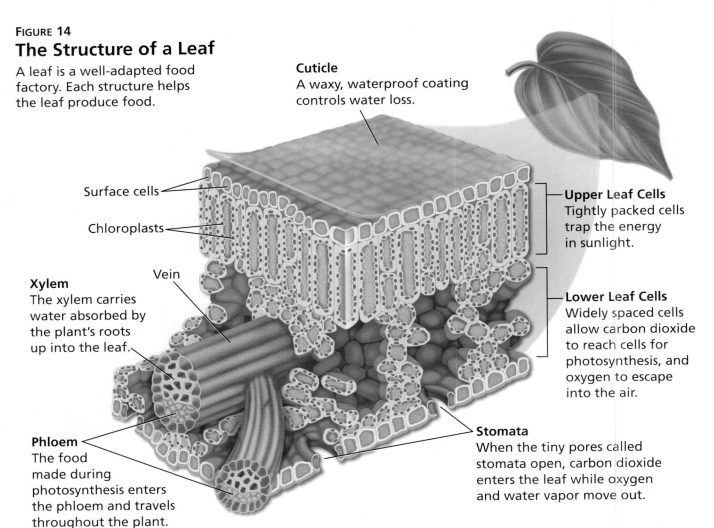

Cuticle
A waxy, waterproof coating controls water loss.

Surface cells

Chloroplasts

Upper Leaf Cells
Tightly packed cells trap the energy in sunlight.

Lower Leaf Cells
Widely spaced cells allow carbon dioxide to reach cells for photosynthesis, and oxygen to escape into the air.

Xylem
The xylem carries water absorbed by the plant's roots up into the leaf.

Vein

Phloem
The food made during photosynthesis enters the phloem and travels throughout the plant.

Stomata
When the tiny pores called stomata open, carbon dioxide enters the leaf while oxygen and water vapor move out.

Leaves

Leaves vary greatly in size and shape. Pine trees, for example, have needle-shaped leaves. Birch trees have small rounded leaves with jagged edges. Regardless of their shape, leaves play an important role in a plant. **Leaves capture the sun's energy and carry out the food-making process of photosynthesis.**

The Structure of a Leaf If you were to cut through a leaf and look at the edge under a microscope, you would see the structures in Figure 14. The leaf's top and bottom surface layers protect the cells inside. Between the layers of cells are veins that contain xylem and phloem.

The surface layers of the leaf have small openings, or pores, called **stomata** (STOH muh tuh) (singular *stoma*). The Greek word *stoma* means "mouth"—and stomata do look like tiny mouths. The stomata open and close to control when gases enter and leave the leaf. When the stomata are open, carbon dioxide enters the leaf, and oxygen and water vapor exit.

Go Online
PHSchool.com

For: More on leaves
Visit: PHSchool.com
Web Code: ced-1051

The Leaf and Photosynthesis The structure of a leaf is ideal for carrying out photosynthesis. The cells that contain the most chloroplasts are located near the leaf's upper surface, where they get the most light. The chlorophyll in the chloroplasts traps the sun's energy.

Carbon dioxide enters the leaf through open stomata. Water, which is absorbed by the plant's roots, travels up the stem to the leaf through the xylem. During photosynthesis, sugar and oxygen are produced from the carbon dioxide and water. Oxygen passes out of the leaf through the open stomata. The sugar enters the phloem and then travels throughout the plant.

Controlling Water Loss Because such a large area of a leaf is exposed to the air, water can quickly evaporate, or be lost, from a leaf into the air. The process by which water evaporates from a plant's leaves is called **transpiration.** A plant can lose a lot of water through transpiration. A corn plant, for example, can lose almost 4 liters of water on a hot summer day. Without a way to slow down the process of transpiration, a plant would shrivel up and die.

Fortunately, plants have ways to slow down transpiration. One way that plants retain water is by closing the stomata. The stomata often close when leaves start to dry out.

 **Reading Checkpoint** How does water get into a leaf?

FIGURE 15
Stomata
Stomata open (top) and close (bottom) to control when gases enter and exit the leaf.
Relating Cause and Effect What gases enter and exit when the stomata open?

Section 2 Assessment

Target Reading Skill Outlining Use the information in your outline about seed plants to help you answer the questions below.

Reviewing Key Concepts

1. **a.** Reviewing What two characteristics do all seed plants share?
   b. Relating Cause and Effect What characteristics enable seed plants to live in a wide variety of environments? Explain.
2. **a.** Listing Name the three main parts of a seed.
   b. Sequencing List the steps in the sequence in which they must occur for a seed to grow into a new plant.
   c. Applying Concepts If a cherry seed were to take root right below its parent tree, what three challenges might the cherry seedling face?

3. **a.** Identifying What are the main functions of a plant's roots, stems, and leaves?
   b. Comparing and Contrasting Compare the path on which water moves through a plant to the path on which sugar moves through a plant.
   c. Applying Concepts How are the structures of a tree's roots and leaves well-suited for their roles in supplying the tree with water and sugar?

Writing in Science

Product Label Write a "packaging label" for a seed. Include a name and description for each part of the seed. Be sure to describe the role of each part in producing a new plant.

Section 3

Gymnosperms

Reading Preview

Key Concepts
- What are the characteristics of gymnosperms?
- How do gymnosperms reproduce?
- What important products come from gymnosperms?

Key Terms
- gymnosperm • cone • ovule
- pollination

Target Reading Skill

Previewing Visuals Before you read, preview Figure 17. Then write two questions that you have about the diagram in a graphic organizer like the one below. As you read, answer your questions.

The Life Cycle of a Gymnosperm

Q.	How does gymnosperm pollination occur?
A.	
Q.	

Go Online
SCi LINKS™ NSTA

For: Links on gymnosperms
Visit: www.SciLinks.org
Web Code: scn-0152

Lab zone — Discover **Activity**

Are All Leaves Alike?

1. Your teacher will give you a hand lens, a ruler, and the leaves from some seed plants.
2. Using the hand lens, examine each leaf. Sketch each leaf in your notebook.
3. Measure the length and width of each leaf. Record your measurements in your notebook.

Think It Over

Classifying Divide the leaves into two groups on the basis of your observations. Explain why you grouped the leaves as you did.

Have you ever seen a tree that is wider than a car? Do trees this huge really exist? The answer is yes. Some giant sequoia trees, which grow almost exclusively in central California, are more than 10 meters wide. You can understand why giant sequoias are commonly referred to as "giants of the forest." It takes a long time for a tree to grow so big. Scientists think that the largest giant sequoias may be about 2,000 years old. One reason they live so long is because their bark is fire resistant.

What Are Gymnosperms?

The giant sequoia trees belong to the group of seed plants known as gymnosperms. A **gymnosperm** (JIM nuh spurm) is a seed plant that produces naked seeds. The seeds of gymnosperms are referred to as "naked" because they are not enclosed by a protective fruit.

Every gymnosperm produces naked seeds. In addition, many gymnosperms have needle-like or scalelike leaves, and deep-growing root systems. Gymnosperms are the oldest type of seed plant. According to fossil evidence, gymnosperms first appeared on Earth about 360 million years ago. Fossils also indicate that there were many more species of gymnosperms on Earth in the past than there are today. Four groups of gymnosperms exist today.

234 ◆

FIGURE 16
Types of Gymnosperms

Gymnosperms are the oldest seed plants. Cycads, conifers, ginkgoes, and gnetophytes are the only groups that exist today.

Gnetophyte: ▲
Welwitschia

Ginkgo: ▲
Ginkgo biloba

Cycad: ▲
Sago palm

Conifer: ▶
Giant
sequoia

Cycads About 175 million years ago, the majority of plants were cycads. Today, cycads (SY kadz) grow mainly in tropical and subtropical areas. Cycads look like palm trees with cones. A cycad cone can grow as large as a football.

Conifers Conifers (KAHN uh furz), or cone-bearing plants, are the largest and most diverse group of gymnosperms today. Most conifers, such as pines, sequoias, and junipers, are evergreens—plants that keep their leaves, or needles, year-round. When needles drop off, they are replaced by new ones.

Ginkgoes Ginkgoes (GING kohz) also grew hundreds of millions of years ago, but today, only one species of ginkgo, *Ginkgo biloba*, exists. It probably survived only because the Chinese and Japanese cared for it in their gardens. Today, ginkgo trees are planted along city streets because they can tolerate air pollution.

Gnetophytes Gnetophytes (NEE tuh fyts) live in hot deserts and in tropical rain forests. Some gnetophytes are trees, some are shrubs, and others are vines. The *Welwitschia* shown in Figure 16 grows in the deserts of West Africa and can live for more than 1,000 years.

 **What are the four types of gymnosperms?**

Reproduction in Gymnosperms

Most gymnosperms have reproductive structures called **cones.** Cones are covered with scales. Most gymnosperms produce two types of cones: male cones and female cones. Usually, a single plant produces both male and female cones. In some types of gymnosperms, however, individual trees produce either male cones or female cones. A few types of gymnosperms produce no cones at all.

In Figure 17, you can see the male and female cones of a Ponderosa pine. Male cones produce tiny grains of pollen—the male gametophyte. Pollen contains the cells that will later become sperm cells. Each scale on a male cone produces thousands of pollen grains.

The female gametophyte develops in structures called ovules. An **ovule** (OH vyool) is a structure that contains an egg cell. Female cones contain at least one ovule at the base of each scale. After fertilization occurs, the ovule develops into a seed.

You can follow the process of gymnosperm reproduction in Figure 17. **First, pollen falls from a male cone onto a female cone. In time, a sperm cell and an egg cell join together in an ovule on the female cone.** After fertilization occurs, the seed develops on the scale of the female cone.

Pollination The transfer of pollen from a male reproductive structure to a female reproductive structure is called **pollination.** In gymnosperms, wind often carries the pollen from the male cones to the female cones. The pollen collects in a sticky substance produced by each ovule.

Fertilization Once pollination has occurred, the ovule closes and seals in the pollen. The scales also close, and a sperm cell fertilizes an egg cell inside each ovule. The fertilized egg then develops into the embryo part of the seed.

Seed Development Female cones remain on the tree while the seeds mature. As the seeds develop, the female cone increases in size. It can take up to two years for the seeds of some gymnosperms to mature. Male cones, however, usually fall off the tree after they have shed their pollen.

Seed Dispersal When the seeds are mature, the scales open. The wind shakes the seeds out of the cone and carries them away. Only a few seeds will land in suitable places and grow into new plants.

 Reading Checkpoint **What is pollen and where is it produced?**

Lab zone Try This **Activity**

The Scoop on Cones

In this activity, you will observe the structure of a female cone.

1. Use a hand lens to look closely at the female cone. Gently shake the cone over a piece of white paper. Observe what happens.

2. Break off one scale from the cone. Examine its base. If the scale contains a seed, remove the seed.

3. With a hand lens, examine the seed from Step 2 or examine a seed that fell on the paper in Step 1.

4. Wash your hands.

Inferring How does the structure of the cone protect the seeds?

FIGURE 17
The Life Cycle of a Gymnosperm

Ponderosa pines have a typical life cycle for a gymnosperm. Follow the steps of pollination, fertilization, seed development, and dispersal in the pine tree.

Interpreting Diagrams *Where do the pine seeds develop?*

1 A pine tree produces male and female cones.

2 A A male cone produces pollen grains, which contain cells that will mature into sperm cells.

Scale on male cone

Scale on female cone

Egg cells   Ovule

2 B Each scale on a female cone has two ovules at its base.

3 In time, two egg cells form inside each ovule.

4 The wind scatters pollen grains. Some become trapped in a sticky substance produced by the ovule.

5 The ovule closes, and a pollen grain produces a tube that grows into the ovule. A sperm cell moves through the tube and fertilizes the egg cell.

6 The ovule develops into a seed. The fertilized egg becomes the seed's embryo. Other parts of the ovule develop into the seed coat and the seed's stored food.

7 Wind disperses the pine seeds. A seed grows into a seedling and then into a tree.

Gymnosperms in Everyday Life

Gymnosperms, especially conifers, provide many useful products. **Paper and other products, such as the lumber used to build homes, come from conifers.** The rayon fibers in clothes as well as the cellophane wrappers on some food products also come from conifers. Other products, such as turpentine and the rosin used by baseball pitchers, gymnasts, and musicians, are made from the sap produced by some conifers.

Because conifers are so useful to humans, they are grown in large, managed forests in many regions of the United States. When adult trees in managed forests are cut down, young trees are planted to replace them. Since different parts of the forest are usually cut at different times, there are always adult trees that can be harvested. These management efforts help ensure a steady supply of these important trees.

FIGURE 18
Uses of Gymnosperms
Conifers provided the lumber for this new house.

 **Reading Checkpoint** What are two products made from the sap of conifers?

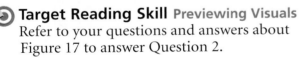

Section 3 Assessment

Target Reading Skill Previewing Visuals Refer to your questions and answers about Figure 17 to answer Question 2.

Reviewing Key Concepts

1. a. **Listing** What characteristics do all gymnosperms share? What other characteristics do many gymnosperms have?
   b. **Comparing and Contrasting** In what way do gymnosperm seeds differ from corn or bean seeds, which are not gymnosperms?
   c. **Predicting** Do you think that the seeds of gymnosperms would likely be dispersed by animals? Why or why not?
2. a. **Reviewing** What is a cone?
   b. **Comparing and Contrasting** What are the two different types of cones? What role does each cone play in gymnosperm reproduction?
   c. **Sequencing** Briefly describe the steps in the reproduction of a gymnosperm.

3. a. **Identifying** Name two important products that come from conifers.
   b. **Making Judgments** Do you think that managed forests guarantee that there will be a steady supply of conifers? Why or why not?

Lab zone At-Home Activity

Everyday Gymnosperms Describe the characteristics of gymnosperms to a family member. Then, with that family member, make a list of things in your home that are made from gymnosperms. Also list the gymnosperms that grow where you live.

Angiosperms

Reading Preview

Key Concepts
- What characteristics do angiosperms share?
- What is the function of an angiosperm's flowers?
- How do angiosperms reproduce?
- How do monocots differ from dicots?

Key Terms
- angiosperm • flower • sepal
- petal • stamen • pistil
- ovary • fruit • monocot
- dicot

Target Reading Skill
Building Vocabulary Using a word in a sentence helps you think about how best to explain the word. After you read the section, reread the paragraphs that contain definitions of Key Terms. Use all the information you have learned to write a meaningful sentence using each Key Term.

Lab zone Discover **Activity**

What Is a Fruit?

1. Your teacher will give you three different fruits that have been cut in half.
2. Use a hand lens to carefully observe the outside of each fruit. For each fruit, record its color, shape, size, and other external features. Record your observations in your notebook.
3. Carefully observe the structures inside the fruit. Record your observations.

Think It Over
Forming Operational Definitions Based on your observations, how would you define the term *fruit?*

You probably associate the word *flower* with a sweet-smelling plant growing in a garden. You certainly wouldn't think of something that smells like rotting meat. But that's exactly what the corpse flower, or rafflesia, smells like. These flowers, which grow on vines in Asia, are huge—nearly 1 meter across! You won't be seeing rafflesia in your local florist shop any time soon.

Rafflesia belongs to the group of seed plants known as **angiosperms** (AN jee uh spurmz). **All angiosperms, or flowering plants, share two important characteristics. First, they produce flowers. Second, in contrast to gymnosperms, which produce uncovered seeds, angiosperms produce seeds that are enclosed in fruits.**

Angiosperms live almost everywhere on Earth. They grow in frozen areas in the Arctic, tropical jungles, and barren deserts. A few angiosperms, such as mangrove trees, can live at the ocean's edge.

◀ **Rafflesia**

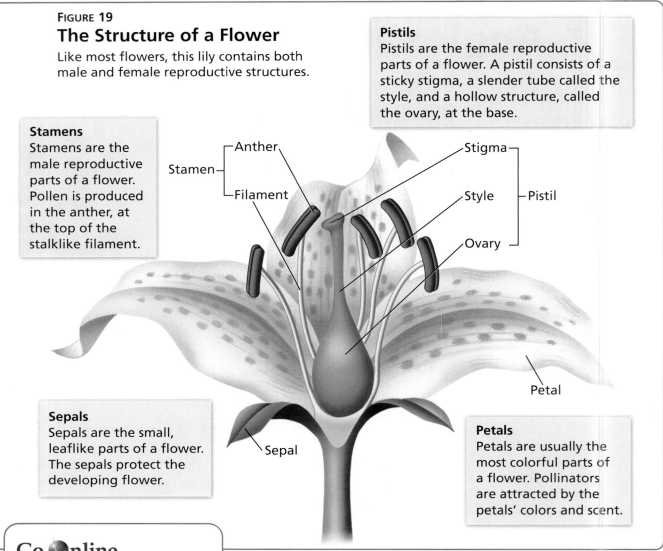

FIGURE 19
The Structure of a Flower
Like most flowers, this lily contains both male and female reproductive structures.

Pistils
Pistils are the female reproductive parts of a flower. A pistil consists of a sticky stigma, a slender tube called the style, and a hollow structure, called the ovary, at the base.

Stamens
Stamens are the male reproductive parts of a flower. Pollen is produced in the anther, at the top of the stalklike filament.

Stamen — Anther
Filament

Stigma
Style — Pistil
Ovary

Petal

Sepals
Sepals are the small, leaflike parts of a flower. The sepals protect the developing flower.

Sepal

Petals
Petals are usually the most colorful parts of a flower. Pollinators are attracted by the petals' colors and scent.

Go Online
active art.

For: The Structure of a Flower activity
Visit: PHSchool.com
Web Code: cep-1053

The Structure of Flowers

Flowers come in all sorts of shapes, sizes, and colors. But, despite their differences, all flowers have the same function— reproduction. A **flower** is the reproductive structure of an angiosperm. Figure 19 shows the parts of a typical flower. As you read about the parts, keep in mind that some flowers lack one or more of the parts. For example, some flowers have only male reproductive parts, and some flowers lack petals.

Sepals and Petals When a flower is still a bud, it is enclosed by leaflike structures called **sepals** (SEE pulz). Sepals protect the developing flower and are often green in color. When the sepals fold back, they reveal the flower's colorful, leaflike **petals.** The petals are generally the most colorful parts of a flower. The shapes, sizes, and number of petals vary greatly from flower to flower.

Stamens Within the petals are the flower's male and female reproductive parts. The **stamens** (STAY munz) are the male reproductive parts. Locate the stamens inside the flower in Figure 19. The thin stalk of the stamen is called the filament. Pollen is produced in the anther, at the top of the filament.

Pistils The female parts, or **pistils** (PIS tulz), are found in the center of most flowers. Some flowers have two or more pistils; others have only one. The sticky tip of the pistil is called the stigma. A slender tube, called a style, connects the stigma to a hollow structure at the base of the flower. This hollow structure is the **ovary,** which protects the seeds as they develop. An ovary contains one or more ovules.

Pollinators The colors and shapes of most petals and the scents produced by most flowers attract insects and other animals. These organisms ensure that pollination occurs. Pollinators include birds, bats, and insects such as bees and flies. The rafflesia flower you read about at the beginning of the section is pollinated by flies. The flies are attracted by the strong smell of rotting meat.

 Reading Checkpoint **What are the male and female reproductive parts of a flower?**

FIGURE 20
Pollinators
Pollinators, such as insects, birds, and bats, are attracted to a flower's color, shape, or scent. *Inferring How might the white color of the cactus flower aid in attracting bats?*

◀ A honeybee is covered in the pollen of an orange flower.

▲ A hummingbird pollinates a bright red flower.

A bat pollinates an organ ▶ pipe cactus flower at night.

Reproduction in Angiosperms

You can follow the process of angiosperm reproduction in Figure 22. **First, pollen falls on a flower's stigma. In time, the sperm cell and egg cell join together in the flower's ovule. The zygote develops into the embryo part of the seed.**

Pollination A flower is pollinated when a grain of pollen falls on the stigma. Like gymnosperms, some angiosperms are pollinated by the wind. But most angiosperms rely on birds, bats, or insects for pollination. Nectar, a sugar-rich food, is located deep inside a flower. When an animal enters a flower to obtain the nectar, it brushes against the anthers and becomes coated with pollen. Some of the pollen can drop onto the flower's stigma as the animal leaves the flower. The pollen can also be brushed onto the sticky stigma of the next flower the animal visits.

Fertilization If the pollen falls on the stigma of a similar plant, fertilization can occur. A sperm cell joins with an egg cell inside an ovule within the ovary at the base of the flower. The zygote then begins to develop into the seed's embryo. Other parts of the ovule develop into the rest of the seed.

Fruit Development and Seed Dispersal As the seed develops after fertilization, the ovary changes into a **fruit**—a ripened ovary and other structures that enclose one or more seeds. Apples and cherries are fruits. So are many foods you usually call vegetables, such as tomatoes and squash. Fruits are the means by which angiosperm seeds are dispersed. Animals that eat fruits help to disperse their seeds.

Reading Checkpoint What flower part develops into a fruit?

FIGURE 21
Fruits
The seeds of angiosperms are enclosed in fruits, which protect and help disperse the seeds.

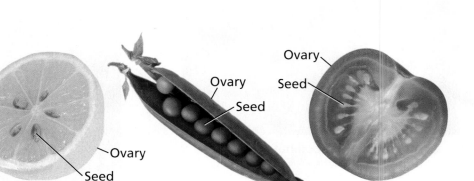

▲ Maple

▲ Lemon

▲ Pea

▲ Tomato

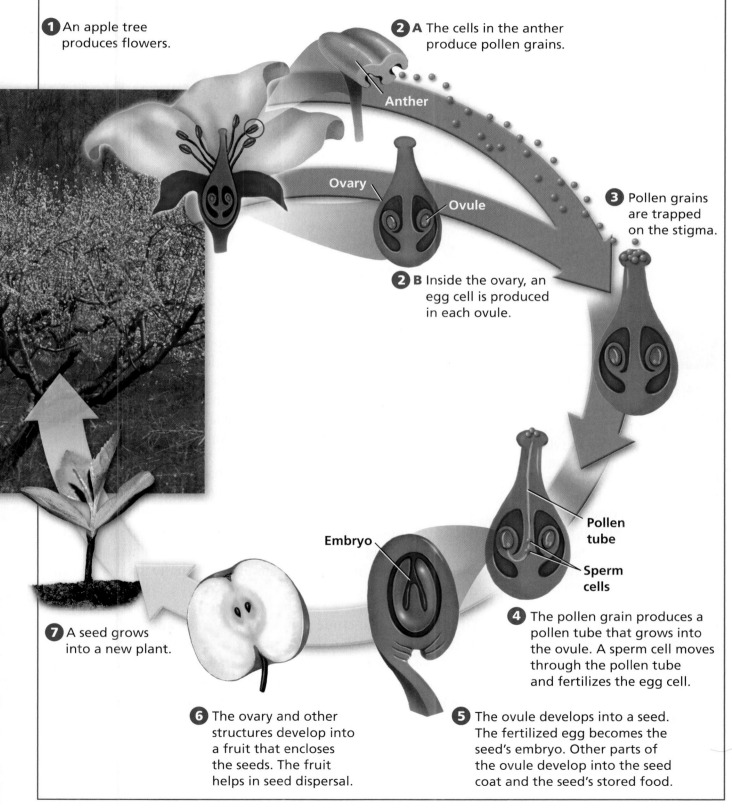

FIGURE 22
The Life Cycle of an Angiosperm
All angiosperms have a similar life cycle. Follow the steps of pollination, fertilization, seed development, and dispersal in this apple tree.
Interpreting Diagrams *What plant part does the ovule develop into?*

1 An apple tree produces flowers.

2 **A** The cells in the anther produce pollen grains.

Anther

Ovary

Ovule

3 Pollen grains are trapped on the stigma.

2 **B** Inside the ovary, an egg cell is produced in each ovule.

Embryo

Pollen tube

Sperm cells

4 The pollen grain produces a pollen tube that grows into the ovule. A sperm cell moves through the pollen tube and fertilizes the egg cell.

7 A seed grows into a new plant.

6 The ovary and other structures develop into a fruit that encloses the seeds. The fruit helps in seed dispersal.

5 The ovule develops into a seed. The fertilized egg becomes the seed's embryo. Other parts of the ovule develop into the seed coat and the seed's stored food.

FIGURE 23
Monocots and Dicots
Monocots and dicots differ in the number of cotyledons, the pattern of veins and vascular tissue, and the number of petals.
Interpreting Tables
How do monocot and dicot leaves differ?

	Comparing Monocots and Dicots		
Plant Part	**Monocots**		**Dicots**
Seed		One cotyledon	Two cotyledons
Leaf		Parallel veins	Branching veins
Stem		Bundles of vascular tissue scattered throughout stem	Bundles of vascular tissue arranged in a ring
Flower		Flower parts in threes	Flower parts in fours or fives

Types of Angiosperms

Angiosperms are divided into two major groups: monocots and dicots. "Cot" is short for *cotyledon*. Recall from Section 2 that the cotyledon, or seed leaf, provides food for the embryo. *Mono* means "one" and *di* means "two." **Monocots** are angiosperms that have only one seed leaf. **Dicots,** on the other hand, produce seeds with two seed leaves. In Figure 23, you can compare the characteristics of monocots and dicots.

Monocots Grasses, including corn, wheat, and rice, and plants such as lilies and tulips are monocots. The flowers of a monocot usually have either three petals or a multiple of three petals. Monocots usually have long, slender leaves with veins that run parallel to one another like train rails. The bundles of vascular tissue in monocot stems are usually scattered randomly throughout the stem.

Dicots Dicots include plants such as roses and violets, as well as dandelions. Both oak and maple trees are dicots, as are food plants such as beans and apples. The flowers of dicots often have either four or five petals or multiples of these numbers. The leaves are usually wide, with veins that branch many times. Dicot stems usually have bundles of vascular tissue arranged in a ring.

 Reading Checkpoint

How do the petals of monocots and dicots differ in number?

Math Skills

Multiples

Is a flower with 6 petals a monocot? To answer this question, you need to determine if 6 is a multiple of 3. A number is a multiple of 3 if there is a nonzero whole number that, when multiplied by 3, gives you that number.

In this case, 6 is a multiple of 3 because you can multiply 2 (a nonzero whole number) by 3 to get 6.

$$2 \times 3 = 6$$

Therefore, a flower with 6 petals is a monocot. Other multiples of 3 include 9 and 12.

Practice Problem Which of these numbers are multiples of 4?

6, 10, 12, 16

Angiosperms in Everyday Life

Angiosperms are an important source of food, clothing, and medicine for other organisms. Plant-eating animals, such as cows, elephants, and beetles, eat flowering plants such as grasses as well as the leaves of trees. People eat vegetables, fruits, and cereals, all of which are angiosperms.

People also produce clothing and other products from angiosperms. For example, the seeds of cotton plants, like the ones you see in Figure 24, are covered with cotton fibers. The stems of flax plants provide linen fibers. The sap of rubber trees is used to make rubber for tires and other products. Furniture is often made from the wood of maple, cherry, and oak trees. Some important medications come from angiosperms, too. For example, the heart medication digitalis comes from the leaves of the foxglove plant.

FIGURE 24
Cotton Bolls
Angiosperms, such as cotton plants, provide many important products. Cotton seeds, which develop in fruits called bolls, are covered with fibers that are manufactured into cotton fabric.

 **Reading Checkpoint** **What are two angiosperms from which people produce clothing?**

Section 4 Assessment

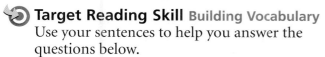

Target Reading Skill Building Vocabulary Use your sentences to help you answer the questions below.

Reviewing Key Concepts

1. a. Reviewing What two characteristics do all angiosperms share?
   b. Comparing and Contrasting Do gymnosperms share either of the two characteristics with angiosperms? Explain.
2. a. Identifying What is the function of an angiosperm's flowers?
   b. Describing Describe the role of a flower's sepals, petals, stamens, and pistil.
3. a. Reviewing On what part of a flower must pollen land for pollination to occur?
   b. Sequencing Briefly describe the steps in the reproduction of an angiosperm, from pollination to seed dispersal.
   c. Making Judgments Do you agree or disagree with the following statement? Animals are essential in order for reproduction in angiosperms to occur. Explain your answer.

4. a. Listing Name the two major groups of angiosperms.
   b. Comparing and Contrasting How do the seeds, leaves, stems, and flowers of these two groups differ?
   c. Classifying A plant's leaves have parallel veins, and each of its flowers has six petals. To which group does it belong? Explain.

Math Practice

5. Multiples Which of the following numbers are multiples of 3? Which of the numbers are multiples of 4?

5, 6, 8, 10, 12, 15

6. Multiples Suppose you found a flower with 12 petals. Would you know from the number of petals whether the flower is a monocot or a dicot? Explain.

Lab zone Skills Lab

A Close Look at Flowers

Problem

What is the function of a flower, and what roles do its different parts play?

Skills Focus

observing, inferring, measuring

Materials

- paper towels
- plastic dropper
- hand lens
- microscope
- slide
- large flower
- coverslip
- scalpel
- tape
- water
- metric ruler
- lens paper

Procedure

PART 1 The Outer Parts of the Flower

1. Tape four paper towel sheets on your work area. Obtain a flower from your teacher. While handling the flower gently, observe its shape and color. Use the ruler to measure it. Notice whether the petals have any spots or other markings. Does the flower have a scent? Record your observations with sketches and descriptions.

2. Observe the sepals. How many are there? How do they relate to the rest of the flower? (*Hint:* The sepals are often green, but not always.) Record your observations.

3. Use a scalpel to carefully cut off the sepals without damaging the structures beneath them. **CAUTION:** *Scalpels are sharp. Cut in a direction away from yourself and others.*

4. Observe the petals. How many are there? Are all the petals the same, or are they different? Record your observations.

PART 2 The Male Part of the Flower

5. Carefully pull off the petals to examine the male part of the flower. Try not to damage the structures beneath the petals.

6. Observe the stamens. How many are there? How are they shaped? How tall are they? Record your observations.

7. Use a scalpel to carefully cut the stamens away from the rest of the flower without damaging the structures beneath them. Lay the stamens on the paper towel.

8. Obtain a clean slide and coverslip. Hold a stamen over the slide, and gently tap some pollen grains from the anther onto the slide. Add a drop of water to the pollen. Then place the coverslip over the water and pollen.

9. Observe the pollen under both the low-power objective and the high-power objective of a microscope. Draw and label a pollen grain.

PART 3 The Female Part of the Flower

10. Use a scalpel to cut the pistil away from the rest of the flower. Measure the height of the pistil. Examine its shape. Observe the top of the pistil. Determine if that surface will stick to and lift a tiny piece of lens paper. Record your observations.

11. Lay the pistil on the paper towel. Holding it firmly at its base, use a scalpel to cut the pistil in half at its widest point, as shown in the diagram below. **CAUTION:** *Cut away from your fingers.* How many compartments do you see? How many ovules do you see? Record your observations.

Analyze and Conclude

1. **Observing** Based on your observations, describe how the sepals, petals, stamens, and pistils of a flower are arranged.

2. **Inferring** How are the sepals, petals, stamens, and pistil involved in the function of this flower?

3. **Measuring** Based on your measurements of the heights of the pistil and stamens, how do you think the flower you examined is pollinated? Use additional observations to support your answer.

4. **Classifying** Did you find any patterns in the number of sepals, petals, stamens, or other structures in your flower? If so, describe that pattern. Is your flower a monocot or a dicot?

5. **Communicating** Write a paragraph explaining all you can learn about a plant by examining one of its flowers. Use your observations in this lab to support your conclusions.

More to Explore

Some kinds of flowers do not have all the parts found in the flower in this lab. Obtain a different flower. Find out which parts that flower has, and which parts are missing. *Obtain your teacher's permission before carrying out your investigation.*

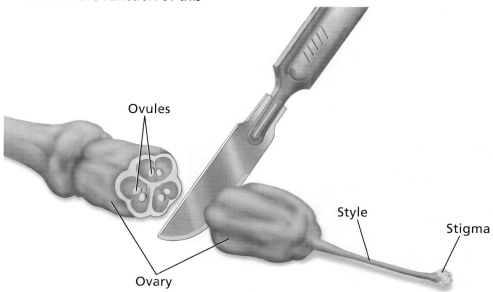

Ovules

Ovary

Style

Stigma

Cotton Boll
The seeds of the cotton plant are hidden by the cotton fibers.

Technology Protection System (TPS)

For centuries, farmers have saved seeds from one year's crop to plant the following year. In the 1990s, scientists discovered that, by adding certain genes to a plant, they could make its seeds sterile—unable to reproduce. Researchers have added these genes to new high-yield strains of cotton, corn, and soybean plants. Farmers who want to grow the new strains must buy the seeds each year.

What's Being Protected?

Developers of the new technology call it Technology Protection System (TPS). They say that it enables the seed companies to be paid, each year, for the seeds their researchers develop. This will give these companies the money to develop stronger crops, which will increase crop yields and feed more people.

However, farmers complain that they can't afford to buy new seeds each year. As a result, they will have to continue growing older, lower-yield strains.

Cotton Field
Cotton was the first crop to be modified with TPS. The technology has since been applied to corn, potato, lettuce, and other crops.

Weigh the Impact

1. Identify the Need
What was the purpose for developing TPS?

2. Research
At the library or on the Internet, research the history of TPS. Find out where, when, and by whom the technology was developed. Record your findings in a table, titled TPS, with four columns headed *Where*, *When*, *Who*, and *What*.

3. Write
A company in the United States offers farmers in India free seed to grow TPS corn for a three-year trial. The farmers ask you whether they should accept the offer. What is your advice? Explain your reasoning.

Feeding the World

Reading Preview

Key Concept
- What technologies may help farmers produce more crops?

Key Terms
- precision farming • hydroponics
- genetic engineering

Target Reading Skill
Identifying Main Ideas As you read the section, write the main idea in a graphic organizer like the one below. Then write three supporting details that give examples of the main idea.

Main Idea

Technologies that may help produce more food include . . .

Detail	Detail	Detail

Discover **Activity**

Will There Be Enough to Eat?

1. Choose a numbered tag from the bag that your teacher provides. If you pick a tag with the number *1* on it, you're from a wealthy country. If you pick a tag with the number *2*, you're from a middle-income country. If you pick a tag with the number *3*, you're from a poor country.

2. Find classmates that have the same number on their tag. Sit down as a group.

3. Your teacher will serve your group a meal. The amount of food you receive will depend on the number on your tag.

4. As you eat, observe the people in your group and in the other groups. After you eat, record your observations. Also, record how you felt and what you were thinking during the meal.

Think It Over
Predicting Based on this activity, predict what effect an increase in the world's population would have on the world's food supply.

More than 6 billion people live on Earth today. By the year 2050, the population could grow as large as 10 billion. Think about how much food will be needed to feed the growing population. How will farmers be able to grow enough food?

Farmers and scientists are hard at work trying to find answers to this question. Farmers are using new technologies that make farming more efficient. People are developing methods for growing crops in areas with poor soil. In addition, scientists are developing plants that are more resistant to insects, diseases, and drought.

A food market ▶
in Turkey

Precision Farming

On the farms of the future, satellite images and computers will be just as important as tractors and harvesters. Such technologies will allow farmers to practice **precision farming,** a farming method in which farmers fine-tune the amount of water and fertilizer they use to the requirements of a specific field.

First, satellite images of a farmer's fields are taken. Then, a computer analyzes the images to determine the makeup of the soil in the different fields. The computer uses the data to prepare a watering and fertilizing plan for each field.

Precision farming can benefit farmers by saving time and money. It also increases crop yields by helping farmers maintain ideal conditions in all fields. Precision farming would also benefit the environment because farmers use only as much fertilizer as the soil needs. When less fertilizer is used, fewer nutrients wash off the land into lakes and rivers. Reducing the use of fertilizers is one way to prevent algal blooms from damaging bodies of water.

Hydroponics

In some areas, people cannot grow crops because the soil is so poor. For example, on some islands in the Pacific Ocean, the soil contains large amounts of salt from the surrounding ocean. Food crops will not grow in salty soil.

On these islands, people may soon use hydroponics to grow food crops. **Hydroponics** (hy druh PAHN iks) is a farming method in which plants are grown in solutions of nutrients instead of in soil. Usually, the plants are grown in containers in which their roots are anchored in gravel or sand. The nutrient solution is pumped through the gravel or sand. **Hydroponics allows people to grow crops in areas with poor soil to help feed a growing population.** Unfortunately, hydroponics is a costly method of growing food crops.

 **What is hydroponics?**

FIGURE 25
Precision Farming
The map on this tractor's computer screen shows the makeup of the soil in a farm's fields. The map was obtained by satellite imaging.
Relating Cause and Effect How can precision farming benefit the environment?

Engineering Better Plants

Wheat, corn, rice, and potatoes are the major sources of food today. To feed more people, the yields of these crops must be increased. This is not an easy task. One challenge facing farmers is that these crops grow only in certain climates. Another challenge is that the size and structure of these plants limit how much food they can produce.

One technique scientists are using to address these challenges is called genetic engineering. In **genetic engineering,** scientists alter an organism's genetic material to produce an organism with qualities that people find useful.

Scientists are using genetic engineering to produce plants that can grow in a wider range of climates. They are also engineering plants to be more resistant to damage from insects. For example, scientists have inserted genetic material from a bacterium into corn and tomato plants. This bacterium is harmless to humans. But its genetic material enables the plants to produce substances that kill insects. Caterpillars or other insects that bite into the leaves of these plants are killed. Today, farmers grow many kinds of genetically engineered plants.

 **Reading Checkpoint** What is one way that genetic engineering can help farmers produce more food?

Go Online
SC*LINKS* NSTA

For: Links on plants as food
Visit: www.SciLinks.org
Web Code: scn-0155

Section 5 Assessment

Target Reading Skill Identifying Main Ideas Use your graphic organizer to help you answer the questions below.

Reviewing Key Concepts

1. **a. Listing** Name three technologies that farmers can use to increase crop yields.
   b. Explaining Describe one farming challenge that each technology addresses.
   c. Making Judgments Which technology do you think holds the most promise for the future? Support your answer with reasons.

Writing in Science

Interview Suppose you could interview a farmer who uses precision farming. Write a one-page interview in which you ask the farmer to explain the technology and its benefits.

Technology Lab
• Tech & Design •

Design and Build a Hydroponic Garden

Problem

Can you design and build a system for growing plants without soil?

Skills Focus

designing a solution, redesigning

Materials

- potted plant
- 2 different types of seedlings
- nutrient solution
- empty 2-liter soda bottles
- paper towels
- optional materials provided by your teacher

Procedure

PART 1 Research and Investigate

1. Copy the data table onto a sheet of paper.

2. Carefully examine the potted plant your teacher gives you. Think about all the factors that are required in order for the plant to grow. List these factors in the first column of the data table.

3. Use your knowledge of plants and additional research to fill in the second column of the data table.

4. For each factor listed in the table, decide whether or not it is "essential" for plant growth. Write this information in the third column of the data table.

PART 2 Design and Build

5. To test whether soil is essential for plant growth, design a "garden" system for growing plants without soil. Your garden must
   - include at least two different types of seedlings
   - use only the amount of nutrient solution provided by your teacher
   - be built using materials that are small and lightweight, yet durable

6. Sketch your garden design on a sheet of paper and make a list of the materials you will use. Then obtain your teacher's approval and build your garden.

PART 3 Evaluate and Redesign

7. Test your garden design by growing your plants for 2 weeks. Each day, measure and record the height of your plants and the number of leaves. Also note the overall appearance of your plants.

8. Evaluate your design by comparing your garden and plants with those of your classmates. Based on your comparison, decide how you might improve your garden's design. Then make any needed changes and monitor plant growth for one more week.

Data Table		
Factor Required for Plant Growth	What This Factor Provides for the Plant	Essential or Nonessential?

Analyze and Conclude

1. **Identifying a Need** In Part 1, did you list soil as a factor required for plant growth? If so, did you think it was an essential or nonessential factor? Explain your thinking.

2. **Designing a Solution** How did the information you gathered in Part 1 help you in designing your garden in Part 2? How did your garden design provide for each of the essential growth factors you listed?

3. **Redesigning** What changes did you make to your garden design and why? Did the changes lead to improved plant growth?

4. **Working With Design Constraints** How did the design constraints in Step 5 limit your design? How did you overcome those limitations?

5. **Evaluating the Impact on Society** Hydroponic gardens are planned for future space flights and as a way to grow plants in cold climates. Explain why hydroponic gardens are a good choice for each of these situations. Then, identify two more situations in which hydroponic gardens would be a good choice and explain why.

Communicate

Create a brochure highlighting the benefits of hydroponic gardening. Be sure to provide details about how a plant's needs are met and about the problems that hydroponic gardens could solve.

Chapter 6

Study Guide

① The Plant Kingdom

Key Concepts

- Plants are autotrophs, organisms that produce their own food. All plants are eukaryotes that contain many cells. In addition, all plant cells are surrounded by cell walls.

- For plants to survive on land, they must have ways to obtain water and other nutrients from their surroundings, retain water, transport materials in their bodies, support their bodies, and reproduce.

- Scientists informally group plants into two major groups—nonvascular plants and vascular plants.

- Plants have complex life cycles that include two different stages, the sporophyte stage and the gametophyte stage.

Key Terms

- photosynthesis • tissue • chloroplast
- vacuole • cuticle • vascular tissue
- fertilization • zygote • nonvascular plant
- vascular plant • chlorophyll • sporophyte
- gametophyte

② The Characteristics of Seed Plants

Key Concepts

- Seed plants have vascular tissue and use pollen and seeds to reproduce.

- Inside a seed is a partially developed plant. If a seed lands in an area where conditions are favorable, it can begin to develop into a plant.

- Roots anchor a plant in the ground and absorb water and nutrients. Stems carry substances between roots and leaves, provide support, and hold up the leaves. Leaves capture the sun's energy for photosynthesis.

Key Terms

- phloem • xylem • pollen
- embryo • cotyledon • germination
- root cap • cambium • stomata
- transpiration

③ Gymnosperms

Key Concepts

- Every gymnosperm produces naked seeds. In addition, many gymnosperms have needle-like or scalelike leaves, and deep-growing roots.

- During reproduction, pollen falls from a male cone onto a female cone. In time, sperm and egg cells join in an ovule on the female cone.

- Paper and other products, such as the lumber used to build homes, come from conifers.

Key Terms

- gymnosperm • cone • ovule • pollination

④ Angiosperms

Key Concepts

- All angiosperms produce flowers and fruits.

- All flowers function in reproduction.

- During reproduction, pollen falls on a flower's stigma. In time, sperm and egg cells join in the flower's ovule. The zygote develops into the embryo part of the seed.

- Angiosperms are divided into two major groups: monocots and dicots.

Key Terms

- angiosperm • flower • sepal • petal
- stamen • pistil • ovary • fruit • monocot
- dicot

⑤ Feeding the World

Key Concept

- Precision farming, hydroponics, and genetic engineering can help farmers produce more crops to feed the world's population.

Key Terms

- precision farming • hydroponics
- genetic engineering

Review and Assessment

Go Online
PHSchool.com

For: Self-Assessment
Visit: PHSchool.com
Web Code: cma-0060

Organizing Information

Concept Mapping Copy the concept map about seed plants onto a sheet of paper. Then complete it and add a title. (For more on Concept Mapping, see the Skills Handbook.)

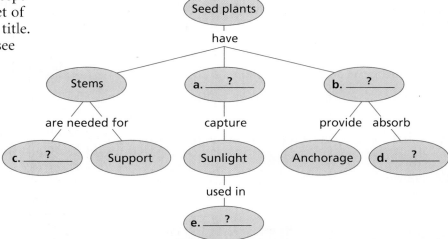

Reviewing Key Terms

Choose the letter of the best answer.

1. The structures in plant cells in which food is made are called
   a. cuticles.
   b. chloroplasts.
   c. vacuoles.
   d. vascular tissues.

2. The process by which a seed sprouts is called
   a. pollination.
   b. fertilization.
   c. dispersal.
   d. germination.

3. In woody stems, new xylem cells are produced by the
   a. bark.
   b. cambium.
   c. phloem.
   d. pith.

4. Which of the following is the male part of a flower?
   a. pistil
   b. ovule
   c. stamen
   d. petal

5. The process of growing crops in a nutrient solution is called
   a. genetic engineering.
   b. hydroponics.
   c. precision farming.
   d. satellite imaging.

If the statement is true, write *true*. If it is false, change the underlined word or words to make the statement true.

6. <u>Vascular tissue</u> is a system of tubelike structures through which water and food move.

7. <u>Stems</u> anchor plants in the soil.

8. The needles of a pine tree are actually its <u>leaves</u>.

9. <u>Gymnosperm</u> seeds are dispersed in fruits.

10. <u>Precision farming</u> uses technology to fine-tune water and fertilizer requirements.

Writing in Science

Firsthand Account Write a story from the viewpoint of a seedling. Describe how you were dispersed as a seed and how you grew into a seedling.

Discovery CHANNEL SCHOOL™

Introduction to Plants
Video Preview
Video Field Trip
▶ Video Assessment

Review and Assessment

Checking Concepts

11. Briefly describe the life cycle of a typical plant.

12. Describe four different ways that seeds can be dispersed.

13. Explain the role that stomata play in leaves.

14. Describe the structure of a female cone.

15. What is the difference between pollination and fertilization?

16. What role does a fruit play in an angiosperm's life cycle?

17. How can the use of hydroponics help increase the amount of food that can be grown on Earth?

Thinking Critically

18. **Comparing and Contrasting** How does the sporophyte generation of a plant differ from the gametophyte generation?

19. **Inferring** Sometimes undersea volcanoes erupt, and new islands form far away from other land masses. Years later, seed plants may be found growing on those islands. How can the presence of those plants be explained?

20. **Relating Cause and Effect** When a strip of bark is removed all the way around the trunk of a tree, the tree dies. Explain why.

21. **Predicting** Pesticides are designed to kill harmful insects. Sometimes, however, pesticides kill helpful insects as well. What effect could this have on angiosperms?

22. **Comparing and Contrasting** Which of the plants below is a monocot? Which is a dicot? Explain your conclusions.

A

B

Math Practice

23. **Multiples** Use what you know about multiples to determine which flower is a monocot and which is a dicot: a flower with nine petals; a flower with ten petals. Explain.

Applying Skills

Use the data in the graph below to answer Questions 24–26.

A scientist measured transpiration in an ash tree over an 18-hour period. She also measured how much water the tree's roots took up in the same period.

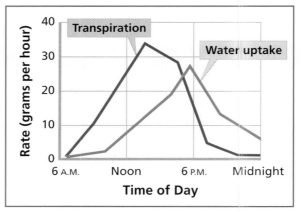

24. **Interpreting Data** At what time is the rate of transpiration highest? At what time is the rate of water uptake highest?

25. **Inferring** Why do you think the transpiration rate increases and decreases as it does during the 18-hour period?

26. **Drawing Conclusions** Based on the graph, what is one conclusion you can reach about the pattern of water loss and gain in the ash tree?

Lab zone Chapter **Project**

Performance Assessment Present your exhibit to your classmates. Describe your original exhibit and how you changed it based on the feedback you received. Explain what you learned by doing this project. What factors are most important in creating a successful educational exhibit for children?

Test-Taking Tip

Sequencing Events

Some test questions require you to arrange a series of events in order. You might be asked which event comes first or last, or which event comes before or after another event. Before looking at the answer choices, try to recall the correct sequence in which the events occur.

Sample Question

Which of the following is the correct sequence of events in the reproduction of a seed plant?

  A pollination, germination, fertilization
  B fertilization, germination, pollination
  C pollination, fertilization, germination
  D germination, fertilization, pollination

Answer

Choice **C** correctly sequences the events of seed plant reproduction. You can eliminate **A** because a seed cannot germinate before fertilization creates that seed. **B** and **D** are incorrect because fertilization cannot take place before pollination.

Choose the letter of the best answer.

1. The diagram below shows the parts of a flower. In which flower part does pollen formation take place?

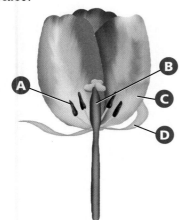

  A part A   **B** part B
  C part C   **D** part D

2. Which of the following is the correct path that water takes once it enters a plant?
  A leaves, stems, roots
  B roots, leaves, stems
  C stems, roots, leaves
  D roots, stems, leaves

3. A scientist examining the annual rings of a tree observes a section with wide rings. What inference can be made from this observation?
  A There was a drought during the years the wide rings were produced.
  B Rainfall was plentiful during the years the wide rings were produced.
  C Forest fires produced the wide rings.
  D There were severe springtime frosts during the years the wide rings were produced.

4. Which would a student expect to find when examining a dicot?
  A one cotyledon
  B flower parts in multiples of threes
  C stems with bundles of vascular tissue arranged in a ring
  D leaves with parallel veins

5. Which of the following statements is a valid comparison of gymnosperms and angiosperms?
  A Both gymnosperms and angiosperms produce flowers.
  B Gymnosperms produce flowers, while angiosperms produce cones.
  C Most gymnosperms have broad leaves, while angiosperms do not.
  D Angiosperm seeds are enclosed within fruits, while gymnosperm seeds are not.

Constructed Response

6. Describe three adaptations that plants have for living on land. Explain why each adaptation is important for a plant to be able to survive on land.

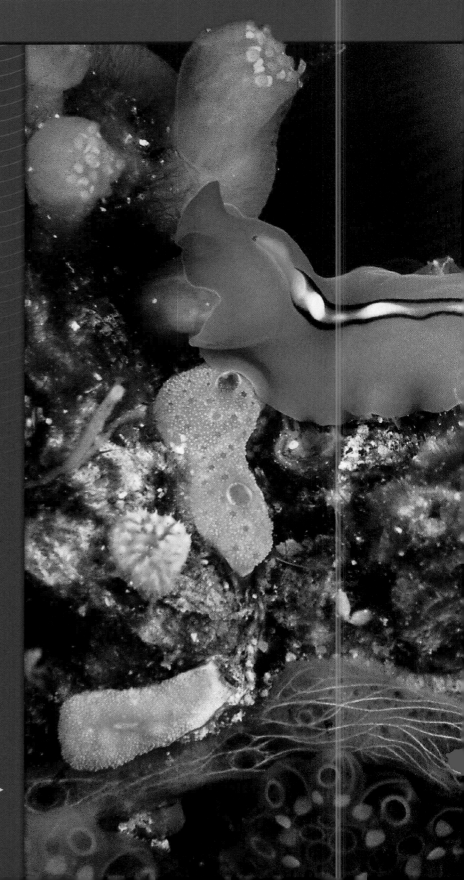

Chapter
7

Animals

Interactive Textbook

A purple flatworm glides along the ocean bottom. ▶

Lab zone™ Chapter **Project**

Design and Build an Animal Habitat

Do all animals require the same things to survive? In this project, you will research what it takes to keep a class pet healthy, and then build a habitat to carry out that objective.

Your Goal To research, design, and build a habitat that will keep an animal healthy for two weeks

To complete this project, you must
- research the needs of your animal
- brainstorm various designs for a habitat that meets your animal's needs and allows you to observe its behavior
- select materials and build a prototype of your design
- test your design by having your animal live in the habitat for two weeks
- follow the safety guidelines in Appendix A

Plan It! Choose your animal. Research where it lives, and what types of climate and food it needs. Use this information to design your habitat. Brainstorm some design ideas and make sketches. Select materials to build the habitat. After your teacher approves your design, build and test the habitat.

What Is an Animal?

Reading Preview

Key Concepts
- How are animal bodies typically organized?
- What are four major functions of animals?
- How are animals classified?

Key Terms
- cell • tissue • organ
- adaptation
- sexual reproduction
- fertilization
- asexual reproduction
- phylum • vertebrate
- invertebrate

Target Reading Skill

Asking Questions Before you read, preview the red headings. In a graphic organizer like the one below, ask a *what* or *how* question for each heading. As you read, write the answers to your questions.

Structure of Animals

Question	Answer
What is a cell?	A cell is . . .

Discover **Activity**

Is It an Animal?
1. Carefully examine each of the organisms that your teacher gives you.
2. Decide which ones are animals. For each organism, write down the reasons for your decision. Wash your hands after handling each of the organisms.

Think It Over
Forming Operational Definitions Use your notes about each organism to write a definition of "animal."

The strange animal, called a barnacle, shown below eats with its feet. Tiny feathery feet flick in and out of the tip of the barnacle's cone, trapping tiny organisms from the ocean. Barnacles and other animals are many-celled organisms that obtain their food by eating other organisms.

Structure of Animals

Animals are composed of many cells. A **cell** is the basic unit of structure and function in living things. **The cells of most animals are organized into higher levels of structure, including tissues, organs, and systems.** A group of similar cells that perform a specific function is called a **tissue.** Tissues may combine to form an **organ,** which is a group of several different tissues. For example, many animals have organs called stomachs, composed of muscle, nerve, and other tissues. Groups of structures that perform the broadest functions of an animal are known as systems. The stomach is part of the digestive system.

A barnacle feeding (inset) ▲ and many barnacles at rest (right)

Functions of Animals

Despite their great diversity, all animals carry out the same basic functions. **The major functions of animals are to obtain food and oxygen, keep internal conditions stable, move, and reproduce.** Structures or behaviors that allow animals to perform these basic functions in their environments are called **adaptations.**

Obtaining Food and Oxygen An animal cannot make food for itself—it obtains food by eating other organisms. Animals may feed on plants, other animals, or a combination of plants and animals. Food provides animals with raw materials for growth and with energy for their bodies' activities, such as breathing and moving. To release energy from food, the body's cells need oxygen. Some animals, like birds, get oxygen from air. Others, like fishes, get oxygen from water.

Keeping Conditions Stable Animals must maintain a stable environment within their bodies. If this balance is lost, the animal cannot survive. For example, cells that get too hot start to die. So, animals are adapted, meaning thay have adaptations, to keep their bodies cool. Earthworms stay in moist soil during hot days, lizards crawl to shady places, and dogs pant.

Movement All animals move in some way at some point in their lives. Most animals move freely from place to place throughout their lives. Some animals, such as barnacles, move from place to place only during the earliest stage of their lives. After they find a good place to attach, these animals stay put. Animal movement is usually related to meeting the basic survival needs. For example, you've probably seen a cat claw its way up a tree trunk to escape from a barking dog.

Reproduction Most animals reproduce sexually. **Sexual reproduction** is the process by which a new organism develops from the joining of two sex cells—a male sperm cell and a female egg cell. The joining of an egg cell and a sperm cell is called **fertilization.**

 What is sexual reproduction?

FIGURE 1
Keeping Cool
This dog is keeping cool by getting wet and panting.

FIGURE 2
Reproduction
Baby alligators are produced by sexual reproduction.
Classifying *Which kind of reproduction involves fertilization?*

Some animals can reproduce asexually as well as sexually. **Asexual reproduction** is the process by which a single organism produces a new organism identical to itself. For example, animals called sea anemones sometimes reproduce by splitting down the middle, producing two identical organisms.

Classification of Animals

Biologists have already identified and named more than 1.5 million animal species. Each year they discover more. Classifying, or sorting animals into categories, helps biologists make sense of this diversity. **An animal is classified based on how it looks, how it develops, and the content of its DNA. Its classification reveals its relationship to other animals.**

Biologists have defined about 35 major groups of animals, each of which is called a **phylum** (FY lum). All **vertebrates,** or animals with a backbone, are classified in only one phylum. All the other animal phyla contain **invertebrates,** or animals without backbones. In fact, of all the types of animals, approximately 97 percent are invertebrates!

 **Reading Checkpoint** What is a phylum?

FIGURE 3
Discovering New Species
Every year, scientists discover new species. This biologist is surveying the leaves of rainforest plants for new insect species.

Section 1 Assessment

🎯 **Target Reading Skill** Asking Questions Use the answers to the questions you wrote about the headings to help you answer the questions below.

Reviewing Key Concepts

1. **a. Defining** What is the basic unit of structure and function in an animal?
   b. Sequencing Arrange in order from simplest to most complex structure: tissue, system, cell, organ.
2. **a. Reviewing** What are four major functions of animals?
   b. Explaining Why must animals obtain food?

   c. Drawing Conclusions Why is movement important for animals?
3. **a. Defining** What is a vertebrate?
   b. Classifying How do biologists classify animals?

Writing in Science

Functional Description Write a few paragraphs about how your classroom pet or a pet at home performs the basic functions of an animal.

Animal Symmetry

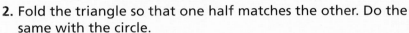

Reading Preview

Key Concepts
- What is symmetry?
- What can you infer about an animal based on its symmetry?

Key Terms
- bilateral symmetry
- radial symmetry

Target Reading Skill
Comparing and Contrasting
As you read, compare and contrast the characteristics of animals with bilateral and radial symmetry in a Venn diagram like the one below. Write the similarities where the circles overlap, and write the differences on the left and right sides.

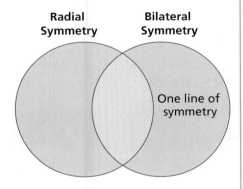

Radial Symmetry | Bilateral Symmetry

One line of symmetry

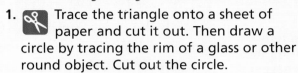

Discover **Activity**

How Many Ways Can You Fold It?

1. Trace the triangle onto a sheet of paper and cut it out. Then draw a circle by tracing the rim of a glass or other round object. Cut out the circle.
2. Fold the triangle so that one half matches the other. Do the same with the circle.
3. See how many different ways you can fold each figure so that the two halves are identical.

Think It Over
Classifying Name an animal whose body shape can be folded in the same number of ways as the triangle.

Bright colors and dark lines crisscross a butterfly's wings in an intricate design. Have you ever watched a butterfly? If so, you may have noticed that the pattern on its left side is a mirror image of the pattern on the right.

The Mathematics of Symmetry

Like a butterfly, most animals have a balanced arrangement of body parts. **The balanced arrangement of parts in animals and other objects is called symmetry.** Look at Figure 5 on page 264 to contrast the types of symmetry. An object has **bilateral symmetry** if there is just one line that divides it into equal halves that are mirror images. This single line is called a line of symmetry.

Objects with **radial symmetry** have many lines of symmetry that all go through a central point. Objects that cannot be divided into equal halves by a line have no symmetry.

FIGURE 4
Butterfly Halves
If you could draw a line through this butterfly's body, it would divide the animal into two mirror-image halves.
Applying Concepts *What is this balanced arrangement called?*

Bilateral Symmetry

Radial Symmetry

No Symmetry

FIGURE 5
Types of Symmetry
Animals have either bilateral or radial symmetry, except for most sponges, which usually have no symmetry.

Go Online
SCiLINKS™ NSTA

For: Links on animal symmetry
Visit: www.SciLinks.org
Web Code: scn-0212

Symmetry and Daily Life

With the exception of most sponges, animal bodies are symmetrical. **You can infer some general characteristics of an animal based on the kind of symmetry it has.**

The external body parts of animals with radial symmetry are equally spaced around a central point, like spokes on a bicycle wheel. Animals with radial symmetry, such as the sea star in Figure 5, do not have distinct front or back ends.

Most animals you know have bilateral symmetry. In general, animals with bilateral symmetry are larger and more complex than those with radial symmetry. Animals with bilateral symmetry move more quickly and efficiently than most animals with radial symmetry. Animals with bilateral symmetry have a front end that typically goes first as the animals move along. Most animals with bilateral symmetry have sense organs, such as eyes and a nose, in their front ends that pick up information about what is in front of them.

Reading Checkpoint Where are the sense organs of an animal with bilateral symmetry typically found?

Section 2 Assessment

Target Reading Skill Comparing and Contrasting Use the information in your Venn diagram about symmetry to help you answer Question 1 below.

Reviewing Key Concepts

1. a. **Reviewing** What is symmetry?
   b. **Comparing and Contrasting** How are bilateral symmetry and radial symmetry alike? How are they different?
   c. **Applying Concepts** What kind of symmetry does a grasshopper have? Explain.
2. a. **Identifying** What general characteristics do animals with radial symmetry share?
   b. **Summarizing** What four body characteristics do animals with bilateral symmetry usually have?

Lab zone **At-Home Activity**

Front-End Advantages With a family member, observe as many different animals as possible in a yard or at a park. Look in lots of different places, such as in the grass, under rocks, and in the air. Explain the advantages an animal with a distinct front end has. Tell the person what this type of body arrangement is called.

Sponges, Cnidarians, Worms, and Mollusks

Reading Preview

Key Concepts
- What are the main characteristics of sponges?
- What are the main characteristics of cnidarians?
- What are the main characteristics of each phylum of worms?
- What are the main characteristics of the major groups of mollusks?

Key Terms
- larva • cnidarian • medusa
- polyp • parasite • host
- mollusk • gastropod
- bivalve • cephalopod

 Target Reading Skill

Comparing and Contrasting
As you read, compare and contrast sponges and cnidarians by completing a table like this one.

Sponges and Cnidarians

Feature	Sponge	Cnidarian
Body structure	Hollow bag with pores	
Cell type that traps food		
Method(s) of reproduction		

Lab zone Discover **Activity**

How Do Natural and Synthetic Sponges Compare?

1. Examine a natural sponge, and then use a hand lens or a microscope to take a closer look. Look carefully at the holes in the sponge. Draw what you see through the lens.
2. ✂ Cut out a small piece of sponge and examine it with a hand lens. Draw what you see.
3. Repeat Steps 1 and 2 with a synthetic kitchen sponge.

Think It Over
Observing What are three ways a natural and a synthetic sponge are similar? What are three ways they are different?

The animal kingdom contains not only familiar organisms such as worms, clams, humans, cats, and dogs. It also contains organisms that look as strange as creatures from a science fiction movie. A few of these unusual organisms are invertebrates called sponges.

Sponges

Sponges live all over the world—mostly in oceans, but also in freshwater rivers and lakes. **Sponges are invertebrate animals that usually have no body symmetry and never have tissues or organs.**

Body Structure and Function A sponge looks something like a hollow bag with a large opening at one end and many tiny pores covering its surface. In fact, the name of the phylum to which sponges belong—phylum Porifera—means "having pores."

Adult sponges are attached to hard surfaces underwater. Water currents carry food and oxygen to them and take away their waste products. A sponge's food consists of tiny one-celled organisms strained from the water. Water currents also play a role in their reproduction and help transport their young to new places to live.

◀ **Diver investigating a barrel sponge**

> **Go Online active art**
>
> **For:** Structure of a Sponge activity
> **Visit:** PHSchool.com
> **Web Code:** cep-2013

A sponge gets its oxygen from water, too. After the water moves through a sponge's pores, it passes over cells inside the sponge. Oxygen in the water then moves into the sponge's cells.

Reproduction Sponges reproduce both asexually and sexually. Budding is one form of asexual reproduction in sponges. In budding, small new sponges grow from the sides of an adult sponge. Eventually, the buds break free and begin life on their own. Sponges reproduce sexually, too, but they do not have separate sexes. A sponge produces both sperm cells and egg cells. The sperm cells are released into the water. They enter another sponge and fertilize its egg. After fertilization, a larva develops. A **larva** (plural larvae) is an immature form of an animal that looks very different from the adult.

FIGURE 6
Structure of a Sponge

Structures surrounding the central cavity are adapted for different functions.
Interpreting Diagrams *Which kind of cell in the sponge digests and distributes food?*

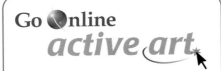

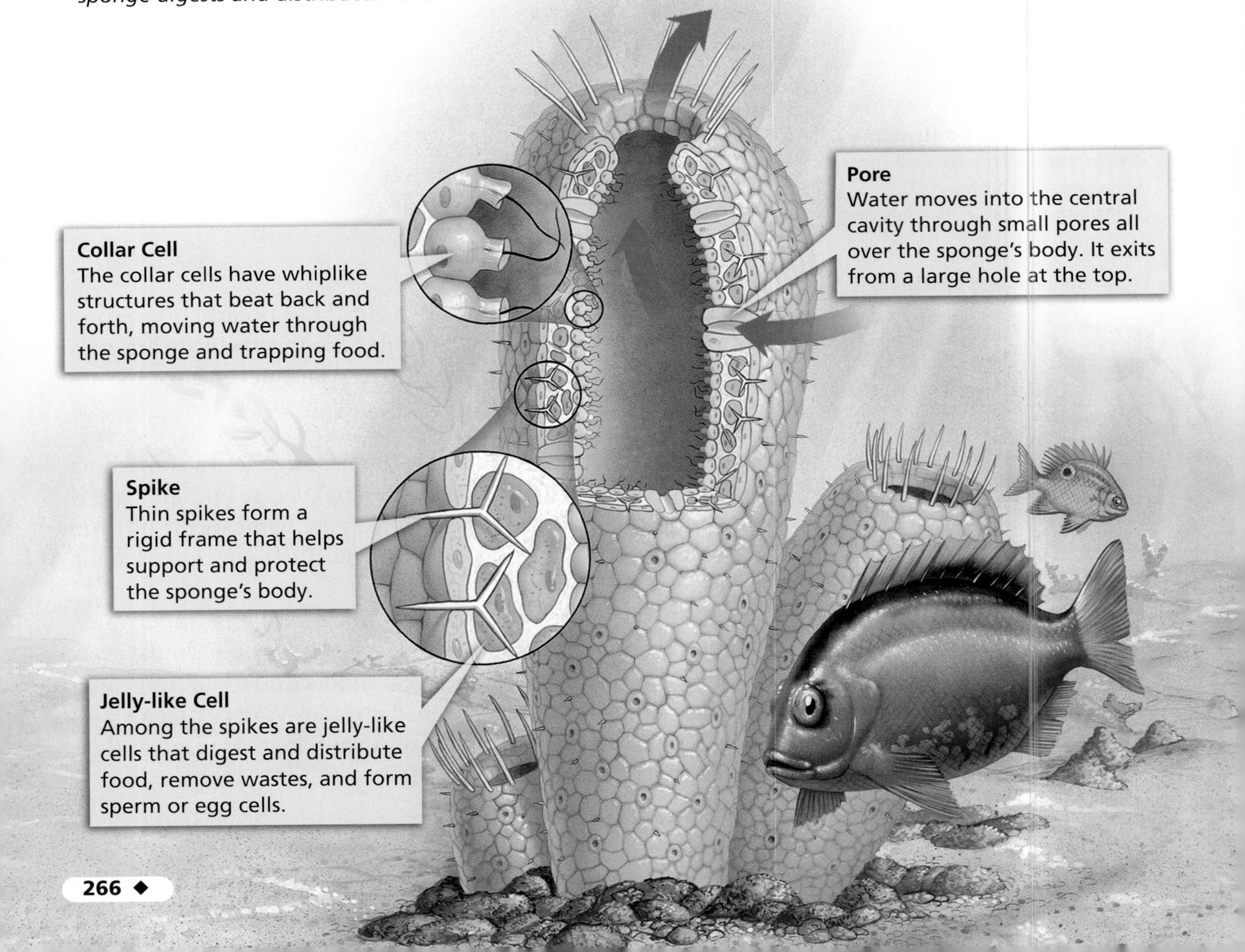

Pore
Water moves into the central cavity through small pores all over the sponge's body. It exits from a large hole at the top.
Collar Cell
The collar cells have whiplike structures that beat back and forth, moving water through the sponge and trapping food.
Spike
Thin spikes form a rigid frame that helps support and protect the sponge's body.
Jelly-like Cell
Among the spikes are jelly-like cells that digest and distribute food, remove wastes, and form sperm or egg cells.

Polyp

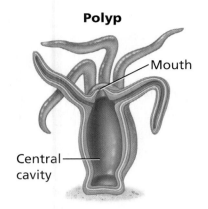
Mouth

Central cavity

Medusa

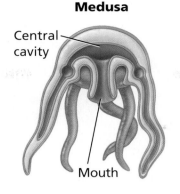
Central cavity

Mouth

FIGURE 7
Cnidarian Body Plans
Cnidarians have two basic body forms, the vase-shaped polyp and the bowl-shaped medusa.
Comparing and Contrasting
Contrast the location of the mouth in the polyp and the medusa.

Cnidarians

If you went on an underwater dive you might notice jellyfishes, corals, and sea anemones—three types of **cnidarians** (ny DEHR ee unz). **Cnidarians are invertebrate animals that use stinging cells to capture food and defend themselves.**

Body Structure and Movement Cnidarians have two different body plans, which you can see in Figure 7. Both plans have radial symmetry, a central hollow cavity, and tentacles that contain stinging cells. The bowl-shaped body plan is called a **medusa** (muh DOO suh). A medusa is adapted for a swimming life. Medusas have mouths that open downward and tentacles that trail down.

The vase-shaped body plan is called a **polyp** (PAHL ip). A polyp's mouth opens at the top and its tentacles spread out from around the mouth. Most polyps are adapted for a life attached to an underwater surface. Tiny polyps called coral live in warm, shallow ocean waters, mainly in tropical regions. The polyps produce limestone structures that build up to form coral reefs. The top layer of a reef is covered with thousands of live coral polyps.

Feeding and Reproduction Cnidarians' stinging cells are key to obtaining food. Some stinging cells inject venom, a substance that paralyzes prey. The cnidarian's tentacles pull the prey to the mouth to a central cavity where it is digested.

Cnidarians reproduce both asexually and sexually. For polyps such as hydras and corals, budding is the most common form of asexual reproduction. Sexual reproduction in cnidarians occurs in a variety of ways. Some species of cnidarians have both sexes within one individual. In others the sexes are in separate individuals. Many cnidarians have life cycles, or a sequence of different stages of development.

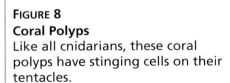
FIGURE 8
Coral Polyps
Like all cnidarians, these coral polyps have stinging cells on their tentacles.

Reading Checkpoint What adaptation allows cnidarians to stun prey and defend themselves?

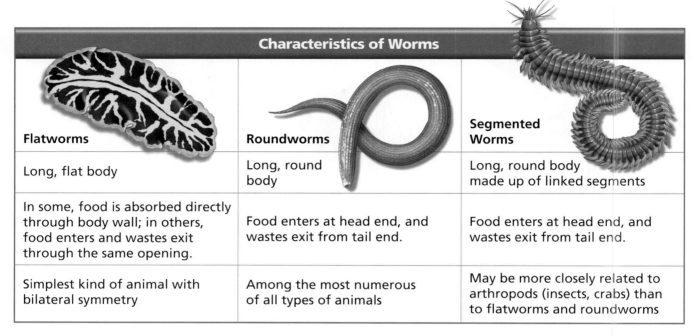

Characteristics of Worms		
Flatworms	**Roundworms**	**Segmented Worms**
Long, flat body	Long, round body	Long, round body made up of linked segments
In some, food is absorbed directly through body wall; in others, food enters and wastes exit through the same opening.	Food enters at head end, and wastes exit from tail end.	Food enters at head end, and wastes exit from tail end.
Simplest kind of animal with bilateral symmetry	Among the most numerous of all types of animals	May be more closely related to arthropods (insects, crabs) than to flatworms and roundworms

FIGURE 9
Three Phyla of Worms
The three major phyla of worms are flatworms, roundworms, and segmented worms.
Observing *How are the body shapes of these three types of worms similar? How are they different?*

Worms

Biologists classify worms into three major phyla—flatworms, roundworms, and segmented worms. Flatworms belong to the phylum Platyhelminthes (plat ee HEL minth eez); roundworms belong to the phylum Nematoda; segmented worms to the phylum Annelida.

All worms are invertebrates with long, narrow bodies and no legs. Their cells are organized into tissues, organs, and body systems. Unlike sponges or cnidarians, worms have bilateral symmetry. Therefore, they have head and tail ends. Worms are the simplest organisms with a brain found in the head end.

Both sexual and asexual reproduction are found in the worm phyla. In many species, there are separate male and female animals, as in humans. In other species of worms, each individual has male and female sex organs.

Flatworms Flatworms include tapeworms, planarians, and flukes. **Flatworms are flat and as soft as jelly.**

Many flatworms are parasites. A **parasite** is an organism that lives inside or on another organism. The parasite takes its food from its **host**, the organism in or on which it lives. All tapeworms and flukes are parasites. There are also some free-living flatworms. A free-living organism does not live in or on other organisms.

Roundworms Unlike flatworms, roundworms have cylindrical bodies. **Unlike cnidarians or flatworms, roundworms have a digestive system that is like a tube, open at both ends.** Food enters at the roundworm's mouth, and wastes exit through the anus, at the far end of the tube.

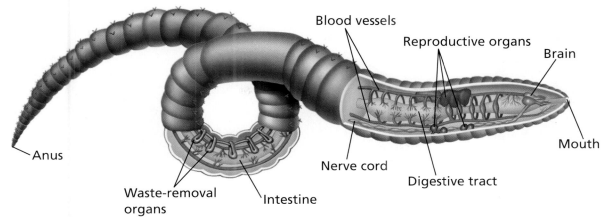

Blood vessels

Reproductive organs

Brain

Mouth

Digestive tract

Nerve cord

Intestine

Waste-removal organs

Anus

There are advantages to a one-way digestive system like that of the roundworm. It allows digestion to happen in orderly stages—from breaking down food to eliminating wastes. This enables the animal's body to absorb much of the needed substances in foods.

Segmented Worms Earthworms, leeches and some sea-floor worms are segmented worms. **Segmented worms have bodies made up of many linked sections called segments.** Look at the diagram of the earthworm in Figure 10. On the outside, the segments look nearly alike. On the inside, some organs are repeated in most segments. Other organs are found only in certain segments.

Segmented worms have a closed circulatory system in which blood moves within a connected network of tubes called blood vessels. Some other animals, including snails and lobsters, have an open circulatory system in which blood leaves the blood vessels and sloshes around inside the body. The blood carries oxygen and food to cells. A closed circulatory system can move blood around an animal's body much more quickly than can an open circulatory system.

 **What type of symmetry do worms have?**

Mollusks

Snails, slugs, and octopuses are invertebrates called **mollusks** (phylum Mollusca). **Mollusks have soft, unsegmented bodies often covered by shells and a thin layer of tissue called a mantle that covers their internal organs, and an organ called a foot.** In various mollusks, the foot is adapted for different functions, such as crawling, digging, or catching prey. In many mollusks, the mantle produces a hard shell. Mollusks have bilateral symmetry and a digestive system with two openings.

Biologists classify mollusks into three major groups based on their physical characteristics. These groups are gastropods (snails and slugs), bivalves (clams and oysters), and cephalopods (octopuses and squids).

FIGURE 10
Structure of an Earthworm
An earthworm's body is divided into more than 100 segments. Some organs are repeated in most of those segments. Other organs exist in only a few segments.
Interpreting Diagrams
Name an example of a body system that runs through all of the worm's segments.

For: More on worms
Visit: PHSchool.com
Web Code: ced-2014

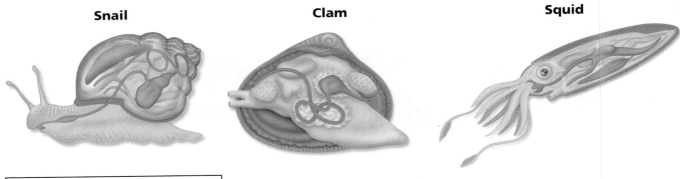

Snail

Clam

Squid

Key

Shell

Mantle

Foot

Gills

Digestive tract

FIGURE 11

A Comparison of Mollusks

Although they don't look much alike at first, a snail, a clam, and a squid have the same basic body structures.

Gastropods are the largest group of mollusks. **Gastropods are mollusks that have a single external shell or no shell at all.** Gastropods feed using a radula, a flexible ribbon of tiny teeth. Some gastropods are herbivores, animals that eat plants.

Bivalves are found in all kinds of watery environments. **Bivalves are mollusks that have two shells held together by hinges and strong muscles.**

Cephalopods are the only mollusks with a closed circulatory system. **A cephalopod is an ocean-dwelling mollusk whose foot is adapted to form tentacles around the mouth.** Cephalopods swim by jet propulsion. They squeeze a current of water out of the space surrounded by the mantle through a tube. Like rockets, they shoot off in the opposite direction.

 **Reading Checkpoint** What are the three main groups of mollusks?

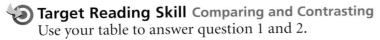

Section 3 Assessment

Target Reading Skill Comparing and Contrasting Use your table to answer question 1 and 2.

Reviewing Key Concepts

1. a. Describing What are the characteristics of a sponge?
  b. Comparing and Contrasting How are the cells of a sponge alike? How are they different?

2. a. Listing List three characteristics that all cnidarians share.
  b. Inferring How might a cnidarian protect itself?

3. a. Listing What are the three main phyla of worms?
  b. Classifying Suppose you use a microscope to look at a tiny worm. What characteristics would you look for to classify it?

4. a. Listing List the characteristics of a mollusk.
  b. Identifying What are three groups of mollusks?

Lab zone At-Home Activity

Edible Mollusks Visit a local supermarket with a family member and identify any mollusks that are being sold as food. Be sure to look in places other than the fish counter, such as the canned-foods section. Discuss the parts of the mollusks that are used for food and the parts that are not edible.

Earthworm Responses

Problem

Do earthworms prefer dry or moist conditions?
Do they prefer light or dark conditions?

Skills Focus

observing, interpreting data

Materials

- plastic dropper   • water   • cardboard
- clock or watch   • paper towels   • flashlight
- 2 earthworms   • storage container   • tray

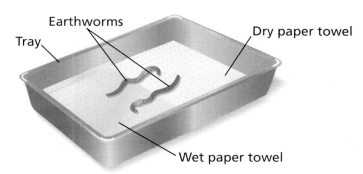

Earthworms

Tray

Dry paper towel

Wet paper towel

Procedure

1. Which environment do you think earthworms prefer—dry or moist? Record your hypothesis in your notebook.

2. Use the dropper to sprinkle water on the worms. Keep the worms moist at all times.

3. Fold a dry paper towel and place it on the bottom of one side of your tray. Fold a moistened paper towel and place it on the other side.

4. Moisten your hands. Then place the earthworms in the center of the tray. Make sure that half of each earthworm's body rests on the moist paper towel and half rests on the dry towel. Handle the worms gently.

5. Cover the tray with the piece of cardboard. After five minutes, remove the cardboard and observe whether the worms are on the moist or dry surface. Record your observations.

6. Repeat Steps 4 and 5.

7. Return the earthworms to their storage container. Moisten the earthworms with water.

8. Which do you think earthworms prefer— strong light or darkness? Record your hypothesis in your notebook.

9. Cover the whole surface of the tray with a moistened paper towel.

10. Place the earthworms in the center of the tray. Cover half of the tray with cardboard. Shine a flashlight onto the other half.

11. After five minutes, note the locations of the worms. Record your observations.

12. Repeat Steps 10 and 11.

13. Moisten the earthworms and put them in the location designated by your teacher. Wash your hands after handling the worms.

Analyze and Conclude

1. **Observing** Which environment did the worms prefer—moist or dry? Bright or dark?

2. **Interpreting Data** Did the worms' behavior support your hypotheses?

3. **Communicating** Explain in a paragraph what knowledge or experiences helped you develop your hypotheses at the beginning of the experiments.

Design an Experiment

Do earthworms prefer a smooth or rough surface? Write your hypothesis. Then design an experiment to answer the question. *Obtain your teacher's permission before carrying out your investigation.*

Arthropods and Echinoderms

Reading Preview

Key Concepts
- What are the main characteristics of arthropods?
- Besides insects, what are the three other major groups of arthropods and how do they differ?
- What are the main characteristics of echinoderms?

Key Terms
- arthropod • exoskeleton
- molting • insect • crustacean
- metamorphosis • arachnid
- echinoderm • endoskeleton
- water vascular system
- tube feet

Target Reading Skill
Asking Questions Before you read, preview the red headings. In a graphic organizer like the one below, ask a *what* or a *how* question for each heading. As you read, write the answers to your questions.

Characteristics of Arthropods

Question	Answer
What is an arthropod?	

FIGURE 12
Black Ants
Ants belong to the arthropod phylum

Discover **Activity**

Will It Bend and Move?
1. Have a partner roll a piece of cardboard around your arm to form a tube that covers your elbow. Your partner should put three pieces of tape around the tube to hold it closed—one at each end and one in the middle.
2. With the tube in place, try to write your name on a piece of paper. Then try to scratch your head.
3. Keep the tube on your arm for 10 minutes. Observe how the tube affects your ability to do things.

Think It Over
Inferring Insects and many other animals have rigid skeletons on the outside of their bodies. Why do their skeletons need joints?

You spread out a blanket and open the picnic basket. You've had just a few bites of your sandwich when you notice some uninvited guests. Ants! They're collecting the crumbs you dropped and are searching for more. One ant uses its front two legs to grasp a large crumb and then walks away on the other four legs. You notice that the legs are jointed, and move very quickly as the ant scurries home with its prize.

Characteristics of Arthropods

The ant is a member of the **arthropod** phylum (phylum Arthropoda), a group that includes animals such as grasshoppers, crabs, lobsters, centipedes, and spiders. **Arthropods are invertebrates that have an external skeleton, a segmented body, and jointed attachments called appendages.**

Comparisons of the Largest Arthropod Groups				
Characteristic	Crustaceans	Arachnids	Centipedes and Millipedes	Insects
Number of body sections	2 or 3	2	2	3
Pairs of legs	5 or more	4	Many	3
Pairs of antennae	2	None	1	1

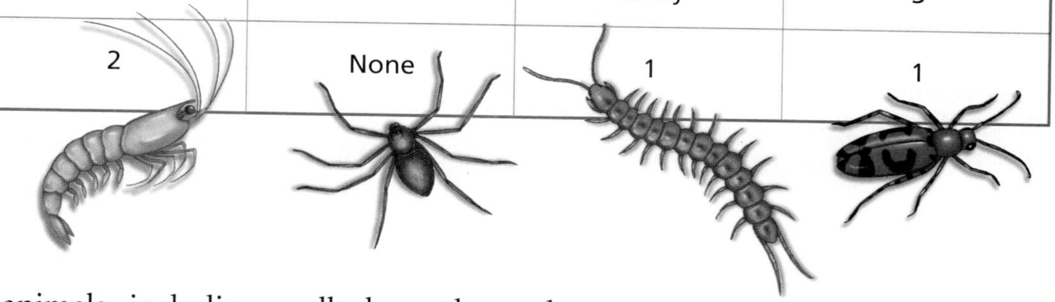

FIGURE 13
Arthropod groups differ in several characteristics.
Interpreting Tables *Which group of arthropods has no antennae?*

Like some other animals, including mollusks, arthropods have bilateral symmetry, an open circulatory system, and a digestive system with two openings. In most arthropods reproduce sexually. Scientists have identified more species of arthropods—more than one million—than all other species of animals combined!

External Skeleton As an arthropod grows larger, its waxy **exoskeleton,** or waterproof outer covering, cannot expand. The growing arthropod is trapped in its exoskeleton, like a knight in armor that is too small. Arthropods solve this problem by occasionally shedding their exoskeletons and growing new ones that are larger. The process of shedding an outgrown exoskeleton is called **molting.** After an arthropod has molted, its new skeleton is soft for a time.

Segmented Body Arthropods' bodies are segmented. The segmented body plan is easiest to see in centipedes and millipedes. You can also see segments on shrimp and lobster tails. In some groups of arthropods, several body segments are grouped together, forming distinct sections.

Jointed Appendages Many arthropods have jointed appendages attached to their bodies, just as your fingers are appendages attached to your palms. Joints give an animal flexibility and enable it to move. Arthropods have specialized appendages used for functions such as walking, obtaining food, reproducing, and sensing the environment.

 **Reading Checkpoint** **What is one type of jointed appendage found on an arthropod and what is its function?**

Go Online
SCi LINKS NSTA

For: Links on arthropods
Visit: www.SciLinks.org
Web Code: scn-0222

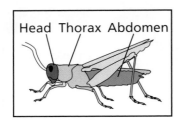

Insects

The major groups of arthropods are insects, crustaceans, centipedes, and millipedes. The largest arthropod group is the insects.

Characteristics of Insects A butterfly is an **insect**, as are dragonflies, grasshoppers, and bees. **Insects are arthropods with three body sections, six legs, one pair of antennae, and usually one or two pairs of wings.** The three body regions are the head, thorax, and abdomen as shown in Figure 14.

Life Cycle Insects begin life as tiny, hard-shelled, fertilized eggs. After they hatch, insects develop into adults by **metamorphosis** (met uh MAWR fuh sis), a process in which an animal's body undergoes dramatic changes in form during its life cycle. Each species of insect undergoes one or two different types of metamorphosis. Complete metamorphosis has four different stages: egg, larva, pupa, and adult. Eggs hatch into larvae. After a time, the larvae enters the next stage of the process, which is called the pupa. Major changes in the body structure take place in this stage, as the pupa becomes an adult. Beetles, butterflies, flies, and ants all undergo complete metamorphosis.

In contrast, the second type of metamorphosis, called gradual metamorphosis, has no distinctly different larval stage. An egg hatches into a stage called a nymph (nimf), which usually looks like the adult insect without the wings. Grasshoppers, termites, cockroaches, and dragonflies go through gradual metamorphosis.

Crustaceans

Crustaceans (krus TAY shunz) include animals such as shrimp, crab, crayfish and lobsters. Nearly every kind of watery environment is home to crustaceans. A few kinds of crustaceans live in damp places on land. **Crustaceans are arthropods with two or three body sections, five or more pairs of legs, and two pairs of antennae.** Each body segment has a pair of legs or another appendage attached to it.

Obtaining Food and Oxygen Crustaceans obtain food in several ways. Many are scavengers that eat dead plants and animals. Others are predators, eating animals they have killed. Like mollusks, water-dwelling crustaceans use gills to obtain oxygen. Their gills are beneath the hard shell, on the head and midsection. Water reaches a crustacean's gills from its underside.

Life Cycle Most crustaceans begin their lives as microscopic, swimming larvae. Crustacean larvae develop into adults by metamorphosis.

Arachnids

Spiders, mites, ticks, and scorpions are the types of **arachnids** (uh RAK nidz) that people most often encounter. **Arachnids are arthropods with two body sections, four pairs of legs, and no antennae.** Their first body section is a combined head and midsection. The hind section, called the abdomen, contains the reproductive organs and part of the digestive system.

Spiders All spiders are predators, and most of them eat insects. Some spiders run down prey. Others spin sticky webs and wait for prey to become trapped.

Spiders have hollow fangs through which they inject venom into their prey. Spider venom turns prey's tissues into mush. Later the spider uses its fangs like drinking straws, sucking in the food. Spiders rarely bite people. When they do bite, most spider bites are painful but not life-threatening. However, the bite of a brown recluse or a black widow may require hospital care.

Ticks Ticks are parasites that live on the outside of a host animal's body. Nearly every kind of land animal has a species of tick that sucks its blood. Some ticks that attack humans can carry diseases. Lyme disease, for example, is spread by the bite of an infected deer tick. You can see a greatly enlarged deer tick in Figure 15.

Mites If chiggers have ever given you an itchy rash, you've had an unpleasant encounter with tiny arachnids called mites. Chiggers and other mites are parasites. Ear mites, for example, give dogs and cats itchy ears. Mites are everywhere. Even the cleanest houses have microscopic dust mites. If you are allergic to dust, you may actually be allergic to the exoskeletons of dust mites. Mites also live in fresh water and in the ocean.

FIGURE 15
Arachnids
This red knee tarantula lives in an underground burrow and uses its fangs to inject venom into its prey. Before this deer tick filled up on blood, it was about the size of a poppy seed.

FIGURE 16
Dust Mite
This microscopic dust mite feeds on dead skin and hair shed by humans.

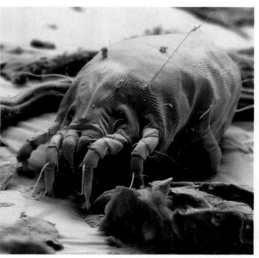

Scorpions Scorpions, which live mainly in hot climates, are also arachnids. They usually are active at night. During the day, scorpions hide in cool places—under rocks and logs, or in holes in the ground, for example. At the end of its abdomen, a scorpion has a spinelike stinger. The scorpion uses the stinger to inject venom into its prey, which is usually a spider or an insect.

 **What are the names of four groups of arachnids?**

Centipedes and Millipedes

You can quickly count the legs of most arthropods, except for centipedes and millipedes. **Centipedes and millipedes are arthropods with two body sections and numerous pairs of legs.** The two body sections are a head with one pair of antennae, and a long abdomen with many segments.

You can see in Figure 18 that centipedes have one pair of legs attached to each segment. Centipedes are swift predators. They inject venom from a pair of claws near their mouths into the smaller animals that they catch for food.

Millipedes, which may have more than 80 segments, have two pairs of legs on each segment—more legs than any other arthropod. Most millipedes are scavengers that graze on partly decayed leaves. When they are disturbed, millipedes can curl up into a ball, protected by their tough exoskeleton. Some will also squirt an awful-smelling liquid at a potential predator.

 **How do centipedes and millipedes differ?**

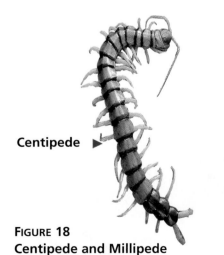

Centipede ▶

FIGURE 18
Centipede and Millipede
Both centipedes and millipedes have numerous pairs of legs. Centipedes are carnivores, while millipedes are herbivores.

Millipede

Echinoderms

The sea star on this page is an **echinoderm** (ee KY noh durmz), member of the phylum Echinodermata. **Echinoderms are invertebrates with an internal skeleton and a system of fluid-filled tubes called a water vascular system.** All echinoderms live in salt water.

Body Structure The skin of most echinoderms is supported by an internal skeleton, or **endoskeleton,** made of hardened plates. Adult echinoderms have a unique kind of radical symmetry in which the body parts usually in multiples of five, are arranged like the spokes of a wheel.

The internal system of fluid-filled tubes in echinoderms is called the **water vascular system.** You can see the sea star's water vascular system in Figure 19. Portions of the tubes can contract, forcing water into connected structures called **tube feet**. The ends of tube feet are sticky and, when filled with water, they act like small, sticky suction cups. The stickiness and suction enable the tube feet to grip the surface beneath the echinoderm.

Reproduction and Life Cycle Most echinoderms are either male or female. Eggs are usually fertilized in the seawater, after a female releases her eggs and a male releases his sperm. The fertilized eggs develop into tiny, swimming larvae that look very different from the adults. The larvae eventually undergo metamorphosis and become adult echinoderms.

Go Online
active art

For: Structure of a Sea Star activity
Visit: PHSchool.com
Web Code: cep-2025

FIGURE 19
Water Vascular System
Echinoderms, such as this sea star, have a water vascular system that helps them move and catch food.
Interpreting Diagrams *Where does water enter the water vascular system?*

Stomach

Tube Feet
The sea star uses tube feet, which line the underside of its arms, to move and capture food.

Bumpy spines

Opening for Water
Water enters the water vascular system partly through an opening in this round plate. Some water probably enters through the tube feet, too.

Water Vascular System
The sea star's water vascular system extends into each arm. Notice that tube feet are part of the water vascular system.

Eyespot

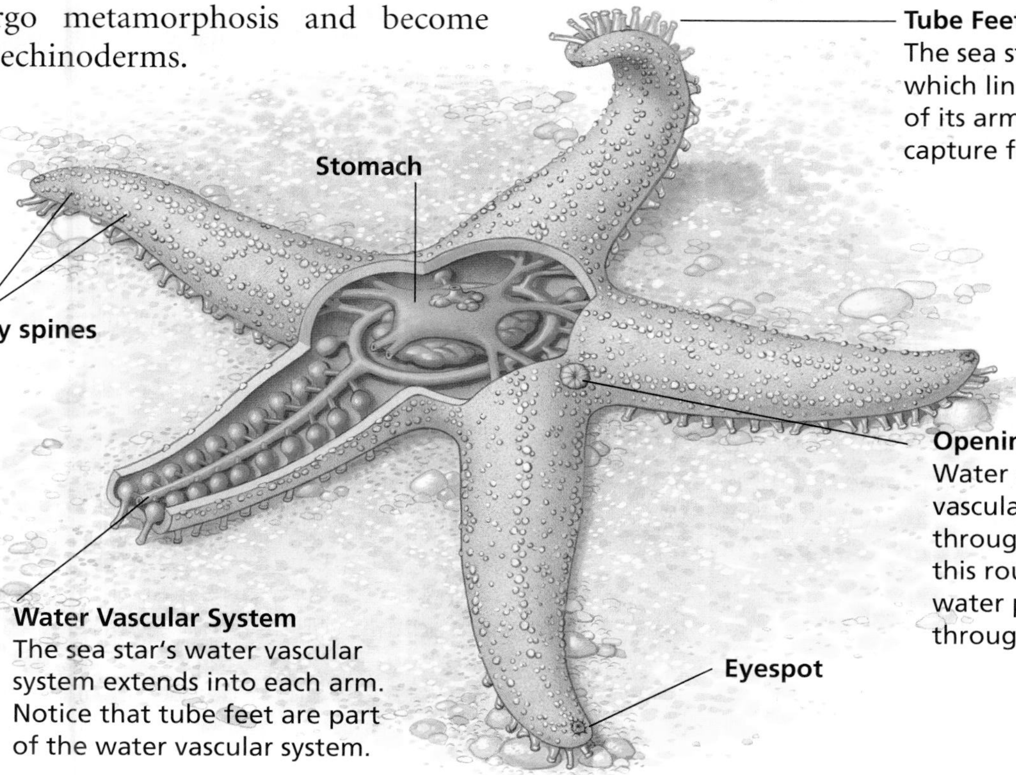

▲ Sea urchins eating seaweed

▲ Sea star eating a clam

▲ Sea cucumber crawling on the ocean floor

FIGURE 20
Diversity of Echinoderms

Echinoderms are diverse in their appearance, but all have radial symmetry and are found in the ocean.

Diversity of Echinoderms Although echinoderms share many internal features, the major groups do not look much alike from the outside. They also have quite different ways of feeding and moving. The major groups of echinoderms are sea stars, brittle stars, sea urchins, and sea cucumbers. Each group's name describes its appearance, as you can see by examining Figure 20.

 Reading Checkpoint **What are the major groups of echinoderms?**

Section 4 Assessment

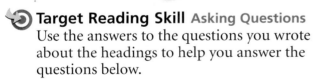 **Target Reading Skill** Asking Questions Use the answers to the questions you wrote about the headings to help you answer the questions below.

Reviewing Key Concepts

1. a. **Naming** What are the major groups of arthropods?
   b. **Summarizing** How are all arthropods alike?
   c. **Applying Concepts** Some restaurants serve soft-shelled crab. What do you think happened to the crab just before it was caught?
2. a. **Identifying** What characterizes a crustacean? An arachnid?
   b. **Comparing and Contrasting** How are centipedes and millipedes alike? How are they different?
3. a. **Reviewing** What characteristics do echinoderms have?
   b. **Summarizing** How does an echinoderm use its tube feet to grip a surface?
   c. **Inferring** Why is movement using tube feet slow?

Writing in Science

Descriptive Paragraph Write about an arthropod that you have observed. Describe details about its physical appearance, its movements, and any other behaviors that you observed.

Fishes, Amphibians, and Reptiles

Reading Preview

Key Concepts
- What characteristics do chordates share, and what characteristics do all vertebrates have?
- What are the main characteristics and groups of fishes?
- What is an amphibian, and how do amphibians differ in their larval and adult stages?
- What are reptiles and how are they adapted to life on land?

Key Terms
- chordate • notochord
- vertebrae • ectotherm
- endotherm • fish • cartilage
- swim bladder • amphibian
- lung • reptile • amniotic egg
- kidney

Target Reading Skill
Building Vocabulary A definition states the meaning of a word or phrase by telling about its most important feature or function. After you read the section, reread the paragraphs that contain definitions of Key Terms. Use all the information you have learned to write a definition of each Key Term in your own words.

Go Online
SciLINKS NSTA

For: Links on vertebrates
Visit: www.SciLinks.org
Web Code: scn-0231

Lab zone Discover **Activity**

How Is an Umbrella Like a Skeleton?

1. Open an umbrella. Turn it upside down and examine how it is made.
2. Now fold the umbrella and watch how the braces and ribs collapse.
3. Think of what would happen if you removed the ribs from the umbrella and then tried to use it during a rainstorm.

Think It Over
Inferring What is the function of the ribs of an umbrella? How are the ribs of the umbrella similar to the bones in your skeleton? How are they different?

Reach back and run your fingertips down the middle of your back. The "bumps" that you feel are the bones of your backbone, or spine. This characteristic is common to vertebrates. You, like so many other familiar animals, are a vertebrate.

Characteristics of Chordates

Members of the phylum Chordata are called **chordates** (KAWR dayts). **At some point in its life, a chordate will have a notochord, a nerve cord that runs down its back, and a slit in its throat area.** Vertebrates like fishes, amphibians, reptiles, birds, and mammals are chordates. The phylum contains a few invertebrates, too.

Chordates get their name from the **notochord,** the flexible rod that supports a chordate's back during part or all of its life. All chordates also have a nerve cord, like your spinal cord, that runs down the back. The nerve cord connects the brain and the nerves, on which messages travel back and forth.

At some point in their lives, chordates have slits in their throat area called gill slits. Invertebrate chordates and some vertebrates, such as fishes, keep these slits as part of their gills all their lives. In other vertebrates, the gill slits disappear before birth.

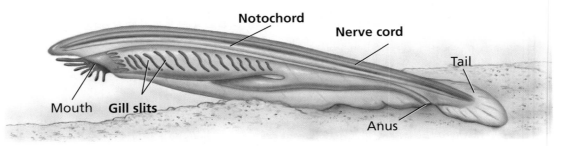

Notochord

Nerve cord

Tail

Mouth   Gill slits

Anus

Backbone

Characteristics of Vertebrates

Most chordates are vertebrates. In addition to the characteristics shared by all chordates, vertebrates share certain other characteristics.

Body Structure **A vertebrate has a backbone that is part of an internal skeletal system.** This endoskeleton supports the body and allows it to move. A vertebrate's backbone runs down the center of its back. The backbone is formed by many bones called **vertebrae** (singular *vertebra*). Joints between the vertebrae give the spine flexibility. Each vertebra has a hole in it that allows the spinal cord to pass through. The backbone protects the body, helps give it shape, and gives muscles a place to attach.

Keeping Conditions Stable One characteristic that distinguishes the major groups of vertebrates from each other is the way they control their body temperature. **The body temperature of most fishes, amphibians, and reptiles is close to the temperature of their environment. In contrast, birds and mammals have a stable body temperature that is often warmer than their environment.**

Fishes, amphibians, and reptiles are ectotherms. An **ectotherm** is an animal whose body does not produce much internal heat. Its body temperature changes depending on the temperature of its environment. An ectotherm regulates its temperature by moving to new locations in its environment.

An **endotherm** is an animal that regulates its body temperature by controlling the internal heat it produces. An endotherm's body temperature usually does not change much, even when the temperature of its environment changes. Birds and mammals are endotherms. Endotherms have adaptations, such as sweat glands and fur or feathers, for maintaining body temperature. On hot days, some endotherms sweat. As the sweat evaporates, the animal is cooled. On cool days, fur or feathers keep endotherms warm. Because endotherms can keep their body temperatures stable, they can live in a greater variety of environments than ectotherms can.

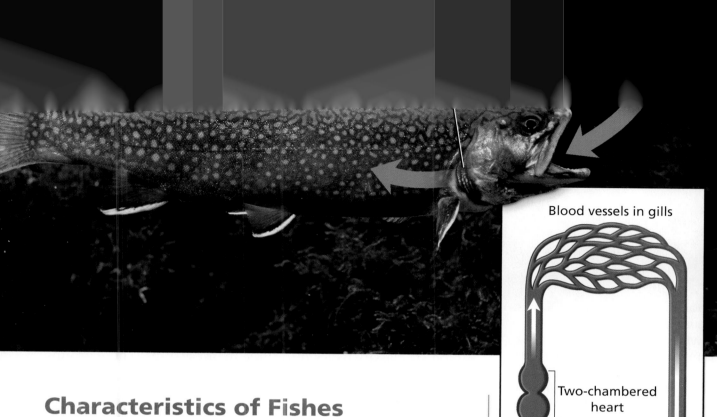

Characteristics of Fishes

Fish are the largest group of vertebrates—nearly half of all vertebrate species are fishes. **Fishes are vertebrates that live in water and have fins, most fishes are ectotherms, obtain oxygen through gills, and have scales.** Scales are thin overlapping plates that cover the skin. Fishes get their oxygen from water. As water flows over the gills, oxygen moves from the water into the fish's blood. You can trace the circular flow of blood through the fish's body using Figure 23.

Fins help fishes swim. A typical fin consists of a thin membrane stretched across bony supports. A fin provides a large surface to push against the water. The push created by this large surface allows for fast movement through water.

Most fishes reproduce by external fertilization. In external fertilization, a female's eggs are fertilized outside of her body. The male fish hovers close to the female and spreads a cloud of sperm over the eggs as she releases them. In contrast, some fishes, including sharks, reproduce by internal fertilization. In internal fertilization, eggs are fertilized inside the female's body. The young fishes develop inside her body. When they are mature enough, she gives birth.

A fish's nervous system and sense organs help it find food and avoid predators. Keen senses of sight, touch, smell, and taste help fishes capture food. Some fishes have taste organs in unusual places; for example, a catfish tastes with its whiskers.

 **Reading Checkpoint** **What are two forms of reproduction in fishes?**

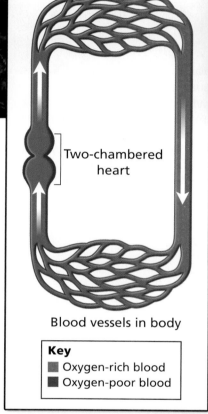

Blood vessels in gills

Two-chambered heart

Blood vessels in body

Key
■ Oxygen-rich blood
■ Oxygen-poor blood

FIGURE 23
Respiration and Circulation
Water flows into the mouth of this fish and then over its gills. Oxygen moves into the blood and is delivered to the cells of the fish.
Interpreting Diagrams *Where does the blood of a fish get oxygen?*

▲ Mouth

Groups of Fishes

Biologists classify fishes into three major groups. These groups are jawless fishes, cartilaginous fishes, and bony fishes.

Jawless Fishes Jaws are hinged bony structures that allow most types of fishes to open and close their mouths. **Jawless fishes are unlike other fishes in that they have no jaws and no scales.** Instead of jaws for biting and chewing their food, jawless fishes have mouths containing structures for scraping, stabbing, and sucking their food. Their skeletons are made of **cartilage,** a tissue that is more flexible than bone. Hagfishes and lampreys are the only kinds of jawless fishes.

Cartilaginous Fishes Sharks, rays, and skates are cartilaginous (kahr tuh LAJ uh nuhs) fishes. **Cartilaginous fishes have jaws, scales, and skeletons made of cartilage.** The scales on many cartilaginous fishes are sharp, giving their skin a texture that is rougher than sandpaper.

Most sharks cannot pump water over their gills. Instead, they must swim continuously or position themselves in currents to keep water moving across their gills. Rays and skates are not as active as sharks. They spend a lot of time partially buried in the sand of the ocean floor. During this time, they take in water through small holes located behind their eyes rather than though their mouths. Water leaves through gill openings on their undersides.

Most cartilaginous fishes are carnivores. Most rays and skates use their teeth to crush mollusks, crustaceans, and small fishes that they hunt on the ocean floor. Sharks will attack and eat nearly anything that smells like food. A shark can smell and taste even a tiny amount of blood—as little as one drop in 115 liters of water!

FIGURE 25
Blue-spotted Ray
This ray is a cartilaginous fish that lives on the ocean floor.

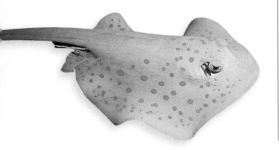

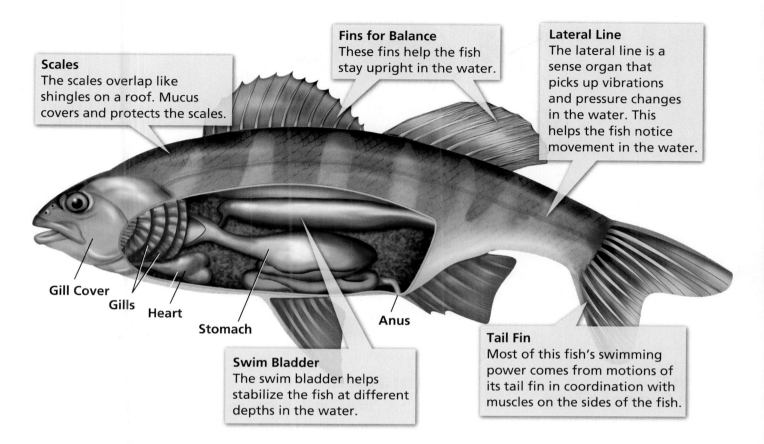

Scales
The scales overlap like shingles on a roof. Mucus covers and protects the scales.

Fins for Balance
These fins help the fish stay upright in the water.

Lateral Line
The lateral line is a sense organ that picks up vibrations and pressure changes in the water. This helps the fish notice movement in the water.

Gill Cover

Gills

Heart

Stomach

Anus

Swim Bladder
The swim bladder helps stabilize the fish at different depths in the water.

Tail Fin
Most of this fish's swimming power comes from motions of its tail fin in coordination with muscles on the sides of the fish.

FIGURE 26
Structure of a Bony Fish
This common freshwater fish, a yellow perch, shows the characteristics typical of a bony fish.

Bony Fishes Bony fishes make up about 95 percent of all fish species. Most familiar kinds of fishes, such as trout, tuna, and goldfishes, are bony fishes. **A bony fish has jaws, scales, a pocket on each side of the head that holds the gills, and a skeleton made of hard bone.** Each gill pocket is covered by a flexible flap that opens to release water. You can see the gill and other major structures of a bony fish in Figure 26.

A bony fish also has an organ called a **swim bladder,** an internal gas-filled sac that helps the fish stay stable at different depths in the water. Gas levels in the swim bladder are adjusted after the fish reaches its desired depth. By adjusting these levels, the fish can stay at a particular depth in the water without using a large amount of energy.

 **Reading Checkpoint** Which organ helps a bony fish maintain its position in the water?

Lab zone Skills Activity

Observing
Put on your goggles and disposable gloves. Observe a preserved fish on your desk and examine it closely. Note its size and shape, and the number and locations of its fins. Lift the gill cover and observe the gill with a hand lens. Make a diagram of your observations, and include a written description. Wash your hands.

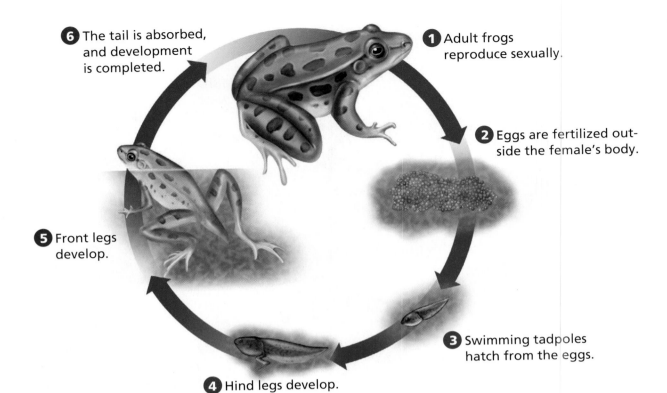

⑥ The tail is absorbed, and development is completed.

① Adult frogs reproduce sexually.

② Eggs are fertilized outside the female's body.

③ Swimming tadpoles hatch from the eggs.

④ Hind legs develop.

⑤ Front legs develop.

FIGURE 27
Life Cycle of a Frog
During its metamorphosis from tadpole to adult, a frog's body undergoes a series of dramatic changes. *Applying Concepts How do these changes prepare a frog for living on land?*

PHSchool.com

For: More on the frog life cycle
Visit: PHSchool.com
Web Code: ced-2033

Amphibians

Salamanders, frogs, and toads are **amphibians.** The word *amphibian* means "double life," and most amphibians have exactly that. **After beginning their lives in water, most amphibians spend their adulthood on land, returning to water to reproduce.** You can distinguish the two major groups of amphibians by the presence of a tail in the adults. Salamanders keep their tails in adulthood, while almost all frogs and toads do not.

Life Cycle Amphibian eggs are coated with clear jelly. Inside each fertilized egg, an embryo develops. In most amphibians, larvae wriggle out of the jelly after a few days and begin a free-swimming, fishlike life. The larvae of most amphibians grow and eventually undergo metamorphosis. You can trace the process of frog metamorphosis in Figure 27. The larva of a frog is called a tadpole.

Obtaining Oxygen and Food The adaptations of larvae and adult amphibians reflect their very different environments of water and land. Amphibian larvae swim and have gills for obtaining oxygen from water. As they become adults, most amphibians lose their gills and develop lungs. **Lungs** are organs of air-breathing vertebrates that exchange oxygen and carbon dioxide with the blood. In addition to breathing with lungs, adult amphibians also exchange gases through their thin, moist skin.

Tadpoles usually are herbivores that feed on rotting pond plants. Most adult frogs and toads are carnivores that feed on insects or other small animals. Rather than actively hunting their prey, frogs and toads usually wait until it comes close. In contrast, salamanders tend actively to stalk and ambush small invertebrates.

Circulatory System A tadpole's circulatory system has a single loop, like that of a fish. In contrast, the circulatory system of many adult amphibians has two loops. It also has a heart with three chambers. You can trace the path of blood through the amphibian's circulatory system in Figure 28. In the first loop, blood flows from the heart to the lungs and skin, and picks up oxygen. This oxygen-rich blood then returns to the heart. In the second loop, the blood flows to the rest of the body, delivering oxygen-rich blood to the cells.

Movement A land vertebrate has a strong skeleton that supports its body against the pull of gravity. In addition, a land animal needs some way of moving. Fins work in water, but they don't work on land. Most adult amphibians have strong skeletons and muscular limbs adapted for moving on land.

Frogs and toads have additional adaptations for another kind of movement—leaping. It requires powerful hind-leg muscles and a skeleton that can absorb the shock of landing.

Reading Checkpoint What is the term for a frog larva?

Go Online
active art

For: Respiration and Circulation activity
Visit: PHSchool.com
Web Code: cep-2032

FIGURE 28
Respiration and Circulation
Most adult amphibians such as this salamander, have internal lungs and a double-loop circulatory system.

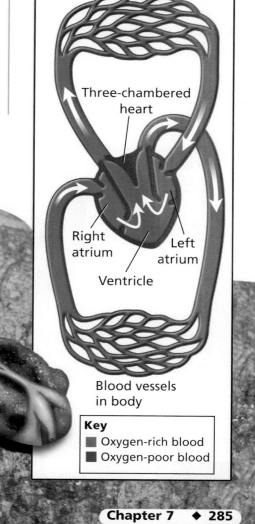

Blood vessels in lungs

Three-chambered heart

Right atrium

Left atrium

Ventricle

Blood vessels in body

Lungs

Key
■ Oxygen-rich blood
■ Oxygen-poor blood

Reptiles

The **reptile** group includes familiar animals such as lizards and alligators. **Reptiles are ectothermic vertebrates with scaly skin that lay their eggs on land.** The skin, eggs, and kidneys of reptiles are particularly adapted to conserve water.

Reptiles get their oxygen from air and breathe entirely with lungs. Even reptiles that live in water breathe with lungs and come ashore to lay eggs. Reptiles' skin, eggs, and kidneys make them well adapted for life on land.

Adaptations To thrive on land, an animal must have adaptations that keep the animal from drying out. Reptiles have dry, tough skin covered with scales. This scaly skin protects reptiles and helps keep water in their bodies.

Reptiles' eggs also are adapted to conserve water. Reptiles have amniotic eggs. An **amniotic egg** is named for the amnion, a membrane inside the shell that holds liquid surrounding the embryo. Look at Figure 29 to see how the amnion and other membranes of a reptile's egg are arranged inside the shell.

The **kidneys** are organs that filter wastes from the blood, producing a waste fluid called urine. A reptile's kidneys concentrate the urine by removing much of its water content before the urine is eliminated. The water that is removed by the kidneys is conserved within the reptile's body.

FIGURE 29
The Amniotic Egg
The membranes and shell of an aminiotic egg protect the developing embryo. **Relating Cause and Effect** *Which parts of the tortoise's egg help keep the embryo from drying out?*

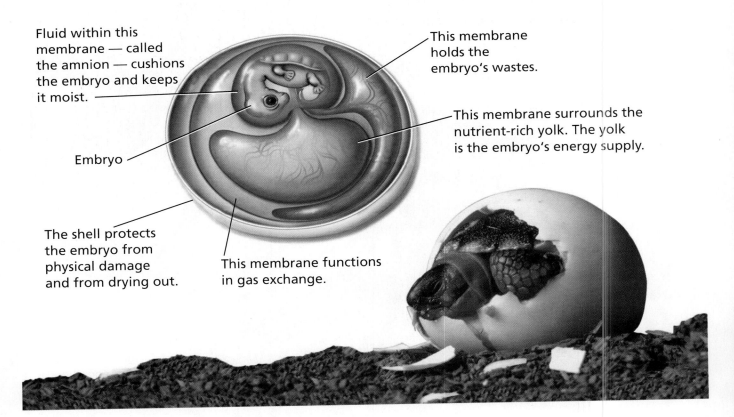

Fluid within this membrane — called the amnion — cushions the embryo and keeps it moist.

Embryo

The shell protects the embryo from physical damage and from drying out.

This membrane functions in gas exchange.

This membrane holds the embryo's wastes.

This membrane surrounds the nutrient-rich yolk. The yolk is the embryo's energy supply.

FIGURE 30
An Egg-eating Snake
The jawbones of this snake's skull have moved to let the snake swallow its food. **Making Generalizations** *How are snakes different from lizards?*

Lizards and Snakes Most reptiles alive today are either lizards or snakes. They are closely related and share some important characteristics. **Both lizards and snakes are reptiles that have skin covered with overlapping scales.** As lizards and snakes grow, they shed their skins, replacing the worn scales with new ones. Most lizards and snakes live in warm areas.

Lizards differ from snakes in several ways. The most obvious difference is that lizards have four legs, while snakes have none. Lizards also have moveable eyelids and a pair of lungs. Snakes have no eyelids, and most have only one lung.

Alligators and Crocodiles Alligators, crocodiles, and their relatives are the largest reptiles still living on Earth. Alligators have broad, rounded snouts. In contrast, crocodiles have pointed snouts. **Alligators and crocodiles are large, carnivores that care for their young.**

After laying eggs in a nest of rotting plant material, a female alligator or crocodile stays near the nest. After the young hatch, the female scoops them up in her huge mouth. She carries them from the nest to the water where they will be safer. She cares for the young until they can feed on their own and protect themselves.

Alligators and crocodiles have several adaptations to help them obtain food. They hunt mostly at night, concealed from their prey. They use their strong, muscular tails to swim rapidly towards prey. Their muscular jaws are equipped with many large, sharp, and pointed teeth. Alligators will eat dogs, raccoons, and deer, but rarely attack humans.

 **Reading Checkpoint** **How are alligators and crocodiles adapted for catching prey?**

For: More on reptiles
Visit: PHSchool.com
Web Code: ced-2034

FIGURE 31

Green Sea Turtles
The green sea turtles lives at sea except to come ashore and lay eggs on sandy beaches.

Turtles Turtles live in the ocean, in fresh water, and on land. Turtles that live on land are commonly called "tortoises." **A turtle is a reptile whose body is covered by a protective shell that includes ribs and backbone.** The body plates of a turtle's shell are covered by large scales made from the same material as the skin's scales. Some turtle shells can cover the whole body. For instance, a box turtle can draw its head, legs, and tail inside its shell for protection.

Turtles lack teeth but have sharp-edged beaks used to tear food. Some are carnivores, such as the leatherback sea turtle. The leatherback's tough skin allows it to feast, mainly on venomous jellyfish without being stung. Other turtles are herbivores, such as the Galápagos tortoise. It feeds mainly on cacti after scraping off the prickly spines.

 **Reading Checkpoint** **What are turtles that live on land called?**

Section 5 Assessment

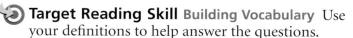 **Target Reading Skill** Building Vocabulary Use your definitions to help answer the questions.

Reviewing Key Concepts

1. a. **Listing** List three characteristics of chordates.
   b. **Reviewing** What are the main characteristics of fishes?
   c. **Identifying** In which group of fishes is a shark classified?
   d. **Predicting** How might a shark's hunting be affected if it were unable to smell?
2. a. **Summarizing** What are the three main characteristics of amphibians?
   b. **Interpreting Diagrams** Review Figure 27. Does a frog have external or internal fertilization?

3. a. **Reviewing** What are the characteristics of a reptile's egg?

Writing in Science

Web Site Design a home page of a web site that introduces people to amphibians. First, come up with a catchy title for your web site. Then, design your home page, the first page people will see. Consider these questions as you come up with your design: What information will you include? What will the illustrations or photos show? What links to specific topics relating to amphibians will you have?

Birds and Mammals

Reading Preview

Key Concepts
• What are the main characteristics of birds?
• How are birds adapted to their environments?
• What characteristics do all mammals share?
• What are the three main groups of mammals?

Key Terms
• bird • contour feather
• down feather • crop
• gizzard • mammal
• diaphragm • monotreme
• marsupial • placental mammal

Target Reading Skill
Building Vocabulary A definition states the meaning of a word or phrase by telling about its most important feature or function. After you read the section, reread the paragraphs that contain definitions of Key Terms. Use all the information you have learned to write a definition of each Key Term.

Lab zone Discover Activity

What Are Feathers Like?
1. Observe the overall shape and structure of a feather. Use a hand lens to examine the feather closely. Notice the many hairlike barbs that project out from the feather's central shaft.
2. Gently separate two barbs in the middle of the feather. How do they feel? Rub the separated edges with your fingertip. What is their texture?
3. Use the hand lens to examine the edges of the two separated barbs. Draw a diagram of what you observe.
4. Rejoin the two separated barbs by gently pulling outward from the shaft. Then wash your hands.

Think It Over
Observing Once the barbs have been separated, is it easy to rejoin them? How might this be an advantage to the bird?

Many people enjoy watching birds. Each species can be identified by its colorful feathers and the notes of its song. Birds are so popular that every state in the United States has a state bird.

Characteristics of Birds

Birds share certain characteristics. **Birds are endothermic vertebrates that lay eggs and have feathers and a four-chambered heart.** Birds have scales on their feet and legs. In addition, most birds can fly.

Body Structure A bird's body is adapted for flight. Of all the animals, only birds have feathers. Different types of feathers have different functions. The large feathers that give shape to a bird's body are **contour feathers.** The contour feathers on the wings and tail help a bird balance and steer during flight. **Down feathers** are specialized to trap heat and keep the bird warm. They grow at the base of contour feathers, against the skin.

▲ **Down feather**

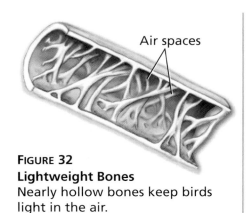

FIGURE 32
Lightweight Bones
Nearly hollow bones keep birds light in the air.

Air spaces

Another adaptation for flight is lightweight bones. A bird's bones are nearly hollow. In addition, the bones of a bird's forelimbs form wings.

Obtaining Food and Oxygen Birds have no teeth. To capture, grip, and handle food, birds mainly use their bills. Each species of bird has a bill shaped to help it feed quickly and efficiently.

After eating, many birds store food in an internal storage tank, or **crop.** After leaving the crop, food enters the first part of the stomach, which is long and has thin walls. Here food is bathed in chemicals that begin to break it down. The partially digested food moves to a thick-walled, muscular part of the stomach called the **gizzard,** which squeezes and grinds the food.

Cells need oxygen to release the energy contained in food. Birds have a four-chambered heart where there is no mixing of oxygen-rich and oxygen-poor blood, as there is in the three-chambered hearts of amphibians and most reptiles. The right side of a bird's heart pumps blood to the lungs, where the blood picks up oxygen. Oxygen-rich blood then returns to the left side of the heart, which pumps it to the rest of the body. You can trace the path of blood through a bird's two-loop circulatory system in Figure 33.

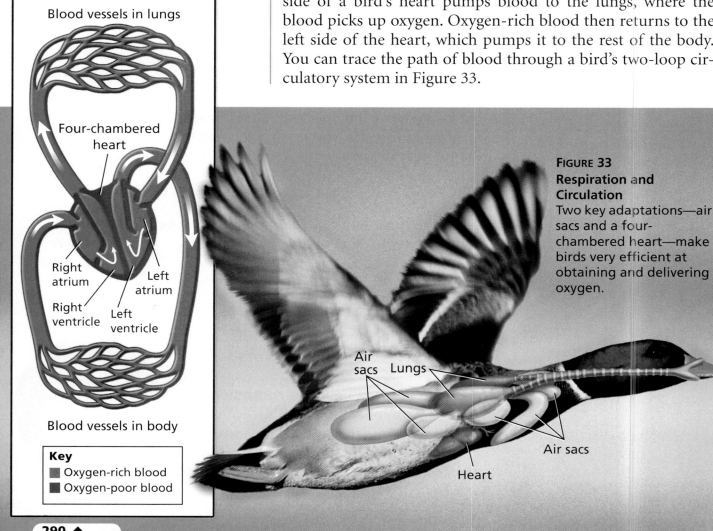

Blood vessels in lungs

Four-chambered heart

Right atrium

Left atrium

Right ventricle

Left ventricle

Blood vessels in body

Key
- Oxygen-rich blood
- Oxygen-poor blood

Air sacs   Lungs

Air sacs

Heart

FIGURE 33
Respiration and Circulation
Two key adaptations—air sacs and a four-chambered heart—make birds very efficient at obtaining and delivering oxygen.

Keeping Conditions Stable Because birds are endotherms, they need a lot of energy to maintain their body temperature. It also takes an enormous amount of energy to power the muscles used in flight. Each day, an average bird eats an amount of food equal to about a quarter of its body weight. Feathers also play a role in maintaining body temperature.

Reproduction and Caring for Young Like reptiles, birds have internal fertilization and lay eggs. In most bird species, the female bird lays the eggs in a nest that has been prepared by one or both parents.

In order to develop, bird eggs need a temperature close to the body temperature of the parent bird. Thus, a parent bird usually incubates the eggs by sitting on them to keep them warm. In some species, incubating the eggs is the job of just one parent. In other species, such as pigeons, the parents take turns incubating the eggs.

When it is ready to hatch, a chick pecks its way out of the eggshell. Most parent birds feed and protect their young at least until they are able to fly.

 **Reading Checkpoint** **What characteristic do bird eggs and reptile eggs share?**

Lab zone Try This **Activity**

"Eggs-amination"
Like reptile eggs, bird eggs protect the developing embryo, provide food for it, and keep it from drying out.

1. Observe the surface of a chicken egg with a hand lens. Then gently crack the egg into a bowl. Do not break the yolk.
2. Note the membrane attached to the inside of the shell. Then look at the blunt end of the egg. What do you see?
3. Fill one part of the eggshell with water. What do you observe?
4. Find the egg yolk. What is its function?
5. Look for a small white spot on the yolk. This marks the spot where the embryo would have developed if the egg had been fertilized.
6. Wash your hands with soap.

Observing Draw a labeled diagram of the egg that names each structure and describes its function.

FIGURE 34
Parental Care
The partridge chicks (above) find food from the day they hatch. In contrast, the blue jay chicks (right) are featherless, blind, and totally dependent on their parents for food.

FIGURE 35
Diversity of Birds

Every bird has adaptations that help it live in its natural environment.

Owls ▲
Sharp vision and keen hearing help owls hunt at night. Razor-sharp claws and great strength allow larger owls, like this eagle owl, to prey on animals as large as deer.

Bee-Eaters ▲
This rainbow bee-eater feeds on bees and other insects, which it catches as it flies. Bee-eaters are found in Africa, Europe, Australia, and Asia.

Game Birds ▶
Wild turkeys are found in North America. When courting females, the male fans his tail feathers, holds his head high, and gobbles.

Birds in the Environment

With almost 10,000 species, birds are the most diverse land-dwelling vertebrates. **Birds are adapted for living in diverse environments. You can see some of these adaptations in the shapes of their legs, claws, and bills.** For example, the long legs and toes of wading birds, such as herons, cranes, and spoonbills, make wading easy. The claws of perching birds, such as goldfinches and mockingbirds, can securely lock onto a branch or other perch. The woodpeckers' bills are tools for chipping into the wood of trees. Birds also have adaptations for flying, finding mates, and caring for their young.

Birds play an important role in the environment. Nectar-eating birds, like hummingbirds, pollinate flowers. Seed-eating birds, like sparrows, carry the seeds of plants to new places. This happens when the birds eat the fruits or seeds of a plant, fly to a new location, and then eliminate some of the seeds in digestive wastes. In addition, birds are some of the chief predators of animals that may be pests. Hawks and owls eat many rats and mice, while many perching birds feed on insect pests.

 **Reading Checkpoint**   **Why do perching birds have claws?**

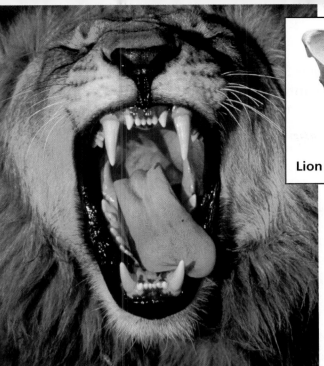

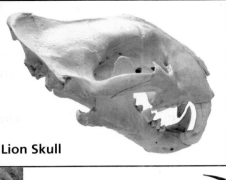

Lion Skull

Springbok Skull

Characteristics of Mammals

The group of vertebrates called **mammals** is a diverse group whose members share many characteristics. **Mammals are endothermic vertebrates with a four-chambered heart and skin covered with fur or hair. The young of most mamals are born alive, and every young mammal is fed milk produced in the mother's body.**

Obtaining Food and Oxygen Mammals need food for energy. Their teeth are adapted to chew their food, breaking it into small bits that make digestion easier. Unlike reptiles and fishes, whose teeth usually all have the same shape, most mammals have teeth with four different shapes. At the front of the jaw are incisors—flat-edged teeth used to bite off and cut parts of food. Next are canines—sharply pointed teeth that stab food and tear into it. Behind the canines are premolars, and farthest back are the molars. Premolars and molars grind and shred food into tiny bits. The size, shape, and hardness of a mammal's teeth reflect its diet.

Like reptiles and birds, all mammals breathe with lungs—even mammals such as whales that live in the ocean. Mammals breathe in and out because of the combined action of rib muscles and a large muscle called the **diaphragm** located at the bottom of the rib cage. The lungs have a huge, moist surface area with a great number of tiny blood vessels where oxygen can move into the bloodstream. Like birds, mammals have a four-chambered heart and a two-loop circulatory system.

FIGURE 36
Teeth of Different Shapes
Lions have sharp, pointed canines. Springboks have broad molars.
Inferring *What kind of diet does each of these mammals eat?*

Keeping Temperature Stable Mammals are endotherms and are adapted to maintain a steady internal temperature. One adaptation is a covering of fur or hair, which all mammals have at some point in their lives. Hair grows from cells located below the surface of the skin. Another adaptation, a layer of fat beneath the skin, allows mammals such as polar bears, to live in cold climates. Fat, like fur and feathers, is an insulating material that keeps heat in the body.

Movement Mammals can move in more ways than any other vertebrates. Most mammals walk or run on four limbs, but some have specialized ways of moving. For example, kangaroos hop, and orangutans swing by their arms from branch to branch. Bats have wings adapted from their front limbs. Dolphins and other sea mammals lack hind limbs, but their front limbs are adapted as flippers for swimming.

Nervous System The brains of mammals are well developed and large in proportion to their bodies, allowing mammals to sense their environments and behave in complex ways. For example, bats navigate in the dark and catch prey by listening to the echoes of their own high-pitched squeaks. The echoes give bats information about the shapes of objects around them and how far away the objects are.

In addition to hearing, sight and smell are well-developed in some mammals. Tarsiers, which are active at night, have huge eyes that enable them to see in the dark. Dogs, cats, and bears often use smell to track their prey. Other mammals can smell approaching predators in time to flee.

FIGURE 37
Fur and Hair
A hippo has hardly any hair. In contrast, a wolf has a thick coat of fur. *Inferring What can you infer about the environment each animal lives in?*

Diversity of Mammals

Consider a duck-billed platypus, a kangaroo, and a panda—each one is furry and feeds its offspring milk. But the ways their offspring develop and receive milk are quite different. Because of this, each of these mammals belongs to a distinct group. **The three main groups of mammals are monotremes, marsupials, and placental mammals.**

Mammals that lay eggs are called **monotremes.** There are just three species in this group—two species of spiny anteaters plus the duck-billed platypus. A female spiny anteater lays one to three leathery-shelled eggs directly into a pouch on her belly. After the young hatch, they stay in the pouch for six to eight weeks. There they drink milk that seeps out of pores on the mother's skin. In contrast, the duck-billed platypus lays her eggs in an underground nest. The tiny young feed by lapping at the milk that oozes onto the fur of their mother's belly.

Koalas, kangaroos, and opossums are some of the better-known marsupials. **Marsupials** are mammals whose young are born at a very early stage of development—they usually continue to develop in a pouch on their mother's body.

Most mammals, including humans, are placental mammals. Unlike a monotreme or a marsupial, a **placental mammal** develops inside its mother's body until its body systems can function independently.

FIGURE 38
A Kangaroo
This gray kangaroo, a marsupial, carries her offspring in a pouch in front. **Classifying** *How do marsupials differ from monotremes?*

Math Analyzing Data

Mammal Diversity

This circle graph shows the percentages of some species of mammals.

1. **Reading Graphs** What percentage of species are bats?

2. **Calculating** What percentage of species are not bats?

3. **Graphing** Suppose you used the data shown in the circle graph to make a bar graph. Which bar would be tallest?

4. **Predicting** What total should all the percentages in the pie chart add up to? Do you have to add the percentages to obtain your answer? Explain.

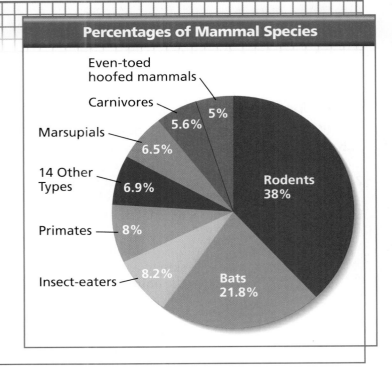

Percentages of Mammal Species

- Even-toed hoofed mammals — 5%
- Carnivores — 5.6%
- Marsupials — 6.5%
- 14 Other Types — 6.9%
- Primates — 8%
- Insect-eaters — 8.2%
- Bats — 21.8%
- Rodents — 38%

FIGURE 39
Diversity of Placental Mammals
From tiny moles to huge elephants, placental mammals exhibit great variety. These photographs show representative animals from three orders of placental mammals.

Carnivores ►
Large canine teeth and clawed toes help carnivores like this river otter catch and eat their prey.

▲ **Marine Mammals**
Whales, manatees, and these Atlantic spotted dolphins are ocean-dwelling mammals that have streamlined bodies adapted for swimming.

Hoofed Mammals ▲
Mammals with hooves are divided into two orders—those with an even number of toes and those with an odd number of toes.

Parental Care Unlike most other kinds of animals, young mammals are usually helpless for a long time after being born. Many are born without a coat of insulating fur. Their eyes are often sealed and may not open for weeks. So young mammals—including humans—usually stay with their mother or both parents for an extended time.

Reading Checkpoint What are three types of movement found in mammals?

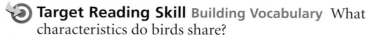

Section 6 Assessment

Target Reading Skill Building Vocabulary What characteristics do birds share?

Reviewing Key Concepts
1. a. **Identifying** What characteristics do birds share?
   b. **Explaining** How is a bird's body adapted for flight?
2. a. **Listing** What are three types of adaptations that allow birds to survive in diverse environments?
3. a. **Defining** What characteristics do mammals share?
   b. **Interpreting Photographs** Look at Figure 37 and compare a hippo's skin to a wolf's skin. Then relate the difference to the animals' environments.

   c. **Making Generalizations** What characteristics enable mammals to live in colder environments than reptiles?
4. a. **Reviewing** What are the three main groups of mammals?

Lab zone **At-Home Activity**

Count Down With the help of a family member, look for products in your home that contain down feathers. (*Hint:* Don't forget to check closets!) What kinds of items contain down feathers? What common purpose do these items have? Explain to your family member what down feathers look like and where they are found on a bird.

Keeping Warm

Problem

Do wool products provide insulation from the cold? How well does wool insulate when it is wet?

Skills Focus

graphing, interpreting data

Materials

- tap water, hot • scissors • beaker, 1-L
- 3 thermometers • clock or watch
- graph paper • a pair of wool socks
- tap water, room temperature
- 3 containers, 250-mL, with lids

Procedure

1. Put one container into a dry woolen sock. Soak a second sock with water at room temperature, wring it out so it's not dripping, and then slide the second container into the wet sock. Both containers should stand upright. Leave the third container uncovered.

2. Create a data table in your notebook, listing the containers in the first column. Provide four more columns in which to record the water temperatures during the experiment.

3. Use scissors to carefully cut a small "X" in the center of each lid. Make the X just large enough for a thermometer to pass through.

4. Fill a beaker with about 800 mL of hot tap water. Then pour hot water nearly to the top of each of the three containers. **CAUTION:** *Avoid spilling hot water on yourself or others.*

5. Place a lid on each of the containers, and insert a thermometer into the water through the hole in each lid. Gather the socks around the thermometers above the first two containers so that the containers are completely covered.

6. Immediately measure the temperature of the water in each container, and record it in your data table. Take temperature readings every 5 minutes for at least 15 minutes.

Analyze and Conclude

1. **Graphing** Graph your results using a different color to represent each container. Graph time in minutes on the horizontal axis and temperature on the vertical axis.

2. **Interpreting Data** Compare the temperature changes in the three containers. Relate your findings to the insulation characteristics of mammal skin coverings.

3. **Communicating** Suppose a company claims that its wool socks keep you warm even if they get wet. Do your findings support this claim? Write a letter to the company explaining why or why not.

Design an Experiment

Design an experiment to compare how wool's insulating properties compare with those of other natural materials (such as cotton) or manufactured materials (such as acrylic). Obtain your teacher's permission before carrying out your investigation.

For: Data sharing
Visit: PHSchool.com
Web Code: ced-2043

1 What Is an Animal?

Key Concepts

- The cells of most animals are organized into higher levels of structure, including tissues, organs, and systems.

- The major functions of animals are to obtain food and oxygen, keep internal conditions stable, move, and reproduce.

Key Terms

- cell • tissue • organ • adaptation
- sexual reproduction • fertilization
- asexual reproduction • phylum • vertebrate
- invertebrate

2 Animal Symmetry

Key Concepts

- The balanced arrangement of parts in animals and other objects is called symmetry.

Key Terms

- bilateral symmetry • radial symmetry

3 Sponges, Cnidarians, Worms, and Mollusks

Key Concepts

- Sponges are invertebrates that usually have no body segments and no tissues or organs.

- Cnidarians use stinging cells to capture food and defend themselves.

- Flatworms are flat and soft as jelly. Round-worms have a digestive system that is like a tube, open at both ends. Segmented worms have bodies made up of many linked sections.

- All mollusks have a mantle that covers their internal organs and a foot.

Key Terms

- larva • cnidarian • polyp • medusa
- parasite • host • mollusk • gastropod
- bivalve • cephalopod

4 Arthropods and Echinoderms

Key Concepts

- Arthropods are invertebrates that have an external skeleton, a segmented body, and jointed attachments called appendages.

- Echinoderms are invertebrates with an internal skeleton and a water vascular system.

Key Terms

- arthropod • exoskeleton • molting • insect
- crustacean • metamorphosis • arachnid
- echinoderm • endoskeleton
- water vascular system • tube feet

5 Fishes, Amphibians, and Reptiles

Key Concepts

- At some point in its life, a chordate will have a notochord, a nerve cord that runs down its back, and a slit in its throat area.

- Fishes are vertebrates that live in water and have fins. In addition, most fishes are ectotherms, obtain oxygen through gills, and have scales.

- After beginning their lives in water, most amphibians spend their adulthood on land, returning to the water to reproduce.

- Reptiles are ectothermic vertebrates with scaly skin that lay their eggs on land.

Key Terms

- chordate • notochord • vertebra
- ectotherm • endotherm • fish • cartilage
- swim bladder • amphibian • lung • reptile
- amniotic egg • kidney

6 Birds and Mammals

Key Concepts

- Birds are endothermic vertebrates that lay eggs and have feathers and a four-chambered heart.

- Mammals are endothermic vertebrates with a four-chambered heart and skin covered with fur or hair. The young of most mammals are born alive, and every young mammal is fed with milk produced in the mother's body.

Key Terms

- bird • contour feather • down feather
- crop • gizzard • mammal • diaphragm
- monotreme • marsupial
- placental mammal

Review and Assessment

Organizing Information

Comparing and Contrasting Copy the table comparing mammal groups onto a sheet of paper. Then fill in the empty spaces and add a title.

Characteristic	Monotremes	Marsupials	Placental Mammals
How Young Begin Life	a. _____?	b. _____?	c. _____?
How Young Are Fed	milk from pores or slits on mother's skin	d. _____?	e. _____?
Example	f. _____?	g. _____?	h. _____?

Reviewing Key Terms

Choose the letter of the best answer.

1. An animal without a backbone is called a(n)
   a. vertebrate.
   b. invertebrate.
   c. larva.
   d. parasite.

2. An animal with many lines of symmetry
   a. has bilateral symmetry.
   b. has radial symmetry.
   c. has no symmetry.
   d. has a distinct head and tail end.

3. A millipede is classified as a(n)
   a. crustacean.
   b. arthropod.
   c. centipede.
   d. arachnid.

4. A sea star is a(n)
   a. mollusk.
   b. arthropod.
   c. echinoderm.
   d. sponge.

5. Which of the following is NOT true of fishes?
   a. They live in water.
   b. They have fins.
   c. They have amniotic eggs.
   d. They are vertebrates.

If the statement is true, write *true*. If it is false, change the underlined word or words to make the statement true.

6. Fishes, amphibians, and reptiles are <u>endotherms.</u>

7. A bird's <u>crop</u> grinds food.

8. Budding is a form of <u>sexual</u> reproduction.

9. Fur and <u>down feathers</u> have a similar function.

10. <u>Marsupials</u> are mammals that lay eggs.

Writing in Science

Letter Suppose that you have just come back from a trip to a coral reef. Write a letter to a friend that compares corals and jellyfish. Be sure to explain how the two animals are alike and how they are different.

DISCOVERY CHANNEL SCHOOL™

Sponges, Cnidarians, and Worms
Video Preview
Video Field Trip
▶ Video Assessment

Review and Assessment

Checking Concepts

11. What are four key functions of animals?

12. Compare and contrast a medusa and a polyp.

13. Describe the main characteristics of chordates.

14. Identify and explain two ways in which mammals are adapted to live in cold climates.

15. What is one way in which the bodies of dolphins are different from those of land mammals?

Thinking Critically

16. **Relating Cause and Effect** Explain why the presence of an endoskeleton allows vertebrates to grow larger than most animals without endoskeletons.

17. **Classifying** Look at the simplified diagram of the circulatory system of a fish below. Is this a single-loop or double-loop system? Explain.

Key
- ■ Oxygen-rich blood
- ■ Oxygen-poor blood

18. **Applying Concepts** Imagine that you are in the hot desert sun with a wet paper towel. You must keep the towel from drying out. What strategy can you copy from reptiles to keep the towel wet?

19. **Predicting** If a rodent were fed a diet consisting only of soft food that it did not need to gnaw, what might its front teeth look like after several months? Explain your prediction.

Applying Skills

Use the information in the table to answer Questions 20–22.

The data table below shows the approximate gestation period of several mammals and the approximate length of time that those mammals care for their young after birth.

Mammal	Gestation Period	Time Spent Caring for Young After Birth
Deer mouse	0.75 month	1 month
Chimpanzee	8 months	24 months
Harp seal	11 months	0.75 month
Elephant	21 months	24 months
Bobcat	2 months	8 months

20. **Graphing** Decide which kind of graph would be best for showing the data in the table. Then construct two graphs—one for gestation period and the other for time spent caring for young.

21. **Interpreting Data** Which mammals listed in the table care for their young for the longest time? The shortest time?

22. **Drawing Conclusions** How are the size of the mammal and the length of time it cares for its young related? Which animal is the exception to this pattern?

Lab zone Chapter Project

Performance Assessment Write a summary explaining what you have learned about your animal. Describe its habitat, the food it eats, its behavior, and any surprising observations that you made. Then introduce your animal to your classmates and share what you have discovered.

End-of-Grade Test Practice

Test-Taking Tip

Interpreting Data Tables

Before you answer a question about a data table, read the title and the headings of the columns and rows. The title identifies the type of data the table contains. The headings reveal how the data are organized. For example, the table below shows that jawless fishes have skeletons made of cartilage. Read the questions about the table before you spend too much time studying the data.

Characteristics of Fishes			
Group	**Skeleton**	**Jaws**	**Scales**
Jawless Fishes	Cartilage	None	None
Cartilaginous Fishes	Cartilage	Yes	Yes
Bony Fishes	Bone	Yes	Yes

Sample Question

Axel has found a fish washed up on the beach that has scales and a skeleton made of cartilage. According to the table, what kind of fish is it?

  A a jawless fish

  B a cartilaginous fish

  C a bony fish

  D The fish cannot be classified using this table.

Answer

The correct answer is **B. A, C,** and **D** cannot be correct because only cartilaginous fishes have a cartilaginous skeleton, jaws, and scales.

Choose the letter of the best answer.

1. An animal that has a soft, unsegmented body surrounded by a hard outer shell is most likely

  A an earthworm.

  B a cnidarian.

  C a mollusk.

  D an arthropod.

2. Which of the following is true of a one-way digestive system?

  A It is found in all parasites.

  B It has two openings.

  C It has one opening.

  D It is found in all parasites and has one opening.

Characteristics of Observed Animals			
Animal	**Skeleton**	**Scales**	**Outer Covering of Egg**
1	Bone	None	Clear jelly
2	Bone	Yes	Leathery shell
3	Bone	Yes	Thin, moist membrane
4	Cartilage	Yes	No eggs observed

3. A scientist observed four different animals and recorded her data in the table shown above. Which of the animals is most likely a reptile?

  A animals 1 and 3

  B animal 2

  C animal 3

  D animal 4

4. Based on the data in the table above, what kind of animal can you infer Animal 3 might be?

  A amphibian

  B bony fish

  C cartilaginous fish

  D reptile

Constructed Response

5. Explain why amphibians can be said to have a "double life." Be sure to include details describing the two different phases in the life of a typical amphibian.

Chapter 8

Bones, Muscles, and Skin

Standard Course of Study

1.01 Identify and create questions and hypotheses.

1.02 Develop appropriate experimental procedures.

1.03 Apply safety procedures.

1.05 Analyze evidence.

1.06 Use mathematics to gather, organize, and present data.

1.07 Prepare models and/or computer simulations.

1.08 Use oral and written language.

2.01 Explore definitions of "technology."

2.02 Use information systems.

2.03 Evaluate technological designs.

2.04 Apply tenets of technological design.

4.01 Analyze how human body systems interact.

4.02 Describe functions of human body systems.

4.04 Evaluate how human body systems regulate the internal environment.

4.05 Analyze imbalances in homeostasis.

4.08 Explain how understanding the human body helps to make informed health decisions.

No matter your age or ability level, playing sports is fun and healthful. ▶

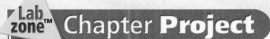

Lab zone™ Chapter **Project**

Design and Build a Hand Prosthesis

A prosthesis is an artificial device that replaces a human body part. Designing artificial replacements, such as prosthetic hands, can be a challenging task. This is because even a simple act, such as picking up a pen, involves a complex interaction of body parts.

Your Goal To design, build, and test a replacement for a human hand

Your prosthesis must

● grasp and lift a variety of objects
● be activated by pulling a cord or string
● spring back when the cord is released
● be built following the safety guidelines in Appendix A

Plan It! Before you design your prosthetic hand, study the human hand. Watch how the fingers move to pick up objects. Make a list of devices that mimic the ability of the hand to pick up objects. Examples include tongs, tweezers, pliers, and chopsticks. Then, choose materials for your hand and sketch your design. When your teacher has approved your design, build and test your prosthetic hand.

Section 1

Body Organization and Homeostasis

Reading Preview

Key Concepts
- What are the levels of organization in the body?
- What is homeostasis?

Key Terms
- cell • cell membrane
- nucleus • cytoplasm
- tissue • muscle tissue
- nervous tissue
- connective tissue
- epithelial tissue
- organ • organ system
- homeostasis • stress

Target Reading Skill

Outlining An outline shows the relationship between main ideas and supporting ideas. As you read, make an outline about body organization and homeostasis. Use the red headings for the main ideas and the blue headings for the supporting ideas.

Body Organization and Homeostasis
I. Cells
A. Structures of cells
B.
II. Tissues

Discover **Activity**

How Does Your Body Respond?

1. Stack one book on top of another one.
2. Lift the two stacked books in front of you so the lowest book is about level with your shoulders. Hold the books in this position for 30 seconds. While you are performing this activity, note how your body responds. For example, how do your arms feel at the beginning and toward the end of the 30 seconds?
3. Balance one book on the top of your head. Walk a few steps with the book on your head.

Think It Over

Inferring List all the parts of your body that worked together as you performed the activities in Steps 1 through 3.

The bell rings—lunchtime! You hurry down the noisy halls to the cafeteria. The unmistakable aroma of hot pizza makes your mouth water. At last, you balance your tray of pizza and salad while you pay the cashier. You look around the cafeteria for your friends. Then, you walk to the table, sit down, and begin to eat.

Think about how many parts of your body were involved in the simple act of getting and eating your lunch. Every minute of the day, whether you are eating, studying, walking, or even sleeping, your body is busily at work. Each part of the body has a specific job to do. And all the different parts of your body usually work together so smoothly that you don't even notice them.

This smooth functioning is due partly to the way in which the body is organized. **The levels of organization in the human body consist of cells, tissues, organs, and organ systems.** The smallest unit of organization is the cell. The next largest unit is tissue; then, organs. Finally, the organ system is the largest unit of organization.

Cells

A **cell** is the basic unit of structure and function in a living thing. Complex organisms are composed of many cells in the same way a brick building is composed of many bricks. The human body contains about 100 trillion cells. Cells are quite tiny, and most cannot be seen without a microscope.

Structures of Cells Most animal cells, including those in the human body, have a structure similar to the cell in Figure 1. The **cell membrane** forms the outside boundary of the cell. Inside the cell membrane is a large structure called the nucleus. The **nucleus** is the control center that directs the cell's activities and contains the information that determines the cell's form and function. When the cell divides, or reproduces, this information is passed along to the newly formed cells. The material within a cell apart from the nucleus is called the **cytoplasm** (SYT uh plaz um). The cytoplasm is made of a clear, jellylike substance containing many cell structures called organelles.

Functions of Cells Cells carry on the processes that keep organisms alive. Inside cells, for example, molecules from digested food undergo chemical reactions that release energy for the body's activities. Cells also grow and reproduce. And they get rid of waste products that result from these activities.

Reading Checkpoint What is the function of the nucleus?

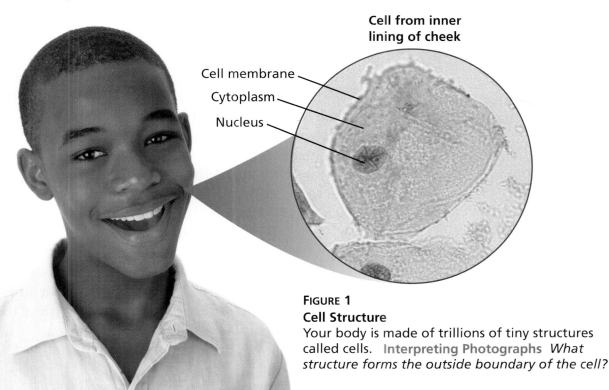

Cell from inner lining of cheek

Cell membrane
Cytoplasm
Nucleus

FIGURE 1
Cell Structure
Your body is made of trillions of tiny structures called cells. **Interpreting Photographs** *What structure forms the outside boundary of the cell?*

FIGURE 2
Types of Tissues

Your body contains four kinds of tissues: muscle, nervous, connective, and epithelial.
Comparing and Contrasting How is the function of nervous tissue different from that of epithelial tissue?

Muscle Tissue
Every movement you make depends on muscle tissue. The muscle tissue shown here allows your body to move.

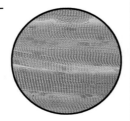

Nervous Tissue
Nervous tissue, such as the brain cells shown here, enables you to see, hear, and think.

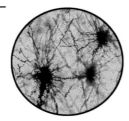

Connective Tissue
Connective tissue, such as the bone shown here, connects and supports parts of your body.

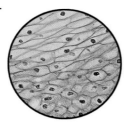

Epithelial Tissue
Epithelial tissue, such as the skin cells shown here, covers the surfaces of your body and lines your internal organs.

Tissues

The next largest unit of organization in your body is a tissue. A **tissue** is a group of similar cells that perform the same function. The human body contains four basic types of tissue: muscle tissue, nervous tissue, connective tissue, and epithelial tissue. To see examples of each of these tissues, look at Figure 2.

Like the muscle cells that form it, **muscle tissue** can contract, or shorten. By doing this, muscle tissue makes parts of your body move. While muscle tissue carries out movement, **nervous tissue** directs and controls the process. Nervous tissue carries electrical messages back and forth between the brain and other parts of the body. Another type of tissue, **connective tissue,** provides support for your body and connects all its parts. Bone tissue and fat are connective tissues.

The surfaces of your body, inside and out, are covered by **epithelial tissue** (ep uh THEE lee ul). Some epithelial tissue, such as your skin, protects the delicate structures that lie beneath it. The lining of your digestive system consists of epithelial tissue that allows you to digest and absorb the nutrients in your food.

 **Reading Checkpoint** **What is the job of muscle tissue?**

Organs and Organ Systems

Your stomach, heart, brain, and lungs are all organs. An **organ** is a structure that is composed of different kinds of tissue. Like a tissue, an organ performs a specific job. The job of an organ, however, is generally more complex than that of a tissue. The heart, for example, pumps blood throughout your body, over and over again. The heart contains all four kinds of tissue—muscle, nervous, connective, and epithelial. Each type of tissue contributes to the organ's overall job of pumping blood.

Each organ in your body is part of an **organ system,** which is a group of organs that work together to perform a major function. Your heart is part of your circulatory system, which carries oxygen and other materials throughout the body. Besides the heart, blood vessels are major structures in the circulatory system. Figure 3 shows some of the major organ systems in the human body.

Figure 3
Organ Systems
The human body is made up of eleven organ systems. Eight of the systems are shown here.
Interpreting Diagrams *Which two systems work together to get oxygen to your cells?*

Circulatory System
Transports materials to and from cells.

Digestive System
Breaks down food and absorbs nutrients.

Nervous System
Detects information from the environment and controls body functions.

Skeletal System
Supports and protects the body.

Endocrine System
Controls many body processes by means of chemicals.

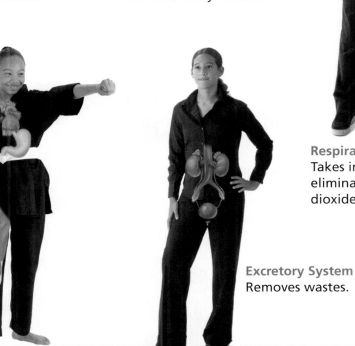

Respiratory System
Takes in oxygen and eliminates carbon dioxide.

Muscular System
Enables movement of the body and internal organs.

Excretory System
Removes wastes.

Go Online

SCi *LINKS* NSTA

For: Links on body systems
Visit: www.SciLinks.org
Web Code: scn-0411

Homeostasis

The different organ systems work together and depend on one another. When you ride a bike, you use your muscular and skeletal systems to steer and push the pedals. But you also need your nervous system to direct your arms and legs to move. Your respiratory, digestive, and circulatory systems work together to fuel your muscles with the energy they need. And your excretory system removes the wastes produced while your muscles are hard at work.

All the systems of the body work together to maintain **homeostasis** (hoh mee oh STAY sis), the body's tendency to keep an internal balance. **Homeostasis is the process by which an organism's internal environment is kept stable in spite of changes in the external environment.**

Homeostasis in Action To see homeostasis in action, all you have to do is take your temperature when the air is cold. Then, take it again in an overheated room. No matter what the temperature of the air around you, your internal body temperature will be close to 37°C. Of course, if you become sick, your body temperature may rise. But when you are well again, it returns to 37°C.

Maintaining Homeostasis Your body has various ways of maintaining homeostasis. For example, when you are too warm, you sweat. Sweating helps to cool your body. On the other hand, when you are cold, you shiver. Shivering occurs when your muscles rapidly contract and relax. This action produces heat that helps keep you warm. Both of these processes help your body maintain homeostasis by regulating your temperature.

FIGURE 4
Maintaining Homeostasis
Regardless of the surrounding temperature, your body temperature remains fairly constant at about 37°C. Sweating (left) and shivering (right) help regulate your body temperature.
Applying Concepts *What is the term for the body's tendency to maintain a stable internal environment?*

Stress and Homeostasis Sometimes, things can happen to throw off homeostasis. As a result, your heart may beat more rapidly or your breathing may increase. These reactions of your circulatory and respiratory systems are signs of stress. **Stress** is the reaction of your body to potentially threatening, challenging, or disturbing events.

Think about what happens when you leave the starting line in a bike race. As you pedal, your heart beats faster and your breathing increases. What is happening in your body? First, your endocrine system releases a chemical called adrenaline into your bloodstream. Adrenaline gives you a burst of energy and prepares your body to take action. As you pedal, your muscles work harder and require more oxygen. Oxygen is carried by the circulatory system, so your heart beats even faster to move more blood to your muscles. Your breath comes faster and faster, too, so that more oxygen can get into your body. Your body is experiencing stress.

If stress is over quickly, your body soon returns to its normal state. Think about the bike race again. After you cross the finish line, you continue to breathe hard for the next few minutes. Soon, however, your breathing and heart rate return to normal. The level of adrenaline in your blood returns to normal. Thus, homeostasis is restored after just a few minutes of rest.

 **Reading Checkpoint** What is stress?

FIGURE 5
Stress
Your body reacts to stress, such as the start of a bike race, by releasing adrenaline and carrying more oxygen to body cells.

Section 1 Assessment

Target Reading Skill Outlining Use the information in your outline to help you answer the questions below.

Reviewing Key Concepts

1. a. Identifying List the four levels of organization in the human body from smallest to largest. Give an example of each level.
  b. Comparing and Contrasting What is the difference between tissues and organs?
  c. Applying Concepts What systems of the body are involved when you prepare a sandwich and then eat it?

2. a. Defining What is homeostasis?
  b. Explaining How does stress affect homeostasis?
  c. Relating Cause and Effect Describe what happens inside your body as you give an oral report in front of your class.

Writing in Science

Summary Write a paragraph that explains what body systems are involved when you sit down to do your homework. Be sure to begin your paragraph with a topic sentence and include supporting details.

The Skeletal System

Reading Preview

Key Concepts
- What are the functions of the skeleton?
- What role do joints play in the body?
- What are the characteristics of bone, and how can you keep your bones strong and healthy?

Key Terms
- skeleton • vertebra • joint
- ligament • cartilage
- compact bone • spongy bone
- marrow • osteoporosis

Target Reading Skill
Asking Questions Before you read, preview the red headings. In a graphic organizer like the one below, ask a *what* or *how* question for each heading. As you read, answer your questions.

The Skeletal System

Question	Answer
What does the skeleton do?	The skeletal system provides shape . . .

Hard as a Rock?

1. Your teacher will give you a rock and a leg bone from a cooked turkey or chicken.
2. Use a hand lens to examine both the rock and the bone.
3. Gently tap both the rock and the bone on a hard surface.
4. Pick up each object to feel how heavy it is.
5. Wash your hands. Then make notes of your observations.

Think It Over
Observing Based on your observations, why do you think bones are sometimes compared to rocks? List some ways in which bones and rocks are similar and different.

A high rise construction site is a busy place. After workers have prepared the building's foundation, they begin to assemble thousands of steel pieces into a frame for the building. People watch as the steel pieces are joined to create a rigid frame that climbs toward the sky. By the time the building is finished, however, the building's framework will no longer be visible.

Like a building, you also have an inner framework, but it isn't made up of steel. Your framework, or **skeleton**, is made up of all the bones in your body. The number of bones in your skeleton, or skeletal system, depends on your age. A newborn has about 275 bones. An adult, however, has about 206 bones. As a baby grows, some of the bones in the body fuse together. For example, as you grew, some of the bones in your skull fused together.

What the Skeletal System Does

Just as a building could not stand without its frame, you would collapse without your skeleton. **Your skeleton has five major functions. It provides shape and support, enables you to move, protects your organs, produces blood cells, and stores minerals and other materials until your body needs them.**

Shape and Support Your skeleton determines the shape of your body, much as a steel frame determines the shape of a building. The backbone, or vertebral column, is the center of the skeleton. Locate the backbone in Figure 6. Notice that the bones in the skeleton are in some way connected to this column. If you move your fingers down the center of your back, you can feel the 26 small bones, or **vertebrae** (VUR tuh bray) (singular: *vertebra*), that make up your backbone. Bend forward at the waist and feel the bones adjust as you move. You can think of each individual vertebra as a bead on a string. Just as a beaded necklace is flexible and able to bend, so too is your vertebral column. If your backbone were just one bone, you would not be able to bend or twist.

✓ **Reading Checkpoint** Why is the vertebral column considered the center of the skeleton?

FIGURE 6
The Skeleton
The skeleton provides a framework that supports and protects many other body parts. **Comparing and Contrasting** *In what ways is the skeleton like the steel framework of a building? In what ways is it different?*

Skull

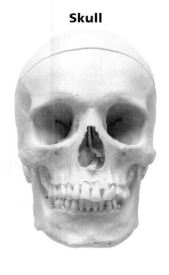

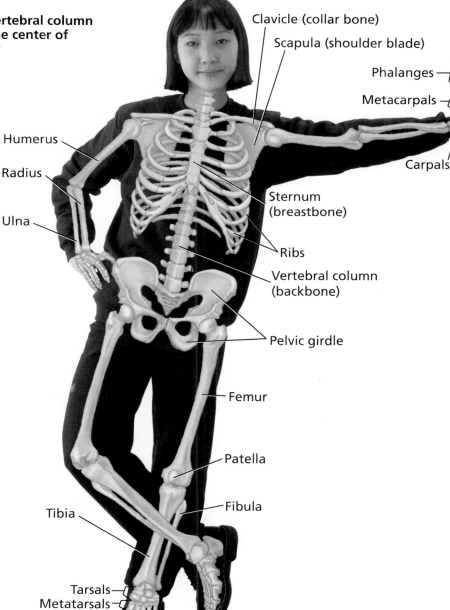

Clavicle (collar bone)

Scapula (shoulder blade)

Phalanges

Metacarpals

Carpals

Humerus

Radius

Ulna

Sternum (breastbone)

Ribs

Vertebral column (backbone)

Pelvic girdle

Femur

Patella

Fibula

Tibia

Tarsals
Metatarsals
Phalanges

Movement and Protection Your skeleton allows you to move. Most of the body's bones are associated with muscles. The muscles pull on the bones to make the body move. Bones also protect many of the organs in your body. For example, your skull protects your brain, and your breastbone and ribs form a protective cage around your heart and lungs.

Production and Storage of Substances Some of your bones produce substances that your body needs. You can think of the long bones of your arms and legs as factories that make certain blood cells. Bones also store minerals such as calcium and phosphorus. When the body needs these minerals, the bones release small amounts of them into the blood.

Joints of the Skeleton

Suppose that a single long bone ran the length of your leg. How would you get out of bed or run for the school bus? Luckily, your body contains many small bones rather than fewer large ones. A **joint** is a place in the body where two bones come together. **Joints allow bones to move in different ways.** There are two kinds of joints—immovable joints and movable joints.

Go Online
active art

For: Movable Joints activity
Visit: PHSchool.com
Web Code: cep-4012

FIGURE 7
Movable Joints

Without movable joints, your body would be as stiff as a board. The different kinds of joints allow your body to move in a variety of ways. Comparing and Contrasting *How is the movement of a hinge joint different from that of a ball-and-socket joint?*

Hinge Joint
A hinge joint allows forward or backward motion. Your knee is a hinge joint that allows you to bend and straighten your leg. Your elbow is also a hinge joint.

Ball-and-Socket Joint
Ball-and-socket joints allow the greatest range of motion. The ball-and-socket joint in your shoulder allows you to swing your arm freely in a circle. Your hips also have ball-and-socket joints.

Immovable Joints Some joints in the body connect bones in a way that allows little or no movement. These joints are called immovable joints. The bones of the skull are held together by immovable joints.

Movable Joints Most of the joints in the body are movable joints. Movable joints allow the body to make a wide range of movements. Look at Figure 7 to see the variety of movements that these joints make possible.

The bones in movable joints are held together by strong connective tissues called **ligaments.** Most joints have a second type of connective tissue, called **cartilage** (KAHR tuh lij), which is more flexible than bone. Cartilage covers the ends of the bones and keeps them from rubbing against each other. For example, in the knee, cartilage acts as a cushion that keeps your femur (thighbone) from rubbing against the bones of your lower leg. In addition, a fluid lubricates the ends of the bones, allowing them to move smoothly over each other.

Reading Checkpoint How are movable joints held together?

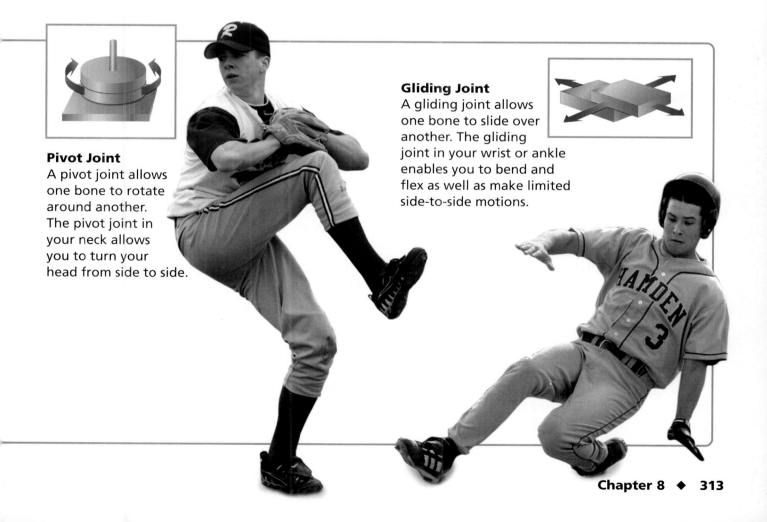

Pivot Joint
A pivot joint allows one bone to rotate around another. The pivot joint in your neck allows you to turn your head from side to side.

Gliding Joint
A gliding joint allows one bone to slide over another. The gliding joint in your wrist or ankle enables you to bend and flex as well as make limited side-to-side motions.

FIGURE 8

Bone Structure

The most obvious feature of a long bone, such as the femur, is its long shaft. Running through the compact bone tissue within the shaft is a system of canals. The canals bring materials to the living bone cells.
Interpreting Diagrams *What different tissues make up the femur?*

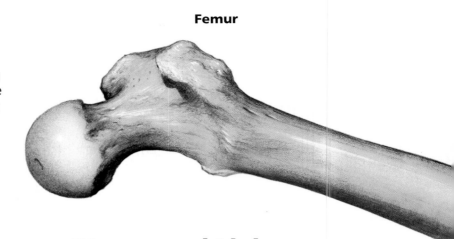

Femur

Try This **Activity**

Soft Bones?

In this activity, you will explore the role that calcium plays in bones.

1. Put on protective gloves. Soak one clean chicken bone in a jar filled with water. Soak a second clean chicken bone in a jar filled with vinegar. (Vinegar causes calcium to dissolve out of bone.)

2. After one week, put on protective gloves and remove the bones from the jars.

3. Compare how the two bones look and feel. Note any differences between the two bones.

Drawing Conclusions Based on your results, explain why it is important to consume a diet that is high in calcium.

Bones—Strong and Living

When you think of a skeleton, you may think of the paper cutouts that are used as decorations at Halloween. Many people connect skeletons with death. The ancient Greeks did, too. The word *skeleton* actually comes from a Greek word meaning "a dried body." The bones of your skeleton, however, are not dead at all. **Bones are complex living structures that undergo growth and development.**

Bone Structure Figure 8 shows the structure of the femur, or thighbone. The femur, which is the body's longest bone, connects the pelvic bones to the lower leg bones. Notice that a thin, tough membrane covers all of the bone except the ends. Blood vessels and nerves enter and leave the bone through the membrane. Beneath the bone's outer membrane is a layer of **compact bone,** which is hard and dense, but not solid. As you can see in Figure 8, small canals run through the compact bone. These canals carry blood vessels and nerves from the bone's surface to the living cells within the bone.

Just inside the femur's compact bone is a layer of spongy bone. Like a sponge, **spongy bone** has many small spaces within it. This structure makes spongy bone tissue lightweight but strong. Spongy bone is also found at the ends of the bone.

The spaces in many bones contain a soft, connective tissue called **marrow.** There are two types of marrow—red and yellow. Red bone marrow produces most of the body's blood cells. As a child, most of your bones contained red bone marrow. As a teenager, only the ends of your femurs, skull, hip bones, and sternum (breastbone) contain red marrow. Your other bones contain yellow marrow. This marrow stores fat that can serve as an energy reserve.

Reading Checkpoint **What are the two types of bone marrow?**

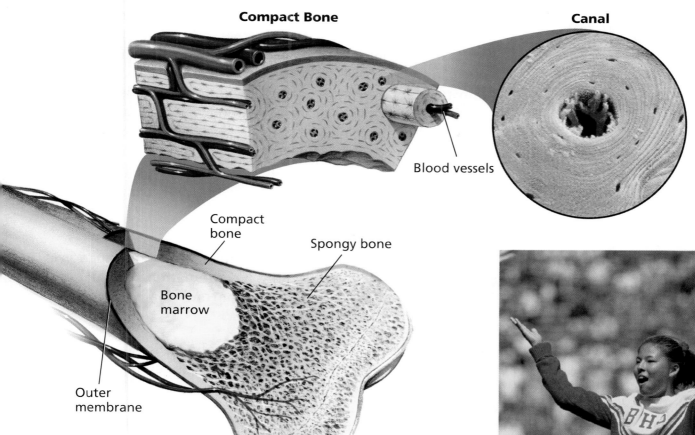

Compact Bone

Canal

Blood vessels

Compact bone

Spongy bone

Bone marrow

Outer membrane

Bone Strength The structure of bone makes it both strong and lightweight. In fact, bones are so strong that they can absorb more force without breaking than can concrete or granite rock. Yet, bones are much lighter than these materials. In fact, only about 20 percent of an average adult's body weight is bone.

Have you ever heard the phrase "as hard as a rock"? Most rock is hard because it is made up of minerals that are packed tightly together. In a similar way, bones are hard because they contain minerals—primarily phosphorus and calcium.

Bone Growth Bones are alive—they contain cells and tissues, such as blood and nerves. Because they are alive, bones also form new bone tissue as you grow. Even after you are grown, however, bone tissue continues to form within your bones. For example, every time you play soccer or basketball, some of your bones absorb the force of your weight. They respond by making new bone tissue.

Sometimes, new bone tissue forms after an accident. If you break a bone, for example, new bone tissue forms to fill the gap between the broken ends of the bone. In fact, the healed region of new bone may be stronger than the original bone!

FIGURE 9
Bone Strength
You can jump up and down or turn cartwheels without breaking bones.

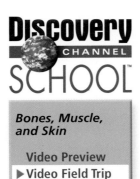

Discovery CHANNEL SCHOOL

Bones, Muscle, and Skin

Video Preview
▶ Video Field Trip
Video Assessment

Bone Development Try this activity: Move the tip of your nose from side to side with your fingers. Notice that the tip of your nose is not stiff. That is because it contains cartilage. As an infant, much of your skeleton was cartilage. Over time, most of the cartilage was replaced with hard bone tissue.

The replacement of cartilage by bone tissue usually is complete by the time you stop growing. You've seen, however, that not all of your body's cartilage is replaced by bone. Even in adults, many joints contain cartilage that protects the ends of the bones.

Taking Care of Your Bones

Because your skeleton performs so many necessary functions, it is important to keep it healthy. **A combination of a balanced diet and regular exercise are important for a lifetime of healthy bones.**

Diet One way to help ensure healthy bones is to eat a well-balanced diet. A well-balanced diet includes enough calcium and phosphorus to keep your bones strong while they are growing. Meats, whole grains, and leafy green vegetables are all good sources of both calcium and phosphorus. Dairy products, including yogurt, are good sources of calcium.

Exercise Another way to build and maintain strong bones is to get plenty of exercise. During activities such as running, skating, or dancing, your bones support the weight of your entire body. These weight-bearing activities help your bones grow stronger and denser. To prevent injuries while exercising, be sure to wear appropriate safety equipment, such as a helmet and pads.

 **Reading Checkpoint** What are two ways to keep your bones healthy?

FIGURE 10
Caring for Your Bones
Exercising regularly and eating a balanced diet help to keep your bones strong and healthy.

Healthy Spine

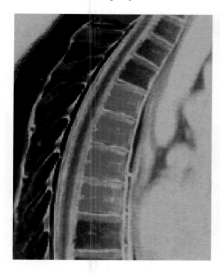

Spine with Osteoporosis

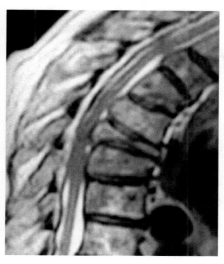

FIGURE 11
Osteoporosis
Without enough calcium in the diet, a person's bones weaken. These photos show how the shape and structure of vertebrae in a healthy spine compare with those in a person with osteoporosis.
Relating Cause and Effect *What can you do to prevent osteoporosis?*

Osteoporosis As people become older, their bones begin to lose some of the minerals they contain. Mineral loss can lead to **osteoporosis** (ahs tee oh puh ROH sis), a condition in which the body's bones become weak and break easily. You can see the effect of osteoporosis in Figure 11. Osteoporosis is more common in women than in men. Evidence indicates that regular exercise throughout life can help prevent osteoporosis. A diet with enough calcium can also help prevent osteoporosis. If you eat enough calcium-rich foods now, during your teenage years, you may help prevent osteoporosis later in life.

Section 2 Assessment

Target Reading Skill Asking Questions Work with a partner to check the answers in your graphic organizer.

Reviewing Key Concepts

1. **a.** Listing What are five functions of the skeleton?
   b. Explaining How does the skeleton protect the body?
   c. Predicting How would your life be different if your backbone consisted of just one long bone?
2. **a.** Naming What are four types of movable joints?
   b. Comparing and Contrasting Compare immovable joints with movable joints.
   c. Classifying Which of your movable joints are ball-and-socket joints?
3. **a.** Describing Describe the structure of the femur.
   b. Relating Cause and Effect How does the structure of bones make them both strong and lightweight?
   c. Applying Concepts How do a well-balanced diet and weight-bearing exercise help keep bones strong?

Lab zone **At-Home Activity**

Model Joints Choose two examples of movable joints from Figure 7. Ask a family member to perform separate movements that involve one joint and then the other. Make drawings to represent the joints and bones involved in each movement. Use the drawings to explain to your family how the motions of the two joints differ.

Diagnosing Bone and Joint Injuries

Reading Preview

Key Concepts
- What are some injuries of the skeletal system, and how can they be identified?
- How can bone and joint injuries be treated?

Key Terms
- fracture   • dislocation
- sprain   • X-ray
- magnetic resonance imaging
- arthritis   • arthroscope

Target Reading Skill
Comparing and Contrasting
When you compare and contrast things, you explain how they are alike and different. As you read, compare and contrast X-rays and MRIs by completing a table like the one below.

Procedure	X-Rays	MRI
Effect on body cells		
Types of injuries identified		

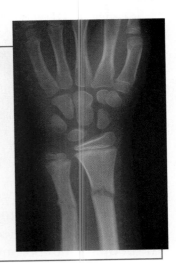

Discover Activity

What Do X-ray Images Show?
1. Examine the photo of an X-ray image.
2. Try to identify what part of the human body the X-ray shows.
3. Locate the break in a bone.

Think It Over
Observing What types of structures are seen clearly in the X-ray? What types of structures cannot be seen?

You're walking home from school on a winter day. It's cold outside, and the ground is icy. Suddenly, you slip. As you lose your balance, you put out your arms to break your fall. The next thing you know, you're on the ground. Your hands sting, and you notice they are scraped. One wrist is starting to swell, and it hurts! If you try to move your wrist, it hurts even more. You need to get to a doctor—and fast.

Common Skeletal System Injuries

On the way to the doctor, you might be wondering, "Is my wrist broken?" Your swollen wrist could be broken, or it could be injured in some other way. **Three common skeletal system injuries are fractures, dislocations, and sprains.**

Fracture A **fracture**, or a break in a bone, can occur when you fall in such a way that all of your weight is placed on only a few bones. There are two kinds of fractures—simple and compound. In a simple fracture, the bone may be cracked or completely broken into two or more pieces. In a compound fracture, the broken ends of the bone stick out through the skin.

Dislocation A second injury of the skeletal system is a dislocation. A **dislocation** occurs when the end of a bone comes out of its joint. Sometimes a doctor can put back a dislocated bone without surgery. Other times surgery is needed.

Sprain A **sprain** occurs when ligaments are stretched too far and tear in places. If you have ever stumbled and turned an ankle, you may have felt a sharp pain. The pain probably occurred because the ligaments on the outside of your ankle stretched too far and partially tore. Sprains, especially of the ankle, are the most common joint injuries. Both sprains and fractures can cause swelling around the injured area.

 **Reading Checkpoint** What is the difference between a simple fracture and a compound fracture?

Go Online
SciLINKS NSTA

For: Links on medical technology
Visit: www.SciLinks.org
Web Code: scn-0413

Identifying Injuries

When you see the doctor, she looks at your wrist and decides she needs to look inside your wrist to determine what's wrong. **Two ways to identify injuries of the skeletal system are X-rays and magnetic resonance imaging.**

X-rays X-ray images can determine whether bones have been broken. **X-rays** are a form of energy that travels in waves, like the light that your eyes can see.

Before an X-ray image is taken, a lead apron is placed on your body to protect you from unnecessary exposure to X-rays. Photographic film is placed under the area to be viewed. Then, a machine that emits a beam of X-rays is aimed at the area. The X-rays pass through soft tissue but not through bone. The X-rays absorbed by the bone do not reach the film. After the film is developed, it shows bones as clearly defined white areas.

One limitation of X-rays is that they cannot be used directly to view injuries to soft tissues, such as muscle and internal organs. In addition, the energy in X-rays can damage your body cells. This is why you should not have unnecessary X-ray images taken.

FIGURE 12
X-ray Diagnosis
X-rays can be used to determine whether or not you have broken a bone or dislocated a joint. Applying Concepts *What are some limitations of X-rays?*

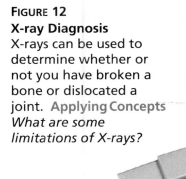

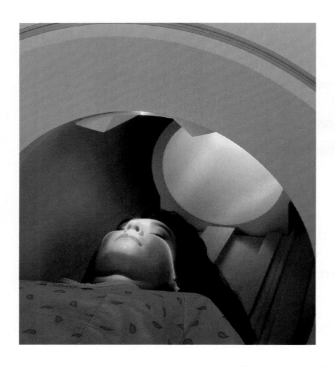

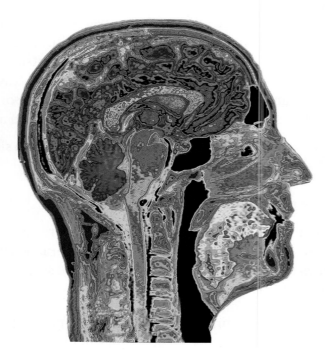

FIGURE 13
Magnetic Resonance Imaging
Magnetic resonance imaging can produce images of muscles and other soft tissues in the body. The image on the right was produced using magnetic resonance imaging.

Magnetic Resonance Imaging A method for taking clear images of both the bones and soft tissues of the body is called **magnetic resonance imaging,** or MRI. An MRI scanner is a large machine that contains electromagnets. The person is placed on a platform that is inside the field of the magnet. The person is then exposed to short bursts of magnetic energy. This magnetic energy causes atoms within the body to vibrate, or resonate. A computer then analyzes the vibration patterns and produces an image of the area.

MRI images are amazingly sharp and clear. MRI can produce images of body tissues at any angle. In addition, MRI can show a clear image of muscles and other soft tissues that an X-ray image cannot show. Another advantage of MRI is that there is no evidence that it can damage cells. Because MRI machines are very expensive to buy and use, this technique is not commonly used to identify possible broken bones.

 **What is one advantage that MRI has over an X-ray?**

Treating Injuries

The doctor determines that your wrist is broken and puts a cast on it. You must wear the cast for six weeks until the bone heals. **In addition to wearing a cast, two other ways to treat skeletal system injuries include surgical procedures such as joint replacement and arthroscopy.**

Joint Replacement Not all injuries to the skeleton involve broken bones. Sometimes, the joints are injured or diseased and require treatment. This is often true for people who have arthritis. **Arthritis** is a disease of the joints that makes movement painful. When movement becomes extremely painful or impossible, the joint may need to be replaced with an artificial one made of metals or plastics. Doctors can replace knees, hips, shoulders, fingers, and wrists. During surgery, the natural joint is removed and an artificial one is cemented in its place.

Arthroscopy Joint injuries can also be treated by arthroscopic surgery. Doctors make a small incision and insert a slim, tube-shaped instrument called an **arthroscope** (AHR thruh skohp) into the joint. Attached to the arthroscope is a camera that projects the image from inside the joint onto a monitor. This allows doctors to look inside the joint to see what is wrong. After the problem is diagnosed, tiny instruments are inserted through one or more additional small incisions to make the necessary repairs. The arthroscope has helped to diagnose and repair many joint problems.

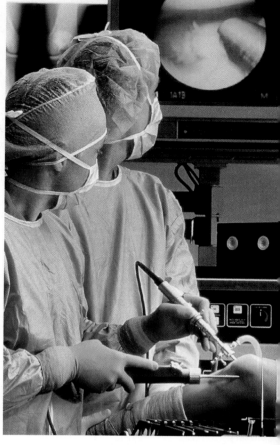

FIGURE 14
Arthroscopic Surgery
To diagnose and treat a knee injury, this surgeon has inserted an arthroscope into the patient's knee.

 **Reading Checkpoint** What is arthritis?

Section 3 Assessment

Target Reading Skill Comparing and Contrasting Use the information in your table about X-rays and MRI to help you answer Question 1 below.

Reviewing Key Concepts

1. **a. Listing** What are three common skeletal system injuries?
   b. Comparing and Contrasting How might each of the different skeletal system injuries be diagnosed?
   c. Applying Concepts Suppose that an X-ray of your injured wrist did not show a fracture. But, after a month, your wrist is still painful and stiff. Why might your doctor order an MRI?

2. **a. Identifying** What are two ways to treat bone and joint injuries surgically?
   b. Summarizing Which joints can be replaced surgically and how is it done?
   c. Making Judgments How has arthroscopic surgery improved the methods for treating skeletal injuries?

Lab zone At-Home Activity

Safety First List the types of exercise you and your family members do. With your family, brainstorm a list of safety gear and precautions to use for each activity in order to prevent skeletal system injuries. (For example, for bicycling, you might list wearing a helmet, stretching before riding, and avoiding busy streets and nighttime riding.) How can you put these safety measures into practice?

The Muscular System

Reading Preview

Key Concepts
- What types of muscles are found in the body?
- Why do skeletal muscles work in pairs?

Key Terms
- involuntary muscle
- voluntary muscle
- skeletal muscle
- tendon
- striated muscle
- smooth muscle
- cardiac muscle

Target Reading Skill
Previewing Visuals When you preview, you look ahead at the material to be read. Preview Figure 15. Then, in a graphic organizer like the one below, write two questions that you have about the diagram. As you read, answer your questions.

Types of Muscle

Q.	How does skeletal muscle help my body move?
A.	
Q.	

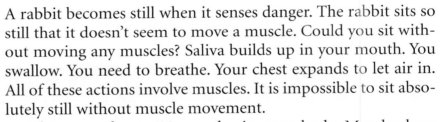

Lab zone Discover Activity

How Do Muscles Work?

1. Grip a spring-type clothespin with the thumb and index finger of your writing hand. Squeeze the clothespin open and shut as quickly as possible for two minutes. Count how many times you can squeeze the clothespin before your muscles tire.

2. Rest for one minute. Then, repeat Step 1.

Think It Over
Predicting What do you think would happen if you repeated Steps 1 and 2 with your other hand? Give a reason for your prediction. Then, test your prediction.

A rabbit becomes still when it senses danger. The rabbit sits so still that it doesn't seem to move a muscle. Could you sit without moving any muscles? Saliva builds up in your mouth. You swallow. You need to breathe. Your chest expands to let air in. All of these actions involve muscles. It is impossible to sit absolutely still without muscle movement.

There are about 600 muscles in your body. Muscles have many functions. For example, they keep your heart beating, pull your mouth into a smile, and move the bones of your skeleton. The girl doing karate on the next page uses many of her muscles to move her arms, legs, hands, feet, and head. Other muscles expand and contract her chest and allow her to breathe.

Types of Muscle

Some of your body's movements, such as smiling, are easy to control. Other movements, such as the beating of your heart, are impossible to control completely. That is because some of your muscles are not under your conscious control. Those muscles are called **involuntary muscles.** Involuntary muscles are responsible for such essential activities as breathing and digesting food.

The muscles that are under your conscious control are called **voluntary muscles.** Smiling, turning a page in a book, and getting out of your chair when the bell rings are all actions controlled by voluntary muscles.

Your body has three types of muscle tissue—skeletal muscle, smooth muscle, and cardiac muscle. Some of these muscle tissues are involuntary, and some are voluntary. In Figure 15, you see a magnified view of each type of muscle in the body. Both skeletal and smooth muscles are found in many places in the body. Cardiac muscle is found only in the heart. Each muscle type performs specific functions in the body.

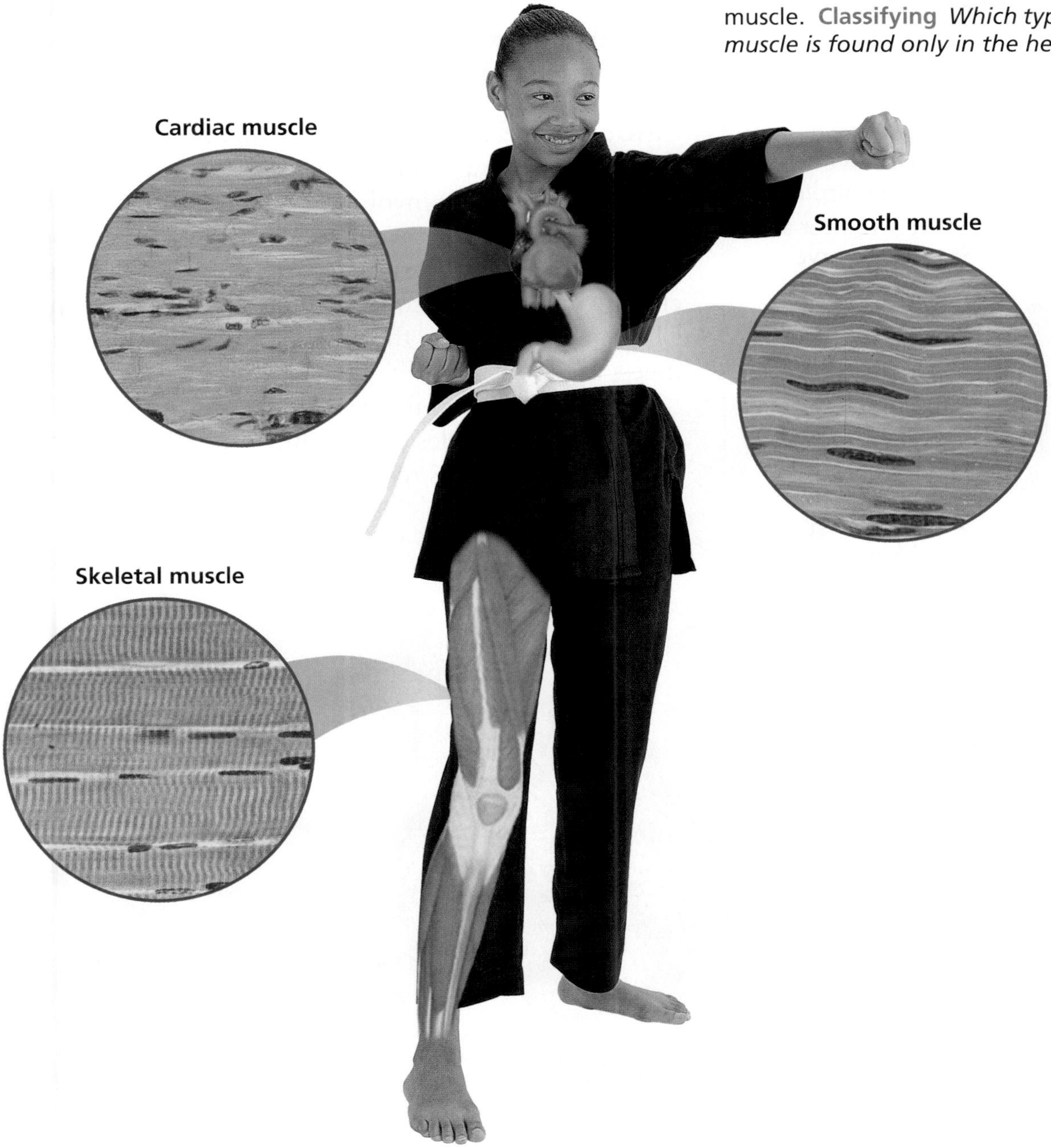

Figure 15
Types of Muscle
Your body has three types of muscle tissue: skeletal muscle, smooth muscle, and cardiac muscle. **Classifying** *Which type of muscle is found only in the heart?*

Cardiac muscle

Smooth muscle

Skeletal muscle

Get a Grip

Are skeletal muscles at work when you're not moving?

1. Hold a stirrer in front of you, parallel to a table top. Do not touch the table.

2. Have a partner place a hairpin on the stirrer.

3. Raise the stirrer until the "legs" of the hairpin just touch the table. The "head" of the hairpin should rest on the stirrer.

4. Hold the stirrer steady for 20 seconds. Observe what happens to the hairpin.

5. Grip the stirrer tighter and repeat Step 4. Observe.

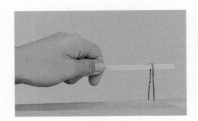

Inferring Are the skeletal muscles in your hand at work when you hold your hand still? Explain.

Skeletal Muscle Every time you walk across a room, you are using skeletal muscles. **Skeletal muscles** are attached to the bones of your skeleton and provide the force that moves your bones. At each end of a skeletal muscle is a tendon. A **tendon** is a strong connective tissue that attaches muscle to bone. Skeletal muscle cells appear banded, or striated. For this reason, skeletal muscle is sometimes called **striated** (STRY ay tid) **muscle.**

Because you have conscious control of skeletal muscles, they are classified as voluntary muscles. One characteristic of skeletal muscles is that they react very quickly. Think about what happens during a swim meet. Immediately after the starting gun sounds, a swimmer's leg muscles push the swimmer off the block into the pool. However, another characteristic of skeletal muscles is that they tire quickly. By the end of the race, the swimmer's muscles are tired and need a rest.

Smooth Muscle The inside of many internal organs, such as the stomach and blood vessels, contain **smooth muscles.** Smooth muscles are involuntary muscles. They work automatically to control certain movements inside your body, such as those involved in digestion. For example, as the smooth muscles of your stomach contract, they produce a churning action. The churning mixes the food with chemicals, and helps to digest the food.

Unlike skeletal muscles, smooth muscle cells are not striated. Smooth muscles behave differently than skeletal muscles, too. Smooth muscles react more slowly and tire more slowly.

 Reading Checkpoint **Where is smooth muscle found?**

Cardiac Muscle The tissue called **cardiac muscle** is found only in your heart. Cardiac muscle has some characteristics in common with both smooth muscle and skeletal muscle. Like smooth muscle, cardiac muscle is involuntary. Like skeletal muscle, cardiac muscle cells are striated. However, unlike skeletal muscle, cardiac muscle does not get tired. It can contract repeatedly. You call those repeated contractions heartbeats.

Muscles at Work

Has anyone ever asked you to "make a muscle"? If so, you probably tightened your fist, bent your arm at the elbow, and made the muscles in your upper arm bulge. Like other skeletal muscles, the muscles in your arm do their work by contracting, becoming shorter and thicker. Muscle cells contract when they receive messages from the nervous system. **Because muscle cells can only contract, not extend, skeletal muscles must work in pairs. While one muscle contracts, the other muscle in the pair relaxes to its original length.**

Muscles Work in Pairs Figure 16 shows the muscle action involved in bending the arm at the elbow. First, the biceps muscle on the front of the upper arm contracts to bend the elbow, lifting the forearm and hand. As the biceps contracts, the triceps on the back of the upper arm relaxes and returns to its original length. Then, to straighten the elbow, the triceps muscle contracts. As the triceps contracts to extend the arm, the biceps relaxes and returns to its original length. Another example of muscles that work in pairs are those in your thigh that bend and straighten the knee joint.

Go Online
PHSchool.com

For: More on muscle types
Visit: PHSchool.com
Web Code: ced-4014

FIGURE 16
Muscle Pairs

Because muscles can only contract, or shorten, they must work in pairs. To bend the arm at the elbow, the biceps contracts while the triceps returns to its original length. **Interpreting Diagrams** *What happens to each muscle to straighten the arm?*

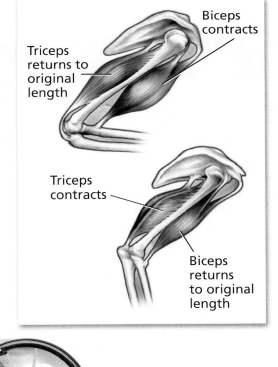

Biceps contracts

Triceps returns to original length

Triceps contracts

Biceps returns to original length

FIGURE 17
Preventing Muscle Injuries
When you warm up before exercising, you increase the flexibility of your muscles.

Muscular Strength and Flexibility Regular exercise is important for maintaining both muscular strength and flexibility. Exercise makes individual muscle cells grow in size. As a result, the whole muscle becomes thicker. The thicker a muscle is, the stronger the muscle is. When you stretch and warm up thoroughly before exercising, your muscles become more flexible. Stretching helps prepare your muscles for exercise or play.

Sometimes, despite taking proper precautions, muscles can become injured. A muscle strain, or pulled muscle, can occur when muscles are overworked or overstretched. Tendons can also be overstretched or partially torn. After a long period of exercise, a skeletal muscle can cramp. When a muscle cramps, the entire muscle contracts strongly and stays contracted. If you injure a muscle or tendon, it is important to follow medical instructions and to rest the injured area so it can heal.

Reading Checkpoint **What are two ways to prepare the muscles for exercise?**

Section 4 Assessment

Target Reading Skill Previewing Visuals Refer to your questions and answers about Figure 15 to help you answer Question 1 below.

Reviewing Key Concepts

1. a. Identifying What are the three types of muscle tissue?
   b. Comparing and Contrasting How do voluntary and involuntary muscles differ? Give an example of each type of muscle.
   c. Predicting The muscles that move your fingers are attached to the bones in your fingers by tendons. Suppose one of the tendons in a person's index finger were cut. How would it affect movement in the finger?

2. a. Identifying Where might you find muscle pairs?
   b. Describing Describe how the muscles in your upper arm work together to bend and straighten your arm.
   c. Applying Concepts When exercising to build muscular strength, why is it important to exercise both muscles in a muscle pair equally?

Writing in Science

Comparison Paragraph Write a paragraph comparing smooth muscle tissue and skeletal muscle tissue. Include whether these muscle tissues are voluntary or involuntary, where they are found and what their functions are. In addition, describe what you might expect to see if you looked at these muscle tissues under a microscope.

A Look Beneath the Skin

Problem

What are some characteristics of skeletal muscles? How do skeletal muscles work?

Skills Focus

observing, inferring, classifying

Materials

- water
- paper towels
- scissors
- dissecting tray
- uncooked chicken wing, treated with bleach

Procedure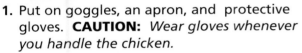

1. Put on goggles, an apron, and protective gloves. **CAUTION:** *Wear gloves whenever you handle the chicken.*

2. Your teacher will give you a chicken wing. Rinse it well with water, dry it with paper towels, and place it in a dissecting tray.

3. Carefully extend the wing to find out how many major parts it has. Draw a diagram of the external structure. Label the upper arm, elbow, lower arm, and hand (wing tip).

4. Use scissors to remove the skin. Cut only through the skin. **CAUTION:** *Cut away from your body and your classmates.*

5. Examine the muscles, which are the bundles of pink tissue around the bones. Find the two groups of muscles in the upper arm. Hold the arm down at the shoulder, and alternately pull on each muscle group. Observe what happens.

6. Find the two groups of muscles in the lower arm. Hold down the arm at the elbow, and alternately pull on each muscle group. Then, make a diagram of the wing's muscles.

7. Find the tendons—shiny white tissue at the ends of the muscles. Notice what parts the tendons connect. Add the tendons to your diagram.

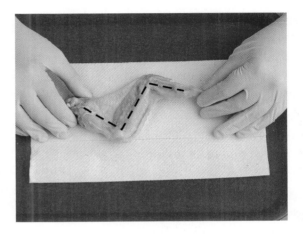

8. Remove the muscles and tendons. Find the ligaments, which are the whitish ribbon-shaped structures between bones. Add them to your diagram.

9. Dispose of the chicken parts according to your teacher's instructions. Wash your hands.

Analyze and Conclude

1. **Observing** How does a chicken wing move at the elbow? How does the motion compare to how your elbow moves? What type of joint is involved?

2. **Inferring** What happened when you pulled on one of the arm muscles? What muscle action does the pulling represent?

3. **Classifying** Categorize the muscles you observed as smooth, cardiac, or skeletal.

4. **Communicating** Why is it valuable to record your observations with accurate diagrams? Write a paragraph in which you describe what your diagrams show.

More to Explore

Use the procedures from this lab to examine an uncooked chicken thigh and leg. Compare how the chicken leg and a human leg move. *Obtain your teacher's permission before carrying out your investigation.*

Reading Preview

Key Concepts
- What are the functions and the structures of skin?
- What habits can help keep your skin healthy?

Key Terms
- epidermis • melanin
- dermis • pore • follicle
- cancer

Target Reading Skill

Identifying Main Ideas As you read the section titled The Body's Tough Covering, write the main idea—the biggest or most important idea—in a graphic organizer like the one below. Then, write five supporting details. The supporting details give examples of the main idea.

Main Idea

The skin has several important functions.

Detail	Detail	Detail

Lab zone — Discover **Activity**

What Can You Observe About Skin?

1. Using a hand lens, examine the skin on your hand. Look for pores and hairs on both the palm and back of your hand.
2. Place a plastic glove on your hand. After five minutes, remove the glove. Then, examine the skin on your hand with the hand lens.

Think It Over

Inferring Compare your hand before and after wearing the glove. What happened to the skin when you wore the glove? Why did this happen?

Here's a question for you: What's the largest organ in the human body? If your answer is the skin, you are right! If an adult's skin were stretched out flat, it would cover an area larger than 1.5 square meters—about the size of a mattress on a twin bed. You may think of the skin as nothing more than a covering that separates the inside of the body from the outside environment. If so, you'll be surprised to learn about the many important roles that the skin plays.

The Body's Tough Covering

The skin performs several major functions in the body. **The skin covers and protects the body from injury, infection, and water loss. The skin also helps regulate body temperature, eliminate wastes, gather information about the environment, and produce vitamin D.**

Protecting the Body The skin protects the body by forming a barrier that keeps disease-causing microorganisms and harmful substances outside the body. In addition, the skin helps keep important substances inside the body. Like plastic wrap that keeps food from drying out, the skin prevents the loss of important fluids such as water.

Maintaining Temperature Another function of the skin is to help the body maintain a steady temperature. Many blood vessels run throughout the skin. When you become too warm, these blood vessels enlarge and the amount of blood that flows through them increases. These changes allow heat to move from your body into the outside environment. In addition, sweat glands in the skin respond to excess heat by producing perspiration. As perspiration evaporates from your skin, your skin is cooled.

Eliminating Wastes Perspiration contains dissolved waste materials that come from the breakdown of chemicals during cellular processes. Thus, your skin is also helping to eliminate wastes whenever you perspire. For example, some of the wastes that come from the breakdown of proteins are eliminated in perspiration.

Gathering Information The skin also gathers information about the environment. To understand how the skin does this, place your fingertips on the skin of your arm and press down firmly. Then lightly pinch yourself. You have just tested some of the nerves in your skin. The nerves in skin provide information about such things as pressure, pain, and temperature. Pain messages are important because they warn you that something in your surroundings may have injured you.

Producing Vitamin D Lastly, some of the skin cells produce vitamin D in the presence of sunlight. Vitamin D is important for healthy bones because it helps the cells in your digestive system to absorb the calcium in your food. Your skin cells need only a few minutes of sunlight to produce all the vitamin D you need in a day.

 **Reading Checkpoint** **How does your skin gather information about the environment?**

FIGURE 18
Eliminating Wastes
Sweat glands in the skin produce perspiration, which leaves the body through pores. The inset photo shows beads of sweat on skin.
Relating Cause and Effect In addition to eliminating wastes, what is another important function of perspiration?

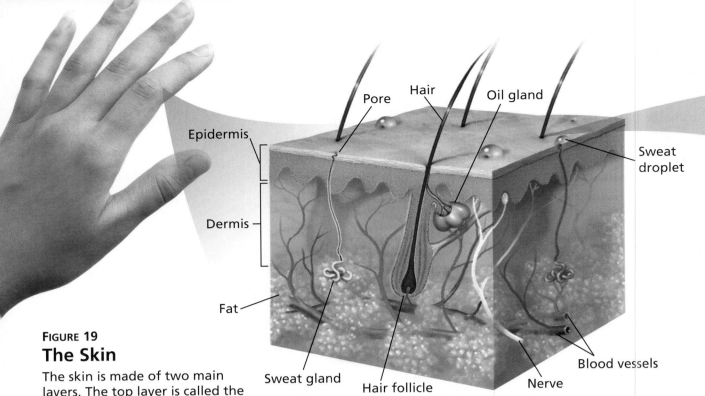

FIGURE 19
The Skin
The skin is made of two main layers. The top layer is called the epidermis. The bottom layer is called the dermis.
Interpreting Diagrams *In which layer of the skin do you find blood vessels?*

The Epidermis

The skin is organized into two main layers, the epidermis and the dermis. The **epidermis** is the outer layer of the skin. In most places, the epidermis is thinner than the dermis. The epidermis does not have nerves or blood vessels. This is why you usually don't feel pain from very shallow scratches, and why shallow scratches do not bleed.

Epidermis Structure Like all cells, the cells in the epidermis have a life cycle. Each epidermal cell begins life deep in the epidermis, where cells divide to form new cells. The new cells mature and move upward in the epidermis as new cells form beneath them. After about two weeks, the cells die and become part of the epidermal surface layer. Under a microscope, this surface layer of dead cells resembles flat bags laid on top of one another. Cells remain in this layer for about two weeks. Then, they are shed and replaced by the dead cells below.

Epidermis Function In some ways, the cells of the epidermis are more valuable dead than alive. Most of the protection provided by the skin is due to the layer of dead cells on the surface. The thick layer of dead cells on your fingertips, for example, protects and cushions your fingertips. Also, the shedding of dead cells carries away bacteria and other substances that settle on the skin. Every time you rub your hands together, you lose thousands of dead skin cells and any bacteria on them.

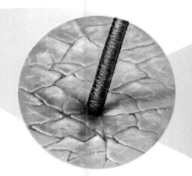

Hair follicle

Some cells in the inner layer of the epidermis help to protect the body, too. On your fingers, for example, some cells produce hard fingernails, which protect the fingertips from injury and help you scratch and pick up objects.

Other cells deep in the epidermis produce **melanin,** a pigment, or colored substance, that gives skin its color. The more melanin in your skin, the darker it is. Exposure to sunlight stimulates the skin to make more melanin. Melanin production helps to protect the skin from burning.

The Dermis

The **dermis** is the inner layer of the skin. Find the dermis in Figure 19. Notice that it is located below the epidermis and above a layer of fat. This fat layer pads the internal organs and helps keep heat in the body.

The dermis contains nerves and blood vessels. The dermis also contains sweat glands, hairs, and oil glands. Sweat glands produce perspiration, which reaches the surface through openings called **pores.** Strands of hair grow within the dermis in structures called **follicles** (FAHL ih kulz). The hair that you see above the skin's surface is made up of dead cells. Oil produced in glands around the hair follicles help to waterproof the hair. In addition, oil that reaches the surface of the skin helps to keep the skin moist.

 **Reading Checkpoint** What is the function of pores in the skin?

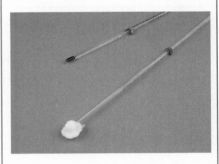

Math · Analyzing Data

Sunscreens and Sunburn

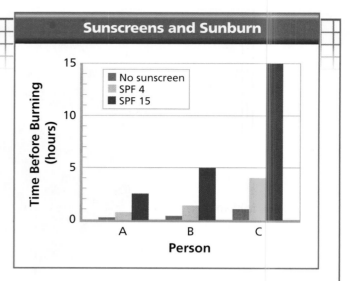

Sunscreen Ratings

The graph shows how sunscreens with different sun protection factor (SPF) ratings extend the time three people can stay in the sun without beginning to get a sunburn.

1. **Reading Graphs** What does the height of each bar in the graph represent?

2. **Interpreting Data** How long can Person B stay in the sun without sunscreen before starting to burn? With a sunscreen of SPF 4? SPF 15?

3. **Inferring** Suppose that Person C was planning to attend an all-day picnic. Which sunscreen should Person C apply? Use data to support your answer.

4. **Calculating** Which is more effective at preventing sunburn—a sunscreen with SPF 4 or one with SPF 15? How much more effective is it? Show your work.

5. **Drawing Conclusions** What does the number in the SPF rating stand for? *(Hint: Note the length of time each person can stay in the sun without sunscreen and compare this value to the length of time each can stay in the sun using SPF 4. Then, do the same for SPF 15.)*

Caring for Your Skin

Because your skin has so many vital functions, taking care of it is important. **Three simple habits can help you keep your skin healthy. Eat a healthful diet. Keep your skin clean and dry. Limit your exposure to the sun.**

Healthful Diet Your skin is always active. Eating a well-balanced diet provides the energy and raw materials needed for the growth and replacement of hair, nails, and skin cells. In addition to what you eat, a healthful diet also includes drinking plenty of water. That way, you can replace the water lost in perspiration.

Keeping Skin Clean When you wash your skin with mild soap, you get rid of dirt and harmful bacteria. Washing your skin also helps to control oiliness.

Good washing habits are particularly important during the teenage years when oil glands are more active. When glands become clogged with oil, the blackheads and whiteheads of acne can form. If acne becomes infected by skin bacteria, your doctor may prescribe an antibiotic to help control the infection.

For: Links on the skin
Visit: www.SciLinks.org
Web Code: scn-0415

Limiting Sun Exposure It is important to protect your skin from the harmful effects of the sun. Repeated exposure to sunlight can damage skin cells, and possibly lead to skin cancer. **Cancer** is a disease in which some cells in the body divide uncontrollably. In addition, repeated exposure to the sun can cause the skin to become leathery and wrinkled.

There are many things you can do to protect your skin from damage by the sun. When you are outdoors, always wear a hat, sunglasses, and use a sunscreen on exposed skin. Choose clothing made of tightly woven fabrics for the greatest protection. In addition, avoid exposure to the sun between the hours of 10 A.M. and 4 P.M. That is the time when sunlight is the strongest.

 **Reading Checkpoint** **What health problems can result from repeated sun exposure?**

FIGURE 20
Skin Protection
This person is wearing a hat to protect his skin from the sun.
Applying Concepts *What other behaviors can provide protection from the sun?*

Section 5 Assessment

Target Reading Skill Identifying Main Ideas Use your graphic organizer to help you answer Question 1 below.

Reviewing Key Concepts

1. **a.** Listing What are five important functions of the skin?
   b. Identifying How does the epidermis protect the body? What structure in the dermis helps to maintain body temperature?
   c. Inferring What could happen if the pores in your dermis become blocked?

2. **a.** Identifying What are three things you can do to keep your skin healthy?
   b. Explaining Why is it important to use sunscreen to protect your skin when outside?
   c. Making Judgments Do you think it is possible to wash your skin too much and damage it as a result? Why or why not?

Lab zone **At-Home Activity**

Protection From the Sun With a family member, look for products in your home that provide protection from the sun. You may also want to visit a store that sells these products. Make a list of the products and place them in categories, such as sunblocks, clothing, eye protectors, and other forms of protection. Explain to your family member why it is important to use such products.

Design Your Own Lab

Sun Safety

Problem

How well do different materials protect the skin from the sun?

Skills Focus

observing, predicting, interpreting data, drawing conclusions

Materials

- scissors
- photosensitive paper
- metric ruler
- white construction paper
- stapler
- pencil
- resealable plastic bag
- plastic knife
- 2 sunscreens with SPF ratings of 4 and 30
- staple remover
- 3 different fabrics

Procedure

PART 1 Sunscreen Protection

1. Read over the procedure for Part 1. Then, write a prediction about how well each of the sunscreens will protect against the sun.

2. Use scissors to cut two strips of photosensitive paper that measure 5 cm by 15 cm.

3. Divide each strip into thirds by drawing lines across the strips.

4. Cover one third of each strip with a square of white construction paper. Staple each square down.

5. Use a pencil to write the lower SPF rating on the back of the first strip. Write the other SPF rating on the back of the second strip.

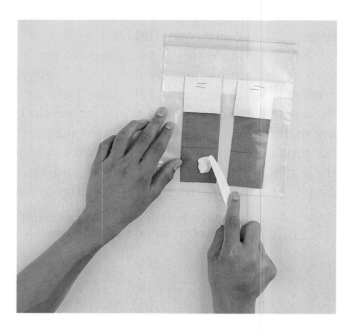

6. Place the two strips side by side in a plastic bag. Seal the bag, then staple through the white squares to hold the strips in place.

7. With a plastic knife, spread a thin layer of each sunscreen on the bag over the bottom square of its labeled strip. This is shown in the photo above. Make certain each strip has the same thickness of sunscreen. Be sure not to spread sunscreen over the middle squares.

8. Place the strips in sunlight until the color of the middle squares stops changing. Make sure the bag is sunscreen-side up when you place it in the sunlight.

9. Remove the staples from the bag, and then take out the strips. Take off the construction paper. Rinse the strips for one minute in cold water, then dry them flat.

10. Observe all the squares. Then, record your observations.

PART 2 | Fabric Protection

11. Your teacher will provide three fabric pieces of different thicknesses.

12. Based on the procedure in Part 1, design an experiment to test how effective the three fabrics are in protecting against the sun. Write a prediction about which fabric you think will be most effective, next most effective, and least effective.

13. Obtain your teacher's approval before carrying out your experiment. Record all of your observations.

Analyze and Conclude

1. **Observing** Did the sunscreens protect against sun exposure? How do you know?

2. **Predicting** Which sunscreen provided more protection? Was your prediction correct? How would you predict a sunscreen with an SPF of 15 would compare to the sunscreens you tested?

3. **Interpreting Data** Did the fabrics protect against sun exposure? How do you know?

4. **Drawing Conclusions** Which of the fabrics provided the most protection? The least protection? How did your results compare with your predictions?

5. **Communicating** What advice would you give people about protecting their skin from the sun? Create a pamphlet in which you address this question by comparing the different sunscreens and fabrics you tested.

More to Explore

Design another experiment, this time to find out whether ordinary window glass protects skin against sun exposure. *Obtain your teacher's permission before carrying out your investigation.*

Study Guide

1 Body Organization and Homeostasis

Key Concepts

- The levels of organization in the body consist of cells, tissues, organs, and organ systems.
- Homeostasis is the process by which an organism's internal environment is kept stable in spite of changes in the external environment.

Key Terms

cell	connective tissue
cell membrane	epithelial tissue
nucleus	organ
cytoplasm	organ system
tissue	homeostasis
muscle tissue	stress
nervous tissue	

2 The Skeletal System

Key Concepts

- Your skeleton provides shape and support, enables you to move, protects your organs, produces blood cells, and stores minerals and other materials until your body needs them.
- Joints allow bones to move in different ways.
- Bones are complex living structures that undergo growth and development.
- A balanced diet and regular exercise are important for a lifetime of healthy bones.

Key Terms

skeleton
vertebra
joint
ligament
cartilage
compact bone
spongy bone
marrow
osteoporosis

3 Diagnosing Bone and Joint Injuries

Key Concepts

- Three common skeletal system injuries are fractures, dislocations, and sprains. Two ways to identify skeletal injuries are X-rays and magnetic resonance imaging (MRI).
- Ways to treat skeletal injuries include wearing a cast, joint replacement, and arthroscopy.

Key Terms

fracture	magnetic resonance
dislocation	imaging
sprain	arthritis
X-ray	arthroscope

4 The Muscular System

Key Concepts

- Your body has three types of muscle tissue—skeletal, smooth, and cardiac.
- Skeletal muscles work in pairs. While one muscle contracts, the other muscle in the pair relaxes to its original length.

Key Terms

involuntary muscle	striated muscle
voluntary muscle	smooth muscle
skeletal muscle	cardiac muscle
tendon	

5 The Skin

Key Concepts

- The skin has several functions: protection, maintaining temperature, eliminating wastes, gathering information, and making vitamin D.
- The two skin layers are epidermis and dermis.
- Three simple habits can help you keep your skin healthy. Eat a healthful diet. Keep your skin clean and dry. Limit your sun exposure.

Key Terms

epidermis	pore
melanin	follicle
dermis	cancer

Review and Assessment

Organizing Information

Concept Mapping Copy the concept map about the types of muscles onto a separate sheet of paper. Then complete it and add a title. (For more on Concept Mapping, see the Skills Handbook.)

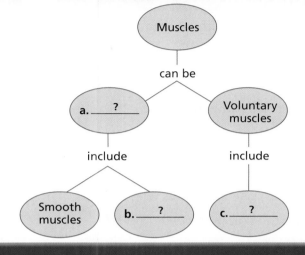

Reviewing Key Terms

Choose the letter of the best answer.

1. A group of similar cells that perform a similar function is called a(n)
   a. cell.
   b. organ.
   c. tissue.
   d. organ system.

2. A soft, connective tissue found inside some bones is
   a. cytoplasm.
   b. marrow.
   c. cartilage.
   d. osteoporosis.

3. The stretching and tearing of ligaments is
   a. a fracture.
   b. a dislocation.
   c. a sprain.
   d. osteoporosis.

4. Muscles that help the skeleton move are
   a. cardiac muscles.
   b. smooth muscles.
   c. skeletal muscles.
   d. involuntary muscles.

5. A colored substance that helps to keep the skin from burning is
   a. the dermis.
   b. the epidermis.
   c. melanin.
   d. a follicle.

If the statement is true, write *true*. If the statement is false, change the underlined word or words to make the statement true.

6. The <u>cytoplasm</u> directs the cell's activities.

7. Spongy bone is filled with <u>cartilage.</u>

8. <u>X-rays</u> produce images of soft tissues.

9. <u>Skeletal</u> muscle is called striated muscle.

10. The <u>epidermis</u> contains nerve endings and blood vessels.

Writing in Science

Descriptive Paragraph Pretend you are a writer for a science magazine for children. Write a few paragraphs that compare the characteristics of cartilage with the characteristics of bones. Be sure to explain the advantages of both types of materials.

Bones, Muscles, and Skin
Video Preview
Video Field Trip
▶ Video Assessment

Review and Assessment

Checking Concepts

11. Explain the relationship among cells, tissues, organs, and organ systems.

12. List the four kinds of movable joints. Describe the type of movement each joint allows.

13. Describe the structure of a bone.

14. How is arthroscopy used to treat injuries?

15. How does the appearance of smooth muscle differ from that of skeletal muscle?

16. Explain how skeletal muscles work in pairs.

17. How does the skin protect your body?

Thinking Critically

18. **Classifying** Identify each of the labeled parts of the cell.

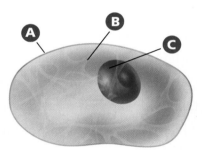

19. **Inferring** In addition to bone, cartilage, and fat, scientists classify blood as a connective tissue. Explain why.

20. **Making Generalizations** How is homeostasis important to survival?

21. **Making Judgments** A patient is admitted to the emergency room with a severe headache after a fall. What kind of image should be taken to diagnose the problem? Explain.

22. **Predicting** If smooth muscle had to be controlled consciously, what problems could you foresee in day-to-day living?

23. **Relating Cause and Effect** A person who is exposed to excessive heat may suffer from heatstroke. The first sign of heatstroke is that the person stops sweating. Why is heatstroke a life-threatening emergency?

Applying Skills

Use the graph to answer Questions 24–26.

The graph below shows the effects of the temperature of the environment on a boy's skin temperature and on the temperature inside his body.

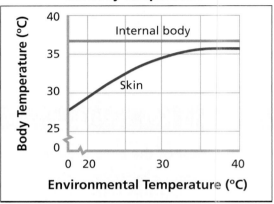

Environmental Temperature vs. Body Temperature

24. **Interpreting Data** As the temperature of the environment rises, what happens to the boy's internal body temperature? How does this demonstrate homeostasis?

25. **Inferring** What happens to the temperature of the boy's skin? Why is this pattern different from the pattern shown by the boy's internal body temperature?

26. **Predicting** Suppose the boy went outdoors on a chilly fall morning. Predict what would happen to his internal body temperature and his skin temperature. Explain.

Lab zone Chapter **Project**

Performance Assessment Before testing your prosthetic hand, explain to your classmates how and why you designed the hand the way you did. When you test the hand, observe how it picks up objects. How does it compare with a real human hand? How could you improve the function of your prosthetic hand?

End-of-Grade Test Practice

Test-Taking Tip
Interpreting a Graph
If a question asks you to interpret a line graph, look first at the graph's title. This tells you the subject of the graph. Next, look at the labels on the axes. The labels tell you what relationship is plotted on the graph—in other words, what variables are being compared. Then, look at the line or lines on the graph to see what trend is shown.

Sample Question

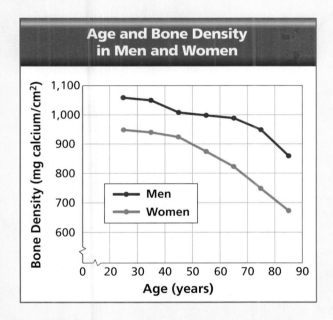

Age and Bone Density in Men and Women

Which of the following relationships is plotted on the graph?
- **A** how exercise affects bone density
- **B** how bone density changes with age
- **C** how calcium intake affects bone density
- **D** how calcium intake changes with age

Answer
The correct answer is **B**. Both the graph title and the labels on the axes tell you that the graph shows the relationship between age and bone density. Choices **A**, **C**, and **D** are incorrect because the graph does not include any information on exercise or calcium intake.

Choose the letter of the best answer.

1. Which of the following statements is true according to the graph shown at left?
   - **A** The bones of women are more dense than the bones of men.
   - **B** The bones of men contain less calcium than do the bones of women.
   - **C** The bone density of both men and women decreases as they age.
   - **D** An average 55-year-old woman has stronger bones than an average 55-year-old man.

2. A doctor cannot identify a sprained ankle by taking an X-ray because
   - **A** X-rays pass through bones.
   - **B** soft tissues block X-rays.
   - **C** X-rays pass through soft tissues.
   - **D** a sprained ankle cannot be viewed on an X-ray until the swelling decreases.

3. The muscles that you use to lift a book are
   - **A** cardiac muscles.
   - **B** smooth muscles.
   - **C** involuntary muscles.
   - **D** skeletal muscles.

4. Which of the following is *not* an important function of the skeletal system?
   - **A** It protects internal organs.
   - **B** It stores minerals until they are needed by the body.
   - **C** It allows the body to move.
   - **D** It regulates body temperature.

5. Which of the following represents the smallest level of organization in the body?
   - **A** cardiac muscle tissue
   - **B** the heart
   - **C** a muscle cell
   - **D** the circulatory system

Constructed Response

6. Compare the dermis and the epidermis layers of the skin. Discuss the following: their thickness, location, nerves, blood vessels, sweat glands, and cell life cycle.

Chapter

9

Food and Digestion

Standard Course of Study

1.02 Develop appropriate experimental procedures.

1.03 Apply safety procedures.

1.04 Analyze variables.

1.05 Analyze evidence.

1.06 Use mathematics to gather, organize, and present data.

1.07 Prepare models and/or computer simulations.

1.08 Use oral and written language.

2.02 Use information systems.

2.04 Apply tenets of technological design.

4.01 Analyze how human body systems interact.

4.02 Describe functions of human body systems.

4.03 Explain how the structure of an organ is adapted to perform specific functions.

4.07 Explain how environmental effects influence human embryo development and health.

4.08 Explain how understanding the human body helps to make informed health decisions.

Let's eat! These baskets of vegetables offer ▶
a wide choice of tasty and healthful foods.

Food and Digestion

▶ Video Preview
Video Field Trip
Video Assessment

Lab zone™ Chapter **Project**

What's for Lunch?

When you're hungry and grab a snack, what do you choose? In this project, you'll take a close look at the foods you select each day.

Your Goal To compare your eating pattern to the recommendations in the Food Guide Pyramid

To complete this project successfully, you must

- keep an accurate record of everything you eat and drink for three days
- create graphs to compare your eating pattern with the recommendations in the Food Guide Pyramid
- make changes in your diet, if needed, during another three-day period

Plan It! Before you begin, study the Food Guide Pyramid in this chapter to understand how foods are grouped. Then, decide how to best keep an accurate, complete food log. How will you make sure you record everything you eat, including snacks and drinks? How will you decide which group each food falls into? How will you determine serving sizes? After your teacher approves your plan, start keeping your food log.

Food and Energy

Reading Preview

Key Concepts
- Why does your body need food?
- How do the six nutrients needed by the body help carry out essential processes?

Key Terms
- nutrient • calorie
- carbohydrate • glucose • fat
- protein • amino acid
- vitamin • mineral

Target Reading Skill
Outlining As you read, make an outline about the six groups of nutrients needed by the body. Use the red headings for the main ideas and the blue headings for the supporting ideas.

Food and Energy
I. Why You Need Food
A. Nutrients
B.
II. Carbohydrates
A.

Lab zone · Discover **Activity**

Food Claims—Fact or Fiction?

1. Examine the list of statements at the right. Copy the list onto a separate sheet of paper.
2. Next to each statement, write *agree* or *disagree*. Give a reason for your response.
3. Discuss your responses with a small group of classmates. Compare the reasons you gave for agreeing or disagreeing with each statement.

Think It Over
Posing Questions List some other statements about nutrition that you have heard. How could you find out whether the statements are true?

Fact or Fiction?
a. Athletes need more protein in their diets than other people do.
b. The only salt that a food contains is the salt that you have added to it.
c. As part of a healthy diet, everyone should take vitamin supplements.

Imagine a Thanksgiving dinner—roast turkey on a platter, delicious stuffing, and lots of vegetables—an abundance of colors and aromas. Food is a central part of many celebrations, of times shared with friends and family. Food is also essential. Every living thing needs food to stay alive.

Why You Need Food

Foods provide your body with materials for growing and for repairing tissues. Food also provides energy for everything you do. For example, running, playing a musical instrument, reading, and even sleeping require energy. Food also helps your body maintain homeostasis. You read in Chapter 1 that the systems of the body work together to help keep the body's internal environment stable. By filling your energy needs, food enables your body to keep this balance during all your activities.

Nutrients Your body breaks down the foods you eat into nutrients. **Nutrients** (NOO tree unts) are the substances in food that provide the raw materials and energy the body needs to carry out all its essential processes. There are six groups of nutrients necessary for human health—carbohydrates, fats, proteins, vitamins, minerals, and water.

Energy When nutrients are used by the body for energy, the amount of energy they release can be measured in units called calories. One **calorie** is the amount of energy needed to raise the temperature of one gram of water by one degree Celsius. Most foods contain many thousands of calories of energy. Biologists use the term *Calorie,* with a capital *C,* to measure the energy in foods. One Calorie is the same as 1 kilocalorie (kcal) or 1,000 calories. For example, one serving of popcorn may contain 60 Calories (60 kcal), or 60,000 calories, of energy. The more Calories a food has, the more energy it contains.

You need to eat a certain number of Calories each day to meet your body's energy needs. Your daily energy requirement depends on your level of physical activity. Your needs also change as you grow and age. As an infant and child, you grew very rapidly, so you likely had very high energy needs. Your current growth and level of physical activity affect the number of Calories you need now. The more active you are, the greater your energy needs are.

 **Reading Checkpoint** How is energy in foods measured?

FIGURE 1
Burning Calories
The number of Calories you burn depends on your weight as well as your level of activity. The more active you are, the more Calories you burn.
Applying Concepts *Which activity do you think burns the most Calories per hour—playing basketball, walking, or reading?*

Playing basketball

Walking

Reading

FIGURE 2
Carbohydrates

Simple carbohydrates, or sugars, are found in fruits, milk, and some vegetables. Sugars are also added to cookies, candies, and soft drinks. Complex carbohydrates are found in rice, corn, pasta, and bread. Fruits, vegetables, nuts, and whole-grain foods also contain fiber.
Applying Concepts Why is fiber important in the diet?

Simple Carbohydrates

Brownie (1 square)
Total Carbohydrates 18 g
    Sugars   10 g
    Starches   7 g
    Fiber   1 g

Watermelon (1 slice)
Total Carbohydrates 22 g
    Sugars   18 g
    Starches   3 g
    Fiber   1 g

Milk (1 cup)
Total Carbohydrates 12 g
    Sugars   12 g
    Starches   0 g
    Fiber   0 g

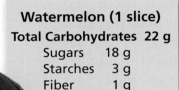

Carbohydrates

The nutrients called **carbohydrates** (kahr boh HY drayts), which are composed of carbon, oxygen, and hydrogen, are a major source of energy. One gram of carbohydrate provides your body with four Calories of energy. **In addition to providing energy, carbohydrates provide the raw materials to make cell parts.** Based on their chemical structure, carbohydrates are divided into simple carbohydrates and complex carbohydrates.

Simple Carbohydrates Simple carbohydrates are also known as sugars. One sugar, **glucose** (GLOO kohs), is the major source of energy for your body's cells. However, most foods do not contain large amounts of glucose. The body converts other types of sugars, such as the sugar found in fruits, into glucose. Glucose is the form of sugar the body can most easily use.

Complex Carbohydrates Complex carbohydrates are made up of many sugar molecules linked together in a chain. Starch is a complex carbohydrate found in foods from plants, such as potatoes, rice, wheat, and corn. To use starch as an energy source, your body first breaks it down into smaller, individual sugar molecules. Only then can your body release the molecules' energy.

Like starch, fiber is a complex carbohydrate found in plants. But unlike starch, fiber cannot be broken down into sugar molecules by your body. Instead, fiber passes through the body and is eliminated.

Complex Carbohydrates

Yellow Corn (1 ear)
Total Carbohydrates 19 g
   Sugars   2 g
   Starches 15 g
   Fiber   2 g

Pasta (1 cup)
Total Carbohydrates 40 g
   Sugars   1 g
   Starches 37 g
   Fiber   2 g

Wheat Bread (1 slice)
Total Carbohydrates 17 g
   Sugars   3.5 g
   Starches 12.0 g
   Fiber   1.5 g

Because your body cannot digest it, fiber is not considered a nutrient. Fiber is an important part of the diet, however, because it helps keep the digestive system functioning properly.

Nutritionists' Recommendations Nutritionists recommend that 45 to 65 percent of the Calories in a diet come from carbohydrates. It is better to eat more complex carbohydrates, such as whole grains, than simple carbohydrates. Foods made with whole grains usually contain a variety of other nutrients. Foods made with a lot of sugar, such as candy and soft drinks, have few valuable nutrients. Also, while sugars can give you a quick burst of energy, starches provide a more even, long-term energy source.

Reading Checkpoint　What are two types of carbohydrates? Give an example of each.

Fats

Like carbohydrates, **fats** are energy-containing nutrients that are composed of carbon, oxygen, and hydrogen. However, fats contain more than twice the energy of an equal amount of carbohydrates. One gram of fat provides your body with nine Calories of energy. **In addition to providing energy, fats have other important functions. Fats form part of the cell membrane, the structure that forms the boundary of a cell. Fatty tissue protects and supports your internal organs and insulates your body.**

Lab zone Skills **Activity**

Predicting

You can do a test to see which foods contain starch.

1. Put on your apron.
2. Obtain food samples from your teacher. Predict which ones contain starch. Write down your predictions.
3. Use a plastic dropper to add three drops of iodine to each food sample. **CAUTION:** *Iodine can stain skin and clothing.* Handle it carefully. If the iodine turns blue-black, starch is present.

Which foods contain starch? Were your predictions correct?

FIGURE 3
Many foods contain saturated, unsaturated, and trans fats. Unsaturated fats are considered to be more healthful than saturated fats and trans fats.
Interpreting Graphs *Which item has the most unsaturated fat—butter, tub margarine, or olive oil?*

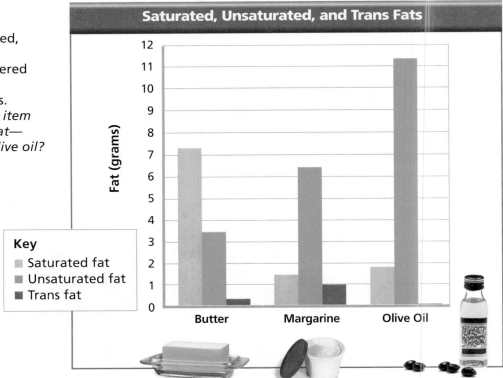

Saturated, Unsaturated, and Trans Fats

Key
- Saturated fat
- Unsaturated fat
- Trans fat

Butter   Margarine   Olive Oil

Fat (grams)

Kinds of Fats Fats may be classified as unsaturated or saturated based on their chemical structure. Unsaturated fats are usually liquid at room temperature. Most cooking oils are unsaturated fats. Saturated fats are usually solid at room temperature. Meat and dairy products contain relatively large amounts of saturated fat.

You may have heard about trans fat. Trans fats are made when manufacturers add hydrogen to vegetable oils. Foods containing trans fats stay fresh longer than foods containing unsaturated fats. Trans fats are found in margarine, chips, and commercially baked goods. Both trans fats and saturated fats are considered to be less healthful than unsaturated fats.

Cholesterol Cholesterol (kuh LES tur awl) is a waxy, fatlike substance found only in animal products. Like fats, cholesterol is an important part of your body's cells. Your liver can make all of the cholesterol your body needs. Therefore, cholesterol is not a necessary part of the diet.

Nutritionists' Recommendations Nutritionists recommend that no more than 30 percent of the Calories eaten each day come from fats. Extra fats and cholesterol in the diet can lead to a buildup of fatty material in the blood vessels. This fatty buildup can cause heart disease.

 Reading Checkpoint **How can you tell the difference between most unsaturated fats and saturated fats?**

Proteins

Proteins are nutrients that contain nitrogen as well as carbon, hydrogen, and oxygen. **Proteins are needed for tissue growth and repair. They also play an important part in chemical reactions within cells.** Proteins can serve as a source of energy, but they are a less important source of energy than carbohydrates or fats. About 10 to 35 percent of your daily Calorie intake should come from proteins.

Amino Acids Proteins are made up of small units called **amino acids** (uh MEE noh), which are linked together chemically to form large protein molecules. Thousands of different proteins are built from only about 20 different amino acids. Your body can make about half of the amino acids it needs. The others, called essential amino acids, must come from the foods you eat.

Complete and Incomplete Proteins Foods from animal sources, such as meat and eggs, are sources of complete proteins because these foods contain all the essential amino acids. Proteins from plant sources, such as beans, grains, and nuts, are called incomplete proteins because they are missing one or more essential amino acid. Different plant sources lack different amino acids. Therefore, to obtain all the essential amino acids from plant sources alone, people need to eat a wide variety of plant foods.

 **Reading Checkpoint** What are the units that make up proteins?

Math Skills

Percentage

A percentage (%) is a ratio that compares a number to 100. For example, 30% means 30 out of 100.

Suppose that a person eats a total of 2,000 Calories in one day. Of those Calories, 300 come from protein. Follow these steps to calculate the percentage of Calories that come from protein.

1. Write the comparison as a fraction:

$$\frac{300}{2,000}$$

2. Multiply the fraction by 100% to express it as a percentage:

$$\frac{300}{2,000} \times 100\% = 15\%$$

Practice Problem Suppose that 540 Calories of the person's 2,000 Calorie total come from fats. What percentage of the Calories comes from fats?

Go Online
SCi LINKS™ NSTA

For: Links on foods and energy
Visit: www.SciLinks.org
Web code: scn-0421

FIGURE 5
Eat Your Vegetables!
Fresh vegetables are full of
vitamins and are fun to pick
as well.

Vitamins and Minerals

Two kinds of nutrients—vitamins and minerals—are needed by the body in very small amounts. Unlike the other nutrients, vitamins and minerals do not provide the body with energy or raw materials. Instead, they help the body carry out various processes.

Vitamins act as helper molecules in a variety of chemical reactions in the body. Vitamin K, for example, helps your blood to clot when you get a cut or a scrape. Figure 6 lists the vitamins necessary for health. The body can make a few of these vitamins. For example, your skin can make vitamin D when exposed to sunlight. Most vitamins, however, must be obtained from foods.

Fat-Soluble and Water-Soluble Vitamins Vitamins are classified as either fat-soluble or water-soluble. Fat-soluble vitamins dissolve in fat, and they are stored in fatty tissues in the body. Vitamins A, D, E, and K are all fat-soluble vitamins. Water-soluble vitamins dissolve in water and are not stored in the body. This fact makes it especially important to include sources of water-soluble vitamins—vitamin C and all of the B vitamins—in your diet every day.

Importance of Vitamins Although vitamins are only needed in small amounts, a lack of certain vitamins in the diet can lead to health problems. In the 1700s, sailors on long voyages survived on hard, dry biscuits, salted meat, and not much else. Because of this limited diet, many sailors developed a serious disease called scurvy. People with scurvy suffer from bleeding gums, stiff joints, and sores that do not heal. Some may even die.

A Scottish doctor, James Lind, hypothesized that scurvy was the result of the sailors' poor diet. Lind divided sailors with scurvy into groups and fed different foods to each group. The sailors who were fed citrus fruits—oranges and lemons—recovered from the disease. Lind recommended that all sailors eat citrus fruits. When Lind's recommendations were carried out, scurvy disappeared. Today scientists know that scurvy is caused by the lack of vitamin C, which is found in citrus fruits.

 **Reading Checkpoint** **List the fat-soluble vitamins.**

FIGURE 6
Essential Vitamins

Both fat-soluble vitamins and water-soluble vitamins are necessary to maintain health. **Interpreting Tables** *What foods provide a supply of both vitamins E and K?*

Fat-Soluble Vitamins		
Vitamin	**Sources**	**Function**
A	Dairy products; eggs; liver; yellow, orange, and dark green vegetables; fruits	Maintains healthy skin, bones, teeth, and hair; aids vision in dim light
D	Fortified dairy products; fish; eggs; liver; made by skin cells in presence of sunlight	Maintains bones and teeth; helps in the use of calcium and phosphorus
E	Vegetable oils; margarine; green, leafy vegetables; whole-grain foods; seeds; nuts	Aids in maintenance of red blood cells
K	Green, leafy vegetables; milk; liver; made by bacteria in the intestines	Aids in blood clotting

Water-Soluble Vitamins		
Vitamin	**Sources**	**Function**
B1 (thiamin)	Pork; liver; whole-grain foods; legumes; nuts	Needed for breakdown of carbohydrates
B2 (riboflavin)	Dairy products; eggs; whole-grain breads and cereals; green, leafy vegetables	Needed for normal growth
B3 (niacin)	Many protein-rich foods; milk; eggs; meat; fish; whole-grain foods; nuts; peanut butter	Needed for release of energy
B6 (pyridoxine)	Green, leafy vegetables; meats; fish; legumes; fruits; whole-grain foods	Helps in the breakdown of proteins, fats, and carbohydrates
B12	Meats; fish; poultry; dairy products; eggs	Maintains healthy nervous system; needed for red blood cell formation
Biotin	Liver; meat; fish; eggs; legumes; bananas; melons	Aids in the release of energy
Folic acid	Green, leafy vegetables; legumes; seeds; liver	Needed for red blood cell formation
Pantothenic acid	Liver; meats; fish; eggs; whole-grain foods	Needed for the release of energy
C	Citrus fruits; tomatoes; potatoes; dark green vegetables; mangoes	Needed to form connective tissue and fight infection

FIGURE 7
Eating a variety of foods each day provides your body with the minerals it needs. *Interpreting Tables* *Which minerals play a role in regulating water levels in the body?*

Essential Minerals

Mineral	Sources	Function
Calcium	Milk; cheese; dark green, leafy vegetables; tofu; legumes	Helps build bones and teeth; aids in blood clotting; muscle and nerve function
Chlorine	Table salt; soy sauce	Helps maintain water balance
Fluorine	Fluoridated drinking water; fish	Helps form bones and teeth
Iodine	Seafood, iodized salt	Helps in the release of energy
Iron	Red meats; seafood; green, leafy vegetables; legumes; dried fruits	Needed for red blood cell function
Magnesium	Green, leafy vegetables; legumes; nuts; whole-grain foods	Aids in muscle and nerve function; helps in the release of energy
Phosphorus	Meat; poultry; eggs; fish; dairy products	Helps produce healthy bones and teeth; helps in the release of energy
Potassium	Grains; fruits; vegetables; meat; fish	Helps maintain water balance; muscle and nerve function
Sodium	Table salt; soy sauce	Helps maintain water balance; nerve function

◄ Source of calcium

◄ Source of potassium

Source of sodium ►

Importance of Minerals Nutrients that are not made by living things are called **minerals.** Minerals are present in soil and are absorbed by plants through their roots. You obtain minerals by eating plant foods or animals that have eaten plants. Figure 7 lists some minerals you need. You probably know that calcium is needed for strong bones and teeth. Iron is needed for the proper functioning of red blood cells.

Both vitamins and minerals are needed by your body in small amounts to carry out chemical processes. If you eat a wide variety of foods, you probably will get enough vitamins and minerals. Most people who eat a balanced diet do not need to take vitamin or mineral supplements.

 Reading Checkpoint   **What are minerals?**

Water

Imagine that a boat is sinking. The people on board are getting into a lifeboat. They have room for only one of these items: a bag of fruit, a can of meat, a loaf of bread, or a jug of water. Which item should they choose?

You might be surprised to learn that the lifeboat passengers should choose the water. Although people can probably survive for weeks without food, they will die within days without fresh water. Water is the most abundant substance in the body. It accounts for about 65 percent of the average person's body weight.

Water is the most important nutrient because the body's vital processes—including chemical reactions such as the breakdown of nutrients—take place in water. Water makes up most of the body's fluids, including blood. Nutrients and other important substances are carried throughout the body dissolved in the watery part of the blood. Your body also needs water to produce perspiration, which helps regulate body temperature and remove wastes.

Under normal conditions, you need to take in about 2 liters of water every day. You can do this by drinking water and other beverages and by eating foods with lots of water, such as fruits and vegetables. If the weather is hot or you are exercising, you need to drink additional water to replace the water that you lose in sweat.

FIGURE 8
Water—An Essential Nutrient
All living things need water. Without regular water intake, an organism would not be able to carry out the processes that keep it alive.

Section 1 Assessment

Target Reading Skill Outlining Use the information in your outline about nutrients to help you answer the questions below.

Reviewing Key Concepts

1. a. **Identifying** Name two ways in which foods are used by the body.
   b. **Defining** What is a calorie? How does it relate to the amount of energy in foods?
   c. **Inferring** Why do young children and active teenagers have high energy needs?
2. a. **Listing** List the six nutrients that are needed by the body.
   b. **Summarizing** For each nutrient you listed, briefly describe the role it plays in the body.
   c. **Applying Concepts** Why is it especially important that vegetarians eat a varied diet?

Math Practice

3. **Percentage** Suppose that a person eats 2,500 Calories in one day. Of those Calories, 1,200 are from carbohydrates, 875 are from fat, and the rest are from protein. What percentages of the person's Calories are from carbohydrates, from fats, and from proteins?

Raisin' the Raisin Question

Problem

Raisins are a good source of the mineral iron. Which raisin bran cereal contains the most raisins?

Skills Focus

measuring, calculating, controlling variables

Materials

- balance
- paper towels
- beaker (250 mL)
- raisin bran cereals (several brands)

Procedure

1. Use a balance to find the mass of a clean 250-mL beaker. Record the mass in a data table like the one below.

2. Fill the beaker to the top with one of the brands of raisin bran cereal, but do not pack down the cereal. **CAUTION:** *Do not put any cereal in your mouth.* Write the brand name in the data table. Measure and record the mass of the beaker plus cereal. Subtract the mass of the empty beaker to get the mass of the cereal alone. Record the result.

3. Pour the cereal onto a paper towel. Separate the raisins from the bran and place the raisins back in the beaker. Measure and record the mass of the beaker plus raisins. Subtract the mass of the empty beaker to get the mass of the raisins alone. Record the result.

4. Repeat Steps 1–3 with each of the other brands of cereal.

Analyze and Conclude

1. **Measuring** Why did you first measure the mass of an empty beaker and then the mass of the beaker plus cereal?

2. **Calculating** Calculate the percentage mass of raisins in each cereal as follows:

$$\% \text{ Mass of raisins} = \frac{\text{Mass of raisins}}{\text{Mass of cereal}} \times 100\%$$

Record the results in your data table.

3. **Interpreting Data** Based on your observations, which brand of cereal had the greatest percentage of raisins by mass?

4. **Controlling Variables** Was it important that all of the cereal samples were collected in the same-size beaker? Why or why not?

5. **Communicating** Based on your results, write a paragraph that could be printed on a box of raisin bran cereal that would help consumers understand that this brand is the best source of iron.

Design an Experiment

In this investigation, you examined a *sample* of cereal rather than the contents of the entire box. Scientists often use samples because it is a more practical way to make observations. Redesign this experiment to improve upon the sampling technique and increase the accuracy of your results. *Obtain your teacher's permission before carrying out your investigation.*

Data Table						
	Mass (g)					Percentage Mass of Raisins (%)
Cereal Brand	Empty Beaker	Beaker plus Cereal	Cereal	Beaker plus Raisins	Raisins	

Healthy Eating

Reading Preview

Key Concepts
- How can the Food Guide Pyramid help you plan a healthy diet?
- What kind of information is included on food labels?

Key Terms
- Food Guide Pyramid
- Percent Daily Value
- Dietary Reference Intakes (DRIs)

Target Reading Skill

Asking Questions Before you read, preview the red headings. In a graphic organizer like the one below, ask a *what* or *how* question for each heading. As you read, write answers to your questions.

Healthy Eating

Question	Answer
What is the Food Guide Pyramid?	The Food Guide Pyramid classifies . . .

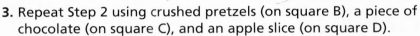

Lab zone Discover Activity

Do Snack Foods Contain Fat?

1. Cut four small squares from a brown paper bag. Label them A, B, C, and D.
2. Rub some crushed potato chips on square A. **CAUTION:** *Do not eat any of the foods in this activity.*
3. Repeat Step 2 using crushed pretzels (on square B), a piece of chocolate (on square C), and an apple slice (on square D).
4. Remove any food. Allow the paper squares to dry.
5. Note which squares have spots of oil on them.

Think It Over

Classifying If a food contains fat, it will leave oily spots on the paper. What does this tell you about the foods you tested?

What does healthy eating mean to you? Eating more fresh fruits and vegetables? Not skipping breakfast? Cutting down on soft drinks and chips? You have just learned about the six types of nutrients—carbohydrates, fats, proteins, vitamins, minerals, and water—that are part of a healthy diet. You may now be wondering how you can use this information to make healthful choices in your diet.

With so many foods available, it may seem more difficult, not easier, to establish a healthful diet. Luckily, nutritionists have developed the Food Guide Pyramid and food labels as a way to help.

FIGURE 9
Healthy Food Choices
Fruits and vegetables are essential parts of a healthy diet. Some people enjoy picking these foods right off the plant.

The Food Guide Pyramid

The **Food Guide Pyramid** is a diagram that was developed to help people plan a healthy diet. **The Food Guide Pyramid classifies foods into six groups. It also indicates how many servings from each group should be eaten every day to maintain a healthy diet.**

The six food groups in the Food Guide Pyramid are shown in Figure 10. You can combine the advice within the pyramid with knowledge of your own food preferences. By doing this, you can have a healthy diet containing foods you like.

Go Online
active.art

For: The Food Guide Pyramid activity
Visit: www.PHSchool.com
Web code: cep-4022

FIGURE 10
The Food Guide Pyramid
The Food Guide Pyramid recommends the number of servings that a person should eat each day from six food groups.

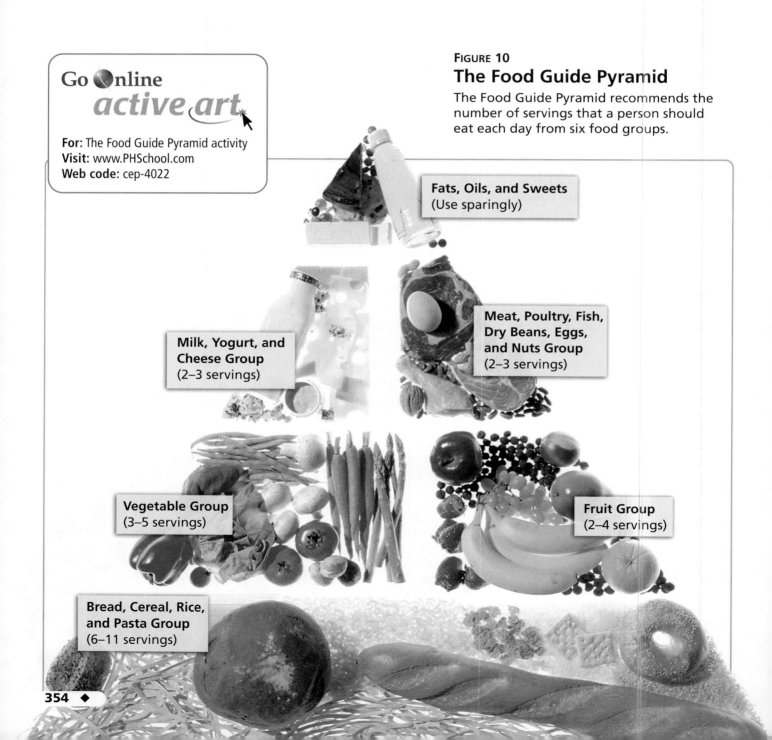

Fats, Oils, and Sweets
(Use sparingly)

Milk, Yogurt, and Cheese Group
(2–3 servings)

Meat, Poultry, Fish, Dry Beans, Eggs, and Nuts Group
(2–3 servings)

Vegetable Group
(3–5 servings)

Fruit Group
(2–4 servings)

Bread, Cereal, Rice, and Pasta Group
(6–11 servings)

Base of the Pyramid Notice in Figure 10 that the food group at the base of the pyramid includes foods made from grains, such as bread, cereal, rice, and pasta. These foods are rich in complex carbohydrates. These foods also provide proteins, fiber, vitamins, and some minerals. This bottom level is the widest part of the pyramid. The large size indicates that these foods should make up the largest part of the diet.

Middle of the Pyramid The second level in the pyramid is made of two food groups, the Fruit group and the Vegetable group. Fruits and vegetables are good sources of carbohydrates, fiber, vitamins, minerals, and water. Notice that this level is not as wide as the bottom level. This size difference indicates that people need fewer servings of these foods than of foods from the bottom level.

The third level of the pyramid contains the Milk, Yogurt, and Cheese group, and the Meat, Poultry, Fish, Dry Beans, Eggs, and Nuts group. Milk and other dairy products are rich in proteins, carbohydrates, vitamins, and minerals. The meat and poultry group contains foods that are high in protein. People need smaller amounts of food from the third level.

Top of the Pyramid At the top of the pyramid are foods containing large amounts of fat, sugar, or both. These foods contain few valuable nutrients. Notice that this is the smallest part of the pyramid. The small size indicates that intake of these foods should be limited. There is a good reason for this advice. Foods in the other groups already contain fats and sugars. Limiting the additional fats and sugars can help you prevent heart disease and other health problems.

 **Reading Checkpoint** Which food groups are in the second level of the Food Guide Pyramid?

Discovery CHANNEL SCHOOL™

Food and Digestion

Video Preview
▶ Video Field Trip
Video Assessment

Lab zone Skills Activity

Graphing
You can graph the nutrient content in a meal. The meal of chicken, beans and rice, and salad has about 27 g of protein, 25 g of carbohydrates, and 4 g of fat. Use this information to draw a bar graph showing protein, carbohydrate, and fat content for this meal.

FIGURE 11
Healthful Eating
The Food Guide Pyramid can help you plan healthy meals. Classifying *Which of the food groups in the Food Guide Pyramid are contained in this meal of chicken, beans, rice, and salad?*

Food Labels

After a long day, you and your friends stop into a store on your way home from school. What snack should you buy? How can you make a wise choice? One thing you can do is to read the information provided on food labels. **Food labels allow you to evaluate a single food as well as to compare the nutritional value of two different foods.**

How to Read a Food Label Figure 12 shows a food label that might appear on a box of cereal. Refer to that label as you read about some of the important nutritional information it contains.

❶ Serving Size This information tells you the size of a single serving and the number of servings in the container. The information on the rest of the label is based on serving size. If you eat twice the serving size, then you'll consume twice the number of Calories.

❷ Calories This information tells you how much energy you get from one serving of this food, including how many Calories come from fat.

❸ Percent Daily Value The **Percent Daily Value** shows you how the nutritional content of one serving fits into the recommended diet for a person who consumes 2,000 Calories a day. For example, one serving of this cereal contains 12% of the total amount of sodium a person should consume in one day. You might eat more or less than 2,000 Calories a day. But, you can still use this percentage as a general guide.

❹ Ingredients The ingredients are listed in order by weight, starting with the main ingredient. The list can alert you to substances that have been added to a food to improve its flavor or color, or to keep it from spoiling. In addition, reading ingredients lists can help you avoid substances that make you ill.

Using Food Labels Food labels can help you make healthful food choices. Suppose you are shopping for breakfast cereals. By reading the labels, you might find that one cereal contains little fat and a high percentage of the Daily Values for complex carbohydrates and several vitamins. Another cereal might have fewer complex carbohydrates and vitamins, and contain significant amounts of fat. You can see that the first cereal would be a better choice as a regular breakfast food.

FIGURE 12
Food Label
By law, specific nutritional information must be listed on food labels.
Calculating How many servings of this product would you have to eat to get 90% of the Daily Value for iron?

Dietary Reference Intakes   Food labels can also help you monitor the nutrients in your diet. Guidelines that show the amounts of nutrients that are needed every day are known as **Dietary Reference Intakes (DRIs).** For example, the DRIs for vitamins recommend that people your age get 45 milligrams of vitamin C every day.

DRIs also show how the Calories that people eat each day should be split among carbohydrates, fats, and proteins. The Percent Daily Values listed on food labels can help you make sure that you are meeting the DRIs for different nutrients.

 **Reading Checkpoint**   What are Dietary Reference Intakes?

FIGURE 13
Reading Food Labels
Food labels allow you to compare the nutritional content of similar kinds of foods.

Section 2 Assessment

Target Reading Skill Asking Questions Work with a partner to check the answers in your graphic organizer.

Reviewing Key Concepts

1. a. Identifying Into how many groups are foods in the Food Guide Pyramid classified?
   b. Interpreting Diagrams Why are foods in the Bread, Cereal, Rice, and Pasta group placed at the bottom of the Food Guide Pyramid?
   c. Applying Concepts Why might a runner need more servings from the Bread, Cereal, Rice, and Pasta group than a less active person?

2. a. Reviewing What are three kinds of information contained on food labels?
   b. Explaining How can food labels help a person make healthy food choices?

   c. Calculating Use Figure 12 to calculate the following: (1) the total number of Calories in 3 servings, (2) the number of servings needed to get 50 percent of the day's Daily Value for Vitamin C, and (3) the number of servings needed to get all the dietary fiber needed for the day.

Lab zone At-Home **Activity**

Menu Planning Work with a family member to plan menus for three days that meet the guidelines in the Food Guide Pyramid. Follow the recommended number of servings for each group. Remember to write down fats, such as butter or margarine, that may be used to add flavor to dishes. Include all snack items as well.

The Digestive Process Begins

Reading Preview

Key Concepts
- What functions are carried out in the digestive system?
- What roles do the mouth, esophagus, and stomach play in digestion?

Key Terms
- digestion • absorption
- saliva • enzyme • epiglottis
- esophagus • mucus
- peristalsis • stomach

Target Reading Skill

Using Prior Knowledge Before you read, look at the section headings and visuals to see what this section is about. Then write what you know about the digestive system in a graphic organizer like the one below. As you read, continue to write in what you learn.

What You Know
1. Food is digested in the stomach.
2.

What You Learned
1.
2.

Discover **Activity**

How Can You Speed Up Digestion?

1. Obtain two plastic jars with lids. Fill the jars with equal amounts of water at the same temperature.
2. Place a whole sugar cube into one jar. Place a crushed sugar cube into the other jar.
3. Fasten the lids on the jars. Holding one jar in each hand, shake the two jars gently and for equal amounts of time.
4. Place the jars on a flat surface. Observe whether the whole cube or the crushed cube dissolves faster.

Think It Over

Predicting Use the results of this activity to predict which would take longer to digest: a large piece of food or one that has been cut up into many small pieces. Explain your answer.

In 1822, a man named Alexis St. Martin was wounded in the stomach. Dr. William Beaumont saved St. Martin's life. The wound, however, left an opening in St. Martin's stomach that never healed completely. Beaumont realized that by looking through the opening in St. Martin's abdomen, he could observe what was happening inside the stomach.

Beaumont observed that food changed chemically inside the stomach. He hypothesized that chemical reactions in the stomach broke down foods into smaller particles. Beaumont removed liquid from St. Martin's stomach and analyzed it. The stomach liquid contained an acid that played a role in the breakdown of foods into simpler substances.

Functions of the Digestive System

Beaumont's observations helped scientists understand the role of the stomach in the digestive system. **The digestive system has three main functions. First, it breaks down food into molecules the body can use. Then, the molecules are absorbed into the blood and carried throughout the body. Finally, wastes are eliminated from the body.** Figure 14 shows the organs of the digestive system, which is about 9 meters long from beginning to end.

Digestion The process by which your body breaks down food into small nutrient molecules is called **digestion.** There are two kinds of digestion—mechanical and chemical. In mechanical digestion, foods are physically broken down into smaller pieces. Mechanical digestion occurs when you bite into a sandwich and chew it into small pieces.

In chemical digestion, chemicals produced by the body break foods into their smaller chemical building blocks. For example, the starch in bread is broken down into individual sugar molecules.

Absorption and Elimination After your food is digested, the molecules are ready to be transported throughout your body. **Absorption** (ab SAWRP shun) is the process by which nutrient molecules pass through the wall of your digestive system into your blood. Materials that are not absorbed, such as fiber, are eliminated from the body as wastes.

Go Online

SCi LINKS™ NSTA

For: Links on digestion
Visit: www.SciLinks.org
Web Code: scn-0423

✓ Reading Checkpoint) **What is chemical digestion?**

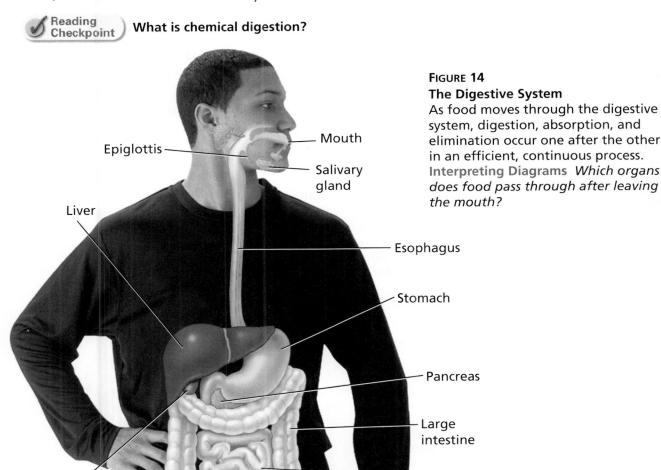

FIGURE 14
The Digestive System
As food moves through the digestive system, digestion, absorption, and elimination occur one after the other in an efficient, continuous process.
Interpreting Diagrams *Which organs does food pass through after leaving the mouth?*

Epiglottis

Mouth

Salivary gland

Liver

Esophagus

Stomach

Pancreas

Large intestine

Small intestine

Gallbladder

Rectum

The Mouth

Have you ever walked past a bakery or restaurant and noticed your mouth watering? Smelling or even just thinking about food when you're hungry is enough to start your mouth watering. This response isn't accidental. When your mouth waters, your body is preparing for the delicious meal it expects. **Both mechanical and chemical digestion begin in the mouth.** The fluid released when your mouth waters is **saliva** (suh LY vuh). Saliva plays an important role in both kinds of digestion.

Mechanical Digestion in the Mouth Your teeth carry out the first stage of mechanical digestion. Your center teeth, or incisors (in SY zurz), cut the food into bite-sized pieces. On either side of the incisors there are sharp, pointy teeth called canines (KAY nynz). These teeth tear and slash the food into smaller pieces. Behind the canines are the premolars and molars, which crush and grind the food. As the teeth do their work, saliva moistens the pieces of food into one slippery mass.

Chemical Digestion in the Mouth As mechanical digestion begins, so does chemical digestion. If you take a bite of a cracker and suck on it, the cracker begins to taste sweet. It tastes sweet because a chemical in the saliva has broken down the starch molecules in the cracker into sugar molecules.

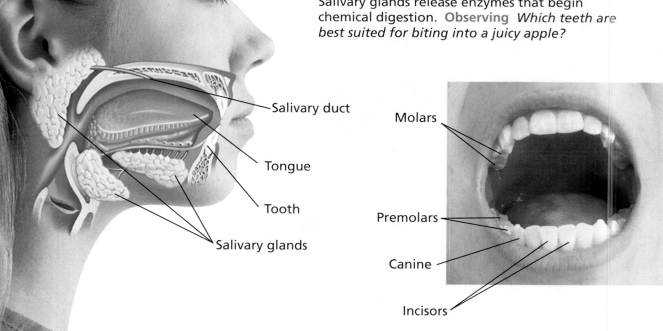

FIGURE 15
Digestion in the Mouth
Mechanical digestion begins in the mouth, where the teeth cut and tear food into smaller pieces. Salivary glands release enzymes that begin chemical digestion. Observing *Which teeth are best suited for biting into a juicy apple?*

Salivary duct

Tongue

Tooth

Salivary glands

Molars

Premolars

Canine

Incisors

FIGURE 16
How Enzymes Work
The shape of an enzyme molecule is specific to
the shape of the food molecule it breaks down.
Here, an enzyme breaks down a starch into sugars.

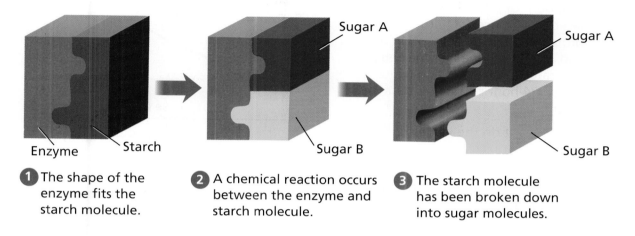

1. The shape of the enzyme fits the starch molecule.

2. A chemical reaction occurs between the enzyme and starch molecule.

3. The starch molecule has been broken down into sugar molecules.

The chemical in saliva that digests starch is an enzyme. **Enzymes** are proteins that speed up chemical reactions in the body. Your body produces many different enzymes. Each enzyme has a specific chemical shape. Its shape enables it to take part in only one kind of chemical reaction. An example of enzyme action is shown in Figure 16.

The Esophagus

If you've ever choked on food, your food may have "gone down the wrong way." That's because there are two openings at the back of your mouth. One opening leads to your windpipe, which carries air into your lungs. As you swallow, a flap of tissue called the **epiglottis** (ep uh GLAHT is) seals off your windpipe, preventing the food from entering. The food goes into the **esophagus** (ih SAHF uh gus), a muscular tube that connects the mouth to the stomach. The esophagus is lined with **mucus,** a thick, slippery substance produced by the body. Mucus makes food easier to swallow and move along.

Food remains in the esophagus for only about 10 seconds. **After food enters the esophagus, contractions of smooth muscles push the food toward the stomach.** These involuntary waves of muscle contraction are called **peristalsis** (pehr ih STAWL sis). Peristalsis also occurs in the stomach and farther down the digestive system. These muscular waves keep food moving in one direction.

 **Reading Checkpoint** How is food prevented from entering the windpipe?

Lab zone Try This Activity

Modeling Peristalsis

1. Obtain a clear, flexible plastic straw.

2. Hold the straw vertically and insert a small bead into the top of the straw. The bead should fit snugly into the straw. **CAUTION:** *Do not put the straw in your mouth or blow into the straw.*

3. Pinch the straw above the bead so the bead begins to move down the length of the tubing.

4. Repeat Step 3 until the bead exits the straw.

Making Models How does this action compare with peristalsis? What do the bead and the straw represent?

Math ▶ Analyzing Data

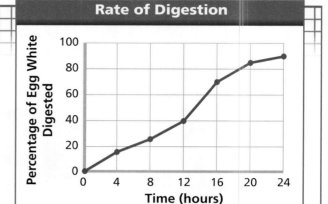

Rate of Digestion

Protein Digestion

A scientist performed an experiment to determine the amount of time needed to digest protein. He placed small pieces of hard-boiled egg white (a protein) in a test tube containing hydrochloric acid, water, and the enzyme pepsin. He measured the rate at which the egg white was digested over a 24-hour period. His data are recorded in the graph.

1. **Reading Graphs** What do the values on the *y*-axis represent?

2. **Interpreting Data** After about how many hours would you estimate that half of the protein was digested?

3. **Interpreting Data** How much digestion occurred in 16 hours?

4. **Drawing Conclusions** During which 4-hour period did the most digestion take place?

The Stomach

When food leaves the esophagus, it enters the **stomach,** a J-shaped, muscular pouch located in the abdomen. As you eat, your stomach expands to hold all of the food that you swallow. **Most mechanical digestion and some chemical digestion occur in the stomach.**

Mechanical Digestion in the Stomach The process of mechanical digestion occurs as three strong layers of smooth muscle contract to produce a churning motion. This action mixes the food with fluids in somewhat the same way that clothes and soapy water are mixed in a washing machine.

Chemical Digestion in the Stomach Chemical digestion occurs as the churning food makes contact with digestive juice, a fluid produced by cells in the lining of the stomach. Digestive juice contains the enzyme pepsin. Pepsin chemically digests the proteins in your food, breaking them down into short chains of amino acids.

Digestive juice also contains hydrochloric acid, a very strong acid. Without this strong acid, your stomach could not function properly. First, pepsin works best in an acid environment. Second, the acid kills many bacteria that you swallow with your food.

Why doesn't stomach acid burn a hole in your stomach? The reason is that cells in the stomach lining also produce mucus, which coats and protects the stomach lining. Also, the cells that line the stomach are quickly replaced as they are damaged or worn out.

362 ◆

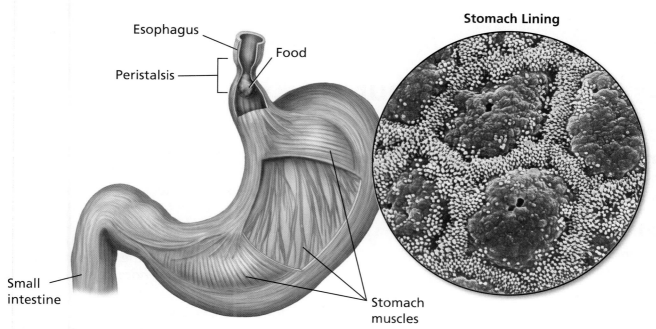

Esophagus

Food

Peristalsis

Small intestine

Stomach muscles

Stomach Lining

Food remains in the stomach until all of the solid material has been broken down into liquid form. A few hours after you finish eating, the stomach completes mechanical digestion of the food. By that time, most of the proteins have been chemically digested into shorter chains of amino acids. The food, now a thick liquid, is released into the next part of the digestive system. That is where final chemical digestion and absorption will take place.

 **Reading Checkpoint** **What is pepsin?**

FIGURE 17
The Stomach
The stomach has three layers of muscle that help to break down foods mechanically. The inset photo shows a microscopic view of the stomach lining. The yellow dots are mucus.
Relating Cause and Effect *What role does mucus play inside the stomach?*

Section 3 Assessment

Target Reading Skill Using Prior Knowledge Review your graphic organizer and revise it based on what you just learned in the section.

Reviewing Key Concepts

1. **a. Listing** What are the functions of the digestive system?
   b. Comparing and Contrasting Distinguish between mechanical and chemical digestion.
   c. Inferring Why must mechanical digestion start before chemical digestion?
2. **a. Reviewing** What key chemicals do the mouth and stomach contain?
   b. Describing How do pepsin and hydrochloric acid work together to digest food in the stomach?
   c. Predicting What could happen if your stomach didn't produce enough mucus? Explain.

Lab zone At-Home Activity

First Aid for Choking Explain to your family what happens when people choke on food. With your family, find out how to recognize when a person is choking and what to do to help the person. Learn about the Heimlich maneuver and how it is used to help someone who is choking.

As the Stomach Churns

Problem

What conditions are needed for the digestion of proteins in the stomach?

Skills Focus

interpreting data, controlling variables, drawing conclusions

Materials

- test-tube rack
- pepsin
- water
- 4 strips of blue litmus paper
- cubes of boiled egg white
- 10-mL plastic graduated cylinder
- 4 test tubes with stoppers
- marking pencil
- diluted hydrochloric acid
- plastic stirrers

Procedure

1. In this lab, you will investigate how acidic conditions affect protein digestion. Read over the entire lab to see what materials you will be testing. Write a prediction stating which conditions you think will speed up protein digestion. Then, copy the data table into your notebook.

2. Label four test tubes A, B, C, and D, and place them in a test-tube rack.

3. In this lab, the protein you will test is boiled egg white, which has been cut into cubes about 1 cm on each side. Add 3 cubes to each test tube. Note and record the size and overall appearance of the cubes in each test tube. **CAUTION:** *Do not put any egg white into your mouth.*

4. Use a graduated cylinder to add 10 mL of the enzyme pepsin to test tube A. Observe the egg white cubes to determine whether an immediate reaction takes place. Record your observations under Day 1 in your data table. If no changes occur, write "no immediate reaction."

5. Use a clean graduated cylinder to add 5 mL of pepsin to test tube B. Then rinse out the graduated cylinder and add 5 mL of water to test tube B. Observe whether or not an immediate reaction takes place.

6. Use a clean graduated cylinder to add 10 mL of hydrochloric acid to test tube C. Observe whether or not an immediate reaction takes place. **CAUTION:** *Hydrochloric acid can burn skin and clothing. Avoid direct contact with it. Wash any splashes or spills with plenty of water, and notify your teacher.*

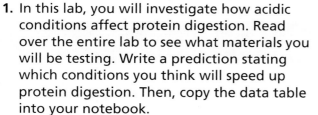

Data Table				
Test Tube	Egg White Appearance		Litmus Color	
	Day 1	Day 2	Day 1	Day 2
A				
B				
C				
D				

7. Use a clean graduated cylinder to add 5 mL of pepsin to test tube D. Then, rinse the graduated cylinder and add 5 mL of hydrochloric acid to test tube D. Observe whether or not an immediate reaction takes place. Record your observations.

8. Obtain four strips of blue litmus paper. (Blue litmus paper turns pink in the presence of an acid.) Dip a clean plastic stirrer into the solution in each test tube, and then touch the stirrer to a piece of litmus paper. Observe what happens to the litmus paper. Record your observations.

9. Insert stoppers in the four test tubes and store the test tube rack as directed by your teacher.

10. The next day, examine the contents of each test tube. Note any changes in the size and overall appearance of the egg white cubes. Then, test each solution with litmus paper. Record your observations in your data table.

Analyze and Conclude

1. **Interpreting Data** Which materials were the best at digesting the egg white? What observations enabled you to determine this?

2. **Inferring** Is the chemical digestion of protein in food a fast or a slow reaction? Explain.

3. **Controlling Variables** Why was it important that the cubes of egg white all be about the same size?

4. **Drawing Conclusions** What did this lab show about the ability of pepsin to digest protein?

5. **Communicating** Write a paragraph in which you describe the purpose of test tube A and test tube C as they relate to the steps you followed in the procedure.

Design an Experiment

Design a way to test whether protein digestion is affected by the size of the food pieces. Write down your hypothesis and the procedure you will follow. *Obtain your teacher's permission before carrying out your investigation.*

Final Digestion and Absorption

Reading Preview

Key Concepts
- What digestive processes occur in the small intestine, and how are other digestive organs involved?
- What role does the large intestine play in digestion?

Key Terms
- small intestine • liver • bile
- gallbladder • pancreas
- villus • large intestine
- rectum • anus

Target Reading Skill

Identifying Main Ideas As you read the section titled The Small Intestine, write the main idea in a graphic organizer like the one below. Then, write three supporting details that further explain the main idea.

Main Idea

Chemical digestion takes place in the . . .

Detail	Detail	Detail

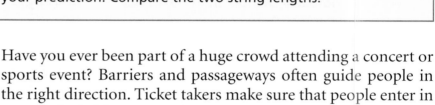

Lab zone Discover **Activity**

Which Surface Is Larger?

1. Work with a partner to carry out this investigation.
2. Begin by placing your hand palm-side down on a table. Keep your thumb and fingers tightly together. Lay string along the outline of your hand. Have your partner help you determine how long a string you need to outline your hand.
3. Use a metric ruler to measure the length of that string.

Think It Over

Predicting How long would you expect your hand outline to be if you spread out your thumb and fingers? Use string to test your prediction. Compare the two string lengths.

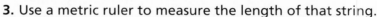

Have you ever been part of a huge crowd attending a concert or sports event? Barriers and passageways often guide people in the right direction. Ticket takers make sure that people enter in an orderly fashion.

In some ways, the stomach can be thought of as the "ticket taker" of the digestive system. Once the food has been changed into a thick liquid, the stomach releases a little of the liquid at a time into the next part of the digestive system. This slow, smooth passage of food through the digestive system ensures that digestion and absorption can take place efficiently.

The Small Intestine

After the thick liquid leaves the stomach, it enters the small intestine. The **small intestine** is the part of the digestive system where most chemical digestion takes place. You may wonder how the small intestine got its name. After all, at about 6 meters—longer than some full-sized cars—it makes up two thirds of the length of the digestive system. The small intestine was named for its small diameter. It is from 2 to 3 centimeters wide, about half the diameter of the large intestine.

When food reaches the small intestine, it has already been mechanically digested into a thick liquid. But chemical digestion has just begun. Starches and proteins have been partially broken down, but fats haven't been digested at all. **Almost all chemical digestion and absorption of nutrients takes place in the small intestine.** As the liquid moves into the small intestine, it mixes with enzymes and secretions that are produced by the small intestine, the liver, and the pancreas. The liver and the pancreas deliver their substances to the small intestine through small tubes.

The Liver As you can see in Figure 18, the **liver** is located in the upper right portion of the abdomen. It is the largest organ inside the body. The liver is like an extremely busy chemical factory and plays a role in many body processes. For example, it breaks down medicines, and it helps eliminate nitrogen from the body. **The role of the liver in the digestive system is to produce bile.**

Bile is a substance that breaks up fat particles. Bile flows from the liver into the **gallbladder,** the organ that stores bile. After you eat, bile passes through a tube from the gallbladder into the small intestine.

Bile is not an enzyme. It does not chemically digest foods. It does, however, physically break up large fat particles into smaller fat droplets. You can compare the action of bile on fats with the action of soap on a greasy frying pan. Soap physically breaks up the grease into small droplets that can mix with the soapy water and be washed away. Bile mixes with the fats in food to form small fat droplets. The droplets can then be chemically broken down by enzymes produced in the pancreas.

![Lab zone] **Try This Activity**

Break Up!
You can model the breakup of fat particles in the small intestine.

1. Fill two plastic jars half full of water. Add a few drops of oil to each jar.
2. Add about $\frac{1}{4}$ spoonful of baking soda to one jar.
3. Stir the contents of both jars. Record your observations.

Observing In which jar did the oil begin to break up? What substance does the baking soda represent?

FIGURE 18
The Liver and Pancreas
Substances produced by the liver and pancreas aid in digestion.
Predicting *How would digestion be affected if the tube leading from the gallbladder to the small intestine became blocked?*

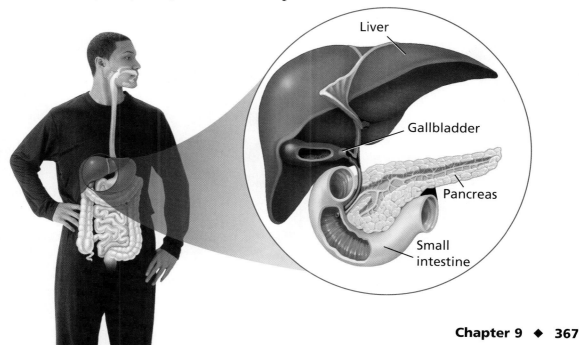

Liver

Gallbladder

Pancreas

Small intestine

For: More on the digestive system
Visit: PHSchool.com
Web Code: ced-4024

FIGURE 19
The Small Intestine
Tiny finger-shaped projections called villi line the inside of the small intestine. Blood vessels in the villi are covered by a single layer of cells.
Relating Cause and Effect How does the structure of the villi help them carry out their function?

The Pancreas The **pancreas** is a triangular organ that lies between the stomach and the first part of the small intestine. Like the liver, the pancreas plays a role in many body processes. **As part of the digestive system, the pancreas produces enzymes that flow into the small intestine and help break down starches, proteins, and fats.**

Digestive enzymes do not break down all food substances. Recall that the fiber in food isn't broken down. Instead, fiber thickens the liquid material in the intestine. This thickening makes it easier for peristalsis to push the material forward.

Absorption in the Small Intestine After chemical digestion takes place, the small nutrient molecules are ready to be absorbed by the body. The structure of the small intestine makes it well suited for absorption. The inner surface, or lining, of the small intestine looks bumpy. Millions of tiny finger-shaped structures called **villi** (VIL eye) (singular *villus*) cover the surface. The villi absorb nutrient molecules. Notice in Figure 19 that tiny blood vessels run through the center of each villus. Nutrient molecules pass from cells on the surface of a villus into blood vessels. The blood carries the nutrients throughout the body for use by body cells.

Villi greatly increase the surface area of the small intestine. If all the villi were laid out flat, the total surface area of the small intestine would be about as large as a tennis court. This increased surface enables digested food to be absorbed much faster than if the walls of the small intestine were smooth.

Reading Checkpoint How does the pancreas aid in digestion?

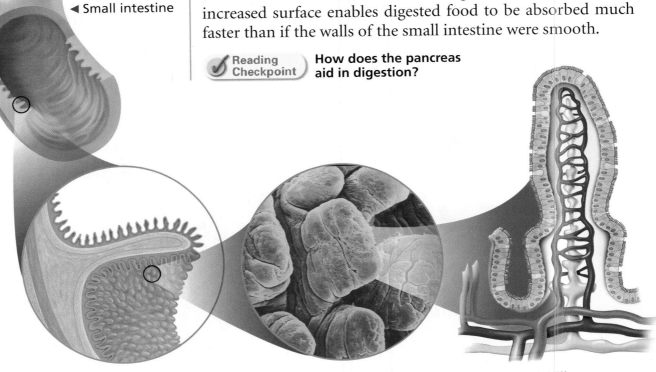

◀ Small intestine

▲ Fold in the wall of the small intestine

▲ Close-up of villi

▲ Villus

The Large Intestine

By the time material reaches the end of the small intestine, most nutrients have been absorbed. The remaining material moves from the small intestine into the large intestine. The **large intestine** is the last section of the digestive system. It is about 1.5 meters long—about as long as the average bathtub. It runs up the right-hand side of the abdomen, across the upper abdomen, and then down the left-hand side. The large intestine contains bacteria that feed on the material passing through. These bacteria normally do not cause disease. In fact, they are helpful because they make certain vitamins, including vitamin K.

The material entering the large intestine contains water and undigested food. **As the material moves through the large intestine, water is absorbed into the bloodstream. The remaining material is readied for elimination from the body.**

The large intestine ends in a short tube called the **rectum**. Here, waste material is compressed into a solid form. This waste material is eliminated from the body through the **anus**, a muscular opening at the end of the rectum.

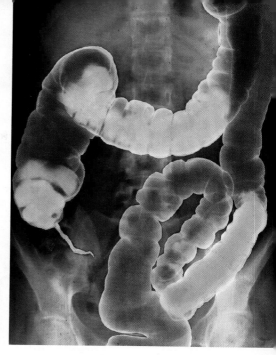

FIGURE 20
The Large Intestine
As material passes through the large intestine, most of the water is absorbed by the body. The remaining material will be eliminated from the body.

 **Reading Checkpoint** What role do bacteria play in the large intestine?

Section 4 Assessment

Target Reading Skill
Identifying Main Ideas Use your graphic organizer to help you answer Question 1 below.

Reviewing Key Concepts

1. a. Reviewing What two digestive processes occur in the small intestine?
  b. Explaining Explain how bile produced by the liver and enzymes produced in the pancreas function in the small intestine.
  c. Relating Cause and Effect Some people are allergic to a protein in wheat. When these people eat foods made with wheat, a reaction destroys the villi in the small intestine. What problems would you expect these people to experience?
2. a. Identifying Which key nutrient is absorbed in the large intestine?
  b. Describing What happens as food moves through the large intestine?
  c. Applying Concepts Diarrhea is a condition in which waste material that is eliminated contains too much water. How might diarrhea upset homeostasis in the body? How could a person reduce the effects of diarrhea on the body?

Writing in Science

Sequence of Events Describe the journey of a bacon, lettuce, and tomato sandwich through a person's digestive system, starting in the mouth and ending with absorption. Include where digestion of fats, carbohydrates, and proteins take place. Use words like *first*, *next*, and *finally* in your writing.

Chapter 9

Study Guide

① Food and Energy

Key Concepts

- Foods provide the body with raw materials and energy.
- Carbohydrates provide energy as well as the raw materials to make cell parts.
- In addition to providing energy, fats form part of the cell membrane. Fatty tissue also protects and supports internal organs and insulates the body.
- Proteins are needed for tissue growth and repair. They also play an important part in chemical reactions within cells.
- Vitamins and minerals are needed in small amounts to carry out chemical processes.
- Water is the most important nutrient because the body's vital processes take place in water.

Key Terms

nutrient	protein
calorie	amino acid
carbohydrate	vitamin
glucose	mineral
fat	

② Healthy Eating

Key Concepts

- The Food Guide Pyramid classifies foods into six groups. It also indicates how many servings from each group should be eaten every day.
- Food labels allow you to evaluate a single food as well as to compare the nutritional value of two different foods.

Key Terms

Food Guide Pyramid
Percent Daily Value
Dietary Reference Intakes (DRIs)

③ The Digestive Process Begins

Key Concepts

- The digestive system breaks down food into molecules the body can use. Then, the molecules are absorbed into the blood and carried throughout the body. Finally, wastes are eliminated.
- Both mechanical and chemical digestion begin in the mouth.
- In the esophagus, contractions of smooth muscles push the food toward the stomach.
- Most mechanical digestion and some chemical digestion occur in the stomach.

Key Terms

digestion	esophagus
absorption	mucus
saliva	peristalsis
enzyme	stomach
epiglottis	

④ Final Digestion and Absorption

Key Concepts

- Almost all chemical digestion and absorption of nutrients takes place in the small intestine.
- The liver produces bile, which breaks up fats.
- The pancreas produces enzymes that help break down starches, proteins, and fats.
- In the large intestine, water is absorbed into the bloodstream. The remaining material is readied for elimination.

Key Terms

small intestine	villus
liver	large intestine
bile	rectum
gallbladder	anus
pancreas	

Review and Assessment

Go Online
PHSchool.com

For: Self-Assessment
Visit: PHSchool.com
Web Code: cea-4020

Organizing Information

Sequencing Copy the flowchart about digestion onto a separate sheet of paper. Then, complete it and add a title. (For more on Sequencing, see the Skills Handbook.)

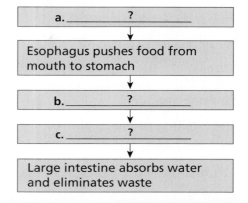

a. _____?_____
↓
Esophagus pushes food from mouth to stomach
↓
b. _____?_____
↓
c. _____?_____
↓
Large intestine absorbs water and eliminates waste

Reviewing Key Terms

Choose the letter of the best answer.

1. The building blocks of proteins are
   a. vitamins.
   b. minerals.
   c. amino acids.
   d. fats.

2. According to the Food Guide Pyramid, from which group should you eat the most servings?
   a. milk, yogurt, and cheese
   b. meat, poultry, fish, beans, eggs, and nuts
   c. vegetables
   d. bread, cereal, rice, and pasta

3. The enzyme in saliva chemically breaks down
   a. fats.
   b. proteins.
   c. glucose.
   d. starches.

4. Most mechanical digestion takes place in the
   a. liver.
   b. esophagus.
   c. stomach.
   d. small intestine.

5. Bile is produced by the
   a. liver.
   b. pancreas.
   c. small intestine.
   d. large intestine.

If the statement is true, write *true*. If it is false, change the underlined word or words to make the statement true.

6. Proteins that come from animal sources are <u>incomplete</u> proteins.

7. <u>Vitamins</u> are nutrients that are not made by living things.

8. To determine which of two cereals supplies more iron, check the <u>Percent Daily Value</u> on the food label.

9. <u>Absorption</u> moves food through the digestive system.

10. Most materials are absorbed into the bloodstream in the <u>large</u> intestine.

Writing in Science

Information Sheet You are a nutritionist assigned to work with a family trying to eat a more healthful diet. Write an instruction sheet outlining what kinds of foods they should eat. Provide some examples of each kind of food.

Discovery CHANNEL SCHOOL

Food and Digestion

Video Preview
Video Field Trip
▶ Video Assessment

Review and Assessment

Checking Concepts

11. How does a person's level of physical activity affect his or her daily energy needs?

12. Why is fiber necessary in a person's diet?

13. Why does the Food Guide Pyramid give the recommended daily servings as a range instead of a single number?

14. Describe the function of the epiglottis.

15. Explain the role of peristalsis.

16. What is the function of the pancreas in the digestive process?

17. What is the function of villi?

Thinking Critically

18. **Applying Concepts** Before winter, animals that hibernate often prepare by eating foods high in fat. How is this behavior helpful?

19. **Predicting** Suppose a medicine killed all the bacteria in your body. How might this affect vitamin production in your body?

20. **Inferring** Why is it important for people to chew their food thoroughly before swallowing?

21. **Relating Cause and Effect** How does the condition illustrated in the diagram below affect the esophagus?

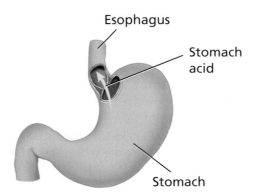

Esophagus

Stomach acid

Stomach

22. **Comparing and Contrasting** The digestive system is sometimes said to be "an assembly line in reverse." Identify some similarities and some differences between your digestive system and an assembly line.

Math Practice

23. **Percentage** Your aunt eats 250 Calories of protein and 1,800 Calories total for the day. Did she get enough protein on that particular day? Show your calculations.

Applying Skills

Use the table to answer Questions 24–27.

Comparing Nutrient Data

Food (1 cup)	Calcium (% Daily Value)	Calories	Calories From Fat
Chocolate milk	30	230	80
Low-fat milk	35	110	20
Plain yogurt	35	110	35

24. **Classifying** To which group in the Food Guide Pyramid do the foods in the chart belong? What is the recommended range of daily servings for that group?

25. **Interpreting Data** How many cups of low-fat milk provide 100% of the day's Daily Value for calcium?

26. **Calculating** Which of the foods meet the recommendation that no more than 30 percent of a food's Calories come from fat? Explain.

27. **Making Judgments** Which of the foods would be the most healthful choice for an afterschool snack? Explain your reasoning.

Lab zone Chapter Project

Performance Assessment Write a summary of what you've learned from keeping a food log. How close were your eating patterns to those recommended in the Food Guide Pyramid? How successful were you in making changes in your diet to match the Food Guide Pyramid?

End-of-Grade Test Practice

Choose the letter of the best answer.

1. Which of the following parts of the digestive system is *best* paired with its function?

  A esophagus—digests carbohydrates

  B stomach—digests fats

  C small intestine—absorbs water

  D liver—produces bile

2. A food label on a cereal box gives you the following information: a serving size equals one cup and there are 110 Calories per serving. You measure the amount of cereal you plan to eat and find that it measures 1 1/2 cups. How many Calories will you consume?

  A 110 Calories

  B 165 Calories

  C 220 Calories

  D 1,100 Calories

Use the table below and your knowledge of science to answer Questions 3 and 4.

Length of Time Food Stays in Organ	
Organ	**Time**
Mouth	Less than 1 minute
Esophagus	Less than 1 minute
Stomach	1–3 hours
Small Intestine	1–6 hours
Large Intestine	12–36 hours

3. If a meal is eaten at noon, what is happening to the food at 1 P.M.?

  A Saliva is breaking down starch into sugar.

  B Proteins are being digested into short chains of amino acids.

  C Fats are being digested.

  D Digested food is being absorbed into the blood.

4. For food eaten at noon, absorption cannot have begun by

  A 1 P.M.

  B 7 P.M.

  C 9 P.M.

  D noon the next day.

5. Which of the following organs is *not* just a digestive organ?

  A stomach

  B liver

  C small intestine

  D large intestine

Constructed Response

6. Compare the processes of mechanical and chemical digestion. How are they similar? How are they different? In what parts of the digestive system do the two processes take place? How do the processes occur?

Chapter 10

Circulation

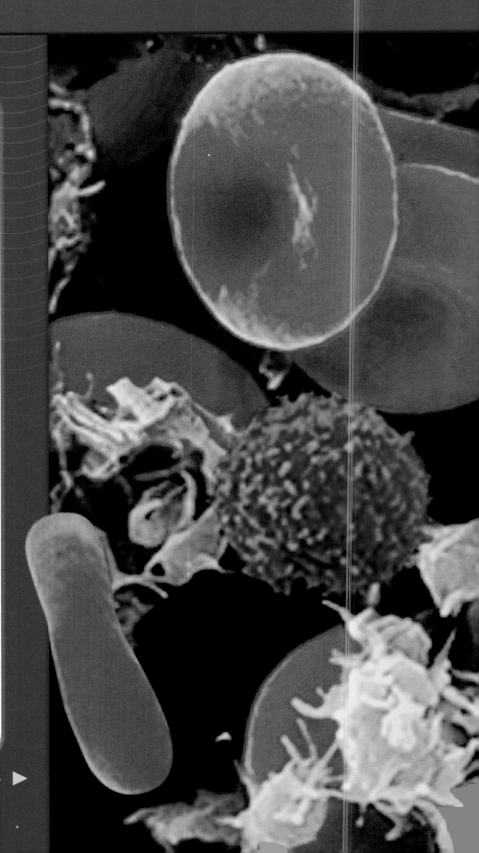

Interactive Textbook

Blood cells travel in blood vessels to all parts of the body. ▶

Lab zone™ Chapter **Project**

Travels of a Red Blood Cell

Every day, you travel from home to school and back home again. Your travel path makes a loop, or circuit, ending where it began. In this chapter, you'll learn how your blood also travels in circuits. In this project, you'll create a display to show how blood circulates throughout the body.

Your Goal To design and construct a display showing a complete journey of a red blood cell through the human body

Your display must
- show a red blood cell that leaves from the heart and returns to the same place
- show where the exchange of oxygen and carbon dioxide takes place
- provide written descriptions of the circuits made by the red blood cell
- be designed following the safety guidelines in Appendix A

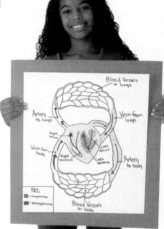

Plan It! Preview the chapter and find diagrams that show the heart, red blood cells, and the pathway of blood throughout the body. Then discuss the kinds of displays you could use, including a three-dimensional model, posters, a series of drawings, a flip book, or a video animation. Write down any content questions you'll need to answer.

The Body's Transport System

Reading Preview

Key Concepts
- What are the functions of the cardiovascular system?
- What is the structure and function of the heart?
- What path does blood take through the cardiovascular system?

Key Terms
- cardiovascular system • heart
- atrium • ventricle • valve
- pacemaker • artery
- capillary • vein • aorta

Target Reading Skill

Sequencing As you read, make a cycle diagram like the one below that shows the path that blood follows as it circulates throughout the body. Write each step of the pathway in a separate circle.

Pathway of Blood

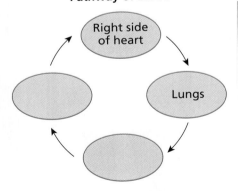

- Right side of heart
- Lungs

Discover Activity

How Hard Does Your Heart Work?

1. Every minute, your heart beats about 75 to 85 times. With each beat, it pumps about 60 milliliters of blood. Can you work as hard and fast as your heart does?

2. Cover a table or desk with newspapers. Place two large plastic containers side by side on the newspapers. Fill one with 2.5 liters of water, which is about the volume of blood that your heart pumps in 30 seconds. Leave the other container empty.

3. With a plastic cup that holds about 60 milliliters, transfer water as quickly as possible into the empty container, trying not to spill any. **CAUTION:** *Wipe up spills on the floor immediately.* Have a partner time you for 30 seconds. As you work, count how many transfers you make in 30 seconds.

4. Multiply your results by 2 to find the number of transfers in 1 minute.

Think It Over
Inferring Compare your performance with the number of times your heart beats every minute. What do your results tell you about the strength and speed of a heartbeat?

Late at night, a truck rolls through the darkness. Loaded with fresh fruits and vegetables, the truck is headed for a city supermarket. The driver steers off the interstate and onto a smaller highway. Finally, after driving through narrow city streets, the truck reaches its destination. As dawn breaks, store workers unload the cargo. At the same time, a garbage truck removes yesterday's trash and drives off down the road.

The Cardiovascular System

Like the roads that link all parts of the country, your body has a "highway" network, called the cardiovascular system, that links all parts of your body. The **cardiovascular system,** also called the circulatory system, consists of the heart, blood vessels, and blood. **The cardiovascular system carries needed substances to cells and carries waste products away from cells. In addition, blood contains cells that fight disease.**

Delivering Needed Materials Most substances that need to get from one part of the body to another are carried by blood. For example, blood carries oxygen from your lungs to your other body cells. Blood also transports the glucose your cells use to produce energy.

Removing Waste Products The cardiovascular system picks up wastes from cells. For example, when cells break down glucose, they produce carbon dioxide as a waste product. The carbon dioxide passes from the cells into the blood. The cardiovascular system then carries carbon dioxide to the lungs, where it is exhaled.

Fighting Disease The cardiovascular system also transports cells that attack disease-causing microorganisms. This process can help keep you from becoming sick. If you do get sick, these disease-fighting blood cells will kill the microorganisms and help you get well.

Reading Checkpoint How does the cardiovascular system help fight disease?

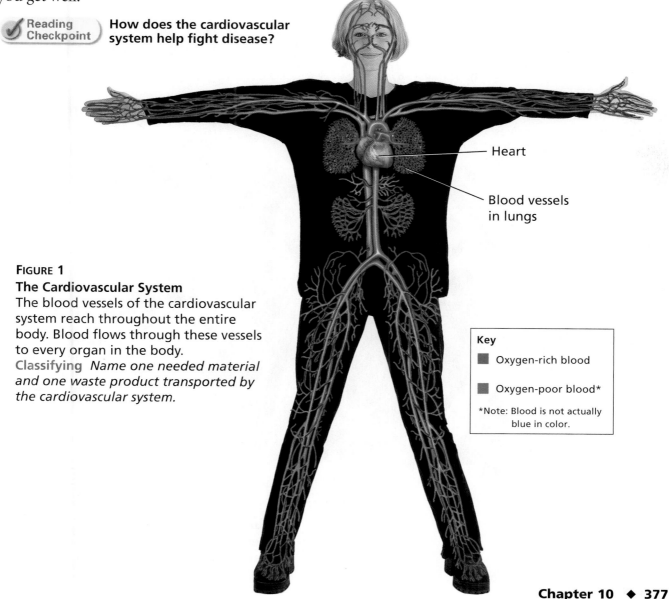

FIGURE 1

The Cardiovascular System
The blood vessels of the cardiovascular system reach throughout the entire body. Blood flows through these vessels to every organ in the body.
Classifying *Name one needed material and one waste product transported by the cardiovascular system.*

Heart

Blood vessels in lungs

Key
■ Oxygen-rich blood
■ Oxygen-poor blood*

*Note: Blood is not actually blue in color.

The Heart

Without the heart, blood wouldn't go anywhere. The **heart** is a hollow, muscular organ that pumps blood throughout the body. Your heart, which is about the size of your fist, is located in the center of your chest. The heart lies behind the sternum (breastbone) and inside the rib cage. These bones protect the heart from injury.

Each time the heart beats, it pushes blood through the blood vessels of the cardiovascular system. The heart is made of cardiac muscle, which can contract over and over without getting tired. Figure 2 shows the structure of the heart.

Go Online
active art

For: The Heart activity
Visit: PHSchool.com
Web Code: cep-4031

FIGURE 2
The Heart

Every second of your life, your heart pumps blood through your body. In a year, the heart pumps enough blood to fill more than 30 competition-size swimming pools.

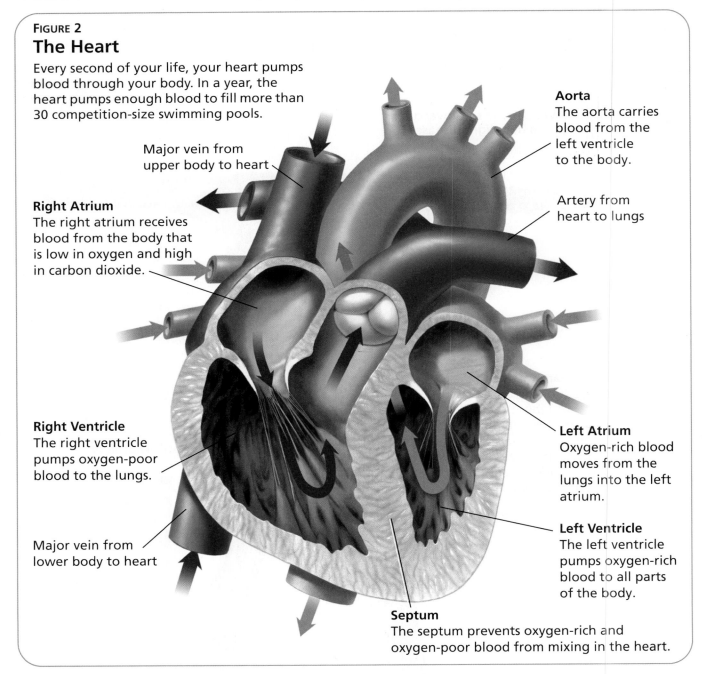

Major vein from upper body to heart

Aorta
The aorta carries blood from the left ventricle to the body.

Artery from heart to lungs

Right Atrium
The right atrium receives blood from the body that is low in oxygen and high in carbon dioxide.

Right Ventricle
The right ventricle pumps oxygen-poor blood to the lungs.

Left Atrium
Oxygen-rich blood moves from the lungs into the left atrium.

Major vein from lower body to heart

Left Ventricle
The left ventricle pumps oxygen-rich blood to all parts of the body.

Septum
The septum prevents oxygen-rich and oxygen-poor blood from mixing in the heart.

The Heart's Structure Notice in Figure 2 that the heart has a right side and a left side. **The right side of the heart is completely separated from the left side by a wall of tissue called the septum. Each side has two compartments, or chambers— an upper chamber and a lower chamber.** Each of the two upper chambers, called an **atrium** (AY tree um) (plural *atria*), receives blood that comes into the heart.

Each lower chamber, called a **ventricle,** pumps blood out of the heart. The atria are separated from the ventricles by valves. A **valve** is a flap of tissue that prevents blood from flowing backward. Valves are also located between the ventricles and the large blood vessels that carry blood away from the heart.

How the Heart Works The action of the heart has two main phases. In one phase, the heart muscle relaxes and the heart fills with blood. In the other phase, the heart muscle contracts and pumps blood forward. A heartbeat, which sounds something like *lub-dup,* can be heard during the pumping phase.

When the heart muscle relaxes, blood flows into the chambers. Then, the atria contract. This muscle contraction squeezes blood out of the atria, through the valves, and into the ventricles. Next, the ventricles contract. This contraction closes the valves between the atria and ventricles, making the *lub* sound and squeezing blood into large blood vessels. As the valves between the ventricles and the blood vessels snap shut, they make the *dup* sound. All of this happens in less than a second.

The Force of the Ventricles When muscle cells in the ventricles contract, they exert a force on the blood. A force is a push or a pull. The force exerted by the ventricles pushes blood out of your heart and into arteries.

The contraction of the left ventricle exerts much more force than the contraction of the right ventricle. The right ventricle pumps blood only to the lungs. In contrast, the left ventricle pumps blood throughout the body.

FIGURE 3
Open and Closed Heart Valves
As blood flows out of the heart and toward the lungs, it passes through a valve like the one in the photograph. **Applying Concepts** *What is the function of a closed heart valve?*

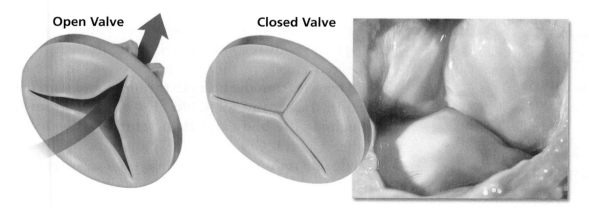

Open Valve   **Closed Valve**

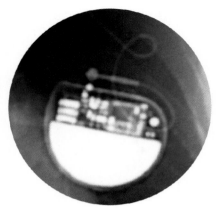

FIGURE 4
An Artificial Pacemaker
This pacemaker has been implanted beneath a patient's skin and connected with wires to the heart. The pacemaker will regulate the patient's heartbeat.

Regulation of Heartbeat A group of heart cells called the **pacemaker** sends out signals that make the heart muscle contract. The pacemaker is located in the right atrium of the heart.

The pacemaker constantly receives messages about the body's oxygen needs. It then adjusts the heart rate to match. For example, your heart beats much faster when you are exercising than when you are sitting quietly. When you exercise, the entire process from the beginning of one heartbeat to the beginning of the next can take less than half a second. Your muscles need more oxygen during exercise. Your rapid heartbeat supplies blood that carries the oxygen throughout your body.

In some people, the pacemaker becomes damaged as a result of disease or an accident. Damage to the pacemaker often results in an irregular or slow heartbeat. In the 1950s, doctors and engineers developed an artificial, battery-operated pacemaker. Modern artificial pacemakers are implanted beneath the skin and are connected by wires to the heart. Tiny electrical impulses travel from the battery through the wires, and make the heart contract.

 Reading Checkpoint **What is the function of the heart's pacemaker?**

Two Loops

After leaving the heart, blood travels in blood vessels through the body. Your body has three kinds of blood vessels—arteries, capillaries, and veins. **Arteries** are blood vessels that carry blood away from the heart. From the arteries, blood flows into tiny, narrow vessels called **capillaries.** In the capillaries, substances are exchanged between the blood and body cells. From capillaries, blood flows into **veins,** blood vessels that carry blood back to the heart.

Pattern of Blood Flow The overall pattern of blood flow through the body is something like a figure eight. The heart is at the center where the two loops cross. **In the first loop, blood travels from the heart to the lungs and then back to the heart. In the second loop, blood is pumped from the heart throughout the body and then returns again to the heart.** The heart is really two pumps, one on the right and one on the left. The right side pumps blood to the lungs, and the left side pumps blood to the rest of the body.

Blood travels in only one direction. If you were a drop of blood, you could start at any point and eventually return to the same point. The entire trip would take less than a minute. As you read about the path that blood takes through the cardiovascular system, trace the path in Figure 5.

Loop One: To the Lungs and Back When blood from the body flows into the right atrium, it contains little oxygen but a lot of carbon dioxide. This oxygen-poor blood is dark red. The blood then flows from the right atrium into the right ventricle. Then, the ventricle pumps the oxygen-poor blood into the arteries that lead to the lungs.

As blood flows through the lungs, large blood vessels branch into smaller ones. Eventually, blood flows through tiny capillaries that are in close contact with the air that comes into the lungs. The air in the lungs has more oxygen than the blood in the capillaries. Therefore, oxygen moves from the lungs into the blood. For the same reason, carbon dioxide moves in the opposite direction—from the blood into the lungs. As the blood leaves the lungs, it is now rich in oxygen and contains little carbon dioxide. This blood, which is bright red, flows to the left side of the heart and will be pumped through the second loop.

Circulation

Video Preview
▶ Video Field Trip
Video Assessment

FIGURE 5
Direction of Blood Flow
Blood circulates through the body in two loops, with the heart at the center. Loop one goes from the heart to the lungs and back. Loop two circulates blood throughout the rest of the body.
Interpreting Diagrams *Where does the blood that enters the left atrium come from?*

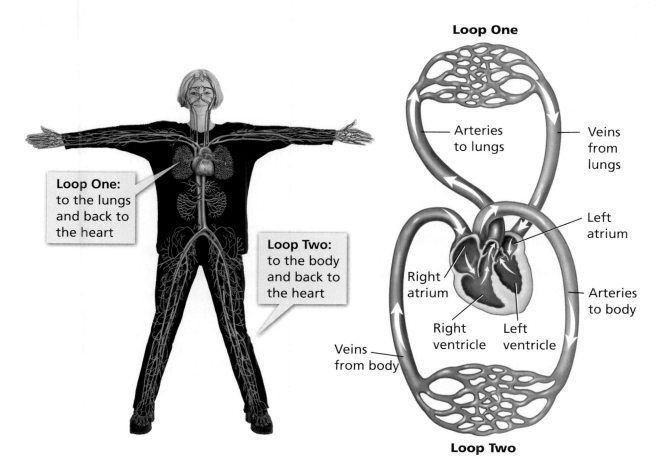

Loop One

Loop One: to the lungs and back to the heart

Loop Two: to the body and back to the heart

Arteries to lungs

Veins from lungs

Left atrium

Right atrium

Arteries to body

Right ventricle

Left ventricle

Veins from body

Loop Two

Loop Two: To the Body and Back The second loop begins as the left atrium fills with oxygen-rich blood coming from the lungs. The blood then moves into the left ventricle. From the left ventricle, the blood is pumped into the **aorta** (ay AWR tuh), the largest artery in the body.

Eventually, after passing through branching arteries, blood flows through tiny capillaries in different parts of your body, such as your brain, liver, and legs. These vessels are in close contact with body cells. Oxygen moves out of the blood and into the body cells. At the same time, carbon dioxide passes from the body cells into the blood. This blood, which is low in oxygen, then flows back to the right atrium of the heart through veins, completing the second loop.

 **Reading Checkpoint** **What is the largest artery in the body?**

FIGURE 6
Getting Blood to Body Cells
In loop two, oxygen-rich blood is pumped throughout the body. The oxygen moves out of the blood and into the body cells in this swimmer's arms and legs.

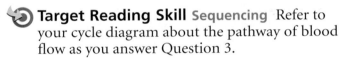

Section 1 Assessment

Target Reading Skill Sequencing Refer to your cycle diagram about the pathway of blood flow as you answer Question 3.

Reviewing Key Concepts
1. **a.** **Reviewing** What three functions does the cardiovascular system perform?
   b. **Comparing and Contrasting** Distinguish between substances that the cardiovascular system transports to cells and substances that it transports away from cells.
2. **a.** **Listing** Name the four chambers of the heart. What structures in the heart separate one chamber from another?
   b. **Summarizing** What function does the heart perform?
   c. **Predicting** What would happen if the valve between the right atrium and right ventricle did not work properly?

3. **a.** **Identifying** Where does blood returning from the body enter the heart?
   b. **Sequencing** Where does the blood move next?
   c. **Interpreting Diagrams** Review Figure 5. How does the blood in the artery leaving the right ventricle differ from the blood in the artery leaving the left ventricle? To where does the artery leaving the right ventricle carry blood?

Writing in Science

Comparison Paragraph Write a paragraph comparing the cardiovascular system in the body to a system of roads, telephone lines, or any other "network" you can think of. How are the two systems alike? How do they differ?

A Closer Look at Blood Vessels

Reading Preview

Key Concepts
- What are the structures and functions of arteries?
- What are the structures and functions of capillaries and veins?
- What causes blood pressure?

Key Terms
- coronary artery • pulse
- diffusion • blood pressure

Target Reading Skill
Comparing and Contrasting As you read, compare and contrast the three kinds of blood vessels by completing a table like the one below.

Comparing Blood Vessels

Blood Vessel	Function	Structure of Wall
Artery	Carries blood away from heart	
Capillary		
Vein		

How Does Pressure Affect Blood Flow?

1. Spread newspapers over a table or desktop. Then, fill a plastic squeeze bottle with water.
2. Hold the bottle over a dishpan. Squeeze the bottle with one hand. Observe how far the water travels. **CAUTION:** *Wipe up spills on the floor to prevent anyone from slipping.*
3. Now, grasp the bottle with both hands and squeeze again. Observe how far the water travels this time.

Think It Over
Inferring Blood is pushed through arteries with much more force than it is pushed through veins. Which part of the activity models an artery? Which part models a vein? Which organ in the body provides the pushing force for blood transport?

Like corridors in a large building, blood vessels run through all of the tissues of your body. Although some blood vessels are as wide as your thumb, most of them are much finer than a human hair. If all the arteries, capillaries, and veins in your body were hooked together end to end, they would stretch a distance of almost 100,000 kilometers. That's long enough to wrap around Earth twice—with a lot left over!

FIGURE 7
Blood Vessels
Thousands of kilometers of blood vessels throughout your body transport the liquid vital to your survival—blood. This model shows the major arteries and veins in the arm.

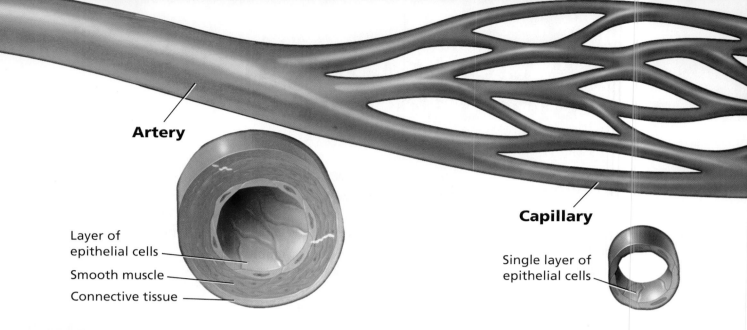

Artery

Layer of
epithelial cells

Smooth muscle

Connective tissue

Capillary

Single layer of
epithelial cells

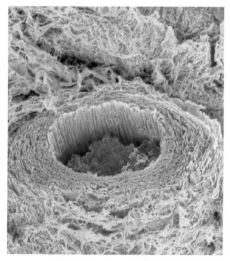

▲ The artery wall appears as a
thick pink band surrounding a
clump of red blood cells.

Arteries

When blood leaves the heart, it travels through arteries. The right ventricle pumps blood into the arteries that go to the lungs. The left ventricle pumps blood into the aorta. Smaller arteries branch off the aorta. The first branches, called the **coronary arteries,** carry blood to the heart itself. Other branches carry blood to the brain, intestines, and other organs. Each artery branches into smaller and smaller arteries.

Artery Structure The walls of arteries are generally very thick. In fact, artery walls consist of three cell layers. The innermost layer, which is made up of epithelial cells, is smooth. This smooth surface enables blood to flow freely. The middle layer consists mostly of muscle tissue. The outer wall is made up of flexible connective tissue. Because of this layered structure, arteries have both strength and flexibility. Arteries are able to withstand the enormous pressure of blood as it is pumped by the heart and to expand and relax between heart beats.

Pulse If you lightly touch the inside of your wrist, you can feel the artery in your wrist rise and fall repeatedly. This **pulse** is caused by the alternating expansion and relaxation of the artery wall. Every time the heart's ventricles contract, they send a spurt of blood out through all the arteries in your body. As this spurt travels through the arteries, it pushes the artery walls and makes them expand. After the spurt passes, the artery walls relax and become narrower again.

When you count the number of times an artery pulses beneath your fingers, you are counting heartbeats. By taking your pulse rate, you can determine how fast your heart is beating.

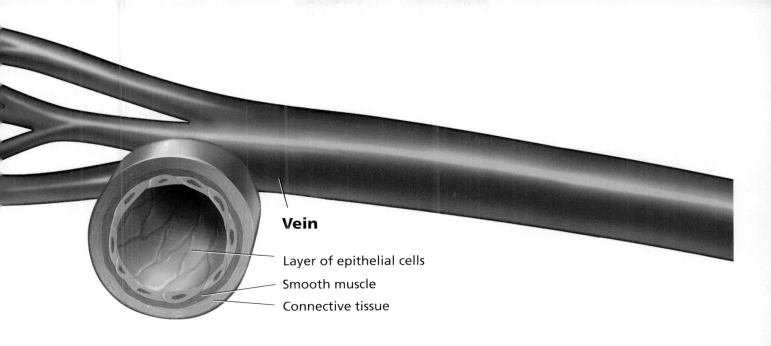

Vein

Layer of epithelial cells

Smooth muscle

Connective tissue

Regulating Blood Flow The layer of muscle in an artery acts as a control gate, adjusting the amount of blood sent to different organs. When the muscle contracts, the opening in the artery becomes smaller. When the muscle relaxes, the opening becomes larger. For example, after you eat, your stomach and intestines need a greater blood supply for digestion. The arteries leading to those organs open wider, and more blood flows through them. In contrast, when you are running, your stomach and intestines need less blood than the muscles in your legs. The arteries leading to the digestive organs become narrower, decreasing the blood flow to these organs.

 **What causes your pulse?**

Capillaries

Eventually, blood flows from small arteries into the tiny capillaries. **In the capillaries, materials are exchanged between the blood and the body's cells. Capillary walls are only one cell thick.** Thus, materials can pass easily through them. Materials such as oxygen and glucose pass from the blood, through the capillary walls, to the cells. Cellular waste products travel in the opposite direction—from cells, through the capillary walls, and into the blood.

One way that materials are exchanged between the blood and body cells is by diffusion. **Diffusion** is the process by which molecules move from an area of higher concentration to an area of lower concentration. For example, glucose is more highly concentrated in the blood than it is in the body cells. Therefore, glucose diffuses from the blood into the body cells.

Math Skills

Calculating a Rate

A rate is the speed at which something happens. When you calculate a rate, you compare the number of events with the time period in which they occur. Here's how to calculate the pulse rate of a person whose heart beats 142 times in 2 minutes.

1. Write the comparison as a fraction.

$$\frac{142 \text{ heartbeats}}{2 \text{ minutes}}$$

2. Divide the numerator and the denominator by 2.

$$\frac{142 \div 2}{2 \div 2} = \frac{71}{1}$$

The person's pulse rate is 71 heartbeats per minute.

Practice Problem Calculate your pulse rate if your heart beats 170 times in 2.5 minutes.

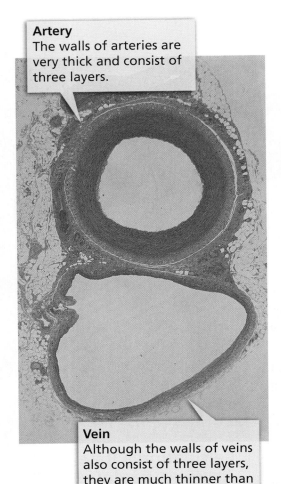

Artery
The walls of arteries are very thick and consist of three layers.

Vein
Although the walls of veins also consist of three layers, they are much thinner than the walls of arteries.

FIGURE 9
Artery and Vein
In this photo, you can compare the wall of an artery (top) with the wall of a vein (bottom).
Comparing and Contrasting
Where is the pushing force of the heart greater—in arteries or in veins?

Veins

After blood moves through capillaries, it enters larger blood vessels called veins, which carry blood back to the heart. The walls of veins, like those of arteries, have three layers, with muscle in the middle layer. However, the walls of veins are generally much thinner than those of arteries.

By the time blood flows into veins, the pushing force of the heart has much less effect than it did in the arteries. Several factors help move blood through veins. First, because many veins are located near skeletal muscles, the contraction of the muscles helps push the blood along. For example, as you run or walk, the skeletal muscles in your legs contract and squeeze the veins in your legs. Second, larger veins in your body have valves in them that prevent blood from flowing backward. Third, breathing movements, which exert a squeezing pressure against veins in the chest, also force blood toward the heart.

 **Reading Checkpoint** How do skeletal muscles help move blood in veins?

Blood Pressure

Suppose that you are washing a car. You attach the hose to the faucet and turn on the faucet. The water flows out in a slow, steady stream. Then, while your back is turned, your little brother turns the faucet on all the way. Suddenly, the water spurts out rapidly, and the hose almost jumps out of your hand.

As water flows through a hose, it pushes against the walls of the hose, creating pressure on the walls. Pressure is the force that something exerts over a given area. When your brother turned on the faucet all the way, the additional water flow increased the pressure exerted on the inside of the hose. The extra pressure made the water spurt out of the nozzle faster.

What Causes Blood Pressure? Blood traveling through blood vessels behaves in a manner similar to that of water moving through a hose. Blood exerts a force, called **blood pressure,** against the walls of blood vessels. **Blood pressure is caused by the force with which the ventricles contract.** In general, as blood moves away from the heart, blood pressure decreases. This change happens because the farther away from the ventricle the blood moves, the lower its force is. Blood flowing near the heart arteries exerts the highest pressure. Blood pressure in arteries farther from the heart is much lower.

Measuring Blood Pressure Blood pressure can be measured with an instrument called a sphygmomanometer (sfig moh muh NAHM uh tur). A cuff is wrapped around the upper arm. Air is pumped into the cuff until the blood flow through the artery is stopped. As the pressure is released, the examiner listens to the pulse and records two numbers. Blood pressure is expressed in millimeters of mercury. The first number is a measure of the blood pressure while the heart's ventricles contract and pump blood into the arteries. The second number, which is lower, measures the blood pressure while the ventricles relax. The two numbers are expressed as a fraction: the contraction pressure over the relaxation pressure.

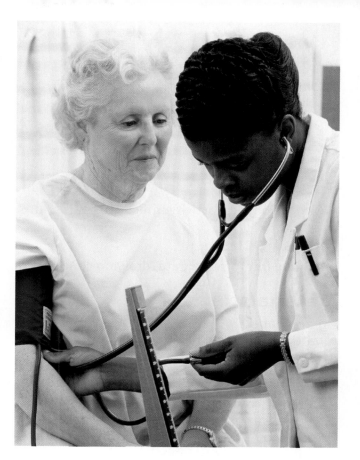

FIGURE 10
Measuring Blood Pressure
Blood pressure can be measured with a sphygmomanometer. A typical blood pressure reading for a healthy person is 120/80 or lower.

Section 2 Assessment

Target Reading Skill Comparing and Contrasting Use the information in your table about blood vessels to help you answer the questions below.

Reviewing Key Concepts

1. a. **Identifying** In which direction do arteries carry blood?
   b. **Explaining** How does the structure of arteries enable them to withstand high pressure?
   c. **Applying Concepts** Arteries adjust the amount of blood flowing to different parts of the body, depending on where blood is needed. Use this fact to explain why you should not exercise vigorously shortly after you eat.

2. a. **Reviewing** What is the function of capillaries in the body?
   b. **Summarizing** Summarize the factors that enable blood in your leg veins to return to the heart in spite of the downward pull of gravity.

3. a. **Defining** What is blood pressure?
   b. **Relating Cause and Effect** Why is blood pressure lower in leg veins than in the aorta?
   c. **Predicting** How might having low blood pressure affect your body?

Math Practice

Before a run, you take your pulse rate for 30 seconds and count 29 beats. Immediately after the run, you count 63 beats in 30 seconds. After resting for 15 minutes, you count 31 beats in 30 seconds.

4. **Calculating a Rate** What was your pulse rate per minute before the run?

5. **Calculating a Rate** What was your pulse rate immediately after the run? After resting for 15 minutes?

Heart Beat, Health Beat

Problem

How does physical activity affect your pulse rate?

Skills Focus

graphing, interpreting data, drawing conclusions

Materials

- graph paper
- watch with second hand or heart rate monitor

Procedure

1. Predict how your pulse rate will change as you go from resting to being active, then back to resting again. Then, copy the data table into your notebook.

2. Locate your pulse by placing the index and middle finger of one hand on your other wrist at the base of your thumb. Move the two fingers slightly until you feel your pulse. If you are using a heart rate monitor, see your teacher for instructions.

3. Work with a partner for the rest of this lab. Begin by determining your resting pulse rate. Count the number of beats in your pulse for exactly 1 minute while your partner times you. Record your resting pulse rate in your data table. **CAUTION:** *Do not complete the rest of this lab if there is any medical reason why you should avoid physical activities.*

4. Walk in place for 1 minute while your partner times you. Stop and immediately take your pulse for 1 minute. Record the number in your data table.

5. Run in place for 1 minute. Take your pulse again, and record the result.

6. Sit down right away, and have your partner time you as you rest for 1 minute. Then, take your pulse rate again.

7. Have your partner time you as you rest for 3 more minutes. Then take your pulse rate again and record it.

Analyze and Conclude

1. **Graphing** Use the data you obtained to create a bar graph of your pulse rate under the different conditions you tested.

2. **Interpreting Data** What happens to the pulse rate when the physical activity has stopped?

3. **Inferring** What can you infer about the heartbeat when the pulse rate increases?

4. **Drawing Conclusions** What conclusion can you draw about the relationship between physical activity and a person's pulse rate?

5. **Communicating** How could you improve the accuracy of your pulse measurements? Write a paragraph in which you discuss this question in relation to the steps you followed in your procedure.

Design an Experiment

Design an experiment to determine whether the resting pulse rates of adults, teens, and young children differ. *Obtain your teacher's permission before carrying out your investigation.*

Data Table	
Activity	Pulse Rate
Resting	
Walking	
Running	
Resting after exercise (1 min)	
Resting after exercise (3+ min)	

For: Data sharing
Visit: PHSchool.com
Web Code: ced-4032

Blood and Lymph

Reading Preview

Key Concepts
- What are the components of blood?
- What determines the type of blood that a person can receive in transfusion?
- What are the structures and functions of the lymphatic system?

Key Terms
- plasma • red blood cell
- hemoglobin
- white blood cell • platelet
- lymphatic system • lymph
- lymph node

Target Reading Skill

Identifying Main Ideas As you read the section titled Blood, write the main idea in a graphic organizer like the one below. Then, write four supporting details that give examples of the main idea.

Main Idea

Blood is made up of...

Detail	Detail	Detail	Detail

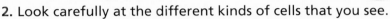

Lab zone Discover Activity

What Kinds of Cells Are in Blood?

1. Obtain a microscope slide of human blood. Look at the slide under the microscope, first under low power and then under high power.
2. Look carefully at the different kinds of cells that you see.
3. Make several drawings of each kind of cell. Use red pencil for the red blood cells.

Think It Over
Observing How many kinds of cells did you see? How do they differ from one another?

While riding your bike through the neighborhood, you take a tumble and scrape your knee. Your knee begins to sting, and you notice blood oozing from the wound. You go inside to clean the wound. As you do, you wonder, "Just what is blood?"

Blood

Blood may seem like just a plain red liquid, but it is actually a complex tissue that has several parts. **Blood is made up of four components: plasma, red blood cells, white blood cells, and platelets.** About 45 percent of the volume of blood is cells. The rest is plasma.

Plasma Most of the materials transported in the blood travel in the plasma. **Plasma** is the liquid part of the blood. Water makes up 90 percent of plasma. The other 10 percent is dissolved materials. Plasma carries nutrients, such as glucose, fats, vitamins, and minerals. Plasma also carries chemical messengers that direct body activities such as the uptake of glucose by your cells. In addition, many wastes produced by cell processes are carried away by plasma.

Protein molecules give plasma its yellow color. There are three groups of plasma proteins. One group helps to regulate the amount of water in blood. The second group, which is produced by white blood cells, helps fight disease. The third group of proteins interacts with platelets to form blood clots.

Red Blood Cells Without red blood cells, your body could not use the oxygen that you breathe in. **Red blood cells** take up oxygen in the lungs and deliver it to cells elsewhere in the body. Red blood cells, like most blood cells, are produced in bone marrow. Under a microscope, these cells look like disks with pinched-in centers. Because of their pinched shape, red blood cells are thin in the middle and can bend and twist easily. This flexibility enables them to squeeze through narrow capillaries.

A red blood cell is made mostly of **hemoglobin** (HEE muh gloh bin), which is an iron-containing protein that binds chemically to oxygen molecules. When hemoglobin combines with oxygen, the cells become bright red. Without oxygen, the cells are dark red. Thus, blood leaving the heart through the aorta is bright red, whereas blood returning from the body to the heart through veins is dark red. Hemoglobin picks up oxygen in the lungs and releases it as blood travels through capillaries in the rest of the body. Hemoglobin also picks up some of the carbon dioxide produced by cells. However, most of the carbon dioxide is carried by plasma. The blood carries the carbon dioxide to the lungs, where it is released from the body.

Mature red blood cells have no nuclei. Without a nucleus, a red blood cell cannot reproduce or repair itself. Mature red blood cells live only about 120 days. Every second, about 2 million red blood cells in your body die. Fortunately, your bone marrow produces new red blood cells at the same rate.

✔ **Reading Checkpoint** **What is hemoglobin?**

White Blood Cells Like red blood cells, white blood cells are produced in bone marrow. **White blood cells** are the body's disease fighters. Some white blood cells recognize disease-causing organisms, such as bacteria, and alert the body that it has been invaded. Other white blood cells produce chemicals to fight the invaders. Still others surround and kill the organisms.

White blood cells are different from red blood cells in several important ways. There are fewer of them—only about one white blood cell for every 500 to 1,000 red blood cells. White blood cells are also larger than red blood cells. In addition, white blood cells contain nuclei. Most white blood cells can live for months or even years.

FIGURE 11
Parts of Blood
Blood consists of liquid plasma and three kinds of cells—red blood cells, white blood cells, and platelets.
Observing *Describe the shape of a red blood cell.*

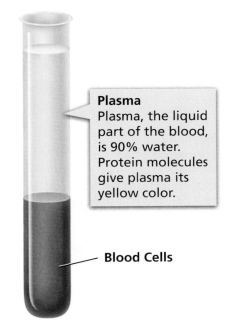

Plasma
Plasma, the liquid part of the blood, is 90% water. Protein molecules give plasma its yellow color.

Blood Cells

Red Blood Cells
Oxygen is carried throughout your body by red blood cells. Your blood contains more red blood cells than any other kind of cell.

White Blood Cells
By finding and destroying disease-causing organisms, white blood cells fight disease.

Platelets
When you cut yourself, platelets help form the blood clot that stops the bleeding. Platelets aren't really whole cells. Instead, they are small pieces of cells and do not have nuclei.

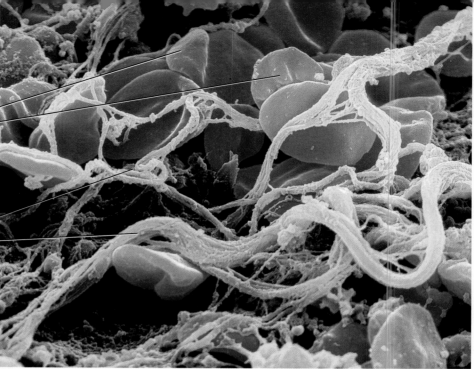

Red blood cells

Fibrin

FIGURE 12
Formation of a Blood Clot
When you cut your skin, a blood clot forms. The blood clot consists of blood cells trapped in a fiber net.
Relating Cause and Effect *How is this net of fibers produced?*

Caught in the Web

In this activity, you will model part of the process by which a blood clot forms.

1. Cover the opening of a sturdy plastic cup with a piece of cheesecloth. Use a rubber band to hold the cheesecloth in place.

2. Put some water, paper clips, and coins in another cup.

3. Carefully pour the water, coins, and paper clips into the middle of the cheesecloth.

Making Models The paper clips and coins represent blood cells. What does the cheesecloth represent? What starts the production of the substance that the cheesecloth represents?

Platelets When you scraped your knee, blood oozed out of the wound. After a short time, however, a blood clot formed, stopping the blood flow. **Platelets** (PLAYT lits) are cell fragments that play an important part in forming blood clots.

When a blood vessel is cut, platelets collect and stick to the vessel at the site of the wound. The platelets release chemicals that start a chain reaction. This series of reactions eventually produces a protein called fibrin (FY brin). Fibrin gets its name from the fact that it weaves a net of tiny fibers across the cut in the blood vessel. Look at Figure 12 to see how the fiber net traps the blood cells. As more and more platelets and blood cells become trapped in the net, a blood clot forms. A scab is a dried blood clot on the skin surface.

Reading Checkpoint What is the role of platelets?

Blood Types

If a person loses a lot of blood—either from a wound or during surgery—he or she may be given a blood transfusion. A blood transfusion is the transfer of blood from one person to another. Most early attempts at blood transfusion failed, but no one knew why until the early 1900s. At that time, Karl Landsteiner, an Austrian American physician, tried mixing blood samples from pairs of people. Sometimes the two blood samples blended smoothly. In other cases, however, the red blood cells clumped together. This clumping accounted for the failure of many blood transfusions. If clumping occurs within the body, it clogs the capillaries and may lead to death.

Marker Molecules Landsteiner went on to discover that there are four major types of blood—A, B, AB, and O. Blood types are determined by proteins known as marker molecules that are on the red blood cells. If your blood type is A, you have the A marker. If your blood type is B, you have the B marker. People with type AB blood have both A and B markers. People with type O blood have neither A nor B markers.

Your plasma contains clumping proteins that recognize red blood cells with "foreign" markers (not yours) and make those cells clump together. For example, if you have blood type A, your blood contains clumping proteins that act against cells with B markers. So, if you receive a transfusion of type B blood, your clumping proteins will make the "foreign" type B cells clump together.

Safe Transfusions Landsteiner's work led to a better understanding of transfusions. **The marker molecules on your red blood cells determine your blood type and the type of blood that you can safely receive in transfusions.** A person with type A blood can receive transfusions of either type A or type O blood. Neither of these two blood types has B markers. Thus they would not be recognized as foreign by the clumping proteins in type A blood. A person with type AB blood can receive all blood types in transfusion because type AB blood has no clumping proteins. Figure 13 shows which transfusions are safe for each blood type.

If you ever receive a transfusion, your blood type will be checked first. Then, donated blood that you can safely receive will be found. This process is called cross matching. You may have heard a doctor on a television show give the order to "type and cross." The doctor wants to find out what blood type the patient has and then cross match it with donated blood.

Go Online

SciLINKS NSTA

For: Links on blood
Visit: www.SciLinks.org
Web Code: scn-0433

FIGURE 13
Blood Types and Their Markers
The chemical markers on a person's red blood cells determine the types of blood he or she can safely receive in a transfusion.
Interpreting Tables *What types of blood can be given safely to a person with blood type AB?*

Blood Types and Their Markers				
Blood Type Characteristic	**Blood Type A**	**Blood Type B**	**Blood Type AB**	**Blood Type O**
Marker Molecules on Red Blood Cells				
Clumping Proteins	anti-B	anti-A	no clumping proteins	anti-A and anti-B
Blood Types That Can Be Safely Received in a Transfusion	A and O	B and O	A, B, AB, and O	O

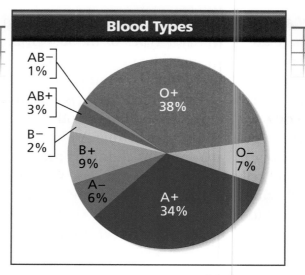

Math — Analyzing Data

Blood Type Distribution

The circle graph shows the percentage of each blood type found in the U.S. population.

1. **Reading Graphs** What does each wedge of the graph represent?

2. **Interpreting Data** Rank the four major blood types—A, B, AB, and O—from least common to most common. What is the percentage of each type?

3. **Calculating** According to the graph, what percentage of the population is Rh positive? What percentage is Rh negative?

4. **Predicting** What type of blood can someone who is B negative (blood type B and Rh negative) receive? What percentage of the population does that represent?

5. **Creating Data Tables** Use the data to make a table of the eight possible blood types. Include columns for the A, B, AB, and O blood types and Rh factor (positive or negative), and a row for percentage of the population.

Rh Factor Landsteiner also discovered the presence of another protein on red blood cells, which he called Rh factor. About 85 percent of the people he tested had this protein, and about 15 percent lacked it. Like the A, B, AB, and O blood types, the presence of Rh factor is determined by a marker on the red blood cell. If your blood type is Rh positive, you have the Rh marker. If your blood type is Rh negative, you lack the marker on your cells. If you are Rh negative and ever received Rh positive blood, you would develop Rh clumping proteins in your plasma. This situation is potentially dangerous.

 **Reading Checkpoint** Where is the Rh marker found?

The Lymphatic System

As blood travels through the capillaries in the cardiovascular system, some of the fluid leaks out. It moves through the walls of capillaries and into surrounding tissues. This fluid carries materials that the cells in the tissues need.

After bathing the cells, this fluid moves into your body's drainage system, called the **lymphatic system** (lim FAT ik). **The lymphatic system is a network of veinlike vessels that returns the fluid to the bloodstream.** The lymphatic system acts something like rain gutters after a rainstorm, carrying the excess fluid away.

Lymph Once the fluid is inside the lymphatic system, it is called **lymph.** Lymph consists of water and dissolved materials such as glucose. It also contains some white blood cells that have left the capillaries.

The lymphatic system has no pump, so lymph moves slowly. Lymphatic vessels, which are part of the cardiovascular system, connect to large veins in the chest. Lymph empties into these veins, and the fluid once again becomes part of blood plasma.

Lymph Nodes As lymph flows through the lymphatic system, it passes through small knobs of tissue called lymph nodes. The **lymph nodes** filter lymph, trapping bacteria and other disease-causing microorganisms in the fluid. When the body is fighting an infection, the lymph nodes enlarge. If you've ever had "swollen glands" when you've been sick, you've actually had swollen lymph nodes.

 **Reading Checkpoint** **What is lymph?**

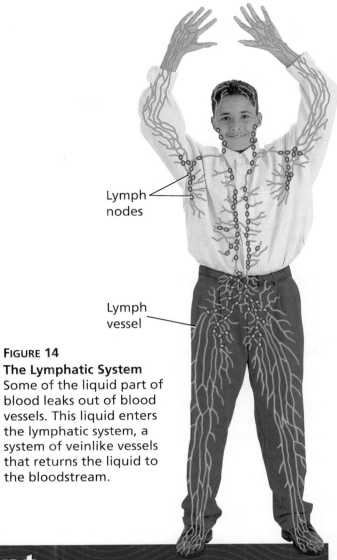

FIGURE 14
The Lymphatic System
Some of the liquid part of blood leaks out of blood vessels. This liquid enters the lymphatic system, a system of veinlike vessels that returns the liquid to the bloodstream.

Lymph nodes

Lymph vessel

Section 3 Assessment

Target Reading Skill Identifying Main Ideas Use your graphic organizer to help you answer Question 1 below.

Reviewing Key Concepts

1. a. Listing Name the four components of blood. Identify whether each is a cell, a part of a cell, or a liquid.
   b. Summarizing Briefly describe what happens to stop the bleeding when you cut yourself.
   c. Relating Cause and Effect People with the disorder hemophilia do not produce the protein fibrin. Explain why hemophilia is a serious disorder.
2. a. Reviewing What is a marker molecule?
   b. Explaining Explain why a person with type O blood cannot receive a transfusion of type A blood.

   c. Predicting Can a person with type AB, Rh negative blood safely receive a transfusion of type O, Rh negative blood? Explain.
3. a. Identifying Where does lymph come from?
   b. Sequencing What happens to lymph after it travels through the lymphatic system?

Lab zone **At-Home Activity**

What's Your Blood Type? If possible, find out your blood type. Explain to family members the types of blood you can receive and to whom you can donate blood. Create a chart to help with your explanation.

Cardiovascular Health

Reading Preview

Key Concepts
- What are some diseases of the cardiovascular system?
- What behaviors can help maintain cardiovascular health?

Key Terms
- atherosclerosis
- heart attack
- hypertension

Target Reading Skill

Asking Questions Before you read, preview the red headings. In a graphic organizer like the one below, ask a *what* or *how* question for each heading. As you read, write the answers to your questions.

Cardiovascular Health

Question	Answer
What are some cardiovascular diseases?	Cardiovascular diseases include...

Lab zone · Discover Activity

Which Foods Are "Heart Healthy"?

1. Your teacher will give you an assortment of foods. If they have nutrition labels, read the information.
2. Sort the foods into three groups. In one group, put those foods that you think are good for your cardiovascular system. In the second group, put foods that you think might damage your cardiovascular system if eaten often. Place foods you aren't sure about in the third group.

Think It Over
Forming Operational Definitions How did you define a "heart-healthy" food?

Shortly after sunrise, when most people are just waking up, a team of rowers is already out on the river. Rhythmically, with perfectly coordinated movement, the rowers pull on the oars, making the boat glide swiftly through the water. Despite the chilly morning air, sweat glistens on the rowers' faces and arms. Inside their chests, their hearts are pounding, delivering blood to the arm and chest muscles that power the oars.

FIGURE 15
Exercising for Health
Strenuous exercise, such as rowing, requires a healthy cardiovascular system. In turn, exercise keeps the cardiovascular system healthy.

Healthy, unblocked artery

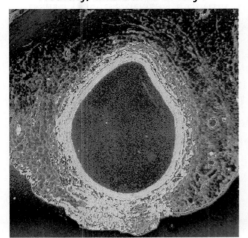

Partially blocked artery

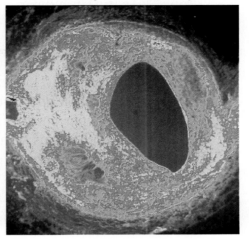

FIGURE 16
Effect of Atherosclerosis
The artery on the right shows atherosclerosis, which is caused by deposits of fat on the artery walls.
Relating Cause and Effect *What kind of diet can lead to atherosclerosis?*

Cardiovascular Diseases

Rowers cannot perform at their peaks unless their cardiovascular systems are in excellent condition. But cardiovascular health is important for all people, not just for athletes. Cardiovascular disease is the leading cause of death in the United States today. **Diseases of the cardiovascular system include atherosclerosis and hypertension.**

Atherosclerosis Compare the photos of the two arteries in Figure 16. The one on the left is a healthy artery. It has a large space in the center through which blood can flow easily. The artery on the right, in contrast, has a smaller space in the middle. This artery exhibits **atherosclerosis** (ath uh roh skluh ROH sis), a condition in which an artery wall thickens as a result of the buildup of fatty materials. One of these fatty materials is cholesterol, a waxy substance. Atherosclerosis results in a reduced flow of blood in the affected artery.

Atherosclerosis can develop in the coronary arteries, which supply the heart muscle. When that happens, the heart muscle receives less blood and therefore less oxygen. This condition may lead to a heart attack. A **heart attack** occurs when blood flow to part of the heart muscle is blocked. Cells die in the part of the heart that does not receive blood and oxygen. This permanently damages the heart.

Treatment for mild atherosclerosis usually includes a low-fat diet and a moderate exercise program. In addition, medications that lower the levels of cholesterol and fats in the blood may be prescribed. People with severe atherosclerosis may need to undergo surgery or other procedures to unclog the blocked arteries.

Lab zone Try This Activity

Blocking the Flow
Use this activity to model how fatty deposits affect the flow of blood through an artery.

1. Put a funnel in the mouth of a plastic jar. The funnel will represent an artery.

2. Slowly pour 100 mL of water into the funnel. Have your partner time how many seconds it takes for all the water to flow through the funnel. Then, discard the water.

3. Use a plastic knife to spread a small amount of paste along the bottom of the funnel's neck. Then, with a toothpick, carve out a hole in the paste so that the funnel is partly, but not completely, clogged.

4. Repeat Steps 1 and 2.

Predicting If the funnels were arteries, which one—blocked or unblocked—would do a better job of supplying blood to tissues? Explain.

Hypertension High blood pressure, or **hypertension** (hy pur TEN shun), is a disorder in which a person's blood pressure is consistently higher than normal—usually defined as greater than 140/90.

Hypertension makes the heart work harder to pump blood throughout the body. It also may damage the walls of the blood vessels. Over time, both the heart and arteries can be severely harmed by hypertension. Because people with hypertension often have no obvious symptoms to warn them of the danger until damage is severe, hypertension is sometimes called the "silent killer."

• Tech & Design in History •

Advances in Cardiovascular Medicine

Scientists today have an in-depth understanding of how the cardiovascular system works and how to treat cardiovascular problems. This timeline describes some of the advances in cardiovascular medicine.

**1930s–1940s
Blood Banks**
Charles Drew demonstrated that emergency blood transfusions could be done with plasma if whole blood was not available. During World War II, Drew established blood banks for storing donated blood. His work helped save millions of lives on and off the battlefield.

**1958
Artificial Pacemaker**
Electrical engineer Earl Baaken developed an external pacemaker to correct irregular heartbeats. A small electric generator connected to the pacemaker generated electric pulses that regulated heart rate. The first pacemakers had a fixed rate of 70 to 75 pulses per minute.

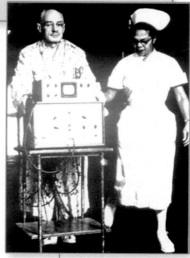

**1961
Heart Valve
Replacement**
The first successful artificial heart valve was inserted into a patient's heart by surgeons Albert Starr and M. L. Edwards in Oregon. The valve was a rubberlike ball inside a stainless steel cage.

1930	1940	1950	1960

Hypertension and atherosclerosis are closely related. As the arteries narrow, blood pressure increases. For mild hypertension, regular exercise and careful food choices may be enough to lower blood pressure. People with hypertension may need to limit their intake of sodium, which can increase blood pressure. Sodium is found in table salt and in processed foods such as soups and packaged snack foods. For many people who have hypertension, however, medications are needed to reduce their blood pressure.

 **Reading Checkpoint** **Why is hypertension called the "silent killer"?**

Writing in Science

Research and Write Choose one of the scientists whose work is described in the timeline. Imagine that you are on a committee that has chosen this scientist to receive an award. Write the speech you would give at the award ceremony, explaining the scientist's contributions.

1967
First Heart Transplant
Christiaan Barnard, a South African surgeon, performed the first transplant of a human heart. Louis Washkanksky, the man who received the heart, lived for only 18 days after the transplant. But Barnard's work paved the way for future successes in transplanting hearts and other organs.

1977
Angioplasty
The first coronary balloon angioplasty was performed by Andreas Gruentizig and a team of surgeons in San Francisco. A balloon is inserted into the coronary artery and inflated, thus opening the artery. In 2001, more than two million angioplasties were performed worldwide.

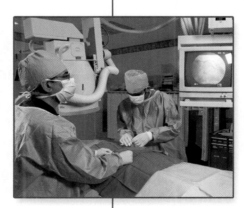

2001
Replacement Heart
The first replacement heart was implanted by a team of surgeons in Louisville, Kentucky. Unlike the first artificial heart, the Jarvik-7, the replacement heart has its own internal batteries. The patient does not have to be "plugged in" to an external power source. The first patient to receive the replacement heart lived for more than 500 days.

| 1970 | 1980 | 1990 | 2000 |

Keeping Healthy

Few young people have heart attacks, but signs of atherosclerosis can be found in some people as young as 18 to 20 years old. You can establish habits now that will lessen your risk of developing atherosclerosis and hypertension. **To help maintain cardiovascular health, people should exercise regularly; eat a balanced diet that is low in saturated fats and trans fats, cholesterol, and sodium; and avoid smoking.**

Exercise and Diet Do you participate in sports, ride a bike, swim, dance, or climb stairs instead of taking the elevator? Every time you do one of those activities, you are helping to strengthen your heart muscle and prevent atherosclerosis.

Foods that are high in cholesterol, saturated fats, and trans fats can lead to atherosclerosis. Foods such as red meats, eggs, and cheese are high in cholesterol. But because they also contain substances that your body needs, a smart approach might be to eat them only in small quantities. Foods that are high in saturated fat include butter, whole milk, and ice cream. Foods high in trans fat include margarine, potato chips, and doughnuts.

Avoid Smoking Smokers are more than twice as likely to have a heart attack as are nonsmokers. Every year, about 180,000 people in the United States who were smokers die from cardiovascular disease. If smokers quit, however, their risk of death from cardiovascular disease decreases.

FIGURE 17
Eating for Health
Eating foods that are low in fat can help keep your cardiovascular system healthy.
Applying Concepts *What are some heart-healthy low-fat foods?*

 Reading Checkpoint **What are some foods that are high in cholesterol?**

Section 4 Assessment

Target Reading Skill Asking Questions Use the answers to the questions you wrote about the headings to help you answer the questions below.

Reviewing Key Concepts

1. **a. Defining** What is atherosclerosis? What is hypertension?
   b. Relating Cause and Effect How do these two diseases affect the heart?
2. **a. Listing** List three things you can do to help your cardiovascular system stay healthy.
   b. Explaining Why it is important to exercise?
   c. Inferring Coronary heart disease is less common in some countries than in the United States. What factors might account for this difference?

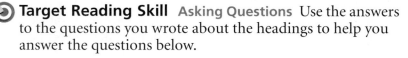

Lab zone At-Home **Activity**

Heart-Healthy Activities With your family, discuss things you all can do to maintain heart health. Make a list of activities that you can enjoy together. You might also work with your family to cook and serve a "heart-healthy" meal. List the foods you would serve at the meal.

Do You Know Your A-B-O's?

Problem

Which blood types can safely receive transfusions of type A blood? Which can receive type O blood?

Skills Focus

interpreting data, drawing conclusions

Materials

- 4 paper cups
- 8 plastic petri dishes
- marking pen
- 4 plastic droppers
- white paper
- toothpicks
- four model "blood" types

Procedure

1. Write down your ideas about why type O blood might be in higher demand than other blood types. Then, make two copies of the data table in your notebook.

2. Label four paper cups A, B, AB, and O. Fill each cup about one-third full with the model "blood" supplied by your teacher. Place one clean plastic dropper into each cup. Use each dropper to transfer only that one type of blood.

3. Label the side of each of four petri dishes with a blood type: A, B, AB, or O. Place the petri dishes on a sheet of white paper.

Data Table			
Donor: Type _____			
Potential Receiver	Original Color	Final Color of Mixture	Safe or Unsafe?
A			
B			
AB			
O			

4. Use the plastic droppers to place 10 drops of each type of blood in its labeled petri dish. Each sample represents the blood of a potential receiver of a blood transfusion. Record the original color of each sample in your data table as yellow, blue, green, or colorless.

5. Label your first data table Donor: Type A. To test whether each potential receiver can safely receive type A blood, add 10 drops of type A blood to each sample. Stir each mixture with a separate, clean toothpick.

6. Record the final color of each mixture in the data table. If the color stayed the same, write "safe" in the last column. If the color of the mixture changed, write "unsafe."

7. Label your second data table Donor: Type O. Obtain four clean petri dishes, and repeat Steps 3 through 6 to determine who could safely receive type O blood.

Analyze and Conclude

1. **Interpreting Data** Which blood types can safely receive a transfusion of type A blood? Type O blood?

2. **Inferring** Use what you know about marker molecules to explain why some transfusions of type A blood are safe while others are unsafe.

3. **Drawing Conclusions** If some blood types are not available, how might type O blood be useful?

4. **Communicating** Write a paragraph in which you discuss why it is important for hospitals to have an adequate supply of different types of blood.

More to Explore

Repeat this activity to find out which blood types can safely receive donations of type B and type AB blood.

The Immune System

If a pathogen infection is severe enough to cause a fever, it triggers the body's third line of defense—the **immune response.** The immune response is controlled by the immune system, the body's disease-fighting system. **The cells of the immune system can distinguish between different kinds of pathogens. The immune system cells react to each kind of pathogen with a defense targeted specifically at that pathogen.**

The white blood cells that distinguish between different kinds of pathogens are called **lymphocytes** (LIM fuh syts). There are two major kinds of lymphocytes—T lymphocytes and B lymphocytes, which are also called T cells and B cells.

What Are T Cells?

A major function of **T cells** is to identify pathogens and distinguish one kind of pathogen from another. You have tens of millions of T cells circulating in your blood. Each kind of T cell recognizes a different kind of pathogen. What T cells actually recognize are marker molecules, called antigens, found on each pathogen. **Antigens** are molecules that the immune system recognizes either as part of your body or as coming from outside your body.

You can think of antigens as something like the uniform that athletes wear. When you watch a track meet, you can look at the runners' uniforms to tell which school each runner comes from. Like athletes from different schools, each different pathogen has its own kind of antigen. Antigens differ from one another because each kind of antigen has a different chemical structure from another.

What Are B Cells?

The lymphocytes called **B cells** produce proteins that help destroy pathogens. These proteins are called **antibodies.** Each kind of B cell produces only one kind of antibody, and each kind of antibody has a different structure. Antigen and antibody molecules fit together like pieces of a puzzle. An antigen on a flu virus will only bind to one kind of antibody— the antibody that acts against that flu virus.

When antibodies bind to the antigens on a pathogen, they mark the pathogen for destruction. Some antibodies make pathogens clump together. Others keep pathogens from attaching to the body cells that they might damage. Still other antibodies make it easier for phagocytes (white blood cells that engulf pathogens and destroy them) to destroy the pathogens.

What Do You Think?

1. **Identify the Problem**
   A vaccine is a substance introduced into the body to stimulate the production of antibodies that destroy viruses or bacteria which cause that disease. Explain how this action keeps the person from becoming ill.

2. **Analyze the Options**
   Flu vaccines are available to combat specific flu viruses. Research how vaccines work. Write two or three paragraphs summarizing your research.

3. **Find a Solution**
   Some people choose not to be vaccinated for certain flu viruses. Interview a health professional about who should or should not receive the vaccine.

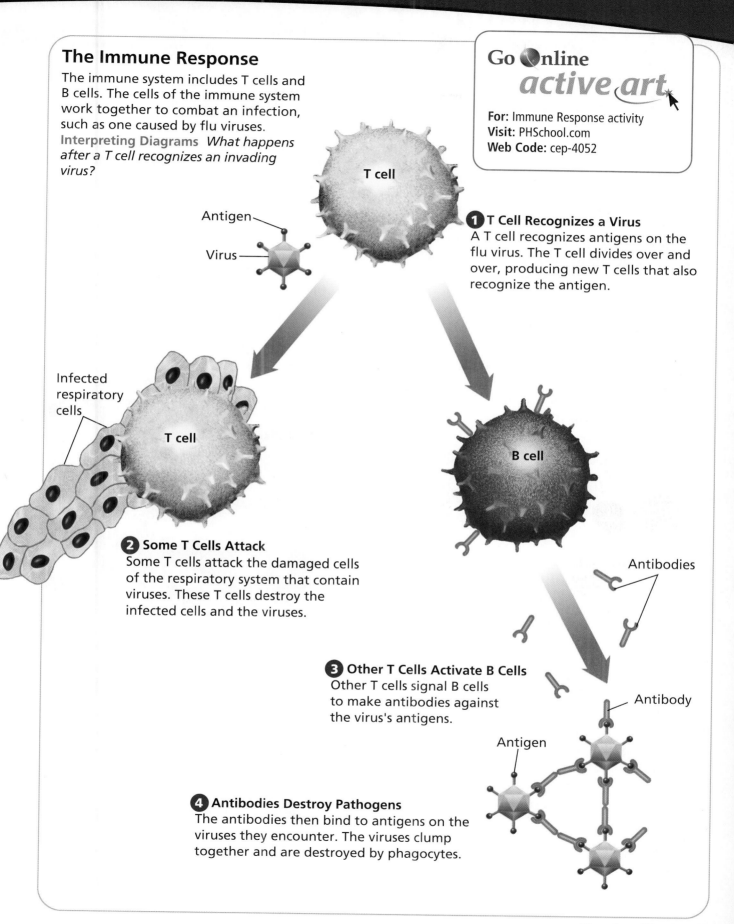

The Immune Response

The immune system includes T cells and B cells. The cells of the immune system work together to combat an infection, such as one caused by flu viruses. **Interpreting Diagrams** *What happens after a T cell recognizes an invading virus?*

Go Online
active art

For: Immune Response activity
Visit: PHSchool.com
Web Code: cep-4052

Antigen

Virus

T cell

❶ T Cell Recognizes a Virus
A T cell recognizes antigens on the flu virus. The T cell divides over and over, producing new T cells that also recognize the antigen.

Infected respiratory cells

T cell

B cell

Antibodies

❷ Some T Cells Attack
Some T cells attack the damaged cells of the respiratory system that contain viruses. These T cells destroy the infected cells and the viruses.

❸ Other T Cells Activate B Cells
Other T cells signal B cells to make antibodies against the virus's antigens.

Antibody

Antigen

❹ Antibodies Destroy Pathogens
The antibodies then bind to antigens on the viruses they encounter. The viruses clump together and are destroyed by phagocytes.

① The Body's Transport System

Key Concepts

- The cardiovascular system carries needed substances to cells and carries waste products away from cells. In addition, blood contains cells that fight disease.

- When the heart beats, it pushes blood through the blood vessels of the cardiovascular system.

- The right side of the heart is completely separated from the left side by a wall of tissue called the septum. Each side has two compartments, or chambers—an upper chamber and a lower chamber.

- Blood circulates in two loops. In the first loop, blood travels from the heart to the lungs and back to the heart. In the second loop, blood is pumped from the heart throughout the body and then returns to the heart.

Key Terms

cardiovascular system	pacemaker
heart	artery
atrium	capillary
ventricle	vein
valve	aorta

② A Closer Look at Blood Vessels

Key Concepts

- When blood leaves the heart, it travels through arteries. Artery walls are thick and consist of three cell layers.

- In the capillaries, materials are exchanged between the blood and the body's cells. Capillary walls are only one cell thick.

- After blood moves through capillaries, it enters larger blood vessels called veins, which carry blood back to the heart. The walls of veins have three layers, with muscle in the middle layer.

- Blood pressure is caused by the force with which the ventricles contract.

Key Terms

coronary artery	diffusion
pulse	blood pressure

③ Blood and Lymph

Key Concepts

- Blood is made up of four components: plasma, red blood cells, white blood cells, and platelets.

- The marker molecules on your red blood cells determine your blood type and the type of blood that you can safely receive in transfusions.

- The lymphatic system is a network of vein-like vessels that returns the fluid to the bloodstream.

Key Terms

plasma	platelet
red blood cell	lymphatic system
hemoglobin	lymph
white blood cell	lymph node

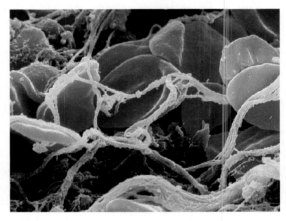

④ Cardiovascular Health

Key Concepts

- Diseases of the cardiovascular system include atherosclerosis and hypertension.

- To help maintain cardiovascular health, people should exercise regularly; eat a balanced diet that is low in saturated fats and trans fats, cholesterol, and sodium; and avoid smoking.

Key Terms

atherosclerosis	hypertension
heart attack	

Review and Assessment

Go Online
PHSchool.com

For: Self-Assessment
Visit: PHSchool.com
Web Code: cea-4030

Organizing Information

Comparing and Contrasting Copy the compare/contrast table about the two loops of the circulatory system onto a sheet of paper. Then complete it and add a title. (For more on Comparing and Contrasting, see the Skills Handbook.)

Loop	Side of heart where loop starts	Where blood flows to	Where blood returns to
Loop One	a. ___?___	Lungs	b. ___?___
Loop Two	Left side	c. ___?___	d. ___?___

Reviewing Key Terms

Choose the letter of the best answer.

1. The heart's upper chambers are called
   a. ventricles.
   b. atria.
   c. valves.
   d. arteries.

2. Nutrients are exchanged between the blood and body cells in the
   a. capillaries.
   b. veins.
   c. aorta.
   d. arteries.

3. The alternating expansion and relaxation of the artery that you feel in your wrist is your
   a. pulse.
   b. coronary artery.
   c. blood pressure.
   d. plasma.

4. Blood components that help the body to control bleeding are
   a. platelets.
   b. red blood cells.
   c. white blood cells.
   d. hemoglobin.

5. Cholesterol is a waxy substance associated with
   a. lymph nodes.
   b. white blood cells.
   c. atherosclerosis.
   d. plasma.

If the statement is true, write *true*. If it is false, change the underlined word or words to make the statement true.

6. The two lower chambers of the heart are called <u>atria</u>.

7. The <u>veins</u> are the narrowest blood vessels in the body.

8. <u>White blood cells</u> contain hemoglobin.

9. The <u>lymphatic system</u> is involved in returning fluid to the bloodstream.

10. Elevated blood pressure is called <u>atherosclerosis</u>.

Writing in Science

Letter Write a letter to a friend describing what you do to stay active. For example, do you participate in team sports, jog, or take long walks with your dog? Include in your letter additional ways you can be even more active.

Discovery CHANNEL SCHOOL

Circulation
Video Preview
Video Field Trip
▶ Video Assessment

Review and Assessment

Checking Concepts

11. A red blood cell is moving through an artery in your leg. Describe the path that the blood cell will follow back to your heart. Identify the chamber of the heart to which it will return.

12. Contrast the forces with which the right and left ventricles contract. How does this relate to each ventricle's function?

13. How is a capillary's structure adapted to its function?

14. What is the function of hemoglobin?

15. What is lymph? How does lymph return to the cardiovascular system?

16. Give two reasons why food choices are important to cardiovascular health.

Thinking Critically

17. **Predicting** Some babies are born with an opening between the left and right ventricles of the heart. How would this heart defect affect the ability of the cardiovascular system to deliver oxygen to body cells?

18. **Classifying** Which two chambers of the heart shown below are the ventricles? Through which chamber does oxygen-poor blood enter the heart from the body?

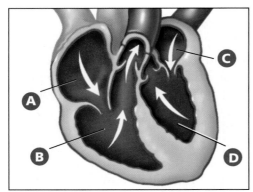

19. **Relating Cause and Effect** People who do not have enough iron in their diets sometimes develop a condition in which their blood cannot carry a normal amount of oxygen. Explain why this is so.

20. **Making Generalizations** Why is atherosclerosis sometimes called a "lifestyle disease"?

Math Practice

21. **Calculating a Rate** The veterinarian listens to your cat's heart and counts 30 beats in 15 seconds. What is your cat's heart rate?

Applying Skills

Use the graph to answer Questions 22–25.

The graph below shows how average blood pressure changes as men and women grow older.

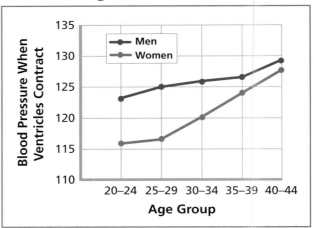

22. **Reading Graphs** What is plotted on each axis?

23. **Interpreting Data** At age 20, who is likely to have higher blood pressure—men or women?

24. **Drawing Conclusions** In general, what happens to blood pressure as people age?

25. **Predicting** Do you think that there is some age at which both men and women have about the same blood pressure? Use the graph lines to explain your prediction.

Lab zone Chapter **Project**

Performance Assessment You should now be ready to present your display. First show it to a small group of classmates to make sure it is clear and accurate. When you present your display, be ready to answer questions.

🌀 End-of-Grade Test Practice

Choose the letter of the best answer.

1. The most important function of the cardiovascular system is to
   A transport needed materials to body cells and remove wastes.
   B provide structural support for the lungs.
   C generate blood pressure so the arteries and veins do not collapse.
   D produce blood and lymph.

2. The correct sequence for the path of blood through the body is
   A heart—lungs—other body parts.
   B heart—lungs—heart—other body parts.
   C lungs—other body parts—heart.
   D heart—other body parts—lungs—heart.

3. Which of the following is true about blood in the aorta?
   A The blood is going to the lungs.
   B The blood is oxygen-rich.
   C The blood is dark red in color.
   D The blood is going to the heart.

Use the table below and your knowledge of science to answer Questions 4 and 5.

Blood Types		
Blood Type	**Marker Molecules**	**Clumping Proteins**
A	A	anti-B
B	B	anti-A
AB	A and B	none
O	none	anti-A and anti-B

4. A person who has type O blood can safely receive blood from a person with
   A type O blood.
   B type A blood.
   C type AB blood.
   D type B blood.

5. A person who has type O blood can safely donate blood to a person with
   A type AB blood.
   B type O blood.
   C types A, B, AB, or O blood.
   D type A or type B blood.

Constructed Response

6. Explain what blood pressure is and what causes it. How is blood pressure measured and what is the significance of the two numbers in a blood pressure reading? Why can high blood pressure be dangerous?

Chapter 11

Respiration and Excretion

Standard Course of Study

1.01 Identify and create questions and hypotheses.

1.02 Develop appropriate experimental procedures.

1.03 Apply safety procedures.

1.05 Analyze evidence.

1.06 Use mathematics to gather, organize, and present data.

1.07 Prepare models and/or computer simulations.

1.08 Use oral and written language.

1.09 Use technologies and information systems.

2.02 Use information systems.

4.01 Analyze how human body systems interact.

4.03 Explain how the structure of an organ is adapted to perform specific functions.

4.04 Evaluate how human body systems regulate the internal environment.

4.07 Explain how environmental effects influence human embryo development and health.

4.08 Explain how understanding the human body helps to make informed health decisions.

Playing the pan flute requires ▶ strong, healthy lungs.

Lab zone™ Chapter **Project**

Get the Message Out

Imagine that you're part of a team of writers and designers who create advertisements. You've just been given the job of creating anti-smoking ads for different age groups. As you read this chapter and learn about the respiratory system, you can use your knowledge in your ad campaign.

Your Goal To design three different anti-smoking ads: one telling young children about the dangers of smoking, the second one discouraging teenagers from trying cigarettes, and the third encouraging adult smokers to quit

To complete this project successfully, each ad must

- accurately communicate at least three health risks associated with smoking
- address at least two pressures that influence people to start or continue smoking
- use images and words in convincing ways that gear your message to each audience

Plan It! Brainstorm a list of reasons why people smoke. Consider the possible influences of family and friends as well as that of ads, movies, videos, and television. Also, decide which types of ads you will produce, such as magazine ads or billboards. After your teacher approves your plan, begin to design your ads.

The Respiratory System

Reading Preview

Key Concepts
- What are the functions of the respiratory system?
- What structures does air pass through as it travels to the lungs?
- What happens during gas exchange and breathing?

Key Terms
- respiration • cilia • pharynx
- trachea • bronchi • lungs
- alveoli • diaphragm • larynx
- vocal cords

Target Reading Skill

Sequencing As you read, make a flowchart that shows the path of air in the respiratory system. Write each step of the process in a separate box in the order in which it occurs.

Path of Air

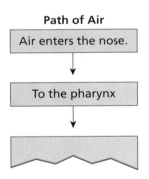

Air enters the nose.

↓

To the pharynx

↓

Lab zone Discover **Activity**

How Big Can You Blow Up a Balloon?

1. Take a normal breath, then blow as much air as possible into a balloon. Twist the end and hold it closed. Have your partner measure around the balloon at its widest point.
2. Let the air out of the balloon. Repeat Step 1 and calculate the average of the two measurements.
3. Compare your results with those of your classmates. The bigger the circumference, the greater the volume of air exhaled.

Think It Over
Inferring What factors might affect the volume of air a person can exhale?

Jerry, the main character in Doris Lessing's story "Through the Tunnel," is on vacation at the seaside. Day after day, he watches some older boys dive into deep water on one side of a huge rock. The boys mysteriously reappear on the other side. Jerry figures out that there must be an underwater tunnel in the rock. He finds the tunnel beneath the water and decides to swim through it. Once inside, though, he is terrified. The walls are slimy, and rocks scrape his body. He can barely see where he is going. But worst of all, Jerry has to hold his breath for far longer than ever before. The author describes Jerry this way: "His head was swelling, his lungs were cracking."

Hold your breath!

Respiratory System Functions

No one can go for very long without breathing. Your body cells need oxygen, and they get that oxygen from the air you breathe. **The respiratory system moves oxygen from the outside environment into the body. It also removes carbon dioxide and water from the body.**

Taking in Oxygen The oxygen your body needs comes from the atmosphere—the mixture of gases that blankets Earth. Your body doesn't use most of the other gases in the air you breathe in. When you exhale, most of the air goes back into the atmosphere.

Oxygen is needed for the energy-releasing chemical reactions that take place inside your cells. Like a fire, which cannot burn without oxygen, your cells cannot "burn" enough fuel to keep you alive without oxygen. The process in which oxygen and glucose undergo a complex series of chemical reactions inside cells is called **respiration.** Respiration, which is also called cellular respiration, is different from breathing. Breathing refers to the movement of air into and out of the lungs. Respiration, on the other hand, refers to the chemical reactions inside cells. As a result of respiration, your cells release the energy that fuels growth and other cell processes.

Removing Carbon Dioxide and Water In addition to the release of energy, respiration produces carbon dioxide and water. Your respiratory system eliminates the carbon dioxide and some of the water through your lungs.

Math · Analyzing Data

The Air You Breathe

The air you breathe in contains several different gases, shown in the circle graph on the left. The air you breathe out contains the same gases, but in the amounts shown in the circle graph on the right.

1. **Reading Graphs** What does each wedge in the graphs represent?

2. **Interpreting Data** Based on the data, which gas is used by the body? Explain.

3. **Drawing Conclusions** Compare the percentage of carbon dioxide in inhaled air with the percentage in exhaled air. How can you account for the difference?

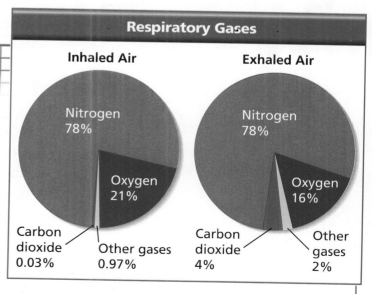

Respiratory Gases

Inhaled Air

Exhaled Air

Nitrogen 78%

Oxygen 21%

Carbon dioxide 0.03%

Other gases 0.97%

Nitrogen 78%

Oxygen 16%

Carbon dioxide 4%

Other gases 2%

4. **Inferring** Explain why the percentage of nitrogen is the same in both inhaled air and exhaled air.

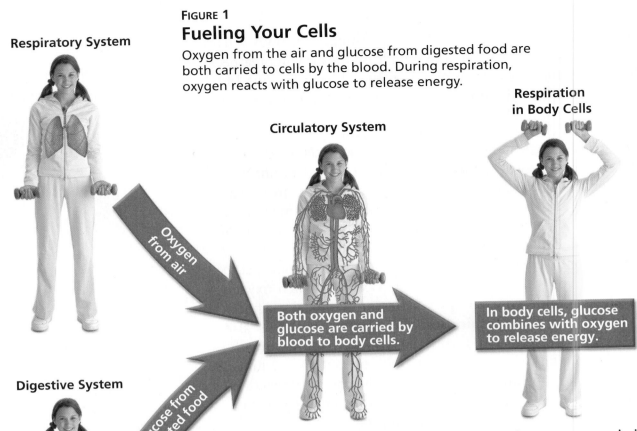

FIGURE 1

Fueling Your Cells

Oxygen from the air and glucose from digested food are both carried to cells by the blood. During respiration, oxygen reacts with glucose to release energy.

Respiratory System

Circulatory System

Respiration in Body Cells

Oxygen from air

Glucose from digested food

Both oxygen and glucose are carried by blood to body cells.

In body cells, glucose combines with oxygen to release energy.

Digestive System

Systems Working Together The respiratory system is just one of the body systems that makes respiration possible. As you can see in Figure 1, respiration could not take place without the digestive and circulatory systems as well. Your respiratory system brings oxygen into your lungs. Meanwhile, your digestive system absorbs glucose from the food you eat. Then, your circulatory system carries both the oxygen and the glucose to your cells, where respiration occurs.

The Path of Air

If you look toward a window on a bright day, you may see tiny particles dancing in the air. These particles include such things as floating grains of dust, plant pollen, and ash from fires. Though you can't see them, air also contains microorganisms. Some of these microorganisms can cause diseases in humans. When you breathe in, all these materials enter your body along with the air.

However, most of these materials never reach your lungs. On its way to the lungs, air passes through a series of structures that filter and trap particles. These organs also warm and moisten the air. **As air travels from the outside environment to the lungs, it passes through the following structures: nose, pharynx, trachea, and bronchi.** It takes air only a few seconds to complete the route from the nose to the lungs.

The Nose Air enters the body through the nose and then moves into spaces called the nasal cavities. Some of the cells lining the nasal cavities produce mucus. This sticky material moistens the air and keeps the lining from drying out. Mucus also traps particles such as dust.

The cells that line the nasal cavities have **cilia** (SIL ee uh), tiny hairlike extensions that can move together in a sweeping motion. The cilia sweep the mucus into the throat, where you swallow it. Stomach acid destroys the mucus, along with everything trapped in it.

Some particles and bacteria can irritate the lining of your nose or throat, causing you to sneeze. The powerful force of a sneeze shoots the particles out of your nose and into the air.

The Pharynx Next, air enters the **pharynx** (FAR ingks), or throat. The pharynx is the only part of the respiratory system that is shared with another system—the digestive system. Both the nose and the mouth connect to the pharynx.

Reading Checkpoint What is the role of cilia?

FIGURE 2
The Respiratory System
On its path from outside the body into the lungs, air passes through several structures that clean, warm, and moisten it. Once in the lungs, the oxygen in the air can enter your bloodstream.
Classifying *Which part of the respiratory system is also part of the digestive system?*

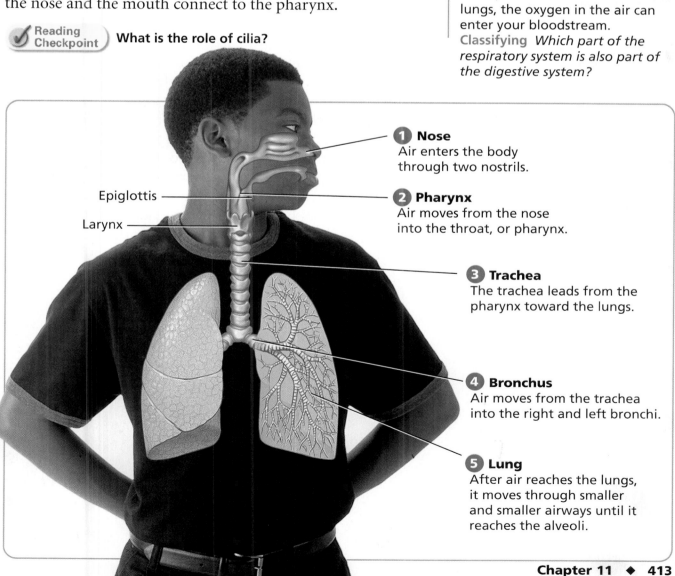

Epiglottis

Larynx

1 Nose
Air enters the body through two nostrils.

2 Pharynx
Air moves from the nose into the throat, or pharynx.

3 Trachea
The trachea leads from the pharynx toward the lungs.

4 Bronchus
Air moves from the trachea into the right and left bronchi.

5 Lung
After air reaches the lungs, it moves through smaller and smaller airways until it reaches the alveoli.

What Do You Exhale?
Learn whether carbon dioxide is present in exhaled air.

1. Label two test tubes *A* and *B*.
2. Fill each test tube with 10 mL of water and a few drops of bromthymol blue solution. Bromthymol blue solution turns green or yellow in the presence of carbon dioxide.
3. Using a straw, gently blow air into the liquid in test tube A for a few seconds. **CAUTION:** *Do not suck the solution back through the straw.*
4. Compare the solutions in the test tubes.

Predicting Suppose you had exercised immediately before you blew into the straw. Predict how this would have affected the results.

The Trachea From the pharynx, air moves into the **trachea** (TRAY kee uh), or windpipe. You can feel your trachea if you gently run your fingers down the center of your neck. The trachea feels like a tube with a series of ridges. The firm ridges are rings of cartilage that strengthen the trachea and keep it open.

The trachea, like the nose, is lined with cilia and mucus. The cilia in the trachea sweep upward, moving mucus toward the pharynx, where it is swallowed. The trachea's cilia and mucus continue the cleaning and moistening of air that began in the nose. If particles irritate the lining of the trachea, you cough. A cough, like a sneeze, sends the particles into the air.

Normally, only air—not food—enters the trachea. If food does enter the trachea, the food can block the opening and prevent air from getting to the lungs. When that happens, a person chokes. Fortunately, food rarely gets into the trachea. The epiglottis, a small flap of tissue that folds over the trachea, seals off the trachea while you swallow.

The Bronchi and Lungs Air moves from the trachea to the **bronchi** (BRAHNG ky) (singular *bronchus*), the passages that direct air into the lungs. The **lungs** are the main organs of the respiratory system. The left bronchus leads into the left lung, and the right bronchus leads into the right lung. Inside the lungs, each bronchus divides into smaller and smaller tubes in a pattern that resembles the branches of a tree.

At the end of the smallest tubes are structures that look like bunches of grapes. The "grapes" are **alveoli** (al VEE uh ly) (singular *alveolus*), tiny sacs of lung tissue specialized for the movement of gases between air and blood. Notice in Figure 3 that each alveolus is surrounded by a network of capillaries. It is here that the blood picks up its cargo of oxygen from the air.

✓ Reading Checkpoint **How is food prevented from entering the trachea?**

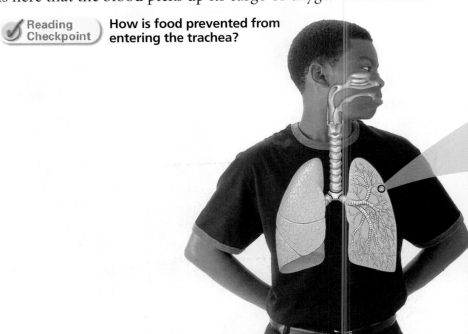

Gas Exchange

Because the walls of both the alveoli and the capillaries are very thin, certain materials can pass through them easily. **After air enters an alveolus, oxygen passes through the wall of the alveolus and then through the capillary wall into the blood. Carbon dioxide and water pass from the blood into the alveoli. This whole process is known as gas exchange.**

How Gas Exchange Occurs Imagine that you are a drop of blood beginning your journey through a capillary that wraps around an alveolus. When you begin that journey, you are carrying a lot of carbon dioxide and little oxygen. As you move through the capillary, oxygen gradually attaches to the hemoglobin in your red blood cells. At the same time, you are getting rid of carbon dioxide. At the end of your journey around the alveolus, you are rich in oxygen and poor in carbon dioxide.

Discovery CHANNEL SCHOOL

Respiration and Excretion

Video Preview
▶ Video Field Trip
Video Assessment

FIGURE 3
Gas Exchange in the Alveoli

Alveoli are hollow air sacs surrounded by capillaries. As blood flows through the capillaries, oxygen moves from the alveoli into the blood. At the same time, carbon dioxide moves from the blood into the alveoli.
Interpreting Diagrams *How is the structure of the alveoli important for gas exchange?*

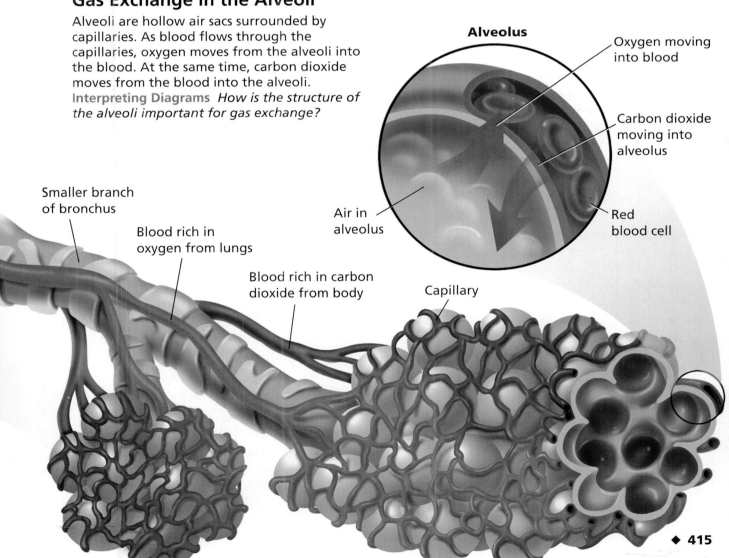

Alveolus

Oxygen moving into blood

Carbon dioxide moving into alveolus

Air in alveolus

Red blood cell

Smaller branch of bronchus

Blood rich in oxygen from lungs

Blood rich in carbon dioxide from body

Capillary

◆ 415

FIGURE 4
Oxygen for Activities
The huge surface area of the alveoli supplies the oxygen these trombone players need to march and play.

Surface Area

Surface area refers to the total area of all of the surfaces of a three-dimensional object. Consider a cube, which has six equal sides. Each side measures 2 cm by 2 cm.

1. To find the surface area of the cube, first calculate the area of one of the six sides:
   Area = length × width
         = 2 cm × 2 cm = 4 cm²
   Each side has an area of 4 cm².

2. Next, add the areas of the six sides together to find the total surface area:
   4 cm² + 4 cm² + 4 cm² + 4 cm² + 4 cm² + 4 cm² = 24 cm²
   The surface area of the cube is 24 cm².

Practice Problem Calculate the surface area of a cube whose side measures 3 cm.

Surface Area for Gas Exchange Your lungs can absorb a large amount of oxygen because of the large surface area of the alveoli. An adult's lungs contain about 300 million alveoli. If you opened the alveoli and spread them out on a flat surface, you would have a surface area of about 70 square meters.

The huge surface area of the alveoli enables the lungs to absorb a large amount of oxygen. The lungs can, therefore, supply the oxygen that people need—even when they are performing strenuous activities. When you play a wind instrument or a fast-paced game of basketball, you have your alveoli to thank.

Your lungs are not the only organs that provide a large surface area in a relatively small space. Recall from Chapter 9 that the small intestine contains numerous, tiny villi that increase the surface available to absorb food molecules.

 **What gases are exchanged across the alveoli?**

How You Breathe

In an average day, you may breathe more than 20,000 times. The rate at which you breathe depends on your body's need for oxygen. The more oxygen you need, the faster you breathe.

Muscles for Breathing Breathing, like other body movements, is controlled by muscles. Figure 5 shows the structure of the chest, including the muscles that enable you to breathe. Notice that the lungs are surrounded by the ribs, which have muscles attached to them. At the base of the lungs is the **diaphragm** (DY uh fram), a large, dome-shaped muscle that plays an important role in breathing.

The Process of Breathing When you breathe, the actions of your rib muscles and diaphragm expand or contract your chest. As a result, air flows in or out.

Here's what happens when you inhale, or breathe in. The rib muscles contract, lifting the chest wall upward and outward. At the same time, the diaphragm contracts and moves downward. The combined action of these muscles makes the chest cavity larger. The same amount of air now occupies a larger space, causing the pressure of the air inside your lungs to decrease. This change means that the pressure of air inside the chest cavity is lower than the pressure of the atmosphere pushing on the body. Because of this difference in air pressure, air rushes into your chest, in the same way that air is sucked into a vacuum cleaner.

When you exhale, or breathe out, the rib muscles and diaphragm relax. This reduces the size of the chest cavity. This decrease in size squeezes air out of the lungs, the way squeezing a container of ketchup pushes ketchup out of the opening.

 **Reading Checkpoint** What muscles cause the chest to expand during breathing?

FIGURE 5
The Breathing Process
When you inhale, the diaphragm moves downward and pressure in the lungs decreases, causing air to flow in. When you exhale, the diaphragm moves upward and the pressure in the lungs increases, pushing the air out.
Interpreting Diagrams *How does the movement of the diaphragm affect the size of the chest cavity?*

For: The Breathing Process activity
Visit: PHSchool.com
Web Code: cep-4041

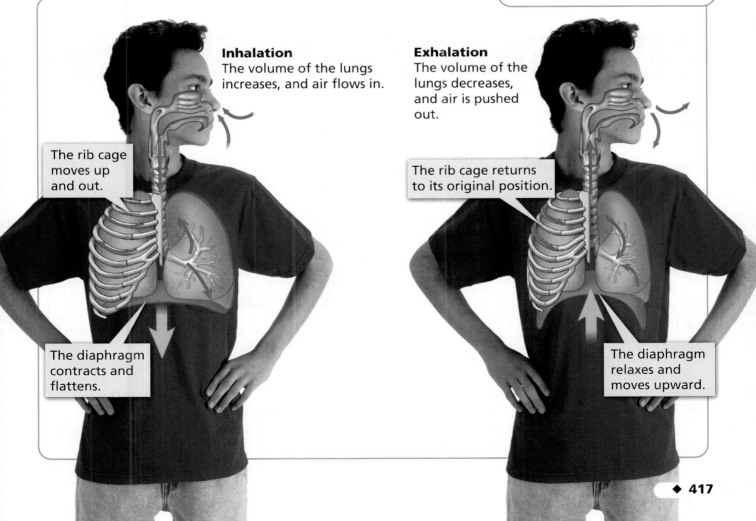

Inhalation
The volume of the lungs increases, and air flows in.

Exhalation
The volume of the lungs decreases, and air is pushed out.

The rib cage moves up and out.

The rib cage returns to its original position.

The diaphragm contracts and flattens.

The diaphragm relaxes and moves upward.

◆ 417

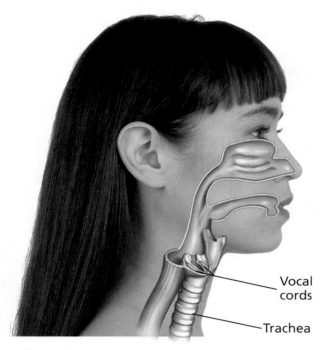

FIGURE 6
The Vocal Cords
Air moving over the vocal cords causes them to vibrate and produce sound.
Interpreting Diagrams *Where are the vocal cords located?*

Vocal cords

Trachea

Relating Breathing and Speaking The air that moves out of your lungs as you breathe also helps you speak. The **larynx** (LAR ingks), or voice box, is located in the top part of the trachea, underneath the epiglottis. Place your fingers on your Adam's apple, which sticks out from the front of your neck. You can feel some of the cartilage that makes up the larynx. Two **vocal cords,** folds of connective tissue that produce your voice, stretch across the opening of the larynx.

If you've ever let air out of a balloon while stretching its neck, you've heard the squeaking sound that the air makes. The neck of the balloon is something like your vocal cords. If you look at Figure 6 you can see that the vocal cords have a slitlike opening between them. When you speak, muscles make the vocal cords contract, narrowing the opening. Air from the lungs rushes through this opening. The movement of the vocal cords makes the air molecules vibrate, or move rapidly back and forth. This vibration creates a sound— your voice.

Section 1 Assessment

Target Reading Skill Sequencing With a partner, review your flowchart about the path of air. Add any necessary information.

Reviewing Key Concepts

1. a. Listing What are the functions of the respiratory system?
   b. Comparing and Contrasting Explain the difference between respiration and breathing.
   c. Predicting How might respiration in your body cells be affected if your respiratory system did not work properly?

2. a. Identifying Name the structures of the respiratory system.
   b. Sequencing Describe the path that a molecule of oxygen takes as it moves from the air outside your body into the alveoli.
   c. Relating Cause and Effect In a healthy person, how do coughing and sneezing protect the respiratory system?

3. a. Reviewing What three substances are exchanged in the alveoli?
   b. Explaining What happens to the carbon dioxide in the blood when it flows through the capillaries in the alveoli?
   c. Applying Concepts How would gas exchange be affected at the top of a tall mountain, where air pressure is lower and there is less oxygen than at lower elevations? Explain.

Math Practice

4. **Surface Area** A cube measures 4 cm × 4 cm on a side. Find its surface area.
5. **Surface Area** Suppose you cut up the cube into eight smaller cubes, each 2 cm × 2 cm on a side. If the larger cube represents a lung, and the smaller cubes represent alveoli, which would provide a larger surface area for oxygen exchange?

A Breath of Fresh Air

Problem

What causes your body to inhale and exhale air?

Skills Focus

making models, observing, drawing conclusions

Materials

- small balloon
- large balloon
- scissors
- transparent plastic bottle with narrow neck

Procedure

1. In your notebook, explain how you think air gets into the lungs during the breathing process.

2. Cut off and discard the bottom of a small plastic bottle. Trim the cut edge so there are no rough spots.

3. Stretch a small balloon; then blow it up a few times to stretch it further. Insert the round end of the balloon through the mouth of the bottle. Then, with a partner holding the bottle, stretch the neck of the balloon and pull it over the mouth of the bottle.

4. Stretch a large balloon; then blow it up a few times to stretch it further. Cut off and discard the balloon's neck.

5. Have a partner hold the bottle while you stretch the remaining part of the balloon over the bottom opening of the bottle, as shown in the photo.

6. Use one hand to hold the bottle firmly. With the knuckles of your other hand, push upward on the large balloon, causing it to form a dome. Remove your knuckles from the balloon, letting the balloon flatten. Repeat this procedure a few times. Observe what happens to the small balloon. Record your observations in your notebook.

Analyze and Conclude

1. **Making Models** Make a diagram of the completed model in your notebook. Add labels to show which parts of your model represent the chest cavity, diaphragm, lungs, and trachea.

2. **Observing** In this model, what is the position of the "diaphragm" just after you have made the model "exhale"? What do the lungs look like just after you have exhaled?

3. **Drawing Conclusions** In this model, how does the "diaphragm" move? How do these movements of the "diaphragm" affect the "lungs"?

4. **Communicating** Write a paragraph describing how this model shows that pressure changes are responsible for breathing.

More to Explore

How could you improve on this model to show more closely what happens in the chest cavity during the process of breathing? *Obtain your teacher's permission before carrying out your investigation.*

Smoking and Your Health

Reading Preview

Key Concepts
- What harmful chemicals are found in tobacco smoke?
- How can tobacco smoke affect a person's health over time?

Key Terms
- tar • carbon monoxide
- nicotine • addiction
- bronchitis • emphysema

Target Reading Skill
Relating Cause and Effect As you read, identify the effects of smoking on the body. Write the information in a graphic organizer like the one below.

Effects

Cause		Effects
Smoking	→	Increase in breathing and heart rate due to carbon monoxide in smoke
	→	
	→	

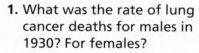
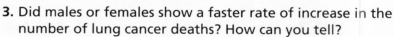

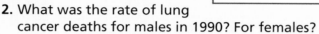

Lab zone Discover Activity

What Are the Dangers of Smoking?

The graph shows the rate of lung cancer deaths in the United States from 1930 to 2000.

1. What was the rate of lung cancer deaths for males in 1930? For females?
2. What was the rate of lung cancer deaths for males in 1990? For females?
3. Did males or females show a faster rate of increase in the number of lung cancer deaths? How can you tell?
4. Cigarette smoking increased until 1965 but then decreased between 1965 and 1990. How does the trend in smoking compare with the rate of lung cancer deaths?

Think It Over

Predicting Do you think that the rate of lung cancer deaths is likely to increase, decrease, or remain the same by 2010? Explain.

Whoosh! Millions of tiny but dangerous aliens are invading the respiratory system. The aliens are pulled into the mouth with an inhaled breath. The cilia trap some aliens, and others get stuck in mucus. But thousands of the invaders get past these defenses and enter the lungs. The aliens then land on the surface of the alveoli!

The "aliens" are not tiny creatures from space. They are the substances found in cigarette smoke. In this section you will learn how tobacco smoke damages the respiratory system.

A heavy smoker may smoke two packs of cigarettes in a day.

Chemicals in Tobacco Smoke

With each puff, a smoker inhales more than 4,000 different chemicals. **Some of the most deadly chemicals in tobacco smoke are tar, carbon monoxide, and nicotine.**

Tar The dark, sticky substance that forms when tobacco burns is called **tar.** When someone inhales tobacco smoke, some tar settles on cilia that line the trachea, bronchi, and smaller airways. Tar makes cilia clump together so they can't function to prevent harmful materials from getting into the lungs. Tar also contains chemicals that have been shown to cause cancer.

Carbon Monoxide When substances—including tobacco—are burned, a colorless, odorless gas called **carbon monoxide** is produced. Carbon monoxide is dangerous because its molecules bind to hemoglobin in red blood cells. When carbon monoxide binds to hemoglobin, it takes the place of some of the oxygen that the red blood cells normally carry. The carbon monoxide molecules are something like cars that are parked in spaces reserved for other cars.

When carbon monoxide binds to hemoglobin, red blood cells carry less than their normal load of oxygen throughout the body. To make up for the decrease in oxygen, the breathing rate increases and the heart beats faster. Smokers' blood may contain too little oxygen to meet their bodies' needs.

Nicotine Another dangerous chemical found in tobacco is **nicotine.** Nicotine is a stimulant drug that increases the activities of the nervous system and heart. It makes the heart beat faster and increases blood pressure. Over time, nicotine produces an **addiction,** or physical dependence. Smokers feel an intense craving for a cigarette if they go without one. Addiction to nicotine is one reason why smokers have difficulty quitting.

 **Reading Checkpoint** How does the tar in cigarettes affect the body?

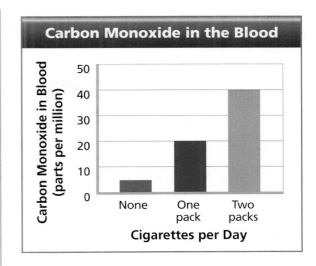

FIGURE 7
Carbon Monoxide in the Blood
The more cigarettes a person smokes, the more carbon monoxide he or she inhales. **Relating Cause and Effect** *How does carbon monoxide deprive the body of oxygen?*

SURGEON GENERAL'S WARNING: Cigarette Smoke Contains Carbon Monoxide.

SURGEON GENERAL'S WARNING: Smoking Causes Lung Cancer, Heart Disease, Emphysema, and May Complicate Pregnancy.

SURGEON GENERAL'S WARNING: Smoking By Pregnant Women May Result in Fetal Injury, Premature Birth, and Low Birth Weight.

FIGURE 8
Staying Healthy by Not Smoking
People stay healthy by exercising and by choosing not to smoke.

Lung of a nonsmoker

Health Problems and Smoking

Tobacco smoke causes health problems in several ways. For example, because the cilia can't sweep away mucus, many smokers have a frequent cough. The mucus buildup also limits the space for airflow, thus decreasing oxygen intake. Because they are not getting enough oxygen, long-term or heavy smokers may be short of breath during even light exercise.

You probably know that smoking damages the respiratory system, but did you know that it strains the circulatory system as well? The respiratory and circulatory systems work together to get oxygen to body cells. If either system is damaged, the other one must work harder. Serious health problems can result from long-term smoking. **Over time, smokers can develop chronic bronchitis, emphysema, lung cancer, and atherosclerosis.** Every year in the United States, more than 400,000 people die from smoking-related illnesses. That's one out of every five deaths. Tobacco smoke is the most important preventable cause of major illness and death.

Chronic Bronchitis Bronchitis (brahng KY tis) is an irritation of the breathing passages in which the small passages become narrower than normal and may be clogged with mucus. People with bronchitis have difficulty breathing. If the irritation continues over a long time, it is called chronic bronchitis. Chronic bronchitis can cause permanent damage to the breathing passages. It is often accompanied by infection with disease-causing microorganisms. Chronic bronchitis is five to ten times more common in heavy smokers than in nonsmokers.

Lab zone Skills **Activity**

Calculating

Heavy smokers may smoke two packs of cigarettes every day. Find out what one pack of cigarettes costs. Then, use that price to calculate how much a person would spend on cigarettes if he or she smoked two packs a day for 30 years.

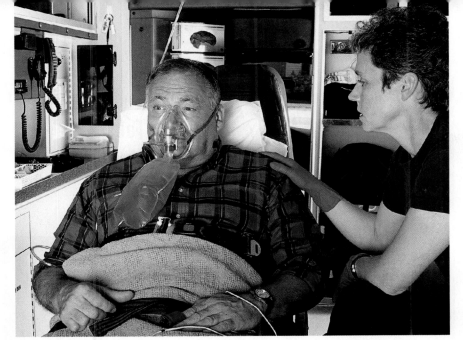

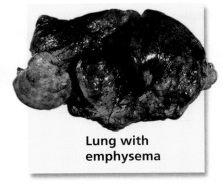

Lung with emphysema

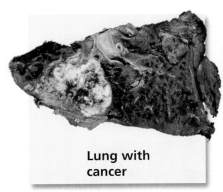

Lung with cancer

FIGURE 9
Effects of Smoking on the Lungs
Over time, smoking damages the lungs and leads to serious health problems. **Comparing and Contrasting** *Compare the lungs of a person with emphysema and a person with lung cancer to the lung of a nonsmoker shown in Figure 8.*

Emphysema The chemicals in tobacco smoke damage lung tissue as well as breathing passages. **Emphysema** (em fuh SEE muh) is a serious disease that destroys lung tissue and causes breathing difficulties. People with emphysema do not get enough oxygen and cannot adequately eliminate carbon dioxide. Therefore, they are always short of breath. Some people with emphysema even have trouble blowing out a match. Unfortunately, the damage caused by emphysema is permanent, even if a person stops smoking.

Lung Cancer About 140,000 Americans die each year from lung cancer caused by smoking. Cigarette smoke contains more than 50 different chemicals that cause cancer, including the chemicals in tar. Cancerous growths, or tumors, take away space in the lungs that are used for gas exchange. Unfortunately, lung cancer is rarely detected early, when treatment would be most effective.

Atherosclerosis The chemicals in tobacco smoke also harm the circulatory system. Some of the chemicals get into the blood and are absorbed by the blood vessels. The chemicals then irritate the walls of the blood vessels. This irritation contributes to the buildup of fatty material on the blood vessel walls that causes atherosclerosis. Atherosclerosis can lead to heart attacks. Compared to nonsmokers, smokers are more than twice as likely to have heart attacks.

 **Reading Checkpoint** **How does emphysema affect a person's lungs?**

FIGURE 10
Passive Smoking
Billboards like this one increase people's awareness that nonsmokers can also suffer from the effects of tobacco smoke.

Go Online

SciLINKS NSTA

For: Links on respiratory disorders
Visit: www.SciLinks.org
Web Code: scn-0442

Passive Smoking Smokers are not the only people to suffer from the effects of tobacco smoke. In passive smoking, people involuntarily inhale the smoke from other people's cigarettes, cigars, or pipes. This smoke contains the same harmful chemicals that smokers inhale. Each year, passive smoking is associated with the development of bronchitis and other respiratory problems, such as asthma, in about 300,000 young children in the United States.

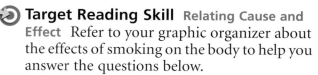

Section 2 Assessment

Target Reading Skill Relating Cause and Effect Refer to your graphic organizer about the effects of smoking on the body to help you answer the questions below.

Reviewing Key Concepts

1. a. **Listing** What are three harmful substances in tobacco smoke?
   b. **Relating Cause and Effect** How does each of the harmful substances directly affect the body?
   c. **Developing Hypotheses** Why might nicotine-containing products, such as chewing gums or skin patches, help a person who is trying to quit smoking?

2. a. **Reviewing** Identify four health problems that can develop in smokers over time.
   b. **Describing** How does smoking contribute to atherosclerosis?
   c. **Inferring** What effect would it have on the circulatory system if a person quit smoking?

Lab zone **At-Home Activity**

Warning Labels With a family member, make a list of the warning statements found on cigarette labels. What chemicals found in tobacco smoke and health problems do the labels identify? Summarize the information you find to share with the class.

Section 3

The Excretory System

Reading Preview

Key Concepts
- What are the structures and functions of the excretory system?
- How do the kidneys filter wastes from the blood?
- How does excretion contribute to homeostasis?

Key Terms
- excretion • urea • kidney
- urine • ureter
- urinary bladder • urethra
- nephron

Target Reading Skill

Previewing Visuals Before you read, preview Figure 11. Then, write two questions that you have about the diagram in a graphic organizer like the one below. As you read, answer your questions.

How the Kidneys Filter Wastes

Q.	Where are nephrons located?
A.	
Q.	

Lab zone Discover Activity

How Does Filtering a Liquid Change the Liquid?

1. Your teacher will give you 50 mL of a liquid in a small container. Pour a small amount of sand into the liquid.
2. Use a glucose test strip to determine whether glucose is present in the liquid.
3. Put filter paper in a funnel. Then, put the funnel into the mouth of a second container. Slowly pour the liquid through the funnel into the second container.
4. Look for any solid material on the filter paper. Remove the funnel, and carefully examine the liquid that passed through the filter.
5. Test the liquid again to see whether it contains glucose.

Think It Over

Observing Which substances passed through the filter, and which did not? How might a filtering device be useful in the body?

The human body faces a challenge that is a bit like trying to keep your room clean. Magazines, notebook paper, and CD wrappers tend to pile up in your room. You use all of these things, but sooner or later you must clean your room if you don't want to be buried in trash. Something similar happens in your body. As your cells use nutrients in respiration and other processes, wastes are created. Different organs in the body have roles for the removal of these wastes. The removal process is known as **excretion.**

If wastes were not removed from your body, they would pile up and make you sick. Excretion helps keep the body's internal environment stable and free of harmful materials. **The excretory system is the system in the body that collects wastes produced by cells and removes the wastes from the body.**

The Excretory System

Two wastes that your body must eliminate are excess water and urea. **Urea** (yoo REE uh) is a chemical that comes from the breakdown of proteins. **The structures of the excretory system that eliminate urea, water, and other wastes include the kidneys, ureters, urinary bladder, and urethra.**

Your two **kidneys,** which are the major organs of the excretory system, remove urea and other wastes from the blood. The kidneys act like filters. They remove wastes but keep materials that the body needs. The wastes are eliminated in **urine**, a watery fluid that contains urea and other wastes. Urine flows from the kidneys through two narrow tubes called **ureters** (yoo REE turz). The ureters carry urine to the **urinary bladder,** a sacklike muscular organ that stores urine. Urine leaves the body through a small tube called the **urethra** (yoo REE thruh).

 **Reading Checkpoint** **What is the role of the ureters?**

Filtration of Wastes

The kidneys are champion filters. Each of your kidneys contains about a million **nephrons,** tiny filtering factories that remove wastes from blood and produce urine. **The nephrons filter wastes in stages. First, both wastes and needed materials, such as glucose, are filtered out of the blood. Then, much of the needed material is returned to the blood, and the wastes are eliminated from the body.** Follow this process in Figure 11.

Filtering Out Wastes During the first stage of waste removal, blood enters the kidneys. Here, the blood flows through smaller and smaller arteries. Eventually it reaches a cluster of capillaries in a nephron. The capillaries are surrounded by a thin-walled, hollow capsule that is connected to a tube. In the capillary cluster, urea, glucose, and some water move out of the blood and into the capsule. Blood cells and most protein molecules do not move into the capsule. Instead, they remain in the capillaries.

Formation of Urine Urine forms from the filtered material in the capsule. This material flows through the long, twisting tube. As the liquid moves through the tube, many of the substances are returned to the blood. Normally, all the glucose, most of the water, and small amounts of other materials pass back into the blood in the capillaries that surround the tube. In contrast, urea and other wastes remain in the tube.

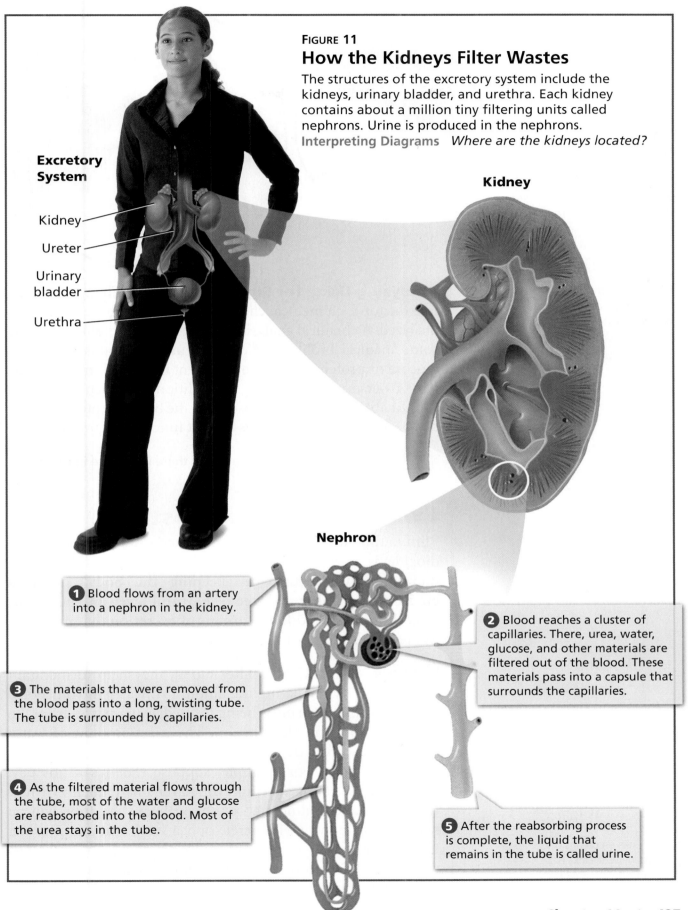

FIGURE 11
How the Kidneys Filter Wastes

The structures of the excretory system include the kidneys, urinary bladder, and urethra. Each kidney contains about a million tiny filtering units called nephrons. Urine is produced in the nephrons.
Interpreting Diagrams *Where are the kidneys located?*

Excretory System

Kidney

Ureter

Urinary bladder

Urethra

Kidney

Nephron

❶ Blood flows from an artery into a nephron in the kidney.

❷ Blood reaches a cluster of capillaries. There, urea, water, glucose, and other materials are filtered out of the blood. These materials pass into a capsule that surrounds the capillaries.

❸ The materials that were removed from the blood pass into a long, twisting tube. The tube is surrounded by capillaries.

❹ As the filtered material flows through the tube, most of the water and glucose are reabsorbed into the blood. Most of the urea stays in the tube.

❺ After the reabsorbing process is complete, the liquid that remains in the tube is called urine.

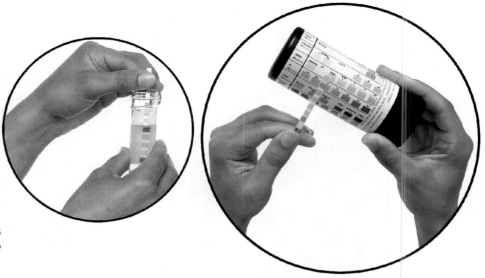

FIGURE 12
Analyzing Urine
Lab technicians can analyze urine by using a dipstick that changes color in the presence of glucose and other substances. The technician dips the dipstick into a urine sample and compares the results to a color chart.
Applying Concepts What are two substances for which urine can be tested?

Analyzing Urine for Signs of Disease When people go to a doctor for a medical checkup, they usually have their urine analyzed. A chemical analysis of urine can be useful in detecting some medical problems. Normally, urine contains almost no glucose or protein. If glucose is present in urine, it may indicate that a person has diabetes, a condition in which body cells cannot absorb enough glucose from the blood. Protein in urine can be a sign that the kidneys are not functioning properly.

 **Reading Checkpoint** What could it mean if there is glucose in the urine?

Excretion and Homeostasis

Eliminating wastes, such as urea, excess water, and carbon dioxide, is important for maintaining homeostasis. **Excretion maintains homeostasis by keeping the body's internal environment stable and free of harmful levels of chemicals. In addition to the kidneys, organs of excretion that maintain homeostasis include the lungs, skin, and liver.**

Kidneys As the kidneys filter blood, they help to maintain homeostasis by regulating the amount of water in your body. Remember that as urine is being formed, water passes from the tube back into the bloodstream. The exact amount of water that is reabsorbed depends on conditions both outside and within the body. For example, suppose that it's a hot day. You've been sweating a lot, and you haven't had much to drink. In that situation, almost all of the water in the tube will be reabsorbed, and you will excrete only a small amount of urine. If, however, the day is cool and you've drunk a lot of water, less water will be reabsorbed. Your body will produce a larger volume of urine.

Go Online
SciLINKS NSTA

For: Links on organs of excretion
Visit: www.SciLinks.org
Web Code: scn-0443

Lungs and Skin Most of the wastes produced by the body are removed through the kidneys. However, the lungs and skin remove some wastes from the body as well. When you exhale, carbon dioxide and some water are removed from the body by the lungs. Sweat glands in the skin also serve an excretory function because water and urea are excreted in perspiration.

Liver Have you ever torn apart a large pizza box so that it could fit into a wastebasket? If so, then you understand that some wastes need to be broken down before they can be excreted. The liver performs this function. For example, urea, which comes from the breakdown of proteins, is produced by the liver. The liver also converts part of the hemoglobin molecule from old red blood cells into substances such as bile. Because the liver produces a usable material from old red blood cells, you can think of the liver as a recycling facility.

FIGURE 13
Excretion Through the Lungs
Your lungs function as excretory organs. When you exhale on a cold morning, you can see the water in your breath.

 **Reading Checkpoint** What substances are excreted in perspiration?

Section 3 Assessment

Target Reading Skill Previewing Visuals Compare your questions and answers about Figure 11 with those of a partner.

Reviewing Key Concepts

1. a. Reviewing What is the role of the excretory system in the body?
   b. Sequencing Name the structures of the excretory system in order of their roles in producing and eliminating urine. Describe the function of each structure.
2. a. Reviewing What are the two main stages of waste removal by the kidneys?
   b. Describing What happens as wastes are filtered in a nephron?
   c. Relating Cause and Effect Why is protein in the urine a sign that something could be wrong with the kidneys?

3. a. Identifying What is the role of excretion in maintaining homeostasis?
   b. Explaining How do the kidneys help maintain homeostasis?
   c. Predicting On a long bus trip, a traveler does not drink any water for several hours. How will the volume of urine she produces that day compare to the volume on a day when she drinks several glasses of water? Explain.

Writing in Science

Explanation Write a paragraph explaining how wastes are filtered in the kidneys. To help you with your writing, first make two lists—one that includes materials removed from the blood in the kidneys and one that includes materials returned to the blood.

Clues About Health

Problem

How can you test urine for the presence of glucose and protein?

Skills Focus

observing, interpreting data, drawing conclusions

Materials

- 6 test tubes
- test-tube rack
- 6 plastic droppers
- water
- glucose solution
- protein solution
- marking pencil
- white paper towels
- 6 glucose test strips
- Biuret solution
- 3 simulated urine samples

Procedure 🔬👕🥽🧤🧪🖐

PART 1 Testing for Glucose

1. Label six test tubes as follows: *W* for water, *G* for glucose, *P* for protein, and *A, B,* and *C* for three patients' "urine samples." Place the test tubes in a test-tube rack.

2. Label six glucose test strips with the same letters: *W, G, P, A, B,* and *C.*

3. Copy the data table into your notebook.

4. Fill each test tube about $\frac{3}{4}$ full with the solution that corresponds to its label.

5. Place glucose test strip W on a clean, dry section of a paper towel. Then, use a clean plastic dropper to place 2 drops of the water from test tube W on the test strip. Record the resulting color of the test strip in your data table. If no color change occurs, write "no reaction."

6. Use the procedure in Step 5 to test each of the other five solutions with the correctly labeled glucose test strip. Record the color of each test strip in the data table.

PART 2 Testing for Protein

7. Obtain a dropper bottle containing Biuret solution. Record the original color of the solution in your notebook.

8. Carefully add 30 drops of Biuret solution to test tube W. **CAUTION:** *Biuret solution can harm skin and damage clothing. Handle it with care.* Gently swirl the test tube to mix the two solutions together. Hold the test tube against a white paper towel to help you detect any color change. Observe the color of the final mixture, and record that color in your data table.

9. Repeat Step 8 for each of the other test tubes.

Data Table						
	Test Tube					
Test for	W (water)	G (glucose)	P (protein)	A (Patient A)	B (Patient B)	C (Patient C)
Glucose						
Protein						

Analyze and Conclude

1. **Observing** What color reaction occurred when you used the glucose test strip on sample W? On sample G?

2. **Interpreting Data** What do the changes in color you observed in Part 1 indicate? Explain.

3. **Observing** What happened when you added Biuret solution to test tube W? To test tube P?

4. **Interpreting Data** What do the changes in color of the Biuret solution you observed in Part II indicate? Explain.

5. **Drawing Conclusions** Which of the three patients' urine samples tested normal? How do you know?

6. **Drawing Conclusions** Which urine sample(s) indicated that diabetes might be present? How do you know?

7. **Drawing Conclusions** Which urine sample(s) indicated that kidney disease might be present? How do you know?

8. **Communicating** Do you think a doctor should draw conclusions about the presence of a disease based on a single urine sample? Write a paragraph in which you discuss this question based on what you know about gathering data in experiments.

More to Explore

Propose a way to determine whether a patient with glucose in the urine could reduce the level through changes in diet.

① The Respiratory System

Key Concepts

- The respiratory system moves oxygen from the outside environment into the body. It also removes carbon dioxide and water from the body.

- As air travels from the outside environment to the lungs, it passes through the following structures: nose, pharynx, trachea, and bronchi.

- After air enters an alveolus, oxygen passes through the wall of the alveolus and then through the capillary wall into the blood. Carbon dioxide and water pass from the blood into the alveoli. This whole process is known as gas exchange.

- When you breathe, the actions of your rib muscles and diaphragm expand or contract your chest, causing air to flow in or out.

Key Terms

respiration	lungs
cilia	alveoli
pharynx	diaphragm
trachea	larynx
bronchi	vocal cords

② Smoking and Your Health

Key Concepts

- Some of the most deadly chemicals in tobacco smoke are tar, carbon monoxide, and nicotine.

- Over time, smokers can develop chronic bronchitis, emphysema, lung cancer, and atherosclerosis.

Key Terms

tar	addiction
carbon monoxide	bronchitis
nicotine	emphysema

③ The Excretory System

Key Concepts

- The excretory system is the system in the body that collects wastes produced by cells and removes the wastes from the body.

- The structures of the excretory system that eliminate urea, water, and other wastes include the kidneys, ureters, the urinary bladder, and the urethra.

- The nephrons filter wastes in stages. First, both wastes and needed materials, such as glucose, are filtered from the blood into a nephron. Then, much of the needed material is returned to the blood, and the wastes are eliminated from the body.

- Excretion maintains homeostasis by keeping the body's internal environment stable and free of harmful levels of chemicals. In addition to the kidneys, organs of excretion that maintain homeostasis include the lungs, skin, and liver.

Key Terms

excretion	ureter
urea	urinary bladder
kidney	urethra
urine	nephron

SURGEON GENERAL'S WARNING: Cigarette Smoke Contains Carbon Monoxide.

SURGEON GENERAL'S WARNING: Smoking Causes Lung Cancer, Heart Disease, Emphysema, and May Complicate Pregnancy.

SURGEON GENERAL'S WARNING: Smoking By Pregnant Women May Result in Fetal Injury, Premature Birth, and Low Birth Weight.

Review and Assessment

Go Online
PHSchool.com

For: Self-Assessment
Visit: PHSchool.com
Web Code: cea-4040

Organizing Information

Sequencing Copy the flowchart about excretion onto a separate sheet of paper. Then, fill in the empty spaces and add a title. (For more on Sequencing, see the Skills Handbook.)

Blood flows into the nephron's capillary cluster.

↓

a. _____ ?

↓

b. _____ ?

↓

c. _____ ?

↓

d. _____ ?

Reviewing Key Terms

Choose the letter of the best answer.

1. The process in which glucose and oxygen react in cells to release energy is called
   a. excretion.
   b. respiration.
   c. bronchitis.
   d. emphysema.

2. The trachea divides into two tubes called
   a. bronchi.
   b. alveoli.
   c. ureters.
   d. vocal cords.

3. Your voice is produced by the
   a. pharynx.   b. larynx.
   c. trachea.   d. alveoli.

4. A colorless, odorless gas produced by burning tobacco is
   a. carbon monoxide.
   b. tar.
   c. nicotine.
   d. urea.

5. The filtration of wastes takes place inside the kidneys in the
   a. ureters.
   b. urethra.
   c. urinary bladder.
   d. nephrons.

If the statement is true, write *true*. If it is false, change the underlined word or words to make the statement true.

6. Dust particles trapped in mucus are swept away by tiny, hairlike <u>alveoli</u>.

7. Clusters of air sacs in the lungs are <u>bronchi</u>.

8. <u>Tar</u> is a chemical in tobacco smoke that makes the heart beat faster.

9. Urine leaves the body through the <u>ureter</u>.

10. Urine is stored in the <u>urethra</u>.

Writing in Science

Informational Brochure Pretend you are a doctor advising high-altitude climbers. Develop an informational brochure that focuses on the effects that high altitude has on the human body. Be sure to include one method climbers can use to become used to the higher altitudes.

Discovery CHANNEL SCHOOL

Respiration and Excretion
Video Preview
Video Field Trip
▶ Video Assessment

Review and Assessment

Checking Concepts

11. Explain the difference between breathing and respiration.

12. Explain how the alveoli provide a large surface area for gas exchange in the lungs.

13. Describe how the diaphragm and rib muscles work together to control inhaling and exhaling.

14. Describe what happens when carbon monoxide enters the body. How does this affect the body?

15. Explain two ways in which the kidneys help to maintain homeostasis in the body.

Thinking Critically

16. **Comparing and Contrasting** How is respiration similar to the burning of fuel? How is it different?

17. **Relating Cause and Effect** What process is shown in the diagram below? What role do changes in pressure play in this process?

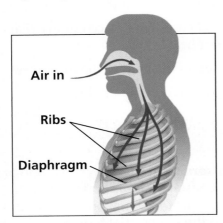

18. **Applying Concepts** Explain how babies can develop smoking-related respiratory problems.

19. **Making Judgments** Do you think that drugstores, which sell medicines, should also sell cigarettes and other tobacco products? Why or why not?

20. **Predicting** If the walls of the capillary cluster in a nephron were damaged or broken, what substance might you expect to find in urine that is not normally present? Explain.

Math Practice

21. **Surface Area** Which has a greater surface area, a cube that is 2 cm × 2 cm on a side, or eight cubes that are each 1 cm × 1 cm on a side? Show your work.

Applying Skills

Use your knowledge of the excretory system and the information in the data table below to answer Questions 22–25.

Average Daily Water Loss in Humans (mL)

Source	Normal Weather	Hot Weather	Extended Heavy Exercise
Lungs	350	250	650
Urine	1,400	1,200	500
Sweat	450	1,750	5,350
Digestive waste	200	200	200

22. **Interpreting Data** Identify the major source of water loss during normal weather and the major source of water loss during hot weather.

23. **Drawing Conclusions** How do the data for normal weather and hot weather show that the body is maintaining homeostasis?

24. **Calculating** What is the total amount of water lost on a hot-weather day? What is the total amount of water lost during extended heavy exercise?

25. **Inferring** Use the data to explain why it is important to drink a lot of water when you are exercising heavily.

Lab zone Chapter Project

Performance Assessment Your three anti-smoking ads should be ready for display. Be prepared to explain why you chose the message you did for each group of viewers. What health risks do each of your ads identify? Why do you think your ads would be effective?

End-of-Grade Test Practice

Some test questions ask you to arrange a series of events in order. For example, you may be asked which event comes first or last. You may also be asked to put a series of events in their correct sequence. Before looking at the answer choices, try to recall the correct sequence in which the events appear. Answer the sample question below by recalling the pathway that urine travels through the excretory system.

Sample Question
On its way out of the body, urine passes LAST through the
 A urinary bladder.
 B kidney.
 C ureter.
 D urethra.

Answer
Answer choice **D** is correct. The urethra is the tube that carries urine out of the body. Choice **B** is incorrect because the kidney is the first body part through which urine passes. Choice **C**, the ureter, is the tube that connects the kidney to the bladder. Choice **A**, urinary bladder, is incorrect because it is not the last body part through which urine passes.

Choose the letter of the best answer.

1. Which of the following organs functions as both a respiratory organ and an excretory organ?
 A the liver
 B the lungs
 C the skin
 D the kidneys

2. The correct sequence of organs through which air travels when it is breathed into the body is
 A pharynx, nose, trachea, bronchi.
 B nose, trachea, pharynx, bronchi.
 C nose, pharynx, bronchi, trachea.
 D nose, trachea, pharynx, bronchi.

The graph below shows the percentage of total lung function in people who have never smoked and in smokers from ages 25–75. Use the graph to answer Questions 3 and 4.

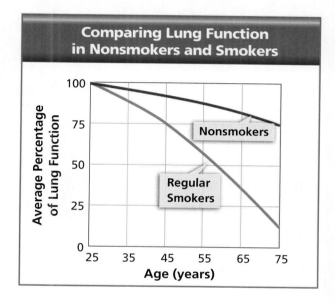

3. At approximately what age do the lungs of a smoker have the same capacity as the lungs of a 75-year-old who has never smoked?
 A 25
 B 45
 C 65
 D 75

4. What general conclusion about lung function and smoking could you draw from this graph?
 A Smoking does not affect lung function.
 B People who smoke are more likely to have greater lung function than those who have never smoked.
 C By the age of 50, a smoker will likely have 50 percent lung function.
 D Smoking significantly reduces the lung function of smokers compared to people who have never smoked.

Constructed Response

5. What is respiration? Explain where this process occurs and what body systems are involved in making respiration possible.

Chapter 12

The Nervous System

Standard Course of Study

1.01 Identify and create questions and hypotheses.

1.02 Develop appropriate experimental procedures.

1.03 Apply safety procedures.

1.04 Analyze variables.

1.05 Analyze evidence.

1.06 Use mathematics to gather, organize, and present data.

1.08 Use oral and written language.

1.09 Use technologies and information systems.

2.03 Evaluate technological designs.

4.01 Analyze how human body systems interact.

4.02 Describe functions of human body systems.

4.03 Explain how the structure of an organ is adapted to perform specific functions.

4.04 Evaluate how human body systems regulate the internal environment.

4.05 Analyze imbalances in homeostasis.

4.07 Explain how environmental effects influence human embryo development and health.

4.08 Explain how understanding the human body helps to make informed health decisions.

Interactive Textbook

Without your nervous system, a sport like windsurfing would be impossible! ▶

Lab zone™ Chapter **Project**

Tricks and Illusions

Things aren't always what they seem. For example, an optical illusion is a picture or other visual effect that tricks you into seeing something incorrectly. In this project, you'll investigate how your senses sometimes can be fooled by illusions.

Your Goal To set up a science fair booth to demonstrate how different people respond to one or more illusions

To complete this project, you must

● try out a variety of illusions, including some that involve the senses of hearing or touch as well as sight
● select one or more illusions and set up an experiment to monitor people's responses to the illusions
● learn why the illusions fool the senses
● follow the safety guidelines in Appendix A

Plan It! In a small group, discuss optical illusions or other illusions that you know about. Look in books to learn about others. Try them out. Which illusions would make an interesting experiment? How could you set up such an experiment at a science fair?

How the Nervous System Works

Reading Preview

Key Concepts
- What are the functions of the nervous system?
- What is the structure of a neuron and what kinds of neurons are found in the body?
- How do nerve impulses travel from one neuron to another?

Key Terms
- stimulus • response
- neuron • nerve impulse
- dendrite • axon • nerve
- sensory neuron • interneuron
- motor neuron • synapse

Target Reading Skill

Previewing Visuals Before you read, preview Figure 3. Then, write two questions that you have about the diagram in a graphic organizer like the one below. As you read, answer your questions.

The Path of a Nerve Impulse

Q.	What is a sensory neuron?
A.	
Q.	

Lab zone Discover **Activity**

How Simple Is a Simple Task?
1. Trace the outline of a penny in twelve different places on a piece of paper.
2. Number the circles 1 through 12. Write the numbers randomly, in no particular order.
3. Now, pick up the penny again. Put it in each circle, one after another, in numerical order, beginning with 1 and ending with 12.

Think It Over
Inferring Make a list of all the sense organs, muscle movements, and thought processes used in this activity. Compare your list with your classmates' lists. What organ system coordinated all the different processes involved in this task?

The ball whizzes toward the soccer goalie. She lunges for the ball, and in one swift movement blocks it from entering the net. To tend goal, soccer players need excellent coordination and keen vision. In addition, they must remember what they have learned from years of practice.

Whether or not you play soccer, you too need coordination, memory, and the ability to learn. Your nervous system carries out all these functions. The nervous system includes the brain, spinal cord, and nerves that run throughout the body. It also includes sense organs, such as the eyes and ears.

Functions of the Nervous System

The Internet lets people gather information from anywhere in the world with the click of a button. Like the Internet, your nervous system is a communications network. But it is much more efficient than the Internet.

The nervous system receives information about what is happening both inside and outside your body. It also directs the way in which your body responds to this information. In addition, your nervous system helps maintain homeostasis. Without your nervous system, you could not move, think, feel pain, or taste a spicy taco.

Receiving Information Because of your nervous system, you are aware of what is happening in the environment around you. For example, you know that a fly is buzzing around your head, that the wind is blowing, or that a friend is telling a funny joke. Your nervous system also checks conditions inside your body, such as the level of glucose in your blood.

Responding to Information Any change or signal in the environment that can make an organism react is called a **stimulus** (STIM yoo lus) (plural: *stimuli*). A buzzing fly is a stimulus. After your nervous system analyzes the stimulus, it causes a response. A **response** is what your body does in reaction to a stimulus—you swat at the fly.

Some nervous system responses, such as swatting a fly, are voluntary, or under your control. However, many processes necessary for life, such as heart rate, are controlled by involuntary actions of the nervous system.

Maintaining Homeostasis The nervous system helps maintain homeostasis by directing the body to respond appropriately to the information it receives. For example, when you are hungry, your nervous system prompts you to eat. This action maintains homeostasis by supplying your body with the nutrients and energy it needs.

Reading Checkpoint What is a stimulus?

FIGURE 1
The Nervous System at Work
The zooming soccer ball is a stimulus. The goalie responds by lunging toward the ball and blocking the shot.
Interpreting Diagrams How does the goalie's nervous system help her body maintain homeostasis?

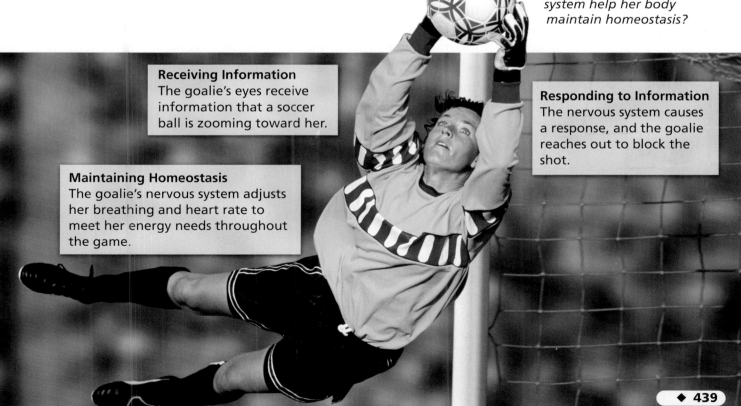

Receiving Information
The goalie's eyes receive information that a soccer ball is zooming toward her.

Responding to Information
The nervous system causes a response, and the goalie reaches out to block the shot.

Maintaining Homeostasis
The goalie's nervous system adjusts her breathing and heart rate to meet her energy needs throughout the game.

FIGURE 2

Structure of a Neuron
A neuron has one axon and many dendrites that extend from the cell body.

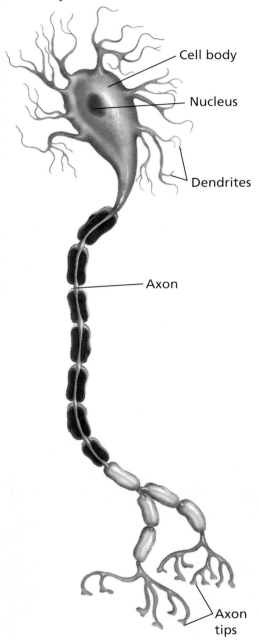

Cell body

Nucleus

Dendrites

Axon

Axon tips

The Neuron

Your nervous system includes various organs, tissues, and cells. For example, your brain is an organ, and the nerves running throughout your body are tissues. The cells that carry information through your nervous system are called **neurons** (NOO rahnz), or nerve cells. The message that a neuron carries is called a **nerve impulse.**

The Structure of a Neuron The structure of a neuron enables it to carry nerve impulses. **A neuron has a large cell body that contains the nucleus, threadlike extensions called dendrites, and an axon.** The **dendrites** carry impulses toward the neuron's cell body. The **axon** carries impulses away from the cell body. Nerve impulses begin in a dendrite, move toward the cell body, and then move down the axon. A neuron can have many dendrites, but it has only one axon. An axon, however, can have more than one tip, so the impulse can go to more than one other cell.

Axons and dendrites are sometimes called nerve fibers. Nerve fibers are often arranged in parallel bundles covered with connective tissue, something like a package of uncooked spaghetti wrapped in cellophane. A bundle of nerve fibers is called a **nerve.**

Kinds of Neurons Three kinds of neurons are found in the body—sensory neurons, interneurons, and motor neurons. Figure 3 shows how these three kinds of neurons work together.

A **sensory neuron** picks up stimuli from the internal or external environment and converts each stimulus into a nerve impulse. The impulse travels along the sensory neuron until it reaches an interneuron, usually in the brain or spinal cord. An **interneuron** is a neuron that carries nerve impulses from one neuron to another. Some interneurons pass impulses from sensory neurons to motor neurons. A **motor neuron** sends an impulse to a muscle or gland, and the muscle or gland reacts in response.

 **Reading Checkpoint** **What is the function of an axon?**

How a Nerve Impulse Travels

Every day of your life, billions of nerve impulses travel through your nervous system. Each of those nerve impulses begins in the dendrites of a neuron. The impulse moves rapidly toward the neuron's cell body and then down the axon until it reaches the axon tip. A nerve impulse travels along the neuron in the form of electrical and chemical signals. Nerve impulses can travel as fast as 120 meters per second!

FIGURE 3

The Path of a Nerve Impulse

When you hear your phone ring, you pick it up to answer it. Many sensory neurons, interneurons, and motor neurons are involved in this action.

Interpreting Diagrams To where does the impulse pass from the sensory neurons?

Receptors in ear

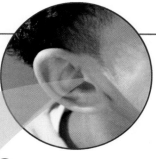

1 Sensory Neuron
Nerve impulses begin when receptors pick up stimuli from the environment. Receptors in the ear pick up the sound of the phone ringing. The receptors trigger nerve impulses in sensory neurons.

2 Interneuron
From the sensory neurons, the nerve impulse passes to interneurons in the brain. Your brain interprets the impulses from many interneurons and makes you realize that the phone is ringing. Your brain also decides that you should answer the phone.

Muscle in hand

3 Motor Neuron
Impulses then travel along thousands of motor neurons. The motor neurons send the impulses to muscles. The muscles carry out the response, and you reach for the phone.

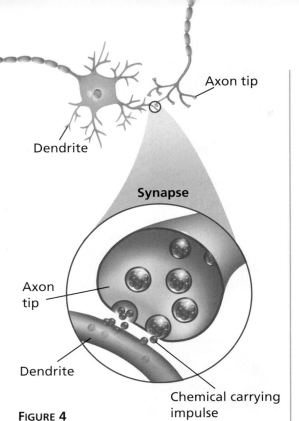

Axon tip

Dendrite

Synapse

Axon tip

Dendrite

Chemical carrying impulse

FIGURE 4
The Synapse
When a nerve impulse reaches the tip of an axon, chemicals are released into the gap at the synapse. The chemicals carry the nerve impulse across the gap.

The Synapse What happens when a nerve impulse reaches the axon tip at the end of a neuron? At that point, the impulse can pass to the next structure. Sometimes the structure is the dendrite of another neuron. Other times, the structure is a muscle or a cell in another organ, such as a sweat gland. The junction where one neuron can transfer an impulse to another structure is called a **synapse** (SIN aps).

How an Impulse is Transferred Figure 4 shows a synapse between the axon tip of one neuron and the dendrite of another neuron. Notice that a small gap separates these two structures. **For a nerve impulse to be carried along at a synapse, it must cross the gap between the axon and the next structure. The axon tips release chemicals that carry the impulse across the gap.**

You can think of the gap at a synapse as a river, and an axon as a road that leads up to the riverbank. The nerve impulse is like a car traveling on the road. To get to the other side, the car has to cross the river. The car gets on a ferry boat, which carries it across the river. The chemicals that the axon tips release are like the ferry, carrying the nerve impulse across the gap.

Section 1 Assessment

Target Reading Skill Previewing Visuals Refer to your questions and answers about Figure 3 to help you answer Question 2 below.

Reviewing Key Concepts

1. a. **Listing** What are three functions of the nervous system?
   b. **Describing** Give an example of a stimulus and describe how the nervous system produces a response.
   c. **Predicting** Your heart rate is controlled by involuntary actions of the nervous system. What would life be like if your heartbeat were under voluntary control?

2. a. **Identifying** Identify the three kinds of neurons that are found in the nervous system.
   b. **Explaining** How do the three kinds of neurons interact to carry nerve impulses?

   c. **Comparing and Contrasting** How do sensory neurons and motor neurons differ?

3. a. **Reviewing** What is a synapse?
   b. **Sequencing** Outline the steps by which a nerve impulse reaches and then crosses the gap at a synapse.

Lab zone At-Home **Activity**

Pass the Salt, Please During dinner, ask a family member to pass the salt and pepper to you. Observe what your family member then does. Explain that the words you spoke were a stimulus and that the family member's reaction was a response. Discuss other examples of stimuli and responses with your family.

Lab zone — Design Your Own Lab

Ready or Not!

Problem

Do people's reaction times vary at different times of the day?

Skills Focus

developing hypotheses, controlling variables, drawing conclusions

Material

• meter stick

Procedure

PART 1 Observing a Response to a Stimulus

1. Have your partner hold a meter stick with the zero end about 50 cm above a table.

2. Get ready to catch the meter stick by positioning the top of your thumb and forefinger just at the zero position, as shown in the photograph.

3. Your partner should drop the meter stick without any warning. Using your thumb and forefinger only (no other part of your hand), catch the meter stick as soon as you can. Record the distance in centimeters that the meter stick fell. This distance is a measure of your reaction time.

PART 2 Designing Your Experiment

4. With your partner, discuss how you can use the activity from Part 1 to find out whether people's reaction times vary at different times of day. Consider the questions below. Then, write up your experimental plan.
   • What hypothesis will you test?
   • What variables do you need to control?
   • How many people will you test? How many times will you test each person?

5. Submit your plan for your teacher's review. Make any changes your teacher recommends. Create a data table to record your results. Then, perform your experiment.

Analyze and Conclude

1. **Inferring** In this lab, what is the stimulus? What is the response? Is the response voluntary or involuntary? Explain.

2. **Developing Hypotheses** What hypothesis did you test in Part 2?

3. **Controlling Variables** In Part 2, why was it important to control all variables except the time of day?

4. **Drawing Conclusions** Based on your results in Part 2, do people's reaction times vary at different times of the day? Explain.

5. **Communicating** Write a paragraph to explain why you can use the distance on the meter stick as a measure of reaction time.

More to Explore

Do you think people can do arithmetic problems more quickly and accurately at certain times of the day? Design an experiment to investigate this question. *Obtain your teacher's permission before carrying out your investigation.*

Divisions of the Nervous System

Reading Preview

Key Concepts

- What are the structures and functions of the central nervous system?
- What are the structures and functions of the peripheral nervous system?
- What is a reflex?
- What are two ways in which the nervous system can be injured?

Key Terms

- central nervous system
- peripheral nervous system
- brain • spinal cord
- cerebrum • cerebellum
- brain stem
- somatic nervous system
- autonomic nervous system
- reflex • concussion

Target Reading Skill

Building Vocabulary After you read this section, reread the paragraphs that contain definitions of Key Terms. Use all the information you have learned to write a definition of each Key Term in your own words.

Discover **Activity**

How Does Your Knee React?

1. Sit on a table or counter so that your legs dangle freely. Make sure that your partner is not directly in front of your legs.
2. Have your partner use the side of his or her hand to tap one of your knees gently just below the kneecap. Observe what happens to your leg. Note whether you have any control over your reaction.
3. Change places with your partner. Repeat Steps 1 and 2.

Think It Over
Inferring When might it be an advantage for your body to react very quickly and without your conscious control?

You are standing at a busy street corner, waiting to cross the street. A traffic cop blows his whistle and waves his arms energetically. For the heavy traffic to move smoothly, there needs to be a traffic cop and responsive drivers. The traffic cop coordinates the movements of the drivers, and they maneuver the cars safely through the intersection.

Similarly, your nervous system has two divisions that work together. The **central nervous system** consists of the brain and spinal cord. The **peripheral nervous system** (puh RIF uh rul) includes all the nerves located outside of the central nervous system. The central nervous system is like a traffic cop. The peripheral nervous system is like the drivers and pedestrians.

The traffic cop keeps everybody moving.

Central Nervous System

You can see the central and peripheral nervous systems in Figure 5. **The central nervous system is the control center of the body. It includes the brain and spinal cord.** All information about what is happening in the world inside or outside your body is brought to the central nervous system. The **brain,** located in the skull, is the part of the central nervous system that controls most functions in the body. The **spinal cord** is the thick column of nervous tissue that links the brain to most of the nerves in the peripheral nervous system.

Most impulses from the peripheral nervous system travel through the spinal cord to get to the brain. Your brain then directs a response. The response usually travels from the brain, through the spinal cord, and then to the peripheral nervous system.

For example, here is what happens when you reach under the sofa to find a lost quarter. Your fingers move over the floor, searching for the quarter. When your fingers finally touch the quarter, the stimulus of the touch triggers nerve impulses in sensory neurons in your fingers. These impulses travel through nerves of the peripheral nervous system to your spinal cord. Then the impulses race up to your brain. Your brain interprets the impulses, telling you that you've found the quarter. Your brain starts nerve impulses that move down the spinal cord. From the spinal cord, the impulses travel through motor neurons in your arm and hand. The impulses in the motor neurons cause your fingers to grasp the quarter.

 **Reading Checkpoint** What are the parts of the central nervous system?

Go Online
active art

For: Nervous System activity
Visit: PHSchool.com
Web Code: cep-4062

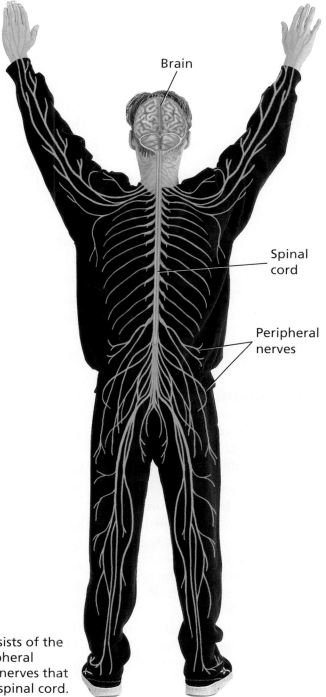

Brain

Spinal cord

Peripheral nerves

FIGURE 5
The Nervous System
The central nervous system consists of the brain and spinal cord. The peripheral nervous system includes all the nerves that branch out from the brain and spinal cord.

The Brain and Spinal Cord

Your brain contains about 100 billion neurons, all of which are interneurons. Each of those neurons may receive messages from up to 10,000 other neurons and may send messages to about 1,000 more! Three layers of connective tissue cover the brain. The space between the middle layer and innermost layer is filled with a watery fluid. The skull, the layers of connective tissue, and the fluid all help protect the brain from injury.

There are three main regions of the brain that receive and process information. These are the cerebrum, the cerebellum, and the brain stem. Find each in Figure 6.

Cerebrum The largest part of the brain is called the cerebrum. The **cerebrum** (suh REE brum) interprets input from the senses, controls movement, and carries out complex mental processes such as learning and remembering. Because of your cerebrum, you can locate your favorite comic strip in the newspaper, read it, and laugh at its funny characters.

The cerebrum is divided into a right and a left half. The right half sends impulses to skeletal muscles on the left side of the body. In contrast, the left half controls the right side of the body. When you reach with your right hand for a pencil, the messages that tell you to do so come from the left half of the cerebrum. In addition, each half of the cerebrum controls slightly different kinds of mental activity. The right half is usually associated with creativity and artistic ability. The left half is usually associated with mathematical skills and logical thinking.

As you can see in Figure 6, certain areas of the cerebrum are associated with smell, touch, taste, hearing, and vision. Other areas control movement, speech, written language, and abstract thought.

Cerebellum and Brain Stem The second largest part of your brain is called the cerebellum. The **cerebellum** (sehr uh BEL um) coordinates the actions of your muscles and helps you keep your balance. When you walk, the impulses that tell your feet to move start in your cerebrum. However, your cerebellum gives you the muscular coordination and sense of balance that keep you from falling down.

The **brain stem,** which lies between the cerebellum and spinal cord, controls your body's involuntary actions—those that occur automatically. For example, neurons in the brain stem regulate your breathing and help control your heartbeat.

 **Reading Checkpoint** **What actions does the brain stem control?**

FIGURE 6

The Brain

Each of the three main parts of the human brain—the cerebrum, cerebellum, and brain stem—carries out specific functions.
Interpreting Diagrams *What are three functions of the cerebrum?*

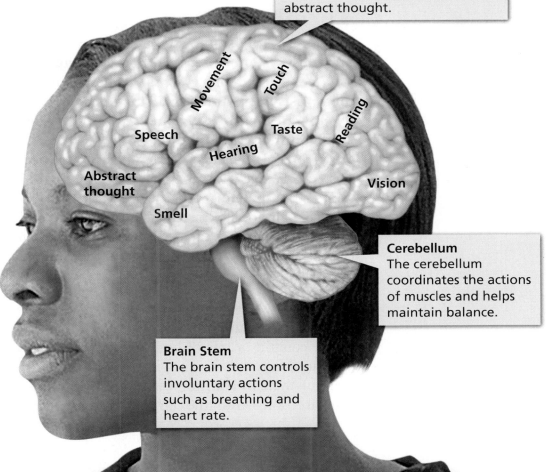

Cerebrum
The cerebrum is the largest part of the brain. Different areas of the cerebrum control such functions as movement, the senses, speech, and abstract thought.

Movement

Touch

Speech

Reading

Taste

Hearing

Abstract thought

Vision

Smell

Cerebellum
The cerebellum coordinates the actions of muscles and helps maintain balance.

Brain Stem
The brain stem controls involuntary actions such as breathing and heart rate.

Top View of Cerebrum

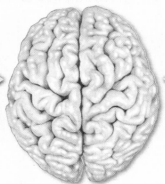

Left Half
The left half of the cerebrum is associated with mathematical and logical thinking.

Right Half
The right half of the cerebrum is associated with creativity and artistic ability.

The Spinal Cord Run your fingers down the center of your back to feel the bones of the vertebral column. The vertebral column surrounds and protects the spinal cord. **The spinal cord is the link between your brain and the peripheral nervous system.** The layers of connective tissue that surround and protect the brain also cover the spinal cord. In addition, like the brain, the spinal cord is further protected by a watery fluid.

Peripheral Nervous System

The second division of the nervous system is the peripheral nervous system. **The peripheral nervous system consists of a network of nerves that branch out from the central nervous system and connect it to the rest of the body. The peripheral nervous system is involved in both involuntary and voluntary actions.**

A total of 43 pairs of nerves make up the peripheral nervous system. Twelve pairs originate in the brain. The other 31 pairs—the spinal nerves—begin in the spinal cord. One nerve in each pair goes to the left side of the body, and the other goes to the right. As you can see in Figure 7, spinal nerves leave the spinal cord through spaces between the vertebrae.

How Spinal Nerves Function A spinal nerve is like a two-lane highway. Impulses travel on a spinal nerve in two directions—both to and from the central nervous system. Each spinal nerve contains axons of both sensory and motor neurons. The sensory neurons carry impulses from the body to the central nervous system. The motor neurons carry impulses in the opposite direction—from the central nervous system to the body.

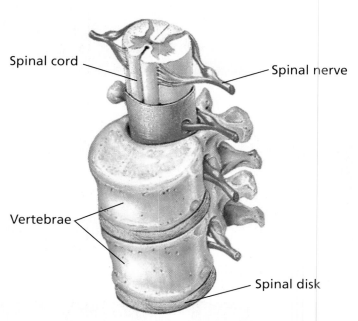

FIGURE 7
The Spinal Nerves
The spinal nerves, which connect to the spinal cord, emerge from spaces between the vertebrae. Each spinal nerve consists of both sensory and motor neurons.

Spinal cord

Spinal nerve

Vertebrae

Spinal disk

FIGURE 8
Somatic and Autonomic Nervous Systems
The somatic nervous system controls voluntary actions. The autonomic nervous system controls involuntary actions. **Classifying** *Which system helps regulate the artist's heartbeat?*

Actions Controlled by the Somatic Nervous System
• Hands shape the clay.
• Foot turns the wheel.
• Mouth smiles.

Actions Controlled by the Autonomic Nervous System
• Heartbeat is regulated.
• Breathing rate is kept steady.
• Body temperature remains constant.

Somatic and Autonomic Systems The nerves of the peripheral nervous system can be divided into two groups, the somatic (soh MAT ik) and autonomic (awt uh NAHM ik) nervous systems. The nerves of the **somatic nervous system** control voluntary actions such as using a fork or tying your shoes. In contrast, nerves of the **autonomic nervous system** control involuntary actions. For example, the autonomic nervous system regulates the contractions of the smooth muscles that adjust the diameter of blood vessels.

 **Reading Checkpoint** What kinds of actions are controlled by the autonomic nervous system?

Reflexes

Imagine that you are watching an adventure movie. The movie is so thrilling that you don't notice a fly circling above your head. When the fly zooms right in front of your eyes, however, your eyelids immediately blink shut. You didn't decide to close your eyes. The blink, which is a **reflex,** is a response that happened automatically. **A reflex is an automatic response that occurs very rapidly and without conscious control. Reflexes help to protect the body.** If you did the Discover activity for this section, you observed another reflex.

Lab zone **Try This Activity**

You Blinked!

Can you make yourself *not* blink? To answer this question, try the following activity.

1. Put on safety goggles.

2. Have your partner stand across from you and gently toss ten cotton balls toward your goggles. Your partner should not give you any warning before tossing the cotton balls.

3. Count the number of times you blink and the number of times you are able to keep from blinking.

Interpreting Data Compare the two numbers. Why is blinking considered a reflex?

A Reflex Pathway As you have learned, the contraction of skeletal muscles is usually controlled by the brain. However, in some reflex actions, skeletal muscles contract with the involvement of the spinal cord only—not the brain.

Figure 9 shows the reflex action that occurs when you touch a sharp object. When your finger touches the object, sensory neurons send impulses to the spinal cord. The impulses may then pass to interneurons in the spinal cord. From there the impulses pass directly to motor neurons in your arm and hand. The muscles then contract, and your hand jerks up and away from the sharp object. By removing your hand quickly, this reflex protects you from getting badly cut.

Signaling the Brain At the same time that some nerve impulses make your arm muscles contract, other nerve impulses travel up your spinal cord to your brain. When these impulses reach your brain, your brain interprets them. You then feel a sharp pain in your finger.

It takes longer for the pain impulses to get to the brain and be interpreted than it does for the reflex action to occur. By the time you feel the pain, you have already moved your hand away.

Reading Checkpoint What is an example of a reflex?

FIGURE 9
A Reflex Action
If you touch a sharp object, your hand immediately jerks away. This action, which is known as a reflex, happens automatically. Follow the numbered steps to understand how a reflex happens.
Sequencing *Do you pull your hand away before or after you feel the pain? Explain.*

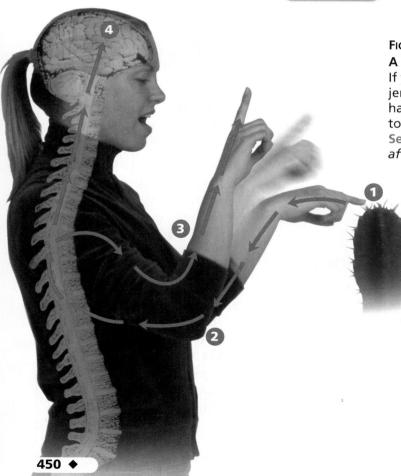

1 Sensory neurons in your fingertip detect a pain stimulus.

2 Nerve impulses travel to your spinal cord.

3 Nerve impulses return to motor neurons in your hand, and you pull your hand away.

4 As you pull your hand away, nerve impulses travel to your brain. You feel the pain.

Nervous System Injuries

The nervous system can suffer injuries that interfere with its functioning. **Concussions and spinal cord injuries are two ways in which the central nervous system can be damaged.**

Concussions A **concussion** is a bruiselike injury of the brain. A concussion occurs when the soft tissue of the brain collides against the skull. Concussions can happen when you bump your head in a hard fall, an automobile accident, or a contact sport such as football.

With most concussions, you may have a headache for a short time, but the injured tissue heals by itself. However, with more serious concussions, you may lose consciousness, experience confusion, or feel drowsy after the injury. To decrease your chances of getting a brain injury, wear a helmet during activities in which you risk bumping your head.

Spinal Cord Injuries Spinal cord injuries occur when the spinal cord is cut or crushed. As a result, axons in the injured region are damaged, so impulses cannot pass through them. This type of injury usually results in paralysis, which is the loss of movement in some part of the body. Car crashes are the most common cause of spinal cord injuries.

FIGURE 10
Protecting the Nervous System
You can help protect yourself from a spinal cord injury by wearing a seatbelt when you travel in a car.

 **Reading Checkpoint** What is paralysis?

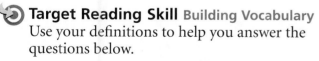

Section 2 Assessment

Target Reading Skill Building Vocabulary Use your definitions to help you answer the questions below.

Reviewing Key Concepts

1. **a.** Listing What two structures are part of the central nervous system?
   b. Describing Describe the functions of the three main regions of the brain.
   c. Relating Cause and Effect What symptoms might indicate that a person's cerebellum has been injured?
2. **a.** Identifying What are the two groups of nerves into which the peripheral nervous system is divided?
   b. Comparing and Contrasting How do the functions of the two groups of peripheral nerves differ?

3. **a.** Defining What is a reflex?
   b. Sequencing Trace the pathway of a reflex in the nervous system.
   c. Inferring How do reflexes help protect the body from injury?
4. **a.** Reviewing What is a concussion?
   b. Applying Concepts How can you reduce your risk of concussion?

Writing in Science

Comparison Paragraph Write a paragraph in which you compare the functions of the left and right halves of the cerebrum. Discuss what kinds of mental activities each half controls as well as which side of the body it controls.

Should People Be Required to Wear Bicycle Helmets?

Bicycling is an enjoyable activity. Unfortunately, many bicyclists are injured while riding. Each year, more than 500,000 people in the United States are treated in hospitals for bicycling injuries. Many of those people suffer head injuries. Head injuries can affect everything your brain does—thinking, remembering, seeing, and being able to move.

Depending on the age group and geographic location, helmet use ranges from less than 10 percent to about 80 percent of bicyclists. What is the best way to get bicyclists to protect themselves from head injury?

The Issues

Should Laws Require the Use of Bicycle Helmets?

Experts estimate that bicycle helmets could reduce the risk of bicycle-related head injuries by as much as 85 percent. Today, about 19 states have passed laws requiring bicycle riders to wear helmets. Most of these statewide laws, however, apply only to children.

Some supporters of helmet laws want to see the laws extended to all riders. They claim that laws are the most effective way to increase helmet use.

What Are the Drawbacks of Helmet Laws?

Opponents of helmet laws believe it is up to the individual to decide whether or not to wear a helmet. They say it is not the role of government to stop people from taking risks. They argue that, rather than making people pay fines if they don't wear bicycle helmets, governments should educate people about the benefits of helmets. Car drivers should also be educated about safe driving procedures near bicycles.

Are There Alternatives to Helmet Laws?

Instead of laws requiring people to wear helmets, some communities and organizations have set up educational programs that teach about the advantages of helmets. Effective programs teach about the dangers of head injuries and the protection that helmets provide. Effective education programs, though, can be expensive. They also need to reach a wide audience, including children, teens, and adults.

You Decide

1. Identify the Problem
In your own words, explain the issues concerning laws requiring people to wear bicycle helmets.

2. Analyze the Options
List two different plans for increasing helmet use by bicycle riders. List at least one advantage and one drawback of each plan.

3. Find a Solution
You are a member of the city government hoping to increase helmet use. Write a speech outlining your position for either a helmet law or an alternative plan. Support your position.

Go Online
PHSchool.com

For: More on bicycle helmets
Visit: PHSchool.com
Web Code: ceh-4060

The Senses

Reading Preview

Key Concepts

- How do your eyes enable you to see?
- How do you hear and maintain your sense of balance?
- How do your senses of smell and taste work together?
- How is your skin related to your sense of touch?

Key Terms

- cornea • pupil • iris • lens
- retina • nearsightedness
- farsightedness • eardrum
- cochlea • semicircular canal

Target Reading Skill

Outlining As you read, make an outline about the senses. Use the red headings for the main ideas and the blue headings for the supporting ideas.

The Senses
I. Vision
A. How light enters your eye
B.
C.

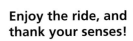

Discover Activity

What's in the Bag?

1. Your teacher will give you a paper bag that contains several objects. Your challenge is to use only your sense of touch to identify each object. You will not look inside the bag.
2. Put your hand in the bag and carefully touch each object. Observe the shape of each object. Note whether its surface is rough or smooth. Also note other characteristics, such as its size, what it seems to be made of, and whether it can be bent.
3. After you have finished touching each object, write your observations on a sheet of paper. Then, write your inference about what each object is.

Think It Over
Observing What could you determine about each object without looking at it? What could you not determine?

You waited in line to get on the ride, and now it's about to begin. You grip the wheel as the bumper cars jerk into motion. The next thing you know, you are zipping around crazily and bumping into cars driven by your friends.

You can thrill to the motion of amusement park rides because of your senses. The sense organs pick up information about your environment, change the information into nerve impulses, and send the impulses to your brain. Your brain then interprets the information. Your senses and brain working together enable you to respond to things in your environment, such as the other bumper cars around you.

Enjoy the ride, and thank your senses!

Pupil in Bright Light

Pupil in Dim Light

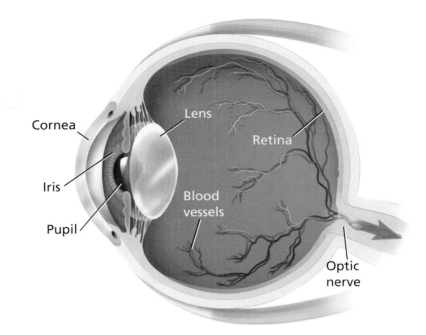

Cornea

Lens

Iris

Retina

Pupil

Blood
vessels

Optic
nerve

Vision

Your eyes are the sense organs that enable you to see the objects in your environment. They let you see this textbook in front of you, the window across the room, and the world outside the window. **Your eyes respond to the stimulus of light. They convert that stimulus into impulses that your brain interprets, enabling you to see.**

How Light Enters Your Eye When rays of light strike the eye, they pass through the structures shown in Figure 11. First, the light strikes the **cornea** (KAWR nee uh), the clear tissue that covers the front of the eye. The light then passes through a fluid-filled chamber behind the cornea and reaches the pupil. The **pupil** is the opening through which light enters the eye.

You may have noticed that people's pupils change size when they go from a dark room into bright sunshine. In bright light, the pupil becomes smaller. In dim light, the pupil becomes larger. The size of the pupil is adjusted by muscles in the iris. The **iris** is a circular structure that surrounds the pupil and regulates the amount of light entering the eye. The iris also gives the eye its color. If you have brown eyes, it is actually your irises that are brown.

How Light Is Focused Light that passes through the pupil strikes the lens. The **lens** is a flexible structure that focuses light. The lens of your eye functions something like the lens of a camera, which focuses light on photographic film. Because of the way in which the lens of the eye bends the light rays, the image it produces is upside down and reversed. Muscles that attach to the lens adjust its shape, producing an image that is in focus.

FIGURE 11
The Eye

The eye is a complex organ that allows you to sense light. The pupil is the opening through which light enters the eye. In bright light, the pupil becomes smaller. In dim light, the pupil enlarges and allows more light to enter the eye.
Interpreting Diagrams *What structure adjusts the size of the pupil?*

DISCOVERY
CHANNEL
SCHOOL

The Nervous System

Video Preview
▶ Video Field Trip
Video Assessment

FIGURE 12
How You See

Light coming from an object enters your eye and is focused by the lens. The light produces an upside-down image on your retina. Receptors in your retina then send impulses to your cerebrum, which turns the image right-side up.
Comparing and Contrasting *Which receptors work best in dim light?*

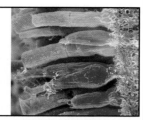

Rods and Cones
Receptors in the retina include rods (shown in green) and cones (shown in blue).

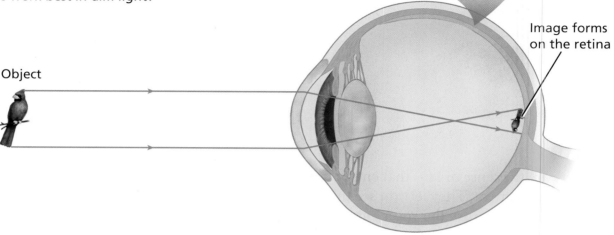

Object

Image forms on the retina

Working Together

Discover how your two eyes work together.

1. With your arms fully extended, hold a drinking straw in one hand and a pipe cleaner in the other.

2. With both eyes open, try to insert the pipe cleaner into the straw.

3. Now close your right eye. Try to insert the pipe cleaner into the straw.

4. Repeat Step 3 with your left eye closed.

Inferring How does closing one eye affect your ability to judge distances?

How You See an Image After passing through the lens, the focused light rays pass through a transparent, jellylike fluid. Then the light rays strike the **retina** (RET 'n uh), the layer of receptor cells that lines the back of the eye. The retina contains about 130 million receptor cells that respond to light. There are two types of receptors: rods and cones. Rod cells work best in dim light and enable you to see black, white, and shades of gray. In contrast, cone cells work best in bright light and enable you to see colors. This difference between rods and cones explains why you see colors best in bright light, but you see only shadowy gray images in dim light.

When light strikes the rods and cones, nerve impulses travel to the cerebrum through the optic nerves. One optic nerve comes from the left eye and the other one comes from the right eye. In the cerebrum, two things happen. The brain turns the reversed image right-side up, and it also combines the images from each eye to produce a single image.

Correcting Nearsightedness A lens—whether it is in your eye or in eyeglasses—is a curved, transparent object that bends light rays as they pass through it. If the lens of the eye does not focus light properly on the retina, vision problems result. The lenses in eyeglasses can help correct vision problems.

FIGURE 13
Correcting Vision Problems

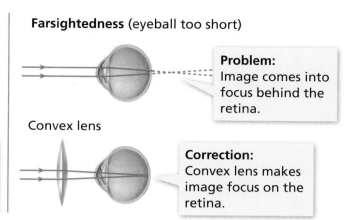

Nearsightedness (eyeball too long)

Concave lens

Problem:
Image comes into focus in front of the retina.

Correction:
Concave lens makes image focus on the retina.

Farsightedness (eyeball too short)

Convex lens

Problem:
Image comes into focus behind the retina.

Correction:
Convex lens makes image focus on the retina.

People with **nearsightedness** can see nearby objects clearly. However, they have trouble seeing objects far away. Nearsightedness results when the eyeball is too long. Because of the extra length that light must travel to reach the retina, distant objects do not focus sharply on the retina. Instead, the lens of the eye makes the image come into focus at a point in front of the retina, as shown in Figure 13.

To correct nearsightedness, eyeglasses with concave lenses are worn. A concave lens is thicker at the edges than it is in the center. When light rays pass through a concave lens, they are bent away from the center of the lens. The concave lenses in glasses make light rays spread out before they reach the lens of the eye. After the rays pass through the lens of the eye, they focus on the retina rather than in front of it.

Correcting Farsightedness People with **farsightedness** can see distant objects clearly. Nearby objects, however, look blurry. The eyeballs of people with farsightedness are too short. Because of this, the lens of the eye bends light from nearby objects so that the image does not focus properly on the retina. If light could pass through the retina, the image would come into sharp focus at a point behind the retina, as shown in Figure 13.

Convex lenses are used to help correct farsightedness. A convex lens is thicker in the middle than at the edges. The convex lens makes the light rays bend toward each other before they reach the eye. Then the lens of the eye bends the rays even more. This bending makes the image focus exactly on the retina.

 **Reading Checkpoint** What type of lens corrects nearsightedness?

Hearing and Balance

What wakes you up in the morning? Maybe an alarm clock buzzes, or perhaps your parent calls you. On a summer morning, you might hear birds singing. Whatever wakes you up, there's a good chance that it's a sound of some sort. **Your ears are the sense organs that respond to the stimulus of sound. The ears convert the sound to nerve impulses that your brain interprets.** So when you hear an alarm clock or another morning sound, your brain tells you that it's time to wake up.

How Sound Is Produced Sound is produced by vibrations. The material that is vibrating, or moving rapidly back and forth, may be almost anything—a guitar string, an insect's wings, or a stereo speaker.

The vibrations move outward from the source of the sound, something like ripples moving out from a stone dropped in water. The vibrations cause particles, such as the gas molecules that make up air, to vibrate. In this way, sound is carried. When you hear a friend's voice, for example, sound has traveled from your friend's larynx to your ears. In addition to being able to travel through gases such as those in air, sound waves can also travel through liquids, such as water, and solids, such as wood.

Math Analyzing Data

Sound Intensity

Sound intensity, or loudness, is measured in units called decibels. The threshold of hearing for the human ear is 0 decibels. For every 10-decibel increase, the sound intensity increases ten times. Thus, a 20-decibel sound is ten times more intense than a 10-decibel sound, not twice as intense. A 30-decibel sound is 100 times more intense than a 10-decibel sound. Sound levels for several sound sources are shown in the bar graph.

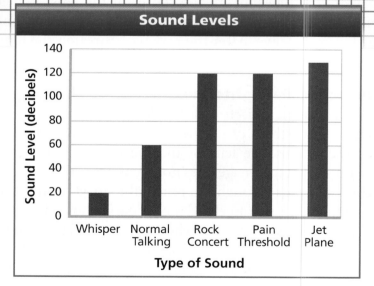

1. **Reading Graphs** What unit of measure is represented on the *y*-axis? What is represented on the *x*-axis?

2. **Interpreting Data** What is the sound intensity in decibels of a whisper? Normal talking? A rock concert?

3. **Calculating** How much more intense is normal talking than a whisper? Explain.

4. **Predicting** Based on the graph, what types of sound could be painful if you were exposed to them?

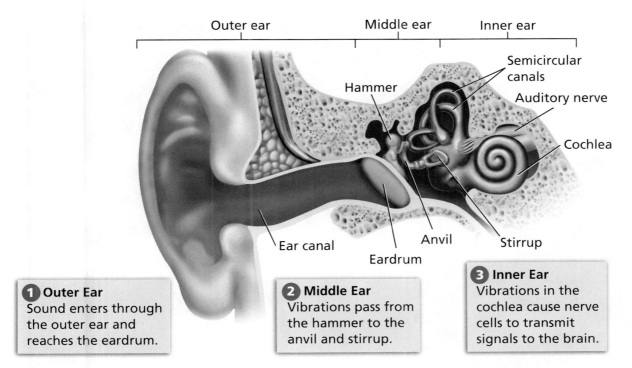

Outer ear   Middle ear   Inner ear

Hammer

Semicircular canals

Auditory nerve

Cochlea

Ear canal

Anvil

Stirrup

Eardrum

1 **Outer Ear**
Sound enters through the outer ear and reaches the eardrum.

2 **Middle Ear**
Vibrations pass from the hammer to the anvil and stirrup.

3 **Inner Ear**
Vibrations in the cochlea cause nerve cells to transmit signals to the brain.

FIGURE 14
The Ear

Sound waves enter the outer ear and make structures in the middle ear vibrate. When the vibrations reach the inner ear, nerve impulses travel to the cerebrum through the auditory nerve. Predicting *What would happen if the bones of the middle ear were stuck together and could not move?*

The Outer Ear The ear is structured to receive sound vibrations. The three regions of the ear—the outer ear, middle ear, and inner ear—are shown in Figure 14. The visible part of the outer ear is shaped like a funnel. This funnel-like shape enables the outer ear to gather sound waves. The sound vibrations then travel down the ear canal, which is also part of the outer ear.

The Middle Ear At the end of the ear canal, sound vibrations reach the eardrum. The **eardrum,** which separates the outer ear from the middle ear, is a membrane that vibrates when sound strikes it. Your eardrum vibrates in much the same way that a drum vibrates when it is struck. Vibrations from the eardrum pass to the middle ear, which contains the three smallest bones in the body—the hammer, anvil, and stirrup. These bones are named for their shapes. The vibrating eardrum makes the hammer vibrate. The hammer passes the vibrations to the anvil, and the anvil passes them to the stirrup.

The Inner Ear The stirrup vibrates against a thin membrane that covers the opening of the inner ear. The membrane channels the vibrations into the fluid in the cochlea. The **cochlea** (KAHK le uh) is a snail-shaped tube that is lined with receptor cells that respond to sound. When the fluid in the cochlea vibrates, it stimulates these receptors. Sensory neurons then send nerve impulses to the cerebrum through the auditory nerve. These impulses are interpreted as sounds that you hear.

Go Online
SCiLINKS NSTA

For: Links on the senses
Visit: www.SciLinks.org
Web Code: scn-0463

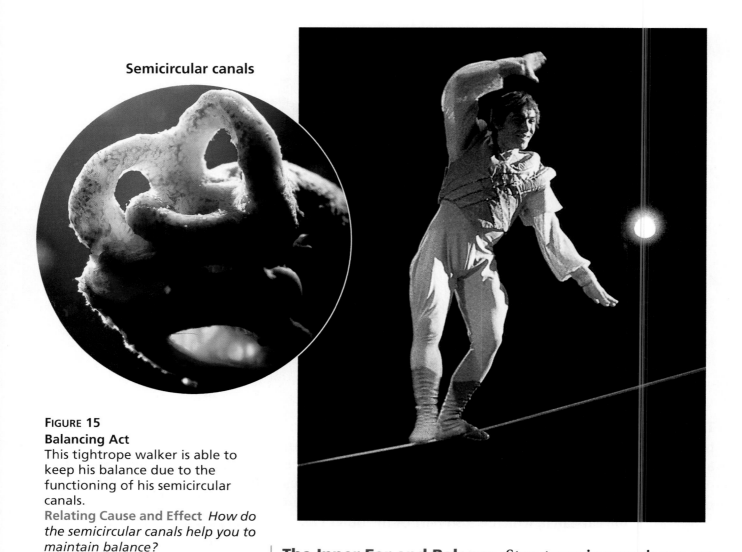

Semicircular canals

Figure 15
Balancing Act
This tightrope walker is able to keep his balance due to the functioning of his semicircular canals.
Relating Cause and Effect How do the semicircular canals help you to maintain balance?

The Inner Ear and Balance Structures in your inner ear control your sense of balance. Above the cochlea in your inner ear are the **semicircular canals,** which are the structures in the ear that are responsible for your sense of balance. You can see how these structures got their name if you look at Figure 15. These canals, as well as the two tiny sacs located behind them, are full of fluid. The canals and sacs are also lined with tiny cells that have hairlike extensions.

When your head moves, the fluid in the semicircular canals is set in motion. The moving fluid makes the cells' hairlike extensions bend. This bending produces nerve impulses in sensory neurons. The impulses travel to the cerebellum. The cerebellum then analyzes the impulses to determine the way your head is moving and the position of your body. If the cerebellum senses that you are losing your balance, it sends impulses to muscles that help you restore your balance.

 **Reading Checkpoint** **Where in the ear are the semicircular canals located?**

Smell and Taste

You walk into the house and smell the aroma of freshly baked cookies. You bite into one and taste its rich chocolate flavor. When you smelled the cookies, receptors in your nose reacted to chemicals carried by the air from the cookies to your nose. When you took a bite of a cookie, taste buds on your tongue responded to chemicals in the food. These food chemicals were dissolved in saliva, which came in contact with your taste buds.

The senses of smell and taste work closely together. Both depend on chemicals in food or in the air. The chemicals trigger responses in receptors in the nose and mouth. Nerve impulses then travel to the brain, where they are interpreted as smells or tastes.

The nose can distinguish at least 50 basic odors. In contrast, there are only five main taste sensations—sweet, sour, salty, bitter, and a meatlike taste called *umami*. When you eat, however, you experience a much wider variety of tastes. The flavor of food is influenced by both smell and taste. When you have a cold, foods may not taste as good as they usually do. That is because a stuffy nose decreases your ability to smell food.

Lab zone **Skills Activity**

Designing Experiments

Can people tell one food from another if they can taste the foods but not smell them? Design an experiment to find out. Use these foods: a peeled pear, a peeled apple, and a peeled raw potato. Be sure to control all variables except the one you are testing. Write your hypothesis and a description of your procedure. Obtain your teacher's approval before carrying out your experiment.

 **Reading Checkpoint** What basic tastes can the tongue detect?

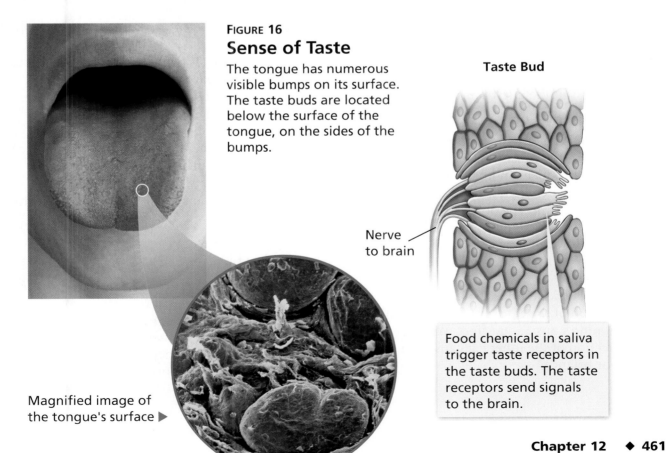

FIGURE 16
Sense of Taste

The tongue has numerous visible bumps on its surface. The taste buds are located below the surface of the tongue, on the sides of the bumps.

Taste Bud

Nerve to brain

Food chemicals in saliva trigger taste receptors in the taste buds. The taste receptors send signals to the brain.

Magnified image of the tongue's surface ▶

Touch

Unlike vision, hearing, balance, smell, and taste, the sense of touch is not found in one specific place. Instead, the sense of touch is found in all areas of your skin. Your skin is your largest sense organ! **Your skin contains different kinds of touch receptors that respond to a number of stimuli.** Some of these receptors respond to light touch and others to heavy pressure. Still other receptors pick up sensations of pain and temperature change.

The receptors that respond to light touch are in the upper part of the dermis. They tell you when something brushes against your skin. These receptors also let you feel the textures of objects, such as smooth glass and rough sandpaper. Receptors deeper in the dermis pick up the feeling of pressure. Press down hard on the top of your desk, for example, and you will feel pressure in your fingertips.

The dermis also contains receptors that respond to temperature and pain. Pain is unpleasant, but it can be one of the body's most important feelings because it alerts the body to possible danger. Have you ever stepped into a bathtub of very hot water and then immediately pulled your foot out? If so, you can appreciate how pain can trigger an important response in your body.

FIGURE 17
Reading by Touch
People who are blind use their sense of touch to read. To do this, they run their fingers over words written in Braille. Braille uses raised dots to represent letters and numbers. Here, a teacher shows a blind child how to read Braille.

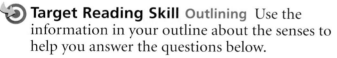

Section 3 Assessment

Target Reading Skill Outlining Use the information in your outline about the senses to help you answer the questions below.

Reviewing Key Concepts

1. **a.** Listing What are the parts of the eye?
   b. Sequencing Describe the process by which the eye produces an image. Begin at the point at which light is focused by the lens.
   c. Inferring If nearby objects seem blurry, what type of vision problem might you have? How can it be corrected?

2. **a.** Identifying What are the three regions of the ear?
   b. Describing Describe the location and function of the eardrum and the cochlea.
   c. Relating Cause and Effect Why may an infection of the inner ear cause you to lose your balance?

3. **a.** Reviewing What two senses work together to influence the flavor of food?
   b. Comparing and Contrasting How are the senses of taste and smell similar? How are they different?

4. **a.** Identifying What kinds of touch receptors are found in the skin?
   b. Applying Concepts What happens in the dermis when you accidentally touch a hot stove?

Writing in Science

Cause-and-Effect Paragraph Write a description of how you feel after an amusement park ride. Explain how your feeling is related to the structure and function of the semicircular canals. Be sure to include a topic sentence and three to four supporting points.

Alcohol and Other Drugs

Reading Preview

Key Concepts
- What are the immediate and long-term effects of drug abuse?
- What are some commonly abused drugs and how does each affect the body?
- How does alcohol abuse harm the body?

Key Terms
- drug • drug abuse
- tolerance • addiction
- withdrawal • depressant
- stimulant • anabolic steroid
- alcoholism

Target Reading Skill

Relating Cause and Effect As you read, identify commonly abused drugs and how they affect the body. Write the information in a graphic organizer like the one below.

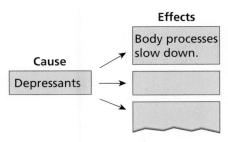

Effects

Body processes slow down.

Cause

Depressants

Lab zone Discover **Activity**

How Can You Best Say No?

1. In this activity, you will use marbles to represent drugs. Your teacher will divide the class into groups of three students. In each group, your teacher will appoint two students to try to convince the other person to take the "drugs."

2. Depending on your role, you should think of arguments to get the person to accept the marbles or arguments against accepting them. After everyone has had a chance to think of arguments, begin the discussion.

3. After a while, students in each group should exchange roles.

Think It Over

Inferring What role does peer pressure play in whether or not a person decides to abuse drugs?

Drugs! You probably hear and see that word in a lot of places. Drugstores sell drugs to relieve headaches, soothe upset stomachs, and stop coughs. Radio and television programs and magazine articles explore drug-related problems. Your school probably has a program to educate students about drugs. When people talk about drugs, what do they mean? To a scientist, a **drug** is any chemical taken into the body that causes changes in a person's body or behavior. Many drugs affect the functioning of the central nervous system.

Drug Abuse

The deliberate misuse of drugs for purposes other than medical ones is called **drug abuse.** Even medicines can be abused drugs if they are used in a way for which they were not intended. Many abused drugs, however, such as cocaine and heroin, are illegal under any circumstances. The use of these drugs is against the law because their effects on the body are almost always dangerous.

Effects of Abused Drugs Abused drugs start to affect the body shortly after they are taken. **Most commonly abused drugs, such as marijuana, alcohol, and cocaine, are especially dangerous because of their immediate effects on the brain and other parts of the nervous system. In addition, long-term drug abuse can lead to addiction and other health and social problems.**

Different drugs have different effects. Some drugs cause nausea and a fast, irregular heartbeat. Others can cause sleepiness. Drug abusers may also experience headaches, dizziness, and trembling. Alcohol can cause confusion, poor muscle coordination, and blurred vision. These effects are especially dangerous in situations in which an alert mind is essential, such as driving a car.

Most abused drugs can alter, or change, a person's mood and feelings. Because of this effect, these drugs are often called mood-altering drugs. For example, the mood of a person under the influence of marijuana may change from calm to anxious. Alcohol can sometimes make a person angry and even violent. Mood-altering drugs also affect patterns of thinking and the way in which the brain interprets information from the senses.

Tolerance If a person takes a drug regularly, the body may develop a tolerance to the drug. **Tolerance** is a state in which a drug user needs larger and larger amounts of the drug to produce the same effect on the body. Tolerance can cause people to take a very large amount of a drug, or an overdose. People who take an overdose may become unconscious or even die.

FIGURE 18
Drug Abuse
Drug abuse can have serious consequences. However, there are ways to tell if someone is abusing drugs and ways to help that person. *Interpreting Diagrams*
What are two ways you can help if someone you know is abusing drugs?

Signs of Drug Abuse

- Sudden changes in mood
- Lying, cheating
- Forgetfulness, withdrawn attitude, aggressiveness
- Poor coordination
- Slurred speech

Addiction For many commonly abused drugs, repeated use can result in addiction. In **addiction,** the body becomes physically dependent on the drug. If a drug addict misses a few doses of the drug, the body reacts to the lack of the drug. The person may experience headaches, dizziness, fever, vomiting, body aches, and muscle cramps. The person is experiencing **withdrawal,** a period of adjustment that occurs when a person stops taking a drug on which the body is dependent.

Some drugs may also cause a person to become emotionally dependent on them. The person becomes accustomed to the feelings and moods produced by the drug. Therefore, the person has a strong desire to continue using the drug.

Other Effects of Drug Abuse Drugs can also affect a person's health indirectly. Some drug users sometimes share needles. When a person uses a needle to inject a drug, some of the person's blood remains in the needle after it is withdrawn. If the person has HIV or another pathogen in the blood, the next person to use the needle may become infected with the pathogen.

The abuse of drugs also has serious legal and social effects. A person who is caught using or selling an illegal drug may have to pay a fine or go to jail. Drug abuse can also make a person unable to get along with others. Drug abusers often have a hard time doing well in school or holding a job.

 **Reading Checkpoint** **What is withdrawal?**

Lab zone Skills **Activity**

Communicating
Plan a 30-second television commercial aimed at teenagers to help them avoid the pressure to try drugs. Your commercial should reveal some harmful effects of drugs and give strategies for avoiding drugs. Create several storyboards to show what the commercial will look like. Then, write a script for your commercial.

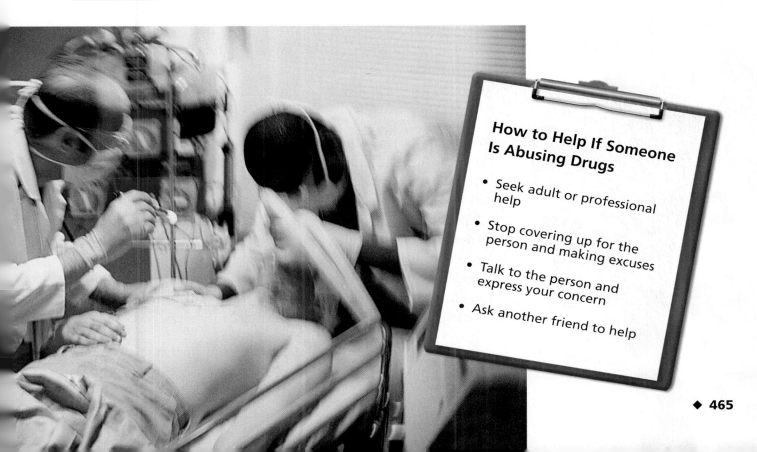

How to Help If Someone Is Abusing Drugs

- Seek adult or professional help
- Stop covering up for the person and making excuses
- Talk to the person and express your concern
- Ask another friend to help

Kinds of Abused Drugs

There are many kinds of drugs, with a wide range of effects on the body. Some are legitimate medicines that a doctor prescribes to help the body fight disease and injury. However, many kinds of drugs are frequently abused. **Commonly abused drugs include depressants, stimulants, inhalants, hallucinogens, anabolic steroids, and alcohol. Many drugs affect the central nervous system, while others affect the overall chemical balance in the body.** Figure 20 lists and describes the characteristics of some commonly abused drugs.

Depressants Notice in Figure 20 that some drugs are classified as depressants. **Depressants** are drugs that slow down the activity of the central nervous system. When people take depressants, their muscles relax and they may become sleepy. They may take longer than normal to respond to stimuli. For example, depressants may prevent people from reacting quickly to the danger of a car rushing toward them. Alcohol and narcotics, such as heroin, are depressants.

Stimulants In contrast to depressants, **stimulants** speed up body processes. They make the heart beat faster and make the breathing rate increase. Cocaine and nicotine are stimulants, as are amphetamines (am FET uh meenz). Amphetamines are prescription drugs that are sometimes sold illegally.

Inhalants and Hallucinogens Some substances, called inhalants, produce mood-altering effects when they are inhaled, or breathed in. Inhalants include paint thinner, nail polish remover, and some kinds of cleaning fluids. Hallucinogens, such as LSD and mescaline, can make people see or hear things that do not really exist.

Steroids Some athletes try to improve their performance by taking drugs known as steroids. **Anabolic steroids** (an uh BAH lik STEER oydz) are synthetic chemicals that are similar to hormones produced in the body.

Anabolic steroids may increase muscle size and strength. However, steroids can cause mood changes that lead to violence. In addition, steroid abuse can cause serious health problems, such as heart damage, liver damage, and increased blood pressure. Steroid use is especially dangerous for teenagers, whose growing bodies can be permanently damaged.

 **Reading Checkpoint** What kinds of drugs are classified as stimulants?

FIGURE 19
Making a Statement About Drug Abuse
Many teens are becoming active in antidrug campaigns.

FIGURE 20

Abused drugs can have many serious effects on the body. **Interpreting Tables** *What are the long-term effects of using inhalants?*

Some Effects of Commonly Abused Drugs				
Drug Type	**Short-Term Effects**	**Long-Term Effects**	**Addiction?**	**Emotional Dependence?**
Marijuana (including hashish)	Unclear thinking, loss of coordination, increased heart rate	Difficulty with concentration and memory; respiratory disease and lung cancer	Probably not	Yes
Nicotine (in cigarettes, cigars, chewing tobacco)	Stimulant; nausea, loss of appetite, headache	Heart and lung disease, difficulty breathing, heavy coughing	Yes, strongly so	Yes
Alcohol	Depressant; decreased alertness, poor reflexes, nausea, emotional depression	Liver and brain damage, inadequate nutrition	Yes	Yes
Inhalants (glue, nail polish remover, paint thinner)	Sleepiness, nausea, headaches, emotional depression	Damage to liver, kidneys, and brain; hallucinations	No	Yes
Cocaine (including crack)	Stimulant; nervousness, disturbed sleep, loss of appetite	Mental illness, damage to lining of nose, irregular heartbeat, heart or breathing failure, liver damage	Yes	Yes, strongly so
Amphetamines	Stimulant; restlessness, rapid speech, dizziness	Restlessness, irritability, irregular heartbeat, liver damage	Possible	Yes
Hallucinogens (LSD, mescaline, PCP)	Hallucinations, anxiety, panic; thoughts and actions not connected to reality	Mental illness; fearfulness; behavioral changes, including violence	No	Yes
Barbiturates (Phenobarbital, Nembutal, Seconal)	Depressant; decreased alertness, slowed thought processes, poor muscle coordination	Sleepiness, irritability, confusion	Yes	Yes
Tranquilizers (Valium, Xanax)	Depressant; blurred vision, sleepiness, unclear speech, headache, skin rash	Blood and liver disease	Yes	Yes
Narcotics (opium, codeine, morphine, heroin)	Depressant; sleepiness, nausea, hallucinations	Convulsion, coma, death	Yes, very rapid development	Yes, strongly so
Anabolic steroids	Mood swings	Heart, liver, and kidney damage; hypertension; overgrowth of skull and facial bones	No	Yes

Alcohol

Alcohol is a drug found in many beverages, including beer, wine, cocktails, and hard liquor. Alcohol is a powerful depressant. In all states, it is illegal for people under the age of 21 to buy or possess alcohol. In spite of this fact, alcohol is the most commonly abused legal drug in people aged 12 to 17.

How Alcohol Affects the Body Alcohol is absorbed by the digestive system quickly. If a person drinks alcohol on an empty stomach, the alcohol enters the blood and gets to the brain and other organs almost immediately. If alcohol is drunk with a meal, it takes longer to get into the blood.

The chart in Figure 21 describes what alcohol does to the body. The more alcohol in the blood, the more serious the effects. The amount of alcohol in the blood is usually expressed as blood alcohol concentration, or BAC. A BAC value of 0.1 percent means that one tenth of one percent of the fluid in the blood is alcohol. In some states, if car drivers have a BAC of 0.08 percent or more, they are legally drunk. In other states, drivers with a BAC of 0.1 are considered legally drunk.

Alcohol produces serious negative effects, including loss of normal judgment, at a BAC of less than 0.08 percent. This loss of judgment can have serious consequences. People who have been drinking may not realize that they cannot drive a car safely. About every two minutes, a person in the United States is injured in a car crash related to alcohol.

FIGURE 21
Alcohol's Effects
Alcohol affects every system of the body. It also impacts a person's thought processes, judgment, and reaction time. In the bottom photo, a police officer tests the blood alcohol concentration of a driver suspected of drinking.

Short-Term Effects of Alcohol	
Body System	**Effect**
Cardiovascular system	First, heartbeat rate and blood pressure increase. Later, they may decrease.
Digestive system	Alcohol is absorbed directly from the stomach and small intestine, which allows it to enter the bloodstream quickly.
Excretory system	The kidneys produce more urine, causing the drinker to excrete more water than usual.
Nervous system	Vision blurs. Speech becomes unclear. Control of behavior is reduced. Judgment becomes poor.
Skin	Blood flow to the skin increases, causing rapid loss of body heat.

Long-Term Alcohol Abuse Many adults drink occasionally and in moderation, without serious safety or health problems. However, heavy drinking, especially over a long period, can result in significant health problems. **Alcohol abuse can cause the destruction of cells in the brain and liver, and can lead to addiction and emotional dependence.** Damage to the brain can cause mental disturbances, such as hallucinations and loss of consciousness. The liver, which breaks down alcohol for elimination from the body, can become so scarred that it does not function properly. In addition, long-term alcohol abuse can increase the risk of getting certain kinds of cancer.

Abuse of alcohol can result in **alcoholism,** a disease in which a person is both physically addicted to and emotionally dependent on alcohol. To give up alcohol, as with any addictive drug, alcoholics must go through withdrawal. To give up drinking, alcoholics need both medical and emotional help. Medical professionals, psychologists, and organizations such as Alcoholics Anonymous can help a person stop drinking.

 **What organs are affected by alcohol abuse?**

Healthy Liver

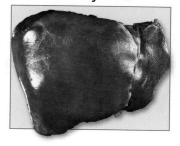

Alcohol-damaged Liver

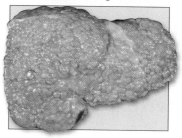

FIGURE 22
Alcohol's Effect on the Liver
Long-term alcohol abuse can cause serious damage to the liver. **Relating Cause and Effect** *What other effects can alcohol abuse have on the body?*

Section 4 Assessment

Target Reading Skill Relating Cause and Effect Refer to your graphic organizer about commonly abused drugs to help you answer Question 2.

Reviewing Key Concepts

1. a. **Defining** In your own words, explain what a drug is. What is drug abuse?
   b. **Explaining** How can the repeated use of some drugs lead to addiction and emotional dependence?
   c. **Applying Concepts** What reasons would you give someone to not try drugs in the first place?
2. a. **Listing** Name two commonly abused depressants and two commonly abused stimulants.
   b. **Comparing and Contrasting** Contrast the effects that depressants and stimulants have on the body.

   c. **Inferring** Why might a person's risk of a heart attack increase with the use of stimulants?
3. a. **Reviewing** What type of drug is alcohol?
   b. **Explaining** What immediate effects does alcohol have on the body?
   c. **Relating Cause and Effect** Based on alcohol's effect on the nervous system, explain why drinking and driving is extremely dangerous.

Lab zone **At-Home Activity**

Medicine Labels Collect several medicine bottles and read the warning labels. Make a list of the kinds of warnings you find. Discuss these warnings with a family member. Why do you think medicines provide warnings?

With Caffeine or Without?

Problem

What body changes does caffeine produce in blackworms *(Lumbriculus)*?

Skills Focus

observing, controlling variables, drawing conclusions

Materials

- blackworms
- plastic dropper
- adrenaline solution
- stereomicroscope
- paraffin specimen trough
- noncarbonated spring water
- beverages with and without caffeine
- stopwatch or clock with second hand

Procedure

PART 1 Observing the Effects of a Known Stimulant

1. Copy the data table in your notebook. Use a dropper to remove one worm and a drop or two of water from the blackworm population provided by your teacher.

2. Place the worm and the water in the trough of the paraffin block. Use the dropper or the corner of a paper towel to remove any excess water that does not fit in the trough. Let the blackworm adjust for a few minutes.

3. Place the paraffin block under the stereomicroscope. Select the smallest amount of light and the lowest possible power to view the blackworm.

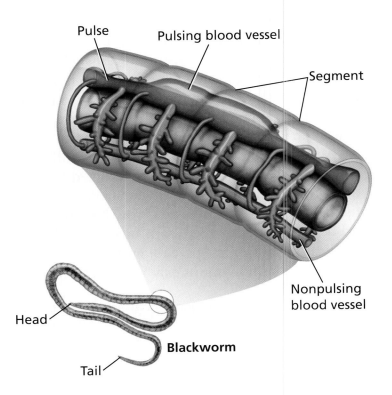

4. Look through the stereomicroscope and locate a segment near the middle of the worm. Count the number of times blood pulses through this segment for 30 seconds. Multiply this number by two to get the pulse in beats per minute. Record the pulse in your data table.

Data Table	
Condition	Pulse Rate
No adrenaline	
With adrenaline	
Beverage without caffeine	
Beverage with caffeine	

5. Remove the block from the stereomicroscope. Use the dropper to add 1 drop of adrenaline solution to the trough. (Adrenaline is a substance produced by the human body that acts as a stimulant.) Let the worm sit in the adrenaline solution for 5 minutes.

6. Place the paraffin block under the stereomicroscope. Again locate a segment near the middle of the worm. Count the number of pulses through this segment for 30 seconds. Multiply this number by two to get the pulse in beats per minute. Record the blackworm's pulse with adrenaline.

PART 2 Testing the Effects of Caffeine

7. Using the procedures you followed in Part 1, design an experiment that tests the effect of caffeine on the blackworm's pulse. You can use beverages with and without caffeine in your investigation. Be sure to write a hypothesis and control all necessary variables.

8. Submit your experimental plan to your teacher for review. After making any necessary changes, carry out your experiment.

Analyze and Conclude

1. **Observing** In Part 1, what was the blackworm's pulse rate before you added adrenaline? After you added adrenaline?

2. **Interpreting Data** Use the data you collected in Part 1 to explain how you know that adrenaline acts as a stimulant.

3. **Controlling Variables** In the experiment you performed in Part 2, what was your control? Explain.

4. **Drawing Conclusions** Based on your results in Part 2, does caffeine act as a stimulant? Explain your answer.

5. **Communicating** Write a paragraph to explain how you think your body would react to drinks with caffeine and without caffeine. Use the results from this investigation to support your viewpoint.

Design an Experiment

Do you think that "decaffeinated" products will act as a stimulant in blackworms? Design a controlled experiment to find out. *Obtain your teacher's permission before carrying out your investigation.*

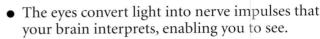

① How the Nervous System Works

Key Concepts

- The nervous system directs how your body responds to information about what is happening inside and outside your body. Your nervous system also helps maintain homeostasis.

- The three kinds of neurons found in the body are sensory neurons, interneurons, and motor neurons.

- For a nerve impulse to be carried along at a synapse, it must cross the gap between an axon and the next structure.

Key Terms

stimulus	axon
response	nerve
neuron	sensory neuron
nerve impulse	interneuron
dendrite	motor neuron
	synapse

② Divisions of the Nervous System

Key Concepts

- The central nervous system is the control center of the body. It includes the brain and spinal cord.

- The peripheral nervous system consists of a network of nerves that branch out from the central nervous system and connect it to the rest of the body.

- A reflex is an automatic response that occurs very rapidly and without conscious control.

- Concussions and spinal cord injuries are two ways the central nervous system can be damaged.

Key Terms

central nervous system	brain stem
peripheral nervous system	somatic nervous system
brain	autonomic nervous system
spinal cord	reflex
cerebrum	concussion
cerebellum	

③ The Senses

Key Concepts

- The eyes convert light into nerve impulses that your brain interprets, enabling you to see.

- The ears convert sound into nerve impulses that your brain interprets, enabling you to hear. Structures in your inner ear control your sense of balance.

- The senses of smell and taste work together.

- The skin contains touch receptors that respond to a number of stimuli.

Key Terms

cornea	nearsightedness
pupil	farsightedness
iris	eardrum
lens	cochlea
retina	semicircular canal

④ Alcohol and Other Drugs

Key Concepts

- Most abused drugs are dangerous because of their immediate effects on the nervous system. Long-term drug abuse can lead to addiction and other health and social problems.

- Commonly abused drugs include depressants, stimulants, inhalants, steroids, and alcohol.

- Alcohol use can destroy cells in the brain and liver, and lead to addiction.

Key Terms

drug
drug abuse
tolerance
addiction
withdrawal
depressant
stimulant
anabolic steroid
alcoholism

Review and Assessment

Organizing Information

Concept Mapping Copy the concept map about neurons and their functions onto a separate sheet of paper. Then, complete it and add a title. (For more on Concept Mapping, see the Skills Handbook.)

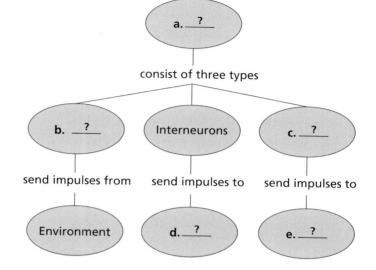

Reviewing Key Terms

Choose the letter of the best answer.

1. A change or signal in the environment that makes the nervous system react is called a
   a. stimulus.
   b. response.
   c. nerve impulse.
   d. synapse.

2. The structures that carry messages toward a neuron's cell body are
   a. axons.
   b. dendrites.
   c. nerves.
   d. nerve impulses.

3. Which structure links the brain and the peripheral nervous system?
   a. the cerebrum
   b. the cerebellum
   c. the cochlea
   d. the spinal cord

4. Which structure adjusts the size of the pupil?
   a. the cornea   b. the retina
   c. the lens   d. the iris

5. Physical dependence on a drug is called
   a. withdrawal.   b. response.
   c. addiction.   d. tolerance.

If the statement is true, write *true*. If it is false, change the underlined word or words to make the statement true.

6. A nerve message is also called a <u>synapse</u>.

7. The <u>cerebrum</u> is the part of the brain that controls involuntary actions.

8. In <u>nearsightedness</u>, a person can see distant objects clearly.

9. The <u>cochlea</u> is part of the inner ear.

10. Alcohol is a <u>depressant</u>.

Writing in Science

Descriptive Paragraph Draw a diagram of the human eye, and label the key parts. Then, write a paragraph that describes how each part helps a person "see" an image.

Discovery CHANNEL SCHOOL

The Nervous System

Video Preview
Video Field Trip
▶ Video Assessment

Review and Assessment

Checking Concepts

11. Compare the functions of axons and dendrites.

12. How do the cerebrum and cerebellum work together when you ride a bicycle?

13. What is the function of the autonomic nervous system?

14. What is the result if the spinal cord is cut?

15. Describe how lenses in eyeglasses correct nearsightedness and farsightedness.

16. List in order all the structures in your ear that must vibrate before you hear a sound.

17. How do anabolic steroids affect the body?

Thinking Critically

18. **Interpreting Diagrams** The diagram below shows a synapse. Explain how a nerve impulse crosses the gap.

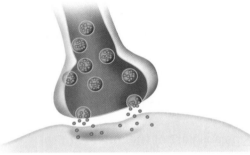

19. **Relating Cause and Effect** When a person has a stroke, blood flow to part of the brain is reduced, and some brain cells die. Suppose that after a stroke, a woman is unable to move her right arm and right leg. In which side of her brain did the stroke occur? Explain.

20. **Applying Concepts** As a man walks barefoot along a beach, he steps on a sharp shell. His foot automatically jerks upward, even before he feels pain. What process is this an example of? How does it help protect the man?

21. **Making Judgments** If someone tried to persuade you to take drugs, what arguments would you use as a way of refusing? Why do you think these arguments would be effective?

Applying Skills

Use the graph to answer Questions 22–25.

A person with normal vision stood at different distances from an eye chart and tried to identify the letters on the chart. The line graph gives the results.

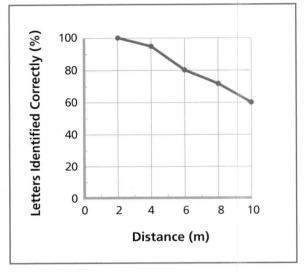

22. **Reading Graphs** What variable is plotted on the *x*-axis? On the *y*-axis?

23. **Interpreting Data** As the distance from the eye chart increases, what happens to the percentage of letters identified correctly?

24. **Controlling Variables** What was the manipulated variable in this experiment? What was the responding variable?

25. **Predicting** How would you expect the results to differ for a farsighted person? Explain.

![Lab zone] Chapter **Project**

Performance Assessment Explain to your classmates how you set up your experiment, which illusions you used, which senses were involved in the illusions, and why the illusions worked. Include information on how the nervous system was involved in your illusions.

🦅 End-of-Grade Test Practice

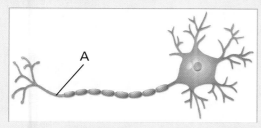
Choose the letter of the best answer.

1. A scientist studying the brain is studying part of the
  A peripheral nervous system.
  B somatic nervous system.
  C autonomic nervous system.
  D central nervous system.

Use the diagram below and your knowledge of science to answer Questions 2 and 3.

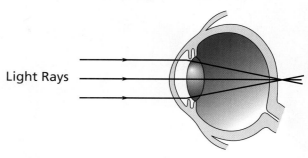

Light Rays

2. To correct the vision of the eye shown above, a lens would have to make the light rays
  A bend toward each other before they reach the eye's lens.
  B spread out before they reach the eye's lens.
  C focus on the eye's lens.
  D focus behind the retina.

3. Which of the following correctly pairs the vision problem in the eye shown above with the proper corrective lens?
  A farsightedness; convex lens
  B farsightedness; concave lens
  C nearsightedness; convex lens
  D nearsightedness; concave lens

4. The brain stem is involved in controlling
  A breathing.
  B the ability to learn.
  C movement of skeletal muscles.
  D balance.

5. You can infer that a person who has lost his or her sense of smell is also likely to have a poor
  A sense of balance.
  B sense of touch.
  C sense of taste.
  D sense of hearing.

Constructed Response

6. Outline the path of the reflex action that takes place when you step on a tack. What is the advantage of the nerve impulse not needing to go through the brain before action is taken?

Standard Course of Study

This chapter addresses the following North Carolina Objectives:

1.01 Identify and create questions and hypotheses.

1.02 Develop appropriate experimental procedures.

1.05 Analyze evidence.

1.06 Use mathematics to gather, organize, and present data.

1.07 Prepare models and/or computer simulations.

1.08 Use oral and written language.

4.01 Analyze how human body systems interact.

4.02 Describe functions of human body systems.

4.04 Evaluate how human body systems regulate the internal environment.

4.06 Describe human growth and development.

4.07 Explain how environmental effects influence human embryo development and health.

▶ Identical twins result when a single fertilized egg splits and forms two embryos.

Lab zone™ Chapter Project

A Precious Bundle

As you learn about reproduction and development, you'll experience what it's like to care for a "baby." Although your baby will be only a model, you'll have a chance to learn about the responsibilities of parenthood.

Your Goal Develop and follow a plan to care for a "baby" for three days and nights.

You must

● list all the essential tasks involved in caring for a young infant, and prepare a 24-hour schedule of those tasks

● make a model "baby" from a bag of flour, and care for the baby according to your schedule

● keep a journal of your thoughts and feelings as you care for your "baby," making entries at least twice a day

Plan It! With classmates, write down all the things that parents must do when caring for infants. Prepare a plan describing how to carry out those activities with your "baby." List the materials you'll need. If you require more information, write down your questions, then consult adult caregivers, day-care facilities, or other resources.

The Endocrine System

Reading Preview

Key Concepts
- How does the endocrine system control body processes?
- What are the endocrine glands?
- How does negative feedback control hormone levels?

Key Terms
- endocrine gland • hormone
- target cell • hypothalamus
- pituitary gland
- negative feedback

Target Reading Skill

Relating Cause and Effect As you read, identify the effects of pituitary hormones. Write the information in a graphic organizer like the one below.

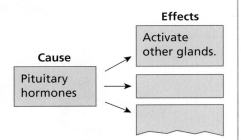

Effects

Cause → Activate other glands.

Pituitary hormones →

→

Lab zone Discover Activity

What's the Signal?

1. Stand up and move around the room until your teacher says "Freeze!" Then, stop moving immediately. Stay perfectly still until your teacher says "Start!" Then, begin moving again.
2. Anyone who moves between the "Freeze!" command and the "Start!" command has to leave the game.
3. When only one person is left, that person wins.

Think it Over

Inferring Why is it important for players in this game to respond to signals? What types of signals does the human body use?

Imagine that you are trapped in a damp, dark dungeon. Somewhere near you is a deep pit with water at the bottom. Overhead swings a pendulum with a razor-sharp edge. With each swing, the pendulum lowers closer and closer to your body.

The main character in Edgar Allan Poe's story "The Pit and the Pendulum" finds himself in that very situation. Here is his reaction: "A fearful idea now suddenly drove the blood in torrents upon my heart. . . . I at once started to my feet, trembling convulsively in every fibre. . . . Perspiration burst from every pore, and stood in cold, big beads upon my forehead."

Poe's character is terrified. When people are badly frightened, their bodies react in the ways that the character describes. These physical reactions, such as sweating and rapid heartbeat, are caused mainly by the body's endocrine system.

Hormones and the Endocrine System

The human body has two systems that regulate its activities, the nervous system and the endocrine system. The nervous system regulates most activities by sending nerve impulses throughout the body. **The endocrine system produces chemicals that control many of the body's daily activities. The endocrine system also regulates long-term changes such as growth and development.**

The endocrine system is made up of glands. A gland is an organ that produces or releases a chemical. Some glands, such as those that produce saliva and sweat, release their chemicals into tiny tubes. The tubes deliver the chemicals to a specific location within the body or to the skin's surface.

Unlike sweat glands, the glands of the endocrine system do not have delivery tubes. **Endocrine glands** (EN duh krin) produce and release their chemical products directly into the bloodstream. The blood then carries those chemicals throughout the body.

Hormones The chemical product of an endocrine gland is called a **hormone.** Hormones turn on, turn off, speed up, or slow down the activities of different organs and tissues. You can think of a hormone as a chemical messenger. Hormones are carried throughout the body by the blood. Therefore, hormones can regulate activities in tissues and organs that are not close to the glands that produce them.

FIGURE 1
Endocrine Control
The endocrine system controls the body's response to an exciting situation such as a roller-coaster ride. Endocrine glands also regulate the changes that occur as a baby grows.
Applying Concepts *What are the substances produced by endocrine glands called?*

Hormone Production What causes the release of hormones? Often, nerve impulses from the brain make that happen. Suppose, for example, a person sees a deadly, knife-edged pendulum. Nerve impulses travel from the person's eyes to the brain. The brain interprets the information and then sends an impulse to an endocrine gland. That gland, in turn, releases the hormone adrenaline into the bloodstream. Adrenaline immediately makes the heart rate and breathing rate increase.

Hormone Action In contrast to the body's response to a nerve impulse, hormones usually cause a slower, but longer-lasting, response. For example, the brain sends a signal to an endocrine gland to release adrenaline into the bloodstream. When the adrenaline reaches the heart, it makes the heart beat more rapidly. The heart continues to race until the amount of adrenaline in the blood drops to a normal level.

Target Cells When a hormone enters the bloodstream, it affects some organs but not others. Why? The answer lies in the hormone's chemical structure. A hormone interacts only with specific target cells. **Target cells** are cells that recognize the hormone's chemical structure. A hormone and its target cell fit together the way a key fits into a lock. Hormones will travel through the bloodstream until they find the "lock"— or particular cell type—that they fit.

 **Reading Checkpoint** What is a target cell?

Functions of Endocrine Glands

Each endocrine gland releases different hormones and thus controls different processes. **The endocrine glands include the hypothalamus, pituitary, thyroid, parathyroid, adrenal, thymus, and pancreas. They also include the ovaries in females and testes in males.** Figure 2 shows the locations of the endocrine glands and describes some activities they control.

The Hypothalamus The nervous system and the endocrine system work together. The **hypothalamus** (hy poh THAL uh mus), a tiny part of the brain near the middle of your head, is the link between the two systems. Nerve messages controlling sleep, hunger, and other basic body processes come from the hypothalamus. The hypothalamus also produces hormones that control other endocrine glands and organs. The hypothalamus plays a major role in maintaining homeostasis because of the nerve impulses and hormones it produces.

Lab zone Skills **Activity**

Making Models
Make a model that shows a hormone and a target cell that the hormone affects. Your model should show how the structures of the hormone and target cell enable the two to fit together. Make your model from materials such as construction paper, pipe cleaners, or modeling clay. When you have finished your model, write an explanation of how it shows the relationship between a hormone and its target cell.

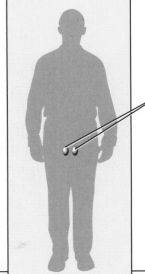

FIGURE 2
Glands of the Endocrine System

Each of the endocrine glands has an important regulatory role in the body. Note the location of each gland and the functions of the hormones it produces.

Hypothalamus
The hypothalamus links the nervous and endocrine systems and controls the pituitary gland.

Thyroid Gland
This gland controls the release of energy from food molecules inside cells.

Pituitary Gland
The pituitary gland controls other endocrine glands and regulates growth, blood pressure, and water balance.

Parathyroid Glands
These tiny glands regulate the amount of calcium in the blood.

Thymus Gland
Hormones from this gland help the immune system develop during childhood.

Pancreas
The pancreas produces the hormones insulin and glucagon, which control the level of glucose in the blood.

Adrenal Glands
These glands release several hormones. Adrenaline triggers the body's response to emergency situations. Other hormones affect salt and water balance in the kidneys and sugar in the blood.

Testes
The testes release the sex hormone testosterone, which controls changes in a male's body and regulates sperm production.

Ovaries
The ovaries release female sex hormones. Estrogen controls changes in a female's body. Estrogen and progesterone trigger egg development.

Female

Male

FIGURE 3
The Pituitary Gland
The pituitary gland is located below the hypothalamus. The pituitary controls several important body functions either directly or indirectly by signaling other endocrine glands.

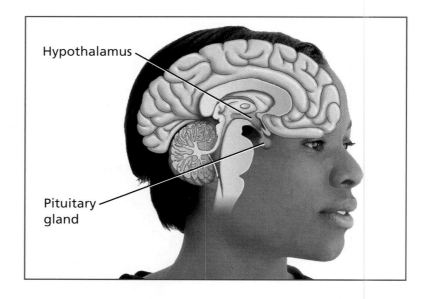

Hypothalamus

Pituitary gland

The Pituitary Gland Just below the hypothalamus is an endocrine gland about the size of a pea. The **pituitary gland** (pih TOO ih tehr ee) communicates with the hypothalamus to control many body activities. In response to nerve impulses or hormone signals from the hypothalamus, the pituitary gland releases its hormones. Some of those hormones act as an "on" switch for other endocrine glands. For example, one pituitary hormone signals the thyroid gland to produce hormones. Other pituitary hormones control body activities directly. Growth hormone regulates growth from infancy to adulthood. Another pituitary hormone directs the kidneys to regulate the amount of water in the blood.

 **Reading Checkpoint** What causes the pituitary gland to release hormones?

Negative Feedback

In some ways, the endocrine system works like a heating system. Suppose you set a thermostat at 20°C. If the temperature falls below 20°C, the thermostat signals the furnace to turn on. When the furnace heats the area to the proper temperature, information about the warm conditions "feeds back" to the thermostat. The thermostat then gives the furnace a signal that turns the furnace off. The type of signal used in a heating system is called **negative feedback** because the system is turned off by the condition it produces.

The endocrine system often uses negative feedback to maintain homeostasis. **Through negative feedback, when the amount of a particular hormone in the blood reaches a certain level, the endocrine system sends signals that stop the release of that hormone.**

You can see an example of negative feedback in Figure 4. Like a thermostat in a cool room, the endocrine system senses when there's not enough thyroxine in the blood. Thyroxine is a thyroid hormone that controls how much energy is available to cells. When there's not enough energy available, the hypothalamus signals the pituitary gland to release thyroid-stimulating hormone (TSH). That hormone signals the thyroid gland to release thyroxine. When the amount of thyroxine reaches the right level, the endocrine system signals the thyroid gland to stop releasing thyroxine.

 **Reading Checkpoint** **How is thyroxine involved in negative feedback?**

Go Online
active art

For: Negative Feedback activity
Visit: PHSchool.com
Web Code: cep-4071

FIGURE 4
Negative Feedback
The release of the hormone thyroxine is controlled through negative feedback. When enough thyroxine is present, the system signals the thyroid gland to stop releasing the hormone. **Predicting** *What happens when the amount of thyroxine becomes too low?*

Hypothalamus senses cells need more energy.

Thyroid stops producing thyroxine.

Pituitary releases TSH.

Pituitary stops producing TSH.

Thyroid produces thyroxine.

Hypothalamus senses cells have enough energy.

Section 1 Assessment

Target Reading Skill
Relating Cause and Effect For Question 2, refer to your graphic organizer about the pituitary gland.

Reviewing Key Concepts

1. a. **Identifying** What is the role of the endocrine system?
   b. **Explaining** How does adrenaline affect the heart?
   c. **Predicting** What could happen if your body continued to release adrenaline into your bloodstream, and the amount of adrenaline did not return to normal?

2. a. **Listing** List the endocrine glands.
   b. **Summarizing** How do the hypothalamus and the pituitary gland interact?

   c. **Relating Cause and Effect** Explain how the hypothalamus indirectly controls growth from infancy to adulthood.

3. a. **Defining** Define negative feedback.
   b. **Applying Concepts** How does negative feedback help to maintain homeostasis?

Writing in Science

Cause-and-Effect Paragraph Explain how the nervous system and endocrine system work together when adrenaline is released.

Chapter 13 ◆ **483**

Technology Lab
• Tech & Design •

Modeling Negative Feedback

Problem

How can you model negative feedback?

Skills Focus

observing, making models, evaluating the design

Materials

- duct tape
- round balloon
- scissors
- rubber stopper
- string, 40 cm
- large plastic soda bottle (2 L) with bottom removed
- small plastic soda bottle (1 L)
- plastic tray
- water

Procedure

PART 1 Research and Investigate

1. Figure 1 shows how a flush toilet uses negative feedback to regulate the water level. In your notebook, describe which part of the process involves negative feedback.

FIGURE 1

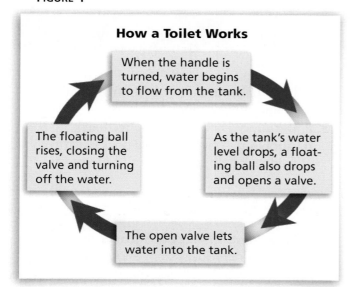

How a Toilet Works

When the handle is turned, water begins to flow from the tank.

As the tank's water level drops, a floating ball also drops and opens a valve.

The open valve lets water into the tank.

The floating ball rises, closing the valve and turning off the water.

FIGURE 2

PART 2 Design and Build

2. As you hold the open end of a balloon, push its closed end through the mouth of a small plastic bottle. Do not push the open end of the balloon into the bottle. Then, slide a straw partway into the bottle so that the air inside the bottle can escape as you blow up the balloon.

3. Partially blow up the balloon inside the bottle as shown in Figure 2. The partially inflated balloon should be about the size of a tennis ball. Remove the straw. Tie the balloon tightly, then push it into the bottle.

4. Place the large plastic bottle mouth to mouth with the small bottle. Tape the two bottles together. Make sure that the seal is waterproof.

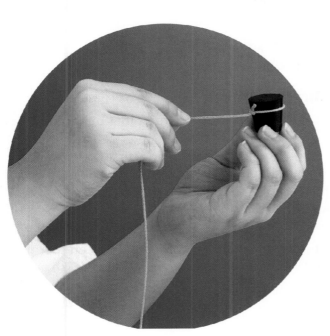

FIGURE 3

FIGURE 4

5. Tie one end of a piece of string around the top of a rubber stopper as shown in Figure 3.

6. Place the attached bottles on the tray with the smaller bottle on the bottom. Place the stopper loosely into the mouth of the larger bottle as shown in Figure 4.

7. While one partner holds the bottles upright, add water to the large bottle until it is about three fourths full. Then gently pull the string to remove the stopper. Watch what happens. Pay close attention to the following: What does the balloon do as water rises in the small bottle? Does the small bottle completely fill with water? Record your observations.

8. In your notebook, record which part of your device models negative feedback.

PART 3 Evaluate and Redesign

9. In the human endocrine system, negative feedback occurs as part of a cycle. With your partner, think of one or more ways that you could modify the model from Part 2 to show a cycle.

Analyze and Conclude

1. **Inferring** Summarize your research from Part 1 by describing an example of negative feedback.

2. **Observing** Describe the events you observed in Step 7.

3. **Making Models** In Step 7, which part of the process involves negative feedback? Explain your answer.

4. **Evaluating the Design** Suggest one way that you could change the model to show that negative feedback can be part of a cycle.

Communicating

Suppose you are a TV health reporter preparing a program on human hormones. You need to do a 30-second segment on hormones and negative feedback. Write a script for your presentation. Include references to a model to help viewers understand how negative feedback works in the endocrine system.

The Male and Female Reproductive Systems

Reading Preview

Key Concepts
- What is sexual reproduction?
- What are the structures and functions of the male and female reproductive systems?
- What events occur during the menstrual cycle?

Key Terms
- egg • sperm • fertilization
- zygote • testis • testosterone
- scrotum • semen • penis
- ovary • estrogen
- fallopian tube • uterus
- vagina • menstrual cycle
- ovulation • menstruation

Target Reading Skill
Sequencing As you read, make a cycle diagram like the one below that shows the menstrual cycle. Write each event of the process in a separate circle.

The Menstrual Cycle

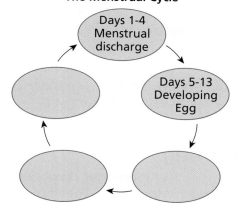

Days 1-4
Menstrual
discharge

Days 5-13
Developing
Egg

Lab zone Discover **Activity**

What's the Big Difference?

1. Your teacher will provide prepared slides of eggs and sperm.
2. Examine each slide under the microscope, first under low power, then under high power. Be sure you view at least one sample of egg and sperm from the same species.
3. Sketch and label each sample.

Think It Over
Observing What differences did you observe between sperm cells and egg cells? What general statement can you make about eggs and sperm?

Many differences between an adult animal and its young are controlled by the endocrine system. In humans, two endocrine glands—the ovaries and the testes—control many of the changes that occur as a child matures. These glands release hormones that cause the body to develop as a person grows older. They also produce sex cells that are part of sexual reproduction.

Hormones control growth and development.

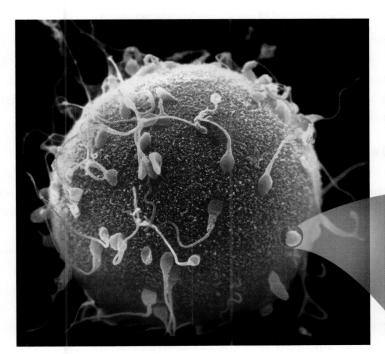

FIGURE 5
Egg and Sperm
An egg is one of the largest cells in the body. A sperm, which is much smaller than an egg, has a head (rounded end) and a tail that allows it to move. In the photograph on the left, sperm are swarming around the large egg. On the right, a sperm, which has been colored blue, has penetrated the egg. **Applying Concepts** *What structure results when the sperm fertilizes the egg?*

Sexual Reproduction

You may find it hard to believe that you began life as a single cell. That single cell was produced by the joining of two other cells, an egg and a sperm. An **egg** is the female sex cell. A **sperm** is the male sex cell.

The joining of a sperm and an egg is called **fertilization.** Fertilization is an important part of sexual reproduction, the process by which male and female living things produce new individuals. **Sexual reproduction involves the production of eggs by the female and sperm by the male. The egg and sperm join together during fertilization.** When fertilization occurs, a fertilized egg, or **zygote,** is produced. Every one of the trillions of cells in your body is descended from the single cell that formed during fertilization.

Like other cells in the body, sex cells contain rod-shaped structures called chromosomes. Chromosomes (KROH muh sohmz) carry the information that controls inherited characteristics, such as eye color and blood type. Every cell in the human body that has a nucleus, except the sex cells, contains 46 chromosomes. Each sex cell contains half that number, or 23 chromosomes. During fertilization, the 23 chromosomes in a sperm join the 23 chromosomes in an egg. The result is a zygote with 46 chromosomes. The zygote contains all of the information needed to produce a new human being.

 **Reading Checkpoint** **What happens to the number of chromosomes when a male sex cell and a female sex cell join?**

Male Reproductive System

The organs of the male reproductive system are shown in Figure 6. **The male reproductive system is specialized to produce sperm and the hormone testosterone. The structures of the male reproductive system include the testes, scrotum, and penis.**

The Testes The oval-shaped **testes** (TES teez) (singular *testis*) are the organs of the male reproductive system in which sperm are produced. The testes consist of clusters of hundreds of tiny coiled tubes and the cells between the tubes. Sperm are formed inside the tubes.

The testes also produce testosterone. **Testosterone** (tes TAHS tuh rohn) is a hormone that controls the development of physical characteristics in mature men. Some of those characteristics include facial hair, deepening of the voice, broadening of the shoulders, and the ability to produce sperm.

Notice in Figure 6 that the testes are located in an external pouch of skin called the **scrotum** (SKROH tum). The external location keeps the testes about 2°C to 3°C below 37°C, which is the usual temperature within the body. That temperature difference is important. Sperm need the slightly cooler conditions to develop normally.

FIGURE 6
The Male Reproductive System

In the male reproductive system, the testes produce sperm and the hormone testosterone.
Interpreting Diagrams *Trace the pathway of sperm in the male reproductive system. What structures does a sperm cell pass through before exiting the body?*

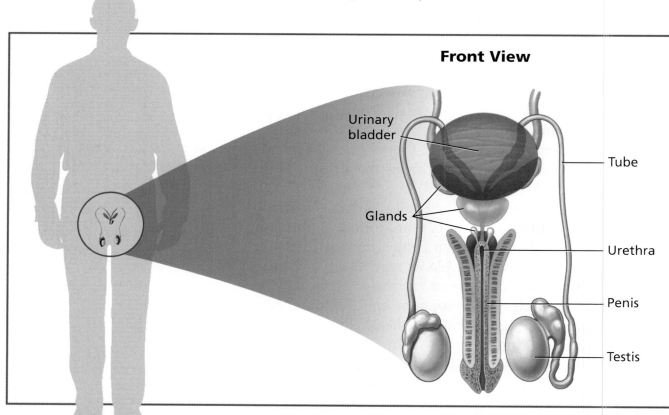

Front View

Urinary bladder

Glands

Tube

Urethra

Penis

Testis

Sperm Production The production of sperm cells begins in males at some point during the teenage years. Each sperm cell is composed of a head that contains chromosomes and a long, whiplike tail. Basically, a sperm cell is a tiny package of chromosomes that can swim.

The Path of Sperm Cells Once sperm cells form in the testes, they travel through other structures in the male reproductive system. During this passage, sperm mix with fluids produced by nearby glands. This mixture of sperm cells and fluids is called **semen** (SEE mun). Semen contains a huge number of sperm—about 5 to 10 million per drop! The fluids in semen provide an environment in which sperm are able to swim. Semen also contains nutrients that the moving sperm use as a source of energy.

Semen leaves the body through an organ called the **penis.** The tube in the penis through which the semen travels is called the urethra. Urine also leaves the body through the urethra. When semen passes through the urethra, however, muscles near the bladder contract. Those muscles prevent urine and semen from mixing.

Go Online
SciLINKS™ NSTA

For: Links on the reproductive system
Visit: www.SciLinks.org
Web Code: scn-0472

Reading Checkpoint — **What is the pouch of skin in which the testes are located?**

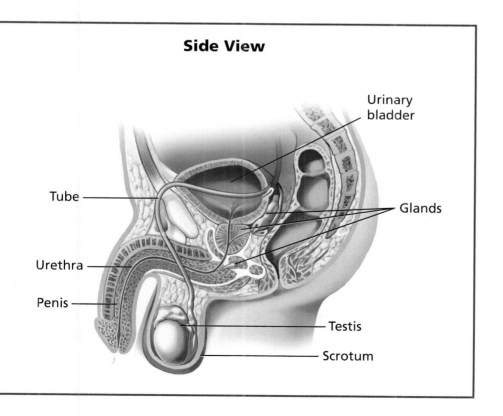

Side View

Urinary bladder

Tube

Glands

Urethra

Penis

Testis

Scrotum

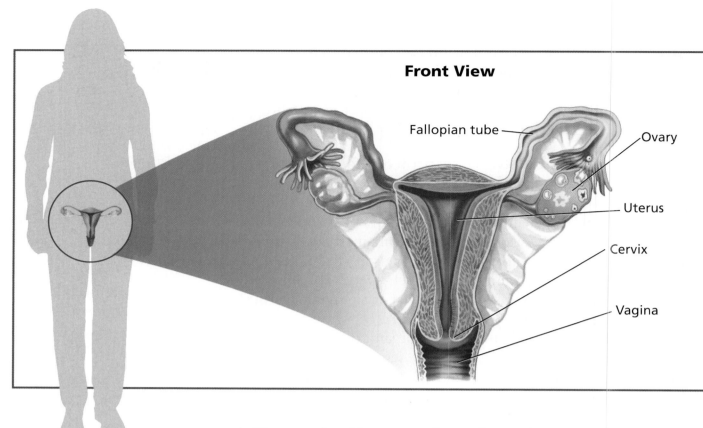

Front View

Fallopian tube

Ovary

Uterus

Cervix

Vagina

Female Reproductive System

Figure 7 shows the female reproductive system. **The role of the female reproductive system is to produce eggs and, if an egg is fertilized, to nourish a developing baby until birth. The organs of the female reproductive system include the ovaries, fallopian tubes, uterus, and vagina.**

The Ovaries The **ovaries** (OH vuh reez) are the female reproductive structures that produce eggs. The ovaries are located slightly below the waist, one ovary on each side of the body. The name for these organs comes from the Latin word *ova*, meaning "eggs."

Female Hormones Like the testes in males, the ovaries also are endocrine glands that produce hormones. One hormone, **estrogen** (ES truh jun), triggers the development of some adult female characteristics. For example, estrogen causes the hips to widen and the breasts to develop. Estrogen also plays a role in the process by which egg cells develop.

The Path of the Egg Cell Each ovary is located near a fallopian tube. The **fallopian tubes,** also called oviducts, are passageways for eggs as they travel from the ovary to the uterus. Each month, one of the ovaries releases a mature egg, which enters the nearest fallopian tube. Fertilization usually occurs within a fallopian tube.

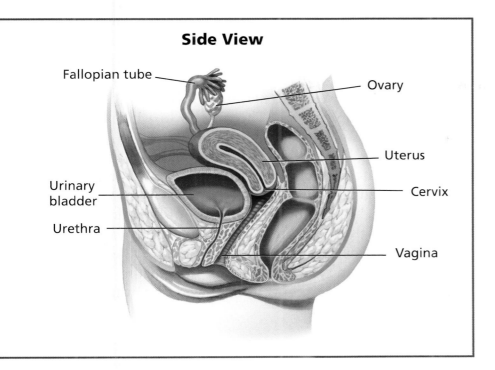

Side View

Fallopian tube

Ovary

Uterus

Cervix

Urinary bladder

Urethra

Vagina

The egg moves through the fallopian tube, which leads to the uterus. The **uterus** (YOO tur us) is a hollow muscular organ about the size of a pear. If an egg has been fertilized, it becomes attached to the wall of the uterus.

An egg that has not been fertilized starts to break down in the uterus. It leaves the uterus through an opening at the base of the uterus, called the cervix. The egg then enters the vagina. The **vagina** (vuh JY nuh) is a muscular passageway leading to the outside of the body. The vagina, or birth canal, is the passageway through which a baby leaves the mother's body.

 **Reading Checkpoint** **What is the role of the fallopian tube?**

The Menstrual Cycle

When the female reproductive system becomes mature, usually during the teenage years, there are about 400,000 undeveloped eggs in the ovaries. However, only about 500 of those eggs will actually leave the ovaries and reach the uterus. An egg is released about once a month in a mature woman's body. The monthly cycle of changes that occur in the female reproductive system is called the **menstrual cycle** (MEN stroo ul).

During the menstrual cycle, an egg develops in an ovary. At the same time, the uterus prepares for the arrival of an embryo. In this way, the menstrual cycle prepares the woman's body for pregnancy, which begins after fertilization.

Lab zone Skills **Activity**

Calculating
An egg is about 0.1 mm in diameter. In contrast, the head of a sperm is about 0.005 mm. Calculate how much bigger an egg is than a sperm.

FIGURE 8
Release of an Egg
The ovary releases an egg, shown here in pink. The egg will then travel down the fallopian tube to the uterus. *Applying Concepts* *Through what opening does an unfertilized egg pass when leaving the uterus?*

Stages of the Menstrual Cycle Follow the stages of the menstrual cycle in Figure 9. Early in the menstrual cycle, an egg starts to mature in one of the ovaries. At the same time, the lining of the uterus begins to thicken. About halfway through a typical menstrual cycle, the mature egg is released from the ovary into a fallopian tube. The process in which an egg is released is called **ovulation** (ahv yuh LAY shun).

Once the egg is released, it can be fertilized for the next few days if sperm are present in the fallopian tube. If the egg is not fertilized, it begins to break down. The lining of the uterus also breaks down. The extra blood and tissue of the thickened lining pass out of the body through the vagina in a process called **menstruation** (men stroo AY shun). On average, menstruation lasts about four to six days. At the same time that menstruation takes place, a new egg begins to mature in the ovary, and the cycle continues.

Endocrine Control The menstrual cycle is controlled by hormones of the endocrine system. Hormones also trigger a girl's first menstruation. Many girls begin menstruation sometime between the ages of 10 and 14 years. Some girls start earlier, while others start later. Women continue to menstruate until about the age of 50. At around that age, the production of sex hormones drops. As a result, the ovaries stop releasing mature egg cells.

Reading Checkpoint How often is an egg released from an ovary?

Changing Hormone Levels

A woman's hormone levels change throughout the menstrual cycle. The graph shows the levels of one female hormone, known as LH, during the menstrual cycle.

1. **Reading Graphs** What does the *y*-axis show?

2. **Interpreting Data** What is the level of LH on day 1? On day 17? On day 21?

3. **Calculating** What is the difference between LH levels on days 9 and 13?

4. **Drawing Conclusions** On what day does LH reach its highest level? What event takes place at about the same time?

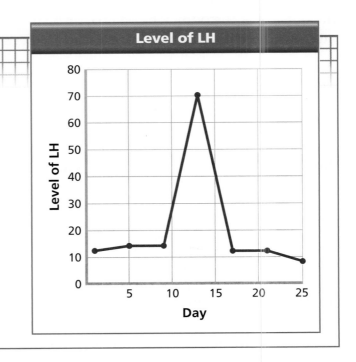

492 ◆

FIGURE 9
The Menstrual Cycle

During the menstrual cycle, the lining of the uterus builds up with extra blood and tissue. About halfway through a typical cycle, ovulation takes place. *Predicting* *What happens if the egg is not fertilized?*

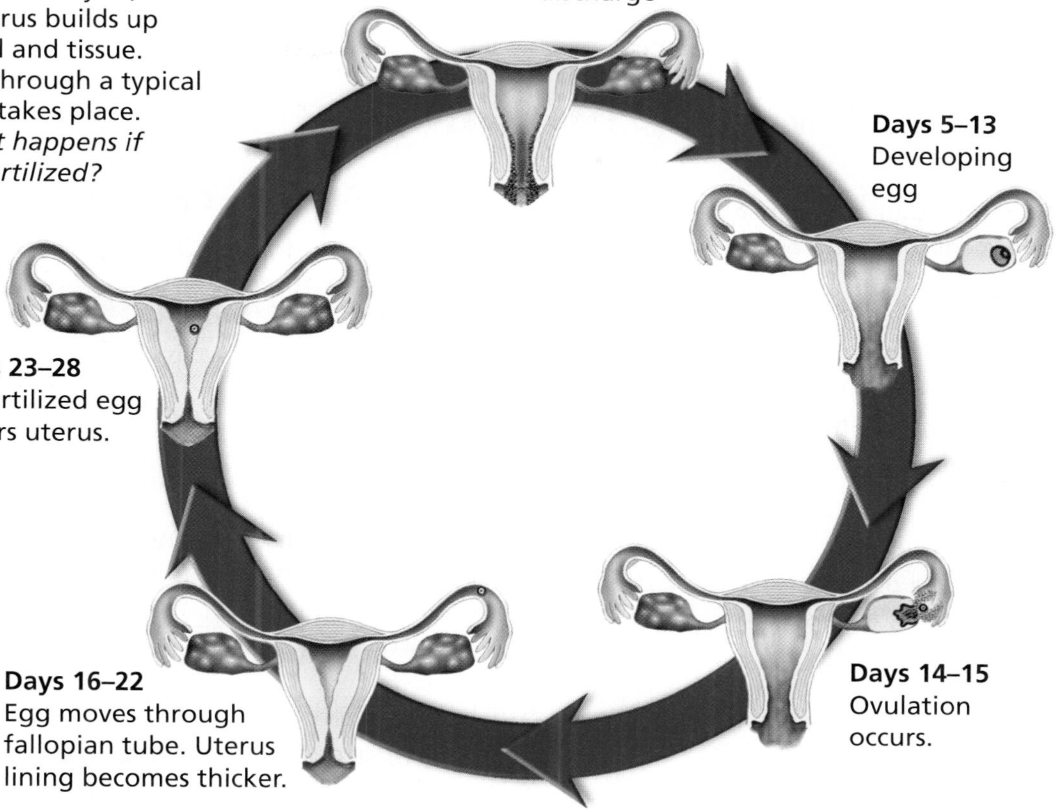

Days 1–4
Menstrual discharge

Days 5–13
Developing egg

Days 14–15
Ovulation occurs.

Days 16–22
Egg moves through fallopian tube. Uterus lining becomes thicker.

Days 23–28
Unfertilized egg enters uterus.

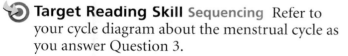

Section 2 Assessment

Target Reading Skill Sequencing Refer to your cycle diagram about the menstrual cycle as you answer Question 3.

Reviewing Key Concepts

1. a. Reviewing What is fertilization?
   b. Explaining Explain how fertilization produces a new individual.
   c. Comparing and Contrasting Contrast the number of chromosomes in sex cells and in a zygote. Explain why the zygote has the number of chromosomes that it does.
2. a. Listing List the structures of the male and female reproductive systems.
   b. Describing Describe the functions of the structures you named in Question 2a.

   c. Comparing and Contrasting In what ways are the functions of the ovaries and the testes similar? How do their functions differ?
3. a. Defining What is the menstrual cycle?
   b. Sequencing Events At what point in the menstrual cycle does ovulation occur?

Writing in Science

Explanatory Paragraph Write a paragraph explaining why the ovaries and testes are part of both the endocrine system and the reproductive system.

Chapter 13 ◆ **493**

The Human Life Cycle

Reading Preview

Key Concepts
- What are the stages of human development that occur before birth?
- How is the developing embryo protected and nourished?
- What happens during childbirth?
- What changes occur from infancy to adulthood?

Key Terms
- embryo • fetus
- amniotic sac • placenta
- umbilical cord • adolescence
- puberty

Target Reading Skill
Building Vocabulary After you read Section 3, reread the paragraphs that contain definitions of Key Terms. Use all the information you have learned to write sentences using each Key Term.

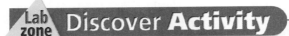

Discover Activity

How Many Ways Does a Child Grow?

1. Compare the two photographs. One shows a baby girl. The other shows the same girl at the age of five.
2. List the similarities you see. Also list the differences.
3. Compare your lists with those of your classmates.

Think It Over
Observing Based on your observations, list three physical changes that occur in early childhood.

An egg can be fertilized during the first few days after ovulation. When sperm are deposited into the vagina, the sperm move into and through the uterus and then into the fallopian tubes. If a sperm fertilizes an egg, pregnancy can occur. Then, the amazing process of human development begins.

Development Before Birth

A fertilized egg, or zygote, is no larger than the period at the end of this sentence. Yet after fertilization, the zygote undergoes changes that result in the formation of a new human. **The zygote develops first into an embryo and then into a fetus.** About nine months after fertilization, a baby is born.

Four-cell stage
48 hours after fertilization

FIGURE 10
Development of the Fetus
As a fetus grows and develops, it gains mass, increases in length, and develops all its body systems.
Applying Concepts *How large is a zygote?*

Zygote

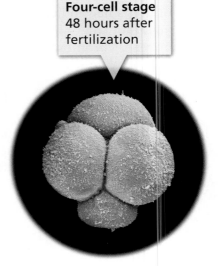

Zygote and Embryo After an egg and sperm join, the zygote moves down the fallopian tube toward the uterus. During this trip, which takes about four days, the zygote begins to divide. The original cell divides to make two cells. These two cells divide to make four, and so on. Eventually, the growing mass of hundreds of cells forms a hollow ball. The ball attaches to the lining of the uterus. From the two-cell stage through the eighth week of development, the developing human is called an **embryo** (EM bree oh).

Fetus From about the ninth week of development until birth, the developing human is called a **fetus** (FEE tus). Although at first the fetus is only the size of a whole walnut shell, it now looks more like a baby. Many internal organs have developed. The head is about half the body's total size. The fetus's brain is developing rapidly. The fetus also has dark eye patches, fingers, and toes. By the end of the third month, the fetus is about 9 centimeters long and has a mass of about 26 grams.

Between the fourth and sixth months, bones become distinct. A heartbeat can be heard with a stethoscope. A layer of soft hair grows over the skin. The arms and legs develop more completely. The fetus begins to move and kick, a sign that its muscles are growing. At the end of the sixth month, the mass of the fetus is approaching 700 grams. Its body is about 30 centimeters long.

The final three months prepare the fetus to survive outside the mother's body. The brain surface develops grooves and ridges. The lungs become ready to carry out the exchange of oxygen and carbon dioxide. The eyelids can open. The fetus doubles in length. Its mass may reach 3 kilograms or more.

 **Reading Checkpoint** At what point during development can a heartbeat be detected in a fetus?

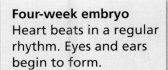
Four-week embryo Heart beats in a regular rhythm. Eyes and ears begin to form.

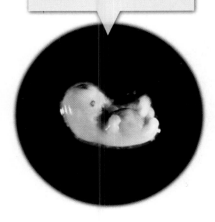

Eight-week embryo Heart has left and right chambers.

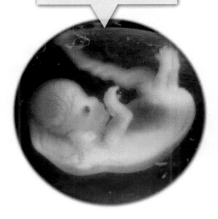

24-week fetus All parts of the eye are present. Fingerprints are forming.

Graphing

The table lists the recommended dietary intake of several nutrients for pregnant women. Make a bar graph showing the recommended dietary intakes for these nutrients.

Recommended Dietary Intake

Nutrient	Percent (%)
Vitamin C	120
Vitamin B_6	140
Calcium	150
Iron	200

Graphing Which nutrient do pregnant women need in the greatest amount?

Protection and Nourishment

Just like you, the embryo and fetus need nourishment and protection to develop properly. Soon after the embryo attaches to the uterus, many changes take place. The hollow ball of cells grows inward. New membranes form. **The membranes and other structures that form during development protect and nourish the developing embryo, and later the fetus.**

Amniotic Sac One membrane surrounds the embryo and develops into a fluid-filled sac called the **amniotic sac** (am NEE aht ik). Locate the amniotic sac in Figure 12. The fluid in the amniotic sac cushions and protects the developing baby.

Placenta Another membrane also forms, which helps to form the placenta. The **placenta** (pluh SEN tuh) is the link between the embryo and the mother. In the placenta, the embryo's blood vessels are located next to the mother's blood vessels. Blood from the two systems does not mix, but many substances are exchanged between the two blood supplies. The embryo receives nutrients, oxygen, and other substances from the mother. It gives off carbon dioxide and other wastes.

FIGURE 12

The Placenta

The placenta provides a connection between the mother and the developing fetus. But the mother's and the fetus's blood vessels remain separate, as you can see in the close-up of the placenta. *Interpreting Diagrams What structure carries nutrients and oxygen from the placenta to the fetus?*

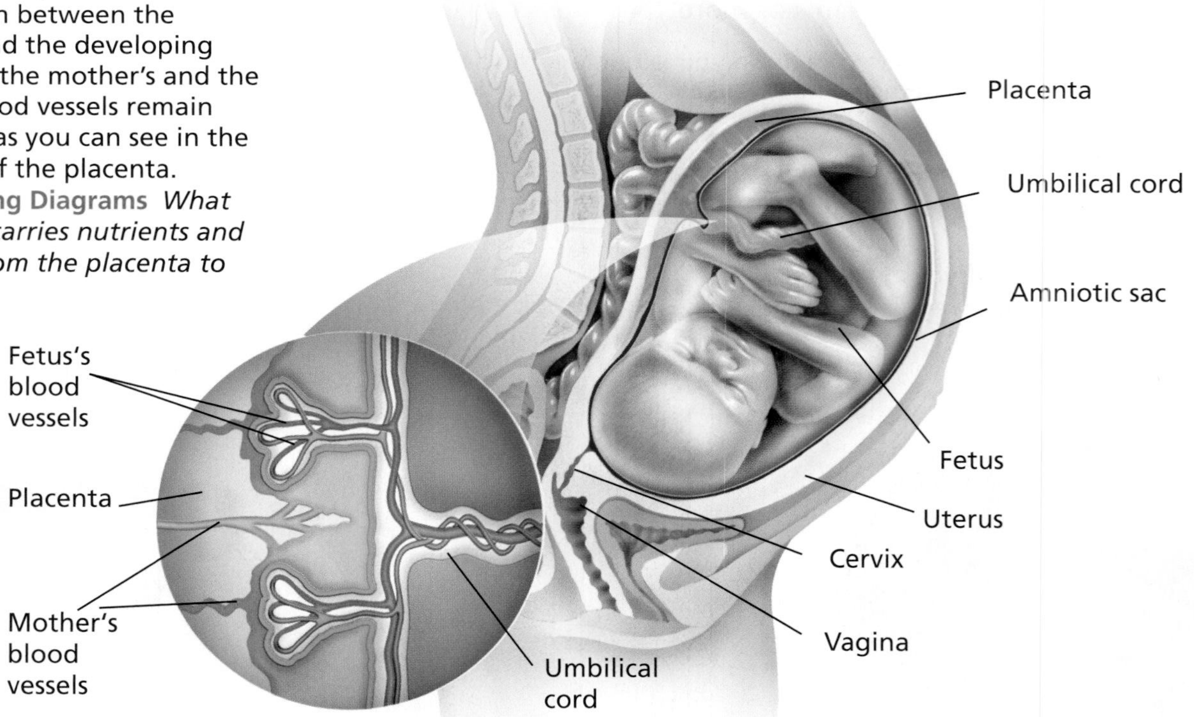

Placenta

Umbilical cord

Amniotic sac

Fetus

Uterus

Cervix

Vagina

Umbilical cord

Fetus's blood vessels

Placenta

Mother's blood vessels

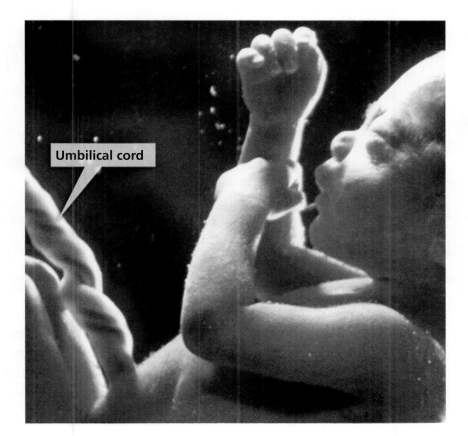

Umbilical cord

Umbilical Cord A ropelike structure called the **umbilical cord** forms between the fetus and the placenta. It contains blood vessels that link the fetus to the mother. However, the two circulatory systems remain separated by a thin barrier.

The barrier that separates the fetus's and mother's blood prevents some diseases from spreading from the mother to the fetus. However, substances such as alcohol, chemicals in tobacco, and many other drugs can pass through the barrier to the fetus. For this reason, pregnant women should not smoke, drink alcohol, or take any drug without a doctor's approval.

Reading Checkpoint **How does a fetus obtain oxygen?**

Birth

After about nine months of development inside the uterus, the baby is ready to be born. **The birth of a baby takes place in three stages—labor, delivery, and afterbirth.**

Labor During the first stage of birth, strong muscular contractions of the uterus begin. These contractions are called labor. The contractions cause the cervix to enlarge, eventually allowing the baby to fit through the opening. Labor may last from about 2 hours to more than 20 hours.

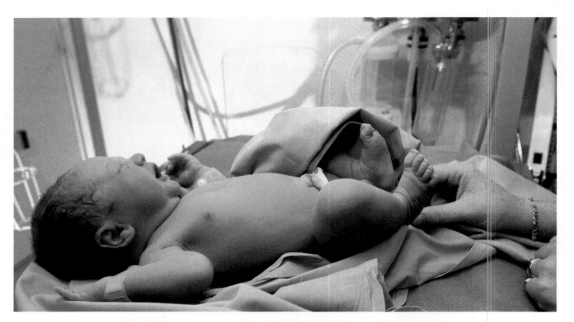

FIGURE 14
Birth
After about nine months of growth and development inside the uterus, a baby is born. You can see where the umbilical cord of this newborn was tied and cut.

Delivery The second stage of birth is called delivery. During delivery, the baby is pushed completely out of the uterus, through the vagina, and out of the mother's body. The head usually comes out first. At this time, the baby is still connected to the placenta by the umbilical cord. Delivery of the baby usually takes less time than labor does—from several minutes to an hour or so.

Shortly after delivery, the umbilical cord is clamped, then cut about 5 centimeters from the baby's abdomen. Within seven to ten days, the remainder of the umbilical cord dries up and falls off, leaving a scar called the navel, or belly button.

Afterbirth About 15 minutes after delivery, the third stage of the birth process begins. Contractions of the uterus push the placenta and other membranes out of the uterus through the vagina. This stage, called afterbirth, is usually completed in less than an hour.

Birth and the Baby The birth process is stressful for both the baby and the mother. The baby is pushed and squeezed as it travels out of the mother's body. Contractions put pressure on the placenta and umbilical cord, briefly decreasing the baby's supply of oxygen.

In response to the changes, the baby's endocrine system releases adrenaline. The baby's heart rate increases. Within a few seconds of delivery, the baby begins breathing with a cry or a cough. This action helps rid the lungs of fluid and fills them with air. The newborn's heart rate then slows to a steady pace. Blood travels to the lungs and picks up oxygen from the air that the baby breathes in. The newborn's cry helps it adjust to the changes in its surroundings.

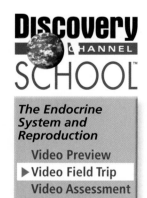

Discovery
CHANNEL
SCHOOL

The Endocrine System and Reproduction
Video Preview
▶ Video Field Trip
Video Assessment

Multiple Births The delivery of more than one baby from a single pregnancy is called a multiple birth. In the United States, about 1 out of every 30 babies born each year is a twin. Multiple births of more than two babies, such as triplets and quadruplets, occur less frequently than do twin births.

There are two types of twins: identical twins and fraternal twins. Identical twins develop from a single fertilized egg, or zygote. Early in development, the embryo splits into two identical embryos. The two embryos have identical inherited traits and are the same sex. Fraternal twins develop when two eggs are released from the ovary and are fertilized by two different sperm. Fraternal twins are no more alike than any other brothers or sisters. Fraternal twins may or may not be the same sex.

 **Reading Checkpoint** What events occur during labor?

FIGURE 15
Twins

Identical twins (left) develop from the same fertilized egg. They share identical characteristics. Fraternal twins (right) develop from two different fertilized eggs. **Applying Concepts** *Why can fraternal twins be different sexes while identical twins cannot?*

Identical Twins

A sperm fertilizes a single egg.

The single egg splits and forms two identical embryos.

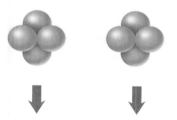

Identical twins result.

Fraternal Twins

Two different sperm fertilize two eggs.

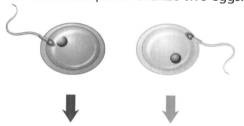

Each of the eggs develops into an embryo.

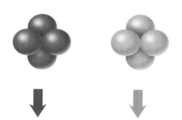

Fraternal twins result.

▲ **Infancy**

▲ **Early childhood**

▲ **Childhood**

FIGURE 16
Development
You can see the changes in development from infancy through adolescence.
Applying Concepts *What mental development takes place during childhood?*

Go Online
SCI*LINKS* NSTA

For: Links on before birth
Visit: www.SciLinks.org
Web Code: scn-0473

Growth and Development

What can a newborn baby do? You might say "Not much!" A newborn can perform only simple actions, such as crying, sucking, yawning, and blinking. You can do a lot more, from playing sports to solving math problems. Many changes have taken place in you that allow you to do these things. **The changes that have taken place as you've grown from infancy to adolescence include physical changes, such as an increase in size and coordination, and mental changes, such as the ability to communicate and solve complex problems.**

Infancy During infancy—the first two years of life—babies undergo many changes and learn to do many things. A baby's shape and size change greatly. When a baby is born, its head makes up about one fourth of its body length. As the infant develops, its head grows more slowly, and its body, legs, and arms begin to catch up. Its nervous and muscular systems become better coordinated. After about 3 months, it can hold its head up and reach for objects. At about 7 months, most infants can move around by crawling. Somewhere between 10 and 16 months, most infants begin to walk by themselves.

You may think that babies display feelings mostly by crying. But young infants can show pleasure by smiling and laughing. Sometime between the ages of one and three years, many children speak their first word. By the end of two years, children can do many things for themselves, such as understand simple directions, feed themselves, and play with toys.

▲ **Early adolescence**　　　　　▲ **Adolescence**

Childhood Infancy ends and childhood begins at about two years of age. Childhood continues until about the age of 12 years. Throughout childhood, children continue to grow. They become taller and heavier as their bones and muscles increase in size. They become more coordinated as they practice skills such as walking, holding a fork, using a pencil, and playing games. Toward the end of childhood, the bones, especially the legs, begin to grow faster. An increased appetite signals that the body needs more nutrients for its next stage of growth and development.

As they develop, children show a growing curiosity and increasing mental abilities. With the help of family members and teachers, children learn to read and to solve problems. Language skills improve rapidly. For example, most four-year-olds can express themselves clearly and can carry on conversations. Over time, children learn to make friends, care about others, and behave responsibly. Between the ages of three and six, they learn to share and play with others. About the age of ten, children develop a strong wish to fit in with others of their age group. As their independence increases, children take on more responsibilities at home and school.

Adolescence If you compared a current photo of yourself with one taken three years ago, you would notice many changes. Starting at about the age of 12, you gradually begin to change from a child to an adult. **Adolescence** (ad ul ES uns) is the stage of development when children become adults physically and mentally.

Puberty Some time between the ages of about 9 and 15 years, a child enters puberty. **Puberty** (PYOO bur tee) is the period of sexual development in which the body becomes able to reproduce. In girls, hormones produced by the pituitary gland and the ovaries control the physical changes of puberty. The sex organs develop. Ovulation and menstruation begin. The breasts begin to enlarge, and the hips start to widen. In boys, hormones from the testes and the pituitary gland govern the changes. The sex organs develop, and sperm production begins. The voice deepens. Hair appears on the face and chest.

Many important mental and social changes take place during adolescence. Adolescents may notice changes in the way they think, feel, and get along with others. Because friends' opinions become very important during adolescence, peer pressure may influence the decisions and actions of teenagers. **Peer pressure** consists of pressure from your friends and classmates to behave in certain ways. Peer pressure can produce both negative and positive results. Negative peer pressure can lead teens to do things that go against their values. The support of friends, on the other hand, can encourage teens to work toward their goals or develop new interests and skills.

 **Reading Checkpoint** What is peer pressure?

FIGURE 17
Growing Up
Adolescence is a time when many teens try new experiences and take on more responsibilities, such as helping others.

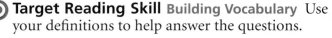

Section 3 Assessment

Target Reading Skill Building Vocabulary Use your definitions to help answer the questions.

Reviewing Key Concepts

1. a. Identifying What three steps of development does a fertilized egg go through before birth?
   b. Describing What happens to the fetus between the fourth and sixth months?
   c. Making Generalizations What are the major differences between the embryo and fetus?

2. a. Reviewing What are the structures that help to protect and nourish the developing embryo?
   b. Explaining What is the function of the placenta?
   c. Relating Cause and Effect Why is it dangerous for a pregnant woman to drink alcohol or to smoke cigarettes?

3. a. Listing What are the three stages of birth?
   b. Summarizing What happens during labor?

4. a. Sequencing What are the stages of growth that take place after you are born?
   b. Explaining What is puberty, and when does it occur?

Lab zone **At-Home Activity**

Parenting Skills Interview a family member about what is involved in being a parent. Ask the following questions: What skills do parents need? What are some of the rewards of parenthood? What are some of the challenges?

Growing Up

Problem

How do the proportions of the human body change during development?

Skills Focus

calculating, predicting

Procedure

1. Examine the diagram below. Notice that the figures are drawn against a graph showing percentages. You can use this diagram to determine how the lengths of major body parts compare to each figure's height. Make a data table in which to record information about each figure's head size and leg length.

2. Look at Figure D. You can use the graph to estimate that the head is about 15 percent of the figure's full height. Record that number in your data table.

3. Examine Figures A through C. Determine the percentage of the total height that the head makes up. Record your results.

4. Next, compare the length of the legs to the total body height for Figures A through D. Record your results. (*Hint:* Figure A shows the legs folded. You will need to estimate the data for that figure.)

Analyze and Conclude

1. **Calculating** How do the percentages for head size and leg length change from infancy to adulthood?

2. **Predicting** If you made a line graph using the data in the diagram, what would be on the horizontal axis? On the vertical axis? What additional information could you gain from this line graph?

3. **Communicating** What can you infer about the rate at which different parts of the body grow? Write a paragraph in which you discuss the answer to this question.

Design an Experiment

Make a prediction about the relationship between the circumference of the head compared with body height. Then, design an experiment to test your prediction, using people for test subjects. *Obtain your teacher's permission before carrying out your investigation.*

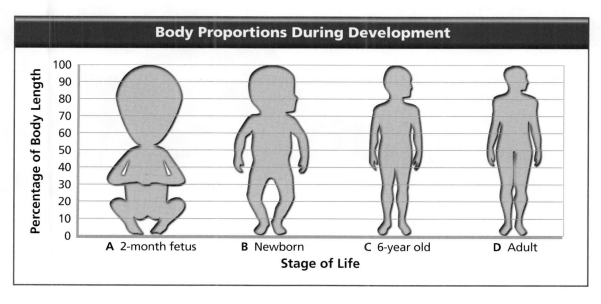

Body Proportions During Development

Percentage of Body Length

A 2-month fetus   B Newborn   C 6-year old   D Adult

Stage of Life

1 The Endocrine System

Key Concepts

● The endocrine system produces chemicals that control many of the body's daily activities as well as growth and development.

● The endocrine glands include the pituitary, hypothalamus, thyroid, parathyroid, adrenal, thymus, and pancreas. They include ovaries in females and testes in males.

● Through negative feedback, when the amount of a particular hormone in the blood reaches a certain level, the endocrine system sends signals that stop the release of that hormone.

Key Terms

endocrine gland	hypothalamus
hormone	pituitary gland
target cell	negative feedback

2 The Male and Female Reproductive Systems

Key Concepts

● Sexual reproduction involves the production of eggs by the female and sperm by the male, which join together during fertilization.

● The male reproductive system produces sperm and the hormone testosterone. Its structures include the testes, scrotum, and penis.

● The female reproductive system produces eggs and nourishes a developing baby until birth. Its structures include the ovaries, fallopian tubes, uterus, and vagina.

● During the menstrual cycle, an egg develops in an ovary. At the same time, the uterus prepares for the arrival of a fertilized egg.

Key Terms

egg	ovary
sperm	estrogen
fertilization	fallopian tube
zygote	uterus
testis	vagina
testosterone	menstrual cycle
scrotum	ovulation
semen	menstruation
penis	

3 The Human Life Cycle

Key Concepts

● The zygote develops first into an embryo and then into a fetus.

● The membranes and other structures that form during development protect and nourish the developing embryo and then the fetus.

● The birth of a baby takes place in three stages— labor, delivery, and afterbirth.

● The changes that have taken place as you've grown from infancy to adolescence include physical changes, such as an increase in size and coordination, and mental changes, such as the ability to communicate and solve complex problems.

Key Terms

embryo	umbilical cord
fetus	adolescence
amniotic sac	puberty
placenta	peer pressure

Review and Assessment

Organizing Information

Sequencing Copy the flowchart showing the main stages that occur between fertilization and birth onto a sheet of paper. Then, complete it and add a title. (For more on Sequencing, see the Skills Handbook.)

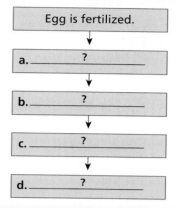

Egg is fertilized.

a. _____ ?

b. _____ ?

c. _____ ?

d. _____ ?

Reviewing Key Terms

Choose the letter of the best answer.

1. The structure that links the nervous system and the endocrine system is the
   a. thyroid gland.
   b. target cell.
   c. umbilical cord.
   d. hypothalamus.

2. The male sex cell is called the
   a. testis.
   b. sperm.
   c. egg.
   d. ovary.

3. The release of an egg from an ovary is known as
   a. ovulation.
   b. fertilization.
   c. menstruation.
   d. negative feedback.

4. The structure that protects and cushions the embryo is called the
   a. umbilical cord.
   b. scrotum.
   c. amniotic sac.
   d. ovary.

5. Sex organs develop rapidly during
   a. fertilization.
   b. ovulation.
   c. puberty.
   d. menstruation.

If the statement is true, write *true*. If it is false, change the underlined word or words to make the statement true.

6. A <u>target cell</u> recognizes a hormone's chemical structure.

7. The joining of a sperm and an egg is called <u>menstruation</u>.

8. A fluid that contains sperm is <u>testosterone</u>.

9. A <u>fallopian tube</u> is the passageway through which an egg travels from the ovary to the uterus.

10. The <u>amniotic sac</u> contains blood vessels that link the fetus to the mother.

Writing in Science

Creative Writing Imagine you just found out that you have an identical twin who was raised in another country. Write a description of what you think your twin would be like. Be sure to include information about what your twin looks like, his or her interests, and unique characteristics of your twin.

Discovery CHANNEL SCHOOL™

The Endocrine System and Reproduction
Video Preview
Video Field Trip
▶ Video Assessment

Review and Assessment

Checking Concepts

11. What is the function of the hypothalamus?

12. When enough thyroxine has been released into the blood, what signal is sent to the thyroid gland? How is that signal sent?

13. What changes occur in the uterus during the menstrual cycle?

14. How does a zygote form? What happens to the zygote about four days after it forms?

15. Describe how a fetus receives food and oxygen and gets rid of wastes.

Math Practice

16. **Ratios** In the Skills Lab, you compared leg length to overall height using percent. Another way to make this comparison is a ratio. A boy is 160 cm tall, and his legs are 76 cm long. What is the ratio of his height to his length?

Thinking Critically

17. **Inferring** Study the diagram below. Then, suggest how the two hormones, glucagon and insulin, might work together to maintain homeostasis in the body.

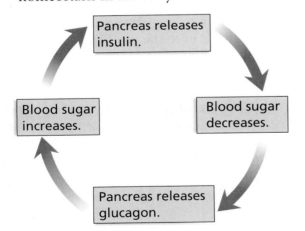

18. **Calculating** The average menstrual cycle is 28 days in length but can vary from 24 to 32 days. Ovulation usually occurs 14 days before the end of the cycle. How long after the start of a 24-day cycle will ovulation occur? A 32-day cycle?

19. **Relating Cause and Effect** How can playing games help children develop important skills?

20. **Comparing and Contrasting** In what way is development during adolescence similar to development before birth? How are the two stages different?

Applying Skills

Use the table to answer Questions 21–23.

The data table below shows how the length of a developing baby changes during pregnancy.

Length of Fetus			
Week of Pregnancy	Average Length (mm)	Week of Pregnancy	Average Length (mm)
4	4	24	300
8	30	28	350
12	75	32	410
16	180	36	450
20	250	38	500

21. **Measuring** Use a metric ruler to mark each length on a piece of paper. During which four-week period did the greatest increase in length occur?

22. **Graphing** Graph the data by plotting time on the x-axis and length on the y-axis.

23. **Interpreting Data** At the twelfth week, a developing baby measures about 75 mm. By which week has the fetus grown to four times that length? Six times that length?

Lab zone Chapter Project

Performance Assessment What did you learn about parenting that you didn't know before? Consider reading passages from your journal to the class.

🦉 End-of-Grade Test Practice

Choose the letter of the best answer.

1. You are riding your bike when a small child suddenly darts out in front of you. Which of your endocrine glands is most likely to release a hormone in response to this situation?
   A pituitary gland
   B adrenal glands
   C thyroid gland
   D parathyroid gland

2. On day 10 of a woman's menstrual cycle, the egg is most likely
   A moving through the fallopian tube.
   B in the uterus.
   C in the ovary.
   D leaving the body.

Use the table below and your knowledge of science to answer Questions 3 and 4.

Number of Chromosomes in Body Cells of Various Animals	
Organism	**Chromosome Number**
Roundworm	2
Fruit Fly	8
Cricket	22
Mouse	40
Human	46
Pigeon	80

3. An egg cell produced by a female mouse probably contains
   A 20 chromosomes.
   B 40 chromosomes.
   C 60 chromosomes.
   D 80 chromosomes.

4. How many chromosomes will a pigeon zygote have?
   A 20
   B 40
   C 60
   D 80

5. A woman gives birth to twins that developed from a single fertilized egg that split early in development. Which of the following is a reasonable prediction that you can make about the twins?
   A They will be the same sex.
   B They will be different sexes.
   C They will not look alike.
   D They will have different inherited traits.

Constructed Response

6. What is negative feedback? Choose an example of a hormone, and describe in a general way how negative feedback regulates its release.

Chapter 14

Genetics: The Science of Heredity

This chapter addresses the following North Carolina Objectives:

1.01 Identify and create questions and hypotheses.

1.02 Develop appropriate experimental procedures.

1.05 Analyze evidence.

1.06 Use mathematics to gather, organize, and present data.

1.07 Prepare models and/or computer simulations.

1.08 Use oral and written language.

2.01 Explore definitions of "technology."

2.02 Use information systems.

2.03 Evaluate technological designs.

5.01 Explain the significance of genes to inherited characteristics.

5.02 Explain the significance of reproduction.

5.03 Identify examples and patterns of human genetic traits.

5.04 Analyze the role of probability in heredity.

These spaniel puppies and their mother resemble each other in many ways. ▶

Lab zone™ Chapter **Project**

All in the Family

Did you ever wonder why some offspring resemble their parents while others do not? In this chapter, you'll learn how offspring come to have traits similar to those of their parents. You'll create a family of "paper pets" to explore how traits pass from parents to offspring.

Your Goal To create a "paper pet" that will be crossed with a class-mate's pet, and to determine what traits the offspring will have

To complete this project success-fully, you must

- create your own unique paper pet with five different traits
- cross your pet with another pet to produce six offspring
- determine what traits the offspring will have, and explain how they came to have those traits
- follow the safety guidelines in Appendix A

Plan It! Cut out your pet from either blue or yellow construction paper. Choose other traits for your pet from this list: square eyes or round eyes; oval nose or triangular nose; pointed teeth or square teeth. Then create your pet using materials of your choice.

Discovering Cells

Reading Preview

Key Concepts
- What are cells?
- How did the invention of the microscope contribute to knowledge about living things?
- What is the cell theory?
- How do microscopes produce magnified images?

Key Terms
- cell • microscope • cell theory

Target Reading Skill
Sequencing A sequence is the order in which a series of events occurs. As you read, construct a flowchart showing how the work of Hooke, Leeuwenhoek, Schleiden, Schwann, and Virchow contributed to scientific understanding of cells.

Discovering Cells

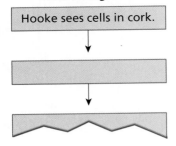

Hooke sees cells in cork.

Lab zone Discover **Activity**

Is Seeing Believing?

1. ✂ Cut a black-and-white photograph out of a page in a newspaper. With only your eyes, closely examine the photo. Record your observations.

2. Examine the same photo with a hand lens. Again, record your observations.

3. Place the photo on the stage of a microscope. Use the clips to hold the photo in place. Shine a light down on the photo. Focus the microscope on part of the photo. (See Appendix B for instructions on using the microscope.) Record your observations.

Think It Over

Observing What did you see in the photo with the hand lens that you could not see with only your eyes? What additional details could you see with the microscope?

A forest is filled with an amazing variety of living things. Some are easy to see, but you have to look closely to find others. If you look carefully at the floor of a forest, you can often find spots of bright color. A beautiful pink coral fungus grows beneath tall trees. Beside the pink fungus, a tiny red newt perches on a fallen leaf.

What do you think a fungus, a tree, and a red newt have in common? They are all living things, or organisms, and, like all organisms, they are made of cells.

FIGURE 1
Newt and Coral Fungus
All living things are made of cells, including this pink fungus and the red newt that perches next to it.

An Overview of Cells

You are made of cells. **Cells are the basic units of structure and function in living things.** This means that **cells** form the parts of an organism and carry out all of an organism's processes, or functions.

Cells and Structure When you describe the structure of an object, you describe what it is made of and how its parts are put together. The structures of many buildings, for example, are determined by the way in which bricks, steel beams, and other materials are arranged. The structures of living things are determined by the amazing variety of ways in which cells are put together. A tall tree, for example, consists of cells arranged to form a high trunk and leafy branches. A red newt's cells form a body with a head and four legs.

Cells and Function An organism's functions are the processes that enable it to stay alive and reproduce. Some functions in organisms include obtaining oxygen, getting rid of wastes, obtaining food, and growing. Cells are involved in all these functions. For example, cells in your digestive system absorb food. The food provides your body with energy and materials needed for growth.

Many and Small Figure 2 shows human skin cells. One square centimeter of your skin's surface contains more than 100,000 cells. But no matter how closely you look with your eyes alone, you won't be able to see individual skin cells. That is because, like most cells, those of your skin are very small. Until the late 1600s, no one knew cells existed because there was no way to see them.

 **Reading Checkpoint** What are some functions that cells perform in living things?

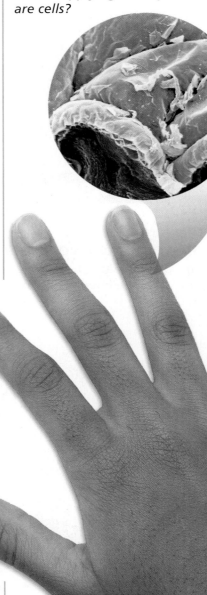

FIGURE 2
FIGURE 2
Skin Cells
Your skin is made of cells such as these. **Applying Concepts** *What are cells?*

First Observations of Cells

Around 1590, the invention of the microscope enabled people to look at very small objects. **The invention of the microscope made it possible for people to discover and learn about cells.** A **microscope** is an instrument that makes small objects look larger. Some microscopes do this by using lenses to focus light. The lenses used in light microscopes are similar to the clear, curved pieces of glass or plastic used in eyeglasses. A simple microscope contains only one lens. A light microscope that has more than one lens is called a compound microscope.

Robert Hooke One of the first people to observe cells was the English scientist and inventor Robert Hooke. Hooke built his own compound microscope, which was one of the best microscopes of his time. In 1663, Hooke used his microscope to observe the structure of a thin slice of cork. Cork, the bark of the cork oak tree, is made up of cells that are no longer alive. To Hooke, the empty spaces in the cork looked like tiny rectangular rooms. Therefore, Hooke called the empty spaces *cells*, which is a word meaning "small rooms."

Hooke described his observations this way: "These pores, or cells, were not very deep, but consisted of a great many little boxes. . . ." What most amazed Hooke was how many cells the cork contained. He calculated that in a cubic inch there were about twelve hundred million cells—a number he described as "almost incredible."

• Tech & Design in History •

The Microscope: Improvements Over Time

The microscope made the discovery of cells possible. Microscopes have improved in many ways over the last 400 years.

1590 First Compound Microscope
Dutch eyeglass makers Zacharias and Hans Janssen made one of the first compound microscopes. It was a tube with a lens at each end.

1674 Leeuwenhoek's Simple Microscope
Although Anton Von Leeuwenhoek's simple microscope used only one tiny lens, it could magnify a specimen up to 266 times.

1660 Hooke's Compound Microscope
Robert Hooke's compound microscope included an oil lamp for lighting. A lens focuses light from the flame onto the specimen.

1500　　　　1600　　　　1700

Anton van Leeuwenhoek At about the same time that Robert Hooke made his discovery, Anton van Leeuwenhoek (LAY vun hook) also began to observe tiny objects with microscopes. Leeuwenhoek was a Dutch businessman who sold cloth. In his spare time, he built simple microscopes.

Leeuwenhoek looked at drops of lake water, scrapings from teeth and gums, and water from rain gutters. In many materials, Leeuwenhoek was surprised to find a variety of one-celled organisms. Leeuwenhoek noted that many of these tiny organisms moved. Some whirled, some hopped, and some shot through water like fast fish. He called these moving organisms *animalcules* (an ih MAL kyoolz), meaning "little animals."

Reading Checkpoint Which type of microscope—simple or compound—did Leeuwenhoek make and use?

Writing in Science

Research and Write Find out more about one of the microscopes. Then write an advertisement for it that might appear in a popular science magazine. Be creative. Emphasize the microscope's usefulness or describe the wonders that can be seen with it.

1965 Scanning Electron Microscope (SEM)
An SEM sends electrons over the surface of a specimen, rather than through it. The result is a three-dimensional image of the specimen's surface. SEMs can magnify a specimen up to 150,000 times.

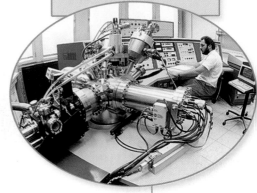

1981 Scanning Tunneling Microscope (STM)
An STM measures electrons that leak, or "tunnel," from the surface of a specimen. STMs can magnify a specimen up to 1,000,000 times.

1886 Modern Compound Light Microscope
German scientists Ernst Abbé and Carl Zeiss made a compound light microscope with complex lenses that greatly improved the image. A mirror focuses light up through the specimen. Modern compound microscopes can effectively magnify a specimen up to 1,000 times.

1933 Transmission Electron Microscope (TEM)
German physicist Ernst Ruska created the first electron microscope. TEMs send electrons through a very thinly sliced specimen. TEMs can magnify a specimen up to 500,000 times.

1800	1900	2000

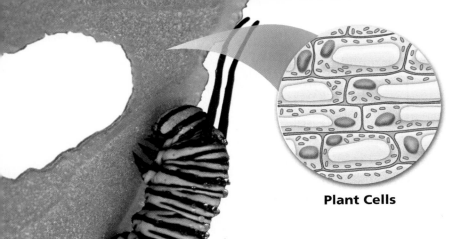

FIGURE 3
Monarch and Milkweed
The monarch butterfly caterpillar and the milkweed leaf that the caterpillar nibbles on are both made of cells.

Plant Cells

Animal Cells

Development of the Cell Theory

Leeuwenhoek's exciting discoveries caught the attention of other researchers. Like Hooke, Leeuwenhoek, and all good scientists, these other researchers were curious about the world around them, including things they couldn't normally see. Many other people began to use microscopes to discover what secrets they could learn about cells.

Schleiden, Schwann, and Virchow Three German scientists made especially important contributions to people's knowledge about cells. These scientists were Matthias Schleiden (SHLY dun), Theodor Schwann, and Rudolf Virchow (FUR koh). In 1838, Schleiden concluded that all plants are made of cells. He based this conclusion on his own research and on the research of others before him. The next year, Theodor Schwann concluded that all animals are also made up of cells. Thus, stated Schwann, all living things are made up of cells.

Schleiden and Schwann had made an important discovery about living things. However, they didn't explain where cells came from. Until their time, most people thought that living things could come from nonliving matter. In 1855, Virchow proposed that new cells are formed only from cells that already exist. "All cells come from cells," wrote Virchow.

What the Cell Theory Says Schleiden, Schwann, Virchow, and others helped develop the cell theory. The **cell theory** is a widely accepted explanation of the relationship between cells and living things. **The cell theory states the following:**

- **All living things are composed of cells.**

- **Cells are the basic units of structure and function in living things.**

- **All cells are produced from other cells.**

The cell theory holds true for all living things, no matter how big or how small. Since cells are common to all living things, they can provide information about the functions that living things perform. Because all cells come from other cells, scientists can study cells to learn about growth and reproduction.

 **Reading Checkpoint** What did Schleiden and Schwann conclude about cells?

Light and Electron Microscopes

The cell theory could not have been developed without microscopes. For a microscope to be useful, it must combine two important properties—magnification and resolution. Scientists today use two kinds of microscopes: light microscopes and electron microscopes.

Magnification and Lenses The first property, magnification, is the ability to make things look larger than they are. **The lenses in light microscopes magnify an object by bending the light that passes through them.** If you examine a hand lens, such as the one in Figure 4, you will see that the lens is curved, not flat. The center of the lens is thicker than the edge. A lens with this curved shape is called a convex lens. The light passing through the sides of the lens bends inward. When this light hits the eye, the eye sees the object as larger than it really is.

Lab zone Skills **Activity**

Observing

1. Read about using the microscope (Appendix B) before beginning this activity.
2. Place a prepared slide of a thin slice of cork on the stage of a microscope.
3. Observe the slide under low power. Draw what you see.
4. Place a few drops of pond water on another slide and cover it with a coverslip.
5. Observe the slide under low power. Draw what you see. Wash your hands after handling pond water.

How does your drawing in Step 3 compare to Hooke's description of cells on page 8? Based on your observations in Step 5, why did Leeuwenhoek call the organisms he saw "little animals"?

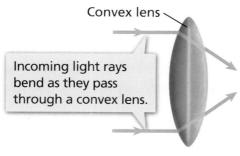

Convex lens

Incoming light rays bend as they pass through a convex lens.

FIGURE 4
A Convex Lens
A magnifying glass is a convex lens. The lines in the diagram represent rays of light, and the arrows show the direction in which the light travels. **Interpreting Diagrams** *Describe what happens to light rays as they pass through a convex lens.*

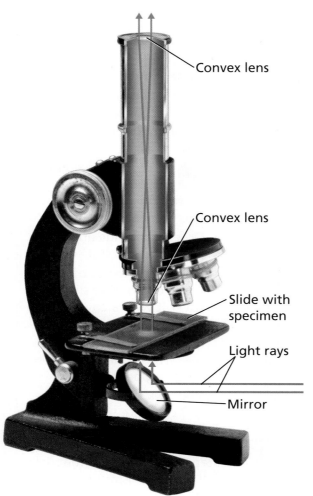

Convex lens

Convex lens

Slide with specimen

Light rays

Mirror

FIGURE 5
A Compound Microscope

FIGURE 5
A Compound Microscope
A compound microscope has two convex lenses.
Calculating If one lens has a magnification of 10, and the other lens has a magnification of 50, what is the total magnification?

Compound Microscope Magnification Since a compound microscope uses more than one lens, it can magnify an object more than one lens by itself. Light passes through a specimen and then through two lenses, as shown in Figure 5. The first lens, near the specimen, magnifies the object. Then a second lens, near the eye, further magnifies the enlarged image. The total magnification of the microscope is equal to the magnifications of the two lenses multiplied together. For example, suppose the first lens makes an object look 10 times bigger than it actually is, and the second lens makes the object look 40 times bigger than it actually is. The total magnification of the microscope is 10×40, or 400.

Resolution To create a useful image, a microscope must also help you see individual parts clearly. The ability to clearly distinguish the individual parts of an object is called resolution. Resolution is another term for the sharpness of an image. For example, a photograph in a newspaper is really made up of a collection of small dots. If you put the photo under a microscope, you can see the dots. You see the dots not only because they are magnified but also because the microscope improves resolution. Good resolution is needed when you study cells.

FIGURE 6
Light Microscope Photos
The pictures of the water flea and the threadlike *Spirogyra* were both taken with a light microscope.

Water flea
40 times actual size

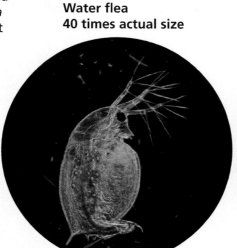

Spirogyra
300 times actual size

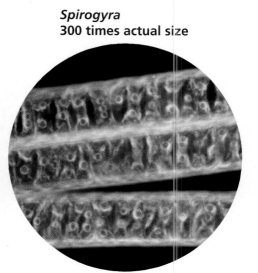

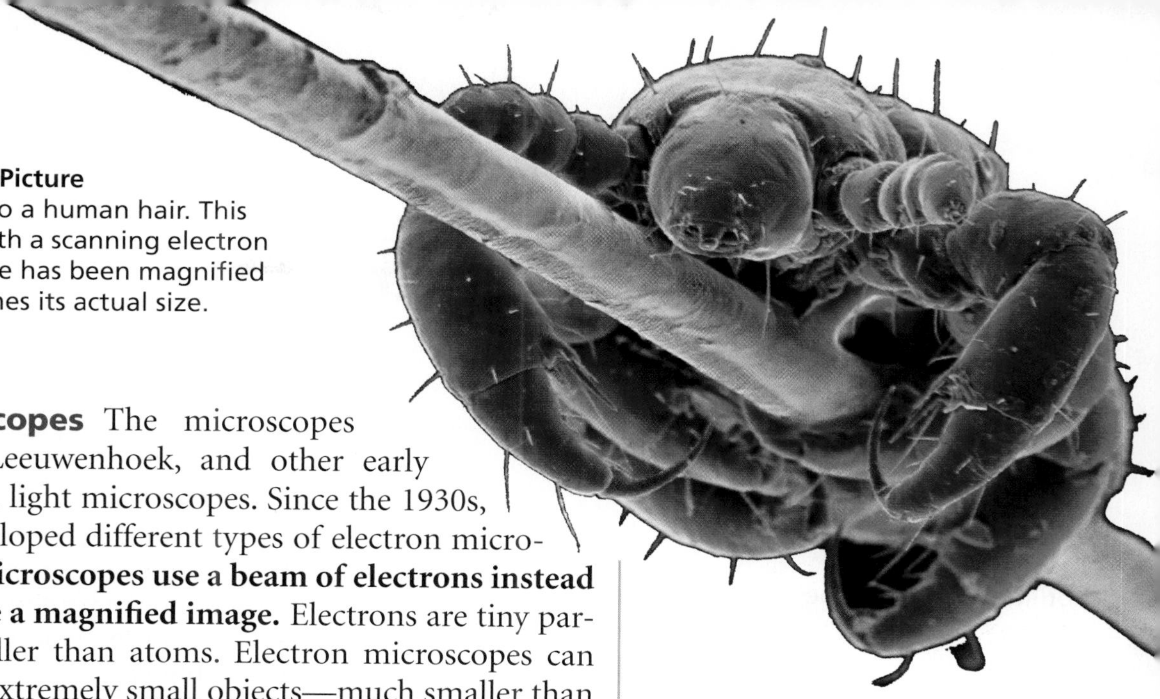

FIGURE 7
Electron Microscope Picture
A head louse clings to a human hair. This picture was taken with a scanning electron microscope. The louse has been magnified to more than 100 times its actual size.

Electron Microscopes The microscopes used by Hooke, Leeuwenhoek, and other early researchers were all light microscopes. Since the 1930s, scientists have developed different types of electron microscopes. **Electron microscopes use a beam of electrons instead of light to produce a magnified image.** Electrons are tiny particles that are smaller than atoms. Electron microscopes can obtain pictures of extremely small objects—much smaller than those that can be seen with light microscopes. The resolution of electron microscopes is much better than the resolution of light microscopes.

 **Reading Checkpoint** What do electron microscopes use to produce magnified images?

Section 1 Assessment

⟳ **Target Reading Skill** Sequencing Review your flowchart and use it to answer Questions 2 and 3 below.

Reviewing Key Concepts

1. a. Defining Define *structure* and *function*.
  b. Explaining Explain this statement: Cells are the basic units of structure and function in organisms.
  c. Applying Concepts In what important function are the cells in your eyes involved?
2. a. Reviewing What does a microscope enable people to do?
  b. Summarizing Summarize Hooke's observations of cork under a microscope.
  c. Relating Cause and Effect Why would Hooke's discovery have been impossible without a microscope?
3. a. Reviewing What are the main ideas of the cell theory?
  b. Explaining What did Virchow contribute to the cell theory?

  c. Applying Concepts Use the ideas of Virchow to explain why plastic plants and stuffed animals are not alive.
4. a. Defining What is magnification?
  b. Comparing and Contrasting Contrast the way light microscopes and electron microscopes magnify objects.

Writing in Science

Writing an Award Speech Suppose you are a member of a scientific society that is giving an award to one of the early cell scientists. Choose the scientist, and write a speech that you might give at the award ceremony. Your speech should describe the scientist's accomplishments.

Technology Lab
• Tech & Design •

Design and Build a Microscope

Problem

How can you design and build a compound microscope?

Design Skills

building a prototype, evaluating design constraints

Materials

- book
- 2 dual magnifying glasses, each with one high-power and one low-power lens
- metric ruler
- 2 cardboard tubes from paper towels, or black construction paper
- tape

Procedure

PART 1 Research and Investigate

1. Work with a partner. Using only your eyes, examine words in a book. Then use the high-power lens to examine the same words. In your notebook, contrast what you saw with and without the magnifying lens.

2. Hold the high-power lens about 5–6 cm above the words in the book. When you look at the words through the lens, they will look blurry.

3. Keep the high-power lens about 5–6 cm above the words. Hold the low-power lens above the high-power lens, as shown in the photograph on the right.

4. Move the low-power lens up and down until the image is in focus and upside down. (*Hint:* You may have to move the high-power lens up or down slightly too.)

5. Once the image is in focus, experiment with raising and lowering both lenses. Your goal is to produce the highest magnification while keeping the image in clear focus.

6. When the image is in focus at the position of highest magnification, have your lab partner measure and record the distance between the book and the high-power lens. Your lab partner should also measure and record the distance between the two lenses.

7. Write a description of how the magnified words viewed through two lenses compares with the words seen without magnification.

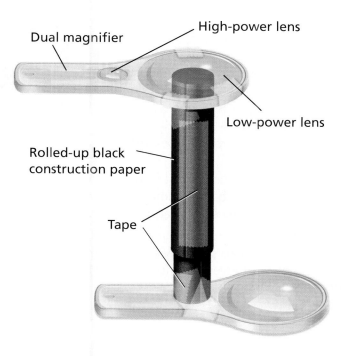

Dual magnifier

High-power lens

Low-power lens

Rolled-up black
construction paper

Tape

PART 2 **Design and Build**

8. Based on what you learned in Part 1, work with a partner to design your own two-lens (compound) microscope. Your microscope should
   - consist of one high-power lens and one low-power lens, each attached to a tube of paper or rolled-up cardboard
   - allow one tube to fit snugly inside the other tube so the distance between the two lenses can be easily adjusted
   - focus to produce a clear, enlarged, upside-down image of the object
   - be made from dual magnifying glasses, cardboard tubes, and tape

9. Sketch your design on a sheet of paper. Obtain your teacher's approval for your design. Then construct your microscope.

PART 3 **Evaluate and Redesign**

10. Test your microscope by examining printed words or a printed photograph. Then, examine other objects such as a leaf or your skin. Record your observations. Did your microscope meet the criteria listed in Step 8?

11. Examine microscopes made by other students. Based on your tests and your examination of other microscopes, list ways you could improve your microscope.

Analyze and Conclude

1. **Observing** Compare the images you observed using one lens with the image from two lenses.

2. **Evaluating** When you used two lenses, how did moving the top lens up and down affect the image? What was the effect of moving the bottom lens up and down?

3. **Building a Prototype** Describe how you built your microscope and explain why you built it that way.

4. **Evaluating the Impact on Society** Describe some of the ways that microscopes have aided scientists in their work.

Communicate

Imagine it is 1675. Write an explanation that will convince scientists to use your new microscope rather than the single-lens variety used by Leeuwenhoek.

Looking Inside Cells

Reading Preview

Key Concepts
- What role do the cell wall and cell membrane play in the cell?
- What are the functions of cell organelles?
- How are cells organized in many-celled organisms?
- How do bacterial cells differ from plant and animal cells?

Key Terms
- organelle • cell wall
- cell membrane • nucleus
- cytoplasm • mitochondria
- endoplasmic reticulum
- ribosome • Golgi body
- chloroplast • vacuole
- lysosome

Target Reading Skill
Previewing Visuals Before you read, preview Figure 12. Then write two questions that you have about the illustrations in a graphic organizer like the one below. As you read, answer your questions.

Plant and Animal Cells

Q.	How are animal cells different from plant cells?
A.	
Q.	

Lab zone | Discover **Activity**

How Large Are Cells?

1. Look at the organism in the photo. The organism is an amoeba (uh MEE buh), a large single-celled organism. This type of amoeba is about 1 mm long.

2. Multiply your height in meters by 1,000 to get your height in millimeters. How many amoebas would you have to stack end-to-end to equal your height?

3. Many of the cells in your body are about 0.01 mm long—one hundredth the size of an amoeba. How many body cells would you have to stack end-to-end to equal your height?

Think It Over

Inferring Look at a metric ruler to see how small 1 mm is. Now imagine a distance one one-hundredth as long, or 0.01 mm. Why can't you see your body's cells without the aid of a microscope?

Nasturtiums brighten up many gardens with green leaves and colorful flowers. How do nasturtiums carry out all the functions necessary to stay alive? To answer this question, you are about to take an imaginary journey. You will travel inside a nasturtium leaf, visiting its tiny cells. You will observe some of the structures found in plant cells. You will also learn some differences between plant and animal cells.

As you will discover on your journey, there are even smaller structures inside a cell. These tiny cell structures, called **organelles,** carry out specific functions within the cell. Just as your stomach, lungs, and heart have different functions in your body, each organelle has a different function within the cell. Now it's time to hop aboard your imaginary ship and sail into a typical plant cell.

Nasturtiums ▶

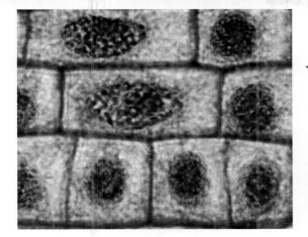

◀ Onion root cells

Paramecium ▼

Enter the Cell

Your ship doesn't have an easy time getting inside the cell. It has to pass through the cell wall and the cell membrane.

Cell Wall As you travel through the plant cell, refer to Figure 12. First, you must slip through the cell wall. The **cell wall** is a rigid layer of nonliving material that surrounds the cells of plants and some other organisms. The cells of animals, in contrast, do not have cell walls. **A plant's cell wall helps to protect and support the cell.** The cell wall is made mostly of a strong material called cellulose. Although the cell wall is tough, many materials, including water and oxygen, can pass through easily.

Cell Membrane After you sail through the cell wall, the next barrier you must cross is the **cell membrane**. All cells have cell membranes. In cells with cell walls, the cell membrane is located just inside the cell wall. In other cells, the cell membrane forms the outside boundary that separates the cell from its environment.

 The cell membrane controls what substances come into and out of a cell. Everything the cell needs, from food to oxygen, enters the cell through the cell membrane. Fortunately, your ship can slip through, too. Harmful waste products leave the cell through the cell membrane. For a cell to survive, the cell membrane must allow these materials to pass in and out. In addition, the cell membrane prevents harmful materials from entering the cell. In a sense, the cell membrane is like a window screen. The screen allows air to enter and leave a room, but it keeps insects out.

FIGURE 8
Cell Wall and Cell Membrane
The onion root cells have both a cell wall and a cell membrane. The single-celled paramecium has only a cell membrane.
Interpreting Photographs *What shape do the cell walls give to the onion root cells?*

Reading Checkpoint **What is the function of the cell wall?**

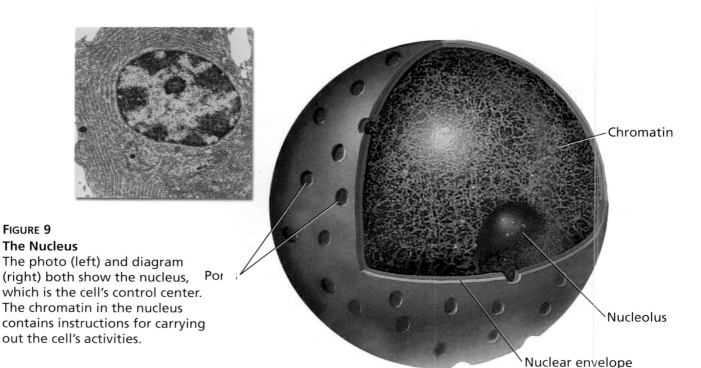

FIGURE 9
The Nucleus
The photo (left) and diagram (right) both show the nucleus, which is the cell's control center. The chromatin in the nucleus contains instructions for carrying out the cell's activities.

Chromatin

Por

Nucleolus

Nuclear envelope

Sail on to the Nucleus

As you sail inside the cell, a large, oval structure comes into view. This structure, called the **nucleus** (NOO klee us), acts as the "brain" of the cell. **You can think of the nucleus as the cell's control center, directing all of the cell's activities.**

Nuclear Envelope Notice in Figure 9 that the nucleus is surrounded by a membrane called the nuclear envelope. Just as a mailing envelope protects the letter inside it, the nuclear envelope protects the nucleus. Materials pass in and out of the nucleus through pores in the nuclear envelope. So aim for that pore just ahead and carefully glide into the nucleus.

Chromatin You might wonder how the nucleus "knows" how to direct the cell. The answer lies in those thin strands floating directly ahead in the nucleus. These strands, called chromatin, contain genetic material, the instructions for directing the cell's functions. For example, the instructions in the chromatin ensure that leaf cells grow and divide to form more leaf cells.

Nucleolus As you prepare to leave the nucleus, you spot a small object floating by. This structure, a nucleolus, is where ribosomes are made. Ribosomes are the organelles where proteins are produced. Proteins are important chemicals in cells.

 **Reading Checkpoint** **Where in the nucleus is genetic material found?**

Lab zone **Try This Activity**

Gelatin Cell

Make your own model of a cell.

1. Dissolve a packet of colorless gelatin in warm water. Pour the gelatin into a rectangular pan (for a plant cell) or a round pan (for an animal cell).

2. Choose different materials that resemble each of the cell structures found in the cell you are modeling. Insert these materials into the gelatin before it begins to solidify.

Making Models On a sheet of paper, develop a key that identifies each cell structure in your model. Describe the function of each structure.

FIGURE 10
Mitochondrion
The mitochondria produce most of the cell's energy. **Inferring** *In what types of cells would you expect to find a lot of mitochondria?*

Organelles in the Cytoplasm

As you leave the nucleus, you find yourself in the **cytoplasm,** the region between the cell membrane and the nucleus. Your ship floats in a clear, thick, gel-like fluid. The fluid in the cytoplasm is constantly moving, so your ship does not need to propel itself. Many cell organelles are found in the cytoplasm.

Mitochondria Suddenly, rod-shaped structures loom ahead. These organelles are **mitochondria** (my tuh KAHN dree uh) (singular *mitochondrion*). **Mitochondria are known as the "powerhouses" of the cell because they convert energy in food molecules to energy the cell can use to carry out its functions.** Figure 10 shows a mitochondrion up close.

Endoplasmic Reticulum As you sail farther into the cytoplasm, you find yourself in a maze of passageways called the **endoplasmic reticulum** (en duh PLAZ mik rih TIK yuh lum). **The endoplasmic reticulum's passageways carry proteins and other materials from one part of the cell to another.**

Ribosomes Attached to some surfaces of the endoplasmic reticulum are small, grainlike bodies called **ribosomes.** Other ribosomes float in the cytoplasm. **Ribosomes function as factories to produce proteins.** Some newly made proteins are released through the wall of the endoplasmic reticulum. From the interior of the endoplasmic reticulum, the proteins will be transported to the Golgi bodies.

FIGURE 11
Endoplasmic Reticulum
The endoplasmic reticulum is similar to the system of hallways in a building. Proteins and other materials move throughout the cell by way of the endoplasmic reticulum. The spots on this organelle are ribosomes, which produce proteins.

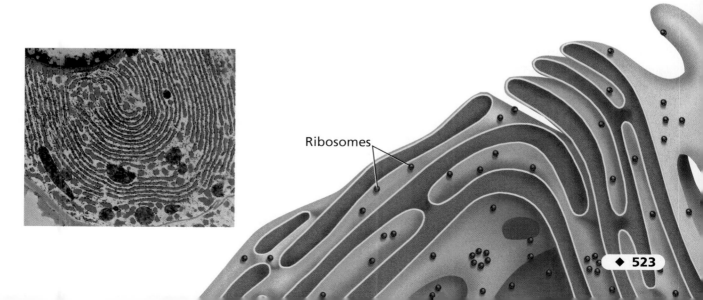

Ribosomes

FIGURE 12
Plant and Animal Cells

These illustrations show typical structures found in plant and animal cells. **Comparing and Contrasting** *Identify one structure found in plant cells but not animal cells.*

Nucleus
The nucleus directs all of the cell's activities, including reproduction.

Endoplasmic Reticulum
This network of passageways carries materials from one part of the cell to another.

Cytoplasm

Ribosomes

Cell Wall
In a plant cell, a stiff wall surrounds the membrane, giving the cell a rigid, boxlike shape.

Golgi Body

Mitochondrion

Chloroplasts
These organelles capture energy from sunlight and use it to produce food for the cell.

Vacuole
Most mature plant cells have one large vacuole. This sac within the cytoplasm stores water, food, waste products, and other materials.

Cell Membrane
The cell membrane protects the cell and regulates what substances enter and leave the cell.

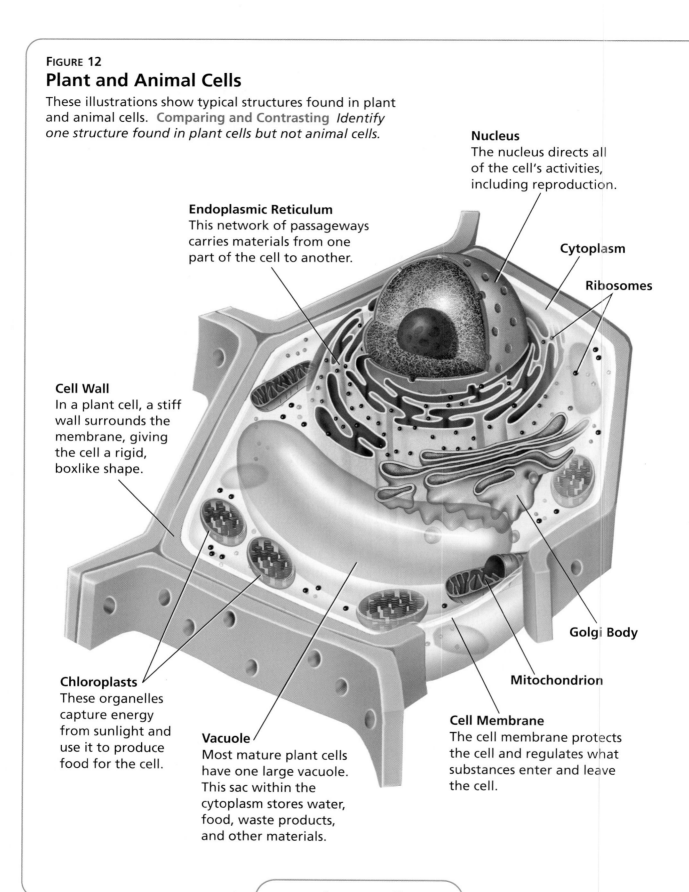

Plant Cell

Ribosomes
These small structures function as factories to produce proteins. Ribosomes may be attached to the endoplasmic reticulum, or they may float in the cytoplasm.

Cytoplasm
The cytoplasm includes a gel-like fluid in which many different organelles are found.

Nucleus
The nucleus directs all of the cell's activities, including reproduction.

Mitochondria
Most of the cell's energy is produced within these rod-shaped organelles.

Endoplasmic Reticulum

Golgi Body
The Golgi bodies receive materials from the endoplasmic reticulum and send them to other parts of the cell. They also release materials outside the cell.

Lysosomes
These small organelles contain chemicals that break down food particles and worn-out cell parts.

Vacuole
Some animal cells have vacuoles that store food, water, waste, and other materials.

Cell Membrane
Since an animal cell does not have a cell wall, the cell membrane forms a barrier between the cytoplasm and the environment outside the cell.

Animal Cell

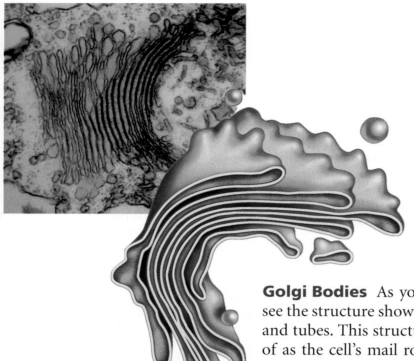

FIGURE 13
A Golgi Body
Golgi bodies are organelles that transport materials.

Golgi Bodies As you leave the endoplasmic reticulum, you see the structure shown in Figure 13. It looks like flattened sacs and tubes. This structure, called a **Golgi body,** can be thought of as the cell's mail room. **The Golgi bodies receive proteins and other newly formed materials from the endoplasmic reticulum, package them, and distribute them to other parts of the cell.** The Golgi bodies also release materials outside the cell.

Chloroplasts Have you noticed the many large green structures floating in the cytoplasm? Only the cells of plants and some other organisms have these green organelles called **chloroplasts. Chloroplasts capture energy from sunlight and use it to produce food for the cell.** Chloroplasts make leaves green.

Vacuoles Steer past the chloroplasts and head for that large, water-filled sac, called a **vacuole** (VAK yoo ohl), floating in the cytoplasm. **Vacuoles are the storage areas of cells.** Most plant cells have one large vacuole. Some animal cells do not have vacuoles; others do. Vacuoles store food and other materials needed by the cell. Vacuoles can also store waste products.

Lysosomes Your journey through the cell is almost over. Before you leave, take another look around you. If you carefully swing your ship around the vacuole, you may be lucky enough to see a **lysosome** (LY suh sohm). **Lysosomes are small, round structures containing chemicals that break down certain materials in the cell.** Some chemicals break down large food particles into smaller ones. Lysosomes also break down old cell parts and release the substances so they can be used again. In this sense, you can think of lysosomes as the cell's cleanup crew.

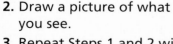

Try This Activity

Comparing Cells
Observe the characteristics of plant and animal cells.

1. Obtain a prepared slide of plant cells from your teacher. Examine these cells under the low-power and high-power lenses of a microscope.
2. Draw a picture of what you see.
3. Repeat Steps 1 and 2 with a prepared slide of animal cells.

Observing How are plant and animal cells alike? How are they different?

Reading Checkpoint **What organelle captures the energy of sunlight and uses it to make food for the cell?**

Specialized Cells

Plants and animals (including yourself) contain many cells. In a many-celled organism, the cells are often quite different from each other and are specialized to perform specific functions. Contrast, for example, the nerve cell and red blood cells in Figure 14. Nerve cells are specialized to transmit information from one part of your body to another, and red blood cells carry oxygen throughout your body.

In many-celled organisms, cells are often organized into tissues, organs, and organ systems. A tissue is a group of similar cells that work together to perform a specific function. For example, your brain is made mostly of nervous tissue, which consists of nerve cells. An organ, such as your brain, is made of different kinds of tissues that function together. In addition to nervous tissue, the brain contains other kinds of tissue that support and protect it. Your brain is part of your nervous system, which is an organ system that directs body activities and processes. An organ system is a group of organs that work together to perform a major function.

Reading Checkpoint What is an organ system? Give an example.

Nerve cell ▼

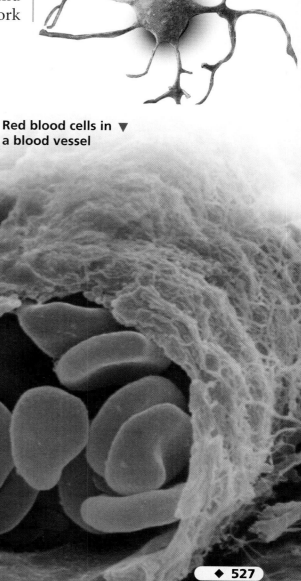

Red blood cells in ▼
a blood vessel

FIGURE 14
Specialized Cells
Nerve cells carry information throughout the human body. Red blood cells carry oxygen. Bone cells produce chemicals that strengthen bone.
Comparing and Contrasting
Compare the structures of these three types of cells.

Bone cells ▼

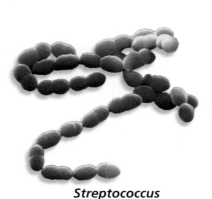

Streptococcus

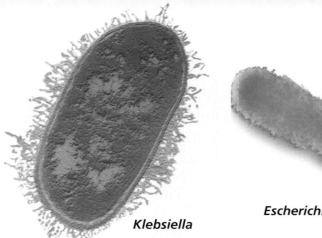

Klebsiella

Escherichia coli

FIGURE 15
Bacterial Cells
Bacterial cells have no nuclei.

Bacterial Cells

The plant and animal cells that you just learned about are very different from the bacterial cells you see in Figure 15. First, bacterial cells are usually much smaller than plant or animal cells. A human skin cell, for example, is about ten times as large as an average bacterial cell. **While a bacterial cell does have a cell wall and a cell membrane, it does not contain a nucleus. The bacterial cell's genetic material, which looks like a thick, tangled string, is found in the cytoplasm.** Bacterial cells contain ribosomes, but none of the other organelles found in plant or animal cells.

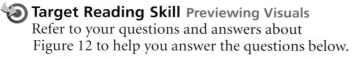

Section 2 Assessment

Target Reading Skill Previewing Visuals
Refer to your questions and answers about Figure 12 to help you answer the questions below.

Reviewing Key Concepts

1. a. **Comparing and Contrasting** Compare the functions of the cell wall and the cell membrane.
   b. **Describing** What is a characteristic of cellulose?
   c. **Inferring** How does cellulose help with the functions of the cell wall?

2. a. **Identifying** Identify the functions of ribosomes and Golgi bodies.
   b. **Describing** Describe the characteristics of the endoplasmic reticulum.
   c. **Applying Concepts** How are the functions of ribosomes, Golgi bodies, and the endoplasmic reticulum related to one another?

3. a. **Reviewing** What is a tissue? What is an organ?
   b. **Explaining** What is the relationship among cells, tissues, and organs?
   c. **Inferring** Would a tissue or an organ have more kinds of specialized cells? Explain.

4. a. **Reviewing** Where is the genetic material in a bacterial cell?
   b. **Comparing and Contrasting** Contrast the location of genetic material in bacterial cells to its location in plant and animal cells.

Writing in Science

Writing a Description Write a paragraph describing a typical animal cell. Your paragraph should include all the structures generally found in animal cells and a brief explanation of the functions of those structures.

What Is Biotechnology?

A fairly new branch of science called biotechnology uses the data and techniques of engineering and technology for the study and solution of problems concerning living things and tiny parts of living things (like cells and molecules). Some biotechnology projects involve genomics, the study of genes and how they function. The word *genomics* comes from the word *genome,* which refers to all the genes in an organism.

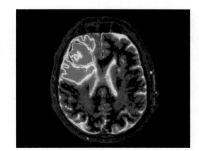

Cancerous Tumor
The bright spot on this X-ray of the brain shows where a cancerous tumor is located. Doctors remove DNA from cancer cells and normal cells to compare the genes.

Biotechnology and Disease

Some of the genomics projects currently underway are searching for links between genes and cancer. A device called a microarray helps scientists compare the genes of healthy cells with the genes of cancerous cells. Gene sequences from the cells are placed on the microarray. A computer scans the microarray and determines which genes are active.

A gene that is active in a cancer cell but not active in a healthy cell might be the cause of the cancer. By identifying such genes, scientists can focus their research on finding ways to block the function of these genes. This area of biotechnology is called gene therapy. Because each disease-causing gene is different, a specific gene therapy must be developed for each disease.

Microarray
Active genes can be identified by using a microarray. Brighter spots indicate more active genes.

What Do You Think?

1. What is one way biotechnology can be used to help people?

2. At the library or on the Internet, do research to find one disease for which scientists are trying to develop gene therapy. Write two or three paragraphs in which you describe the disease and how scientists expect gene therapy will fight it.

3. Gene therapy experiments will be very costly. Should all the people who need gene therapy receive it regardless of the cost? Should only those who can afford gene therapy be treated? Give reasons for your answers.

Mendel's Work

Reading Preview

Key Concepts
- What were the results of Mendel's experiments, or crosses?
- What controls the inheritance of traits in organisms?

Key Terms
- heredity • trait • genetics
- fertilization • purebred • gene
- alleles • dominant allele
- recessive allele • hybrid

Target Reading Skill
Outlining As you read, make an outline about Mendel's work. Use the red headings for the main ideas and the blue headings for the supporting ideas.

Mendel's Work
I. Mendel's experiments
A. Crossing pea plants
B.
C.

Lab zone Discover Activity

What Does the Father Look Like?

1. Observe the colors of the kitten in the photo. Record the kitten's coat colors and pattern. Include as many details as you can.

2. Observe the mother cat in the photo. Record her coat color and pattern.

Think It Over
Inferring Based on your observations, describe what you think the kitten's father might look like. Identify the evidence on which you based your inference.

In the mid nineteenth century, a priest named Gregor Mendel tended a garden in a central European monastery. Mendel's experiments in that peaceful garden would one day revolutionize the study of heredity. **Heredity** is the passing of physical characteristics from parents to offspring.

Mendel wondered why different pea plants had different characteristics. Some pea plants grew tall, while others were short. Some plants produced green seeds, while others had yellow seeds. Each different form of a characteristic, such as stem height or seed color, is called a **trait.** Mendel observed that the pea plants' traits were often similar to those of their parents. Sometimes, however, the plants had different traits from those of their parents.

Mendel experimented with thousands of pea plants to understand the process of heredity. Today, Mendel's discoveries form the foundation of **genetics,** the scientific study of heredity.

**Gregor ▶
Mendel**

Mendel's Experiments

Figure 16 shows a pea plant's flower. The flower's petals surround the pistil and the stamens. The pistil produces female sex cells, or eggs. The stamens produce pollen, which contains the male sex cells, or sperm. A new organism begins to form when egg and sperm join in the process called **fertilization.** Before fertilization can happen in pea plants, pollen must reach the pistil of a pea flower. This process is called pollination.

Pea plants are usually self-pollinating. In self-pollination, pollen from a flower lands on the pistil of the same flower. Mendel developed a method by which he cross-pollinated, or "crossed," pea plants. To cross two plants, he removed pollen from a flower on one plant. He then brushed the pollen onto a flower on a second plant.

Crossing Pea Plants Suppose you wanted to study the inheritance of traits in pea plants. What could you do? Mendel decided to cross plants with contrasting traits—for example, tall plants and short plants. He started his experiments with pure-bred plants. A **purebred** organism is the offspring of many generations that have the same trait. For example, purebred short pea plants always come from short parent plants.

FIGURE 16
Crossing Pea Plants
Gregor Mendel crossed pea plants that had different traits. The illustrations show how he did this. **Interpreting Diagrams** *How did Mendel prevent self-pollination?*

1 To prevent self-pollination, Mendel removed the pollen-producing structures from a pink flower.

2 He used a brush to remove pollen from a white flower on another plant. He brushed this pollen onto the pink flower.

3 The egg cells in the pink flower were then fertilized by sperm from the white flower. After a time, peas formed in the pod.

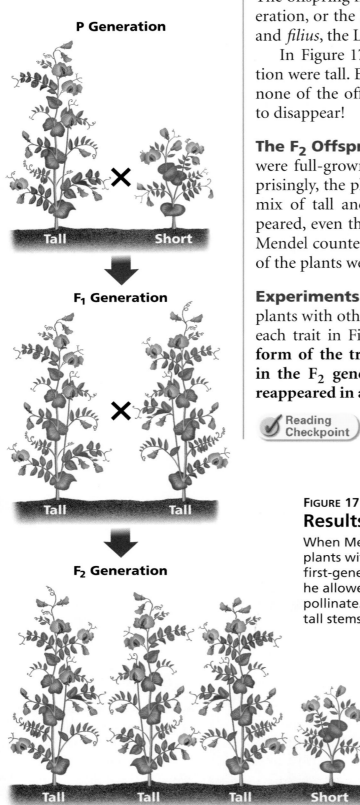

P Generation

Tall × Short

F₁ Generation

Tall × Tall

F₂ Generation

Tall   Tall   Tall   Short

The F₁ Offspring In one experiment, Mendel crossed pure-bred tall plants with purebred short plants. Scientists today call these parent plants the parental generation, or P generation. The offspring from this cross are the first filial (FIL ee ul) generation, or the F₁ generation. The word *filial* comes from *filia* and *filius*, the Latin words for "daughter" and "son."

In Figure 17, notice that all the offspring in the F₁ generation were tall. Even though one of the parent plants was short, none of the offspring were short. The shortness trait seemed to disappear!

The F₂ Offspring When the plants in the F₁ generation were full-grown, Mendel allowed them to self-pollinate. Surprisingly, the plants in the F₂ (second filial) generation were a mix of tall and short plants. The shortness trait had reappeared, even though none of the F₁ parent plants were short. Mendel counted the tall and short plants. About three fourths of the plants were tall, while one fourth were short.

Experiments With Other Traits Mendel also crossed pea plants with other contrasting traits. Compare the two forms of each trait in Figure 18. **In all of Mendel's crosses, only one form of the trait appeared in the F₁ generation. However, in the F₂ generation, the "lost" form of the trait always reappeared in about one fourth of the plants.**

✓ **Reading Checkpoint** What did Mendel observe about the F₂ plants?

FIGURE 17
Results of a Cross
When Mendel crossed purebred tall-stemmed plants with purebred short-stemmed plants, the first-generation offspring all had tall stems. Then he allowed the first-generation plants to self-pollinate. About 75 percent of the offspring had tall stems, and about 25 percent had short stems.

Genetics of Pea Plants

Traits	Seed Shape	Seed Color	Seed Coat Color	Pod Shape	Pod Color	Flower Position	Stem Height
Controlled by Dominant Allele	Round	Yellow	Gray	Smooth	Green	Side	Tall
Controlled by Recessive Allele	Wrinkled	Green	White	Pinched	Yellow	End	Short

Dominant and Recessive Alleles

Mendel reached several conclusions on the basis of his experimental results. He reasoned that individual factors, or sets of genetic "information," must control the inheritance of traits in peas. The factors that control each trait exist in pairs. The female parent contributes one factor, while the male parent contributes the other factor. Finally, one factor in a pair can mask, or hide, the other factor. The tallness factor, for example, masked the shortness factor.

Genes and Alleles Today, scientists use the word **gene** for the factors that control a trait. **Alleles** (uh LEELZ) are the different forms of a gene. The gene that controls stem height in peas, for example, has one allele for tall stems and one allele for short stems. Each pea plant inherits two alleles from its parents—one allele from the egg and the other from the sperm. A pea plant may inherit two alleles for tall stems, two alleles for short stems, or one of each.

An organism's traits are controlled by the alleles it inherits from its parents. Some alleles are dominant, while other alleles are recessive. A **dominant allele** is one whose trait always shows up in the organism when the allele is present. A **recessive allele,** on the other hand, is hidden whenever the dominant allele is present. A trait controlled by a recessive allele will only show up if the organism does not have the dominant allele. Figure 18 shows dominant and recessive alleles in Mendel's crosses.

FIGURE 18
Mendel studied several traits in pea plants.
Interpreting Diagrams *Is yellow seed color controlled by a dominant allele or a recessive allele?*

Lab zone Skills Activity

Predicting

In fruit flies, long wings are dominant over short wings. A scientist crossed a purebred long-winged male fruit fly with a purebred short-winged female. Predict the wing length of the F_1 offspring. If the scientist crossed a hybrid male F_1 fruit fly with a hybrid F_1 female, what would their offspring probably be like?

In pea plants, the allele for tall stems is dominant over the allele for short stems. Pea plants with one allele for tall stems and one allele for short stems will be tall. The allele for tall stems masks the allele for short stems. Only pea plants that inherit two recessive alleles for short stems will be short.

Alleles in Mendel's Crosses In Mendel's cross for stem height, the purebred tall plants in the P generation had two alleles for tall stems. The purebred short plants had two alleles for short stems. The F_1 plants each inherited an allele for tall stems from the tall parent and an allele for short stems from the short parent. Therefore, each F_1 plant had one allele for tall stems and one for short stems. The F_1 plants are called hybrids. A **hybrid** (HY brid) organism has two different alleles for a trait. All the F_1 plants are tall because the dominant allele for tall stems masks the recessive allele for short stems.

When Mendel crossed the F_1 plants, some of the offspring in the F_2 generation inherited two dominant alleles for tall stems. These plants were tall. Other F_2 plants inherited one dominant allele for tall stems and one recessive allele for short stems. These plants were also tall. The rest of the F_2 plants inherited two recessive alleles for short stems. These plants were short.

Symbols for Alleles Geneticists use letters to represent alleles. A dominant allele is represented by a capital letter. For example, the allele for tall stems is represented by *T*. A recessive allele is represented by the lowercase version of the letter. So, the allele for short stems would be represented by *t*. When a plant inherits two dominant alleles for tall stems, its alleles are written as *TT*. When a plant inherits two recessive alleles for short stems, its alleles are written as *tt*. When a plant inherits one allele for tall stems and one allele for short stems, its alleles are written as *Tt*.

FIGURE 19
Black Fur, White Fur
In rabbits, the allele for black fur is dominant over the allele for white fur. **Inferring** *What combination of alleles must the white rabbit have?*

534 ◆

Significance of Mendel's Contribution Mendel's discovery of genes and alleles eventually changed scientists' ideas about heredity. Before Mendel, most people thought that the traits of an individual organism were simply a blend of their parents' characteristics. According to this idea, if a tall plant and a short plant were crossed, the offspring would all have medium height.

However, when Mendel crossed purebred tall and purebred short pea plants, the offspring were all tall. Mendel's experiments demonstrated that parents' traits do not simply blend in the offspring. Instead, traits are determined by individual, separate alleles inherited from each parent. Some of these alleles, such as the allele for short height in pea plants, are recessive. If a trait is determined by a recessive allele, the trait can seem to disappear in the offspring.

Unfortunately, the importance of Mendel's discovery was not recognized during his lifetime. Then, in 1900, three different scientists rediscovered Mendel's work. These scientists quickly recognized the importance of Mendel's ideas. Because of his work, Mendel is often called the Father of Genetics.

FIGURE 20
The Mendel Medal
Every year, to honor the memory of Gregor Mendel, an outstanding scientist is awarded the Mendel Medal.

Reading Checkpoint If an allele is represented by a capital letter, what does this indicate?

Section 3 Assessment

 **Target Reading Skill** Outlining Use the information in your outline about Mendel's work to help you answer the questions below.

Reviewing Key Concepts

1. a. Identifying In Mendel's cross for stem height, what contrasting traits did the pea plants in the P generation exhibit?

b. Explaining What trait or traits did the plants in the F_1 generation exhibit? When you think of the traits of the parent plants, why is this result surprising?

c. Comparing and Contrasting Contrast the offspring in the F_1 generation to the offspring in the F_2 generation. What did the differences in the F_1 and F_2 offspring show Mendel?

2. a. Defining What is a dominant allele? What is a recessive allele?

b. Relating Cause and Effect Explain how dominant and recessive alleles for the trait of stem height determine whether a pea plant will be tall or short.

c. Applying Concepts Can a short pea plant ever be a hybrid for the trait of stem height? Why or why not? As part of your explanation, write the letters that represent the alleles for stem height of a short pea plant.

Lab zone **At-Home Activity**

Gardens and Heredity Some gardeners save the seeds produced by flowers and plant them in the spring. If there are gardeners in your family, ask them how closely the plants that grow from these seeds resemble the parent plants. Are the offspring's traits ever different from those of the parents?

Take a Class Survey

Problem

Are traits controlled by dominant alleles more common than traits controlled by recessive alleles?

Skills Focus

developing hypotheses, interpreting data

Materials

- mirror (optional)

Procedure

PART 1 Dominant and Recessive Alleles

1. Write a hypothesis reflecting your ideas about the problem. Then copy the data table.

2. For each of the traits listed in the data table, work with a partner to determine which trait you have. Circle that trait in your data table.

3. Count the number of students in your class who have each trait. Record that number in your data table. Also record the total number of students.

PART 2 Are Your Traits Unique?

4. Look at the circle of traits on the opposite page. All the traits in your data table appear in the circle. Place the eraser end of your pencil on the trait in the small central circle that applies to you—either free ear lobes or attached ear lobes.

5. Look at the two traits touching the space your eraser is on. Move your eraser onto the next description that applies to you. Continue using your eraser to trace your traits until you reach a number on the outside rim of the circle. Share that number with your classmates.

Analyze and Conclude

1. **Observing** The traits listed under Trait 1 in the data table are controlled by dominant alleles. The traits listed under Trait 2 are controlled by recessive alleles. Which traits controlled by dominant alleles were shown by a majority of students? Which traits controlled by recessive alleles were shown by a majority of students?

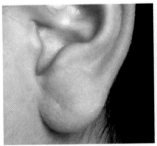
Free ear lobe

Widow's peak

Cleft chin

Dimple

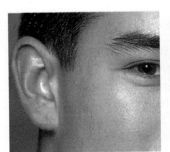
Attached ear lobe

No widow's peak

No cleft chin

No dimple

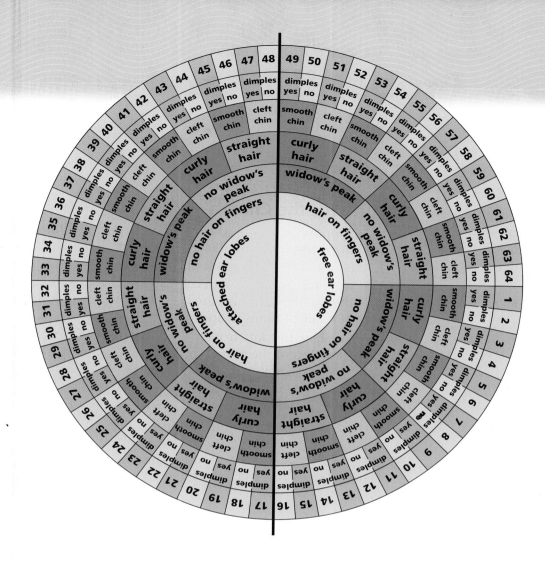

2. **Interpreting Data** How many students ended up on the same number on the circle of traits? How many students were the only ones to have their number? What do the results suggest about each person's combination of traits?

3. **Developing Hypotheses** Do your data support the hypothesis you proposed in Step 1? Write an answer with examples.

Design an Experiment

Do people who are related to each other show more genetic similarity than unrelated people? Write a hypothesis. Then design an experiment to test your hypothesis. *Obtain your teacher's permission before carrying out your investigation.*

Data Table				
Total Number of Students_____				
	Trait 1	Number	Trait 2	Number
A	Free ear lobes		Attached ear lobes	
B	Hair on fingers		No hair on fingers	
C	Widow's peak		No widow's peak	
D	Curly hair		Straight hair	
E	Cleft chin		Smooth chin	
F	Smile dimples		No smile dimples	

Probability and Heredity

Reading Preview

Key Concepts
- What is probability and how does it help explain the results of genetic crosses?
- What is meant by genotype and phenotype?
- What is codominance?

Key Terms
- probability
- Punnett square
- phenotype
- genotype
- homozygous
- heterozygous
- codominance

🎯 Target Reading Skill
Building Vocabulary After you read the section, reread the paragraphs that contain definitions of Key Terms. Use all the information you have learned to write a definition of each Key Term in your own words.

Go Online
SCiLINKS NSTA

For: Links on probability and genetics
Visit: www.SciLinks.org
Web Code: scn-0332

Lab zone Discover **Activity**

What's the Chance?

1. Suppose you were to toss a coin 20 times. Predict how many times the coin would land with heads up and how many times it would land with tails up.

2. Now test your prediction by tossing a coin 20 times. Record the number of times the coin lands with heads up and the number of times it lands with tails up.

3. Combine the data from the entire class. Record the total number of tosses, the number of heads, and the number of tails.

Think It Over

Predicting How did your results in Step 2 compare to your prediction? How can you account for any differences between your results and the class results?

On a brisk fall afternoon, the stands are packed with cheering football fans. Today is the big game between Riverton's North and South high schools, and it's almost time for the kickoff. Suddenly, the crowd becomes silent, as the referee is about to toss a coin. The outcome of the coin toss will decide which team kicks the ball and which receives it. The captain of the visiting North High team says "heads." If the coin lands with heads up, North High wins the toss and the right to decide whether to kick or receive the ball.

What is the chance that North High will win the coin toss? To answer this question, you need to understand the principles of probability.

Principles of Probability

If you did the Discover activity, you used the principles of **probability** to predict the results of a particular event. In this case, the event was the toss of a coin. **Probability is a number that describes how likely it is that an event will occur.**

Mathematics of Probability Each time you toss a coin, there are two possible ways that the coin can land—heads up or tails up. Each of these two events is equally likely to occur. In mathematical terms, you can say that the probability that a tossed coin will land with heads up is 1 in 2. There is also a 1 in 2 probability that the coin will land with tails up. A 1 in 2 probability can also be expressed as the fraction $\frac{1}{2}$ or as a percent—50 percent.

The laws of probability predict what is likely to occur, not necessarily what will occur. If you tossed a coin 20 times, you might expect it to land with heads up 10 times and with tails up 10 times. However, you might not get these results. You might get 11 heads and 9 tails, or 8 heads and 12 tails. The more tosses you make, the closer your actual results will be to the results predicted by probability.

 **Reading Checkpoint** What is probability?

Independence of Events When you toss a coin more than once, the results of one toss do not affect the results of the next toss. Each event occurs independently. For example, suppose you toss a coin five times and it lands with heads up each time. What is the probability that it will land with heads up on the next toss? Because the coin landed heads up on the previous five tosses, you might think that it would be likely to land heads up on the next toss. However, this is not the case. The probability of the coin landing heads up on the next toss is still 1 in 2, or 50 percent. The results of the first five tosses do not affect the result of the sixth toss.

FIGURE 21
A Coin Toss
The result of a coin toss can be explained by probability.

◆ **539**

1 Start by drawing a box and dividing it into four squares.

2 Write the male parent's alleles along the top of the square and the female parent's alleles along the left side.

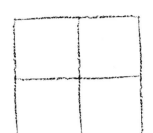

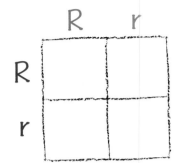

FIGURE 22
How to Make a Punnett Square

The diagrams show how to make a Punnett square. In this cross, both parents are heterozygous for the trait of seed shape. *R* represents the dominant round allele, and *r* represents the recessive wrinkled allele.

Coin Crosses

Here's how you can use coins to model Mendel's cross between two *Tt* pea plants.

1. Place a small piece of masking tape on each side of two coins.

2. Write a *T* (for tall) on one side of each coin and a *t* (for short) on the other.

3. Toss both coins together 20 times. Record the letter combinations that you obtain from each toss.

Interpreting Data How many of the offspring would be tall plants? (*Hint:* What different letter combinations would result in a tall plant?) How many would be short? Convert your results to percentages. Then compare your results to Mendel's.

Probability and Genetics

How is probability related to genetics? To answer this question, think back to Mendel's experiments with peas. Remember that Mendel carefully counted the offspring from every cross that he carried out. When Mendel crossed two plants that were hybrid for stem height (Tt), three fourths of the F_1 plants had tall stems. One fourth of the plants had short stems.

Each time Mendel repeated the cross, he obtained similar results. Mendel realized that the mathematical principles of probability applied to his work. He could say that the probability of such a cross producing a tall plant was 3 in 4. The probability of producing a short plant was 1 in 4. Mendel was the first scientist to recognize that the principles of probability can be used to predict the results of genetic crosses.

Punnett Squares A tool that can help you understand how the laws of probability apply to genetics is called a Punnett square. A **Punnett square** is a chart that shows all the possible combinations of alleles that can result from a genetic cross. Geneticists use Punnett squares to show all the possible outcomes of a genetic cross, and to determine the probability of a particular outcome.

Figure 22 shows how to construct a Punnett square. In this case, the Punnett square shows a cross between two hybrid pea plants with round seeds (Rr). The allele for round seeds (R) is dominant over the allele for wrinkled seeds (r). Each parent can pass either of its alleles, R or r, to its offspring. The boxes in the Punnett square represent the possible combinations of alleles that the offspring can inherit.

Reading Checkpoint What is a Punnett square?

3 Copy the female parent's alleles into the boxes to their right.

4 Copy the male parent's alleles into the boxes beneath them.

5 The completed Punnett square shows all the possible allele combinations in the offspring.

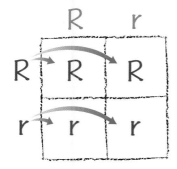

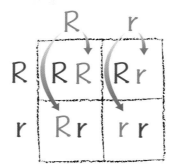

R r

R | RR | Rr
r | Rr | rr

Using a Punnett Square

You can use a Punnett square to calculate the probability that offspring with a certain combination of alleles will result. **In a genetic cross, the allele that each parent will pass on to its offspring is based on probability.** The completed Punnett square in Figure 22 shows four possible combinations of alleles. The probability that an offspring will be *RR* is 1 in 4, or 25 percent. The probability that an offspring will be *rr* is also 1 in 4, or 25 percent. Notice, however, that the *Rr* allele combination appears in two boxes in the Punnett square. This is because there are two possible ways in which this combination can occur. So the probability that an offspring will be *Rr* is 2 in 4, or 50 percent.

When Mendel crossed hybrid plants with round seeds, he discovered that about three fourths of the plants (75 percent) had round seeds. The remaining one fourth of the plants (25 percent) produced wrinkled seeds. Plants with the *RR* allele combination would produce round seeds. So too would those plants with the *Rr* allele combination. Remember that the dominant allele masks the recessive allele. Only those plants with the *rr* allele combination would have wrinkled seeds.

Predicting Probabilities

You can use a Punnett square to predict probabilities. For example, Figure 8 shows a cross between a purebred black guinea pig and a purebred white guinea pig. The allele for black fur is dominant over the allele for white fur. Notice that only one allele combination is possible in the offspring—*Bb*. All of the offspring will inherit the dominant allele for black fur. Because of this, all of the offspring will have black fur. There is a 100 percent probability that the offspring will have black fur.

FIGURE 23
Guinea Pig Punnett Square
This Punnett square shows a cross between a black guinea pig (*BB*) and a white guinea pig (*bb*).
Calculating What is the probability that an offspring will have white fur?

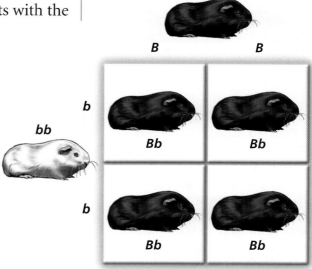

Math › Analyzing Data

What Are the Genotypes?

Mendel allowed several F_1 pea plants with yellow seeds to self-pollinate. The graph shows the approximate numbers of the F_2 offspring with yellow seeds and with green seeds.

1. **Reading Graphs** How many F_2 offspring had yellow seeds? How many had green seeds?

2. **Calculating** Use the information in the graph to calculate the total number of offspring that resulted from this cross. Then calculate the percentage of the offspring with yellow peas, and the percentage with green peas.

3. **Inferring** Use the answers to Question 2 to infer the probable genotypes of the parent plants.

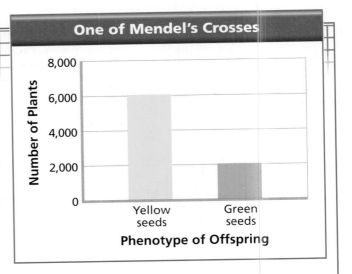

One of Mendel's Crosses

Number of Plants (y-axis: 0, 2,000, 4,000, 6,000, 8,000)

Phenotype of Offspring (x-axis: Yellow seeds, Green seeds)

(*Hint:* Construct Punnett squares with the possible genotypes of the parents.)

Phenotypes and Genotypes

Two useful terms that geneticists use are **phenotype** (FEE noh typ) and **genotype** (JEN uh typ). **An organism's phenotype is its physical appearance, or visible traits. An organism's genotype is its genetic makeup, or allele combinations.**

To understand the difference between phenotype and genotype, look at Figure 24. The allele for smooth pea pods (S) is dominant over the allele for pinched pea pods (s). All of the plants with at least one dominant allele have the same phenotype—they all produce smooth pods. However, the plants can have two different genotypes—SS or Ss. If you were to look at the plants with smooth pods, you would not be able to tell the difference between those with the SS genotype and those with the Ss genotype. The plants with pinched pods, on the other hand, would all have the same phenotype—pinched pods—as well as the same genotype—ss.

Geneticists use two additional terms to describe an organism's genotype. An organism that has two identical alleles for a trait is said to be **homozygous** (hoh moh ZY gus) for that trait. A smooth-pod plant that has the alleles SS and a pinched-pod plant with the alleles ss are both homozygous. An organism that has two different alleles for a trait is **heterozygous** (het ur oh ZY gus) for that trait. A smooth-pod plant with the alleles Ss is heterozygous. Mendel used the term *hybrid* to describe heterozygous pea plants.

SS Ss ss

Phenotypes and Genotypes	
Phenotype	**Genotype**
Smooth pods	SS
Smooth pods	Ss
Pinched pods	ss

FIGURE 24
The phenotype of an organism is its physical appearance. Its genotype is its genetic makeup.
Interpreting Tables How many genotypes are there for the smooth-pod phenotype?

Reading Checkpoint If a pea plant's genotype is Ss, what is its phenotype?

Codominance

For all of the traits that Mendel studied, one allele was dominant while the other was recessive. This is not always the case. For some alleles, an inheritance pattern called **codominance** exists. **In codominance, the alleles are neither dominant nor recessive. As a result, both alleles are expressed in the offspring.**

Look at Figure 25. Mendel's principle of dominant and recessive alleles does not explain why the heterozygous chickens have both black and white feathers. The alleles for feather color are codominant—neither dominant nor recessive. As you can see, neither allele is masked in the heterozygous chickens. Notice also that the codominant alleles are written as capital letters with superscripts—F^B for black feathers and F^W for white feathers. As the Punnett square shows, heterozygous chickens have the $F^B F^W$ allele combination.

 **Reading Checkpoint** How are the symbols for codominant alleles written?

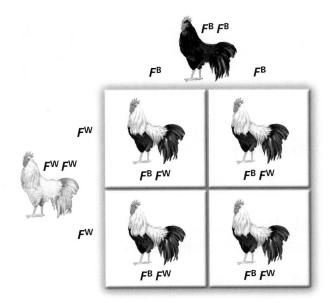

FIGURE 25
Codominance
The offspring of the cross in this Punnett square will have both black and white feathers.
Classifying *Will the offspring be heterozygous or homozygous? Explain your answer.*

Section 4 Assessment

Target Reading Skill **Building Vocabulary** Use your definitions to help you answer the questions.

Reviewing Key Concepts

1. a. **Reviewing** What is probability?
   b. **Explaining** If you know the parents' alleles for a trait, how can you use a Punnett square to predict the probable genotypes of the offspring?
   c. **Predicting** A pea plant with round seeds has the genotype *Rr*. You cross this plant with a wrinkled-seed plant, genotype *rr*. What is the probability that the offspring will have wrinkled seeds? (Use a Punnett square to help with the prediction.)

2. a. **Defining** Define *genotype* and *phenotype*.
   b. **Relating Cause and Effect** Explain how two organisms can have the same phenotype but different genotypes. Give an example.
   c. **Applying Concepts** A pea plant has a tall stem. What are its possible genotypes?

3. a. **Explaining** What is codominance? Give an example of codominant alleles and explain why they are codominant.
   b. **Applying Concepts** What is the phenotype of a chicken with the genotype $F^B F^W$?

Math Practice

4. **Ratios** A scientist crossed a tall pea plant with a short pea plant. Of the offspring, 13 were tall and 12 were short. Write the ratio of each phenotype to the total number of offspring. Express the ratios as fractions.

5. **Percentage** Use the fractions to calculate the percentage of the offspring that were tall and the percentage that were short.

Make the Right Call!

Problem

How can you predict the possible results of genetic crosses?

Skills Focus

making models, interpreting data

Materials

- 2 small paper bags • marking pen
- 3 blue marbles • 3 white marbles

Procedure

1. Label one bag "Bag 1, Female Parent." Label the other bag "Bag 2, Male Parent." Then read over Part 1, Part 2, and Part 3 of this lab. Write a prediction about the kinds of off-spring you expect from each cross.

PART 1 Crossing Two Homozygous Parents

2. Copy the data table and label it *Data Table 1*. Then place two blue marbles in Bag 1. This pair of marbles represents the female parent's alleles. Use the letter *B* to represent the dominant allele for blue color.

3. Place two white marbles in Bag 2. Use the letter *b* to represent the recessive allele for white color.

4. For Trial 1, remove one marble from Bag 1 without looking in the bag. Record the result in your data table. Return the marble to the bag. Again, without looking in the bag, remove one marble from Bag 2. Record the result in your data table. Return the marble to the bag.

5. In the column labeled Offspring's Alleles, write *BB* if you removed two blue marbles, *bb* if you removed two white marbles, or *Bb* if you removed one blue marble and one white marble.

6. Repeat Steps 4 and 5 nine more times.

PART 2 Crossing Homozygous and Heterozygous Parents

7. Place two blue marbles in Bag 1. Place one white marble and one blue marble in Bag 2. Copy the data table again, and label it *Data Table 2*.

8. Repeat Steps 4 and 5 ten times.

Data Table			
Number _____			
Trial	Allele From Bag 1 (Female Parent)	Allele From Bag 2 (Male Parent)	Offspring's Alleles
1			
2			
3			
4			
5			
6			

PART 3 Crossing Two Heterozygous Parents

9. Place one blue marble and one white marble in Bag 1. Place one blue marble and one white marble in Bag 2. Copy the data table again and label it *Data Table 3*.

10. Repeat Steps 4 and 5 ten times.

Analyze and Conclude

1. **Making Models** Make a Punnett square for each of the crosses you modeled in Part 1, Part 2, and Part 3.

2. **Interpreting Data** According to your results in Part 1, how many different kinds of offspring are possible when the homozygous parents (*BB* and *bb*) are crossed? Do the results you obtained using the marble model agree with the results shown by a Punnett square?

3. **Predicting** According to your results in Part 2, what percentage of offspring are likely to be homozygous when a homozygous parent (*BB*) and a heterozygous parent (*Bb*) are crossed? What percentage of offspring are likely to be heterozygous? Does the model agree with the results shown by a Punnett square?

4. **Communicating** According to your results in Part 3, what different kinds of offspring are possible when two heterozygous parents (*Bb* × *Bb*) are crossed? What percentage of each type of offspring are likely to be produced? Does the model agree with the results of a Punnett square?

5. **Inferring** For Part 3, if you did 100 trials instead of 10 trials, would your results be closer to the results shown in a Punnett square? Explain.

6. **Communicating** In a paragraph, explain how the marble model compares with a Punnett square. How are the two methods alike? How are they different?

More to Explore

In peas, the allele for yellow seeds (*Y*) is dominant over the allele for green seeds (*y*). What possible crosses do you think could produce a heterozygous plant with yellow seeds (*Yy*)? Use the marble model and Punnett squares to test your predictions.

The Cell and Inheritance

Reading Preview

Key Concepts
- What role do chromosomes play in inheritance?
- What events occur during meiosis?
- What is the relationship between chromosomes and genes?

Key Term
- meiosis

Target Reading Skill
Identifying Supporting Evidence As you read, identify the evidence that supports the hypothesis that genes are found on chromosomes. Write the evidence in a graphic organizer.

Evidence

(Grasshoppers: 24 chromosomes in body cells, 12 in sex cells)

Hypothesis

(Chromosomes are important in inheritance.)

Lab zone Discover **Activity**

Which Chromosome Is Which?
Mendel did not know about chromosomes or their role in genetics. Today we know that genes are located on chromosomes.

1. Label two craft sticks with the letter *A*. The craft sticks represent a pair of chromosomes in the female parent. Turn the sticks face down on a piece of paper.
2. Label two more craft sticks with the letter *a*. These represent a pair of chromosomes in the male parent. Turn the sticks face down on another piece of paper.
3. Turn over one craft stick "chromosome" from each piece of paper. Move both sticks to a third piece of paper. These represent a pair of chromosomes in the offspring. Note the allele combination that the offspring received.

Think It Over
Making Models Use this model to explain how chromosomes are involved in the inheritance of alleles.

Mendel's work showed that genes exist. But scientists in the early twentieth century did not know what structures in cells contained genes. The search for the answer to this puzzle is something like a mystery story. The story could be called "The Clue in the Grasshopper's Cells."

In 1903, Walter Sutton, an American geneticist, was studying the cells of grasshoppers. He wanted to understand how sex cells (sperm and egg) form. Sutton focused on the movement of chromosomes during the formation of sex cells. He hypothesized that chromosomes were the key to understanding how offspring have traits similar to those of their parents.

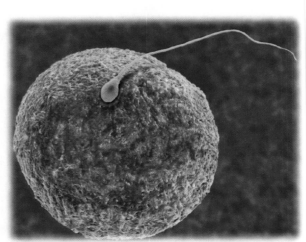

◄ Sperm

Egg ►

FIGURE 26
Sex Cells
The large egg is a female sex cell, and the smaller sperm is a male sex cell.

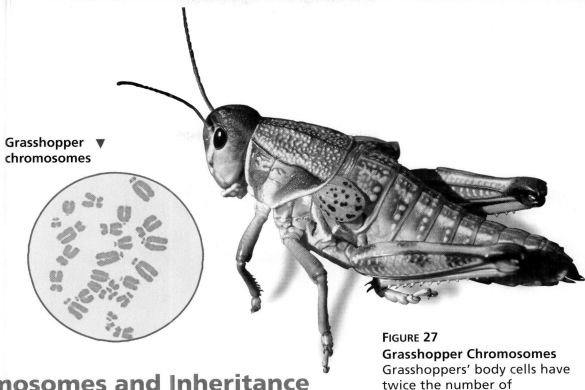

Grasshopper ▼
chromosomes

FIGURE 27
Grasshopper Chromosomes
Grasshoppers' body cells have twice the number of chromosomes as their sex cells.
Applying Concepts *What is the function of chromosomes?*

Chromosomes and Inheritance

Sutton needed evidence to support his hypothesis that chromosomes were important in the inheritance of traits. He found that evidence in grasshoppers' cells. The body cells of a grasshopper have 24 chromosomes. To his surprise, Sutton found that the grasshopper's sex cells have only 12 chromosomes. In other words, a grasshopper's sex cells have exactly half the number of chromosomes found in its body cells.

Chromosome Pairs Sutton observed what happened when a sperm cell and an egg cell joined during fertilization. The fertilized egg that formed had 24 chromosomes. As a result, the grasshopper offspring had exactly the same number of chromosomes in its cells as did each of its parents. The 24 chromosomes existed in 12 pairs. One chromosome in each pair came from the male parent, while the other chromosome came from the female parent.

Genes on Chromosomes Recall that alleles are different forms of a gene. Because of Mendel's work, Sutton knew that alleles exist in pairs in an organism. One allele in a pair comes from the organism's female parent and the other allele comes from the male parent. Sutton realized that paired alleles were carried on paired chromosomes. Sutton's idea came to be known as the chromosome theory of inheritance. **According to the chromosome theory of inheritance, genes are carried from parents to their offspring on chromosomes.**

 Reading Checkpoint) **What is the relationship between alleles and chromosomes?**

FIGURE 28
Meiosis

During meiosis, a cell produces sex cells with half the number of chromosomes. **Interpreting Diagrams** *What happens before meiosis?*

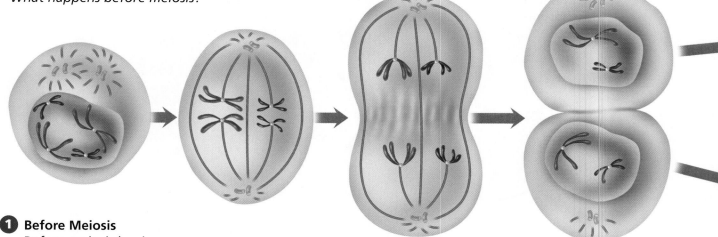

1 Before Meiosis
Before meiosis begins, every chromosome in the parent cell is copied. Centromeres hold the two chromatids together.

2 Meiosis I
A The chromosome pairs line up in the center of the cell.

B The pairs separate and move to opposite ends of the cell.

C Two cells form, each with half the number of chromosomes. Each chromosome still has two chromatids.

Meiosis

How do sex cells end up with half the number of chromosomes as body cells? To answer this question, you need to understand the events that occur during meiosis. **Meiosis** (my OH sis) is the process by which the number of chromosomes is reduced by half to form sex cells—sperm and eggs.

What Happens During Meiosis You can trace the events of meiosis in Figure 28. In this example, each parent cell has four chromosomes arranged in two pairs. **During meiosis, the chromosome pairs separate and are distributed to two different cells. The resulting sex cells have only half as many chromosomes as the other cells in the organism.** The sex cells end up with only two chromosomes each—half the number found in the parent cell. Each sex cell has one chromosome from each original pair.

When sex cells combine to form an organism, each sex cell contributes half the normal number of chromosomes. Thus, the offspring gets the normal number of chromosomes—half from each parent.

Go Online
SciLINKS NSTA

For: Links on meiosis
Visit: www.SciLinks.org
Web Code: scn-0333

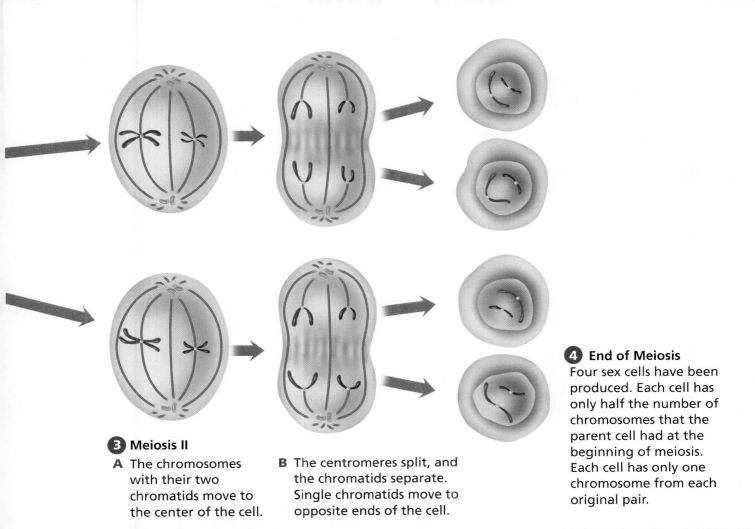

3 Meiosis II

A The chromosomes with their two chromatids move to the center of the cell.

B The centromeres split, and the chromatids separate. Single chromatids move to opposite ends of the cell.

4 End of Meiosis
Four sex cells have been produced. Each cell has only half the number of chromosomes that the parent cell had at the beginning of meiosis. Each cell has only one chromosome from each original pair.

Meiosis and Punnett Squares   A Punnett square is actually a way to show the events that occur at meiosis. When the chromosome pairs separate and go into two different sex cells, so do the alleles carried on each chromosome. One allele from each pair goes to each sex cell.

In Figure 29, you can see how the Punnett square accounts for the separation of alleles during meiosis. As shown across the top of the Punnett square, half of the sperm cells from the male parent will receive the chromosome with the *T* allele. The other half of the sperm cells will receive the chromosome with the *t* allele. In this example, the same is true for the egg cells from the female parent, as shown down the left side of the Punnett square. Depending on which sperm cell combines with which egg cell, one of the allele combinations shown in the boxes will result.

FIGURE 29
Meiosis Punnett Square
Both parents are heterozygous for the trait of stem height. The Punnett square shows the possible allele combinations after fertilization.

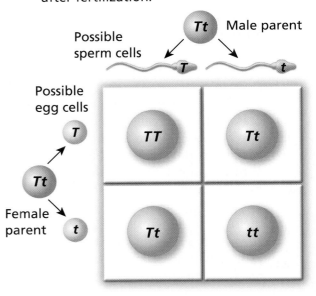

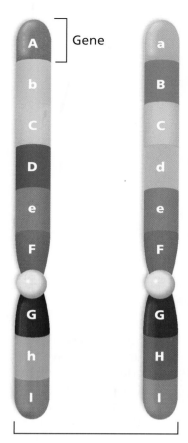

Gene

Chromosome pair

A Lineup of Genes

The body cells of humans contain 23 chromosome pairs, or 46 chromosomes. **Chromosomes are made up of many genes joined together like beads on a string.** Although you have only 23 pairs of chromosomes, your body cells each contain about 35,000 genes. Each gene controls a trait.

In Figure 30, one chromosome in the pair came from the female parent. The other chromosome came from the male parent. Notice that each chromosome in the pair has the same genes. The genes are lined up in the same order on both chromosomes. However, the alleles for some of the genes might be different. For example, the organism has the *A* allele on one chromosome and the *a* allele on the other. As you can see, this organism is heterozygous for some traits and homozygous for others.

FIGURE 30
Genes on Chromosomes
Genes are located on chromosomes. The chromosomes in a pair may have different alleles for some genes and the same alleles for others.
Classifying *For which genes is this organism homozygous? For which genes is it heterozygous?*

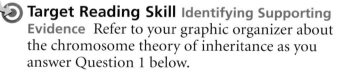

Section 5 Assessment

↻ **Target Reading Skill** Identifying Supporting Evidence Refer to your graphic organizer about the chromosome theory of inheritance as you answer Question 1 below.

Reviewing Key Concepts

1. a. **Comparing and Contrasting** According to Sutton's observations, how does the number of chromosomes in a grasshopper's body cells compare to the number in its sex cells?
   b. **Describing** Describe what happens to the number of chromosomes when two grasshopper sex cells join in fertilization.
   c. **Explaining** How do Sutton's observations about chromosome number support the chromosome theory of inheritance?
2. a. **Defining** What is meiosis?
   b. **Interpreting Diagrams** Briefly describe meiosis I and meiosis II. Refer to Figure 28.
   c. **Sequencing** Use the events of meiosis to explain why a sex cell normally does not receive both chromosomes from a pair.

3. a. **Describing** How are genes arranged on a chromosome?
   b. **Comparing and Contrasting** How does the order of genes in one member of a chromosome pair compare to the order of genes on the other chromosome?

Writing in Science

Newspaper Interview You are a newspaper reporter in the early 1900s. You want to interview Walter Sutton about his work with chromosomes. Write three questions you would like to ask Sutton. Then, for each question, write answers that Sutton might have given.

The DNA Connection

Reading Preview

Key Concepts
- What forms the genetic code?
- How does a cell produce proteins?
- How can mutations affect an organism?

Key Terms
- messenger RNA
- transfer RNA

Target Reading Skill
Sequencing A sequence is the order in which the steps in a process occur. As you read, make a flowchart that shows protein synthesis. Put the steps of the process in separate boxes in the flowchart in the order in which they occur.

Protein Synthesis

DNA provides code to form messenger RNA.

↓

Messenger RNA attaches to ribosome.

↓

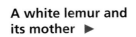

Lab zone | Discover **Activity**

Can You Crack the Code?

1. Use the Morse code in the chart to decode the question in the message below. The letters are separated by slash marks.

   • – – / • • • • / • / • – • / • / • – / • – • /
   • / – – • / • / – • / • / • • • / • – • • / – – –/
   – • – • / • – / – • / – • • /

2. Write your answer to the question in Morse code.

3. Exchange your coded answer with a partner. Then decode your partner's answer.

Think It Over
Forming Operational Definitions Based on your results from this activity, write a definition of the word *code*. Then compare your definition to one in a dictionary.

A • –	N – •
B – • • •	O – – –
C – • – •	P • – – •
D – • •	Q – – • –
E •	R • – •
F • • – •	S • • •
G – – •	T –
H • • • •	U • • –
I • •	V • • • –
J • – – –	W • – –
K – • –	X – • • –
L • – • •	Y – • – –
M – –	Z – – • •

The young, white, ring-tailed lemur in the photograph below was born in a forest in southern Madagascar. White lemurs are extremely rare. Why was this lemur born with such an uncommon phenotype? To answer this question, you need to know how the genes on a chromosome control an organism's traits.

A white lemur and its mother ▶

The Genetic Code

The main function of genes is to control the production of proteins in an organism's cells. Proteins help to determine the size, shape, color, and many other traits of an organism.

Genes and DNA Recall that chromosomes are composed mostly of DNA. In Figure 31, you can see the relationship between chromosomes and DNA. Notice that a DNA molecule is made up of four different nitrogen bases—adenine (A), thymine (T), guanine (G), and cytosine (C). These bases form the rungs of the DNA "ladder."

A gene is a section of a DNA molecule that contains the information to code for one specific protein. A gene is made up of a series of bases in a row. The bases in a gene are arranged in a specific order—for example, ATGACGTAC. A single gene on a chromosome may contain anywhere from several hundred to a million or more of these bases. Each gene is located at a specific place on a chromosome.

Order of the Bases A gene contains the code that determines the structure of a protein. **The order of the nitrogen bases along a gene forms a genetic code that specifies what type of protein will be produced.** Remember that proteins are long-chain molecules made of individual amino acids. In the genetic code, a group of three DNA bases codes for one specific amino acid. For example, the base sequence CGT (cytosine-guanine-thymine) always codes for the amino acid alanine. The order of the three-base code units determines the order in which amino acids are put together to form a protein.

FIGURE 31
The DNA Code

Chromosomes are made of DNA. Each chromosome contains thousands of genes. The sequence of bases in a gene forms a code that tells the cell what protein to produce. **Interpreting Diagrams** *Where in the cell are chromosomes located?*

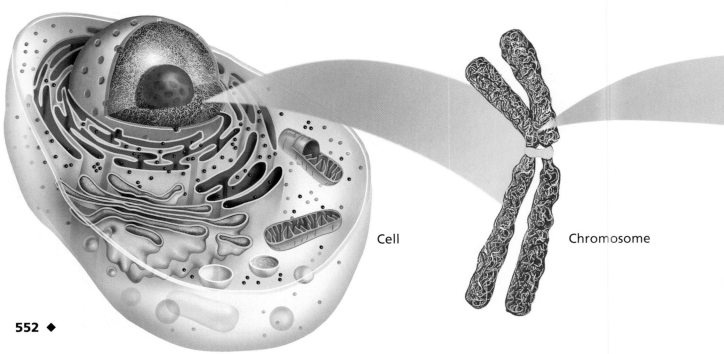

Cell

Chromosome

How Cells Make Proteins

The production of proteins is called protein synthesis. **During protein synthesis, the cell uses information from a gene on a chromosome to produce a specific protein.** Protein synthesis takes place on the ribosomes in the cytoplasm of a cell. As you know, the cytoplasm is outside the nucleus. The chromosomes, however, are found inside the nucleus. How, then, does the information needed to produce proteins get out of the nucleus and into the cytoplasm?

The Role of RNA Before protein synthesis can take place, a "messenger" must first carry the genetic code from the DNA inside the nucleus into the cytoplasm. This genetic messenger is called ribonucleic acid, or RNA.

Although RNA is similar to DNA, the two molecules differ in some important ways. Unlike DNA, which has two strands, RNA has only one strand. RNA also contains a different sugar molecule from the sugar found in DNA. Another difference between DNA and RNA is in their nitrogen bases. Like DNA, RNA contains adenine, guanine, and cytosine. However, instead of thymine, RNA contains uracil (YOOR uh sil).

Types of RNA There are several types of RNA involved in protein synthesis. **Messenger RNA** copies the coded message from the DNA in the nucleus, and carries the message to the ribosome in the cytoplasm. Another type of RNA, called **transfer RNA,** carries amino acids to the ribosome and adds them to the growing protein.

 **Reading Checkpoint** **How is RNA different from DNA?**

Lab zone Skills Activity

Drawing Conclusions

The following is a sequence of nitrogen bases on one strand of a nucleic acid molecule.

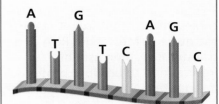

Does the strand come from DNA or RNA? Explain your answer.

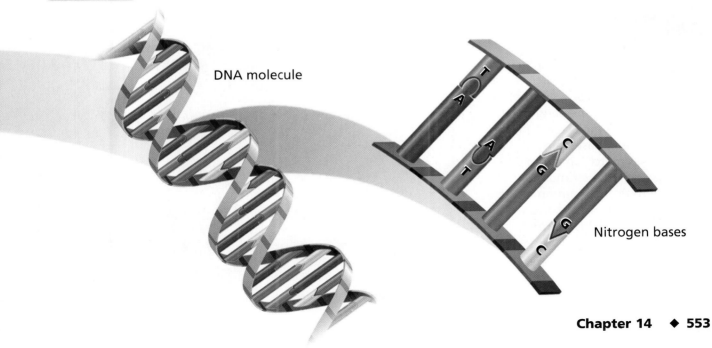

DNA molecule

Nitrogen bases

Translating the Code The process of protein synthesis is shown in Figure 32. Look at the illustration as you read the following steps.

① The first step is for a DNA molecule to "unzip" between its base pairs. Then one of the strands of DNA directs the production of a strand of messenger RNA. To form the RNA strand, RNA bases pair up with the DNA bases. The process is similar to the process in which DNA replicates. Cytosine always pairs with guanine. However, uracil—not thymine— pairs with adenine.

② The messenger RNA then leaves the nucleus and enters the cytoplasm. In the cytoplasm, messenger RNA attaches to a ribosome. On the ribosome, the messenger RNA provides the code for the protein molecule that will form. During protein synthesis, the ribosome moves along the messenger RNA strand.

FIGURE 32
Protein Synthesis

To make proteins, messenger RNA copies information from DNA in the nucleus. Messenger RNA and transfer RNA then use this information to produce proteins.
Interpreting Diagrams In which organelle of the cell are proteins manufactured?

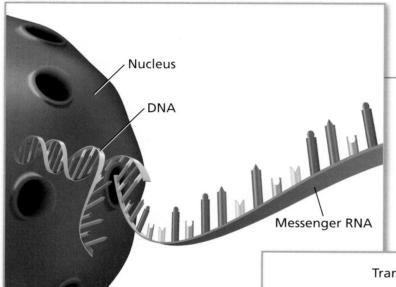

Nucleus

DNA

Messenger RNA

① **Messenger RNA Production** ▲
In the nucleus, a DNA molecule serves as a "pattern" for making messenger RNA. The DNA molecule "unzips" between base pairs. RNA bases match up along one of the DNA strands. The genetic information in the DNA is transferred to the messenger RNA strand.

② **Messenger RNA Attaches to a Ribosome** ▼
When the messenger RNA enters the cytoplasm, it attaches to a ribosome, where production of the protein chain begins. The ribosome moves along the messenger RNA strand.

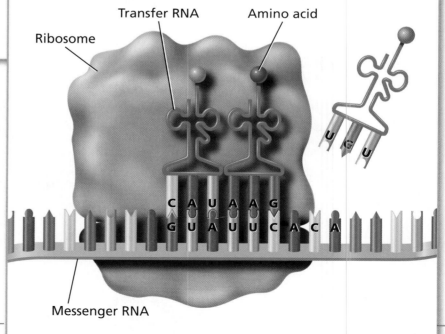

Transfer RNA   Amino acid

Ribosome

Messenger RNA

❸ Molecules of transfer RNA attach to the messenger RNA. The bases on the transfer RNA "read" the message by pairing up three-letter codes to bases on the messenger RNA. For example, you can see that a molecule of transfer RNA with the bases AAG pairs with the bases UUC on the messenger RNA. The molecules of transfer RNA carry specific amino acids. The amino acids link in a chain. The order of the amino acids in the chain is determined by the order of the three-letter codes on the messenger RNA.

❹ The protein molecule grows longer as each transfer RNA molecule puts the amino acid it is carrying along the growing protein chain. Once an amino acid is added to the protein chain, the transfer RNA is released into the cytoplasm and can pick up another amino acid. Each transfer RNA molecule always picks up the same kind of amino acid.

 **Reading Checkpoint** What is the function of transfer RNA?

Go Online
active art

For: Protein Synthesis activity
Visit: PHSchool.com
Web Code: cep-3034

❸ **Transfer RNA Attaches to Messenger RNA** ▼
Transfer RNA molecules carry specific amino acids to the ribosome. There they "read" the message in messenger RNA by matching up with three-letter codes of bases. The protein chain grows as each amino acid is attached.

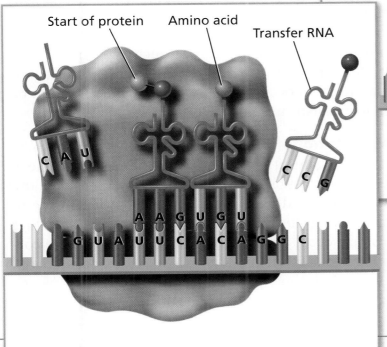

Start of protein   Amino acid   Transfer RNA

C A U   C C G

A A G U G U
G U A U U C A C A G G C

❹ **Protein Production Continues** ▲
The protein chain continues to grow until the ribosome reaches a three-letter code that acts as a stop sign. The ribosome then releases the completed protein.

Growing protein

C C G
G G C

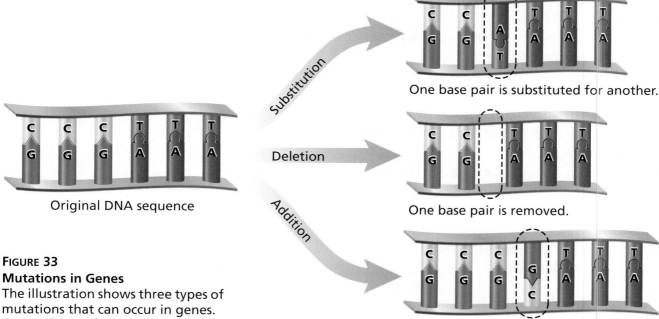

FIGURE 33
Mutations in Genes
The illustration shows three types of mutations that can occur in genes. *Comparing and Contrasting* *How are these mutations different from the mutations that occur when chromosomes do not separate during meiosis?*

Original DNA sequence

Substitution — One base pair is substituted for another.

Deletion — One base pair is removed.

Addition — One base pair is added.

Mutations

Suppose that a mistake occurred in one gene of a chromosome. Instead of the base A, for example, the DNA molecule might have the base G. Such a mistake is one type of mutation that can occur in a cell's hereditary material. Recall that a mutation is any change in a gene or chromosome. **Mutations can cause a cell to produce an incorrect protein during protein synthesis. As a result, the organism's trait, or phenotype, may be different from what it normally would have been.** In fact, the term *mutation* comes from a Latin word that means "change."

If a mutation occurs in a body cell, such as a skin cell, the mutation will not be passed on to the organism's offspring. If, however, a mutation occurs in a sex cell, the mutation can be passed on to an offspring and affect the offspring's phenotype.

Types of Mutations Some mutations are the result of small changes in an organism's hereditary material. For example, a single base may be substituted for another, or one or more bases may be removed from a section of DNA. This type of mutation can occur during the DNA replication process. Other mutations may occur when chromosomes don't separate correctly during meiosis. When this type of mutation occurs, a cell can end up with too many or too few chromosomes. The cell could also end up with extra segments of chromosomes.

Effects of Mutations Because mutations can introduce changes in an organism, they can be a source of genetic variety. Some mutations are harmful to an organism. A few mutations, however, are helpful, and others are neither harmful nor helpful. A mutation is harmful to an organism if it reduces the organism's chance for survival and reproduction.

Whether a mutation is harmful or not depends partly on the organism's environment. The mutation that led to the production of a white lemur would probably be harmful to an organism in the wild. The lemur's white color would make it more visible, and thus easier for predators to find. However, a white lemur in a zoo has the same chance for survival as a brown lemur. In a zoo, the mutation neither helps nor harms the lemur.

Helpful mutations, on the other hand, improve an organism's chances for survival and reproduction. Antibiotic resistance in bacteria is an example. Antibiotics are chemicals that kill bacteria. Gene mutations have enabled some kinds of bacteria to become resistant to certain antibiotics—that is, the antibiotics do not kill the bacteria that have the mutations. The mutations have improved the bacteria's ability to survive and reproduce.

FIGURE 34
Six-Toed Cat
Because of a mutation in one of its ancestors, this cat has six toes on each front paw.

 Reading Checkpoint **What are two types of mutations?**

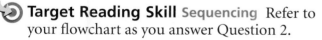

Section 6 Assessment

Target Reading Skill Sequencing Refer to your flowchart as you answer Question 2.

Reviewing Key Concepts

1. a. Explaining What is the relationship between a gene, a DNA molecule, and a protein?
   b. Relating Cause and Effect How does a DNA molecule determine the structure of a specific protein?
   c. Inferring The DNA base sequence GGG codes for the amino acid proline. Could this same base sequence code for a different amino acid? Why or why not?
2. a. Listing List the sequence of events that happens during protein synthesis.
   b. Describing What is messenger RNA? Describe how it performs its function.

   c. Inferring Does transfer RNA perform its function in the nucleus or cytoplasm? Explain your answer.
3. a. Reviewing How does a mutation in a gene affect the order of DNA bases?
   b. Relating Cause and Effect How can a mutation in a gene cause a change in an organism's phenotype?

Writing in Science

Compare/Contrast Paragraph Write a paragraph comparing and contrasting gene mutations and chromosome mutations. In your paragraph, explain what the two types of mutations are, and how they are similar and different.

1 Discovering Cells

Key Concepts

- The invention of the microscope enabled people to discover and learn about cells.

- All living things are composed of cells. Cells are the basic units of structure and function in living things. All cells are produced from other cells.

- The lenses in light microscopes magnify an object by bending the light that passes through them. Electron microscopes use a beam of electrons instead of light to produce a magnified image.

Key Terms
- cell • microscope • cell theory

2 Looking Inside Cells

Key Concepts

- A plant's cell wall protects and supports the cell. The cell membrane controls what substances come into and out of a cell.

- The nucleus directs the cell's activities. Mitochondria release energy from food molecules.

- Ribosomes produce proteins.

- Chloroplasts capture energy from sunlight and use it to produce food for the cell.

- Vacuoles are the storage areas of cells. Lysosomes contain chemicals that break down certain materials in the cell.

- In many-celled organisms, cells are often organized into tissues, organs, and organ systems.

- A bacterial cell has a cell wall and cell membrane, but no nucleus.

Key Terms
- organelle • cell wall • cell membrane
- nucleus • cytoplasm • mitochondria
- endoplasmic reticulum • ribosome • Golgi body • chloroplast • vacuole • lysosome

3 Mendel's Work

Key Concepts

- An organism's traits are controlled by the alleles it inherits from its parents.

Key Terms
- heredity • trait • genetics • fertilization
- purebred • gene • alleles • dominant allele
- recessive allele • hybrid

4 Probability and Heredity

Key Concepts

- Probability is the likelihood that a particular event will occur.

- In a genetic cross, the allele that each parent will pass on to its offspring is based on probability.

- An organism's phenotype is its physical appearance. An organism's genotype is its genetic makeup.

- In codominance, the alleles are neither dominant nor recessive.

Key Terms
- probability • Punnett square • phenotype
- genotype • homozygous • heterozygous
- codominance

5 The Cell and Inheritance

Key Concepts

- Genes are carried from parents to their offspring on chromosomes that are made up of many genes.

- During meiosis, the chromosome pairs separate and are distributed to two different cells. The resulting sex cells have only half as many chromosomes as the organism's other cells.

Key Term
meiosis

6 The DNA Connection

Key Concepts

- The order of the nitrogen bases along a gene forms a genetic code that specifies what type of protein will be produced.

- During protein synthesis, the cell uses information from a gene on a chromosome to produce a specific protein.

- Mutations can cause a cell to produce an incorrect protein during protein synthesis.

Key Terms
- messenger RNA • transfer RNA

Review and Assessment

Go Online
PHSchool.com

For: Self-Assessment
Visit: PHSchool.com
Web Code: cna-0010

Organizing Information

Concept Mapping Copy the concept map onto a separate sheet of paper. Then complete the concept map. (For more on Concept Mapping, see the Skills Handbook.)

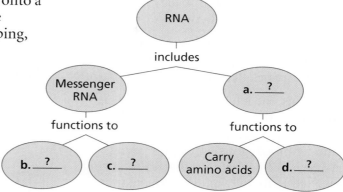

Reviewing Key Terms

Choose the letter of the best answer.

1. In plant and animal cells, the control center of the cell is the
   a. chloroplast.   **b.** cytoplasm.
   c. nucleus.   **d.** Golgi body.

2. The different forms of a gene are called
   a. alleles.   **b.** chromosomes.
   c. phenotypes.   **d.** genotypes.

3. The likelihood that a particular event will occur is called
   a. chance.   **b.** Punnett square.
   c. probability.   **d.** recessive.

4. An organism with two identical alleles for a trait is
   a. heterozygous.   **b.** homozygous.
   c. recessive.   **d.** dominant.

5. If the body cells of an organism have 10 chromosomes, then the sex cells produced during meiosis would have
   a. 5 chromosomes.
   b. 10 chromosomes.
   c. 15 chromosomes.
   d. 20 chromosomes.

6. During protein synthesis, messenger RNA
   a. links one amino acid to another.
   b. releases the completed protein chain.
   c. provides a code from DNA in the nucleus.
   d. carries amino acids to the ribosome.

If the statement is true, write *true*. If it is false, change the underlined word or words to make the statement true.

7. <u>Ribosomes</u> produce proteins.

8. The study of heredity is called <u>genetics</u>.

9. An organism's physical appearance is its <u>genotype</u>.

10. In <u>codominance</u>, neither of the alleles is dominant or recessive.

11. Each transfer RNA molecule picks up one kind of <u>protein</u>.

12. Mutations in <u>body cells</u> are passed to offspring.

Writing in Science

Science Article You are a science reporter for a newspaper. Write an article about gene mutations. Explain what a mutation is and what determines whether it is helpful or harmful.

Discovery CHANNEL SCHOOL™

Genetics: The Science of Heredity
Video Preview
Video Field Trip
▶ Video Assessment

Review and Assessment

Checking Concepts

13. What role did the microscope play in the development of the cell theory?

14. Describe what happened when Mendel crossed purebred tall pea plants with purebred short pea plants.

15. In guinea pigs, the allele for black fur (*B*) is dominant over the allele for white fur (*b*). In a cross between a heterozygous black guinea pig (*Bb*) and a homozygous white guinea pig (*bb*), what is the probability that an offspring will have white fur? Use a Punnett square to answer the question.

16. Describe the role of transfer RNA in protein synthesis.

17. How can mutations affect protein synthesis?

Thinking Critically

18. **Comparing and Contrasting** To compare plant and animal cells, make a list of the different organelles in each cell. Explain how each organelle is vital to the life and function of a plant or animal.

19. **Applying Concepts** In rabbits, the allele for a spotted coat is dominant over the allele for a solid-colored coat. A spotted rabbit was crossed with a solid-colored rabbit. The offspring all had spotted coats. What are the probable genotypes of the parents? Explain.

20. **Interpreting Diagrams** The diagram below shows a chromosome pair. For which genes is the organism heterozygous?

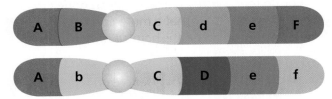

21. **Predicting** A new mutation in mice causes the coat to be twice as thick as normal. In what environments would this mutation be helpful? Why?

22. **Applying Concepts** If the body cells have 12 chromosomes, how many will the sex cells have?

23. **Relating Cause and Effect** Why are mutations that occur in an organism's body cells not passed on to its offspring?

Math Practice

24. **Percentage** A garden has 80 pea plants. Of the plants, 20 have short stems and 60 have tall stems. What percentage of the plants have short stems? What percentage have tall stems?

Applying Skills

Use the information in the table to answer Questions 25–27.

In peas, the allele for green pods (G) is dominant over the allele for yellow pods (g). The table shows the phenotypes of offspring produced from a cross of two plants with green pods.

Phenotype	Number of Offspring
Green pods	27
Yellow pods	9

25. **Calculating Percent** Calculate what percent of the offspring produce green pods. Calculate what percent have yellow pods.

26. **Inferring** What is the genotype of the offspring with yellow pods? What are the possible genotypes of the offspring with green pods?

27. **Drawing Conclusions** What are the genotypes of the parents? How do you know?

Lab zone Chapter Project

Performance Assessment Finalize your display of your pet's family. Be prepared to discuss the inheritance patterns in your pet's family. Examine your classmates' exhibits. See which offspring look most like, and least like, their parents. Can you find any offspring that "break the laws" of inheritance?

End-of-Grade Test Practice

Test-Taking Tip
Sequencing Events

A test question may ask you to arrange a series of events in order. You might be asked which event comes last, or which event comes before another event. Before you answer the question, think about the process the question asks about. Then think of the process's main events and try to put them in order.

For example, the question below asks about protein synthesis. Before looking at the answer choices, try to recall the correct sequence in which the events of protein synthesis occur. Then choose the answer that the question asks for.

Sample Question

Which of the following is the first event in the process of protein synthesis?

  A Messenger RNA enters the cytoplasm and attaches to a ribosome.
  B The coded message in DNA is copied when a molecule of messenger RNA is formed.
  C The protein chain grows until a stop code is reached.
  D Transfer RNA molecules carrying amino acids attach to messenger RNA.

Answer

The correct answer is **B**. For protein synthesis to begin, instructions must be carried from DNA in the nucleus to the cytoplasm. Messenger RNA performs that function.

Choose the letter of the best answer.

1. A tissue in an animal produces and releases chemicals that are used by cells throughout the animal's body. Cells in that tissue probably have a larger than normal number of
   A lysosomes.
   B mitochondria.
   C Golgi bodies.
   D nuclei.

The Punnett square below shows a cross between two pea plants, each with round seeds. Use the Punnett square to answer Questions 2–4.

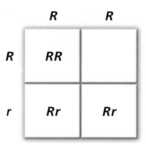

2. The missing genotype in the empty square is correctly written as
   A Rr.
   B rR.
   C rr.
   D RR.

3. Which statement is true about the cross shown in the Punnett square?
   A Both parents are heterozygous for the trait.
   B Both parents are homozygous for the trait.
   C One parent is heterozygous and the other is homozygous for the trait.
   D The trait is controlled by codominant alleles.

4. What percentage of the offspring of this cross will produce round seeds?
   A 0%
   B 25%
   C 50%
   D 100%

5. A section of DNA has the base sequence GCTTAA. The corresponding messenger RNA base sequence will be
   A GCTTAA.
   B CGAAUU.
   C CGAATT.
   D UUTTCG.

Constructed Response

6. Describe the process of meiosis. What is the outcome of meiosis?

Chapter 15

Modern Genetics

Standard Course of Study

This chapter addresses the following North Carolina Objectives:

1.01 Identify and create questions and hypotheses.

1.05 Analyze evidence.

1.06 Use mathematics to gather, organize, and present data.

1.08 Use oral and written language.

1.09 Use technologies and information systems.

2.01 Explore definitions of "technology."

2.02 Use information systems.

4.01 Analyze how human body systems interact.

5.01 Explain the significance of genes to inherited characteristics.

5.02 Explain the significance of reproduction.

5.03 Identify examples and patterns of human genetic traits.

5.04 Analyze the role of probability in heredity.

5.05 Summarize the genetic transmittance of disease.

5.06 Evaluate the evidence that produces human characteristics.

Interactive Textbook

▶ The members of this family resemble one another because they share some alleles.

Lab zone™ **Chapter Project**

Teach Others About a Trait

People inherit alleles for traits from their parents. Some traits, such as keen eyesight, are beneficial. Other traits, such as colorblindness, can present challenges. In this project you will design a display to help teach younger children about a genetically inherited trait. You and your group will need to research the inheritance pattern of your selected trait.

Your Goal To design and build an educational tool or display that can be used to educate young children

The display you create should

- illustrate how the trait is inherited and whom it can affect
- explain whether the trait is dominant, recessive, or codominant
- contain an interactive question and answer section that includes a way of predicting the probability that a person will inherit the trait
- stand by itself and be easy to set up

Plan It! Begin by choosing a trait and researching its inheritance pattern. Then determine how the display will look and the materials you need. Determine what is the best method to make the display interactive. Plan to test your display on a younger audience to assess their understanding and then revise your design.

Human Inheritance

Reading Preview

Key Concepts
- What are some patterns of inheritance in humans?
- What are the functions of the sex chromosomes?
- What is the relationship between genes and the environment?

Key Terms
- multiple alleles
- sex chromosomes
- sex-linked gene
- carrier

Target Reading Skill
Identifying Main Ideas
As you read the Patterns of Human Inheritance section, write the main idea—the biggest or most important idea—in a graphic organizer like the one below. Then write three supporting details that further explain the main idea.

Main Idea

Human traits are controlled by single genes with two alleles, single genes with . . .

Detail	Detail	Detail

Lab zone Discover Activity

How Tall Is Tall?

1. Choose a partner. Measure each other's height to the nearest 5 centimeters. Record your measurements on the chalkboard.
2. Create a bar graph showing the number of students at each height. Plot the heights on the horizontal axis and the number of students on the vertical axis.

Think It Over
Inferring Do you think height in humans is controlled by a single gene, as it is in peas? Explain your answer.

The arrival of a baby is a happy event. Eagerly, the parents and grandparents gather around to admire the newborn baby. "Don't you think she looks like her father?" "Yes, but she has her mother's eyes."

When a baby is born, the parents, their families, and their friends try to determine whom the baby resembles. Chances are good that the baby will look a little bit like both parents. That is because both parents pass alleles for traits on to their offspring.

FIGURE 1
Family Resemblance
Because children inherit alleles for traits from their mother and father, children often look like their parents.

Patterns of Human Inheritance

Take a few seconds to look at the other students in your classroom. Some people have curly hair; others have straight hair. Some people are tall, some are short, and many others are in between. You'll probably see eyes of many different colors, ranging from pale blue to dark brown. The different traits you see are determined by a variety of inheritance patterns. **Some human traits are controlled by single genes with two alleles, and others by single genes with multiple alleles. Still other traits are controlled by many genes that act together.**

Single Genes With Two Alleles A number of human traits are controlled by a single gene with one dominant allele and one recessive allele. These human traits have two distinctly different phenotypes, or physical appearances.

For example, a widow's peak is a hairline that comes to a point in the middle of the forehead. The allele for a widow's peak is dominant over the allele for a straight hairline. The Punnett square in Figure 2 illustrates a cross between two parents who are heterozygous for a widow's peak. Trace the possible combinations of alleles that a child may inherit. Notice that each child has a 3 in 4, or 75 percent, probability of having a widow's peak. There is only a 1 in 4, or 25 percent, probability that a child will have a straight hairline. When Mendel crossed peas that were heterozygous for a trait, he obtained similar percentages in the offspring.

FIGURE 2
Widow's Peak Punnett Square
This Punnett square shows a cross between two parents with widow's peaks.
Interpreting Diagrams *What are the possible genotypes of the offspring? What percentage of the offspring will have each genotype?*

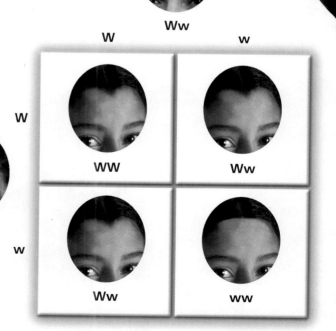

FIGURE 3
Inheritance of Blood Type
Blood type is determined by a single gene with three alleles. This chart shows which combinations of alleles result in each blood type.

Alleles of Blood Types	
Blood Type	Combination of Alleles
A	$I^A I^A$ or $I^A i$
B	$I^B I^B$ or $I^B i$
AB	$I^A I^B$
O	ii

Single Genes With Multiple Alleles Some human traits are controlled by a single gene that has more than two alleles. Such a gene is said to have **multiple alleles**—three or more forms of a gene that code for a single trait. Even though a gene may have multiple alleles, a person can carry only two of those alleles. This is because chromosomes exist in pairs. Each chromosome in a pair carries only one allele for each gene.

Human blood type is controlled by a gene with multiple alleles. There are four main blood types—A, B, AB, and O. Three alleles control the inheritance of blood types. The allele for blood type A and the allele for blood type B are codominant. The allele for blood type A is written as I^A. The allele for blood type B is written I^B. The allele for blood type O—written i—is recessive. Recall that when two codominant alleles are inherited, neither allele is masked. A person who inherits an I^A allele from one parent and an I^B allele from the other parent will have type AB blood. Figure 3 shows the allele combinations that result in each blood type. Notice that only people who inherit two i alleles have type O blood.

Traits Controlled by Many Genes If you completed the Discover activity, you saw that height in humans has more than two distinct phenotypes. In fact, there is an enormous variety of phenotypes for height. Some human traits show a large number of phenotypes because the traits are controlled by many genes. The genes act together as a group to produce a single trait. At least four genes control height in humans, so there are many possible combinations of genes and alleles. Skin color is another human trait that is controlled by many genes.

 Reading Checkpoint **Why do some traits exhibit a large number of phenotypes?**

FIGURE 4
Many Phenotypes
Skin color in humans is determined by three or more genes. Different combinations of alleles for each of the genes result in a wide range of possible skin colors.

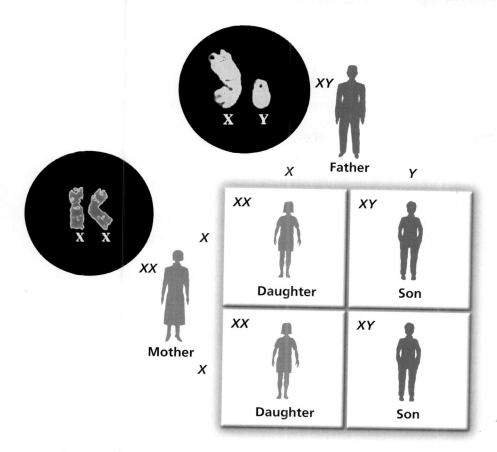

FIGURE 5
Male or Female?
As this Punnett square shows, there is a 50 percent probability that a child will be a girl and a 50 percent probability that a child will be a boy.
Interpreting Diagrams *What sex will the child be if a sperm with a Y chromosome fertilizes an egg?*

The Sex Chromosomes

The **sex chromosomes** are one of the 23 pairs of chromosomes in each body cell. **The sex chromosomes carry genes that determine whether a person is male or female. They also carry genes that determine other traits.**

Girl or Boy? The sex chromosomes are the only chromosome pair that do not always match. If you are a girl, your two sex chromosomes match. The two chromosomes are called X chromosomes. If you are a boy, your sex chromosomes do not match. One of them is an X chromosome, and the other is a Y chromosome. The Y chromosome is much smaller than the X chromosome.

Sex Chromosomes and Fertilization What happens to the sex chromosomes when egg and sperm cells form? Since both of a female's sex chromosomes are X chromosomes, all eggs carry one X chromosome. Males, however, have two different sex chromosomes. Therefore, half of a male's sperm cells carry an X chromosome, while half carry a Y chromosome.

When a sperm cell with an X chromosome fertilizes an egg, the egg has two X chromosomes. The fertilized egg will develop into a girl. When a sperm with a Y chromosome fertilizes an egg, the egg has one X chromosome and one Y chromosome. The fertilized egg will develop into a boy.

Lab zone **Try This Activity**

The Eyes Have It
One inherited trait is eye dominance—the tendency to use one eye more than the other. Here's how you can test yourself for this trait.

1. Hold your hand out in front of you at arm's length. Point your finger at an object across the room.
2. Close your right eye. With only your left eye open, observe how far your finger appears to move.
3. Repeat Step 2 with the right eye open. With which eye did your finger seem to remain closer to the object? That eye is dominant.

Designing Experiments Is eye dominance related to hand dominance—whether a person is right-handed or left-handed? Design an experiment to find out. *Obtain your teacher's permission before carrying out your experiment.*

Sex-Linked Genes The genes for some human traits are carried on the sex chromosomes. Genes on the X and Y chromosomes are often called **sex-linked genes** because their alleles are passed from parent to child on a sex chromosome. Traits controlled by sex-linked genes are called sex-linked traits. One sex-linked trait is red-green colorblindness. A person with this trait cannot distinguish between red and green.

Recall that females have two X chromosomes, whereas males have one X chromosome and one Y chromosome. Unlike most chromosome pairs, the X and Y chromosomes have different genes. Most of the genes on the X chromosome are not on the Y chromosome. Therefore, an allele on an X chromosome may have no corresponding allele on a Y chromosome.

Like other genes, sex-linked genes can have dominant and recessive alleles. In females, a dominant allele on one X chromosome will mask a recessive allele on the other X chromosome. But in males, there is usually no matching allele on the Y chromosome to mask the allele on the X chromosome. As a result, any allele on the X chromosome—even a recessive allele—will produce the trait in a male who inherits it. Because males have only one X chromosome, males are more likely than females to have a sex-linked trait that is controlled by a recessive allele.

FIGURE 6
Colorblindness
The lower photo shows how a red barn and green fields look to a person with red-green colorblindness.

Normal vision
▼

Red-green colorblind vision
▼

Inheritance of Colorblindness Colorblindness is a trait controlled by a recessive allele on the X chromosome. Many more males than females have red-green colorblindness. You can understand why this is the case by examining the Punnett square in Figure 7. Both parents in this example have normal color vision. Notice, however, that the mother is a carrier of color-blindness. A **carrier** is a person who has one recessive allele for a trait and one dominant allele. A carrier of a trait controlled by a recessive allele does not have the trait. However, the carrier can pass the recessive allele on to his or her offspring. In the case of sex-linked traits, only females can be carriers.

As you can see in Figure 7, there is a 25 percent probability that this couple will have a colorblind child. Notice that none of the couple's daughters will be colorblind. On the other hand, the sons have a 50 percent probability of being color-blind. For a female to be colorblind, she must inherit two recessive alleles for colorblindness, one from each parent. A male needs to inherit only one recessive allele. This is because there is no gene for color vision on the Y chromosome. Thus, there is no allele that could mask the recessive allele on the X chromosome.

 **Reading Checkpoint** **What is the sex of a person who is a carrier for colorblindness?**

Go Online
SciLINKS NSTA

For: Links on genetics
Visit: www.SciLinks.org
Web Code: scn-0341

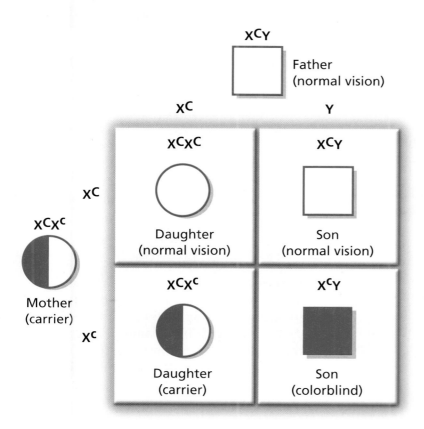

FIGURE 7
Colorblindness Punnett Square
Red-green colorblindness is a sex-linked trait. A girl who receives only one recessive allele (written X^c) for red-green colorblindness will not have the trait. However, a boy who receives one recessive allele will be colorblind.
Applying Concepts *What allele combination would a daughter need to inherit to be colorblind?*

The Effect of Environment

In humans and other organisms, the effects of genes are often influenced by the environment—an organism's surroundings. **Many of a person's characteristics are determined by an interaction between genes and the environment.**

You have learned that several genes work together to help determine human height. However, people's heights are also influenced by their environments. People's diets can affect their height. A diet lacking in protein, certain minerals, or certain vitamins can prevent a person from growing as tall as might be possible.

Environmental factors can also affect human skills, such as playing a musical instrument. For example, physical traits such as muscle coordination and a good sense of hearing will help a musician play well. But the musician also needs instruction on how to play the instrument. Musical instruction is an environmental factor.

FIGURE 8
Heredity and Environment
When a person plays a violin, genetically determined traits such as muscle coordination interact with environmental factors such as time spent in practice.

Reading Checkpoint How can environmental factors affect a person's height?

Section 1 Assessment

Target Reading Skill Identifying Main Ideas
Use your graphic organizer to help you answer
Question 1 below.

Reviewing Key Concepts

1. a. **Identifying** Identify three patterns of inheritance in humans. Give an example of a trait that follows each pattern.
   b. **Summarizing** How many human blood types are there? Summarize how blood type is inherited.
   c. **Drawing Conclusions** Aaron has blood type O. Can either of his parents have blood type AB? Explain your answer.
2. a. **Reviewing** What are the functions of the sex chromosomes?
   b. **Comparing and Contrasting** Contrast the sex chromosomes found in human females and human males.

   c. **Relating Cause and Effect** Explain how red-green colorblindness is inherited. Why is the condition more common in males than in females?
3. a. **Reviewing** Are a person's characteristics determined only by genes? Explain.
   b. **Applying Concepts** Explain what factors might work together to enable a great soccer player to kick a ball a long distance.

Writing in Science

Heredity and Environment Think of an ability you admire, such as painting, dancing, snowboarding, or playing games skillfully. Write a paragraph explaining how genes and the environment might work together to enable a person to develop this ability.

Human Genetic Disorders

Reading Preview

Key Concepts
- What are two major causes of genetic disorders in humans?
- How do geneticists trace the inheritance of traits?
- How are genetic disorders diagnosed and treated?

Key Terms
- genetic disorder • pedigree
- karyotype

Target Reading Skill
Comparing and Contrasting
As you read, compare and contrast the types of genetic disorders by completing a table like the one below.

Disorder	Description	Cause
Cystic fibrosis	Abnormally thick mucus	Loss of three DNA bases

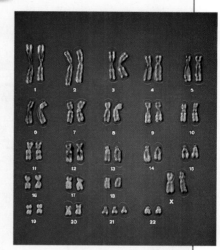

Lab zone — Discover **Activity**

How Many Chromosomes?
The photo at right shows the chromosomes from a cell of a person with Down syndrome, a genetic disorder. The chromosomes have been sorted into pairs.

1. Count the number of chromosomes in the photo.
2. How does the number of chromosomes compare to the usual number of chromosomes in human cells?

Think It Over
Inferring How do you think a cell could have ended up with this number of chromosomes? (*Hint:* Think about the events that occur during meiosis.)

The air inside the stadium was hot and still. The crowd cheered loudly as the runners approached the starting blocks. At the crack of the starter's gun, the runners leaped into motion and sprinted down the track. Seconds later, the race was over. The runners, bursting with pride, hugged each other and their coaches. These athletes were running in the Special Olympics, a competition for people with disabilities. Many of the athletes who compete in the Special Olympics have disabilities that result from genetic disorders.

◄ **Runners in the Special Olympics**

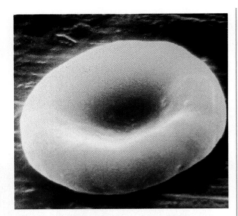

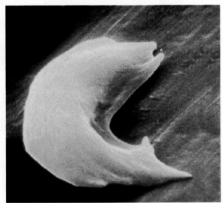

FIGURE 9
Sickle-Cell Disease
Normally, red blood cells are shaped like round disks (top). In a person with sickle-cell disease, red blood cells can become sickle-shaped (bottom).

Lab zone **Skills Activity**

Predicting
A man has sickle-cell disease. His wife does not have the disease, but is heterozygous for the sickle-cell trait. Predict the probability that their child will have sickle-cell disease. (*Hint:* Construct a Punnett square.)

Causes of Genetic Disorders

A **genetic disorder** is an abnormal condition that a person inherits through genes or chromosomes. **Some genetic disorders are caused by mutations in the DNA of genes. Other disorders are caused by changes in the overall structure or number of chromosomes.** In this section, you will learn about some common genetic disorders.

Cystic Fibrosis Cystic fibrosis is a genetic disorder in which the body produces abnormally thick mucus in the lungs and intestines. The thick mucus fills the lungs, making it hard for the affected person to breathe. Cystic fibrosis is caused by a recessive allele on one chromosome. The recessive allele is the result of a mutation in which three bases are removed from a DNA molecule.

Sickle-Cell Disease Sickle-cell disease affects hemoglobin, a protein in red blood cells that carries oxygen. When oxygen concentrations are low, the red blood cells of people with the disease have an unusual sickle shape. Sickle-shaped red blood cells clog blood vessels and cannot carry as much oxygen as normal cells. The allele for the sickle-cell trait is codominant with the normal allele. A person with two sickle-cell alleles will have the disease. A person with one sickle-cell allele will produce both normal hemoglobin and abnormal hemoglobin. This person usually will not have symptoms of the disease.

Hemophilia Hemophilia is a genetic disorder in which a person's blood clots very slowly or not at all. People with the disorder do not produce one of the proteins needed for normal blood clotting. The danger of internal bleeding from small bumps and bruises is very high. Hemophilia is caused by a recessive allele on the X chromosome. Because hemophilia is a sex-linked disorder, it occurs more frequently in males than in females.

Down Syndrome In Down syndrome, a person's cells have an extra copy of chromosome 21. In other words, instead of a pair of chromosomes, a person with Down syndrome has three of that chromosome. Down syndrome most often occurs when chromosomes fail to separate properly during meiosis. People with Down syndrome have some degree of mental retardation. Heart defects are also common, but can be treated.

 **Reading Checkpoint** **How is the DNA in the sickle-cell allele different from the normal allele?**

Pedigrees

Imagine that you are a geneticist who is interested in tracing the occurrence of a genetic disorder through several generations of a family. What would you do? **One important tool that geneticists use to trace the inheritance of traits in humans is a pedigree.** A **pedigree** is a chart or "family tree" that tracks which members of a family have a particular trait.

The trait in a pedigree can be an ordinary trait, such as a widow's peak, or a genetic disorder, such as cystic fibrosis. Figure 10 shows a pedigree for albinism, a condition in which a person's skin, hair, and eyes lack normal coloring.

Go Online
active.art

For: Pedigree activity
Visit: PHSchool.com
Web Code: cep-3042

FIGURE 10
A Pedigree

The father in the photograph has albinism. The pedigree shows the inheritance of the allele for albinism in three generations of a family. **Interpreting Diagrams** *Where is an albino male shown in the pedigree?*

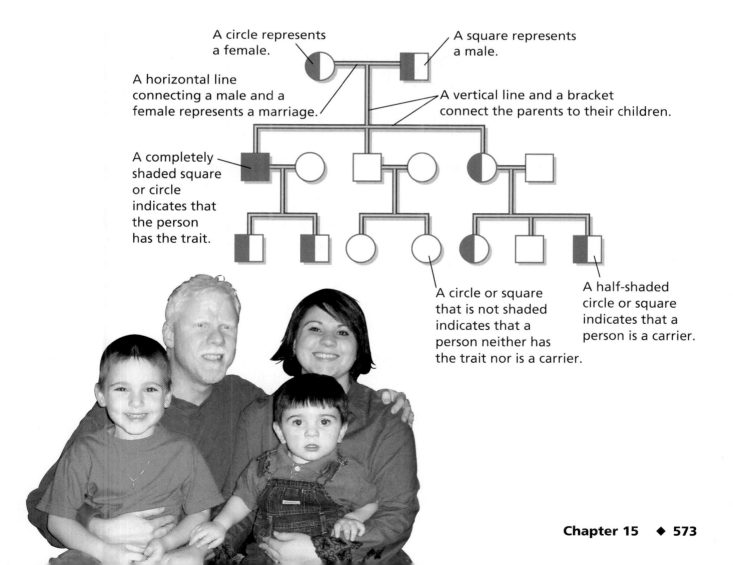

A circle represents a female.

A square represents a male.

A horizontal line connecting a male and a female represents a marriage.

A vertical line and a bracket connect the parents to their children.

A completely shaded square or circle indicates that the person has the trait.

A circle or square that is not shaded indicates that a person neither has the trait nor is a carrier.

A half-shaded circle or square indicates that a person is a carrier.

FIGURE 11
Living With Hemophilia

With proper care, people with hemophilia can manage their disorder. **Interpreting Diagrams** *In the pedigree, how many people have hemophilia?*

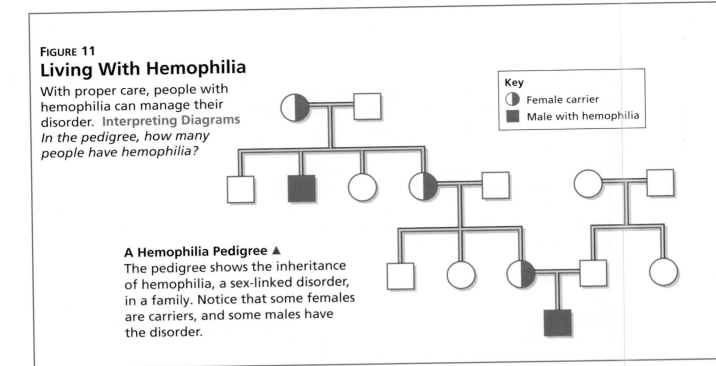

Key
◐ Female carrier
■ Male with hemophilia

A Hemophilia Pedigree ▲
The pedigree shows the inheritance of hemophilia, a sex-linked disorder, in a family. Notice that some females are carriers, and some males have the disorder.

Managing Genetic Disorders

Years ago, doctors had only Punnett squares and pedigrees to help them predict whether a child might have a genetic disorder. **Today, doctors use tools such as karyotypes to help diagnose genetic disorders. People with genetic disorders are helped through medical care, education, job training, and other methods.**

Karyotypes To detect chromosomal disorders such as Down syndrome, a doctor examines the chromosomes from a person's cells. The doctor uses a karyotype to examine the chromosomes. A **karyotype** (KA ree uh typ) is a picture of all the chromosomes in a cell. The chromosomes in a karyotype are arranged in pairs. A karyotype can reveal whether a person has the correct number of chromosomes in his or her cells. If you did the Discover activity, you saw a karyotype from a girl with Down syndrome.

Genetic Counseling A couple that has a family history of a genetic disorder may turn to a genetic counselor for advice. Genetic counselors help couples understand their chances of having a child with a particular genetic disorder. Genetic counselors use tools such as karyotypes, pedigree charts, and Punnett squares to help them in their work.

 **Reading Checkpoint** **What do genetic counselors do?**

Physical Therapy ▶
Trained medical workers help hemophilia patients cope with their disorder. Here, a boy receives physical therapy.

Sports ▶
A boy with hemophilia learns how to play golf. The disorder does not stop people from living active lives.

Dealing With Genetic Disorders People with genetic disorders face serious challenges, but help is available. Medical treatments help people with some disorders. For example, physical therapy helps remove mucus from the lungs of people with cystic fibrosis. People with sickle-cell disease take folic acid, a vitamin, to help their bodies manufacture red blood cells. Because of education and job training, adults with Down syndrome can find work in hotels, banks, restaurants, and other places of employment. Fortunately, most genetic disorders do not prevent people from living active, productive lives.

Section 2 Assessment

Target Reading Skill
Comparing and Contrasting Use the information in your table to help you answer Question 1 below.

Reviewing Key Concepts
1. a. **Identifying** Identify the two major causes of genetic disorders in humans.
   b. **Explaining** Which of those two major causes is responsible for Down syndrome?
   c. **Describing** How are the cells of a person with Down syndrome different from those of a person without the disorder?
2. a. **Defining** What is a pedigree?
   b. **Inferring** Why are pedigrees helpful in understanding genetic disorders?

   c. **Applying Concepts** Sam has hemophilia. Sam's brother, mother, and father do not have hemophilia. Draw a pedigree showing who has the disorder and who is a carrier.
3. a. **Reviewing** What is a karyotype?
   b. **Inferring** Would a karyotype reveal the presence of sickle-cell disease? Why or why not?

Writing in Science

Creating a Web Site Create an imaginary Web site to inform the public about genetic disorders. Write a description of one disorder for the Web site.

Family Puzzle

Problem

A husband and wife want to understand the probability that their children might inherit cystic fibrosis. How can you use the information in the box labeled Case Study to predict the probability?

Skills Focus

interpreting data, predicting

Materials

- 12 index cards • scissors • marker

Procedure

1. Read the Case Study. In your notebook, draw a pedigree that shows all the family members. Use circles to represent the females, and squares to represent the males. Shade in the circles or squares representing the individuals who have cystic fibrosis.

2. You know that cystic fibrosis is controlled by a recessive allele. To help you figure out Joshua and Bella's family pattern, create a set of cards to represent the alleles. Cut each of six index cards into four smaller cards. On 12 of the small cards, write *N* to represent the dominant normal allele. On the other 12 small cards, write *n* for the recessive allele.

Case Study: Joshua and Bella

- Joshua and Bella have a son named Ian. Ian has been diagnosed with cystic fibrosis.
- Joshua and Bella are both healthy.
- Bella's parents are both healthy.
- Joshua's parents are both healthy.
- Joshua's sister, Sara, has cystic fibrosis.

3. Begin by using the cards to represent Ian's alleles. Since he has cystic fibrosis, what alleles must he have? Write in this genotype next to the pedigree symbol for Ian.

4. Joshua's sister, Sara, also has cystic fibrosis. What alleles does she have? Write in this genotype next to the pedigree symbol that represents Sara.

5. Now use the cards to figure out what genotypes Joshua and Bella must have. Write their genotypes next to their symbols in the pedigree.

6. Work with the cards to figure out the genotypes of all other family members. Fill in each person's genotype next to his or her symbol in the pedigree. If more than one genotype is possible, write in both genotypes.

Analyze and Conclude

1. **Interpreting Data** What were the possible genotypes of Joshua's parents? What were the genotypes of Bella's parents?

2. **Predicting** Joshua also has a brother. What is the probability that he has cystic fibrosis? Explain.

3. **Communicating** Imagine that you are a genetic counselor. A couple asks why you need information about many generations of their families to draw conclusions about a hereditary condition. Write an explanation you can give to them.

More to Explore

Review the pedigree that you just studied. What data suggest that the traits are not sex-linked? Explain.

Advances in Genetics

Reading Preview

Key Concepts
- What are three ways of producing organisms with desired traits?
- What is the goal of the Human Genome Project?

Key Terms
- selective breeding
- inbreeding • hybridization
- clone • genetic engineering
- gene therapy • genome

Target Reading Skill

Asking Questions Before you read, preview the red headings. In a graphic organizer like the one below, ask a question for each heading. As you read, write answers to your questions.

Advances in Genetics

Question	Answer
What is selective breeding?	Selective breeding is . . .

Lab zone — Discover **Activity**

What Do Fingerprints Reveal?

1. Label a sheet of paper with your name. Then roll one of your fingers from side to side on an ink pad. Make a fingerprint by carefully rolling your inked finger on the paper.
2. Divide into groups. Each group should choose one member to use the same finger to make a second fingerprint on a sheet of paper. Leave the paper unlabeled.
3. Exchange your group's fingerprints with those from another group. Compare each labeled fingerprint with the fingerprint on the unlabeled paper. Decide whose fingerprint it is.
4. Wash your hands after completing this activity.

Think It Over

Observing Why are fingerprints used to identify people?

Would you like to have your picture taken with a 9,000-year-old family member? Adrian Targett, a history teacher in the village of Cheddar in England, has actually done that. All that's left of his ancient relative, known as "Cheddar Man," is a skeleton. The skeleton was discovered in a cave near the village. DNA analysis indicates that Targett and Cheddar Man are relatives.

Like your fingerprints, your DNA is different from everyone else's. Because of advances in genetics, DNA evidence can show many things, such as family relationships.

FIGURE 12
Distant Relatives
Adrian Targett visits his distant relative, Cheddar Man. Unfortunately, Cheddar Man cannot respond to questions about life 9,000 years ago.

FIGURE 13

Inbreeding
Turkeys such as the one with white feathers were developed by inbreeding. Breeders started with wild turkeys.

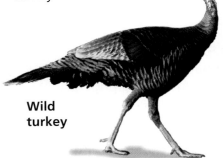

Wild turkey

Domestic turkey

Selective Breeding

Genetic techniques have enabled people to produce organisms with desirable traits. **Selective breeding, cloning, and genetic engineering are three methods for developing organisms with desirable traits.**

The process of selecting organisms with desired traits to be parents of the next generation is called **selective breeding**. Thousands of years ago, in what is now Mexico, the food that we call corn was developed in this way. Every year, farmers saved seeds from the healthiest plants that produced the best food. In the spring, they planted those seeds. By repeating this process over and over, farmers developed plants that produced better corn. People have used selective breeding with many different plants and animals. Two selective breeding techniques are inbreeding and hybridization.

Inbreeding The technique of **inbreeding** involves crossing two individuals that have similar characteristics. For example, suppose a male and a female turkey are both plump and grow quickly. Their offspring will probably also have those desirable qualities. Inbred organisms have alleles that are very similar to those of their parents.

Inbred organisms are genetically very similar. Therefore, inbreeding increases the probability that organisms may inherit alleles that lead to genetic disorders. For example, inherited hip problems are common in many breeds of dogs.

Hybridization In **hybridization** (hy brid ih ZAY shun), breeders cross two genetically different individuals. The hybrid organism that results is bred to have the best traits from both parents. For example, a farmer might cross corn that produces many kernels with corn that is resistant to disease. The result might be a hybrid corn plant with both of the desired traits.

Reading Checkpoint **What is the goal of hybridization?**

FIGURE 14
Hybridization
McIntosh and Red Delicious apples were crossed to produce Empire apples.
Applying Concepts What desirable traits might breeders have been trying to produce?

McIntosh   **Red Delicious**   **Empire**

Changing Rice Production

The graph shows how worldwide rice production changed between 1965 and 2000. New, hybrid varieties of rice plants are one factor that has affected the amount of rice produced.

1. **Reading Graphs** According to the graph, how did rice production change between 1965 and 2000?

2. **Reading Graphs** How many metric tons of rice per hectare were produced in 1965? How many were produced in 2000?

3. **Calculating** Calculate the approximate difference between rice production in 1965 and 2000.

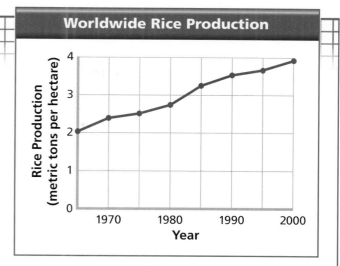

Worldwide Rice Production

4. **Developing Hypotheses** What factors besides new varieties of plants might help account for the difference in rice production between 1965 and 2000?

Cloning

For some organisms, a technique called cloning can be used to produce offspring with desired traits. A **clone** is an organism that has exactly the same genes as the organism from which it was produced. It isn't hard to clone some kinds of plants, such as an African violet. Just cut a stem from one plant, and put the stem in soil. Water it, and soon you will have a whole new plant. The new plant is genetically identical to the plant from which the stem was cut.

Researchers have also cloned animals such as sheep and pigs. The methods for cloning these animals are complex. They involve taking the nucleus of an animal's body cell and using that nucleus to produce a new animal.

Discovery CHANNEL SCHOOL

Modern Genetics

Video Preview
► Video Field Trip
Video Assessment

 **Reading Checkpoint** How can a clone of a plant be produced?

FIGURE 15
Cloned Goats
These goats were produced by cloning.

Genetic Engineering

Geneticists have developed another powerful technique for producing organisms with desired traits. In this process, called **genetic engineering**, genes from one organism are transferred into the DNA of another organism. Genetic engineering can produce medicines and improve food crops.

Genetic Engineering in Bacteria One type of genetically engineered bacteria produces a protein called insulin. Injections of insulin are needed by many people with diabetes. Recall that bacteria have a single DNA molecule in the cytoplasm. Some bacterial cells also contain small circular pieces of DNA called plasmids. In Figure 16, you can see how scientists insert the DNA for a human gene into the plasmid of a bacterium.

FIGURE 16
Genetic Engineering

Scientists use genetic engineering to create bacterial cells that produce important human proteins such as insulin.
Interpreting Diagrams *How does a human insulin gene become part of a plasmid?*

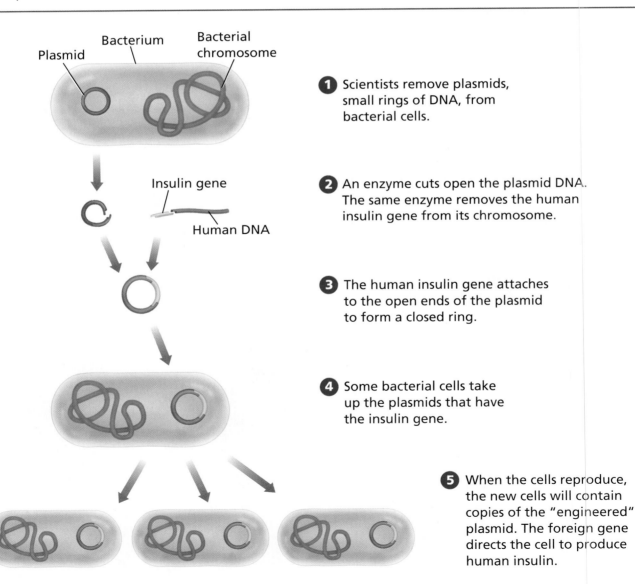

Plasmid Bacterium Bacterial chromosome

Insulin gene

Human DNA

❶ Scientists remove plasmids, small rings of DNA, from bacterial cells.

❷ An enzyme cuts open the plasmid DNA. The same enzyme removes the human insulin gene from its chromosome.

❸ The human insulin gene attaches to the open ends of the plasmid to form a closed ring.

❹ Some bacterial cells take up the plasmids that have the insulin gene.

❺ When the cells reproduce, the new cells will contain copies of the "engineered" plasmid. The foreign gene directs the cell to produce human insulin.

580 ◆

Normal
zebra danio ▲

Genetically ▶
engineered
zebra danios

Once the gene is inserted into the plasmid, the bacterial cell and all its offspring will contain this human gene. As a result, the bacteria produce the protein that the human gene codes for—in this case, insulin. Because bacteria reproduce quickly, large amounts of insulin can be produced in a short time.

Genetic Engineering in Other Organisms Scientists can also use genetic engineering techniques to insert genes into animals. For example, human genes can be inserted into the cells of cows. The cows then produce the human protein for which the gene codes in their milk. Scientists have used this technique to produce the blood clotting protein needed by people with hemophilia.

Genes have also been inserted into the cells of plants, such as tomatoes and rice. Some of the genes enable the plants to survive in cold temperatures or in poor soil. Other genetically engineered crops can resist insect pests.

Gene Therapy Someday it may be possible to use genetic engineering to correct some genetic disorders in humans. This process, called **gene therapy**, will involve inserting copies of a gene directly into a person's cells. For example, doctors may be able to treat hemophilia by replacing the defective allele on the X chromosome. The person's blood would then clot normally.

Concerns About Genetic Engineering Some people are concerned about the long-term effects of genetic engineering. For example, some people think that genetically engineered crops may not be entirely safe. People fear that these crops may harm the environment or cause health problems in humans. To address such concerns, scientists are trying to learn more about the effects of genetic engineering.

 **Reading Checkpoint** How do genetic engineering techniques enable scientists to produce clotting proteins?

FIGURE 17
Genetically Engineered Fish
The bright red zebra danios are the result of genetic engineering.

For: Links on genetic engineering
Visit: www.SciLinks.org
Web Code: scn-0343

Lab zone Skills Activity

Communicating
Suppose you work for a drug company that uses genetically engineered bacteria to produce insulin. Write an advertisement for the drug that includes a simplified explanation of how the drug is produced.

Learning About Human Genetics

Recent advances have enabled scientists to learn a great deal about human genetics. The Human Genome Project and DNA fingerprinting are two applications of this new knowledge.

The Human Genome Project Imagine trying to crack a code that is 6 billion letters long. That's exactly what scientists working on the Human Genome Project have been doing. A **genome** is all the DNA in one cell of an organism. **The main goal of the Human Genome Project has been to identify the DNA sequence of every gene in the human genome.** The Human Genome Project has completed a "first draft" of the human genome. The scientists have learned that the DNA of humans has at least 30,000 genes. The average gene has about 3,000 bases. Scientists will some day know the DNA sequence of every human gene.

DNA Fingerprinting DNA technology used in the Human Genome Project can also identify people and show whether people are related. DNA from a person's cells is broken down into small pieces, or fragments. Selected fragments are used to produce a pattern called a DNA fingerprint. Except for identical twins, no two people have exactly the same DNA fingerprint. You will learn more about DNA fingerprinting in Technology and Society.

 **Reading Checkpoint** **About how many genes are in the human genome?**

FIGURE 18
The Human Genome Project
Scientists on the Human Genome Project continue to study human DNA.

Section 3 Assessment

Target Reading Skill Asking Questions Work with a partner to check your answers in your graphic organizer.

Reviewing Key Concepts

1. a. Listing List three methods that scientists can use to develop organisms with desirable traits.
   b. Describing Briefly describe each method.
   c. Applying Concepts Lupita has a houseplant. Which method would be the best way of producing a similar plant for a friend? Explain your answer.
2. a. Defining What is a genome?
   b. Explaining What is the Human Genome Project?

c. Relating Cause and Effect How might knowledge gained from the Human Genome Project be used in gene therapy?

Lab zone At-Home **Activity**

Food and Selective Breeding Go to a grocery store with a parent or other family member. Discuss how fruits and vegetables have been produced by selective breeding. Choose a fruit or vegetable, and identify the traits that make it valuable.

Guilty or Innocent?

Problem

A crime scene may contain hair, skin, or blood from a criminal. These materials all contain DNA that can be used to make a DNA fingerprint. A DNA fingerprint, which consists of a series of bands, is something like a bar code. How can a DNA fingerprint identify individuals?

Skills Focus

drawing conclusions, inferring

Materials

- 4–6 bar codes
- hand lens

Procedure

1. Look at the photograph of DNA band patterns shown at right. Each person's DNA produces a unique pattern of these bands.

2. Now look at the Universal Product Code, also called a bar code, shown below the DNA bands. A bar code can be used as a model of a DNA band pattern. Compare the bar code with the DNA bands to see what they have in common. Record your observations.

3. Suppose that a burglary has taken place, and you're the detective leading the investigation. Your teacher will give you a bar code that represents DNA from blood found at the crime scene. You arrange to have DNA samples taken from several suspects. Write a sentence describing what you will look for as you try to match each suspect's DNA to the DNA sample from the crime scene.

4. You will now be given bar codes representing DNA samples taken from the suspects. Compare those bar codes with the bar code that represents DNA from the crime scene.

5. Use your comparisons to determine whether any of the suspects was present at the crime scene.

Analyze and Conclude

1. **Drawing Conclusions** Based on your findings, were any of the suspects present at the crime scene? Support your conclusion with specific evidence.

2. **Inferring** Why do people's DNA patterns differ so greatly?

3. **Drawing Conclusions** How would your conclusions be affected if you learned that the suspect whose DNA matched the evidence had an identical twin?

4. **Communicating** Suppose you are a defense lawyer. DNA evidence indicates that the bloodstain at the scene of a crime belongs to your client. Do you think this DNA evidence should be enough to convict your client? Write a speech you might give to the jury in defense of your client.

More to Explore

Do you think the DNA fingerprints of a parent and a child would show any similarities? Explain your thinking.

DNA Fingerprinting

What do you have that no one else has? Unless you are an identical twin, your DNA is unique. Because one person's DNA is like no one else's, it can be used to produce genetic "fingerprints." These fingerprints can tie a person to the scene of a crime. They can prevent the wrong person from going to jail. They can also be used to identify skeletal remains. Today, soldiers and sailors give blood and saliva samples so their DNA fingerprints can be saved. Like the identification tags that soldiers wear, DNA records can be used to identify the bodies of unknown soldiers or civilians.

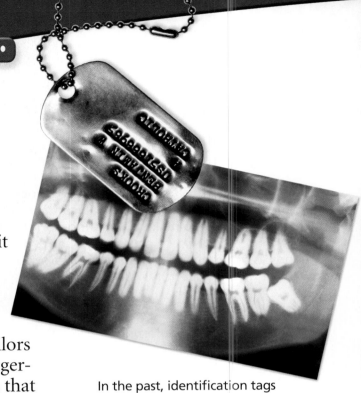

In the past, identification tags and dental records were the main methods for identifying skeletal remains.

T T C G A A T T C G A A T T C T G A A T T C T A G A A T T C G A A

T T C G | A A T T C G | A A T T C T G | A A T T C T A G | A A T T C G A A

4 bases 6 bases 7 bases 8 bases 8 bases

This enzyme cuts the DNA every time it encounters the DNA sequence GAATTC.

1 After a sample of DNA is extracted from the body, an enzyme cuts the DNA strand into several smaller pieces.

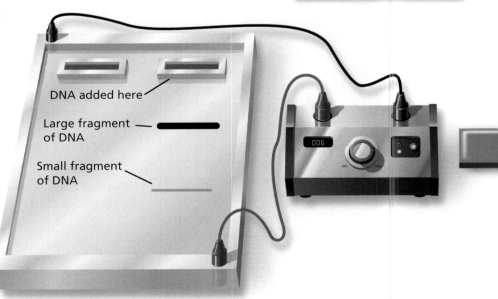

DNA added here

Large fragment of DNA

Small fragment of DNA

2 The cut-up DNA fragments are loaded into a gel that uses electric current to separate fragments. Larger fragments of DNA move through the gel more slowly than the smaller fragments.

Analyzing DNA

In one method of DNA analysis, DNA from saliva, blood, bones, teeth, or other fluids or tissues is taken from cells. Special enzymes are added to cut the DNA into small pieces. Selected pieces are put into a machine that runs an electric current through the DNA and sorts the pieces by size. The DNA then gets stained and photographed. When developed, a unique banded pattern, similar to a product bar code, is revealed. The pattern can be compared to other samples of DNA to determine a match.

Limitations of DNA Fingerprinting

Like all technology, DNA fingerprinting has its limitations. DNA is very fragile and the films produced can be difficult to read if the DNA samples are old. In rare instances, DNA from the people testing the samples can become mixed in with the test samples and produce inaccurate results. DNA testing is also time consuming and expensive.

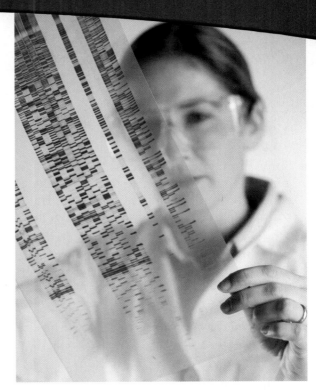

▲ **Scientist reading a DNA fingerprint**

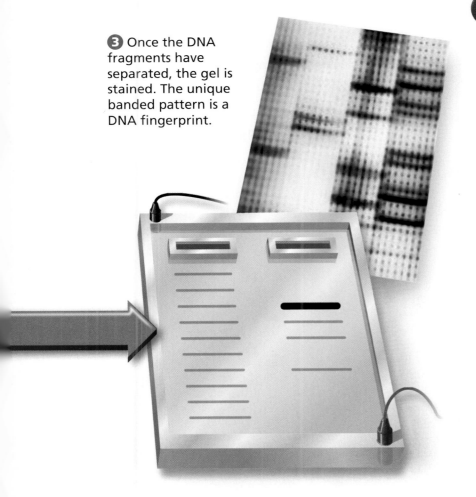

3 Once the DNA fragments have separated, the gel is stained. The unique banded pattern is a DNA fingerprint.

Weigh the Impact

1. **Identify the Need**
   Make a list of at least five situations in which DNA fingerprinting could be useful.

2. **Research**
   Research the situations you listed in Question 1 to find out if DNA analysis is or can be used in each.

3. **Write**
   Choose one application of DNA analysis and write one or two paragraphs to explain when the application can be used.

For: More on DNA fingerprinting
Visit: PHSchool.com
Web Code: ceh-3040

1 Human Inheritance

Key Concepts

- Some human traits are controlled by single genes with two alleles, and others by single genes with multiple alleles. Still other traits are controlled by many genes that act together.

- The sex chromosomes carry genes that determine whether a person is male or female. They also carry genes that determine other traits.

- Many of a person's characteristics are determined by an interaction between genes and the environment.

Key Terms

multiple alleles
sex chromosomes
sex-linked gene
carrier

2 Human Genetic Disorders

Key Concepts

- Some genetic disorders are caused by mutations in the DNA of genes. Other disorders are caused by changes in the overall structure or number of chromosomes.

- One important tool that geneticists use to trace the inheritance of traits in humans is a pedigree.

- Today doctors use tools such as karyotypes to help detect genetic disorders. People with genetic disorders are helped through medical care, education, job training, and other methods.

Key Terms

genetic disorder
pedigree
karyotype

3 Advances in Genetics

Key Concepts

- Selective breeding, cloning, and genetic engineering are three methods for developing organisms with desirable traits.

- The main goal of the Human Genome Project has been to identify the DNA sequence of every gene in the human genome.

Key Terms

selective breeding
inbreeding
hybridization
clone
genetic engineering
gene therapy
genome

Review and Assessment

Organizing Information

Concept Mapping Copy the concept map about human traits onto a separate sheet of paper. Then complete it and add a title. (For more on Concept Mapping, see the Skills Handbook.)

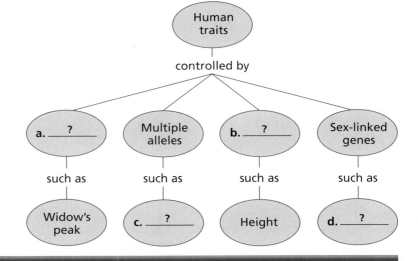

Reviewing Key Terms

Choose the letter of the best answer.

1. A human trait that is controlled by a single gene with multiple alleles is
   a. dimples.
   b. blood type.
   c. height.
   d. skin color.

2. A sex-linked disorder is
   a. cystic fibrosis.
   b. sickle-cell disease.
   c. hemophilia.
   d. Down syndrome.

3. Which of the following would most likely be used to diagnose Down syndrome?
   a. a karyotype
   b. a pedigree
   c. a blood-clotting test
   d. a Punnett square

4. Inserting a human gene into a bacterial plasmid is an example of
   a. inbreeding.
   b. selective breeding.
   c. DNA fingerprinting.
   d. genetic engineering.

5. An organism that has the same genes as the organism from which it was produced is called a
   a. clone.
   b. hybrid.
   c. genome.
   d. pedigree.

If the statement is true, write *true*. If it is false, change the underlined word or words to make the statement true.

6. A widow's peak is a human trait that is controlled by <u>a single gene</u>.

7. A <u>male</u> inherits two X chromosomes.

8. A <u>karyotype</u> tracks which members of a family have a trait.

9. <u>Hybridization</u> is the crossing of two genetically similar organisms.

10. A <u>genome</u> is all the DNA in one cell of an organism.

Writing in Science

Fact Sheet You are a scientist in a cloning lab. Write a fact sheet that explains what the process of cloning involves. Describe at least one example.

Modern Genetics

Video Preview
Video Field Trip
▶ Video Assessment

Review and Assessment

Checking Concepts

11. Explain why there are a wide variety of phenotypes for skin color in humans.

12. Traits controlled by recessive alleles on the X chromosome are more common in males than in females. Explain why.

13. What is sickle-cell disease? How is this disorder inherited?

14. What is a pedigree? How do geneticists use pedigrees?

15. Describe two ways in which people with genetic disorders can be helped.

16. Explain how a horse breeder might use selective breeding to produce horses that have golden coats.

17. Describe how gene therapy might be used in the future to treat a person with hemophilia.

18. What is the Human Genome Project?

Thinking Critically

19. **Problem Solving** A woman with normal color vision has a colorblind daughter. What are the genotypes and phenotypes of both parents?

20. **Calculating** If a mother is a carrier of hemophilia and the father does not have hemophilia, what is the probability that their son will have the trait? Explain your answer.

21. **Interpreting Diagrams** The allele for cystic fibrosis is recessive. Identify which members of the family in the pedigree have cystic fibrosis and which are carriers.

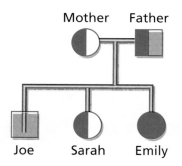

Mother   Father

Joe   Sarah   Emily

Applying Skills

Use the Punnett square to answer Questions 22–24.

The Punnett square below shows how muscular dystrophy, a sex-linked recessive disorder, is inherited.

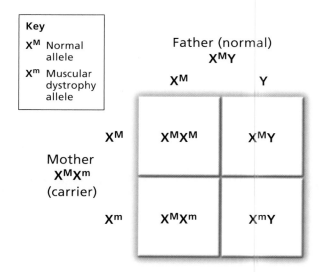

22. **Interpreting Data** What is the probability that a daughter of these parents will have muscular dystrophy? Explain your answer.

23. **Interpreting Data** What is the probability that a son of these parents will have muscular dystrophy? Explain your answer.

24. **Inferring** Is it possible for a woman to have muscular dystrophy? Why or why not?

Lab zone Chapter **Project**

Performance Assessment Present your display board to your class. Highlight important facts about the genetic trait you selected. Discuss the innovative designs you incorporated into the display board. In your presentation, highlight the interactive part of your project.

End-of-Grade Test Practice

Choose the letter of the best answer.

1. A woman is heterozygous for the trait of hemophilia. Her husband does not have hemophilia. What is the probability that their son will have hemophilia?
   A 0%
   B 25%
   C 50%
   D 100%

2. Down syndrome is an example of a genetic disorder in which
   A one DNA base has been added.
   B one DNA base has been deleted.
   C one chromosome is substituted for another.
   D an extra chromosome is added to a pair.

Use the pedigree to answer Questions 3–4.

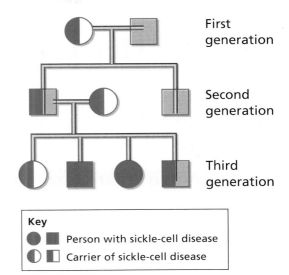

First generation

Second generation

Third generation

Key
- Person with sickle-cell disease
- Carrier of sickle-cell disease

3. How many people in the second generation have sickle-cell disease?
   A none   B one person
   C two people D three people

4. Which statement is true about the third generation in the pedigree?
   A No one has sickle-cell disease.
   B Everyone has sickle-cell disease.
   C Everyone has at least one allele for sickle-cell disease.
   D No one has any alleles for sickle-cell disease.

5. To produce a human protein through genetic engineering, scientists use
   A a bacterial gene inserted into a human chromosome.
   B a human gene inserted into a plasmid.
   C a bacterial gene inserted into a plasmid.
   D a human gene inserted into a human chromosome.

Constructed Response

6. Explain why, for each pregnancy, human parents have a 50 percent probability of having a boy and a 50 percent probability of having a girl. Your answer should include the terms *X chromosome* and *Y chromosome*.

The Olympic Games

What event—

- is the dream of athletes around the world?
- has the motto "faster, higher, stronger"?
- supports amateur sports?

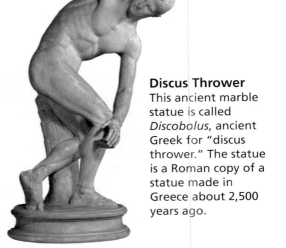

Discus Thrower
This ancient marble statue is called *Discobolus*, ancient Greek for "discus thrower." The statue is a Roman copy of a statue made in Greece about 2,500 years ago.

The Olympic games began more than 2,500 years ago in Olympia, Greece. For one day every four years, the best athletes in Greece gathered to compete. The games honored the Greek god Zeus. The ancient Greeks valued both physical and intellectual achievement. A winning athlete at the Olympic games was rewarded with a lifetime of honor and fame.

For more than a thousand years, the Greeks held the games at Olympia every four years. The games were discontinued in A.D. 394, when the Romans ruled Greece.

Centuries later, in the 1880s, Pierre de Coubertin, a Frenchman, convinced the United States and other nations to bring back the Olympic games. Coubertin hoped that the modern Olympics would promote world peace by bringing together athletes from all nations. The modern Olympics began in Athens in 1896.

Today the summer and winter Olympics alternate every two years. For several weeks, athletes from all around the world experience the excitement of competing against each other. Only a few know the joy of winning. But, all who participate learn about fair play, striving toward a goal, and becoming a little bit faster and stronger through training.

Olympic Torch, 2002
Here the flame burns in Salt Lake City, Utah. It's a symbol of the spirit of competition and fair play.

Sports in Ancient Greece

The ancient Greeks valued physical fitness as much as an educated mind. Men and boys exercised regularly by wrestling, sprinting, throwing the discus, and tossing the javelin. Greek philosophy taught that a sound mind and body created a well-balanced person. Greek art glorified the muscles and movement of the human body in magnificent sculptures and paintings.

The first recorded Olympic games were held in 776 B.C. That year a cook named Coroebus from Elis, Greece, won the only event in the games—a sprint of about 192 meters. The prize was a wreath of olive leaves. In ancient Greece, an olive wreath was the highest mark of honor.

Over the next 130 years, other events were added to the games, including longer running events, wrestling, chariot racing, boxing, and the pentathlon. *Pent-* comes from the Greek word meaning "five." A pentathlon included five competitions: a long jump, javelin toss, discus throw, foot race, and wrestling. Early records indicate that women were not allowed to compete in the games.

Ancient Greece
Rival city-states, such as Athens and Sparta, sent their best athletes to the games at Olympia.

Social Studies Activity

The Olympics encourage peaceful competition among athletes from many nations. But political conflicts sometimes have disrupted or canceled the games. For example, the 1916 games were canceled because of World War I. Other Olympics are remembered for the achievements of certain athletes, such as Babe Didrikson in 1932. Find out what political events affected particular Olympics during the twentieth century. Or research outstanding athletes at different games. Report your findings to the class.

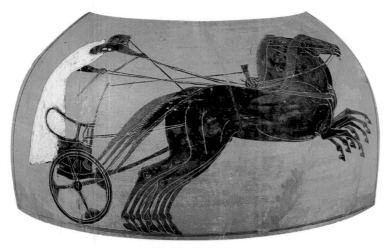

Amphora
Chariot racing became a popular sport in the ancient Olympics. This scene is painted on a Greek amphora, a pottery jar for olive oil or wine.

Modern Olympic Games

At the 1988 Olympic games in Seoul, South Korea, Jackie Joyner-Kersee was one of the star athletes. She won two gold medals there. In total, between 1984 and 1996, she won six Olympic medals (three of them gold), making her one of the world's greatest athletes.

Jackie grew up in East St. Louis, Illinois, where she started running and jumping at age ten. Although she was a natural at the long jump, she wasn't a fast runner. But her coach, Mr. Fennoy, encouraged her. After her final Olympics, Jackie wrote an autobiography—a story of her life. Here is an excerpt from her book *A Kind of Grace*.

Jackie Joyner-Kersee
Jackie jumps to her second gold medal at the 1988 Olympic games.

After school the boys' and girls' teams jogged to Lincoln Park's irregular-shaped track and makeshift long-jump pit. The track was a 36-inch-wide strip of black cinders sprinkled amid the rest of the dirt and grass. We called it the bridle path because that's what it looked like. We ran over, around and through the potholes, rocks, glass and tree limbs that littered the track. After practice, we jogged another two or three miles around the neighborhood to complete our workout.

In winter, when it was too cold to practice outside, we trained inside the Lincoln High building. Every afternoon after school and at 9:00 every Saturday morning, the team of twenty-five girls split into groups on the two floors and ran along the brown concrete corridors. When it was time for hurdling drills, Mr. Fennoy set up hurdles in the center of the hallway on the second floor, and put us through our paces. We sprinted and leaped past the doors to the math and science classrooms.

We ran to the end of the hall, turned around and repeated the drill in the opposite direction.

The running drills, exhausting as they were, eventually paid off. In 1977, between the ninth and tenth grade, I developed booster rockets and cut an astonishing four seconds off my 440 time. I surged to the front of the pack in practice heats. By the time we entered Lincoln High as tenth-graders, I was the fastest 440 runner on the team. The last was—at long last—first.

Language Arts Activity

What does Jackie mean by "the last was—at long last—first"? How did she get to be first? Some people say that Jackie was just a natural athlete. Jackie herself says, "I think it was my reward for all those hours of work on the bridle path, the neighborhood sidewalks and the schoolhouse corridors."

Think about a period in your life when you had to prepare for a math competition, a recital, a performance, a sports event, or other event. Write a short autobiographical sketch describing how you worked to improve your performance.

Yelena Yelesina
Yelena Yelesina of Russia won the women's high jump at the 2000 Olympics in Sydney, Australia. How much higher did she jump than the 1952 winner?

Women's High Jump	
Year	Height
1952	65.75
1960	72.75
1968	71.5
1976	76.0
1984	79.5
1992	79.5
2000	79.0

Olympic Records

To prepare for the Olympic games, top athletes train for years. Sometimes they even move to climates that will help them prepare to compete in their sports. Skiers, for example, might move to a mountain region where they can train year-round. Athletes also use the most advanced equipment available in their sport. This scientific approach to training has helped athletes set new records for speed, height, and distance. In addition, measurement tools such as timing clocks have become more precise. As a result, athletes can now break records by just a few hundredths of a second.

The table and graph at right show how the winning height in the women's high jump has changed over many Olympic games. Notice that the high jump measures height in inches.

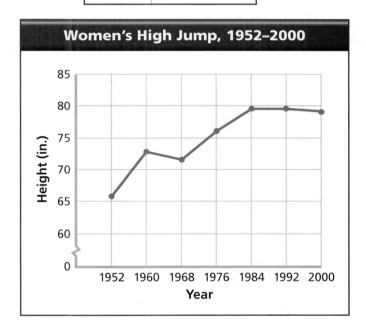

Women's High Jump, 1952–2000

Math Activity

The line graph above shows how the heights in the Olympic women's high jump have changed since 1952. Use the table at right, showing times for the men's 400-meter run, to create your own line graph.

How did the winning performance in the men's 400-meter run change over time? How does your graph differ from that of the women's high jump? Why do the graphs differ?

Men's 400-Meter Run	
Year	Time in Seconds
1952	45.90
1960	44.90
1968	43.86
1976	44.26
1984	44.27
1992	43.50
2000	43.84

High-Tech Training

Recent technology has made training for the Olympics a different process from that used in previous Olympic games. Today's high-tech equipment enables athletes to focus on specific aspects in their training.

One technology that is widely used today is video imaging. Olympic athletes such as figure skaters, gymnasts, and divers use video imaging. Using a video camera that links to a laptop computer, a coach can videotape an athlete practicing. Using software in the laptop, the coach and athlete can immediately replay a routine, like a dive, and discuss possible improvements. Some software allows the user to superimpose one video clip routine "on top" of another for comparison.

If you are a runner, you might use a watch with a chronometer, or timekeeper. But some athletes today use another new technology, sometimes called "wrist-top computers." These watches can measure an athlete's heart rate, speed, distance, and time. Many of these "mini machines" can also be connected to a computer so that athletes can compare their performances.

A third new technology, called a diagnostic system, tracks an athlete's constantly shifting body systems. Each training session can be adapted to provide enough—but not too much—of a workout. Electrodes are attached to the athlete's ankles, wrists, chest, and forehead. In 20 minutes, while the athlete is lying down, the system records and analyzes information, from heart rate and oxygen usage to how well the central nervous system, liver, and kidneys are functioning. These measurements can give all types of athletes an overall picture of their conditioning.

High-Tech Machines
The athlete on this workout machine can monitor her time, distance, speed, calories burned, heart rate, and other data (right). A transmitter attached to the chest sends data to a wrist-top computer that displays the athlete's heart rate and other data (above).

Science Activity

Athletes who are in the best shape often have very low resting heart and breathing rates. Some have resting heart rates below 40 bpm (beats per minute). Yet, while exercising, their heart and breathing rates can speed up to more than 170 bpm. Compare yourself to a top athlete.

1. In a sitting position, feel your pulse and count your heartbeats for 10 seconds. Multiply that number by 6 to get your resting bpm. Record the number. Next, count how many times you inhale and exhale in 30 seconds. Multiply that number by 2 to get your resting breathing rate. Record the data.

2. Walk up and down a staircase with at least 5 steps for 10 minutes without stopping. Keep your pace steady. As soon as the 10 minutes are up, measure your heart and breathing rates again. Record the data. **CAUTION:** *Do not do this part of the activity if you have any limiting physical and/or cardiovascular condition.*

3. What is your heartbeat range before and after exercise? How does that range compare to the top athlete described above? What is your breathing rate range?

Working Out

1. Warm-up
(5–10 minutes)
Slowly move the muscles to be used in the workout.

2. Stretch
(5–10 minutes)
Stretch the muscles to be used in the workout.

3. Workout
(20–45 minutes)
Do an activity such as walking, running, swimming, gymnastics, or riding a bicycle.

4. Cool-down
(5–10 minutes)
Move the muscles used in the workout at a reduced pace.

5. Stretch
(5–10 minutes)
Stretch the muscles used in the workout.

Tie It Together

Plan an Olympic Day!

Design a competition that can be held at your school. Decide the time, place, and kind of contests to hold. Remember that the ancient Greeks honored intellect as well as athletics. So you could include games that test the mind as well as the body.

Research the decathlon, pentathlon, heptathlon, and marathon in the ancient and modern Olympics. You could design your own pentathlon that includes athletic and nonathletic events.

To organize the Olympic day, you should

- set up the sports contests by measuring and marking the ground for each event

- find stopwatches, meter sticks, tape measures, and any necessary equipment

- locate or make prizes for first, second, and third place in each event

- enlist volunteers to compete in the events

- assign someone to take notes and to write a newspaper story on your Olympic day

Chapter

16

Motion

► The wild horses running across this meadow are in motion.

Lab zone™ Chapter Project

Show Some Motion

Your Goal To identify the motion of several common objects and calculate how fast each one moves

To complete this project, you must

● measure distance and time carefully
● calculate the speed of each object using your data
● prepare display cards of your data, diagrams, and calculations
● follow the safety guidelines in Appendix A

Plan It! With your classmates, brainstorm several examples of objects in motion, such as a feather falling, your friend riding a bicycle, or the minute hand moving on a clock. Choose your examples and have your teacher approve them. Create a data table for each example and record your measurements. For accuracy, repeat your measurements. Then calculate the speed of each object. Make display cards for each example that show data, diagrams, and calculations.

Describing and Measuring Motion

Reading Preview

Key Concepts
- When is an object in motion?
- How do you know an object's speed and velocity?
- How can you graph motion?

Key Terms
- motion • reference point
- International System of Units
- meter • speed • average speed
- instantaneous speed
- velocity • slope

Target Reading Skill

Using Prior Knowledge Before you read, write what you know about motion in a graphic organizer like the one below. As you read, write what you learn.

What You Know
1. A moving object changes position. 2.

What You Learned
1. 2.

Lab zone Discover **Activity**

How Fast and How Far?

1. Using a stopwatch, find out how long it takes you to walk 5 meters at a normal pace. Record your time.
2. Now find out how far you can walk in 5 seconds if you walk at a normal pace. Record your distance.
3. Repeat Steps 1 and 2, walking slower than your normal pace. Then repeat Steps 1 and 2 walking faster than your normal pace.

Think It Over
Inferring What is the relationship between the distance you walk, the time it takes you to walk, and your walking speed?

How do you know if you are moving? If you've ever traveled on a train, you know you cannot always tell if you are in motion. Looking at a building outside the window helps you decide. Although the building seems to move past the train, it's you and the train that are moving.

However, sometimes you may see another train that appears to be moving. Is the other train really moving, or is your train moving? How do you tell?

Describing Motion

Deciding if an object is moving isn't as easy as you might think. For example, you are probably sitting in a chair as you read this book. Are you moving? Well, parts of you may be. Your eyes blink and your chest moves up and down. But you would probably say that you are not moving. An object is in **motion** if its distance from another object is changing. Because your distance from your chair is not changing, you are not in motion.

Reference Points To decide if you are moving, you use your chair as a reference point. A **reference point** is a place or object used for comparison to determine if something is in motion. **An object is in motion if it changes position relative to a reference point.**

Objects that we call stationary—such as a tree, a sign, or a building—make good reference points. From the point of view of the train passenger in Figure 1, such objects are not in motion. If the passenger is moving relative to a tree, he can conclude that the train is in motion.

You probably know what happens if your reference point is moving. Have you ever been in a school bus parked next to another bus? Suddenly, you think your bus is moving backward. But, when you look out a window on the other side, you find that your bus isn't moving at all—the other bus is moving forward! Your bus seems to move backward because you used the other bus as a reference point.

FIGURE 1
Reference Points
The passenger can use a tree as a reference point to decide if the train is moving. A tree makes a good reference point because it is stationary from the passenger's point of view.
Applying Concepts *Why is it important to choose a stationary object as a reference point?*

Relative Motion From the Plane
- The plane does not appear to be moving.
- The skydivers appear to be moving away.
- A point on the ground appears to be moving away.

Relative Motion Are you moving as you read this book? The answer to that question depends on your reference point. When your chair is your reference point, you are not moving. But if you choose another reference point, you may be moving.

Suppose you choose the sun as a reference point instead of your chair. If you compare yourself to the sun, you are moving quite rapidly. This is because you and your chair are on Earth, which moves around the sun. Earth moves about 30 kilometers every second. So you, your chair, this book, and everything else on Earth move that quickly as well. Going that fast, you could travel from New York City to Los Angeles in about 2 minutes! Relative to the sun, both you and your chair are in motion. But because you are moving with Earth, you do not seem to be moving.

FIGURE 2
Relative Motion
Whether or not an object is in motion depends on the reference point you choose.
Comparing and Contrasting *Are the skydivers moving relative to each other? Are they moving relative to the airplane from which they jumped? Are they moving relative to the ground?*

Relative Motion From the Skydivers
- The plane appears to be moving away.
- The skydivers do not appear to be moving.
- The ground appears to be moving closer.

Relative Motion From the Ground
- The plane appears to be moving across the sky.
- The skydivers appear to be moving closer.
- The ground does not appear to be moving.

FIGURE 3
Measuring Distance
You can measure distances shorter than 1 meter in centimeters. The wingspan of the butterfly is 7 cm.

Measuring Distance You can use units of measurement to describe motion precisely. You measure in units, or standard quantities of measurement, all the time. For example, you might measure 1 cup of milk for a recipe, run 2 miles after school, or buy 3 pounds of fruit at the store. Cups, miles, and pounds are all units of measurement.

Scientists all over the world use the same system of measurement so that they can communicate clearly. This system of measurement is called the **International System of Units** or, in French, *Système International* (SI).

When describing motion, scientists use SI units to describe the distance an object moves. When you measure distance, you measure length. The SI unit of length is the **meter** (m). A meter is a little longer than a yard. An Olympic-size swimming pool is 50 meters long. A football field is about 91 meters long.

The length of an object smaller than a meter often is measured in a unit called the centimeter (cm). The prefix *centi-* means "one hundredth." A centimeter is one hundredth of a meter, so there are 100 centimeters in a meter. The wingspan of the butterfly shown in Figure 3 can be measured in centimeters. For lengths smaller than a centimeter, the millimeter (mm) is used. The prefix *milli-* means "one thousandth," so there are 1,000 millimeters in a meter. Distances too long to be measured in meters often are measured in kilometers (km). The prefix *kilo-* means "one thousand." There are 1,000 meters in a kilometer.

Scientists also use SI units to describe quantities other than length. You can find more information about SI units in the Skills Handbook at the end of this book.

 **Reading Checkpoint** What system of measurement do scientists use?

Math Skills

Converting Units

Use a conversion factor to convert one metric unit to another. A conversion factor is a fraction in which the numerator and denominator represent equal amounts in different units. Multiply the number you want to convert by the conversion factor.

Suppose you want to know how many millimeters (mm) are in 14.5 meters (m). Since there are 1,000 millimeters in 1 meter, the conversion factor is

$$\frac{1,000 \text{ mm}}{1 \text{ m}}$$

Multiply 14.5 meters by the conversion factor to find millimeters.

$$14.5 \text{ m} \times \frac{1,000 \text{ mm}}{1 \text{ m}}$$

$$= 14.5 \times 1,000 \text{ mm}$$

$$= 14,500 \text{ mm}$$

Practice Problem How many centimeters are in 22.5 meters?

Calculating

Two families meet at the City Museum at 10:00 A.M. Each family uses a different means of transportation to get there. The Gonzalez family leaves at 9:00 A.M. and drives 90 km on a highway. The Browns leave at 9:30 A.M. and ride the train 30 km. What is the average speed for each family's trip? Which family travels at the faster speed?

Calculating Speed

A measurement of distance can tell you how far an object travels. A cyclist, for example, might travel 30 kilometers. An ant might travel 2 centimeters. **If you know the distance an object travels in a certain amount of time, you can calculate the speed of the object.** Speed is a type of rate. A rate tells you the amount of something that occurs or changes in one unit of time. The **speed** of an object is the distance the object travels per unit of time.

The Speed Equation To calculate the speed of an object, divide the distance the object travels by the amount of time it takes to travel that distance. This relationship can be written as an equation.

$$\text{Speed} = \frac{\text{Distance}}{\text{Time}}$$

The speed equation consists of a unit of distance divided by a unit of time. If you measure distance in meters and time in seconds, you express speed in meters per second, or m/s. (The slash is read as "per.") If you measure distance in kilometers and time in hours, you express speed in kilometers per hour, or km/h. For example, a cyclist who travels 30 kilometers in 1 hour has a speed of 30 km/h. An ant that moves 2 centimeters in 1 second is moving at a speed of 2 centimeters per second, or 2 cm/s.

FIGURE 4
Speed
The cyclists' speeds will vary throughout the cross-country race. However, the cyclist with the greatest average speed will win.

Average Speed The speed of most moving objects is not constant. The cyclists shown in Figure 4, for example, change their speeds many times during the race. They might ride at a constant speed along flat ground but move more slowly as they climb hills. Then they might move more quickly as they come down hills. Occasionally, they may stop to fix their bikes.

Although a cyclist does not have a constant speed, the cyclist does have an average speed throughout a race. To calculate **average speed**, divide the total distance traveled by the total time. For example, suppose a cyclist travels 32 kilometers during the first 2 hours. Then the cyclist travels 13 kilometers during the next hour. The average speed of the cyclist is the total distance divided by the total time.

$$\text{Total distance} = 32 \text{ km} + 13 \text{ km} = 45 \text{ km}$$
$$\text{Total time} = 2 \text{ h} + 1 \text{ h} = 3 \text{ h}$$
$$\text{Average speed} = \frac{45 \text{ km}}{3 \text{ h}} = 15 \text{ km/h}$$

The cyclist's average speed is 15 kilometers per hour.

Instantaneous Speed Calculating the average speed of a cyclist during a race is important. However, it is also useful to know the cyclist's instantaneous speed. **Instantaneous speed** is the rate at which an object is moving at a given instant in time.

Reading Checkpoint How do you calculate average speed?

FIGURE 5
Measuring Speed
Cyclists use an electronic device known as a cyclometer to track the distance and time that they travel. A cyclometer can calculate both average and instantaneous speed.
Comparing and Contrasting *Explain why the instantaneous speed and the average speed shown below are different.*

◆ **603**

Motion

Video Preview
▶ Video Field Trip
Video Assessment

Describing Velocity

Knowing the speed at which something travels does not tell you everything about its motion. To describe an object's motion completely, you need to know the direction of its motion. For example, suppose you hear that a thunderstorm is traveling at a speed of 25 km/h. Should you prepare for the storm? That depends on the direction of the storm's motion. Because storms usually travel from west to east in the United States, you need not worry if you live to the west of the storm. But if you live to the east of the storm, take cover.

When you know both the speed and direction of an object's motion, you know the velocity of the object. Speed in a given direction is called **velocity.** You know the velocity of the storm when you know that it is moving 25 km/h eastward.

• Tech & Design in History •

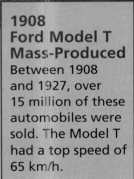

The Speed of Transportation

The speed with which people can travel from one place to another has increased over the years.

1818
National Road Constructed
The speed of transportation has been limited largely by the quality of roadways. The U.S. government paid for the construction of a highway named the Cumberland Road. It ran from Cumberland, Maryland, to Wheeling, in present-day West Virginia. Travel by horse and carriage on the roadway was at a speed of about 11 km/h.

1885
Benz Tricycle Car Introduced
This odd-looking vehicle was the first internal combustion (gasoline-powered) automobile sold to the public. Although it is an ancestor of the modern automobile, its top speed was only about 15 km/h—not much faster than a horse-drawn carriage.

1908
Ford Model T Mass-Produced
Between 1908 and 1927, over 15 million of these automobiles were sold. The Model T had a top speed of 65 km/h.

| 1800 | 1850 | 1900 |

At times, describing the velocity of moving objects can be very important. For example, air traffic controllers must keep close track of the velocities of the aircraft under their control. These velocities continually change as airplanes move overhead and on the runways. An error in determining a velocity, either in speed or in direction, could lead to a collision.

Velocity is also important to airplane pilots. For example, stunt pilots make spectacular use of their control over the velocity of their aircrafts. To avoid colliding with other aircraft, these skilled pilots must have precise control of both their speed and direction. Stunt pilots use this control to stay in close formation while flying graceful maneuvers at high speed.

 **Reading Checkpoint** What is velocity?

Writing in Science

Research and Write What styles of automobile were most popular during the 1950s, 1960s, and 1970s? Were sedans, convertibles, station wagons, or sports cars the bestsellers? Choose an era and research automobiles of that time. Then write an advertisement for one particular style of car. Be sure to include information from your research.

1934 Zephyr Introduced
The first diesel passenger train in the United States was the *Zephyr*. The *Zephyr* set a long-distance record, traveling from Denver to Chicago at an average speed of 125 km/h for more than 1,600 km.

1956 Interstate Highway System Established
The passage of the Federal-Aid Highway Act established the Highway Trust Fund. This act allowed the construction of the Interstate and Defense Highways. Nonstop transcontinental auto travel became possible. Speed limits in many parts of the system were more than 100 km/h.

2003 Maglev in Motion
The first commercial application of high-speed maglev (magnetic levitation) was unveiled in Shanghai, China. During the 30-km trip from Pudong International Airport to Shanghai's financial district, the train operates at a top speed of 430 km/h, reducing commuting time from 45 minutes to just 8 minutes.

1950   2000   2050

Go **Online**

active art

For: Graphing Motion activity
Visit: PHSchool.com
Web Code: cgp-3011

FIGURE 6
Graphing Motion

Distance-versus-time graphs can be used to analyze motion. On the jogger's first day of training, her speed is the same at every point. On the second day of training, her speed varies. **Reading Graphs** *On the first day, how far does the jogger run in 5 minutes?*

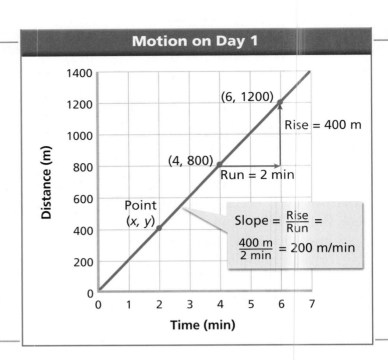

Motion on Day 1

(6, 1200)
Rise = 400 m
(4, 800)
Run = 2 min
Point (x, y)

$$\text{Slope} = \frac{\text{Rise}}{\text{Run}} = \frac{400 \text{ m}}{2 \text{ min}} = 200 \text{ m/min}$$

Distance (m) vs *Time (min)*

Graphing Motion

You can show the motion of an object on a line graph in which you plot distance versus time. The graphs you see in Figure 6 are distance-versus-time motion graphs. Time is shown on the horizontal axis, or *x*-axis. Distance is shown on the vertical axis, or *y*-axis. A point on the line represents the distance an object has traveled at a particular time. The *x* value of the point is time, and the *y* value is distance.

The steepness of a line on a graph is called **slope.** The slope tells you how fast one variable changes in relation to the other variable in the graph. In other words, slope tells you the rate of change. Since speed is the rate that distance changes in relation to time, the slope of a distance-versus-time graph represents speed. The steeper the slope is, the greater the speed. A constant slope represents motion at constant speed.

Calculating Slope You can calculate the slope of a line by dividing the rise by the run. The rise is the vertical difference between any two points on the line. The run is the horizontal difference between the same two points.

$$\text{Slope} = \frac{\text{Rise}}{\text{Run}}$$

In Figure 6, using the points shown, the rise is 400 meters and the run is 2 minutes. To find the slope, you divide 400 meters by 2 minutes. The slope is 200 meters per minute.

 **Reading Checkpoint** What is the slope of a graph?

606 ◆

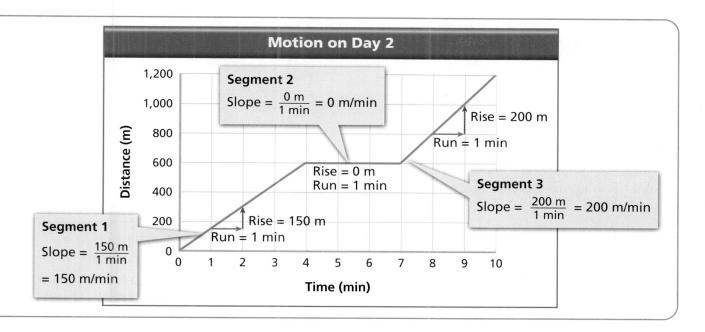

Motion on Day 2

Segment 2
Slope = $\frac{0 \text{ m}}{1 \text{ min}}$ = 0 m/min

Rise = 200 m
Run = 1 min

Rise = 0 m
Run = 1 min

Segment 3
Slope = $\frac{200 \text{ m}}{1 \text{ min}}$ = 200 m/min

Segment 1
Slope = $\frac{150 \text{ m}}{1 \text{ min}}$
= 150 m/min

Rise = 150 m
Run = 1 min

Distance (m) — 0, 200, 400, 600, 800, 1,000, 1,200
Time (min) — 0, 1, 2, 3, 4, 5, 6, 7, 8, 9, 10

Different Slopes Most moving objects do not travel at a constant speed. The graph above shows a jogger's motion on her second day. The line is divided into three segments. The slope of each segment is different. From the steepness of the slopes you can tell that the jogger ran the fastest during the third segment. The horizontal line in the second segment shows that the jogger's distance did not change at all.

Section 1 Assessment

Target Reading Skill

Using Prior Knowledge Review your graphic organizer and revise it based on what you just learned about motion.

Reviewing Key Concepts

1. **a. Reviewing** How do you know if an object is moving?
   b. Explaining Why is it important to know if your reference point is moving?
   c. Applying Concepts Suppose you are riding in a car. Describe your motion relative to the car, the road, and the sun.
2. **a. Defining** What is speed?
   b. Describing What do you know about the motion of an object that has an average speed of 1 m/s?
   c. Comparing and Contrasting What is the difference between speed and velocity?

3. **a. Identifying** What does the slope of a distance-versus-time graph show you about the motion of an object?
   b. Calculating The rise of a line on a distance-versus-time graph is 600 m and the run is 3 minutes. What is the slope of the line?

Math Practice

This week at swim practice, Jamie swam a total of 1,500 m, while Ellie swam 1.6 km.

4. **Converting Units** Convert Ellie's distance to meters. Who swam the greater distance: Jamie or Ellie?
5. **Converting Units** How many kilometers did Jamie swim?

Inclined to Roll

For: Data sharing
Visit: PHSchool.com
Web Code: cgd-3012

Problem

How does the steepness of a ramp affect how fast an object rolling off it moves across the floor?

Skills Focus

measuring, calculating, graphing

Materials

- skateboard   • meter stick   • protractor
- masking tape   • flat board, about 1.5 m long
- small piece of sturdy cardboard
- supports to prop up the board (books, boxes)
- two stopwatches

Procedure

1. In your notebook, make a data table like the one below. Include space for five angles.

2. Lay the board flat on the floor. Using masking tape, mark a starting line in the middle of the board. Mark a finish line on the floor 1.5 m beyond one end of the board. Place a barrier after the finish line.

3. Prop up the other end of the board to make a slight incline. Use a protractor to measure the angle that the board makes with the ground. Record the angle in your data table.

4. Working in groups of three, have one person hold the skateboard so that its front wheels are even with the starting line. As the holder releases the skateboard, the other two students should start their stopwatches.

5. One timer should stop his or her stopwatch when the front wheels of the skateboard reach the end of the incline.

6. The second timer should stop his or her stopwatch when the front wheels reach the finish line. Record the times in your data table in the columns labeled Time 1 and Time 2.

7. Repeat Steps 4–6 two more times. If your results for the three times aren't within 0.2 second of one another, carry out more trials.

Data Table							
Angle (degrees)	Trial Number	Time 1 (to bottom) (s)	Time 2 (to finish) (s)	Avg Time 1 (s)	Avg Time 2 (s)	Avg Time 2 – Avg Time 1 (s)	Avg Speed (m/s)
	1						
	2						
	3						
	1						
	2						
	3						
	1						
	2						

8. Repeat Steps 3–7 four more times, making the ramp gradually steeper each time.

9. For each angle of the incline, complete the following calculations and record them in your data table.
   a. Find the average time the skateboard takes to get to the bottom of the ramp (Time 1).
   b. Find the average time the skateboard takes to get to the finish line (Time 2).
   c. Subtract the average of Time 1 from the average of Time 2.

Analyze and Conclude

1. **Calculating** How can you find the average speed of the skateboard across the floor for each angle of the incline? Determine the average speed for each angle and record it in your data table.

2. **Classifying** Which is your manipulated variable and which is your responding variable in this experiment? Explain. (For a discussion of manipulated and responding variables, see the Skills Handbook.)

3. **Graphing** On a graph, plot the average speed of the skateboard (on the y-axis) against the angle of the ramp (on the x-axis).

4. **Drawing Conclusions** What does your graph show about the relationship between the skateboard's speed and the angle of the ramp?

5. **Measuring** If your measurements for distance, time, or angle were inaccurate, how would your results have been affected?

6. **Communicating** Do you think your method of timing was accurate? Did the timers start and stop their stopwatches exactly at the appropriate points? How could the accuracy of the timing be improved? Write a brief procedure for your method.

Design an Experiment

A truck driver transporting new cars needs to roll the cars off the truck. You offer to design a ramp to help with the task. What measurements would you make that might be useful? Design an experiment to test your ideas. *Obtain your teacher's permission before carrying out your investigation.*

Slow Motion on Planet Earth

Reading Preview

Key Concepts
- How does the theory of plate tectonics explain the movement of Earth's landmasses?
- How fast do Earth's plates move?

Key Terms
- plate • theory of plate tectonics

Target Reading Skill

Previewing Visuals Before you read, preview Figure 8. Then write two questions that you have about the diagram in a graphic organizer like the one below. As you read, answer your questions.

Motion of the Continents

Q.	Why do the continents move over time?
A.	
Q.	

Lab zone Discover **Activity**

How Slow Can It Flow?

1. Put a spoonful of honey on a plate.
2. Place a piece of tape 4 cm from the bottom edge of the honey.
3. Lift one side of the plate just high enough that the honey starts to flow.
4. Reduce the plate's angle until the honey barely moves. Prop up the plate at this angle.
5. Time how long the honey takes to reach the tape. Calculate the speed of the honey.

Think It Over

Forming Operational Definitions When an object doesn't appear to be moving at first glance, how can you tell if it is?

Have you ever noticed that Earth's landmasses resemble pieces of a giant jigsaw puzzle? It's true. The east coast of South America, for example, would fit nicely into the west coast of Africa. The Arabian Peninsula would fit fairly well with the northeastern coast of Africa. Since the 1600s, people have wondered why Earth's landmasses look as if they would fit together. After all, land can't move. Or can it?

These landmasses would fit fairly well if they were pushed together like puzzle pieces. ▶

Earth's Plates

Earth's rocky outer layer consists of pieces that fit together like a jigsaw puzzle. This outer layer is made of more than a dozen major pieces called **plates.** The boundaries between the plates are cracks in Earth's outer layer. As you can see in Figure 7, plate boundaries do not always lie along the edges of continents. The eastern boundary of the North American plate, for example, lies under the Atlantic Ocean. Many plates have both continents and oceans on them.

The Theory of Plate Tectonics Scientists use the concept of plates to explain how landmasses have changed over time. The **theory of plate tectonics** states that Earth's plates move slowly in various directions. Some plates slowly pull away from each other, some plates push toward each other, and some plates slide past each other. **According to the theory of plate tectonics, Earth's landmasses have changed position over time because they are part of plates that are slowly moving.**

Why Do Earth's Plates Move? Have you ever heated a pot of water and watched what happens? The liquid at the bottom gets hotter faster. The hotter liquid rises upward. At the surface it cools, and then hotter water moving upward pushes it aside. The same type of churning motion drives the movement of Earth's plates.

Underneath Earth's rigid plates is somewhat softer rock that moves similarly to boiling water. Scientists think that heat deep inside Earth causes material there to slowly rise upward. As more heated material rises, it pushes aside cooler material at the top of the layer. Eventually the cooler material sinks downward. The rising and sinking of material creates a slow-moving current beneath Earth's outer layer. It is this current that causes Earth's plates to move.

 Reading Checkpoint **What causes Earth's plates to move?**

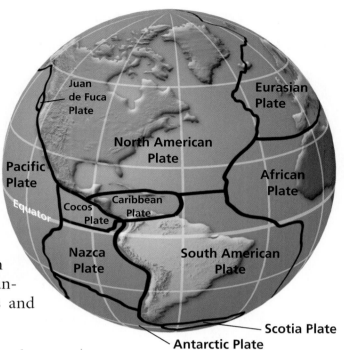

FIGURE 7
Earth's Plates
The black outlines show the boundaries of some of Earth's plates. **Interpreting Maps** *Which plates border the Nazca plate?*

225 Million Years Ago

180-200 Million Years Ago

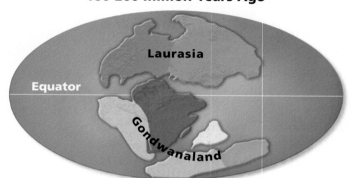

FIGURE 8
Motion of the Continents
The shapes and positions of Earth's continents have changed greatly over time and will continue to change in the future.
Interpreting Maps *Locate Australia on the map. How does its position change over time?*

For: Continental Drift activity
Visit: PHSchool.com
Web Code: cfp-1015

135 Million Years Ago

Present Day

Scientists have found that South America is moving 10 cm west per year. You can use this speed to predict how far the continent will move in 500 years.

Distance = Speed × Time

Distance = $\frac{10 \text{ cm}}{1 \text{ year}}$ × 500 years = 5,000 cm

South America will move 5,000 cm, or 50 m, in the next 500 years.

Plate Movement

Unless you have experienced an earthquake, you have probably never felt Earth's plates moving. Why not? After all, you live on one of Earth's plates. One reason may be that they move so slowly. **Some plates move at a rate of several centimeters each year. Others move only a few millimeters per year.**

Knowing the average speed of Earth's plates allows scientists to explain how Earth's surface has changed over time. It also helps them predict future changes. Figure 8 shows how scientists think the continents may have looked in the past.

Suppose you study the motion of a plate. You find that the plate moved a distance of 5 centimeters in one year. So, the speed of the plate is 5 cm/yr. You can use this speed to predict how far the plate will move in 1,000 years. Start by rearranging the speed formula to find the distance. Then calculate distance.

$$\text{Distance} = \text{Speed} \times \text{Time}$$

$$\text{Distance} = \frac{5 \text{ cm}}{1 \text{ yr}} \times 1{,}000 \text{ yr} = 5{,}000 \text{ cm}$$

In 1,000 years, the plate will move 5,000 centimeters. You could probably walk the same distance in 30 seconds!

 **Reading Checkpoint** Why are scientists interested in the average speed of Earth's plates?

Section 2 Assessment

Target Reading Strategy Previewing Visuals Refer to your questions and answers about Figure 8 to help you answer Question 1 below.

Reviewing Key Concepts

1. **a.** Defining What theory explains the movement of pieces of Earth's surface?
   b. Explaining Why do Earth's plates move?
   c. Interpreting Maps Use the map in Figure 7 to determine which plate contains most of the United States.
2. **a.** Reviewing In general, at what speed do Earth's plates move?
   b. Calculating A plate moves at a speed of 45 mm/yr. How far will the plate move in 100 years?
   c. Predicting Figure 8 shows that North America and Europe are moving apart from each other. In your lifetime, how will this affect the time it takes to travel between the two continents?

Lab zone At-Home **Activity**

Fingernail Growth Have a family member measure in millimeters the length of the white part of one fingernail. Record the result and which finger you used. In exactly three weeks, again measure the white part of the same fingernail. Then calculate the speed, in millimeters per day, at which the fingernail grew. Discuss with your family member how your results compare with the typical speed of Earth's plates.

3 Acceleration

Reading Preview

Key Concepts
- What kind of motion does acceleration refer to?
- How is acceleration calculated?
- What graphs can be used to analyze the motion of an accelerating object?

Key Term
- acceleration

Target Reading Skill

Identifying Main Ideas As you read the What Is Acceleration? section, write the main idea in a graphic organizer like the one below. Then write three supporting details that give examples of the main idea.

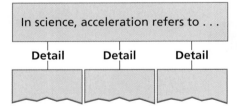

Main Idea

In science, acceleration refers to . . .

Detail	Detail	Detail

Discover Activity

Will You Hurry Up?

1. Measure 10 meters in an open area. Mark the distance with masking tape.
2. Walk the 10 meters in such a way that you keep moving faster throughout the entire distance. Have a partner time you.
3. Repeat Step 2, walking the 10 meters in less time than you did before. Then try it again, this time walking the distance in twice the time as the first. Remember to keep speeding up throughout the entire 10 meters.

Think It Over
Inferring How is the change in your speed related to the time in which you walk the 10-meter course?

The pitcher throws. The ball speeds toward the batter. Off the bat it goes. It's going, going, gone! A home run!

Before landing, the ball went through several changes in motion. It sped up in the pitcher's hand, and lost speed as it traveled toward the batter. The ball stopped when it hit the bat, changed direction, sped up again, and eventually slowed down. Most examples of motion involve similar changes. In fact, rarely does any object's motion stay the same for very long.

What Is Acceleration?

Suppose you are a passenger in a car stopped at a red light. When the light changes to green, the driver steps on the accelerator. As a result, the car speeds up, or accelerates. In everyday language, *acceleration* means "the process of speeding up."

Acceleration has a more precise definition in science. Scientists define **acceleration** as the rate at which velocity changes. Recall that velocity describes both the speed and direction of an object. A change in velocity can involve a change in either speed or direction—or both. **In science, acceleration refers to increasing speed, decreasing speed, or changing direction.**

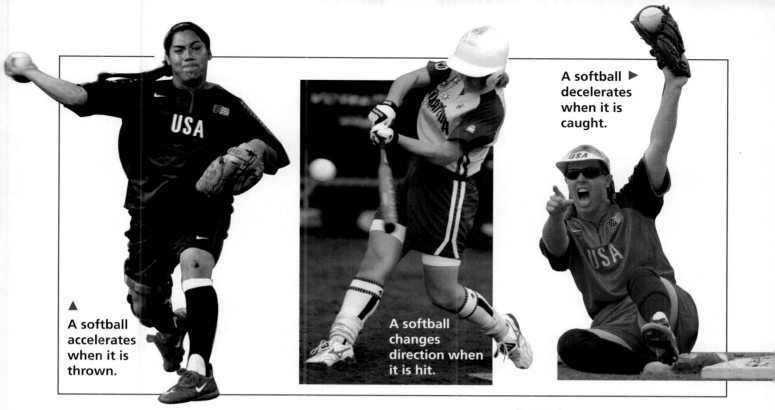

A softball ▶
decelerates
when it is
caught.

▲
A softball
accelerates
when it is
thrown.

A softball
changes
direction when
it is hit.

FIGURE 9
Acceleration
A softball experiences acceleration
when it is thrown, caught, and
hit. **Classifying** *What change in
motion occurs in each example?*

Increasing Speed

Whenever an object's speed increases, the object accelerates. A softball accelerates when the pitcher throws it, and
again when a bat hits it. A car that begins to move from a
stopped position or speeds up to pass another car is accelerating. People can accelerate too. For example, you accelerate
when you coast down a hill on your bike.

Decreasing Speed Just as objects can speed up, they can also
slow down. This change in speed is sometimes called decelera-
tion, or negative acceleration. For example, a softball decelerates
when it lands in a fielder's mitt. A car decelerates when it stops at
a red light. A water skier decelerates when the boat stops pulling.

Changing Direction Even an object that is traveling at a constant speed can be accelerating. Recall that acceleration can be a
change in direction as well as a change in speed. Therefore, a car
accelerates as it follows a gentle curve in the road or changes
lanes. Runners accelerate as they round the curve in a track. A
softball accelerates when it changes direction as it is hit.

Many objects continuously change direction without changing speed. The simplest example of this type of motion is circular motion, or motion along a circular path. For example, the
seats on a Ferris wheel accelerate because they move in a circle.

 **Reading
Checkpoint** How can a car be accelerating if its speed is
constant at 65 km/h?

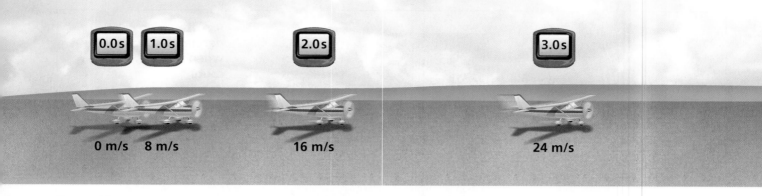

0.0s   1.0s   2.0s   3.0s

0 m/s   8 m/s   16 m/s   24 m/s

FIGURE 10

Analyzing Acceleration
The speed of the airplane above increases by the same amount each second. **Interpreting Diagrams** *How does the distance change in each second?*

Calculating Acceleration

Acceleration describes the rate at which velocity changes. If an object is not changing direction, you can describe its acceleration as the rate at which its speed changes. **To determine the acceleration of an object moving in a straight line, you must calculate the change in speed per unit of time.** This is summarized by the following formula.

$$\text{Acceleration} = \frac{\text{Final speed} - \text{Initial speed}}{\text{Time}}$$

If speed is measured in meters per second (m/s) and time is measured in seconds, the SI unit of acceleration is meters per second per second, or m/s^2. Suppose speed is measured in kilometers per hour and time is measured in hours. Then the unit for acceleration is kilometers per hour per hour, or km/h^2.

To understand acceleration, imagine a small airplane moving down a runway. Figure 10 shows the airplane's motion after each of the first five seconds of its acceleration. To calculate the average acceleration of the airplane, you must first subtract the initial speed of 0 m/s from the final speed of 40 m/s. Then divide the change in speed by the time, 5 seconds.

$$\text{Acceleration} = \frac{40 \text{ m/s} - 0 \text{ m/s}}{5 \text{ s}}$$

$$\text{Acceleration} = 8 \text{ m/s}^2$$

The airplane accelerates at a rate of 8 m/s^2. This means that the airplane's speed increases by 8 m/s every second. Notice in Figure 10 that, after each second of travel, the airplane's speed is 8 m/s greater than it was the previous second.

Go Online
SC*LINKS* NSTA

For: Links on acceleration
Visit: www.SciLinks.org
Web Code: scn-1313

Reading Checkpoint   **What must you know about an object moving in a straight line to calculate its acceleration?**

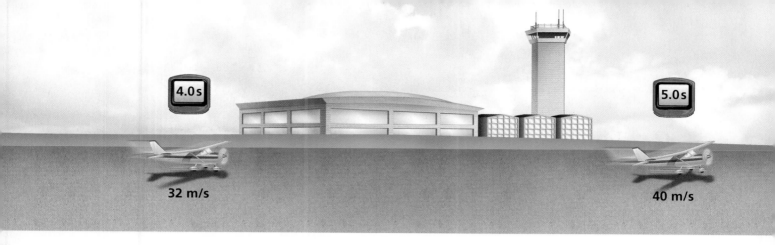

4.0 s   **5.0 s**

32 m/s   40 m/s

Math ▶ Sample Problem

Calculating Acceleration

As a roller coaster car starts down a slope, its speed is 4 m/s. But 3 seconds later, at the bottom, its speed is 22 m/s. What is its average acceleration?

1 **Read and Understand**
What information are you given?

Initial speed = 4 m/s
Final speed = 22 m/s
Time = 3 s

2 **Plan and Solve**
What quantity are you trying to calculate?

The average acceleration of the roller coaster car = ■

What formula contains the given quantities and the unknown quantity?

$$\text{Acceleration} = \frac{\text{Final speed} - \text{Initial speed}}{\text{Time}}$$

Perform the calculation.

$$\text{Acceleration} = \frac{22 \text{ m/s} - 4 \text{ m/s}}{3 \text{ s}}$$

$$\text{Acceleration} = \frac{18 \text{ m/s}}{3 \text{ s}}$$

$$\text{Acceleration} = 6 \text{ m/s}^2$$

The roller coaster car's average acceleration is 6 m/s².

3 **Look Back and Check**
Does your answer make sense?

The answer is reasonable. If the car's speed increases by 6 m/s each second, its speed will be 10 m/s after 1 second, 16 m/s after 2 seconds, and 22 m/s after 3 seconds.

Math ▶ Practice

1. **Calculating Acceleration** A falling raindrop accelerates from 10 m/s to 30 m/s in 2 seconds. What is the raindrop's average acceleration?

2. **Calculating Acceleration** A certain car can accelerate from rest to 27 m/s in 9 seconds. Find the car's average acceleration.

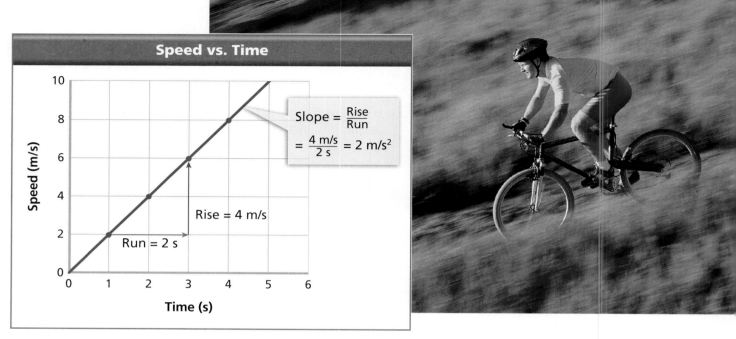

Speed vs. Time

Slope = $\dfrac{\text{Rise}}{\text{Run}}$

= $\dfrac{4 \text{ m/s}}{2 \text{ s}}$ = 2 m/s²

Rise = 4 m/s

Run = 2 s

FIGURE 11

Speed-Versus-Time Graph
The slanted, straight line on this speed-versus-time graph tells you that the cyclist is accelerating at a constant rate. The slope of a speed-versus-time graph tells you the object's acceleration.

Predicting How would the slope of the graph change if the cyclist were accelerating at a greater rate? At a lesser rate?

Graphing Acceleration

Suppose you ride your bicycle down a long, steep hill. At the top of the hill your speed is 0 m/s. As you start down the hill, your speed increases. Each second, you move at a greater speed and travel a greater distance than the second before. During the five seconds it takes you to reach the bottom of the hill, you are an accelerating object. **You can use both a speed-versus-time graph and a distance-versus-time graph to analyze the motion of an accelerating object.**

Speed-Versus-Time Graph Figure 11 shows a speed-versus-time graph for your bicycle ride down the hill. What can you learn about your motion by analyzing this graph? First, since the line slants upward, the graph shows you that your speed was increasing. Next, since the line is straight, you can tell that your acceleration was constant. A slanted, straight line on a speed-versus-time graph means that the object is accelerating at a constant rate. You can find your acceleration by calculating the slope of the line. To calculate the slope, choose any two points on the line. Then, divide the rise by the run.

$$\text{Slope} = \frac{\text{Rise}}{\text{Run}} = \frac{8 \text{ m/s} - 4 \text{ m/s}}{4 \text{ s} - 2 \text{ s}} = \frac{4 \text{ m/s}}{2 \text{ s}}$$

$$\text{Slope} = 2 \text{ m/s}^2$$

During your bike ride, you accelerated down the hill at a constant rate of 2 m/s².

Distance-Versus-Time Graph You can represent the motion of an accelerating object with a distance-versus-time graph. Figure 12 shows a distance-versus-time graph for your bike ride. On this type of graph, a curved line means that the object is accelerating. The curved line in Figure 12 tells you that during each second, you traveled a greater distance than the second before. For example, you traveled a greater distance during the third second than you did during the first second.

The curved line in Figure 12 also tells you that during each second your speed is greater than the second before. Recall that the slope of a distance-versus-time graph is the speed of an object. From second to second, the slope of the line in Figure 12 gets steeper and steeper. Since the slope is increasing, you can conclude that the speed is also increasing. You are accelerating.

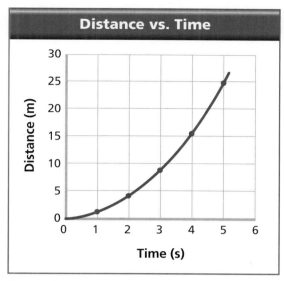

FIGURE 12
Distance-Versus-Time Graph
The curved line on this distance-versus-time graph tells you that the cyclist is accelerating.

 **Reading Checkpoint** What does a curved line on a distance-versus-time graph tell you?

Section 3 Assessment

Target Reading Skill Identifying Main Ideas Use information in your graphic organizer to answer Question 1 below.

Reviewing Key Concepts

1. a. **Describing** What are the three ways that an object can accelerate?
   b. **Summarizing** Describe how a baseball player accelerates as he runs around the bases after hitting a home run.
   c. **Applying Concepts** An ice skater glides around a rink at a constant speed of 2 m/s. Is the skater accelerating? Explain your answer.

2. a. **Identifying** What is the formula used to calculate the acceleration of an object moving in a straight line?
   b. **Calculating** A cyclist's speed changes from 0 m/s to 15 m/s in 10 seconds. What is the cyclist's average acceleration?

3. a. **Naming** What types of graphs can you use to analyze the acceleration of an object?
   b. **Explaining** How is an object moving if a slanted, straight line on a speed-versus-time graph represents its motion?
   c. **Predicting** What would a distance-versus-time graph look like for the moving object in part (b)?

Math ► **Practice**

4. **Calculating Acceleration** A downhill skier reaches the steepest part of a trail. Her speed increases from 9 m/s to 18 m/s in 3 seconds. What is her average acceleration?

5. **Calculating Acceleration** What is a race car's average acceleration if its speed changes from 0 m/s to 40 m/s in 4 seconds?

Stopping on a Dime

Problem

The school will put in a new basketball court in a small area between two buildings. Safety is an important consideration in the design of the court. What is the distance needed between an out-of-bounds line and a wall so that a player can stop before hitting the wall?

Skills Focus

calculating, interpreting data

Materials

• wooden meter stick • tape measure
• 2 stopwatches or watches with second hands

Procedure

PART 1 Reaction Time

1. Have your partner suspend a wooden meter stick, zero end down, between your thumb and index finger, as shown. Your thumb and index finger should be about 3 cm apart.

2. Your partner will drop the meter stick without giving you any warning. Try to grab it with your thumb and index finger.

Reaction Time			
Distance (cm)	Time (s)	Distance (cm)	Time (s)
15	0.175	25	0.226
16	0.181	26	0.230
17	0.186	27	0.235
18	0.192	28	0.239
19	0.197	29	0.243
20	0.202	30	0.247
21	0.207	31	0.252
22	0.212	32	0.256
23	0.217	33	0.260
24	0.221	34	0.263

3. Note the level at which you grabbed the meter stick and use the chart shown to determine your reaction time. Record the time in the class data table.

4. Reverse roles with your partner and repeat Steps 1–3.

PART 2 Stopping Distance

5. On the school field or in the gymnasium, mark off a distance of 25 m. **CAUTION:** *Be sure to remove any obstacles from the course.*

6. Have your partner time how long it takes you to run the course at full speed. After you pass the 25-m mark, come to a stop as quickly as possible and remain standing. You must not slow down before the mark.

7. Have your partner measure the distance from the 25-m mark to your final position. This is the distance you need to come to a complete stop. Enter your time and distance into the class data table.

8. Reverse roles with your partner. Enter your partner's time and distance into the class data table.

Class Data Table			
Student Name	Reaction Time (s)	Running Time (s)	Stopping Distance (m)

Analyze and Conclude

1. **Calculating** Calculate the average speed of the student who ran the 25-m course the fastest.

2. **Interpreting Data** Multiply the speed of the fastest student (calculated in Question 1) by the slowest reaction time listed in the class data table. Why would you be interested in this product?

3. **Interpreting Data** Add the distance calculated in Question 2 to the longest stopping distance in the class data table. What does this total distance represent?

4. **Drawing Conclusions** Explain why it is important to use the fastest speed, the slowest reaction time, and the longest stopping distance in your calculations.

5. **Controlling Variables** What other factors should you take into account to get results that apply to a real basketball court?

6. **Communicating** Suppose you calculate that the distance from the out-of-bounds line to the wall of the basketball court is too short for safety. Write a proposal to the school that describes the problem. In your proposal, suggest a strategy for making the court safer.

More to Explore

Visit a local playground and examine it from the viewpoint of safety. Use what you learned about stopping distance as one of your guidelines, but also try to identify other potentially unsafe conditions. Write a letter to the Department of Parks or to the officials of your town informing them of your findings.

1 Describing and Measuring Motion

Key Concepts

- An object is in motion if it changes position relative to a reference point.
- If you know the distance an object travels in a certain amount of time, you can calculate the speed of the object.
- $\text{Speed} = \dfrac{\text{Distance}}{\text{Time}}$
- When you know both the speed and direction of an object's motion, you know the velocity of the object.
- You can show the motion of an object on a line graph in which you plot distance versus time.
- $\text{Slope} = \dfrac{\text{Rise}}{\text{Run}}$

Key Terms

motion
reference point
International System of Units
meter
speed
average speed
instantaneous speed
velocity
slope

2 Slow Motion on Planet Earth

Key Concepts

- According to the theory of plate tectonics, Earth's landmasses have changed position over time because they are part of plates that are slowly moving.
- Some plates move at a rate of several centimeters each year. Others move only a few millimeters per year.

Key Terms

plate
theory of plate tectonics

3 Acceleration

Key Concepts

- In science, acceleration refers to increasing speed, decreasing speed, or changing direction.
- To determine the acceleration of an object moving in a straight line, you must calculate the change in speed per unit of time.
- $\text{Acceleration} = \dfrac{\text{Final speed} - \text{Initial speed}}{\text{Time}}$
- You can use both a speed-versus-time graph and a distance-versus-time graph to analyze the motion of an accelerating object.

Key Term

acceleration

Review and Assessment

Organizing Information

Concept Mapping Copy the concept map about motion onto a separate sheet of paper. Then complete it and add a title. (For more information on Concept Mapping, see the Skills Handbook.)

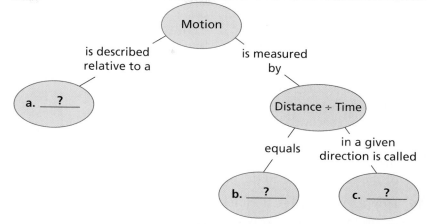

Reviewing Key Terms

Choose the letter of the best answer.

1. A change in position with respect to a reference point is
   a. acceleration.
   b. velocity.
   c. direction.
   d. motion.

2. You do not know an object's velocity until you know its
   a. speed.
   b. reference point.
   c. speed and direction.
   d. acceleration.

3. If you know a car travels 30 km in 20 minutes, you can find its
   a. acceleration.
   b. average speed.
   c. direction.
   d. instantaneous speed.

4. The parts of Earth's outer layer that move are called
   a. reference points.
   b. slopes.
   c. plates.
   d. boundaries.

5. The rate at which velocity changes is called
   a. acceleration.   b. constant speed.
   c. average speed.   d. velocity.

If the statement is true, write *true*. If it is false, change the underlined word or words to make the statement true.

6. The distance an object travels per unit of time is called <u>acceleration</u>.

7. The basic SI unit of length is the <u>meter</u>.

8. The <u>theory of plate tectonics</u> explains how Earth's landmasses have changed position over time.

9. The <u>slope</u> of a speed-versus-time graph represents acceleration.

10. Both <u>speed</u> and acceleration include the direction of an object's motion.

Writing in Science

News Report Two trucks have competed in a race. Write an article describing the race and who won. Explain the role the average speed of the trucks played. Tell how average speed can be calculated.

Motion

Video Preview
Video Field Trip
▶ Video Assessment

Review and Assessment

Checking Concepts

11. A passenger walks toward the rear of a moving train. Describe her motion as seen from a reference point on the train. Then describe it from a reference point on the ground.

12. Which has a greater speed, a heron that travels 600 m in 60 seconds or a duck that travels 60 m in 5 seconds? Explain.

13. You have a motion graph for an object that shows distance and time. How does the slope of the graph relate to the object's speed?

14. How can you tell if an object is moving when its motion is too slow to see?

15. An insect lands on a compact disc that is put into a player. If the insect spins with the disc, is the insect accelerating? Why or why not?

Thinking Critically

16. **Interpreting Graphs** The graph below shows the motion of a remote-control car. During which segment is the car moving the fastest? The slowest? How do you know?

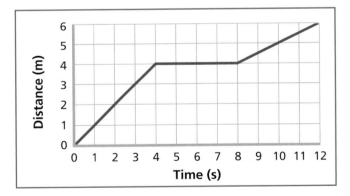

17. **Problem Solving** Two drivers make a 100-km trip. Driver 1 completes the trip in 2 hours. Driver 2 takes 3 hours but stops for an hour halfway. Which driver had a greater average speed? Explain.

18. **Applying Concepts** A family takes a car trip. They travel for an hour at 80 km/h and then for 2 hours at 40 km/h. Find their average speed during the trip.

Math Practice

19. **Converting Units** Convert 119 cm to meters.

20. **Converting Units** Convert 22.4 km to meters.

21. **Calculating Acceleration** During a slap shot, a hockey puck takes 0.5 second to reach the goal. It started from rest and reached a final speed of 35 m/s. What is the puck's average acceleration?

Applying Skills

Use the illustration of the motion of a ladybug to answer Questions 22–24.

Start   Finish

22. **Measuring** Measure the distance from the starting line to line B, and from line B to the finish line. Measure to the nearest tenth of a centimeter.

23. **Calculating** Starting at rest, the ladybug accelerated to line B and then moved at a constant speed until it reached the finish line. If the ladybug took 2.5 seconds to move from line B to the finish line, calculate its constant speed during that time.

24. **Interpreting Data** The speed you calculated in Question 21 is also the speed the ladybug had at the end of its acceleration at line B. If it took 2 seconds for the ladybug to accelerate from the start line to line B, what is its average acceleration during that time?

Lab zone Chapter **Project**

Perfomance Assessment Organize your display cards so that they are easy to follow. Remember to put a title on each card stating the speed that you measured. Place the cards in order from the slowest speed to the fastest. Then display them to your class. Compare your results with those of other students.

Test-Taking Tip

Converting Units

A test question may ask you to change one unit of measurement to another. You do this by using a conversion factor, a fraction that represents the relationship between the units. For example, to convert meters to centimeters, you need to remember that a meter equals 100 centimeters: 1 m = 100 cm. To figure out the answer, you would multiply by the conversion factor $\frac{100\ cm}{1\ m}$.

Sample Question

A garden measures 3.12 meters wide. How many centimeters wide is the garden?

A 0.312 cm
B 31.2 cm
C 312 cm
D 3,120 cm

Answer

The correct answer is **C**. When you multiply 3.12 m by 100 cm, you get 312 cm.

Choose the letter of the best answer.

1. Members of the Fairview Track Club are running a 1.5 km race. What is the distance of the race in meters?
   A 0.15 m
   B 15 m
   C 150 m
   D 1,500 m

2. Your father is driving to the beach. He drives at one speed for two hours. He drives at a different speed for another two hours and a third speed for the final hour. How would you find his average speed for all five hours?
   A Divide the total driving time by the total distance.
   B Multiply the total driving time by the total distance.
   C Divide the total distance by the total driving time.
   D Subtract the total driving time from the total distance.

3. Two objects traveling at the same speed have different velocities if they
   A start at different times.
   B travel different distances.
   C have different masses.
   D move in different directions.

4. The graph below shows the distance versus time for a runner moving at a constant 200 m/min. What could the runner do to make the slope of the line rise?

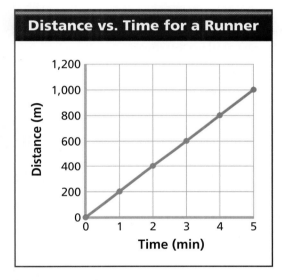

Distance vs. Time for a Runner

   A stop running
   B decrease speed
   C maintain the same speed
   D increase speed

5. An object used as a reference point to determine motion should be
   A accelerating.
   B stationary.
   C decelerating.
   D changing direction.

Constructed Response

6. Explain how speed, velocity, and acceleration are related.

Standard Course of Study

This chapter addresses the following North Carolina Objectives:

1.01 Identify and create questions and hypotheses.

1.02 Develop appropriate experimental procedures.

1.03 Identify and create questions and hypotheses.

1.04 Analyze variables.

1.05 Analyze evidence.

1.06 Use mathematics to gather, organize, and present data.

1.08 Use oral and written language.

1.09 Use technologies and information systems.

2.03 Evaluate technological designs.

6.03 Evaluate motion in terms of Newton's Laws.

6.05 Describe and measure quantities that characterize moving objects and their interactions.

6.06 Investigate and analyze real-world interactions of balanced and unbalanced forces.

A golfer exerts a force on the golf ball. ▶

Lab zone™ Chapter Project

Newton Scooters

Newton's laws of motion describe the relationship between forces and motion. In this Chapter Project, you will use Newton's third law to design a vehicle that moves without the use of gravity or a power source such as electricity. How can you make an object move without pushing or pulling it?

Your Goal To design and build a vehicle that moves without an outside force acting on it

Your vehicle must

● move forward by pushing back on something
● not be powered by any form of electricity or use gravity in order to move
● travel a minimum distance of 1.5 meters
● be built following the safety guidelines in Appendix A

Plan It! Preview the chapter to find out about Newton's laws of motion. Determine factors that will affect the acceleration of your vehicle. Brainstorm possible designs for your vehicle, but be careful not to lock yourself into a single idea. Remember that a car with wheels is only one type of vehicle.

Think of ways to use household materials to build your vehicle. Draw a diagram of your proposed design and identify the force that will propel your vehicle. Have your teacher approve your design. Then build your vehicle and see if it works!

The Nature of Force

Reading Preview

Key Concepts
• How is a force described?
• How are unbalanced and balanced forces related to an object's motion?

Key Terms
• force
• newton
• net force
• unbalanced forces
• balanced forces

Target Reading Skill
Asking Questions Before you read, preview the red headings. In a graphic organizer like the one below, ask a *what* or *how* question for each heading. As you read, write the answers to your questions.

What Is a Force?

Question	Answer
What is a force?	A force is . . .

Lab zone Discover Activity

Is the Force With You?
1. Attach a spring scale to each end of a skateboard.
2. Gently pull on one spring scale with a force of 4 N, while your partner pulls on the other with the same force. Observe the motion of the skateboard.
3. Now try to keep your partner's spring scale reading at 2 N while you pull with a force of 4 N. Observe the motion of the skateboard.

Think It Over
Observing Describe the motion of the skateboard when you and your partner pulled with the same force. How was the motion of the skateboard affected when you pulled with more force than your partner?

A hard kick sends a soccer ball shooting down the field toward the goal. Just in time, the goalie leaps forward, stops the ball, and quickly kicks it in the opposite direction. In a soccer game, the ball is rarely still. Its motion is constantly changing. Why? What causes an object to start moving, stop moving, or change direction? The answer is force.

What Is a Force?

In science, the word *force* has a simple and specific meaning. A **force** is a push or a pull. When one object pushes or pulls another object, you say that the first object exerts a force on the second object. You exert a force on a computer key when you push it and on a chair when you pull it away from a table.

Like velocity and acceleration, a force is described by its strength and by the direction in which it acts. If you push on a door, you exert a force in a different direction than if you pull on the door.

The strength of a force is measured in the SI unit called the **newton** (N). This unit is named after the English scientist and mathematician Isaac Newton. You exert about one newton of force when you lift a small lemon.

The direction and strength of a force can be represented by an arrow. The arrow points in the direction of a force. The length of the arrow tells you the strength of a force—the longer the arrow, the greater the force.

 Reading Checkpoint — **What SI unit is used to measure the strength of a force?**

Combining Forces

Often, more than a single force acts on an object at one time. The combination of all forces acting on an object is called the **net force.** The net force determines whether an object moves and also in which direction it moves.

When forces act in the same direction, the net force can be found by adding the strengths of the individual forces. In Figure 2, the lengths of the two arrows, which represent two forces, are added together to find the net force.

When forces act in opposite directions, they also combine to produce a net force. However, you must pay attention to the direction of each force. Adding a force acting in one direction to a force acting in the opposite direction is the same as adding a positive number to a negative number. So when two forces act in opposite directions, they combine by subtraction. The net force always acts in the direction of the greater force. If the opposing forces are of equal strength, there is no net force. There is no change in the object's motion.

FIGURE 2
Combining Forces
The strength and direction of the individual forces determine the net force. **Calculating** *How do you find the net force when two forces act in opposite directions?*

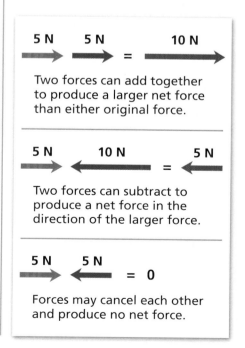

5 N   5 N   =   10 N

Two forces can add together to produce a larger net force than either original force.

5 N   10 N   =   5 N

Two forces can subtract to produce a net force in the direction of the larger force.

5 N   5 N   = 0

Forces may cancel each other and produce no net force.

Individual forces

Net force

Unbalanced Forces in the Same Direction
When two forces act in the same direction, the net force is the sum of the two individual forces. The box moves to the right.

Individual forces

Net force

Unbalanced Forces in the Opposite Direction
When two forces act in opposite directions, the net force is the difference between the two individual forces. The box moves to the right.

Unbalanced Forces Whenever there is a net force acting on an object, the forces are unbalanced. **Unbalanced forces** can cause an object to start moving, stop moving, or change direction. **Unbalanced forces acting on an object result in a net force and cause a change in the object's motion.**

Figure 3 shows two people exerting forces on a box. When they both push a box to the right, their individual forces add together to produce a net force in that direction. Since a net, or unbalanced, force acts on the box, the box moves to the right.

When the two people push the box in opposite directions, the net force on the box is the difference between their individual forces. Because the boy pushes with a greater force than the girl, their forces are unbalanced and a net force acts on the box to the right. As a result, the box moves to the right.

Reading Checkpoint What is the result of unbalanced forces acting on an object?

Balanced Forces When forces are exerted on an object, the object's motion does not always change. In an arm wrestling contest, each person exerts a force on the other's arm, but the two forces are exerted in opposite directions. Even though both people push hard, their arm positions may not change.

Equal forces acting on one object in opposite directions are called **balanced forces.** Each force is balanced by the other.

Go Online
SciLINKS NSTA

For: Links on force
Visit: www.SciLinks.org
Web Code: scn-1321

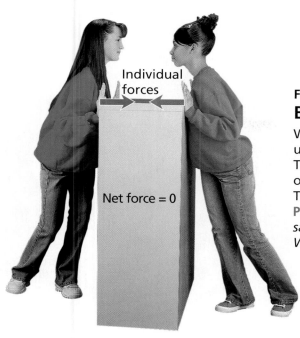

Individual forces

Net force = 0

FIGURE 3
Balanced and Unbalanced Forces

When the forces acting on an object are unbalanced, a net force acts on the object. The object will move. When balanced forces act on an object, no net force acts on the object. The object's motion remains unchanged. **Predicting** *If both girls pushed the box on the same side, would the motion of the box change? Why or why not?*

Balanced Forces in Opposite Directions
When two equal forces act in opposite directions, they cancel each other out. The box doesn't move.

Balanced forces acting on an object do not change the object's motion. When equal forces are exerted in opposite directions, the net force is zero. In Figure 3, when two people push on the box with equal force in opposite directions, the forces cancel out. The box does not move.

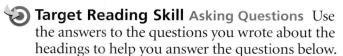

Section 1 Assessment

Target Reading Skill **Asking Questions** Use the answers to the questions you wrote about the headings to help you answer the questions below.

Reviewing Key Concepts

1. a. Defining What is a force?
   b. Explaining How is a force described?
   c. Interpreting Diagrams In a diagram, one force arrow is longer than the other arrow. What can you tell about the forces?
2. a. Reviewing How can you find the net force if two forces act in opposite directions?
   b. Comparing and Contrasting How do balanced forces acting on an object affect its motion? How do unbalanced forces acting on an object affect its motion?

   c. Calculating You exert a force of 120 N on a desk. Your friend exerts a force of 150 N in the same direction. What net force do you and your friend exert on the desk?

Lab zone **At-Home Activity**

House of Cards Carefully set two playing cards upright on a flat surface so that their top edges lean on each other. The cards should be able to stand by themselves. In terms of balanced forces, explain to a family member why the cards don't move. Then exert a force on one of the cards. Explain to a family member the role of unbalanced forces in what happens.

Sticky Sneakers

Problem

Friction is a force that acts in the opposite direction to motion. How does the amount of friction between a sneaker and a surface compare for different brands of sneakers?

Skills Focus

controlling variables, interpreting data

Materials

• three or more different brands of sneakers
• 2 spring scales, 5-N and 20-N, or force sensors
• mass set(s)
• tape
• 3 large paper clips
• balance

Procedure

1. Sneakers are designed to deal with various friction forces, including these:
   • starting friction, which is involved when you start from a stopped position
   • forward-stopping friction, which is involved when you come to a forward stop
   • sideways-stopping friction, which is involved when you come to a sideways stop
2. Prepare a data table in which you can record each type of friction for each sneaker.

3. Place each sneaker on a balance. Then put masses in each sneaker so that the total mass of the sneaker plus the masses is 1,000 g. Spread the masses out evenly inside the sneaker.

4. You will need to tape a paper clip to each sneaker and then attach a spring scale to the paper clip. (If you are using force sensors, see your teacher for instructions.) To measure
   • starting friction, attach the paper clip to the back of the sneaker
   • forward-stopping friction, attach the paper clip to the front of the sneaker
   • sideways-stopping friction, attach the paper clip to the side of the sneaker

Data Table			
Sneaker	Starting Friction (N)	Sideways-Stopping Friction (N)	Forward-Stopping Friction (N)
A			
B			

5. To measure starting friction, pull the sneaker backward until it starts to move. Use the 20-N spring scale first. If the reading is less than 5 N, use a 5-N scale. The force necessary to make the sneaker start moving is equal to the friction force. Record the starting friction force in your data table.

6. To measure either type of stopping friction, use the spring scale to pull each sneaker at a slow, constant speed. Record the stopping friction force in your data table.

7. Repeat Steps 4–6 for the remaining sneakers.

Analyze and Conclude

1. **Controlling Variables** What are the manipulated and responding variables in this experiment? Explain. (See the Skills Handbook to read about experimental variables.)

2. **Observing** Why is the reading on the spring scale equal to the friction force in each case?

3. **Interpreting Data** Which sneaker had the most starting friction? Which had the most forward-stopping friction? Which had the most sideways-stopping friction?

4. **Drawing Conclusions** Do you think that using a sneaker with a small amount of mass in it is a fair test of the friction of the sneakers? Why or why not? (*Hint*: Consider that sneakers are used with people's feet inside them.)

5. **Inferring** Why did you pull the sneaker at a slow speed to test for stopping friction? Why did you pull a sneaker that wasn't moving to test starting friction?

6. **Developing Hypotheses** Can you identify a relationship between the brand of sneaker and the amount of friction you observed? If so, describe the relationship. What do you observe that might cause one sneaker to grip the floor better than another?

7. **Communicating** Draw a diagram for an advertising brochure that shows the forces acting on the sneaker for each type of motion.

Design an Experiment

Wear a pair of your own sneakers. Start running and notice how you press against the floor with your sneaker. How do you think this affects the friction between the sneaker and the floor? Design an experiment that will test for this variable. *Obtain your teacher's permission before carrying out your investigation.*

Friction and Gravity

Reading Preview

Key Concepts
- What factors determine the strength of the friction force between two surfaces?
- What factors affect the gravitational force between two objects?
- Why do objects accelerate during free fall?

Key Terms
- friction • static friction
- sliding friction
- rolling friction • fluid friction
- gravity • mass • weight
- free fall • air resistance
- terminal velocity • projectile

Target Reading Skill
Comparing and Contrasting As you read, compare and contrast friction and gravity by completing a table like the one below.

	Friction	Gravity
Effect on motion	Opposes motion	
Depends on		
Measured in		

Lab zone Discover **Activity**

Which Lands First?
1. Stack three quarters. Place tape between the quarters to hold them tightly together. Place the stack of quarters next to a single quarter near the edge of a desk.
2. Put a ruler flat on the desk behind the coins. Line it up parallel to the edge of the desk and just touching the coins.
3. Keeping the ruler parallel to the edge of the desk, push the coins over the edge at the same time. Observe how long the coins take to land.

Think It Over
Predicting Did you see a difference in the time the coins took to fall? Use what you observed to predict whether a soccer ball will fall more quickly than a marble. Will a pencil fall more quickly than a book? How can you test your predictions?

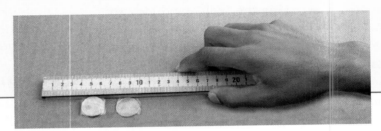

What happens when you jump on a sled on the side of a snow-covered hill? Without actually doing this, you can predict that the sled will slide down the hill. Now think about what happens at the bottom of the hill. Does the sled keep sliding? Again, without actually riding the sled, you can predict that the sled will slow down and stop.

Why does the sled's motion change on the side of the hill and then again at the bottom? In each case, unbalanced forces act on the sled. The force of gravity causes the sled to accelerate down the hill. The force of friction eventually causes the sled to stop. These two forces affect many motions on Earth.

◀ Friction and gravity both act on the sled.

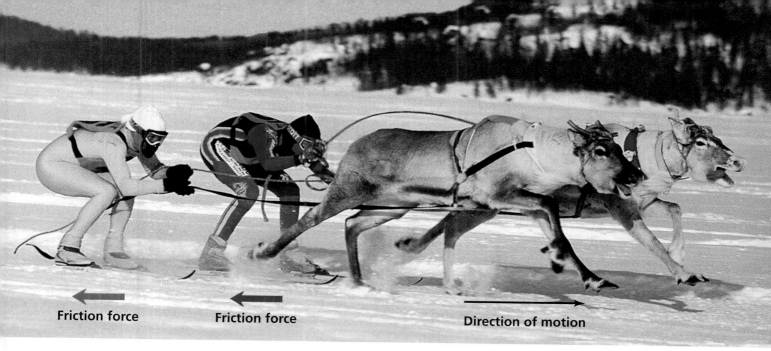

Friction force   Friction force   Direction of motion

FIGURE 4
Friction and Smooth Surfaces The smooth surfaces of
the skis make for a fast ride for these Finnish skiers.
Relating Diagrams and Photos *How does the direction
of friction compare to the direction of motion?*

Friction

When a sled moves across snow, the bottom of the sled rubs
against the surface of the snow. In the same way, the skin of a
firefighter's hands rubs against the polished metal pole during
the slide down the pole. The force that two surfaces exert on
each other when they rub against each other is called **friction.**

The Causes of Friction In general, smooth surfaces produce less friction than rough surfaces. **The strength of the
force of friction depends on two factors: how hard the
surfaces push together and the types of surfaces involved.**
The skiers in Figure 4 get a fast ride because there is very little
friction between their skis and the snow. The reindeer would
not be able to pull them easily over a rough surface such as
sand. Friction also increases if surfaces push hard against each
other. If you rub your hands together forcefully, there is more
friction than if you rub your hands together lightly.

    A snow-packed surface or a metal firehouse pole may seem
quite smooth. But, as you can see in Figure 5, even the smooth-
est objects have irregular, bumpy surfaces. When the irregulari-
ties of one surface come into contact with those of another
surface, friction occurs. Friction acts in a direction opposite to
the direction of the object's motion. Without friction, a moving
object might not stop until it strikes another object.

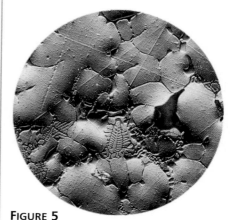

FIGURE 5
A Smooth Surface?
If you look at the polished surface
of an aluminum alloy under a
powerful microscope, you'll find
that it is actually quite rough.

Go Online

SCI_{LINKS} NSTA

For: Links on friction
Visit: www.SciLinks.org
Web Code: scn-1322

Static Friction Four types of friction are shown in Figure 6. The friction that acts on objects that are not moving is called **static friction.** Because of static friction, you must use extra force to start the motion of stationary objects. For example, think about what happens when you try to push a heavy desk across a floor. If you push on the desk with a force less than the force of static friction between the desk and the floor, the desk will not move. To make the desk move, you must exert a force greater than the force of static friction. Once the desk is moving, there is no longer any static friction. However, there is another type of friction—sliding friction.

Sliding Friction **Sliding friction** occurs when two solid surfaces slide over each other. Sliding friction can be useful. For example, you can spread sand on an icy path to improve your footing. Ballet dancers apply a sticky powder to the soles of their ballet slippers so they won't slip on the dance floor. And when you stop a bicycle with hand brakes, rubber pads slide against the tire surfaces, causing the wheels to slow and eventually stop. On the other hand, sliding friction is a problem if you fall off your bike and skin your knee!

Rolling Friction When an object rolls across a surface, **rolling friction** occurs. Rolling friction is easier to overcome than sliding friction for similar materials. This type of friction is important to engineers who design certain products. For example, skates, skateboards, and bicycles need wheels that move freely. So engineers use ball bearings to reduce the friction between the wheels and the rest of the product. These ball bearings are small, smooth steel balls that reduce friction by rolling between moving parts.

Fluid Friction Fluids, such as water, oil, or air, are materials that flow easily. **Fluid friction** occurs when a solid object moves through a fluid. Like rolling friction, fluid friction is easier to overcome than sliding friction. This is why the parts of machines that must slide over each other are often bathed in oil. In this way, the solid parts move through the fluid instead of sliding against each other. When you ride a bike, fluid friction occurs between you and the air. Cyclists often wear streamlined helmets and specially designed clothing to reduce fluid friction.

 **What are two ways in which friction can be useful?**

FIGURE 6

Types of Friction

Types of friction include static, sliding, rolling, and fluid friction. **Making Generalizations** *In what direction does friction act compared to an object's motion?*

Static Friction ▼
To make the sled move, the athlete first has to overcome the force of static friction. Static friction acts in the opposite direction to the intended motion.

Direction of motion → ← Sliding friction

Sliding Friction ▲
Once the sled is moving, it slides over the floor. Sliding friction acts between the sled and the floor in the opposite direction to the sled's motion.

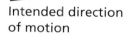

Intended direction → ← Static friction
of motion

Rolling Friction ▼
Rolling friction occurs when an object rolls over a surface. For the skateboarder, rolling friction acts in the direction opposite to the skateboard's motion.

Fluid friction ← Direction → of motion

Fluid Friction ▲
When an object pushes fluid aside, friction occurs. The surfer must overcome the fluid friction of the water.

Direction of motion → ← Rolling friction

Gravity

Would you be surprised if you let go of a pen you were holding and it did not fall? You are so used to objects falling that you may not have thought about why they fall. One person who thought about it was Isaac Newton. He concluded that a force acts to pull objects straight down toward the center of Earth. **Gravity** is a force that pulls objects toward each other.

Universal Gravitation Newton realized that gravity acts everywhere in the universe, not just on Earth. It is the force that makes an apple fall to the ground. It is the force that keeps the moon orbiting around Earth. It is the force that keeps all the planets in our solar system orbiting around the sun.

What Newton realized is now called the law of universal gravitation. The law of universal gravitation states that the force of gravity acts between all objects in the universe. This means that any two objects in the universe, without exception, attract each other. You are attracted not only to Earth but also to all the other objects around you. Earth and the objects around you are attracted to you as well. However, you do not notice the attraction among objects because these forces are small compared to the force of Earth's attraction.

Factors Affecting Gravity Two factors affect the gravitational attraction between objects: mass and distance. **Mass** is a measure of the amount of matter in an object. The SI unit of mass is the kilogram. One kilogram is the mass of about 400 modern pennies. Everything that has mass is made up of matter.

FIGURE 7
Gravity and Acceleration
Divers begin accelerating as soon as they leap from the platform.

FIGURE 8
Gravitational Attraction
Gravity increases with mass and decreases with distance. *Inferring What happens to the force of gravity between two objects if the distance between them decreases?*

The force of gravity acts between all objects.

If mass increases, the force of gravity increases.

If distance increases, the force of gravity decreases.

The more mass an object has, the greater its gravitational force. Because the sun's mass is so great, it exerts a large gravitational force on the planets. That's one reason why the planets orbit the sun.

In addition to mass, gravitational force depends on the distance between the objects. The farther apart two objects are, the lesser the gravitational force between them. For a spacecraft traveling toward Mars, Earth's gravitational pull decreases as the spacecraft's distance from Earth increases. Eventually the gravitational pull of Mars becomes greater than Earth's, and the spacecraft is more attracted toward Mars.

Weight and Mass Mass is sometimes confused with weight. Mass is a measure of the amount of matter in an object; weight is a measure of the gravitational force exerted on an object. The force of gravity on a person or object at the surface of a planet is known as **weight.** So, when you step on a bathroom scale, you are determining the gravitational force Earth is exerting on you.

Weight varies with the strength of the gravitational force but mass does not. Suppose you weighed yourself on Earth to be 450 newtons. Then you traveled to the moon and weighed yourself again. You might be surprised to find out that you weigh only about 75 newtons—the weight of about 8 kilograms on Earth! You weigh less on the moon because the moon's mass is only a fraction of Earth's.

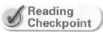 Reading Checkpoint **What is the difference between weight and mass?**

Lab zone Skills Activity

Calculating

You can determine the weight of an object if you measure its mass.

1. Estimate the weight of four objects. (*Hint:* A small lemon weighs about 1 N.)

2. Use a balance to find the mass of each object. If the measurements are not in kilograms, convert them to kilograms.

3. Multiply each mass by 9.8 m/s² to find the weight in newtons.

How close to actual values were your estimates?

FIGURE 9

Mass and Weight This astronaut jumps easily on the moon. **Comparing and Contrasting** *How do his mass and weight on the moon compare to his mass and weight on Earth?*

Astronaut in Spacesuit	
Weight on Moon =	270 N
Weight on Earth =	1,617 N
Mass on Moon =	165 kg
Mass on Earth =	165 kg

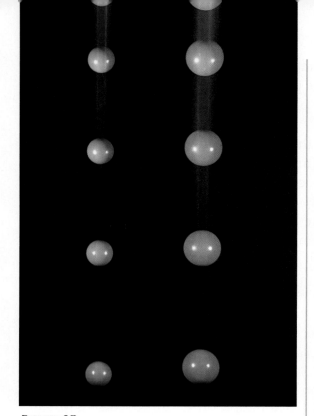

FIGURE 10
Free Fall
In the absence of air, two objects with different masses fall at exactly the same rate.

Gravity and Motion

On Earth, gravity is a downward force that affects all objects. When you hold a book, you exert a force that balances the force of gravity. When you let go of the book, gravity becomes an unbalanced force and the book falls.

Free Fall When the only force acting on an object is gravity, the object is said to be in **free fall.** An object in free fall is accelerating. Do you know why? **In free fall, the force of gravity is an unbalanced force, which causes an object to accelerate.**

How much do objects accelerate as they fall? Near the surface of Earth, the acceleration due to gravity is 9.8 m/s^2. This means that for every second an object is falling, its velocity increases by 9.8 m/s. For example, suppose an object is dropped from the top of a building. Its starting velocity is 0 m/s. After one second, its velocity has increased to 9.8 m/s. After two seconds, its velocity is 19.6 m/s (9.8 m/s + 9.8 m/s). The velocity continues to increase as the object falls.

While it may seem hard to believe at first, all objects in free fall accelerate at the same rate regardless of their masses. The two falling objects in Figure 10 demonstrate this principle.

Math Analyzing Data

Free Fall

Use the graph to answer the following questions.

1. **Interpreting Graphs** What variable is on the horizontal axis? The vertical axis?

2. **Calculating** Calculate the slope of the graph. What does the slope tell you about the object's motion?

3. **Predicting** What will be the speed of the object at 6 seconds?

4. **Drawing Conclusions** Suppose another object of the same size but with a greater mass was dropped instead. How would the speed values change?

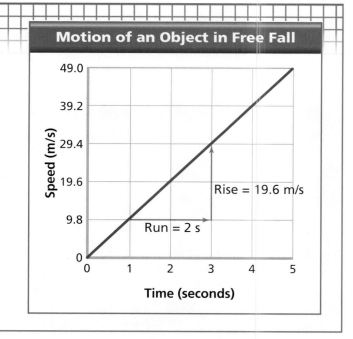

Motion of an Object in Free Fall

Rise = 19.6 m/s
Run = 2 s

Speed (m/s) vertical axis: 0, 9.8, 19.6, 29.4, 39.2, 49.0
Time (seconds) horizontal axis: 0, 1, 2, 3, 4, 5

Air Resistance Despite the fact that all objects are supposed
to fall at the same rate, you know that this is not always the case.
For example, an oak leaf flutters slowly to the ground, while an
acorn drops straight down. Objects falling through air experience a type of fluid friction called **air resistance.** Remember that
friction is in the direction opposite to motion, so air resistance is
an upward force exerted on falling objects. Air resistance is not
the same for all objects. Falling objects with a greater surface
area experience more air resistance. That is why a leaf falls more
slowly than an acorn. In a vacuum, where there is no air, all
objects fall with exactly the same rate of acceleration.

You can see the effect of air resistance if you drop a flat
piece of paper and a crumpled piece of paper at the same time.
Since the flat paper has a greater surface area, it experiences
greater air resistance and falls more slowly. In a vacuum, both
pieces of paper would fall at the same rate.

Air resistance increases with velocity. As a falling object
speeds up, the force of air resistance becomes greater and greater.
Eventually, a falling object will fall fast enough that the upward
force of air resistance becomes equal to the downward force of
gravity acting on the object. At this point the forces on the object
are balanced. Remember that when forces are balanced, there is
no acceleration. The object continues to fall, but its velocity
remains constant. The greatest velocity a falling object reaches is
called its **terminal velocity.** Terminal velocity is reached when
the force of air resistance equals the weight of the object.

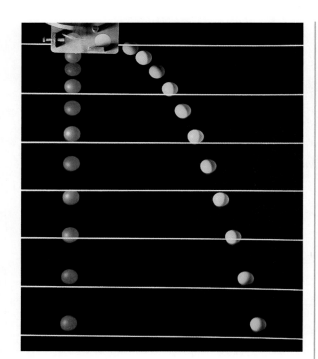

FIGURE 12
Projectile Motion
One ball is dropped vertically and a second ball is thrown horizontally at the same time.
Making Generalizations Does the horizontal velocity of the ball affect how fast it falls?

Projectile Motion Rather than dropping a ball straight down, what happens if you throw it horizontally? An object that is thrown is called a **projectile** (pruh JEK tul). Will a projectile that is thrown horizontally land on the ground at the same time as an object that is dropped?

Look at Figure 12. The yellow ball was given a horizontal push at the same time as the red ball was dropped. Even though the yellow ball moves horizontally, the force of gravity continues to act on it in the same way it acts on the red ball. The yellow ball falls at the same rate as the red ball. Thus, both balls will hit the ground at exactly the same time.

In a similar way, an arrow flying toward a target is a projectile. Because of the force of gravity, the arrow will fall as it flies toward the target. So if you try to hit the bull's-eye, you must aim above it to account for gravity's pull. When you throw a projectile at an upward angle, the force of gravity reduces its vertical velocity. Eventually, the upward motion of the projectile will stop, and gravity will pull it back toward the ground. From this point, the projectile will fall at the same rate as any dropped object.

 Reading Checkpoint **How does gravity affect objects that are moving horizontally?**

Section 2 Assessment

Target Reading Skill

Comparing and Contrasting Use the information in your table about friction and gravity to help you answer the questions below.

Reviewing Key Concepts

1. **a. Listing** What are the four types of friction?
   b. Summarizing What factors affect the friction force between two surfaces?
   c. Classifying What types of friction occur when you ride a bike through a puddle?
2. **a. Identifying** What is the law of universal gravitation?
   b. Explaining How do mass and distance affect the gravitational attraction between objects?
   c. Predicting How would your weight change on the surface of an Earth-sized planet whose mass was greater than Earth's? Why?

3. **a. Reviewing** Why does an object accelerate when it falls toward Earth's surface?
   b. Describing How does the mass of an object affect its acceleration during free fall?
   c. Applying Concepts What force changes when a sky diver's parachute opens? What force stays the same?

Writing in Science

Cause-and-Effect Paragraph Suppose Earth's gravitational force were decreased by half. How would this change affect a game of basketball? Write a paragraph explaining how the motion of the players and the ball would be different.

Newton's First and Second Laws

Reading Preview

Key Concepts
- What is Newton's first law of motion?
- What is Newton's second law of motion?

Key Term
- inertia

 Target Reading Skill

Outlining As you read, make an outline about Newton's first and second laws. Use the red headings for the main topics and the blue headings for the subtopics.

Newton's First and Second Laws
I. The first law of motion
A. Inertia
B.
II. The second law of motion
A.

Isaac Newton ▼

Lab zone **Discover Activity**

What Changes Motion?
1. Stack several metal washers on top of a toy car.
2. Place a heavy book on the floor near the car.
3. Predict what will happen to both the car and the washers if you roll the car into the book. Test your prediction.

Think It Over

Observing What happened to the car when it hit the book? What happened to the washers? What might be the reason for any difference between the motions of the car and the washers?

How and why objects move as they do has fascinated scientists for thousands of years. In the early 1600s, the Italian astronomer Galileo Galilei suggested that, once an object is in motion, no force is needed to keep it moving. Force is needed only to change the motion of an object. Galileo's ideas paved the way for Isaac Newton. Newton proposed the three basic laws of motion in the late 1600s.

The First Law of Motion

Newton's first law restates Galileo's ideas about force and motion. **Newton's first law of motion states that an object at rest will remain at rest, and an object moving at a constant velocity will continue moving at a constant velocity, unless it is acted upon by an unbalanced force.**

If an object is not moving, it will not move until a force acts on it. Clothes on the floor of your room, for example, will stay there unless you pick them up. If an object is already moving, it will continue to move at a constant velocity until a force acts to change either its speed or direction. For example, a tennis ball flies through the air once you hit it with a racket. If your friend doesn't hit the ball back, the forces of gravity and friction will eventually stop the ball. On Earth, gravity and friction are unbalanced forces that often change an object's motion.

FIGURE 13
Inertia The inertia of the objects on the table keeps them from moving. *Inferring Why should the girl use a slippery tablecloth?*

Inertia Whether an object is moving or not, it resists any change to its motion. Galileo's concept of the resistance to a change in motion is called inertia. **Inertia** (in UR shuh) is the tendency of an object to resist a change in motion. Newton's first law of motion is also called the law of inertia.

Inertia explains many common events, such as why you move forward in your seat when a car stops suddenly. When the car stops, inertia keeps you moving forward. A force, such as the pull of a seat belt, is required to change your motion.

Inertia Depends on Mass Some objects have more inertia than other objects. For example, suppose you needed to move an empty aquarium and an aquarium full of water. Obviously, the full aquarium is harder to move than the empty one, because it has more mass. The greater the mass of an object is, the greater its inertia, and the greater the force required to change its motion. The full aquarium is more difficult to move because it has more inertia than the empty aquarium.

✓ **Reading Checkpoint** How is mass related to inertia?

The Second Law of Motion

Suppose you are baby-sitting two children who love wagon rides. Their favorite part is when you accelerate quickly. When you get tired and sit in the wagon, one of the children pulls you. He soon finds he cannot accelerate the wagon nearly as fast as you can. How is the wagon's acceleration related to the force pulling it? How is the acceleration related to the wagon's mass?

Determining Acceleration According to Newton's second law of motion, acceleration depends on the object's mass and on the net force acting on the object. This relationship can be written as an equation.

$$\text{Acceleration} = \frac{\text{Net force}}{\text{Mass}}$$

Acceleration is measured in meters per second per second (m/s^2), and mass is measured in kilograms (kg). According to Newton's second law, then, force is measured in kilograms times meters per second per second $(kg \cdot m/s^2)$. The short form for this unit of force is the newton (N). Recall that a newton is the SI unit of force. You can think of 1 newton as the force required to give a 1-kg mass an acceleration of 1 m/s^2.

Go Online
PHSchool.com

For: More on Newton's laws
Visit: PHSchool.com
Web Code: cgd-3023

Math Sample Problem

Calculating Force

A speedboat pulls a 55-kg water-skier. The force causes the skier to accelerate at 2.0 m/s^2. Calculate the net force that causes this acceleration.

1 Read and Understand
What information are you given?

Mass of the water-skier (m) = 55 kg

Acceleration of the water-skier (a) = 2.0 m/s^2

2 Plan and Solve
What quantity are you trying to calculate?

The net force (F_{net}) = ■

What formula contains the given quantities and the unknown quantity?

$$a = \frac{F_{net}}{m} \quad \text{or} \quad F_{net} = m \times a$$

Perform the calculation.

$F_{net} = m \times a = 55 \text{ kg} \times 2.0 \text{ m/s}^2$

$F = 110 \text{ kg} \cdot \text{m/s}^2$

$F = 110 \text{ N}$

3 Look Back and Check
Does your answer make sense?

A net force of 110 N is required to accelerate the water-skier. This may not seem like enough force, but it does not include the force of the speedboat's pull that overcomes friction.

Math Practice

1. **Calculating Force** What is the net force on a 1,000-kg object accelerating at 3 m/s^2?

2. **Calculating Force** What net force is needed to accelerate a 25-kg cart at 14 m/s^2?

FIGURE 14
Force and Mass
The force of the boy's pull and the mass of the wagon determine the wagon's acceleration.

Changes in Force and Mass How can you increase the acceleration of the wagon? Look again at the equation. One way to increase acceleration is by changing the force. If the mass is constant, acceleration and force change in the same way. So to increase the acceleration of the wagon, you can increase the force used to pull it.

Another way to increase acceleration is to change the mass. According to the equation, acceleration and mass change in opposite ways. If the force is constant, an increase in mass causes a decrease in acceleration. The opposite is also true: A decrease in mass causes an increase in acceleration with a constant force. To increase the acceleration of the wagon, you can decrease its mass. So, instead of you, the children should ride in the wagon.

✓ **Reading Checkpoint** **What are two ways to increase the acceleration of an object?**

Section 3 Assessment

🔄 **Target Reading Skill** Outlining Use the information in your outline about Newton's first and second laws of motion to help you answer the questions below.

Reviewing Key Concepts

1. **a. Reviewing** What does Newton's first law of motion state?
   b. Explaining Why is Newton's first law of motion sometimes called the law of inertia?
   c. Inferring Use what you know about inertia to explain why you feel pressed back into the seat of a car when it accelerates.
2. **a. Defining** State Newton's second law of motion in your own words.
   b. Problem Solving How could you keep an object's acceleration the same if the force acting on the object were doubled?

c. Applying Concepts Using what you know about Newton's second law, explain why a car with a large mass might use more fuel than a car with a smaller mass. Assume both cars drive the same distance.

Math Practice

3. **Calculating Force** Find the force it would take to accelerate an 800-kg car at a rate of 5 m/s^2.

4. **Calculating Force** What is the net force acting on a 0.15-kg hockey puck accelerating at a rate of 12 m/s^2?

Newton's Third Law

Reading Preview

Key Concepts
- What is Newton's third law of motion?
- How can you determine the momentum of an object?
- What is the law of conservation of momentum?

Key Terms
- momentum
- law of conservation of momentum

Target Reading Skill
Previewing Visuals Before you read, preview Figure 18. Then write two questions that you have about the diagram in a graphic organizer like the one below. As you read, answer your questions.

Conservation of Momentum

Q. What happens when two moving objects collide?
A.
Q.

Lab zone Discover **Activity**

How Pushy Is a Straw?
1. Stretch a rubber band around the middle of the cover of a medium-size hardcover book.
2. Place four marbles in a small square on a table. Place the book on the marbles so that the cover with the rubber band is on top.
3. Hold the book steady by placing one index finger on the binding. Then, as shown, push a straw against the rubber band with your other index finger.
4. Push the straw until the rubber band stretches about 10 cm. Then let go of both the book and the straw at the same time.

Think It Over
Developing Hypotheses What did you observe about the motion of the book and the straw? Write a hypothesis to explain what happened in terms of the forces on the book and the straw.

Have you ever tried to teach a friend how to roller-skate? It's hard if you are both wearing skates. When your friend pushes against you to get started, you move too. And when your friend runs into you to stop, you both end up moving! To understand these movements you need to know Newton's third law of motion and the law of conservation of momentum.

Newton's Third Law of Motion

Newton proposed that whenever one object exerts a force on a second object, the second object exerts a force back on the first object. The force exerted by the second object is equal in strength and opposite in direction to the first force. Think of one force as the "action" and the other force as the "reaction." **Newton's third law of motion states that if one object exerts a force on another object, then the second object exerts a force of equal strength in the opposite direction on the first object.** Another way to state Newton's third law is that for every action there is an equal but opposite reaction.

Action force

Reaction force

When the gymnast does a flip, he pushes down on the vaulting horse. The reaction force of the vaulting horse pushes him up to complete the flip.

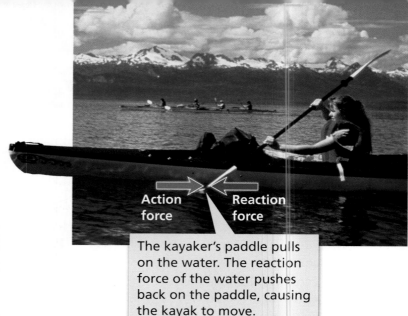

Action force   Reaction force

The kayaker's paddle pulls on the water. The reaction force of the water pushes back on the paddle, causing the kayak to move.

Action force

Reaction force

When the dog leaps, it pushes down on the ground. The reaction force of the ground pushes the dog into the air.

FIGURE 15
Action-Reaction Pairs
Action-reaction pairs explain how a gymnast can flip over a vaulting horse, how a kayaker can move through the water, and how a dog can leap off the ground. Observing *Name some other action-reaction pairs that you have observed.*

Action-Reaction Pairs You're probably familiar with many examples of Newton's third law. Pairs of action and reaction forces are all around you. When you jump, you push on the ground with your feet. This is an action force. The ground pushes back on your feet with an equal and opposite force. This is the reaction force. You move upward when you jump because the ground is pushing you! In a similar way, a kayaker moves forward by exerting an action force on the water with a paddle. The water pushes back on the paddle with an equal reaction force that propels the kayak forward.

Now you can understand what happens when you teach your friend to roller-skate. Your friend exerts an action force when he pushes against you to start. You exert a reaction force in the opposite direction. As a result, both of you move in opposite directions.

Detecting Motion Can you always detect motion when paired forces are in action? The answer is no. For example, when Earth's gravity pulls on an object, you cannot detect Earth's equal and opposite reaction. Suppose you drop your pencil. Gravity pulls the pencil downward. At the same time, the pencil pulls Earth upward with an equal and opposite reaction force. You don't see Earth accelerate toward the pencil because Earth's inertia is so great that its acceleration is too small to notice.

Do Action-Reaction Forces Cancel? Earlier you learned that if two equal forces act in opposite directions on an object, the forces are balanced. Because the two forces add up to zero, they cancel each other out and produce no change in motion. Why then don't the action and reaction forces in Newton's third law of motion cancel out as well? After all, they are equal and opposite.

The action and reaction forces do not cancel out because they are acting on different objects. Look at the volleyball player on the left in Figure 16. She exerts an upward action force on the ball. In return, the ball exerts an equal but opposite downward reaction force back on her wrists. The action and reaction forces act on different objects.

On the other hand, the volleyball players on the right are both exerting a force on the *same* object—the volleyball. When they hit the ball from opposite directions, each of their hands exerts a force on the ball equal in strength but opposite in direction. The forces on the volleyball are balanced and the ball does not move either to the left or to the right.

 **Reading Checkpoint** Why don't action and reaction forces cancel each other?

DISCOVERY CHANNEL SCHOOL
Forces
Video Preview
▶ Video Field Trip
Video Assessment

Force on wrists

Force on ball

FIGURE 16
Action-Reaction Forces
In the photo on the left, the player's wrists exert the action force. In the photo below, the ball exerts reaction forces on both players.
Interpreting Diagrams *In the photo below, which forces cancel each other out? What force is not cancelled? What will happen to the ball?*

Forces on hands

Force on ball   Force on ball

Momentum

All moving objects have what Newton called a "quantity of motion." What is this quantity of motion? Today we call it momentum. **Momentum** (moh MEN tum) is a characteristic of a moving object that is related to the mass and the velocity of the object. **The momentum of a moving object can be determined by multiplying the object's mass and velocity.**

$$\text{Momentum } = \text{ Mass} \times \text{Velocity}$$

Since mass is measured in kilograms and velocity is measured in meters per second, the unit for momentum is kilogram-meters per second (kg·m/s). Like velocity, acceleration, and force, momentum is described by its direction as well as its quantity. The momentum of an object is in the same direction as its velocity.

Math ▸ Sample Problem

Calculating Momentum

Which has more momentum: a 3.0-kg sledgehammer swung at 1.5 m/s, or a 4.0-kg sledgehammer swung at 0.9 m/s?

1 Read and Understand
What information are you given?
- Mass of smaller sledgehammer = **3.0 kg**
- Velocity of smaller sledgehammer = **1.5 m/s**
- Mass of larger sledgehammer = **4.0 kg**
- Velocity of larger sledgehammer = **0.9 m/s**

2 Plan and Solve
What quantities are you trying to calculate?
The momentum of each sledgehammer = ▪

What formula contains the given quantities and the unknown quantity?
Momentum = Mass × Velocity

Perform the calculations.
Smaller sledgehammer: **3.0 kg × 1.5 m/s = 4.5 kg·m/s**
Larger sledgehammer: **4.0 kg × 0.9 m/s = 3.6 kg·m/s**

3 Look Back and Check
Does your answer make sense?
The 3.0-kg hammer has more momentum than the 4.0-kg one. This answer makes sense because it is swung at a greater velocity.

Math ▸ Practice

1. **Calculating Momentum**
   A golf ball travels at 16 m/s, while a baseball moves at 7 m/s. The mass of the golf ball is 0.045 kg and the mass of the baseball is 0.14 kg. Which has greater momentum?

2. **Calculating Momentum**
   What is the momentum of a bird with a mass of 0.018 kg flying at 15 m/s?

FIGURE 17
Momentum
An object's momentum depends on velocity and mass.
Problem Solving *If both dogs have the same velocity, which one has the greater momentum?*

The more momentum a moving object has, the harder it is to stop. The mass of an object affects the amount of momentum the object has. For example, you can catch a baseball moving at 20 m/s, but you cannot stop a car moving at the same speed. The car has more momentum because it has a greater mass. The velocity of an object also affects the amount of momentum an object has. For example, an arrow shot from a bow has a large momentum because, although it has a small mass, it travels at a high velocity.

 **Reading Checkpoint** **What must you know to determine an object's momentum?**

Conservation of Momentum

The word *conservation* has a special meaning in physical science. In everyday language, conservation means saving resources. You might conserve water or fossil fuels, for example. In physical science, conservation refers to the conditions before and after some event. An amount that is conserved is the same amount after an event as it was before.

The amount of momentum objects have is conserved when they collide. Momentum may be transferred from one object to another, but none is lost. This fact is called the law of conservation of momentum.

The **law of conservation of momentum** states that, in the absence of outside forces, the total momentum of objects that interact does not change. The amount of momentum is the same before and after they interact. **The total momentum of any group of objects remains the same, or is conserved, unless outside forces act on the objects.** Friction is an example of an outside force.

Lab zone Try This Activity

Colliding Cars
Momentum is always conserved—even by toys!

1. Find two nearly identical toy cars that roll easily.
2. Make two loops out of masking tape (sticky side out). Put one loop on the front of one of the cars and the other loop on the back of the other car.
3. Place on the floor the car that has tape on the back. Then gently roll the other car into the back of the stationary car. Was momentum conserved? How do you know?

Predicting What will happen if you put masking tape on the fronts of both cars and roll them at each other with equal speeds? Will momentum be conserved in this case? Test your prediction.

FIGURE 18
Conservation of Momentum
In the absence of friction, momentum is conserved when two train cars collide. **Interpreting Diagrams** *In which diagram is all of the momentum transferred from the blue car to the green car?*

Ⓐ Two Moving Objects

Before

4 m/s ⟶   2 m/s ⟶

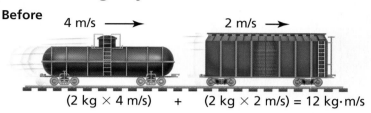

(2 kg × 4 m/s)   +   (2 kg × 2 m/s) = 12 kg·m/s

Before the collision, the blue car moves faster than the green car. Afterward, the green car moves faster. The total momentum stays the same.

After

2 m/s ⟶   4 m/s ⟶

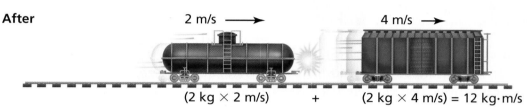

(2 kg × 2 m/s)   +   (2 kg × 4 m/s) = 12 kg·m/s

Ⓑ One Moving Object

When the green car is at rest before the collision, all of the blue car's momentum is transferred to it. Momentum is conserved.

Before

4 m/s ⟶   0 m/s

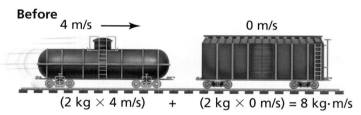

(2 kg × 4 m/s)   +   (2 kg × 0 m/s) = 8 kg·m/s

After

0 m/s   4 m/s ⟶

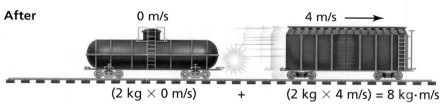

(2 kg × 0 m/s)   +   (2 kg × 4 m/s) = 8 kg·m/s

Ⓒ Two Connected Objects

Before

4 m/s ⟶   0 m/s

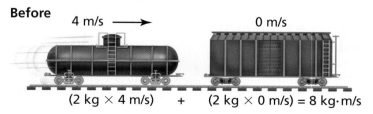

(2 kg × 4 m/s)   +   (2 kg × 0 m/s) = 8 kg·m/s

If the two cars couple together, momentum is still conserved. Together, the cars move slower than the blue car did before the collision.

After

2 m/s ⟶   2 m/s ⟶

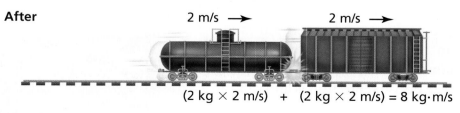

(2 kg × 2 m/s)   +   (2 kg × 2 m/s) = 8 kg·m/s

Collisions With Two Moving Objects In Figure 18A, a train car travels at 4 m/s down the same track as another train car traveling at only 2 m/s. The two train cars have equal masses. The blue car catches up with the green car and bumps into it. During the collision, the speed of each car changes. The blue car slows down to 2 m/s, and the green car speeds up to 4 m/s. Momentum is conserved—the momentum of one train car decreases while the momentum of the other increases.

Collisions With One Moving Object In Figure 18B, the blue car travels at 4 m/s but the green car is not moving. Eventually the blue car hits the green car. After the collision, the blue car is no longer moving, but the green car travels at 4 m/s. Even though the situation has changed, momentum is conserved. All of the momentum has been transferred from the blue car to the green car.

Collisions With Connected Objects Suppose that, instead of bouncing off each other, the two train cars couple together when they hit. Is momentum still conserved in Figure 18C? After the collision, the coupled train cars make one object with twice the mass. The velocity of the coupled trains is 2 m/s—half the initial velocity of the blue car. Since the mass is doubled and the velocity is divided in half, the total momentum remains the same.

 **Reading Checkpoint** What happens to the momentum of two objects after they collide?

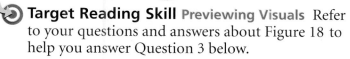

Section 4 Assessment

Target Reading Skill Previewing Visuals Refer to your questions and answers about Figure 18 to help you answer Question 3 below.

Reviewing Key Concepts

1. **a. Reviewing** State Newton's third law of motion.
   b. Summarizing According to Newton's third law of motion, how are action and reaction forces related?
   c. Applying Concepts What would happen if you tried to catch a ball when you were standing on roller skates?
2. **a. Defining** What is momentum?
   b. Predicting What is the momentum of a parked car?
   c. Relating Cause and Effect Why is it important for drivers to allow more distance between their cars when they travel at faster speeds?

3. **a. Identifying** What is conservation of momentum?
   b. Inferring The total momentum of two marbles before a collision is 0.06 kg·m/s. No outside forces act on the marbles. What is the total momentum of the marbles after the collision?

Math Practice

4. **Calculating Momentum** What is the momentum of a 920-kg car moving at a speed of 25 m/s?
5. **Calculating Momentum** Which has more momentum: a 250-kg dolphin swimming at 4 m/s, or a 350-kg manatee swimming at 2 m/s?

Forced to Accelerate

Problem

How is the acceleration of a skateboard related to the force that is pulling it?

Skills Focus

calculating, graphing, interpreting data

Materials

- skateboard • meter stick • string
- stopwatch • masking tape
- spring scale, 5-N
- several bricks or other large mass(es)

Procedure

1. Attach a loop of string to a skateboard. Place the bricks on the skateboard.

2. Using masking tape, mark off a one-meter distance on a level floor. Label one end "Start" and the other "Finish."

3. Attach a spring scale to the loop of string. Pull it so that you maintain a force of 2.0 N. Be sure to pull with the scale straight out in front. Practice applying a steady force to the skateboard as it moves.

4. Copy the data table into your notebook.

5. Find the smallest force needed to pull the skateboard at a slow, constant speed. Do not accelerate the skateboard. Record this force on the first line of the table.

6. Add 0.5 N to the force in Step 5. This will be enough to accelerate the skateboard. Record this force on the second line of the table.

7. Have one of your partners hold the front edge of the skateboard at the starting line. Then pull on the spring scale with the force you found in Step 6.

8. When your partner says "Go" and releases the skateboard, maintain a constant force until the skateboard reaches the finish line. A third partner should time how long it takes the skateboard to go from start to finish. Record the time in the column labeled Trial 1.

9. Repeat Steps 7 and 8 twice more. Record your results in the columns labeled Trial 2 and Trial 3.

10. Repeat Steps 7, 8, and 9 using a force 1.0 N greater than the force you found in Step 5.

11. Repeat Steps 7, 8, and 9 twice more. Use forces that are 1.5 N and 2.0 N greater than the force you found in Step 5.

Data Table							
Force (N)	Trial 1 Time (s)	Trial 2 Time (s)	Trial 3 Time (s)	Average Time (s)	Average Speed (m/s)	Final Speed (m/s)	Acceleration (m/s^2)

Analyze and Conclude

1. **Calculating** For each force, find the average of the three times that you measured. Record the average time in your data table.

2. **Calculating** For each force, find the average speed of the skateboard. Use this formula:

   Average speed = 1 m ÷ Average time

   Record this value for each force.

3. **Calculating** To obtain the final speed of the skateboard, multiply each average speed by 2. Record the result in your data table.

4. **Calculating** To obtain the acceleration, divide each final speed you found by the average time. Record the acceleration in your data table.

5. **Graphing** Make a line graph. Show the acceleration on the y-axis and the force on the x-axis. The y-axis scale should go from 0 m/s^2 to about 1 m/s^2. The x-axis should go from 0 N to 3.0 N. If your data points seem to form a straight line, draw a line through them.

6. **Interpreting Data** Your first data point is the force required for an acceleration of zero. How do you know the force for an acceleration of zero?

7. **Interpreting Data** According to your graph, how is the acceleration of the skateboard related to the pulling force?

8. **Communicating** Write a paragraph in which you identify the manipulated variable and the responding variable in this experiment. Describe other variables that might have affected the outcome of this experiment. (See the Skills Handbook to read about experimental variables.)

Design an Experiment

Design an experiment to test how the acceleration of the loaded skateboard depends on its mass. Think about how you would vary the mass of the skateboard. What quantity would you need to measure that you did not measure in this experiment? Do you have the equipment to make that measurement? If not, what other equipment would you need? *Obtain your teacher's permission before carrying out your investigation.*

Rockets and Satellites

Reading Preview

Key Concepts
- How does a rocket lift off the ground?
- What keeps a satellite in orbit?

Key Terms
- satellite
- centripetal force

Target Reading Skill
Identifying Main Ideas As you read the What Is a Satellite? section, write the main idea in a graphic organizer like the one below. Then write three supporting details that further explain the main idea.

Main Idea

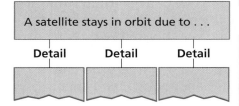

A satellite stays in orbit due to . . .

Detail	Detail	Detail

Lab zone Discover Activity

What Makes an Object Move in a Circle?

1. Tie a small mass, such as an empty thread spool, to the end of a string no more than one meter long.
2. Swing the object rapidly around in a circle that is perpendicular to the floor. Make sure no one is near the swinging object, and don't let it go!
3. Predict what will happen if you decrease the speed of the object. Test your prediction.
4. Predict how the length of the string affects the object's motion. Test your prediction.

Think It Over
Forming Operational Definitions Describe the object's motion. How do you know that the string exerts a force?

In October 1957, 14-year-old Homer Hickam looked upward and saw a speck of light move across the sky. It was the Russian satellite *Sputnik*, the first artificial satellite. It was propelled into space by a powerful rocket. This sight inspired Homer and his friends. They spent the next three years designing, building, and launching rockets in their hometown of Coalwood, West Virginia. Many of their first attempts failed, but they did not give up. Eventually, they built a rocket that soared to a height of almost ten kilometers. Their hard work paid off. In 1960, they won first place in the National Science Fair. Since then, rocket launches have become more familiar, but they are still an awesome sight.

◀ Homer Hickam holds a rocket that he and his friends designed.

How Do Rockets Lift Off?

A space shuttle like the one in Figure 19 has a mass of more than 2 million kilograms when loaded with fuel. To push the shuttle away from the pull of Earth's gravity and into space requires an incredible amount of force. How is this force generated? Rockets and space shuttles lift into space using Newton's third law of motion. As they lift off, they burn fuel and push the exhaust gases downward at a high velocity. In turn, the gases push upward on the rocket with an equal but opposite force. **A rocket can rise into the air because the gases it expels with a downward action force exert an equal but opposite reaction force on the rocket.** As long as this upward pushing force, called thrust, is greater than the downward pull of gravity, there is a net force in the upward direction. As a result, the rocket accelerates upward into space.

What Is a Satellite?

Rockets are often used to carry satellites into space. A **satellite** is any object that orbits another object in space. An artificial satellite is a device that is launched into orbit. Artificial satellites are designed for many purposes, such as communications, military intelligence, weather analysis, and geographical surveys. The International Space Station is an example of an artificial satellite. It was designed for scientific research.

Circular Motion Artificial satellites travel around Earth in an almost circular path. Recall that an object traveling in a circle is accelerating because it constantly changes direction. If an object is accelerating, a force must be acting on it. Any force that causes an object to move in a circular path is a **centripetal force** (sen TRIP ih tul). The word *centripetal* means "center-seeking."

In the Discovery Activity, the string supplies the centripetal force. The string acts to pull the object toward the center, and thereby keeps it moving in a circular path. For a satellite, the centripetal force is the gravitational force that pulls the satellite toward the center of Earth.

 Reading Checkpoint What type of force causes an object to move in a circular path?

Action force

Reaction force

FIGURE 19
A Rocket Launch
The action force pushes the rocket's exhaust gases downward. The reaction force of the gases sends the rocket into space. Predicting *As the rocket ascends, how will its mass change?*

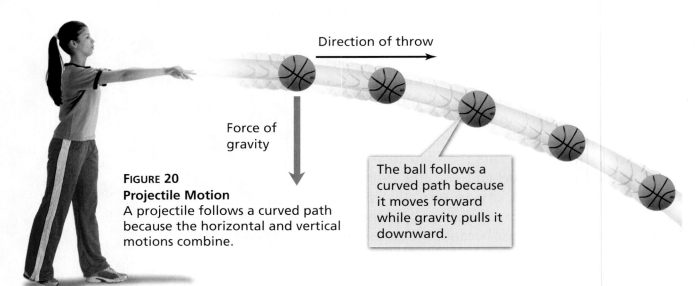

Direction of throw

Force of
gravity

FIGURE 20
Projectile Motion
A projectile follows a curved path
because the horizontal and vertical
motions combine.

The ball follows a
curved path because
it moves forward
while gravity pulls it
downward.

FIGURE 21
Satellite Motion
The faster a projectile is thrown, the farther
it travels before it hits the ground. A
projectile with enough velocity moves in a
circular orbit. **Interpreting Diagrams** *How
does the direction of gravity compare to the
direction of the orbiting projectile's motion
at any point?*

Satellite Motion Gravity pulls satellites toward Earth.
So why don't satellites fall, as a ball thrown into the air
would? The answer is that satellites do not travel straight
up into the air. Instead they move around Earth.

If you throw a ball horizontally, as shown in
Figure 20, the ball will move away from you at the same
time that it is pulled to the ground because of gravity.
The horizontal and vertical motions combine, and the
ball follows a curved path toward the ground. If you
throw the ball faster, it will land even farther in front of
you. The faster you throw a projectile, the farther it
travels before it lands.

Now suppose, as Isaac Newton did, what would
happen if you were on a high mountain and could
throw a ball as fast as you wanted. The faster you threw
it, the farther away it would land. But, at a certain speed,
the path of the ball would match the curve of Earth.
Although the ball would keep falling due to gravity,
Earth's surface would curve away from the ball at the
same rate. Thus the ball would circle Earth, as shown in
Figure 21.

**Satellites in orbit around Earth continuously fall
toward Earth, but because Earth is curved they travel
around it.** In other words, a satellite is a falling projectile
that keeps missing the ground! It falls around Earth
rather than into it. A satellite does not need fuel because
it continues to move ahead due to its inertia. At the same
time, gravity continuously changes the satellite's direction. The speed with which an object must be thrown in
order to orbit Earth turns out to be about 7,900 m/s!
This speed is about 200 times faster than a pitcher can
throw a baseball.

Satellite Location Some satellites, such as mapping and observation satellites, are put into low orbits of less than 1,000 kilometers. In a low orbit, satellites complete a trip around Earth in less than two hours. Other satellites are sent into higher orbits. At those distances, a satellite travels more slowly, taking longer to circle Earth. For example, communications satellites travel about 36,000 kilometers above Earth's surface. At that height, they circle Earth once every 24 hours. Because Earth rotates once every 24 hours, a satellite above the equator always stays at the same point above Earth as it orbits.

✓ **Reading Checkpoint** **How does gravity help keep satellites in orbit?**

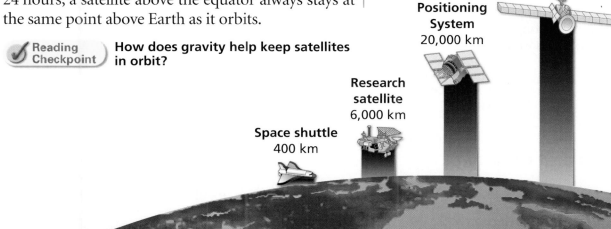

FIGURE 22
Satellite Locations
Depending on their uses, artificial satellites orbit at different heights.

Communications satellite
35,800 km

Global Positioning System
20,000 km

Research satellite
6,000 km

Space shuttle
400 km

Section 5 Assessment

Target Reading Skill Identifying Main Ideas Use your graphic organizer to help you answer Question 2 below.

Reviewing Key Concepts

1. a. **Identifying** Which of Newton's three laws of motion explains how a rocket lifts off?
   b. **Explaining** How do action-reaction pairs explain how a rocket lifts off?
   c. **Applying Concepts** As a rocket travels upward from Earth, air resistance decreases along with the force of gravity. The rocket's mass also decreases as its fuel is used up. If thrust remains the same, how do these factors affect the rocket's acceleration?

2. a. **Defining** What is a satellite?
   b. **Relating Cause and Effect** What causes satellites to stay in orbit rather than falling toward Earth?

   c. **Inferring** In Figure 21, a projectile is thrown with enough velocity to orbit Earth. What would happen if the projectile were thrown with a greater velocity?

Lab zone **At-Home Activity**

Swing the Bucket Fill a small plastic bucket halfway with water and take it outdoors. Challenge a family member to swing the bucket in a vertical circle. Explain that the water won't fall out at the top if the bucket is moving fast enough. Tell your family member that if the bucket falls as fast as the water, the water will stay in the bucket. Relate this activity to a satellite that also falls due to gravity, yet remains in orbit.

1 The Nature of Force

Key Concepts

● Like velocity and acceleration, a force is described by its strength and by the direction in which it acts.

● Unbalanced forces acting on an object result in a net force and cause a change in the object's motion.

● Balanced forces acting on an object do not change the object's motion.

Key Terms

force   unbalanced forces
newton   balanced forces
net force

2 Friction and Gravity

Key Concepts

● The strength of the force of friction depends on two factors: how hard the surfaces push together and the types of surfaces involved.

● Two factors affect the gravitational attraction between objects: mass and distance.

● In free fall, the force of gravity is an unbalanced force, which causes an object to accelerate.

Key Terms

friction   mass
static friction   weight
sliding friction   free fall
rolling friction   air resistance
fluid friction   terminal velocity
gravity   projectile

3 Newton's First and Second Laws

Key Concepts

● An object at rest will remain at rest, and an object moving at a constant velocity will continue moving at a constant velocity, unless it is acted upon by an unbalanced force.

● Acceleration depends on the object's mass and on the net force acting on the object.

● $\text{Acceleration} = \dfrac{\text{Net force}}{\text{Mass}}$

Key Term
inertia

4 Newton's Third Law

Key Concepts

● If one object exerts a force on another object, then the second object exerts a force of equal strength in the opposite direction on the first object.

● The momentum of a moving object is equal to its mass times its velocity.

$$\text{Momentum} = \text{Mass} \times \text{Velocity}$$

● The total momentum of any group of objects remains the same, or is conserved, unless outside forces act on the objects.

Key Terms
momentum
law of conservation of momentum

5 Rockets and Satellites

Key Concepts

● A rocket can rise into the air because the gases it expels with a downward action force exert an equal but opposite reaction force on the rocket.

● Satellites in orbit around Earth continuously fall toward Earth, but because Earth is curved they travel around it.

Key Terms

satellite   centripetal force

Review and Assessment

Go Online
PHSchool.com

For: Self-Assessment
Visit: PHSchool.com
Web Code: cga-3020

Organizing Information

Contrasting Copy the table about the different types of friction onto a sheet of paper. Then complete it and add a title. (For more on Comparing and Contrasting, see the Skills Handbook.)

Type of Friction	Occurs When	Example
Static	An object is not moving	a. ____?____
Sliding	b. ____?____	c. ____?____
Rolling	d. ____?____	e. ____?____
Fluid	f. ____?____	g. ____?____

Reviewing Key Terms

Choose the letter of the best answer.

1. When an unbalanced force acts on an object, the force
   a. changes the motion of the object.
   b. is canceled by another force.
   c. does not change the motion of the object.
   d. is equal to the weight of the object.

2. Air resistance is a type of
   a. rolling friction.
   b. sliding friction.
   c. centripetal force.
   d. fluid friction.

3. Which of the following is not a projectile?
   a. a satellite
   b. a thrown ball
   c. a ball on the ground
   d. a soaring arrow

4. The resistance of an object to any change in its motion is called
   a. inertia.
   b. friction.
   c. gravity.
   d. weight.

5. The product of an object's mass and its velocity is called the object's
   a. net force.
   b. weight.
   c. momentum.
   d. gravitation.

If the statement is true, write *true*. If it is false, change the underlined word or words to make the statement true.

6. <u>Balanced forces</u> are equal forces acting on an object in opposite directions.

7. <u>Rolling friction</u> occurs when two solid surfaces slide over each other.

8. The greatest velocity a falling object reaches is called its <u>momentum</u>.

9. The <u>law of universal gravitation</u> states that the total momentum of objects that interact does not change.

10. The type of force that causes a satellite to orbit Earth is a <u>centripetal force</u>.

Writing in Science

Descriptive Paragraph Suppose you have been asked to design a new amusement park ride. Write a description of how you will design it. Explain the role that friction and gravity will play in the ride's design.

DISCOVERY CHANNEL **SCHOOL**

Forces

Video Preview
Video Field Trip
▶ Video Assessment

Review and Assessment

Checking Concepts

11. Four children pull on the same toy at the same time, yet there is no net force on the toy. How is that possible?

12. Why do slippery fluids such as oil reduce sliding friction?

13. Will a flat sheet of paper dropped from a height of 2 m accelerate at the same rate as a piece of paper crumpled into a ball? Why or why not?

14. Explain how force, mass, and acceleration are related by Newton's second law of motion.

15. Suppose you are an astronaut making a space walk outside your space station when your jet pack runs out of fuel. How can you use your empty jet pack to get you back to the station?

16. Draw a diagram showing the motion of a satellite around Earth. Label the forces acting on the satellite. Is the satellite accelerating?

Thinking Critically

17. Classifying What kind of friction allows you to walk without slipping?

18. Applying Concepts You are moving fast on a skateboard when your wheel gets stuck in a crack on the sidewalk. Using the term *inertia*, explain what happens.

19. Problem Solving Look at the diagram below of two students pulling a bag of volleyball equipment. The friction force between the bag and the floor is 15 N. What is the net force acting on the bag? What is the acceleration of the bag?

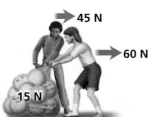

20. Relating Cause and Effect When you drop a golf ball to the pavement, it bounces up. Is a force needed to make it bounce up? If so, what exerts the force?

Math Practice

21. Calculating Force A 7.3-kg bowling ball accelerates at a rate of 3.7 m/s². What force acts on the bowling ball?

22. Calculating Momentum A 240-kg snowmobile travels at 16 m/s. The mass of the driver is 75 kg. What is the momentum of the snowmobile and driver?

Applying Skills

Use the illustration showing a collision between two balls to answer Questions 23–25.

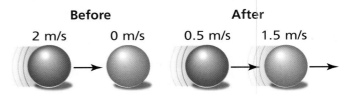

23. Calculating Use the formula for momentum to find the momentum of each ball before and after the collision. Assume the mass of each ball is 0.4 kg.

24. Inferring Find the total momentum before and after collision. Is the law of conservation of momentum satisfied in this collision? Explain.

25. Designing Experiments Design an experiment in which you could show that momentum is not conserved between the balls when friction is strong.

Lab zone — Chapter Project

Performance Assessment Test your vehicle to make sure it will work on the type of floor in your classroom. Will the vehicle stay within the bounds set by your teacher? Identify all the forces acting on the vehicle. What was the most significant source of friction for your vehicle? List at least three features you included in the design of the vehicle that led to an improvement in its performance. For example, did you give it a smooth shape for low air resistance?

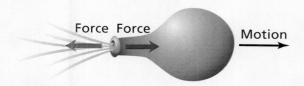
Choose the letter of the best answer.

1. In the balloon diagram above, why don't the two forces cancel each other out?
   A They are not equal.
   B They both act on the air.
   C They both act on the balloon.
   D They act on different objects.

2. What force makes it less likely for a person to slip on a dry sidewalk as opposed to an icy sidewalk?
   A air resistance
   B friction
   C inertia
   D momentum

3. Which of the following is determined by the force of gravity?
   A weight
   B momentum
   C mass
   D distance

4. The table below shows the mass and velocity of four animals. Which animal has the greatest momentum?

Mass and Velocity of Animals		
Animal	Mass (kg)	Velocity (m/s)
Cheetah	45	20
Grizzly bear	200	13
Hyena	70	18
Wild turkey	11	7

   A cheetah
   B grizzly bear
   C hyena
   D wild turkey

5. A 50-car freight train and an 8-car passenger train are stopped on parallel tracks. It is more difficult to move the freight train than the passenger train. What accounts for this fact?
   A terminal velocity
   B inertia
   C centripetal force
   D speed

Constructed Response

6. Write a short paragraph explaining how a parachute works in terms of forces.

Chapter

18

Forces in Fluids

The force of air pushing on a hang glider's wing helps to keep the glider aloft. ▶

Lab zone™ Chapter Project

Staying Afloat

Whether an object sinks or floats depends on more than just its weight. In this Chapter Project, you will design and build a boat that can float in water and carry cargo. You will find out what forces in fluids make an object sink or float.

Your Goal To construct a boat that can float in water and carry cargo

Your boat must

- be made of metal only
- support a cargo of 50 pennies without allowing any water to enter for at least 10 seconds
- travel at least 1.5 meters
- be built following the safety guidelines in Appendix A

Plan It! Before you design your boat, think about the shape of real ships. Preview the chapter to find out what makes an object float. Then look for simple metal objects that you can form into a boat. Compare different materials and designs to build the most efficient boat you can. After your teacher approves your design, build your boat and test it.

Pressure

Reading Preview

Key Concepts
- What does pressure depend on?
- How do fluids exert pressure?
- How does fluid pressure change with elevation and depth?

Key Terms
- pressure • pascal • fluid
- barometer

Target Reading Skill
Previewing Visuals Before you read, preview Figure 5. Then write two questions that you have about the diagram in a graphic organizer like the one below. As you read, answer your questions.

Pressure Variations

Q.	Why does pressure change with elevation and depth?
A.	
Q.	

Can You Blow Up a Balloon in a Bottle?

1. Insert a balloon into the neck of an empty bottle. Try to blow up the balloon.
2. Now insert a straw into the bottle, next to the balloon. Keep one end of the straw sticking out of the bottle. Try again to blow up the balloon.

Think It Over
Developing Hypotheses Did using the straw make a difference? If it did, develop a hypothesis to explain why.

Outside, deep snow covers the ground. You put on your sneakers and head out, shovel in hand. When you step outside, your foot sinks deep into the snow. It's nearly up to your knees! Nearby, a sparrow hops across the surface of the snow. Unlike you, the bird does not sink. In fact, it barely leaves a mark! Why do you sink into the snow while the sparrow rests on the surface? The answer has to do with pressure.

What Is Pressure?

The word *pressure* is related to the word *press*. It refers to a force exerted on a surface. You may recall that the force of Earth's gravity pulls you downward with a force equal to your weight. Due to the force of gravity, your feet exert a force on the ground in the form of pressure.

Exerting pressure on snow ▶

Area = 250 cm²

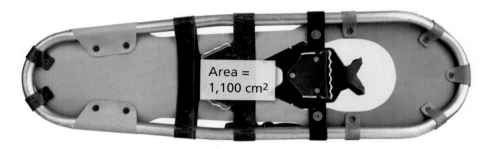
Area = 1,100 cm²

Pressure and Area Force and pressure are closely related, but they are not the same thing. **Pressure decreases as the area over which a force is distributed increases.** The larger the area over which the force is distributed, the less pressure is exerted. In order to stand on snow without sinking, you can't make yourself weigh the same as a bird. However, you can change the area over which you exert the force of your weight.

If you wear sneakers, like those shown in Figure 1, your weight is distributed over the soles of both shoes. You'll exert pressure over an area of about 500 cm² and sink into the snow. But if you wear snowshoes, you'll exert pressure over a much greater area—about 2,200 cm². Because the force of your weight is distributed over a greater area, the overall pressure exerted on the snow is much less. Like a sparrow, you can stand on the snow without sinking!

Calculating Pressure The relationship of force, area, and pressure is summarized by a formula.

$$\text{Pressure} = \frac{\text{Force}}{\text{Area}}$$

Pressure is equal to the force exerted on a surface divided by the total area over which the force is exerted. Force is measured in newtons (N). Area is measured in square meters (m²). Since force is divided by area, the SI unit of pressure is the newton per square meter (N/m²). This unit of pressure is also called the **pascal** (Pa): 1 N/m² = 1 Pa.

Reading Checkpoint What is the SI unit of pressure called?

FIGURE 1
Pressure and Area
Pressure depends on the area over which a force is distributed.
Inferring Which type of shoe would you use to keep from sinking into deep snow?

Math Skills

Area
The area of a surface is the number of square units that it covers. To find the area of a rectangle, multiply its length by its width. The area of the rectangle below is 2 cm × 3 cm, or 6 cm².

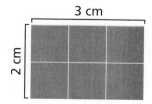
3 cm
2 cm

Practice Problem Which has a greater area: a rectangle that is 4 cm × 20 cm, or a square that is 10 cm × 10 cm?

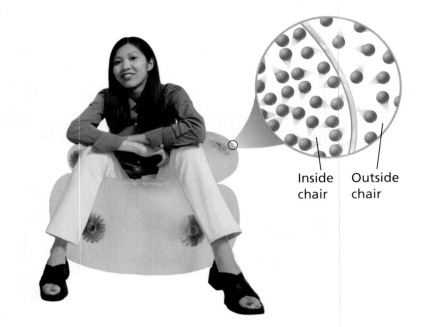

FIGURE 2
Fluid Particles
The particles that make up a fluid move constantly in all directions. When a particle collides with a surface, it exerts a force on the surface.
Relating Cause and Effect
What will happen to the force exerted by the particles in the chair when you add more air to the chair?

Inside chair   Outside chair

Fluid Pressure

Solids such as sneakers are not the only materials that exert pressure. Fluids also exert pressure. A **fluid** is a material that can easily flow. As a result, a fluid can change shape. Liquids such as water and oil and gases such as air and helium are examples of fluids.

What Causes Fluid Pressure? To understand how fluids exert forces that can result in pressure, think about the tiny particles that make up the fluid. Particles in a fluid constantly move in all directions, as shown in Figure 2. As they move, the particles collide with each other and with any surface that they meet.

As each particle in a fluid collides with a surface, it exerts a force on the surface. **All of the forces exerted by the individual particles in a fluid combine to make up the pressure exerted by the fluid.** Because the number of particles is large, you can consider the fluid as a whole. So, the fluid pressure is the total force exerted by the fluid divided by the area over which the force is exerted.

Air Pressure Did you know that you live at the bottom of 100 kilometers of fluid that surrounds Earth? This fluid, called air, is the mixture of gases that makes up Earth's atmosphere. These gases press down on everything on Earth's surface, all the time. Air exerts pressure because it has mass. You may forget that air has mass, but each cubic meter of air around you has a mass of about 1 kilogram. Because the force of gravity pulls down on this mass of air, the air has weight. The weight of the air is the force that produces air pressure, or atmospheric pressure.

Lab zone Try This **Activity**

Card Trick

1. Fill a small plastic cup to the brim with water. Gently place an index card over the top of the cup.

2. Hold the card in place and slowly turn the cup upside down. Let go of the card. What happens? Without touching the card, turn the container on its side.

Inferring Why does the water stay in the cup when you turn the cup upside down?

Balanced Pressure Hold out your hand, palm up. You are holding up air. At sea level, atmospheric pressure is about 10.13 N/cm². The surface area of your hand is about 100 cm². So, the weight supported by the surface area of your hand is about 1,000 newtons, or about the same weight as that of a large washing machine!

How could your hand possibly support that weight and not feel it? In a stationary fluid, pressure at a given point is exerted equally in all directions. The weight of the atmosphere does not just press down on your hand. It presses on your hand from every direction. The pressures balance each other.

Balanced pressures also explain why the tremendous air pressure pushing on you from all sides does not crush you. Your body contains fluids that exert outward pressure. For example, your lungs and sinus cavities contain air. Your cells and blood vessels contain liquids. So pressure from fluids inside your body balances the air pressure outside your body.

What happens when air pressure becomes unbalanced? Look at Figure 4. When the can is full of air, the air pressure inside the can balances the atmospheric pressure outside the can. When air is removed from the can, the unbalanced force of the outside air pressure crushes the can.

 **Reading Checkpoint** How is the pressure on your hand balanced?

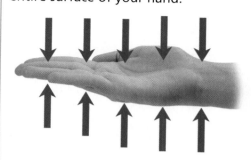

FIGURE 3
Atmospheric Pressure
The pressure of Earth's atmosphere is exerted over the entire surface of your hand.

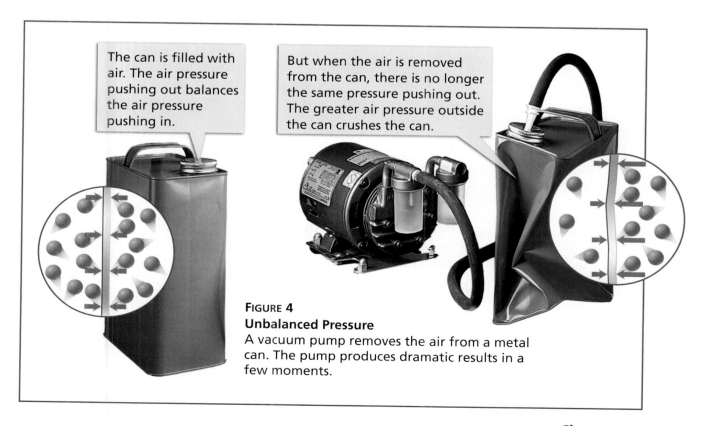

The can is filled with air. The air pressure pushing out balances the air pressure pushing in.

But when the air is removed from the can, there is no longer the same pressure pushing out. The greater air pressure outside the can crushes the can.

FIGURE 4
Unbalanced Pressure
A vacuum pump removes the air from a metal can. The pump produces dramatic results in a few moments.

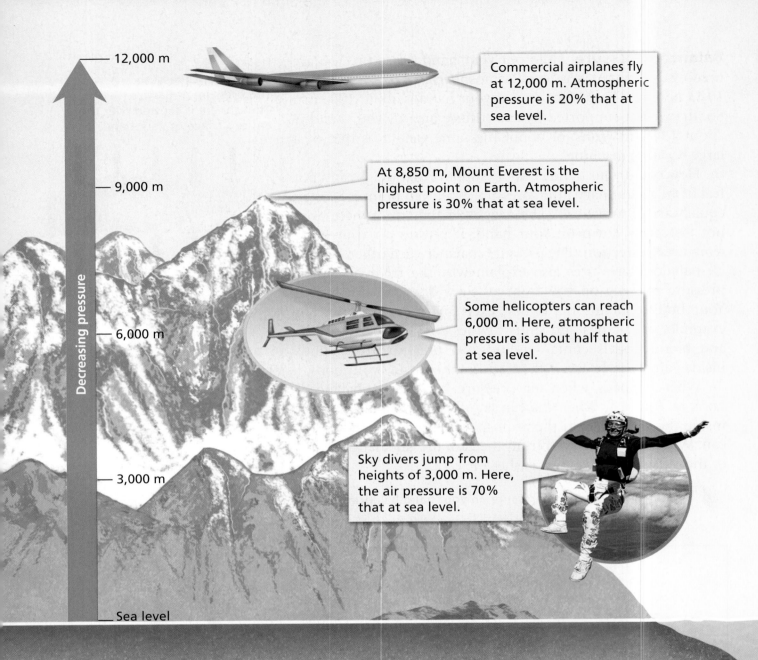

12,000 m — Commercial airplanes fly at 12,000 m. Atmospheric pressure is 20% that at sea level.

9,000 m — At 8,850 m, Mount Everest is the highest point on Earth. Atmospheric pressure is 30% that at sea level.

Decreasing pressure

6,000 m — Some helicopters can reach 6,000 m. Here, atmospheric pressure is about half that at sea level.

3,000 m — Sky divers jump from heights of 3,000 m. Here, the air pressure is 70% that at sea level.

Sea level

FIGURE 5
Pressure Variations

Atmospheric pressure decreases gradually as the elevation above sea level increases. Water pressure increases rapidly as the water depth increases. Applying Concepts *Why do airplanes have pressurized cabins?*

Variations in Fluid Pressure

Does the pressure of a fluid ever change? What happens to pressure as you climb to a higher elevation or sink to a lower depth within a fluid? Figure 5 shows how pressure changes depending on where you are.

Atmospheric Pressure and Elevation Have you ever felt your ears "pop" as you rode up in an elevator? The "popping" has to do with changing air pressure. At higher elevations, there is less air above you and therefore less air pressure. **As your elevation increases, atmospheric pressure decreases.**

The fact that air pressure decreases as you move up in elevation explains why your ears pop. When the air pressure outside your body changes, the air pressure inside adjusts, but more slowly. So, for a moment, the air pressure behind your eardrums is greater than it is in the air outside. Your body releases this pressure with a "pop," balancing the pressures.

Water Pressure and Depth Fluid pressure depends on depth. The pressure at one meter below the surface of a swimming pool is the same as the pressure one meter below the surface of a lake. But if you dive deeper into either body of water, pressure becomes greater as you descend. The deeper you swim, the greater the pressure you feel. **Water pressure increases as depth increases.**

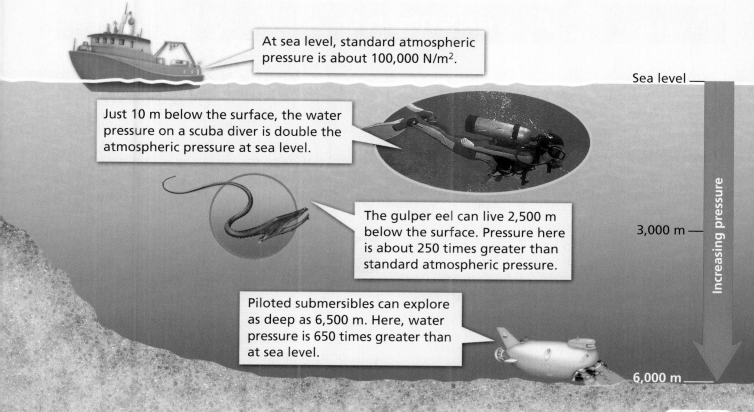

At sea level, standard atmospheric pressure is about 100,000 N/m².

Just 10 m below the surface, the water pressure on a scuba diver is double the atmospheric pressure at sea level.

The gulper eel can live 2,500 m below the surface. Pressure here is about 250 times greater than standard atmospheric pressure.

Piloted submersibles can explore as deep as 6,500 m. Here, water pressure is 650 times greater than at sea level.

Sea level

3,000 m

6,000 m

Increasing pressure

FIGURE 6

Aneroid Barometer
An aneroid barometer measures atmospheric pressure.
Interpreting Photographs *What type of weather might be coming when atmospheric pressure decreases?*

As with air, you can think of water pressure as being due to the weight of the water above a particular point. At greater depths, there is more water above that point and therefore more weight to support. In addition, air in the atmosphere pushes down on the water. Therefore, the total pressure at a given point beneath the water results from the weight of the water plus the weight of the air above it. In the deepest parts of the ocean, the pressure is more than 1,000 times the air pressure you experience every day.

Measuring Pressure You can measure atmospheric pressure with an instrument called a **barometer.** There are two types of barometers: a mercury barometer and an aneroid barometer. The aneroid barometer is the barometer you usually see hanging on a wall. Weather forecasters use the pressure reading from a barometer to help forecast the weather. Rapidly decreasing atmospheric pressure usually means a storm is on its way. Increasing pressure is often a sign of fair weather. You may hear barometric pressure readings expressed in millimeters, inches, or another unit called a millibar. For example, the standard barometric pressure at sea level may be reported as 760 millimeters, 29.92 inches, or 1,013.2 millibars.

Reading Checkpoint What instrument measures atmospheric pressure?

Section 1 Assessment

Target Reading Skill
Previewing Visuals Refer to your questions and answers about Figure 5 to help you answer Question 3 below.

Reviewing Key Concepts
1. a. **Reviewing** What two factors does pressure depend on?
   b. **Comparing and Contrasting** Who exerts more pressure on the ground—a 50-kg woman standing in high heels, or a 50-kg woman standing in work boots?
2. a. **Summarizing** How do fluids exert pressure?
   b. **Explaining** Since most of the weight of the atmosphere is above you, why aren't you crushed by it?
   c. **Inferring** How is your body similar to the can containing air shown in Figure 4?

3. a. **Describing** How does atmospheric pressure change as you move away from the surface of Earth?
   b. **Comparing and Contrasting** Compare the change in atmospheric pressure with elevation to the change in water pressure with depth.
   c. **Applying Concepts** Why must an astronaut wear a pressurized suit in space?

 **Math** **Practice**

4. **Area** Find the area of a rectangular photo that is 20 cm long and 15 cm wide.
5. **Area** Which has a greater area: a square table that measures 120 cm × 120 cm, or a rectangular table that measures 200 cm × 90 cm?

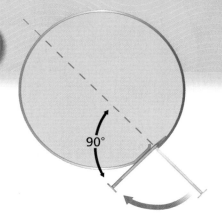

Lab zone Design Your Own Lab

Spinning Sprinklers

Problem

What factors affect the speed of rotation of a lawn sprinkler?

Skills Focus

designing experiments, controlling variables

Materials

- empty soda can
- fishing line, 30 cm
- waterproof marker
- wide-mouth jar or beaker
- stopwatch
- nails of various sizes
- large basin

Procedure

PART 1   Making a Sprinkler

1. Fill the jar with enough water to completely cover a soda can. Place the jar in the basin.

2. Bend up the tab of a can and tie the end of a length of fishing line to it. **CAUTION:** *The edge of the can opening can be sharp.*

3. Place a mark on the can to help you keep track of how many times the can spins.

4. Using the small nail, make a hole in the side of the can about 1 cm up from the bottom. Poke the nail straight in. Then twist the nail until it makes a right angle with the radius of the can as shown in the figure above. **CAUTION:** *Nails are sharp and should be used only to puncture the cans.*

5. Submerge the can in the jar and fill the can to the top with water.

6. Quickly lift the can with the fishing line so that it is 1–2 cm above the water level in the jar. Practice counting how many spins the can completes in 15 seconds.

PART 2   What Factors Affect Spin?

7. How does the size of the hole affect the number of spins made by the can? Propose a hypothesis and then design an experiment to test the hypothesis. Obtain your teacher's approval before carrying out your experiment. Record all your data.

8. How does the number of holes affect the number of spins made by the can? Propose a hypothesis and then design an experiment to test the hypothesis. Obtain your teacher's approval before carrying out your experiment. Record all your data.

Analyze and Conclude

1. **Designing Experiments** How does the size of the hole affect the rate of spin of the can? How does the number of holes affect the rate of spin of the can?

2. **Controlling Variables** What other variables might affect the number of spins made by the can?

3. **Interpreting Data** Explain the motion of the can in terms of water pressure.

4. **Classifying** Which of Newton's three laws of motion could you use to explain the motion of the can? Explain.

5. **Communicating** Use the results of your experiment to write a paragraph that explains why a spinning lawn sprinkler spins.

More to Explore

Some sprinkler systems use water pressure to spin. Examine one of these sprinklers to see the size, direction of spin, and number of holes. What would happen if you connected a second sprinkler to the first with another length of hose? If possible, try it.

Floating and Sinking

Reading Preview

Key Concepts
- What is the effect of the buoyant force?
- How can you use density to determine whether an object will float or sink in a fluid?

Key Terms
- buoyant force
- Archimedes' principle
- density

Target Reading Skill
Relating Cause and Effect
As you read, identify the reasons why an object sinks. Write the information in a graphic organizer like the one below.

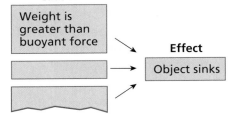

Causes

| Weight is greater than buoyant force |

Effect

| Object sinks |

Lab zone Discover Activity

What Can You Measure With a Straw?
1. Cut a plastic straw to a 10-cm length.
2. Use a waterproof marker to make marks on the straw that are 1 cm apart.
3. Roll some modeling clay into a ball about 1.5 cm in diameter. Stick one end of the straw in the clay. You have built a device known as a hydrometer.
4. Place the hydrometer in a glass of water. About half of the straw should remain above water. If it sinks, remove some of the clay. Make sure no water gets into the straw.
5. Dissolve 10 spoonfuls of sugar in a glass of water. Try out your hydrometer in this liquid.

Think It Over
Predicting Compare your observations in Steps 4 and 5. Then predict what will happen if you use 20 spoonfuls of sugar in a glass of water. Test your prediction.

In April 1912, the *Titanic* departed from England on its first and only voyage. At the time, it was the largest ship afloat—nearly three football fields long. The *Titanic* was also the most technologically advanced ship in existence. Its hull was divided into compartments, and it was considered to be unsinkable.

Yet a few days into the voyage, the *Titanic* struck an iceberg. One compartment after another filled with water. Less than three hours later, the bow of the great ship slipped under the waves. As the stern rose high into the air, the ship broke in two. Both pieces sank to the bottom of the Atlantic Ocean. More than a thousand people died.

◄ **The bow section of the *Titanic* resting on the ocean floor**

Buoyancy

Ships are designed to have buoyancy—the ability to float. How is it possible that a huge ship can float easily on the surface of water under certain conditions, and then in a few hours become a sunken wreck? To answer this question, you need to understand the buoyant force.

Gravity and the Buoyant Force You have probably experienced the buoyant force. If you have ever picked up an object under water, you know that it seems much lighter in water than in air. Water and other fluids exert an upward force called the **buoyant force** that acts on a submerged object. **The buoyant force acts in the direction opposite to the force of gravity, so it makes an object feel lighter.**

As you can see in Figure 7, a fluid exerts pressure on all surfaces of a submerged object. Since the pressure in a fluid increases with depth, the upward pressure on the bottom of the object is greater than the downward pressure on the top. The result is a net force acting upward on the submerged object. This is the buoyant force.

Remember that the weight of a submerged object is a downward force. An object sinks if its weight is greater than the buoyant force because a net force acts downward on the object. If the weight of a submerged object is equal to the buoyant force, no net force acts on the object. The object floats on the surface while partly submerged or floats at a constant level while totally submerged, depending on its weight. For example, both the jellyfish and the turtle shown in Figure 8 have balanced forces acting on them.

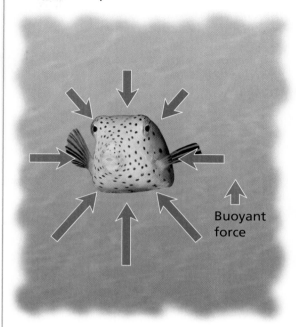

FIGURE 7
Buoyant Force
The pressure on the bottom of a submerged object is greater than the pressure on the top. The result is a net force in the upward direction.

Buoyant force

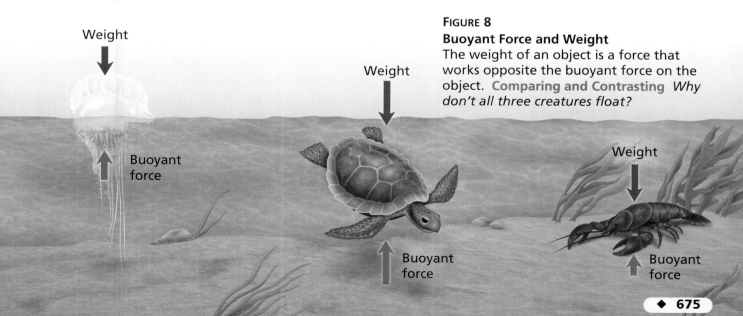

Weight

Buoyant force

Weight

Buoyant force

Weight

Buoyant force

FIGURE 8
Buoyant Force and Weight
The weight of an object is a force that works opposite the buoyant force on the object. **Comparing and Contrasting** *Why don't all three creatures float?*

FIGURE 9
Archimedes' Principle
Archimedes' principle applies to sinking and floating objects.
Predicting If you press down on the floating film can, what will happen to the volume of the displaced fluid in the small beaker?

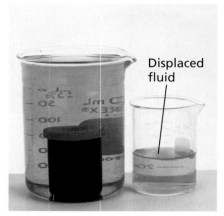
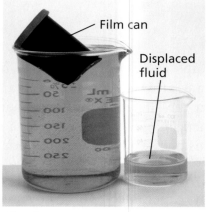

Sinking
When the film can has film in it, it sinks. The volume of fluid displaced by the can is equal to the volume of the can.

Floating
When the film can is empty, it floats. The volume of displaced fluid is equal to the volume of the submerged portion of the can.

Archimedes' Principle You know that all objects take up space. A submerged object displaces, or takes the place of, a volume of fluid equal to its own volume. A partly submerged object, however, displaces a volume of fluid equal to the volume of its submerged portion only. You can see this in Figure 9.

Archimedes, a mathematician of ancient Greece, discovered a connection between the weight of a fluid displaced by an object and the buoyant force acting on it. This connection is known as Archimedes' principle. **Archimedes' principle** states that the buoyant force acting on a submerged object is equal to the weight of the fluid the object displaces. To understand what this means, think about swimming in a pool. Suppose your body displaces 50 liters of water. The buoyant force exerted on you will be equal to the weight of 50 liters of water, or about 500 N.

You can use Archimedes' principle to explain why a ship floats on the surface. Since the buoyant force equals the weight of the displaced fluid, the buoyant force will increase if more fluid is displaced. A large object displaces more fluid than a small object. A greater buoyant force acts on the larger object even if the large object has the same weight as the small object.

Look at Figure 10. The shape of a ship's hull causes the ship to displace a greater volume of water than a solid piece of steel with the same mass. A ship displaces a volume of water equal in weight to the submerged portion of the ship. According to Archimedes' principle, the weight of the displaced water is equal to the buoyant force. Since a ship displaces more water than a block of steel, a greater buoyant force acts on the ship. A ship floats on the surface as long as the buoyant force acting on it is equal to its weight.

Forces in Fluids

Video Preview
▶ Video Field Trip
Video Assessment

 **Reading Checkpoint** **Does a greater buoyant force act on a large object or a small object?**

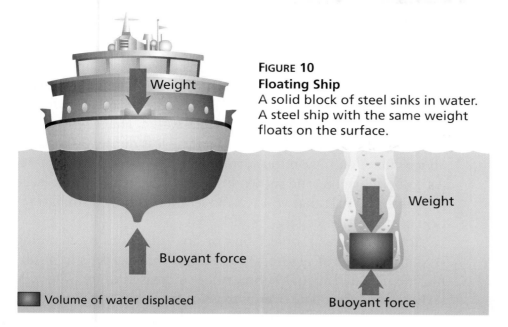

FIGURE 10
Floating Ship
A solid block of steel sinks in water. A steel ship with the same weight floats on the surface.

Weight

Buoyant force

Volume of water displaced

Weight

Buoyant force

Density

Exactly why do some objects float and others sink? To find the answer, you must relate an object's mass to its volume. In other words, you need to know the object's density.

What Is Density? The **density** of a substance is its mass per unit volume.

$$\text{Density} = \frac{\text{Mass}}{\text{Volume}}$$

For example, one cubic centimeter (cm^3) of lead has a mass of 11.3 grams, so its density is 11.3 g/cm^3. In contrast, one cubic centimeter of cork has a mass of only about 0.25 gram. So the density of cork is about 0.25 g/cm^3. Lead is more dense than cork. The density of water is 1.0 g/cm^3. So water is less dense than lead but more dense than cork.

Comparing Densities of Substances In Figure 11, several liquids and other materials are shown along with their densities. Notice that liquids can float on top of other liquids. (You may have seen salad oil floating on top of vinegar.) The liquids and materials with the greatest densities are near the bottom of the cylinder.

By comparing densities, you can predict whether an object will float or sink in a fluid. An object that is more dense than the fluid in which it is immersed sinks. An object that is less dense than the fluid in which it is immersed floats to the surface. And if the density of an object is equal to the density of the fluid in which it is immersed, the object neither rises nor sinks in the fluid. Instead, it floats at a constant depth.

FIGURE 11
Densities of Substances
You can use density to predict whether an object will sink or float when placed in a liquid. **Interpreting Data** *Will a rubber washer sink or float in corn oil?*

Substance	Density (g/cm³)
Wood	0.7
Corn oil	0.925
Plastic	0.93
Water	1.00
Tar ball	1.02
Glycerin	1.26
Rubber washer	1.34
Corn syrup	1.38
Copper wire	8.8
Mercury	13.6

Changing Density Changing density can explain why an object floats or sinks. For example, you can change the density of water by freezing it into ice. Since water expands when it freezes, ice occupies more space than water. That's why ice is less dense than water. But it's just a little less dense! So most of an ice cube floating on the surface is below the water's surface. An iceberg like the one shown in Figure 12 is really a very large ice cube. The part that you see above water is only a small fraction of the entire iceberg.

You can make an object sink or float in a fluid by changing its density. Look at Figure 13 to see how this happens to a submarine. The density of a submarine is increased when water fills its flotation tanks. The overall mass of the submarine increases. Since its volume remains the same, its density increases when its mass increases. So the submarine will dive. To make the submarine float to the surface, water is pumped out of it, decreasing its mass. Its density decreases, and it rises toward the surface.

You can also explain why a submarine dives and floats by means of the buoyant force. Since the buoyant force is equal to the weight of the displaced fluid, the buoyant force on the submerged submarine stays the same. Changing the water level in the flotation tanks changes the weight of the submarine. The submarine dives when its weight is greater than the buoyant force. It rises to the surface when its weight is less than the buoyant force.

Don't forget that air is also a fluid. If you decrease the density of an object, such as a balloon, the object will float and not sink in air. Instead of air, you can fill a balloon with helium gas. A helium balloon rises because helium is less dense than air. A balloon filled with air, however, is denser than the surrounding air because the air inside it is under pressure. The denser air inside, along with the weight of the balloon, make it fall to the ground.

 Reading Checkpoint   **Why does a helium balloon float in air?**

FIGURE 12
Iceberg
An iceberg is dangerous to ships because most of it is under water.

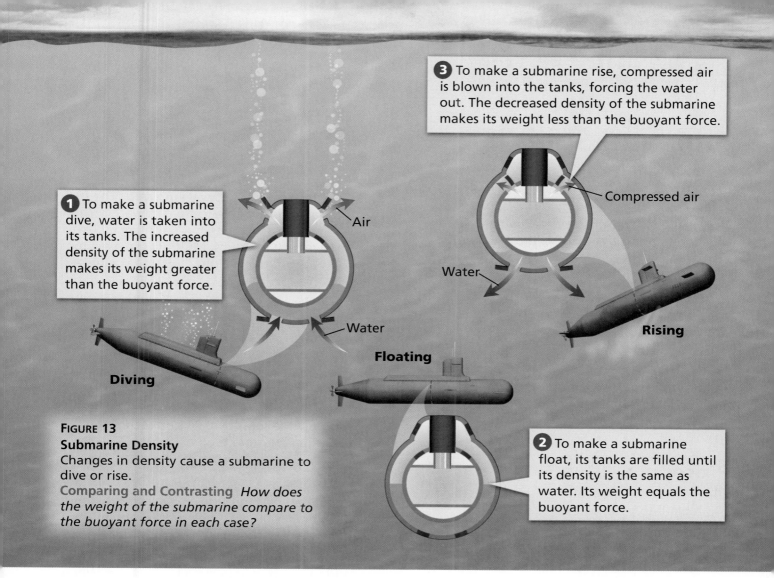

③ To make a submarine rise, compressed air is blown into the tanks, forcing the water out. The decreased density of the submarine makes its weight less than the buoyant force.

Compressed air

Water

Rising

① To make a submarine dive, water is taken into its tanks. The increased density of the submarine makes its weight greater than the buoyant force.

Air

Water

Diving

Floating

② To make a submarine float, its tanks are filled until its density is the same as water. Its weight equals the buoyant force.

FIGURE 13
Submarine Density
Changes in density cause a submarine to dive or rise.
Comparing and Contrasting *How does the weight of the submarine compare to the buoyant force in each case?*

Section 2 Assessment

Target Reading Skill
Relating Cause and Effect Refer to your graphic organizer to help you answer the questions below.

Reviewing Key Concepts

1. a. Explaining How does the buoyant force affect a submerged object?
  b. Summarizing How does Archimedes' principle relate the buoyant force acting on an object to the fluid displaced by the object?
  c. Calculating An object that weighs 340 N floats on a lake. What is the weight of the displaced water? What is the buoyant force?
2. a. Defining What is density?
  b. Explaining How can you use the density of an object to predict whether it will float or sink in water?

  c. Applying Concepts Some canoes have compartments on either end that are hollow and watertight. These canoes won't sink, even when they capsize. Explain why.

Lab zone At-Home **Activity**

Changing Balloon Density Attach paper clips to the string of a helium balloon. Ask a family member to predict how many paper clips you will need to attach to make the balloon sink to the floor. How many paper clips can you attach and still keep the helium balloon suspended in the air? Explain how adding paper clips changes the overall density of the balloon.

Sink and Spill

Problem

How is the buoyant force acting on a floating object related to the weight of the water it displaces?

Skills Focus

controlling variables, interpreting data, drawing conclusions

Materials

- paper towels • pie pan
- triple-beam balance • beaker, 600-mL
- jar with watertight lid, about 30-mL
- table salt

Procedure

1. Preview the procedure and copy the data table into your notebook.

2. Find the mass, in grams, of a dry paper towel and the pie pan together. Multiply the mass by 0.01. This gives you the weight in newtons. Record it in your data table.

3. Place the 600-mL beaker, with the dry paper towel under it, in the middle of the pie pan. Fill the beaker to the very top with water.

4. Fill the jar about halfway with salt. (The jar and salt must be able to float in water.) Then find the mass of the salt and the dry jar (with its cover on) in grams. Multiply the mass by 0.01. Record this weight in your data table.

5. Gently lower the jar into the 600-mL beaker. (If the jar sinks, take it out and remove some salt. Repeat Steps 2, 3, and 4.) Estimate the fraction of the jar that is underwater, and record it.

6. Once all of the displaced water has been spilled, find the total mass of the paper towel and pie pan containing the water. Multiply the mass by 0.01 and record the result in your data table.

7. Empty the pie pan. Dry off the pan and the jar.

8. Repeat Steps 3 through 7 several more times. Each time fill the jar with a different amount of salt, but make sure the jar still floats.

9. Calculate the buoyant force for each trial and record it in your data table. (Hint: When an object floats, the buoyant force is equal to the weight of the object.)

10. Calculate the weight of the displaced water in each case. Record it in your data table.

	Data Table					
Jar	Weight of Empty Pie Pan and Dry Paper Towel (N)	Weight of Jar, Salt, and Cover (N)	Weight of Pie Pan With Displaced Water and Paper Towel (N)	Fraction of Jar Submerged in Water	Buoyant Force (N)	Weight of Displaced Water (N)
1						
2						
3						

Analyze and Conclude

1. **Controlling Variables** In each trial, the jar had a different weight. How did this affect the way that the jar floated?

2. **Interpreting Data** The jar had the same volume in every trial. Why did the volume of displaced water vary?

3. **Drawing Conclusions** What can you conclude about the relationship between the buoyant force and the weight of the displaced water?

4. **Drawing Conclusions** If you put too much salt in the jar, it will sink. What can you conclude about the buoyant force in this case? How can you determine the buoyant force for an object that sinks?

5. **Communicating** Write a paragraph suggesting places where errors may have been introduced into the experiment. Propose some ways to control the errors.

Design an Experiment

How do you think your results would change if you used a liquid that is more dense or less dense than water? Design an experiment to test your hypothesis. What liquid or liquids will you use? Will you need equipment other than what you used for this experiment? If so, what will you need? *Obtain your teacher's permission before carrying out your investigation.*

Pascal's Principle

Reading Preview

Key Concepts
- What does Pascal's principle say about change in fluid pressure?
- How does a hydraulic system work?

Key Terms
- Pascal's principle
- hydraulic system

Target Reading Skill

Asking Questions Before you read, preview the red headings. In a graphic organizer like the one below, ask a *what* or *how* question for each heading. As you read, write the answers to your questions.

Pascal's Principle

Question	Answer
How is pressure transmitted in a fluid?	Pressure is transmitted . . .

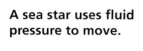

Lab zone ▸ **Discover Activity**

How Does Pressure Change?

1. Fill an empty 2-liter plastic bottle with water. Then screw on the cap. There should be no bubbles in the bottle (or only very small bubbles).
2. Lay the bottle on its side. At one spot, push in the bottle with your left thumb.
3. With your right thumb, push in fairly hard on a spot at the other end, as shown. What does your left thumb feel?
4. Pick another spot on the bottle for your left thumb and repeat Step 3.

Think It Over

Observing When you push in with your right thumb, does the water pressure in the bottle increase, decrease, or remain the same? How do you know?

At first, you hesitate, but then you hold out your hand. The aquarium attendant places the sea star in your palm. You can feel motion on your skin. The many tiny "feet" on the animal's underside look something like suction cups, and they tickle just a bit! The attendant explains that the sea star has a system of tubes containing water in its body. As the water moves around in the tubes, it creates fluid pressure that allows the sea star to move. The sea star also uses this system to obtain its food.

A sea star uses fluid ▸ pressure to move.

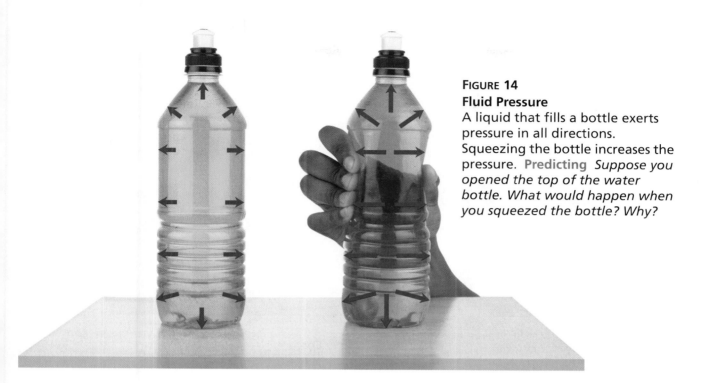

FIGURE 14
Fluid Pressure
A liquid that fills a bottle exerts pressure in all directions. Squeezing the bottle increases the pressure. **Predicting** *Suppose you opened the top of the water bottle. What would happen when you squeezed the bottle? Why?*

Transmitting Pressure in a Fluid

If you did the Discover Activity, you may be surprised to learn that a sea star's water-filled tube system is like the closed bottle you pushed your thumb against. Recall that the fluid pressure in the closed container increased when you pushed against its side. By changing the fluid pressure at any spot in the closed container, you transmitted pressure throughout the container. In the 1600s, a French mathematician named Blaise Pascal developed a principle to explain how pressure is transmitted in a fluid. Pascal's name is used for the unit of pressure.

What Is Pascal's Principle? As you may recall, fluid exerts pressure on any surface it touches. For example, the water in each bottle shown in Figure 14 exerts pressure on the entire surface of the bottle—up, down, and sideways.

What happens if you squeeze the bottle when its top is closed? The water has nowhere to go, so it presses harder on the inside surface of the bottle. The water pressure increases everywhere in the bottle. This is shown by the increased length of the arrows on the right in Figure 14.

Pascal discovered that pressure increases by the same amount throughout an enclosed or confined fluid. **When force is applied to a confined fluid, the change in pressure is transmitted equally to all parts of the fluid.** This relationship is known as **Pascal's principle.**

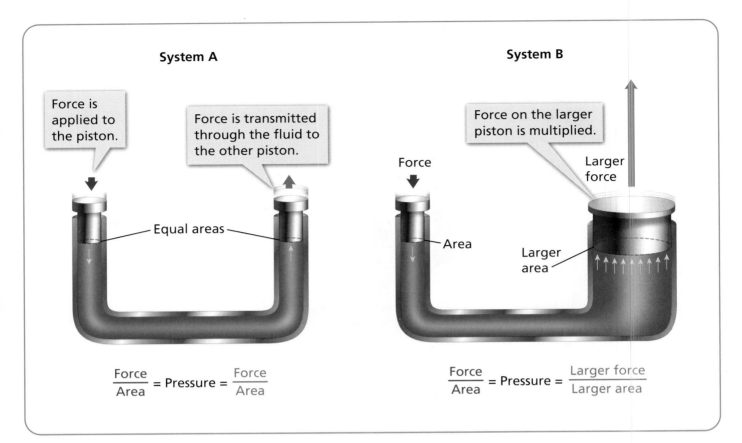

System A

Force is applied to the piston.

Force is transmitted through the fluid to the other piston.

Equal areas

$$\frac{\text{Force}}{\text{Area}} = \text{Pressure} = \frac{\text{Force}}{\text{Area}}$$

System B

Force

Force on the larger piston is multiplied.

Larger force

Area

Larger area

$$\frac{\text{Force}}{\text{Area}} = \text{Pressure} = \frac{\text{Larger force}}{\text{Larger area}}$$

FIGURE 15
Hydraulic Devices
In a hydraulic device, a force applied to one piston increases the fluid pressure equally throughout the fluid. By changing the size of the pistons, the force can be multiplied.
Problem Solving *To multiply the force applied to the left piston four times, how large must the right piston be?*

For: Hydraulic Systems activity
Visit: PHSchool.com
Web Code: cgp-3033

Using Pascal's Principle You can see Pascal's principle at work in Figure 15, which shows a model of a hydraulic device. A hydraulic device is operated by the movement and force of a fluid. The device consists of two pistons, one at each end of a U-shaped tube. A piston is like a stopper that slides up and down in a tube.

Suppose you fill System A with water and then push down on the left piston. The increase in fluid pressure will be transmitted to the right piston. According to Pascal's principle, both pistons experience the same fluid pressure. So, because both pistons have the same surface area, they will experience the same force.

Now look at System B. The right piston has a greater surface area than the left piston. Suppose the area of the small piston is 1 square centimeter and the area of the large piston is 9 square centimeters. Then the right piston has an area nine times greater than the area of the left piston. If you push down on the left piston, pressure is transmitted equally to the right piston. But, because the area of the right piston is nine times greater, the force you exert on the left piston is multiplied nine times on the right piston. By changing the size of the pistons, you can multiply force by almost any amount you wish.

 **Reading Checkpoint** **How is force multiplied in System B?**

Hydraulic Systems

Hydraulic systems make use of hydraulic devices to perform a variety of functions. A **hydraulic system** uses liquids to transmit pressure in a confined fluid. **A hydraulic system multiplies force by applying the force to a small surface area. The increase in pressure is then transmitted to another part of the confined fluid, which pushes on a larger surface area.** You have probably seen a number of hydraulic systems at work, including lift systems and the brakes of a car. Because they use fluids to transmit pressure, hydraulic systems have few moving parts that can jam, break, or wear down.

Hydraulic Lifts Hydraulic lift systems are used to raise cars off the ground so mechanics can repair them with ease. You may be surprised to learn that hydraulic systems are also used to lift the heavy ladder on a fire truck to reach the upper windows of a burning building. In addition, hydraulic lifts are used to operate many pieces of heavy construction equipment such as dump trucks, backhoes, snowplows, and cranes. Next time you see a construction vehicle at work, see if you can spot the hydraulic pistons in action.

 **Reading Checkpoint** What are some uses of hydraulic systems?

Math — Analyzing Data

Comparing Hydraulic Lifts

In the hydraulic device in Figure 15, a force applied to the piston on the left produces a lifting force in the piston on the right. The graph shows the relationship between the applied force and the lifting force for two hydraulic lifts.

1. **Reading Graphs** Suppose a force of 1,000 N is applied to both lifts. Use the graph to determine the lifting force of each lift.

2. **Reading Graphs** For Lift A, how much force must be applied to lift a 12,000-N object?

3. **Interpreting Data** By how much is the applied force multiplied for each lift?

4. **Interpreting Data** What can you learn from the slope of the line for each lift?

5. **Drawing Conclusions** Which lift would you choose if you wanted to produce the greater lifting force?

Hydraulic Lifts

(Graph: x-axis "Applied Force (N)" ranging 0 to 3,000; y-axis "Lifting Force (N)" ranging 0 to 12,000. Lift A is the steeper line; Lift B is the less steep line.)

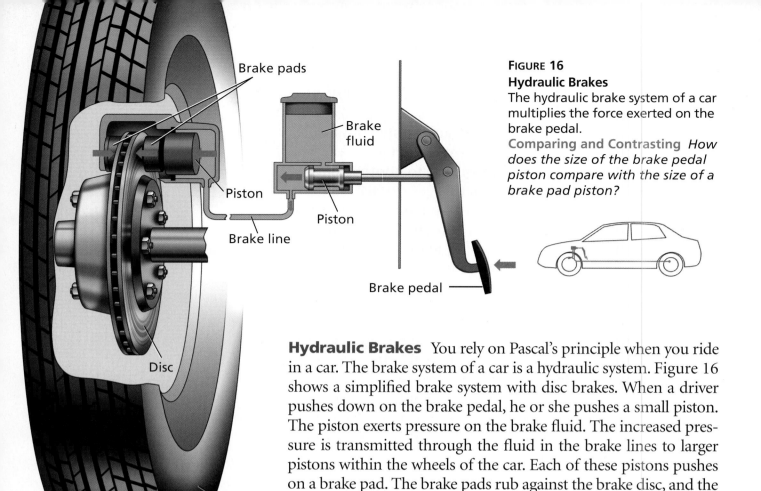

Brake pads

Brake fluid

Piston

Piston

Brake line

Disc

Tire

Brake pedal

FIGURE 16
Hydraulic Brakes
The hydraulic brake system of a car multiplies the force exerted on the brake pedal.
Comparing and Contrasting *How does the size of the brake pedal piston compare with the size of a brake pad piston?*

Hydraulic Brakes You rely on Pascal's principle when you ride in a car. The brake system of a car is a hydraulic system. Figure 16 shows a simplified brake system with disc brakes. When a driver pushes down on the brake pedal, he or she pushes a small piston. The piston exerts pressure on the brake fluid. The increased pressure is transmitted through the fluid in the brake lines to larger pistons within the wheels of the car. Each of these pistons pushes on a brake pad. The brake pads rub against the brake disc, and the wheel's motion is slowed down by the force of friction. Because the brake system multiplies force, a person can stop a large car with only a light push on the brake pedal.

Section 3 Assessment

Target Reading Skill **Asking Questions** Use the answers to the questions you wrote about the headings to help you answer the questions below.

Reviewing Key Concepts

1. a. Reviewing According to Pascal's principle, how is pressure transmitted in a fluid?
  b. Relating Cause and Effect How does a hydraulic device multiply force?
  c. Calculating Suppose you apply a 10-N force to a 10-cm^2 piston in a hydraulic device. If the force is transmitted to another piston with an area of 100 cm^2, by how much will the force be multiplied?

2. a. Defining What is a hydraulic system?
  b. Explaining How does a hydraulic system work?

c. Sequencing Describe what happens in the brake system of a car from the time a driver steps on the brake pedal to the time the car stops.

Writing in Science

Cause-and-Effect Letter You are a mechanic who fixes hydraulic brakes. A customer asks you why his brakes do not work. When you examine the car, you notice a leak in the brake line and repair it. Write a letter to the customer explaining why a leak in the brake line caused his brakes to fail.

Bernoulli's Principle

Reading Preview

Key Concepts
- According to Bernoulli's principle, how is fluid pressure related to the motion of a fluid?
- What are some applications of Bernoulli's principle?

Key Terms
- Bernoulli's principle
- lift

Target Reading Skill
Identifying Main Ideas As you read the Applying Bernoulli's Principle section, write the main idea in a graphic organizer like the one below. Then write three supporting details that give examples of the main idea.

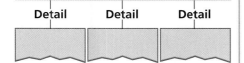

Main Idea

Bernoulli's principle is a factor that helps explain . . .

Detail	Detail	Detail

Lab zone Discover **Activity**

Does the Movement of Air Affect Pressure?

1. Use your thumb and forefinger to hold a sheet of paper by the corners.
2. Hold the paper just below your mouth, so that its edge is horizontal and the paper hangs down.
3. Blow across the top of the paper.
4. Repeat this several times, blowing harder each time.

Think It Over
Inferring On what side of the paper is the pressure lower? How do you know?

In December 1903, Wilbur and Orville Wright brought an odd-looking vehicle to a deserted beach in Kitty Hawk, North Carolina. People had flown in balloons for more than a hundred years, but the Wright brothers' goal was something no one had ever done before. They flew a plane that was heavier (denser) than air! They had spent years experimenting with different wing shapes and surfaces, and they had carefully studied the flight of birds. Their first flight at Kitty Hawk lasted just 12 seconds. The plane flew more than 36 meters and made history.

What did the Wright brothers know about flying that allowed them to construct the first airplane? And how can the principles they used explain how a jet can fly across the country? The answer has to do with fluid pressure and what happens when a fluid moves.

◄ On December 17, 1903, the Wright brothers' plane *Flyer* flew for the first time.

Faucet Force

1. Hold a plastic spoon loosely by the edges of its handle so it swings freely between your fingers.

2. Turn on a faucet to produce a steady stream of water. Predict what will happen if you touch the bottom of the spoon to the stream of water.

3. Test your prediction. Repeat the test several times.

Developing Hypotheses Use your observations to develop a hypothesis explaining why the spoon moved as it did.

Pressure and Moving Fluids

So far in this chapter, you have learned about fluids that are not moving. What makes a fluid flow? And what happens to fluid pressure when a fluid moves?

Fluid Motion A fluid naturally flows from an area of high pressure to an area of low pressure. This happens, for example, when you sip a drink from a straw. When you start to sip, you remove the air from the straw. This creates an area of low pressure in the straw. The higher air pressure pushing down on the surface of your drink forces the drink up into the straw.

What Is Bernoulli's Principle? In the 1700s, Swiss scientist Daniel Bernoulli (bur NOO lee) discovered that the pressure of a moving fluid is different than the pressure of a fluid at rest. **Bernoulli's principle** states that the faster a fluid moves, the less pressure the fluid exerts.

If you did the Discover Activity, you saw that air moving over the paper caused the paper to rise. Bernoulli's principle explains the behavior of the paper. **Bernoulli's principle states that as the speed of a moving fluid increases, the pressure within the fluid decreases.** The air above the paper moves, but the air below the paper does not. The moving air exerts less pressure than the still air. As a result, the still air exerts greater pressure on the bottom of the paper, pushing the paper up.

Reading Checkpoint) **What is Bernoulli's principle?**

FIGURE 17
Making Air Move
Blowing air quickly between two cans lowers the air pressure between them. Higher pressure exerted by the still air to either side pushes the cans toward each other.
Relating Cause and Effect *How does the flowing air affect the air pressure around the two cans?*

High pressure   High pressure

Low pressure

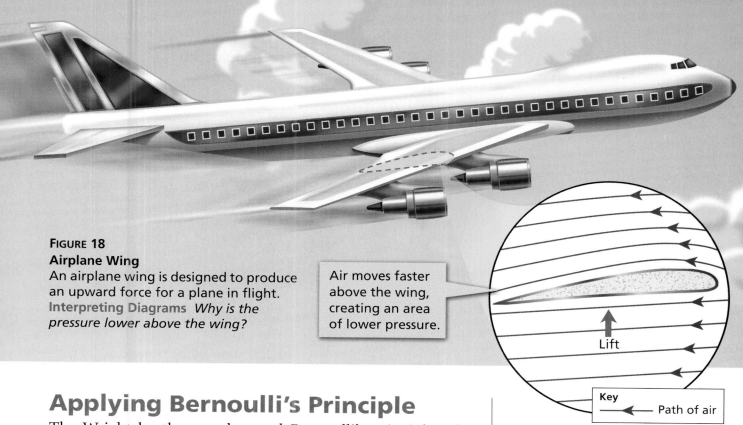

FIGURE 18
Airplane Wing
An airplane wing is designed to produce an upward force for a plane in flight.
Interpreting Diagrams Why is the pressure lower above the wing?

Air moves faster above the wing, creating an area of lower pressure.

Lift

Key — Path of air

Applying Bernoulli's Principle

The Wright brothers understood Bernoulli's principle. They used it when they designed and built their plane. **Bernoulli's principle helps explain how planes fly. It also helps explain why smoke rises up a chimney, how an atomizer works, and how a flying disk glides through the air.**

Objects in Flight Bernoulli's principle is one factor that helps explain flight—from a small kite to a huge airplane. Objects can be designed so that their shapes cause air to move at different speeds above and below them. If the air moves faster above the object, fluid pressure pushes the object upward. If the air moves faster below the object, fluid pressure pushes it downward.

The wing of an airplane is designed to produce **lift**, or an upward force. Look at Figure 18 to see the design of a wing. Both the slant and the shape of the wing are sources of lift. Because the wing is slanted, the air that hits it is forced downward as the plane moves. The air exerts an equal and opposite force on the wing and pushes it upward. This upward force helps an airplane to take off.

The curved shape of a wing also gives an airplane lift. Because the top of the wing is curved, air moving over the top has a greater speed than air moving under the bottom. As a result, the air moving over the top exerts less pressure than the air below. The difference in air pressure above and below the wing creates lift.

Go Online
SC LINKS NSTA

For: Links on Bernoulli's principle
Visit: www.SciLinks.org
Web Code: scn-1334

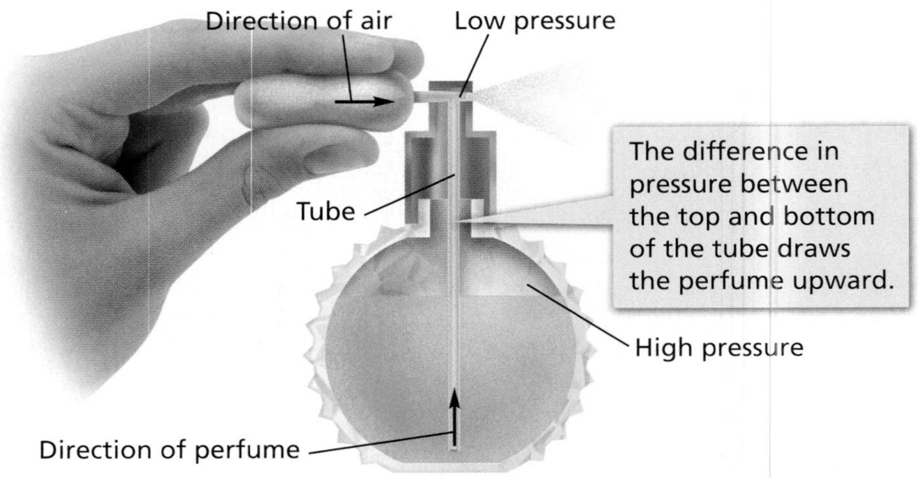

Direction of air   Low pressure

The difference in pressure between the top and bottom of the tube draws the perfume upward.

Tube

High pressure

Direction of perfume

FIGURE 19
Perfume Atomizer
An atomizer is an application of Bernoulli's principle.
Applying Concepts *Why is the perfume pushed up and out of the flask?*

Atomizers Bernoulli's principle can help you understand how the perfume atomizer shown in Figure 19 works. When you squeeze the rubber bulb, air moves quickly past the top of the tube. The moving air lowers the pressure at the top of the tube. The greater pressure in the flask pushes the liquid up into the tube. The air stream breaks the liquid into small drops, and the liquid comes out as a fine mist. In a similar way, pressure differences in the carburetors of older gasoline engines push gasoline up a tube. There, the gasoline combines with air to create the mixture of air and fuel that runs the engine.

Chimneys You can sit next to a fireplace enjoying a cozy fire thanks in part to Bernoulli's principle. Smoke rises up the chimney partly because hot air rises, and partly because it is pushed. Wind blowing across the top of a chimney lowers the air pressure there. The higher pressure at the bottom pushes air and smoke up the chimney. Smoke will rise faster in a chimney on a windy day than on a calm day.

Direction of wind

Lower pressure area

Direction of smoke

Wind blowing across the top of a chimney creates an area of low pressure.

The difference in air pressure between the top and bottom of the chimney helps keep air moving upward.

Higher pressure area

 Reading Checkpoint   **How does an atomizer work?**

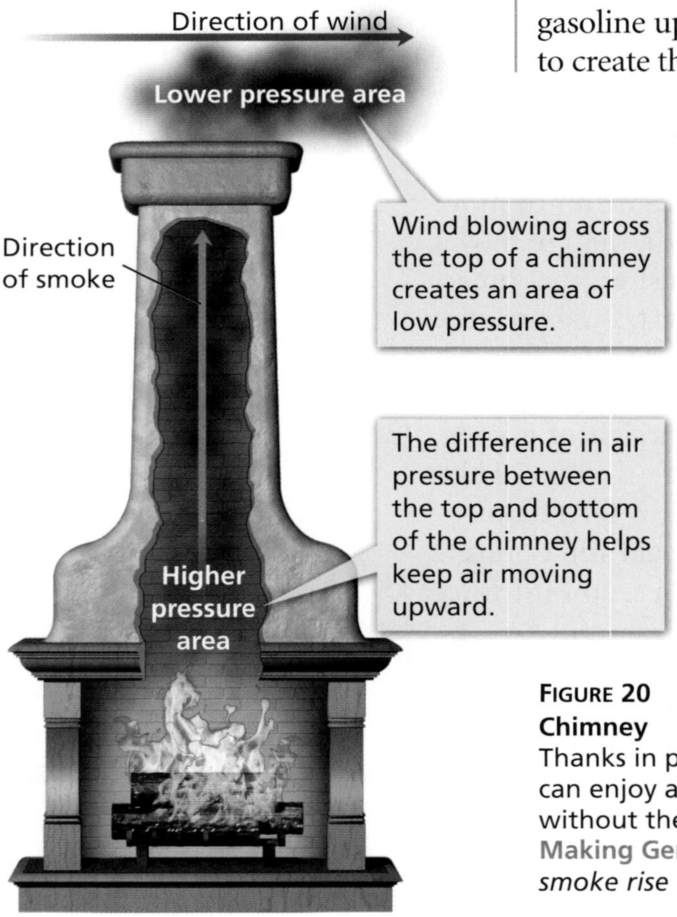

FIGURE 20
Chimney
Thanks in part to Bernoulli's principle, you can enjoy an evening by a warm fireplace without the room filling up with smoke.
Making Generalizations *Why does the smoke rise up the chimney?*

Lift

Key   ←——— Path of air

Flying Disks Did you ever wonder what allows a flying disk to glide through the air? The upper surface of a flying disk is curved like an airplane wing. Bernoulli's principle explains that the faster-moving air following the disk's curved upper surface exerts less pressure than the slower-moving air beneath it. A net force acts upward on the flying disk, creating lift. Tilting the disk slightly toward you as you throw it also helps to keep it in the air. A tilted disk pushes air down. The air exerts an equal and opposite force on the disk, pushing it up. The spinning motion of a flying disk keeps it stable as it flies.

FIGURE 21
Flying Disk
Like an airplane wing, a flying disk uses a curved upper surface to create lift. **Comparing and Contrasting** *How does a flying disk differ from an airplane wing?*

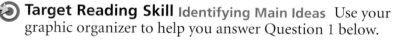

Section 4 Assessment

Target Reading Skill **Identifying Main Ideas** Use your graphic organizer to help you answer Question 1 below.

Reviewing Key Concepts

1. a. **Reviewing** What makes fluids flow?
   b. **Summarizing** What does Bernoulli's principle say about the pressure exerted by a moving fluid?
   c. **Applying Concepts** You are riding in a car on a highway when a large truck speeds by you. Explain why your car is pushed toward the truck.
2. a. **Listing** List four applications of Bernoulli's principle.
   b. **Explaining** Why does the air pressure above an airplane wing differ from the pressure below it? How is this pressure difference involved in flight?
   c. **Relating Cause and Effect** How could strong winds from a hurricane blow the roof off a house?

Lab zone At-Home Activity

Paper Chimney With a family member, see how a chimney works by using a paper cup and a hair dryer. Cut up several small pieces of tissue and place them in the bottom of a paper cup. Hold on to the paper cup with one hand. With your other hand, use the hair dryer to blow cool air across the top of the cup. Explain to your family member how Bernoulli's principle explains how the chimney works.

Helicopters

Most aircraft are like eagles—they take off majestically, glide among the clouds, and land with ease. But helicopters are the hummingbirds of aircraft. They can fly forward, backward, sideways, and up and down. They can stop abruptly and hover in midair. In fact, helicopters can fly circles around other types of aircraft.

Science in Action

On the top of a helicopter are large blades that turn rapidly. These blades are curved on top like the wings of an airplane. Air flowing over the curved blades helps cause lift— the upward force for the helicopter—just as air flowing over wings helps cause lift for most airplanes. Action and reaction forces as described by Newton's third law of motion also play a role in causing lift. As the tilted blades push down on the air, the air pushes up on the blade.

Main Rotor
The main rotor turns the blades and controls their angle.

Blades
Air flows over the curved, rotating blades. Along with action and reaction forces, this helps to give the helicopter lift.

As the main rotor spins, the reaction force pushes the helicopter's body in the opposite direction. If not for the tail rotor, the body would spin too.

Hand Controls and Foot Pedals
These controls are connected to the main rotor. The collective control guides the helicopter up or down. The cyclic control guides the helicopter forward, backward, or sideways. The foot pedals allow the helicopter to rotate in tight circles.

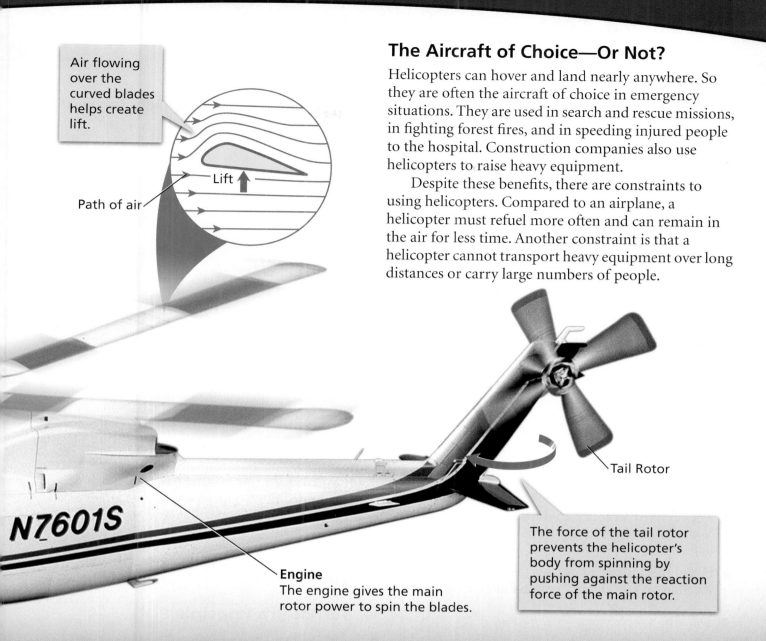

Air flowing over the curved blades helps create lift.

Lift

Path of air

The Aircraft of Choice—Or Not?

Helicopters can hover and land nearly anywhere. So they are often the aircraft of choice in emergency situations. They are used in search and rescue missions, in fighting forest fires, and in speeding injured people to the hospital. Construction companies also use helicopters to raise heavy equipment.

Despite these benefits, there are constraints to using helicopters. Compared to an airplane, a helicopter must refuel more often and can remain in the air for less time. Another constraint is that a helicopter cannot transport heavy equipment over long distances or carry large numbers of people.

Tail Rotor

N7601S

The force of the tail rotor prevents the helicopter's body from spinning by pushing against the reaction force of the main rotor.

Engine
The engine gives the main rotor power to spin the blades.

Weigh the Impact

1. Identify the Need
What advantages do helicopters have over airplanes?

2. Research
Using the Internet, research how helicopters are used in national parks, such as Yellowstone National Park. Choose one helicopter mission. Make notes on the mission's difficulty level, purpose, location, procedures, and outcome.

3. Write
Suppose you are a park ranger. Use your notes to write a report to your supervisor explaining why a helicopter was or was not the best technology to use for this mission.

Go Online
PHSchool.com

For: More on helicopters
Visit: PHSchool.com
Web Code: cgh-3030

① Pressure

Key Concepts

- Pressure decreases as the area over which a force is distributed increases.

- Pressure = $\dfrac{\text{Force}}{\text{Area}}$

- All of the forces exerted by the individual particles in a fluid combine to make up the pressure exerted by the fluid.

- As elevation increases, atmospheric pressure decreases.

- Water pressure increases as depth increases.

Key Terms

pressure
pascal
fluid
barometer

② Floating and Sinking

Key Concepts

- The buoyant force acts in the direction opposite to the force of gravity, so it makes an object feel lighter.

- By comparing densities, you can predict whether an object will float or sink in a fluid.

- Density = $\dfrac{\text{Mass}}{\text{Volume}}$

Key Terms

buoyant force
Archimedes' principle
density

③ Pascal's Principle

Key Concepts

- When force is applied to a confined fluid, the change in pressure is transmitted equally to all parts of the fluid.

- A hydraulic system multiplies force by applying the force to a small surface area. The increase in pressure is then transmitted to another part of the confined fluid, which pushes on a larger surface area.

Key Terms

Pascal's principle
hydraulic system

④ Bernoulli's Principle

Key Concepts

- Bernoulli's principle states that as the speed of a moving fluid increases, the pressure within the fluid decreases.

- Bernoulli's principle helps explain how planes fly. It also helps explain why smoke rises up a chimney, how an atomizer works, and how a flying disk glides through the air.

Key Terms

Bernoulli's principle
lift

Review and Assessment

For: Self-Assessment
Visit: PHSchool.com
Web Code: cga-3030

Organizing Information

Sequencing Create a flowchart that shows how a hydraulic device multiplies force. (For more on Sequencing, see the Skills Handbook.)

How a Hydraulic Device Works

Force applied to small piston

↓

a. _____ ?

↓

b. _____ ?

↓

c. _____ ?

↓

d. _____ ?

Reviewing Key Terms

Choose the letter of the best answer.

1. If you divide the force exerted on a surface by the total area of the surface, you will know
   a. density.
   b. pressure.
   c. lift.
   d. buoyant force.

2. If you know the weight of an object that floats, you know the
   a. object's density.
   b. object's mass.
   c. object's volume.
   d. buoyant force.

3. If you divide the mass of an object by its volume, you know the object's
   a. mass.
   b. weight.
   c. density.
   d. pressure.

4. The concept that an increase in pressure on a confined fluid is transmitted equally to all parts of the fluid is known as
   a. Pascal's principle.
   b. Bernoulli's principle.
   c. Archimedes' principle.
   d. Newton's third law.

5. The concept that the pressure in a fluid decreases as the speed of the fluid increases is known as
   a. Pascal's principle.
   b. Bernoulli's principle.
   c. Archimedes' principle.
   d. Newton's first law.

If the statement is true, write *true*. If it is false, change the underlined word or words to make the statement true.

6. Pressure is force per unit of <u>mass</u>.

7. A <u>fluid</u> is a material that can easily flow.

8. A factor that helps explain flight is <u>Archimedes' principle</u>.

9. A hydraulic system is designed to take advantage of <u>Pascal's principle</u>.

10. <u>Lift</u> is an upward force.

Writing in Science

News Report Suppose that you are a newspaper journalist on the day after the *Titanic* sank. Write a news report that tells what happened. Explain how the buoyancy of a ship is affected when it fills with water. Include information about the various fluid forces involved.

Forces in Fluids
Video Preview
Video Field Trip
▶ Video Assessment

Review and Assessment

Checking Concepts

11. How does the amount of pressure you exert on the floor when you are lying down compare with the amount of pressure you exert when you are standing up?

12. Why aren't deep-sea fish crushed by the tremendous pressure they experience?

13. Why do you seem to weigh more in air than you do in water?

14. In a hydraulic system, why is the force exerted on a small piston multiplied when it acts on a larger piston?

15. Name two hydraulic systems that an auto mechanic would know well.

16. Why is air pressure at the top of a chimney less than air pressure at the bottom?

Thinking Critically

17. Making Generalizations How does the water pressure change at each level in the jug below? How can you tell?

18. Developing Hypotheses A sphere made of steel is put in water and, surprisingly, it floats. Develop a possible explanation for this observation.

19. Applying Concepts One method of raising a sunken ship to the surface is to inflate large bags or balloons inside its hull. Explain why this procedure could work.

20. Problem Solving You have two fluids of unknown density. Suggest a method to determine which is denser, without mixing the two fluids.

Math Practice

21. Area The cover of your textbook measures about 28 cm × 22 cm. Find its area.

22. Area A dollar bill measures about 15.9 cm × 6.7 cm. The Chinese yuan note measures 14.5 cm × 7.0 cm. Which currency uses a larger bill?

Applying Skills

The illustration shows an object supported by a spring scale, both in and out of water. Use the illustration to answer Questions 23–25.

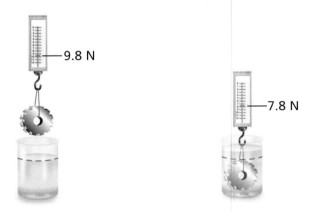

23. Inferring Why is there a difference between the weight of the object in air and its measured weight in water?

24. Calculating What is the buoyant force acting on the object?

25. Drawing Conclusions What can you conclude about the water above the dotted line?

Lab zone Chapter **Project**

Performance Assessment Test your boat to make sure it does not leak. Display the diagrams of different designs you tried and the observations and data you recorded for each design. Then demonstrate for the class how the boat floats. Point out to your classmates the features you used in your final design.

End-of-Grade Test Practice

Choose the letter of the best answer.

1. The upward force that acts on an airplane's wing is called
   A density.
   B inertia.
   C lift.
   D pressure.

2. Which of the following is an example of a hydraulic system?
   A a car's brakes
   B a barometer
   C an airplane's wing
   D a submarine's flotation tanks

3. A boat that weighs 28,800 N is loaded with 7,200 N of cargo. After it is loaded, what is the buoyant force acting on the boat?
   A 400 N
   B 22,000 N
   C 36,000 N
   D 360,000 N

4. Why doesn't air pressure crush human beings standing at sea level?
   A Air pressure at sea level is very low.
   B Clothing on our bodies shields us from air pressure.
   C Air is not as heavy as human beings.
   D Pressure from the fluids inside our bodies balances the air pressure outside.

5. You observe that a chunk of tar sinks in puddles of rainwater but floats on the ocean. An experiment to explain the behavior of the tar should measure
   A the difference between atmospheric pressure and water pressure.
   B the densities of fresh water, salt water, and tar.
   C the height from which the chunk of tar is dropped.
   D the depth of each type of water.

Constructed Response

Use the diagram below and your knowledge of science to help you answer Question 6.

6. Use Bernoulli's principle to explain why the fabric of a domed tent bulges outward on a windy day.

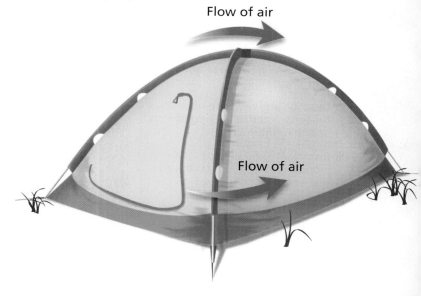

Flow of air

Flow of air

Chapter 19

Work and Machines

Standard Course of Study

1.01 Identify and create questions and hypotheses.

1.02 Develop appropriate experimental procedures.

1.03 Apply safety procedures.

1.04 Analyze variables.

1.05 Analyze evidence.

1.06 Use mathematics to gather, organize, and present data.

1.07 Prepare models and/or computer simulations.

1.08 Use oral and written language.

1.09 Use technologies and information systems.

2.01 Explore definitions of "technology."

2.02 Use information systems.

2.03 Evaluate technological designs.

6.01 Demonstrate how simple machines change force.

6.02 Analyze simple machines for mechanical advantage and efficiency.

6.05 Describe and measure quantities that characterize moving objects and their interactions.

6.06 Investigate and analyze real-world interactions of balanced and unbalanced forces.

Interactive Textbook

▶ A Maori woodcarver in New Zealand creates a traditional carving.

Lab zone™ Chapter **Project**

The Nifty Lifting Machine

In this Chapter Project, you will design and build a lifting machine and then demonstrate it to the class.

Your Goal To design, build, and test a complex machine that can lift a 600-gram soup can 5 centimeters

Your machine must
- be made of materials that are approved by your teacher
- consist of at least two simple machines working in combination
- be able to lift the soup can to a height of at least 5 centimeters
- be built following the safety guidelines in Appendix A

Plan It! Preview the chapter to find out what simple machines you can use and how to use them. Determine the amount of work your machine must do. Brainstorm different machine designs and materials with your classmates. Analyze factors affecting efficiency and mechanical advantage, and then construct your machine. When your teacher has approved your design, build and test your machine.

What Is Work?

Reading Preview

Key Concepts
- When is work done on an object?
- How do you determine the work done on an object?
- What is power?

Key Terms
- work • joule • power

🎯 Target Reading Skill

Asking Questions Before you read, preview the red headings. In a graphic organizer like the one below, ask a *what* or *how* question for each heading. As you read, write the answers to your questions.

Question	Answer
What is work?	Work is . . .

This morning you probably woke up and went to school with your backpack of books. You lifted the backpack and then carried it with you. If you had a lot of books to bring home, carrying your backpack might have felt like a lot of work. But in the scientific definition of work, after you lifted the backpack, you did no work to carry it at all!

The Meaning of Work

In scientific terms, you do **work** when you exert a force on an object that causes the object to move some distance. **Work is done on an object when the object moves in the same direction in which the force is exerted.** If you push a child on a swing, for example, you are doing work on the child. If you pull your books out of your backpack, you do work on the books. If you lift a bag of groceries out of a shopping cart, you do work on the bag of groceries.

FIGURE 1
Doing Work
Lifting books out of a backpack is work, but carrying them to class is not.

No Work Without Motion To do work on an object, the object must move some distance as a result of your force. If the object does not move, no work is done, no matter how much force is exerted.

There are many situations in which you exert a force but don't do any work. Suppose, for example, you are pushing a car that is stuck in the snow. You certainly exert a force on the car, so it might seem as if you do work. But if the force you exert does not make the car move, you are not doing any work on it.

Force in the Same Direction So why didn't you do any work when you carried your books to school? To do work on an object, the force you exert must be in the same direction as the object's motion. When you carry an object at constant velocity, you exert an upward force to hold the object so that it doesn't fall to the ground. The motion of the object, however, is in the horizontal direction. Since the force is vertical and the motion is horizontal, you don't do any work on the object as you carry it.

How much work do you do when you pull a suitcase with wheels? When you pull a suitcase, you pull on the handle at an angle to the ground. As you can see in Figure 2, your force has both a horizontal part and a vertical part. When you pull this way, only part of your force does work—the part in the same direction as the motion of the suitcase. The rest of your force does not help pull the suitcase forward.

 **Reading Checkpoint** **If you pull an object horizontally, what part of your force does work?**

FIGURE 2
Force, Motion, and Work
Whether the girl does work on the suitcase depends on the direction of her force and the suitcase's motion. **Drawing Conclusions** *Why doesn't the girl do work when she carries her suitcase rather than pulling it?*

Direction of motion

A The lifting force is not in the direction of the suitcase's motion, so no work is done.

Force

Direction of motion

B The force acts in the same direction as the suitcase's motion, so the maximum work is done.

Part of the force that does no work

Force

Part of the force that does work

Direction of motion

C Only the horizontal part of the force does work to move the suitcase.

FIGURE 3
Amount of Work
When you lift a plant, you do work. You do more work when you lift a heavier plant the same distance.
Relating Cause and Effect
Why does it take more work to lift the heavier plant?

For: Links on work
Visit: www.SciLinks.org
Web Code: scn-1341

Calculating Work

Which do you think involves more work: lifting a 50-newton potted plant 0.5 meters off the ground onto a table, or lifting a 100-newton plant onto the same table? Your common sense may suggest that lifting a heavier object requires more work than lifting a lighter object. This is true. Is it more work to lift a plant onto a table or up to the top story of a building? As you might guess, moving an object a greater distance requires more work than moving the same object a shorter distance.

The amount of work you do depends on both the amount of force you exert and the distance the object moves. **The amount of work done on an object can be determined by multiplying force times distance.**

> **Work = Force × Distance**

You can use the work formula to calculate the amount of work you do to lift a plant. When you lift an object, the upward force you exert must be at least equal to the object's weight. So, to lift the lighter plant, you would have to exert a force of 50 newtons. The distance you lift the plant is 0.5 meters. The amount of work you do on the plant can be calculated using the work formula.

$$\text{Work} = \text{Force} \times \text{Distance}$$
$$\text{Work} = 50\ \text{N} \times 0.5\ \text{m} = 25\ \text{N·m}$$

To lift the heavier plant, you would have to exert a force of 100 newtons. So the amount of work you do would be 100 newtons × 0.5 meters, or 50 N·m. As you can see, you do more work to lift the heavier object.

When force is measured in newtons and distance in meters, the SI unit of work is the newton × meter (N·m). This unit is also called a joule (JOOL) in honor of James Prescott Joule, a physicist who studied work in the mid-1800s. One **joule** (J) is the amount of work you do when you exert a force of 1 newton to move an object a distance of 1 meter. You would have to exert 25 joules of work to lift the lighter plant and 50 joules of work to lift the heavier plant.

 **Reading Checkpoint** **What is the SI unit for work?**

Power

The amount of work you do on an object is not affected by the time it takes to do the work. For example, if you carry a backpack up a flight of stairs, the work you do is the weight of the backpack times the height of the stairs. Whether you walk or run up the stairs, you do the same amount of work because time is not part of the definition of work.

But time is important when you talk about power. **Power** is the rate at which work is done. **Power equals the amount of work done on an object in a unit of time.** You need more power to run up the stairs with your backpack than to walk because it takes you less time to do the same work.

You can think of power in another way. An object that has more power than another object does more work in the same time. It can also mean doing the same amount of work in less time.

For example, a car's engine does work to accelerate the car from its rest position. The greater a car engine's power, the faster the engine can accelerate the car.

FIGURE 4
Work and Power
Whether you use a rake or a blower, the same amount of work is done to gather leaves. However, the blower has more power.
Inferring *Will the blower or the rake do the same amount of work in less time?*

Calculating Power Whenever you know how fast work is done, you can calculate power. Power is calculated by dividing the amount of work done by the amount of time it takes to do the work. This can be written as the following formula.

$$\text{Power} = \frac{\text{Work}}{\text{Time}}$$

Since work is equal to force times distance, you can rewrite the equation for power as follows.

$$\text{Power} = \frac{\text{Force} \times \text{Distance}}{\text{Time}}$$

Full Serve

Math ▸ Sample Problem

Calculating Power

A tow truck exerts a force of 11,000 N to pull a car out of a ditch. It moves the car a distance of 5 m in 25 seconds. What is the power of the tow truck?

1 Read and Understand
What information are you given?
- Force of the tow truck (F) = **11,000 N**
- Distance (d) = **5.0 m**
- Time (t) = **25 s**

2 Plan and Solve
What quantity are you trying to calculate?
The power (P) of the tow truck = ▪

What formula contains the given quantities and the unknown quantity?

$$\text{Power} = \frac{\text{Force} \times \text{Distance}}{\text{Time}}$$

Perform the calculation.

$$\text{Power} = \frac{11,000 \text{ N} \times 5.0 \text{ m}}{25 \text{ s}}$$

$$\text{Power} = \frac{55,000 \text{ N·m}}{25 \text{ s}} \text{ or } \frac{55,000 \text{ J}}{25 \text{ s}}$$

$$\text{Power} = 2,200 \text{ J/s} = 2,200 \text{ W}$$

3 Look Back and Check
Does your answer make sense?
The answer tells you that the tow truck pulls the car with a power of 2,200 W. This value is about the same power of three horses, so the answer is reasonable.

Math ▸ Practice

1. **Calculating Power** A motor exerts a force of 12,000 N to lift an elevator 8.0 m in 6.0 seconds. What is the power of the motor?

2. **Calculating Power** A crane lifts an 8,000-N beam 75 m to the top of a building in 30 seconds. What is the crane's power?

Power Units When work is measured in joules and time in seconds, the SI unit of power is the joule per second (J/s). This unit is also known as the watt (W), in honor of James Watt, who made great improvements to the steam engine. One joule of work done in one second is one watt of power. In other words, 1 J/s = 1 W.

A watt is a relatively small unit of power. Because a watt is so small, power is often measured in larger units. One kilowatt (kW) equals 1,000 watts.

When people talk about engines for vehicles, they use another power unit instead of the watt. This unit is the horsepower. One horsepower equals 746 watts. (The horsepower is not an SI unit.)

FIGURE 5
Horsepower
James Watt used the word *horsepower* to advertise the advantages of his improved steam engine (next to the chimney) of 1769.

 **Reading Checkpoint** **What is a kilowatt?**

Section 1 Assessment

Target Reading Skill Asking Questions Use the answers to the questions you wrote about the headings to help you answer the questions below.

Reviewing Key Concepts

1. a. Reviewing What is work?
   b. Describing In order for work to be done on an object, what must happen to the object?
   c. Applying Concepts In which of the following situations is work being done: rolling a bowling ball, pushing on a tree for ten minutes, kicking a football?

2. a. Identifying What is a joule?
   b. Explaining How can you determine the amount of work done on an object?
   c. Problem Solving Is more work done when a force of 2 N moves an object 3 m or when a force of 3 N moves an object 2 m? Explain.

3. a. Defining What is power?
   b. Summarizing How are power and work related?

Math Practice

4. Calculating Power Your laundry basket weighs 22 N and your room is 3.0 m above you on the second floor. It takes you 6.0 seconds to carry the laundry basket up. What is your power?

5. Calculating Power If you take only 4.4 seconds to carry the basket upstairs, what is your power?

How Machines Do Work

Reading Preview

Key Concepts
- How do machines make work easier?
- What is a machine's mechanical advantage?
- How can you calculate the efficiency of a machine?

Key Terms
- machine • input force
- output force • input work
- output work
- mechanical advantage
- efficiency

Target Reading Skill
Identifying Main Ideas As you read the What Is a Machine? section, write the main idea in a graphic organizer like the one below. Then write three supporting details.

Main Idea

The mechanical advantage of a machine helps by . . .

Detail	Detail	Detail

Lab zone Discover **Activity**

Is It a Machine?
1. Examine the objects that your teacher gives you.
2. Sort the objects into those that are machines and those that are not machines.
3. Determine how each object that you classified as a machine functions. Explain each object to another student.

Think It Over
Forming Operational Definitions Why did you decide certain objects were machines while other objects were not?

A load of soil for your school garden has been dumped 10 meters from the garden. How can you move the soil easily and quickly? You could move the soil by handfuls, but that would take a long time. Using a shovel would make the job easier. If you had a wheelbarrow, that would make the job easier still! But be careful what you think. Using a machine may make work go faster, but it doesn't mean you do less work.

FIGURE 6
Using Machines
Shovels and rakes make the work of these students easier.

What Is a Machine?

Shovels and wheelbarrows are two examples of machines. A **machine** is a device that allows you to do work in a way that is easier or more effective. You may think of machines as complex gadgets with motors, but a machine can be quite simple. For example, think about using a shovel. A shovel makes the work of moving soil easier, so a shovel is a machine.

Moving a pile of soil will involve the same amount of work whether you use your hands or a shovel. What a shovel or any other machine does is change the way in which work is done. **A machine makes work easier by changing at least one of three factors. A machine may change the amount of force you exert, the distance over which you exert your force, or the direction in which you exert your force.** In other words, a machine makes work easier by changing either force, distance, or direction.

Input and Output Forces When you use a machine to do work, you exert a force over some distance. For example, you exert a force on the shovel when you use it to lift soil. The force you exert on the machine is called the **input force.** The input force moves the machine a certain distance, called the input distance. The machine does work by exerting a force over another distance, called the output distance. The force the machine exerts on an object is called the **output force.**

Input and Output Work The input force times the input distance is called the **input work.** The output force times the output distance is called the **output work.** When you use a machine, the amount of input work equals the amount of output work.

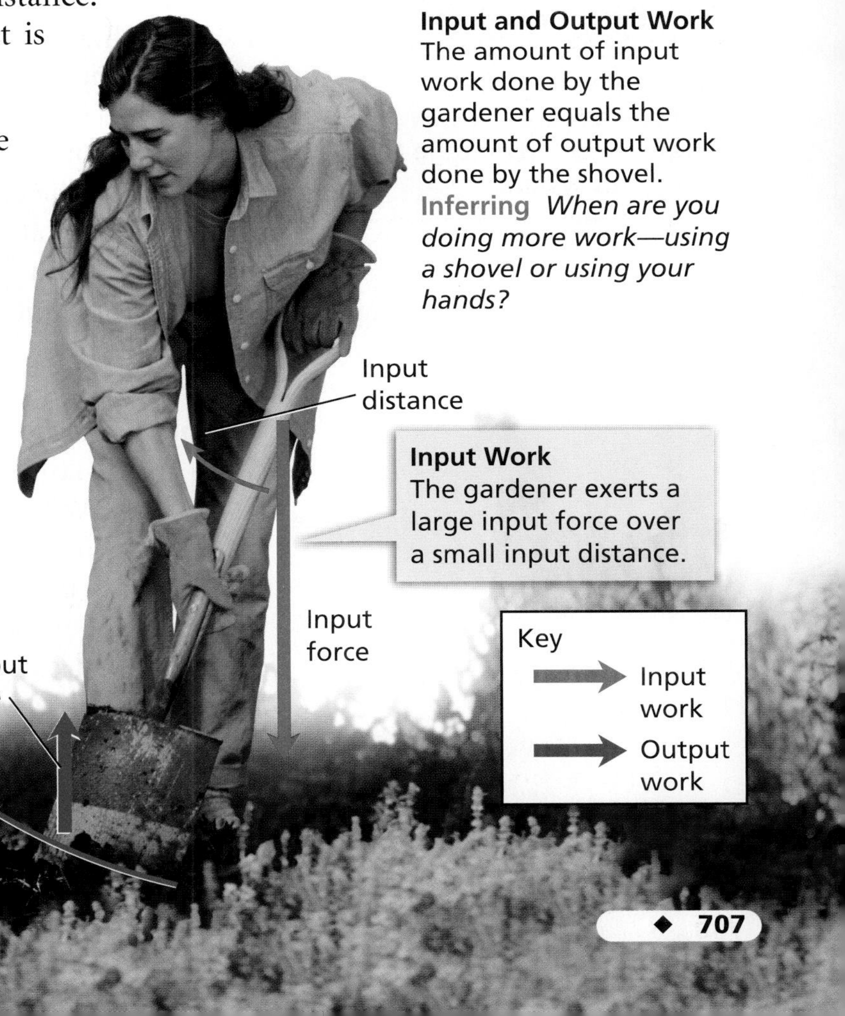

FIGURE 7
Input and Output Work
The amount of input work done by the gardener equals the amount of output work done by the shovel.
Inferring When are you doing more work—using a shovel or using your hands?

Input distance

Input Work
The gardener exerts a large input force over a small input distance.

Input force

Output Work
The shovel exerts a small output force over a large output distance.

Output distance

Output force

Key
→ Input work
→ Output work

Lab zone Try This **Activity**

Going Up
Does a rope simply turn your force upside down? Find out!

1. Tie a piece of string about 50 cm long to an object, such as an empty cooking pot. Make a small loop on the other end of the string.

2. Using a spring scale, slowly lift the pot 20 cm. Note the reading on the scale.

3. Now loop the string over a pencil and pull down on the spring scale to lift the pot 20 cm. Note the reading on the scale.

Developing Hypotheses
How did the readings on the spring scale compare? If the readings were different, suggest a reason why. What might be an advantage to using this system?

Changing Force In some machines, the output force is greater than the input force. How can this happen? Recall the formula for work: Work = Force × Distance. If the amount of work stays the same, a decrease in force must mean an increase in distance. So if a machine allows you to use less input force to do the same amount of work, you must apply that input force over a greater distance.

What kind of machine allows you to exert a smaller input force? Think about a ramp. Suppose you have to lift a heavy box onto a stage. Instead of lifting the box, you could push it up a ramp. Because the length of the ramp is greater than the height of the stage, you exert your input force over a greater distance. However, when you use the ramp, the work is easier because you can exert a smaller input force. The faucet knob in Figure 8 changes force in the same way.

Changing Distance In some machines, the output force is less than the input force. Why would you want to use a machine like this? This kind of machine allows you to exert your input force over a shorter distance. In order to apply a force over a shorter distance, you need to apply a greater input force.

When do you use this kind of machine? Think about taking a shot with a hockey stick. You move your hands a short distance, but the other end of the stick moves a greater distance to hit the puck. When you use chopsticks to eat your food, you move the hand holding the chopsticks a short distance. The other end of the chopsticks moves a greater distance, allowing you to pick up and eat food. When you ride a bicycle in high gear, you apply a force to the pedals over a short distance. The bicycle, meanwhile, travels a much longer distance.

Changing Direction Some machines don't change either force or distance. What could be the advantage of these machines? Well, think about a weight machine. You could stand and lift the weights. But it is much easier to sit on the machine and pull down than to lift up. By running a steel cable over a small wheel at the top of the machine, as shown in Figure 8, you can raise the weights by pulling down on the cable. This cable system is a machine that makes your job easier by changing the direction in which you exert your force.

 **Reading Checkpoint** How does the cable system on a weight machine make raising the weights easier?

FIGURE 8

Making Work Easier

A machine can make work easier in one of three ways.

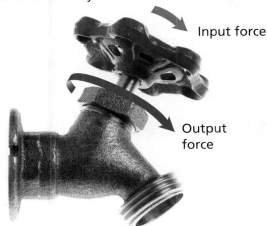

Input force

Output force

When a machine increases force, you must exert the input force over a greater distance.

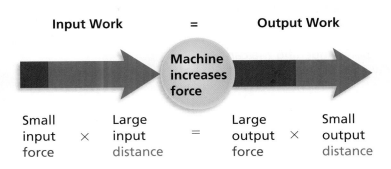

Input Work = **Output Work**

Machine increases force

| Small input force | × | Large input distance | = | Large output force | × | Small output distance |

When a machine increases distance, you must apply a greater input force.

Input Work = **Output Work**

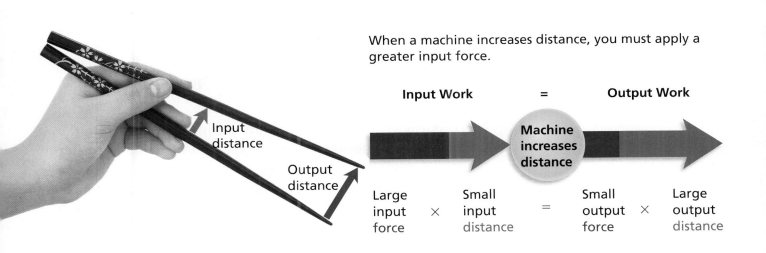

Input distance

Output distance

Machine increases distance

| Large input force | × | Small input distance | = | Small output force | × | Large output distance |

When a machine changes the direction of the input force, the amount of force and the distance remain the same.

Input Work = **Output Work**

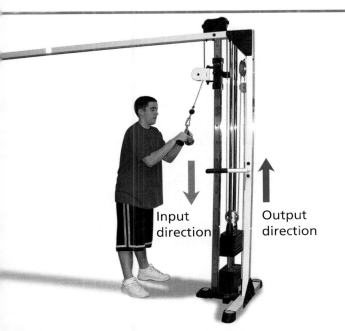

Input direction

Output direction

Machine changes direction

| Small input force | × | Large input distance | = | Large output distance | × | Small output force |

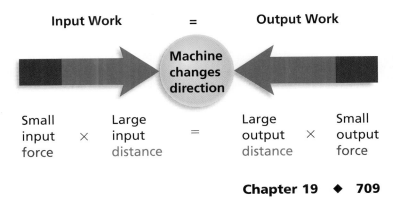

FIGURE 9
Mechanical Advantage
Without the mechanical advantage of the can opener, opening the can would be very difficult.

Mechanical Advantage

If you compare the input force to the output force, you can find the advantage of using a machine. **A machine's mechanical advantage is the number of times a machine increases a force exerted on it.** Finding the ratio of output force to input force gives you the **mechanical advantage** of a machine.

$$\text{Mechanical advantage} = \frac{\text{Output force}}{\text{Input force}}$$

Increasing Force When the output force is greater than the input force, the mechanical advantage of a machine is greater than 1. Suppose you exert an input force of 10 newtons on a hand-held can opener, and the opener exerts an output force of 30 newtons on a can. The mechanical advantage of the can opener is

$$\frac{\text{Output force}}{\text{Input force}} = \frac{30 \text{ N}}{10 \text{ N}} = 3$$

The can opener triples your input force!

Increasing Distance For a machine that increases distance, the output force is less than the input force. So in this case, the mechanical advantage is less than 1. For example, suppose your input force is 20 newtons and the machine's output force is 10 newtons. The mechanical advantage is

$$\frac{\text{Output force}}{\text{Input force}} = \frac{10 \text{ N}}{20 \text{ N}} = 0.5$$

The output force of the machine is half your input force, but the machine exerts that force over a longer distance.

Mechanical Advantage

The input force and output force for three different ramps are shown in the graph.

1. **Reading Graphs** What variable is plotted on the horizontal axis?

2. **Interpreting Data** If an 80-N input force is exerted on Ramp 2, what is the output force?

3. **Interpreting Data** Find the slope of the line for each ramp.

4. **Drawing Conclusions** Why does the slope represent each ramp's mechanical advantage? Which ramp has the greatest mechanical advantage?

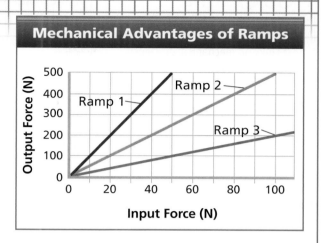

Mechanical Advantages of Ramps

Changing Direction What can you predict about the mechanical advantage of a machine that changes the direction of the force? If only the direction changes, the input force will be the same as the output force. The mechanical advantage will always be 1.

Efficiency of Machines

So far, you have learned that the work you put into a machine is exactly equal to the work done by the machine. In an ideal situation, this equation is true. In real situations, however, the output work is always less than the input work.

Friction and Efficiency If you have ever tried to cut something with scissors that barely open and close, you know that a large part of your work is wasted overcoming the tightness, or friction, between the parts of the scissors.

In every machine, some work is wasted overcoming the force of friction. The less friction there is, the closer the output work is to the input work. The **efficiency** of a machine compares the output work to the input work. Efficiency is expressed as a percent. The higher the percent, the more efficient the machine is. If you know the input work and output work for a machine, you can calculate a machine's efficiency.

FIGURE 10
Efficiency
A rusty pair of shears is less efficient than a new pair of shears.
Applying Concepts *What force reduces the efficiency of the shears?*

Reading Checkpoint **Why is output work always less than input work in real situations?**

Go Online

SC LINKS™ **NSTA**

For: Links on mechanical efficiency
Visit: www.SciLinks.org
Web Code: scn-1342

Calculating Efficiency To calculate the efficiency of a machine, divide the output work by the input work and multiply the result by 100 percent. This is summarized by the following formula.

$$\text{Efficiency} = \frac{\text{Output work}}{\text{Input work}} \times 100\%$$

If the tight scissors described above have an efficiency of 60%, only a little more than half of the work you do goes into cutting the paper. The rest is wasted overcoming the friction in the scissors.

Math ▶ Sample Problem

Calculating Efficiency

You do 250,000 J of work to cut a lawn with a hand mower. If the work done by the mower is 200,000 J, what is the efficiency of the lawn mower?

① **Read and Understand.**
What information are you given?

Input work (W_{input}) = 250,000 J

Output work (W_{output}) = 200,000 J

② **Plan and Solve**
What quantity are you trying to calculate?

The efficiency of the lawn mower = ■

What formula contains the given quantities and the unknown quantity?

$$\text{Efficiency} = \frac{\text{Output work}}{\text{Input work}} \times 100\%$$

Perform the calculation.

$$\text{Efficiency} = \frac{200,000 \text{ J}}{250,000 \text{ J}} \times 100\%$$

$$\text{Efficiency} = 0.8 \times 100\% = 80\%$$

The efficiency of the lawn mower is 80%.

③ **Look Back and Check**
Does your answer make sense?

An efficiency of 80% means that 80 out of every 100 J of work went into cutting the lawn. This answer makes sense because most of the input work is converted to output work.

Math ▶ Practice

1. **Calculating Efficiency** You do 20 J of work while using a hammer. The hammer does 18 J of work on a nail. What is the efficiency of the hammer?

2. **Calculating Efficiency** Suppose you left your lawn mower outdoors all winter. Now it's rusty. Of your 250,000 J of work, only 100,000 J go to cutting the lawn. What is the efficiency of the lawn mower now?

FIGURE 11
An Ideal Machine?
M. C. Escher's print *Waterfall* illustrates an ideal machine. **Inferring** *Why won't Escher's waterfall machine work in real life?*

Real and Ideal Machines If you could find a machine with an efficiency of 100%, it would be an ideal machine. Unfortunately, an ideal machine, such as the one shown in Figure 11, does not exist. In all machines, some work is wasted due to friction. So all machines have an efficiency of less than 100%. The machines you use every day, such as scissors, screwdrivers, and rakes, lose some work due to friction.

A machine's ideal mechanical advantage is its mechanical advantage with 100% efficiency. However, if you measure a machine's input force and output force, you will find the efficiency is always less than 100%. A machine's measured mechanical advantage is called actual mechanical advantage.

Reading Checkpoint **What is a machine's ideal mechanical advantage?**

Section 2 Assessment

Target Reading Skill

Identifying Main Ideas Use your graphic organizer to help you answer Question 1 below.

Reviewing Key Concepts

1. a. Defining What is a machine?
  b. Describing In what three ways can machines make work easier?
  c. Applying Concepts How does a screwdriver make work easier?
2. a. Reviewing What is the mechanical advantage of a machine?
  b. Making Generalizations What is the mechanical advantage of a machine that changes only the direction of the applied force?
  c. Calculating If a machine has an input force of 40 N and an output force of 80 N, what is its mechanical advantage?

3. a. Reviewing What must you know in order to calculate a machine's efficiency?
  b. Explaining What is an ideal machine?
  c. Comparing and Contrasting How is a real machine like an ideal machine, and how is it different?

Math Practice

4. Calculating Efficiency The input work you do on a can opener is 12 J. The output work the can opener does is 6 J. What is the efficiency of the can opener?

5. Calculating Efficiency Suppose the efficiency of a manual pencil sharpener is 58%. If the output work needed to sharpen a pencil is 4.8 J, how much input work must you do to sharpen the pencil?

Seesaw Science

Problem

What is the relationship between distance and weight for a balanced seesaw?

Skills Focus

controlling variables, interpreting data

Materials

- meter stick • masking tape
- 28 pennies, minted after 1982
- small object with a mass of about 50 g
- dowel or other cylindrical object for pivot point, about 10 cm long and 3 cm in diameter

Procedure

1. Begin by using the dowel and meter stick to build a seesaw. Tape the dowel firmly to the table so that it does not roll.

2. Choose the meter stick mark that will rest on the dowel from the following: 55 cm or 65 cm. Record your choice. Position your meter stick so that it is on your chosen pivot point with the 100-cm mark on your right.

3. Slide the 50-g mass along the shorter end of the meter stick until the meter stick is balanced, with both sides in the air. (This is called "zeroing" your meter stick.)

4. Copy the data table into your notebook.

5. Place a stack of 8 pennies exactly over the 80-cm mark. Determine the distance, in centimeters, from the pivot point to the pennies. Record this distance in the "Distance to Pivot" column for the right side of the seesaw.

6. Predict where you must place a stack of 5 pennies in order to balance the meter stick. Test your prediction and record the actual position in the "Position of Pennies" column for the left side of the seesaw.

Data Table					
Your group's pivot point position: _____ cm					
Trial Number	Side of Seesaw	Number of Pennies or Weight of Pennies (pw)	Position of Pennies (cm)	Distance to Pivot (cm)	Weight of Pennies × Distance
1	Right				
	Left				
2	Right				
	Left				
3	Right				

7. Determine the distance, in centimeters, from the pivot point to the left stack of pennies. Record this distance in the "Distance to Pivot" column for the left side of the seesaw.

8. If you use an imaginary unit of weight, the pennyweight (pw), then one penny weighs 1 pw. Multiply the weight of each stack of pennies by the distance to the pivot point. Record the result in the last column of the data table.

9. Predict how the position of the pennies in Step 6 would change if you used 7, 12, 16, and 20 pennies instead of 5 pennies. Test your predictions.

Analyze and Conclude

1. **Controlling Variables** In this experiment, what is the manipulated variable? The responding variable? How do you know which is which?

2. **Interpreting Data** As you increase the number of pennies on the left, what happens to the distance at which you must place the stack in order to balance the meter stick?

3. **Drawing Conclusions** What conclusion can you draw about the relationship between distances and weights needed to balance a seesaw?

4. **Controlling Variables** Why was it important to zero the meter stick with the 50-g mass?

5. **Interpreting Data** Compare your results with those of the other groups. How do different pivot point positions affect the results?

6. **Communicating** Write a dialogue that occurs when two friends try to balance themselves on opposite sides of a seesaw. One friend has a mass of 54 kg and the other friend has a mass of 42 kg.

Design an Experiment

Suppose you have a seesaw with a movable pivot. You want to use it with a younger friend who weighs half what you weigh. If you and your friend sit on the ends of the seesaw, where should you position the pivot point? Develop a hypothesis and then design an experiment to test it. *Obtain your teacher's permission before carrying out your investigation.*

Reading Preview

Key Concepts
- What are the six kinds of simple machines, and how are they used?
- What is the ideal mechanical advantage of each simple machine?
- What is a compound machine?

Key Terms
- inclined plane • wedge
- screw • lever • fulcrum
- wheel and axle • pulley
- compound machine

Target Reading Skill

Previewing Visuals Before you read, preview Figure 17. Then write two questions that you have about the diagram in a graphic organizer like the one below. As you read, answer your questions.

Three Classes of Levers

Q.	What are the three classes of levers?
A.	
Q.	

Discover Activity

Lab zone

How Can You Increase Force?

1. Working with two partners, wrap a rope around two broomsticks as shown.
2. Your two partners should try to hold the brooms apart with the same amount of force throughout the activity. For safety, they should hold firmly, but not with all their strength.
3. Try to pull the two students together by pulling on the broomsticks. Can you do it?
4. Can you pull them together by pulling on the rope?

Think It Over

Predicting What do you think will be the effect of wrapping the rope around the broomsticks several more times?

Look at the objects shown on these pages. Which of them would you call machines? Would it surprise you to find out that each is made up of one or more simple machines? As you learned in the last section, a machine helps you do work by changing the amount or direction of the force you apply.

There are six basic kinds of simple machines: the inclined plane, the wedge, the screw, the lever, the wheel and axle, and the pulley. In this section, you will learn how the different types of simple machines help you do work.

◀ An eggbeater, a bolt, and a fishing pole all make use of simple machines.

Inclined Plane

Have you ever had to lift something from a lower level to a higher level? The job is much easier if you have a ramp. For example, a ramp makes it much easier to push a grocery cart over a curb. A ramp is an example of a simple machine called an inclined plane. An **inclined plane** is a flat, sloped surface.

How It Works An inclined plane allows you to exert your input force over a longer distance. As a result, the input force needed is less than the output force. The input force that you use on an inclined plane is the force with which you push or pull an object. The output force is the force that you would need to lift the object without the inclined plane. Recall that this force is equal to the weight of the object.

Mechanical Advantage You can determine the ideal mechanical advantage of an inclined plane by dividing the length of the incline by its height.

$$\text{Ideal mechanical advantage} = \frac{\text{Length of incline}}{\text{Height of incline}}$$

For example, if you are loading a truck that is 1 meter high using a ramp that is 3 meters long, the ideal mechanical advantage of the ramp is 3 meters ÷ 1 meter, or 3. The inclined plane increases the force you exerted three times. If the height of the incline does not change, increasing the length of the incline will increase the mechanical advantage. The longer the incline, the less input force you need to push or pull an object.

FIGURE 12
Inclined Plane
Although the amount of work is the same whether you lift the boxes or push them up the ramp to the truck, you need less force when you use an inclined plane.
Relating Cause and Effect *When you use a ramp, what happens to the distance over which you exert your force?*

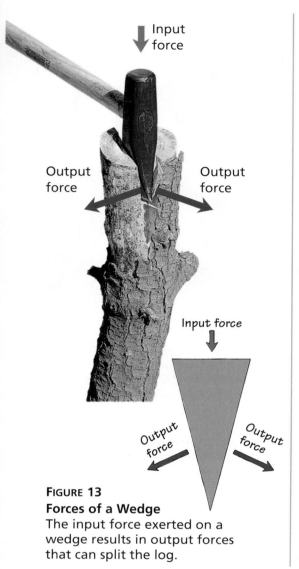

FIGURE 13
Forces of a Wedge
The input force exerted on a wedge results in output forces that can split the log.

Wedge

If you've ever sliced an apple with a knife, pulled up a zipper, or seen someone chop wood with an ax, you are familiar with another simple machine known as a wedge. A **wedge** is a device that is thick at one end and tapers to a thin edge at the other end. It might be helpful to think of a wedge, like the one shown in Figure 13, as an inclined plane (or sometimes two inclined planes back to back) that can move.

How It Works When you use a wedge, instead of moving an object along the inclined plane, you move the inclined plane itself. For example, when an ax is used to split wood, the ax handle exerts a force on the blade of the ax, which is the wedge. That force pushes the wedge down into the wood. The wedge in turn exerts an output force at a 90° angle to its slope, splitting the wood in two.

Wedges are a part of your everyday life. For example, a zipper depends on wedges to close and open. A pencil sharpener, a cheese grater, and a shovel all make use of wedges.

Mechanical Advantage The mechanical advantage of the wedge and the inclined plane are similar. **The ideal mechanical advantage of a wedge is determined by dividing the length of the wedge by its width.** The longer and thinner a wedge is, the greater its mechanical advantage. For example, the cutting edge of a steel carving knife is a wedge. When you sharpen a knife, you make the wedge thinner and increase its mechanical advantage. That is why sharp knives cut better than dull knives.

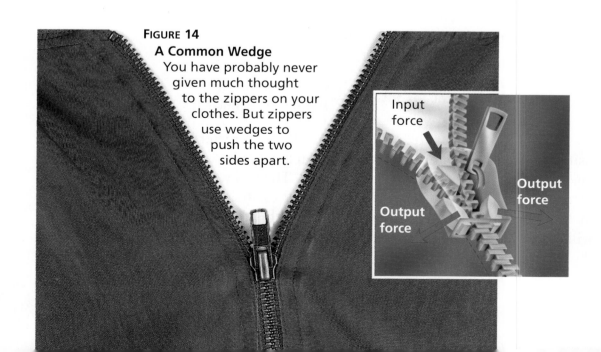

FIGURE 14
A Common Wedge
You have probably never given much thought to the zippers on your clothes. But zippers use wedges to push the two sides apart.

FIGURE 15
It's All in the Threads
Examples of the screw are found in jars and hardware fasteners.
Relating Cause and Effect How does the distance between the threads of a screw affect its mechanical advantage?

Screws

Like a wedge, a screw is a simple machine that is related to the inclined plane. A **screw** can be thought of as an inclined plane wrapped around a cylinder. This spiral inclined plane forms the threads of the screw.

How It Works When you twist a screw into a piece of wood, you exert an input force on the screw. The threads of a screw act like an inclined plane to increase the distance over which you exert the input force. As the threads of the screw turn, they exert an output force on the wood, pulling the screw into the wood. Friction between the screw and the wood holds the screw in place.

Many devices act like screws. Examples include bolts, light bulbs, and jar lids. Look at the jar lid in Figure 15. When you turn the lid, your small input force is greatly increased because of the screw threads on the lid. The threads on the lid are pulled against the matching threads on the jar with a strong enough force to make a tight seal.

Mechanical Advantage The closer together the threads of a screw are, the greater the mechanical advantage. This is because the closer the threads are, the more times you must turn the screw to fasten it into a piece of wood. Your input force is applied over a longer distance. The longer input distance results in an increased output force. Think of the length around the threads as the length of the inclined plane, and the length of the screw as the height of the inclined plane. **The ideal mechanical advantage of a screw is the length around the threads divided by the length of the screw.**

Reading Checkpoint How does the length around the threads of a screw compare to an inclined plane?

Lab zone Try This **Activity**

A Paper Screw
1. To make a paper model of a screw, cut out a triangle from a piece of paper.
2. Tape the wide end of the triangle to a pencil. Then wind the paper around the pencil.

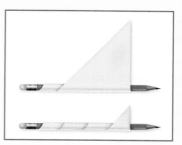

Making Models How does this model represent a real screw? Can you think of a way to calculate the ideal mechanical advantage of your model screw?

Levers

Have you ever ridden on a seesaw or pried open a paint can with an opener? If so, then you are already familiar with another simple machine called a lever. A **lever** is a rigid bar that is free to pivot, or rotate, on a fixed point. The fixed point that a lever pivots around is called the **fulcrum.**

How It Works To understand how levers work, think about using a paint-can opener. The opener rests against the edge of the can, which acts as the fulcrum. The tip of the opener is under the lid of the can. When you push down, you exert an input force on the handle, and the opener pivots on the fulcrum. As a result, the tip of the opener pushes up, thereby exerting an output force on the lid.

Mechanical Advantage A lever like the paint-can opener helps you in two ways. It increases your input force and it changes the direction of your input force. When you use the paint-can opener, you push the handle a long distance down in order to move the lid a short distance up. However, you are able to apply a smaller force than you would have without the opener.

The ideal mechanical advantage of a lever is determined by dividing the distance from the fulcrum to the input force by the distance from the fulcrum to the output force.

$$\text{Ideal mechanical advantage} = \frac{\text{Distance from fulcrum to input force}}{\text{Distance from fulcrum to output force}}$$

In the case of the paint can opener, the distance from the fulcrum to the input force is greater than the distance from the fulcrum to the output force. This means that the mechanical advantage is greater than 1.

Different Types of Levers When a paint-can opener is used as a lever, the fulcrum is located between the input and output forces. But this is not always the case. As shown in Figure 17, there are three different types of levers. Levers are classified according to the location of the fulcrum relative to the input and output forces.

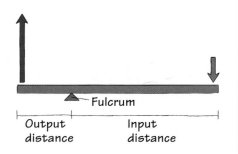

FIGURE 16
Mechanical Advantage of a Lever
A lever's input distance and output distance determine its ideal mechanical advantage.

 **Reading Checkpoint** **What point on a lever does not move?**

720 ◆

FIGURE 17

Three Classes of Levers

The three classes of levers differ in the positions of the fulcrum, input force, and output force.
Applying Concepts *Which type of lever always has an ideal mechanical advantage less than 1?*

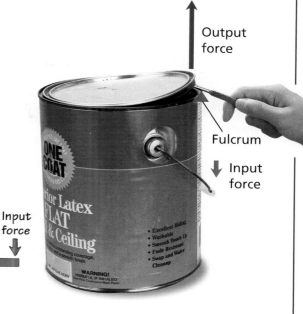

Output force

Fulcrum

Input force

First-Class Levers

First-class levers always change the direction of the input force. If the fulcrum is closer to the output force, these levers also increase force. If the fulcrum is closer to the input force, these levers also increase distance. Other examples include scissors, pliers, and seesaws.

Output force

Input force

Fulcrum

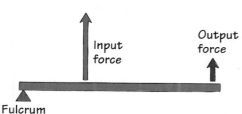

Input force

Output force

Fulcrum

Second-Class Levers

These levers increase force, but do not change the direction of the input force. Other examples include doors, nutcrackers, and bottle openers.

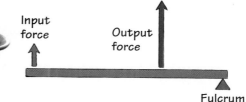

Input force

Output force

Fulcrum

Third-Class Levers

These levers increase distance, but do not change the direction of the input force. Other examples include fishing poles, shovels, and baseball bats.

Input force

Output force

Fulcrum

Fulcrum

Input force

Output force

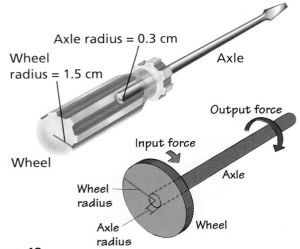

FIGURE 18
Wheel and Axle
A screwdriver increases force by exerting the output force over a shorter distance.
Observing *Which has a larger radius, the wheel or the axle?*

Wheel and Axle

It's almost impossible to insert a screw into a piece of wood with your fingers. But with a screwdriver, you can turn the screw easily. A screwdriver makes use of a simple machine known as the **wheel and axle.** A wheel and axle is a simple machine made of two circular or cylindrical objects fastened together that rotate about a common axis. The object with the larger radius is called the wheel and the object with the smaller radius is called the axle. In a screwdriver, the handle is the wheel and the shaft is the axle. A doorknob and a car's steering wheel are also examples of a wheel and axle.

Science and **History**

Engineering Marvels
Simple machines have been used to create some of the most beautiful and useful structures in the world.

2550 B.C.
Great Pyramid, Giza, Egypt
Workers used wedges to cut 2.3 million blocks of stone to build the pyramid. At the quarry, the wedges were driven into cracks in the rock. The rock split into pieces. Workers hauled the massive blocks up inclined planes to the tops of pyramid walls.

500 B.C.
Theater at Epidaurus, Greece
Instead of ramps, the Greeks relied on a crane powered by pulleys to lift the stone blocks to build this theater. The crane was also used to lower actors to the stage during performances.

3000 B.C.   **2000 B.C.**   **1000 B.C.**

How It Works How does a screwdriver make use of a wheel and axle to do work? Look at Figure 18. When you use a screwdriver, you apply an input force to turn the handle, or wheel. Because the wheel is larger than the shaft, or axle, the axle rotates and exerts a large output force. The wheel and axle increases your force, but you must exert your force over a long distance.

What would happen if the input force were applied to the axle rather than the wheel? For the riverboat in Figure 19 on the next page, the force of the engine is applied to the axle of the large paddle wheel. The large paddle wheel in turn pushes against the water. In this case, the input force is exerted over a short distance. So when the input force is applied to the axle, a wheel and axle multiplies distance.

Writing in Science

Research and Write
Suppose that you are the person who first thought of using a simple machine at one of the construction sites in the timeline. Write out your proposal. You'll need to research the time and place. Explain to the people in charge why the simple machine you suggest will give workers a mechanical advantage.

A.D. 1000 Brihadeshwara Temple, India
The temple's tower at Thanjavur is more than 60 meters high. Workers dragged the dome-shaped capstone, a mass of 70,000 kilograms, to the top of the structure along an inclined plane several kilometers long.

A.D. 1994
The Chunnel, United Kingdom to France
Special drilling equipment was built to tunnel under the English Channel. Opened in May of 1994, the tunnel is 50 kilometers long. It carries only railway traffic.

A.D. 1056
Yingxian Pagoda, China
Slanted wooden beams called *ang* act as first-class levers to hold up the roof of this pagoda. The weight of the center of the roof presses down on one end of the beam. The other end of the beam swings up to support the outer edge of the roof.

| 0 | A.D. 1000 | A.D. 2000 |

Mechanical Advantage You can find the ideal mechanical advantage of a wheel and axle by dividing the radius of the wheel by the radius of the axle. (A radius is the distance from the outer edge of a circle to the circle's center.) The greater the ratio between the radius of the wheel and the radius of the axle, the greater the mechanical advantage.

$$\text{Mechanical advantage} = \frac{\text{Radius of wheel}}{\text{Radius of axle}}$$

Suppose the radius of a screwdriver's wheel is 1.5 cm and its axle radius is 0.3 cm. The screwdriver's ideal mechanical advantage would be 1.5 centimeters ÷ 0.3 centimeter, or 5.

 **Reading Checkpoint** What is a radius?

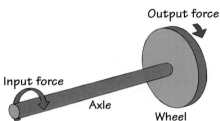
Output force
Input force
Axle
Wheel

FIGURE 19
Increasing Distance
In a riverboat paddle wheel, the axle turns the wheel. The output force is less than the input force, but it is exerted over a longer distance.

Pulley

When you raise a flag on a flagpole or when you open and close window blinds, you are using a pulley. A **pulley** is a simple machine made of a grooved wheel with a rope or cable wrapped around it.

How It Works You use a pulley by pulling on one end of the rope. This is the input force. At the other end of the rope, the output force pulls up on the object you want to move. To move a heavy object over a distance, a pulley can make work easier in two ways. First, it can decrease the amount of input force needed to lift the object. Second, the pulley can change the direction of your input force. For example, you pull down on the flagpole rope, and the flag moves up.

Types of Pulleys There are two basic types of pulleys. A pulley that you attach to a structure is called a fixed pulley. Fixed pulleys are used at the tops of flagpoles. If you attach a pulley to the object you wish to move, you use a movable pulley. Construction cranes often use movable pulleys. By combining fixed and movable pulleys, you can make a pulley system called a block and tackle. **The ideal mechanical advantage of a pulley is equal to the number of sections of rope that support the object.**

 **Reading Checkpoint** A pulley is attached to the object that is being moved. What kind of pulley is it?

Lab zone Skills **Activity**

Communicating

Write a packaging label for a machine that uses a wheel and axle. On your label, describe the advantages of using this simple machine. Include a drawing of the forces that act on the machine.

FIGURE 20
Types of Pulleys

A fixed pulley and a movable pulley are the two basic types of pulleys. A block and tackle combines a fixed and movable pulley.
Comparing and Contrasting *Which type of pulley has the greatest mechanical advantage?*

Fixed Pulley

A fixed pulley does not change the amount of force applied. It does change the direction of the force.

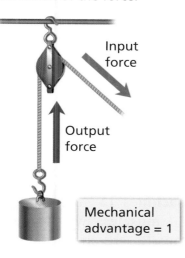

Mechanical advantage = 1

Movable Pulley

A movable pulley decreases the amount of input force needed. It does not change the direction of the force.

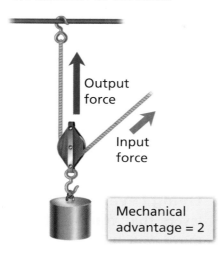

Mechanical advantage = 2

Block and Tackle

A block and tackle is a pulley system made up of fixed and movable pulleys.

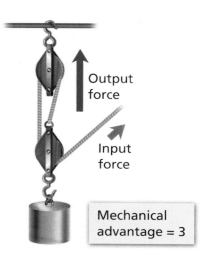

Mechanical advantage = 3

Cranes use block-and-tackle systems to lift heavy loads.

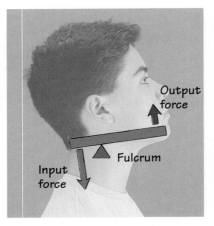

First-Class Lever The joint at the top of your neck is the fulcrum of a first-class lever. The muscles in the back of your neck provide the input force. The output force is used to tilt your head back.

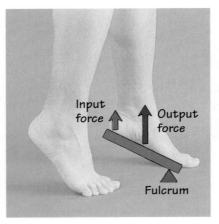

Second-Class Lever The ball of your foot is the fulcrum of a second-class lever. The muscle in the calf of your leg provides the input force. The output force is used to raise your body.

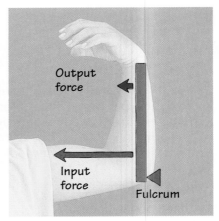

Third-Class Lever Your elbow is the fulcrum of a third-class lever. Your biceps muscle provides the input force. The output force is used to lift your arm.

FIGURE 21
Levers in the Body
You don't need to look further than your own body to find simple machines. Three different types of levers are responsible for many of your movements.

Simple Machines in the Body

You probably don't think of the human body as being made up of machines. Believe it or not, machines are involved in much of the work that your body does.

Living Levers **Most of the machines in your body are levers that consist of bones and muscles.** Every time you move, you use a muscle. Your muscles are attached to your bones by connecting structures called tendons. Tendons and muscles pull on bones, making them work as levers. The joint, near where the tendon is attached to the bone, acts as the fulcrum. The muscles produce the input force. The output force is used for doing work, such as lifting your hand.

Working Wedges When you bite into an apple, you use your sharp front teeth, called incisors. Your incisors are shaped like wedges to enable you to bite off pieces of food. When you bite down on something, the wedge shape of your front teeth produces enough force to break it into pieces, just as an ax splits a log. The next time you take a bite of a crunchy apple, think about the machines in your mouth!

✓ Reading Checkpoint   **What type of simple machine do your front teeth resemble?**

FIGURE 22
Wedges to Help You Eat
Your front teeth, known as incisors, are shaped like wedges.

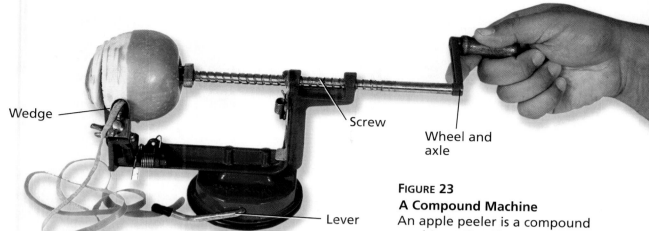

Wedge

Screw

Wheel and axle

Lever

FIGURE 23
A Compound Machine
An apple peeler is a compound machine. Classifying *What other compound machines can you think of? What simple machines make them up?*

Compound Machines

Many machines do not resemble the six simple machines you just read about. That's because many machines consist of combinations of simple machines.

A **compound machine** is a machine that utilizes two or more simple machines. **The ideal mechanical advantage of a compound machine is the product of the individual ideal mechanical advantages of the simple machines that make it up.**

An apple peeler like the one shown in Figure 23 is a compound machine. Four different simple machines make it up. The handle is a wheel and axle. The axle is also a screw that turns the apple. A wedge peels the apple's skin. To hold the machine in place, a lever can be switched to engage a suction cup.

Section 3 Assessment

Target Reading Skill Previewing Visuals Refer to your questions and answers about Figure 17 to help you answer Question 1 below.

Reviewing Key Concepts

1. a. Listing List the six kinds of simple machines.
  b. Classifying What type of simple machine is a door stopper? A rake? A windmill? A slide?
  c. Developing Hypotheses Can you consider your thumb to be a lever? Why or why not?
2. a. Identifying What is the ideal mechanical advantage of each type of simple machine?
  b. Inferring How can you increase a pulley's mechanical advantage?
  c. Drawing Conclusions How is calculating the ideal mechanical advantage of an inclined plane similar to calculating that of a screw?

3. a. Reviewing How many simple machines are needed to make a compound machine?
  b. Describing How do you find the mechanical advantage of a compound machine?

Lab zone **At-Home Activity**

Machines in the Kitchen Look around your kitchen with a family member. Identify at least five machines. Classify each as a simple machine or a compound machine. Explain to your family member how each machine makes work easier.

Angling for Access

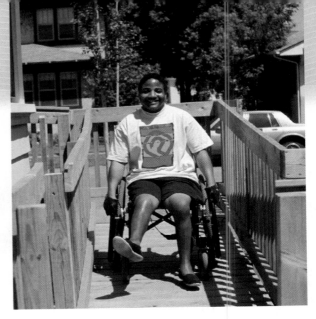

Problem

How does the steepness of a wheelchair-access ramp affect its usefulness?

Skills Focus

making models, calculating

Materials

- 4 books, about 2 cm thick   • metric ruler
- wooden block with eye-hook   • marker
- board, at least 10 cm wide and 50 cm long
- spring scale, 0–10 N, or force sensor

Procedure

1. Preview the following steps that describe how you can construct and use a ramp. Then copy the data table into your notebook.

2. The output force with an inclined plane is equal to the weight of the object. Lift the block with the spring scale to measure its weight. Record this value in the data table. If you are using a force sensor, see your teacher for instructions.

3. Make a mark on the side of the board about 3 cm from one end. Measure the length from the other end of the board to the mark and record it in the data table.

4. Place one end of the board on top of a book. The mark you made on the board should be even with the edge of the book.

5. Measure the vertical distance in centimeters from the top of the table to where the underside of the incline touches the book. Record this value in the data table as "Height of Incline."

6. Lay the block on its largest side and use the spring scale to pull the block straight up the incline at a slow, steady speed. Be sure to hold the spring scale parallel to the incline, as shown in the photograph. Measure the force needed and record it in the data table.

7. Predict how your results will change if you repeat the investigation using two, three, and four books. Test your predictions.

8. For each trial, determine the ideal mechanical advantage and the actual mechanical advantage. Record the calculations in your data table.

Data Table						
Number of Books	Output Force (N)	Length of Incline (cm)	Height of Incline (cm)	Input Force (N)	Ideal Mechanical Advantage	Actual Mechanical Advantage
1						
2						
3						
4						

Analyze and Conclude

1. **Interpreting Data** How did the ideal mechanical advantage and the actual mechanical advantage compare each time you repeated the experiment? Explain your answer.

2. **Making Models** How did the model help you in determining the ramp's usefulness? What kind of limitations does your model have?

3. **Making Models** What happens to the actual mechanical advantage as the inclined plane gets steeper? On the basis of this fact alone, which of the four inclined planes models the best steepness for a wheelchair-access ramp? Explain your answer.

4. **Drawing Conclusions** What other factors, besides mechanical advantage, should you consider when deciding on the steepness of the ramp?

5. **Calculating** Suppose the door of the local public library is 2.0 m above the ground and the distance from the door to the parking lot is 15 m. What is the ideal mechanical advantage of a ramp built from the door to the parking lot?

6. **Communicating** Write a letter to a local business explaining how a ramp could help the employees and customers. Give some examples of work that could be made easier using a ramp. Explain how the steepness of a ramp affects its mechanical advantage.

More to Explore

Find actual ramps that provide access for people with disabilities. Measure the heights and lengths of these ramps and calculate their ideal mechanical advantages. Find out what the requirements are for access ramps in your area. Should your ramp be made of a particular material? Should it level off before it reaches the door? How wide should it be? How does it provide water drainage?

Science and Society

Automation in the Workplace— Lost Jobs or New Jobs?

In the 1800s, the first makers of baseball bats spent long days carving bats by hand. In a modern American factory, bat-making machines can produce a much larger number of bats in a shorter time. Since ancient times, people have invented machines to help with their work. Today, factories can use automated machines to perform jobs that are difficult, dangerous, or even just boring. Like science-fiction robots, these machines can do a whole series of different tasks.

But if a machine does work instead of a person, then someone loses a job. How can society use machines to make work easier and more productive without some people losing their chance to work?

The Issues

What Are the Effects of Automation?

New machines replace some jobs, but they also can create jobs. Suppose an automobile factory starts using machines instead of people to paint cars. At first, some workers may lose their jobs. But the factory may be able to produce more cars. Then it may need to hire more workers—to handle old tasks as well as some new ones. New jobs are created for people who are educated and skilled in operating and taking care of the new machines.

Still, some workers whose skills are no longer needed lose their jobs. Some may find work in different jobs for less money. Others may be unable to find new jobs. Can society provide people who are out of work with the skills they need to start a new career?

Carving a single bat with a lathe can take several hours.

730 ◆

Using automated machines, a modern factory can produce hundreds of baseball bats each day.

What Can People Do?

Education programs can train young people for new jobs and teach older workers new skills. Those who learn how to use computers and other new technologies can take on new tasks. Learning how to sell or design a product can also prepare workers for new careers. Workers who have lost jobs can train for different types of work that cannot be done by machines. For example, a machine cannot replace human skill in day care or medical care.

Who Should Pay?

Teaching young people how to work in new kinds of jobs costs money. So do training programs for adult workers who have lost jobs. How could society pay for these costs? Businesses might share some of the costs. Some businesses give workers full pay until they are retrained or find new work. Also, the government might provide unemployment pay or training for jobless workers. Then all taxpayers would share the costs.

You Decide

1. Identify the Problem
Describe in your own words the benefits and drawbacks of workplace automation.

2. Analyze the Options
List ways society could deal with the effects of automation. For each plan, give the benefits and drawbacks and tell how it would be paid for.

3. Find a Solution
The owner of the pizza shop in your neighborhood has bought an automated pizza-making system. Make a plan for the shop to use the system without having to fire workers.

For: More on automation in the workplace
Visit: PHSchool.com
Web Code: cgh-3040

1 What Is Work?

Key Concepts

- Work is done on an object when the object moves in the same direction in which the force is exerted.
- The amount of work done on an object can be determined by multiplying force times distance.

$$\text{Work} = \text{Force} \times \text{Distance}$$

- Power equals the amount of work done on an object in a unit of time.

$$\text{Power} = \frac{\text{Work}}{\text{Time}}$$

Key Terms

work
joule
power

2 How Machines Do Work

Key Concepts

- A machine makes work easier by changing at least one of three factors. A machine may change the amount of force you exert, the distance over which you exert your force, or the direction in which you exert your force.
- A machine's mechanical advantage is the number of times a machine increases a force exerted on it.
- Mechanical advantage $= \dfrac{\text{Output force}}{\text{Input force}}$
- To calculate the efficiency of a machine, divide the output work by the input work and multiply the result by 100 percent.

$$\text{Efficiency} = \frac{\text{Output work}}{\text{Input work}} \times 100\%$$

Key Terms

machine
input force
output force
input work
output work
mechanical advantage
efficiency

3 Simple Machines

Key Concepts

- There are six basic kinds of simple machines: the inclined plane, the wedge, the screw, the lever, the wheel and axle, and the pulley.
- You can determine the ideal mechanical advantage of an inclined plane by dividing the length of the incline by its height.
- The ideal mechanical advantage of a wedge is determined by dividing the length of the wedge by its width.
- The ideal mechanical advantage of a screw is the length around the threads divided by the length of the screw.
- The ideal mechanical advantage of a lever is determined by dividing the distance from the fulcrum to the input force by the distance from the fulcrum to the output force.
- You can find the ideal mechanical advantage of a wheel and axle by dividing the radius of the wheel by the radius of the axle.
- The ideal mechanical advantage of a pulley is equal to the number of sections of rope that support the object.
- Most of the machines in your body are levers that consist of bones and muscles.
- The ideal mechanical advantage of a compound machine is the product of the individual ideal mechanical advantages of the simple machines that make it up.

Key Terms

inclined plane   fulcrum
wedge   wheel and axle
screw   pulley
lever   compound machine

Review and Assessment

Organizing Information

Comparing and Contrasting Copy the compare/contrast table about simple machines onto a separate sheet of paper. Then complete it for each type of simple machine and add a title. (For more on Comparing and Contrasting, see the Skills Handbook.)

Simple Machine	Mechanical Advantage	Example
Inclined plane	Length of incline ÷ Height of incline	Ramp
a. ___?___	b. ___?___	c. ___?___

Reviewing Key Terms

Choose the letter of the best answer.

1. The amount of work done on an object is obtained by multiplying
   a. input force and output force.
   b. force and distance.
   c. time and force.
   d. efficiency and work.

2. The rate at which work is done is called
   a. output force.
   b. efficiency.
   c. power.
   d. mechanical advantage.

3. One way a machine can make work easier for you is by
   a. decreasing the amount of work you do.
   b. changing the direction of your force.
   c. increasing the amount of work required for a task.
   d. decreasing the friction you encounter.

4. The output force is greater than the input force for a
   a. pizza cutter.
   b. hockey stick.
   c. single fixed pulley.
   d. screw.

5. An example of a second-class lever is a
   a. seesaw.
   b. shovel.
   c. paddle.
   d. wheelbarrow.

If the statement is true, write _true_. If it is false, change the underlined word or words to make the statement true.

6. The SI unit of work is the <u>newton</u>.

7. The work you do on a machine is called the <u>input work</u>.

8. The ratio of output work to input work is <u>mechanical advantage</u>.

9. An <u>inclined plane</u> is a flat, sloped surface.

10. A <u>pulley</u> can be thought of as an inclined plane wrapped around a cylinder.

Writing in Science

Proposed Solution A community of people in Pennsylvania known as the Old Order Amish can build a wooden barn in a single day—without using electricity. Suppose you were faced with this task. Propose how you would use simple machines to help with the construction.

Discovery CHANNEL **SCHOOL**™

Work and Machines
Video Preview
Video Field Trip
▶ Video Assessment

Review and Assessment

Checking Concepts

11. The mythical god Atlas was believed to hold the weight of the sky on his shoulders. Was Atlas performing any work? Explain.

12. The mechanical advantage of a machine is 3. If you exert an input force of 5 N, what output force is exerted by the machine?

13. Which has a greater mechanical advantage, a wedge that is 6 cm long and 3 cm wide, or a wedge that is 12 cm long and 4 cm wide? Explain your answer.

14. Why will decreasing the radius of the axle improve the mechanical advantage of a wheel and axle?

15. Describe a lever in your body. Locate the input force, output force, and fulcrum.

Thinking Critically

16. Relating Cause and Effect Describe the relationship between friction and the efficiency of a machine.

17. Classifying What type of simple machine would be used to lower an empty bucket into a well and then lift the bucket full of water?

18. Applying Concepts To open a door, you push on the part of the door that is farthest from the hinges. Why would it be harder to open the door if you pushed on the center of it?

19. Interpreting Diagrams Which ramp has the greater ideal mechanical advantage?

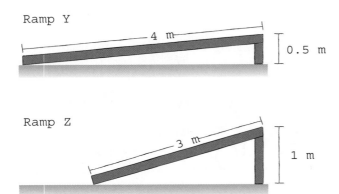

Ramp Y — 4 m, 0.5 m

Ramp Z — 3 m, 1 m

Math Practice

20. Calculating Power A bulldozer does 72,000 J of work in 48 seconds. How much power does the bulldozer use?

21. Calculating Efficiency A machine with 75% efficiency does 3,300 J of work. Using the machine, how much work did you do?

Applying Skills

Use the illustration to answer Questions 22–25.

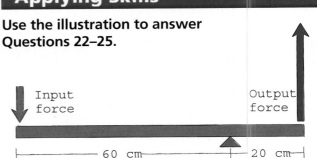

Input force

Output force

60 cm   20 cm

22. Calculating Use the input and output distances to calculate the ideal mechanical advantage of the lever.

23. Predicting What would the ideal mechanical advantage be if the distance from the fulcrum to the input force were 20 cm? 40 cm? 80 cm?

24. Graphing Use your answers to Questions 22 and 23 to graph the distance from the fulcrum to the input force on the x-axis and the ideal mechanical advantage on the y-axis.

25. Interpreting Data What does your graph show you about the relationship between the ideal mechanical advantage of a first-class lever and the distance between the fulcrum and the input force?

Lab zone Chapter Project

Performance Assessment Finalize your design and build your machine. Consider how you can improve the machine's efficiency. Check all measurements and calculations. Does it lift the soup can at least 5 cm? Is it made of two or more simple machines? When you show your machine to the class, explain why you built it as you did.

End-of-Grade Test Practice

Choose the letter of the best answer.

1. What simple machine is used in *all* of the following jobs: moving a flag to the top of a flagpole, lifting equipment with a construction crane, and using a block and tackle to move a crate?
   A lever
   B pulley
   C wedge
   D wheel and axle

2. The table below shows the input work and output work for four different pulleys. Which pulley has the highest efficiency?

Work of Different Pulleys		
Pulley	Input Work	Output Work
Fixed pulley A	20,000 J	8,000 J
Fixed pulley B	20,000 J	10,000 J
Movable pulley	20,000 J	12,000 J
Block and tackle	20,000 J	16,000 J

   A Fixed pulley A   **B** Movable pulley
   C Fixed pulley B   **D** Block and Tackle

3. Which is the *best* definition of a machine?
   A A machine is a time-saving device that uses motors and gears.
   B A machine changes the amount of input force.
   C A machine makes work easier by changing force, distance, or direction.
   D A machine can be either simple or compound.

4. Which of the following will increase the ideal mechanical advantage of a wheel and axle?
   A increasing the wheel's radius
   B decreasing the wheel's radius
   C increasing the axle's radius
   D increasing the wheel's radius and the axle's radius equally

5. Which activity describes work being done on an object?
   A walking a dog on a leash
   B lifting a bag of groceries
   C holding up an umbrella
   D pressing a stamp onto an envelope

Constructed Response

6. Explain why an engineer would design a road to wind around a mountain rather than go straight up the side. Show how this design would be better.

Bridges—
From Vines to Steel

Have you ever
- balanced on a branch or log to cross a brook?
- jumped from rock to rock in a streambed?
- swung on a vine or rope over a river?

Vine Footbridge
A girl crosses over the Hunza River in northern Pakistan.

Then you have used the same ways that early people used to get over obstacles. Fallen trees, twisted vines, and natural stones formed the first bridges.

Bridges provide easy ways of getting over difficult obstacles. For thousands of years, bridges have also served as forts for defense, scenes of great battles, and homes for shops and churches. They have also been sites of mystery, love, and intrigue. They span history—linking cities, nations, and empires and encouraging trade and travel.

But bridges have not always been as elaborate as they are today. The earliest ones were made of materials that were free and plentiful. In deep forests, people used beams made from small trees. In tropical regions where vegetation was thick, people wove together vines and grasses, then hung them to make walkways over rivers and gorges.

No matter what the structures or materials, bridges reflect the people who built them. The ancient civilizations of China, Egypt, Greece, and Rome all designed strong, graceful bridges to connect and control their empires.

Roman Arch Bridge
Ponte Sant'Angelo is in Rome.

The Balance of Forces

What keeps a bridge from falling down? How does it support its own weight and the weight of people and traffic on it? Builders found the answers by considering the various forces that act on a bridge.

The weight of the bridge and the traffic on it are called the *load*. When a heavy truck crosses a beam bridge, the weight of the load forces the beam to curve downward. This creates tension forces that stretch the bottom of the beam. At the same time, the load also creates compression forces at the top of the beam.

Since the bridge doesn't collapse under the load, there must be upward forces to balance the downward forces. In simple beam bridges, builders anchor the beam to the ground or to end supports called abutments. To cross longer spans or distances, they construct piers under the middle span. Piers and abutments are structures that act as upward forces—reaction forces.

Another type of bridge, the arch bridge, supports its load by compression. A heavy load on a stone arch bridge squeezes or pushes the stones together, creating compression throughout the structure. Weight on the arch bridge pushes down to the ends of the arch. The side walls and abutments act as reaction forces.

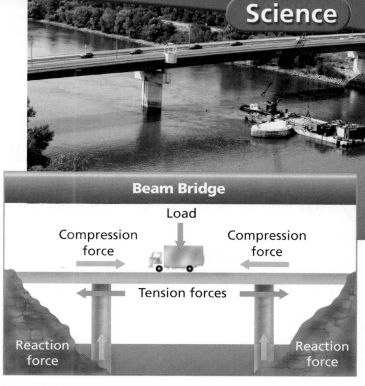

Beam Bridge
A beam bridge spans the Rhone River in France (top).

Early engineers discovered that arch bridges made of stone could span wider distances than simple beam bridges. Arch bridges are also stronger and more durable. Although the Romans were not the first to build arch bridges, they perfected the form in their massive, elegant structures. Early Roman arch bridges were built without mortar, or "glue." The arch held together because the stones were skillfully shaped to work in compression. After nearly 2,000 years, some of these Roman arch bridges are still standing.

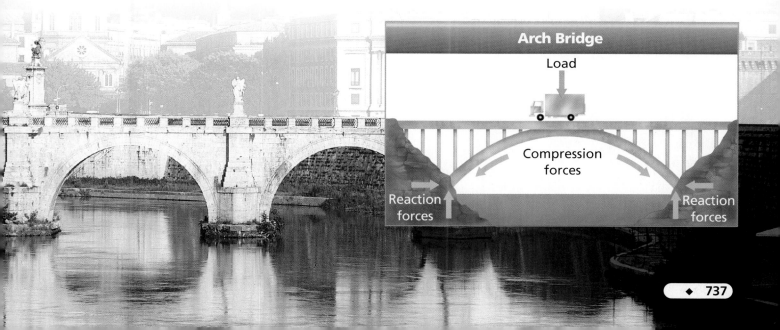

The Structure of Modern Bridges

By the 1800s in the United States, bridge builders began to use cast iron instead of stone and wood. By the late 1800s, they were using steel, which was strong and relatively lightweight. The use of new building materials was not the only change. Engineers began designing different types of bridges as well. They found that they could build longer, larger bridges by using a suspension structure.

Suspension bridges are modern versions of long, narrow, woven bridges found in tropical regions. These simple, woven suspension bridges can span long distances. Crossing one of these natural structures is like walking a tightrope. The weight of people and animals traveling over the bridge pushes down on the ropes, stretching them and creating tension forces.

Modern suspension bridges follow the same principles of tension as do woven bridges. A suspension bridge is strong in tension. In suspension bridges, parallel cables are stretched the entire length of the bridge—over giant towers. The cables are anchored at each end of the bridge. The roadway hangs from the cables, attached by wire suspenders. The weight of the bridge and the load on it act to pull apart or stretch the cables. This pulling apart creates tension forces.

The towers of a suspension bridge act as supports for the bridge cables. The abutments that anchor the cables exert reaction forces as well. So forces in balance keep a suspension bridge from collapsing.

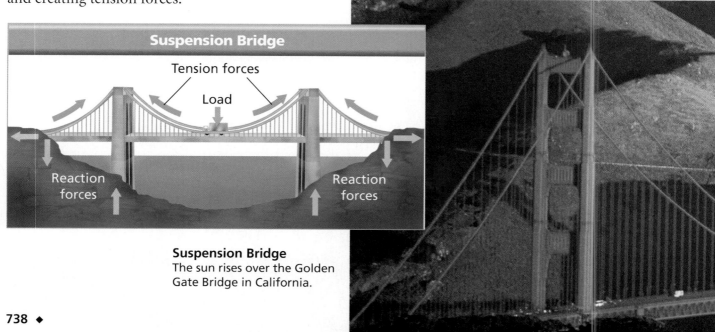

Suspension Bridge
The sun rises over the Golden Gate Bridge in California.

Cable-Stayed Bridge
The Sunshine Skyway Bridge spans a broad section of Tampa Bay in Florida. The cables, attached to the center of the roadway, enable travelers to have a clear view.

Science Activity

Work in groups to make a suspension bridge, using two chairs, a wooden plank, rope, and some books.

- Place two chairs back-to-back and stretch 2 ropes over the backs of the chairs. Hold the ropes at both ends.
- Tie three pieces of rope to the longer ropes. Place the plank through the loops.
- With a partner, hold the ropes tightly at each end. Load books on top of the plank to see how much it will hold.

Why is it important to anchor the ropes tightly at each end?

When the Brooklyn Bridge opened in New York City in 1883, it was the longest suspension bridge in the world. The Golden Gate Bridge in San Francisco, which was opened in 1937, was another great engineering feat.

Recently, engineers have developed a new bridge design called the cable-stayed bridge. It looks similar to a suspension bridge because both are built with towers and cables. But the two bridges are quite different. The cables on the cable-stayed bridge attach to the towers, so the towers bear the weight of the bridge and the load on it. In contrast, the cables on a suspension bridge ride over the towers and anchor at the abutments. So on a suspension bridge, both the towers and abutments bear the load.

Brooklyn Bridge
This bridge connects Brooklyn and Manhattan (above).
It took 14 years for workers to complete the bridge (left).

Against All Odds

When John Roebling was hired in 1868 to build the Brooklyn Bridge, he was already a skilled suspension bridge engineer. He had been working on plans for the bridge since 1855.

But before bridge construction even began in 1869, John Roebling died in a construction accident. Fortunately, he had worked out his bridge design to the last detail. His son, Colonel Washington Roebling, who was also a skilled engineer, dedicated himself to carrying out his father's plans.

The construction dragged on for 14 years and cost nearly 30 lives. Colonel Roebling himself became so disabled that he was forced to direct construction from his home. Using a telescope, Colonel Roebling followed every detail. His remarkable, energetic wife, Emily Warren Roebling, learned enough engineering principles to deliver and explain his orders to the workers.

As soon as the giant towers were up, workers unrolled the steel wire back and forth across the towers to weave the cables. The next step was to twist the wires together. But the workmen were terrified of hanging so high on the bridge and refused to work.

Finally, Frank Farrington, the chief mechanic, crossed the river on a small chair dangling from a wheel that ran across an overhead line. Farrington completed his journey to the roar of the crowd. Somewhat reassured, the builders returned to work. But it took two more years to string the cables. The bridge was one of the greatest engineering achievements of its time.

In the end, the Brooklyn Bridge project succeeded only because of the determination and sacrifices of the Roebling family. It became the model for hundreds of other suspension bridges.

Social Studies Activity

How do you think the Brooklyn Bridge changed the lives of New Yorkers? In groups, research the history of another famous bridge. Present your findings to your class along with drawings and photos. Find out

- when and why the bridge was built
- what type of bridge it is
- what effects the bridge has on people's lives—on trade, travel, and population
- how landforms affected the bridge building
- about events connected to the bridge

TWO GREAT CITIES UNITED

MAY 25, 1883—The Brooklyn Bridge was successfully opened yesterday. The pleasant weather brought visitors by the thousands from all around. Spectators were packed in masses through which it was almost impossible to pass, and those who had tickets to attend the ceremonies had hard work to reach the bridge. Every available house-top and window was filled, and an adventurous party occupied a tall telegraph pole. It required the utmost efforts of the police to keep clear the necessary space.

After the exercises at the bridge were completed the Brooklyn procession was immediately re-formed and the march was taken up to Col. Roebling's residence. From the back study on the second floor of his house Col. Roebling had watched through his telescope the procession as it proceeded along from the New York side until the Brooklyn tower was reached. Mrs. Roebling received at her husband's side and accepted her share of the honors of the bridge.

For blocks and blocks on either side of the bridge there was scarcely a foot of room to spare. Many persons crossed and re-crossed the river on the ferry boats, and in that way watched the display. Almost every ship along the river front was converted into a grand stand.

The final ceremonies of the opening of the great bridge began at eight o'clock, when the first rocket was sent from the center of the great structure, and ended at nine o'clock, when a flight of 500 rockets illuminated the sky. The river-front was one blaze of light, and on the yachts and smaller vessels blue fires were burning and illuminating dark waters around them.

————Excerpted with permission from
The New York Times

Brooklyn Bridge
This historic painting shows fireworks at the opening of the bridge in 1883.

THE GRAND DISPLAY OF FIREWORKS AND ILLUMINATIONS

Language Arts Activity

A reporter's goal is to inform and entertain the reader. Using a catchy opening line draws interest. Then the reader wants to know the facts—who, what, where, when, why, and how (5 W's and H).

You are a school reporter. Write about the opening of a bridge in your area. It could be a highway overpass or a bridge over water, a valley, or railroad tracks.

- Include some of the 5 W's and H.
- Add interesting details and descriptions.

Mathematics

Bridge Geometry

As railroad traffic increased in the late 1800s, truss bridges became popular. Designed with thin vertical and diagonal supports to add strength, truss bridges were actually reinforced beam bridge structures. Many of the early wood truss bridges couldn't support the trains that rumbled over them. Cast iron and steel trusses soon replaced wood trusses.

Using basic triangular structures, engineers went to work on more scientific truss bridge designs. The accuracy of the design is crucial to handling the stress from heavy train loads and constant vibrations. As in all bridge structures, each steel piece has to be measured and fitted accurately—including widths, lengths, angles, and points of intersection and attachment.

Geometric Angles and Figures
Engineers use various geometric figures in drawing bridge plans. Figures that have right angles are squares, rectangles, and right triangles. Figures that have acute angles and obtuse angles can be triangles and parallelograms.

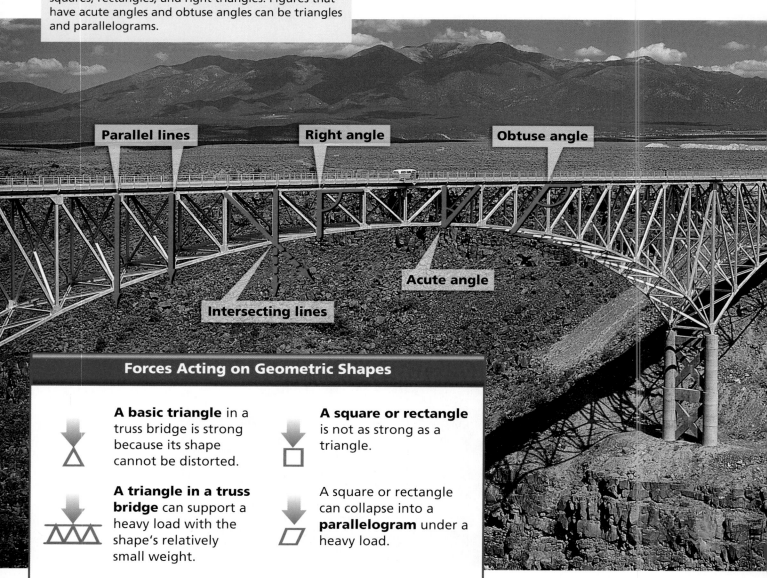

Parallel lines

Right angle

Obtuse angle

Acute angle

Intersecting lines

Forces Acting on Geometric Shapes

A basic triangle in a truss bridge is strong because its shape cannot be distorted.

A square or rectangle is not as strong as a triangle.

A triangle in a truss bridge can support a heavy load with the shape's relatively small weight.

A square or rectangle can collapse into a **parallelogram** under a heavy load.

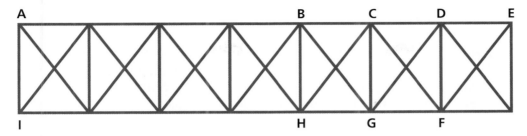

The chief building engineer has asked you to draw up exact plans for a new truss bridge. How well will you do as an assistant? Review the captions and labels on the previous page. Then answer these questions:

1. Which lines are parallel?

2. Which lines intersect?

3. What kind of figure is formed by *ABHI*?

4. What kind of figure is formed by *HCF*?

5. What kind of angle is *BGF*—obtuse or right?

6. What kind of angle is *CHG*?

7. What kind of triangle is *BHG*? What makes it this kind of triangle?

8. Why is a triangle stronger than a square?

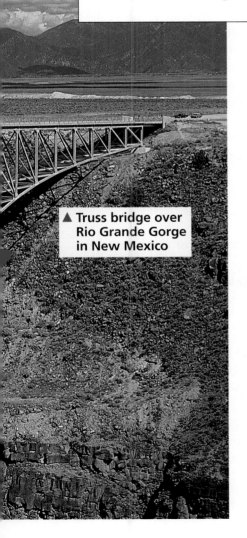

▲ **Truss bridge over Rio Grande Gorge in New Mexico**

Tie It Together

Work in small groups to build a model of a bridge out of a box of spaghetti and a roll of masking tape. Meet as a group to choose the type of bridge you will build. Each bridge should be strong enough to hold a brick. You can build

- a beam bridge

- a truss bridge

- an arch bridge

- a suspension bridge (This one is challenging.)

After drawing a sketch of the bridge design, assign jobs for each team member. Then

- decide how long the bridge span will be

- measure and cut the materials

- build the roadway first for beam, truss, and suspension bridges

- build the arch first in an arch bridge

When your bridge is complete, display it in the classroom. Test the strength of each bridge by placing a brick on the roadway. Discuss the difference in bridge structures. Determine which bridge design is the strongest.

Think Like a Scientist

Scientists have a particular way of looking at the world, or scientific habits of mind. Whenever you ask a question and explore possible answers, you use many of the same skills that scientists do. Some of these skills are described on this page.

Observing

When you use one or more of your five senses to gather information about the world, you are **observing.** Hearing a dog bark, counting twelve green seeds, and smelling smoke are all observations. To increase the power of their senses, scientists sometimes use microscopes, telescopes, or other instruments that help them make more detailed observations.

An observation must be an accurate report of what your senses detect. It is important to keep careful records of your observations in science class by writing or drawing in a notebook. The information collected through observations is called evidence, or data.

Inferring

When you interpret an observation, you are **inferring,** or making an inference. For example, if you hear your dog barking, you may infer that someone is at your front door. To make this inference, you combine the evidence—the barking dog—and your experience or knowledge—you know that your dog barks when strangers approach—to reach a logical conclusion.

Notice that an inference is not a fact; it is only one of many possible interpretations for an observation. For example, your dog may be barking because it wants to go for a walk. An inference may turn out to be incorrect even if it is based on accurate observations and logical reasoning. The only way to find out if an inference is correct is to investigate further.

Predicting

When you listen to the weather forecast, you hear many predictions about the next day's weather—what the temperature will be, whether it will rain, and how windy it will be. Weather forecasters use observations and knowledge of weather patterns to predict the weather. The skill of **predicting** involves making an inference about a future event based on current evidence or past experience.

Because a prediction is an inference, it may prove to be false. In science class, you can test some of your predictions by doing experiments. For example, suppose you predict that larger paper airplanes can fly farther than smaller airplanes. How could you test your prediction?

Classifying

Could you imagine searching for a book in the library if the books were shelved in no particular order? Your trip to the library would be an all-day event! Luckily, librarians group together books on similar topics or by the same author. Grouping together items that are alike in some way is called **classifying.** You can classify items in many ways: by size, by shape, by use, and by other important characteristics.

Like librarians, scientists use the skill of classifying to organize information and objects. When things are sorted into groups, the relationships among them become easier to understand.

Activity

Classify the objects in the photograph into two groups based on any characteristic you choose. Then use another characteristic to classify the objects into three groups.

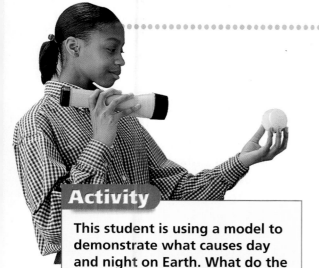

Making Models

Have you ever drawn a picture to help someone understand what you were saying? Such a drawing is one type of model. A model is a picture, diagram, computer image, or other representation of a complex object or process. **Making models** helps people understand things that they cannot observe directly.

Scientists often use models to represent things that are either very large or very small, such as the planets in the solar system, or the parts of a cell. Such models are physical models—drawings or three-dimensional structures that look like the real thing. Other models are mental models—mathematical equations or words that describe how something works.

Activity

This student is using a model to demonstrate what causes day and night on Earth. What do the flashlight and the tennis ball in the model represent?

Communicating

Whenever you talk on the phone, write a report, or listen to your teacher at school, you are communicating. **Communicating** is the process of sharing ideas and information with other people. Communicating effectively requires many skills, including writing, reading, speaking, listening, and making models.

Scientists communicate to share results, information, and opinions. Scientists often communicate about their work in journals, over the telephone, in letters, and on the Internet.

They also attend scientific meetings where they share their ideas with one another in person.

Activity

On a sheet of paper, write out clear, detailed directions for tying your shoe. Then exchange directions with a partner. Follow your partner's directions exactly. How successful were you at tying your shoe? How could your partner have communicated more clearly?

Making Measurements

By measuring, scientists can express their observations more precisely and communicate more information about what they observe.

Measuring in SI

The standard system of measurement used by scientists around the world is known as the International System of Units, which is abbreviated as SI (**Système International d'Unités,** in French). SI units are easy to use because they are based on multiples of 10. Each unit is ten times larger than the next smallest unit and one tenth the size of the next largest unit. The table lists the prefixes used to name the most common SI units.

Length To measure length, or the distance between two points, the unit of measure is the **meter (m).** The distance from the floor to a doorknob is approximately one meter. Long distances, such as the distance between two cities, are measured in kilometers (km). Small lengths are measured in centimeters (cm) or millimeters (mm). Scientists use metric rulers and meter sticks to measure length.

Common Conversions		
1 km	=	1,000 m
1 m	=	100 cm
1 m	=	1,000 mm
1 cm	=	10 mm

Common SI Prefixes		
Prefix	**Symbol**	**Meaning**
kilo-	k	1,000
hecto-	h	100
deka-	da	10
deci-	d	0.1 (one tenth)
centi-	c	0.01 (one hundredth)
milli-	m	0.001 (one thousandth)

Liquid Volume To measure the volume of a liquid, or the amount of space it takes up, you will use a unit of measure known as the **liter (L).** One liter is the approximate volume of a medium-size carton of milk. Smaller volumes are measured in milliliters (mL). Scientists use graduated cylinders to measure liquid volume.

Activity

The larger lines on the metric ruler in the picture show centimeter divisions, while the smaller, unnumbered lines show millimeter divisions. How many centimeters long is the shell? How many millimeters long is it?

Activity

The graduated cylinder in the picture is marked in milliliter divisions. Notice that the water in the cylinder has a curved surface. This curved surface is called the *meniscus.* To measure the volume, you must read the level at the lowest point of the meniscus. What is the volume of water in this graduated cylinder?

Common Conversion
1 L = 1,000 mL

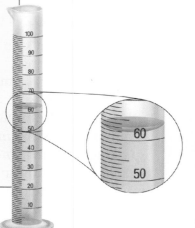

Mass To measure mass, or the amount of matter in an object, you will use a unit of measure known as the **gram (g).** One gram is approximately the mass of a paper clip. Larger masses are measured in kilograms (kg). Scientists use a balance to find the mass of an object.

Common Conversion
1 kg = 1,000 g

Activity

The mass of the potato in the picture is measured in kilograms. What is the mass of the potato? Suppose a recipe for potato salad called for one kilogram of potatoes. About how many potatoes would you need?

`0.25 KG`

Temperature To measure the temperature of a substance, you will use the **Celsius scale.** Temperature is measured in degrees Celsius (°C) using a Celsius thermometer. Water freezes at 0°C and boils at 100°C.

Time The unit scientists use to measure time is the **second (s).**

Activity

What is the temperature of the liquid in degrees Celsius?

Converting SI Units

To use the SI system, you must know how to convert between units. Converting from one unit to another involves the skill of **calculating,** or using mathematical operations. Converting between SI units is similar to converting between dollars and dimes because both systems are based on multiples of ten.

Suppose you want to convert a length of 80 centimeters to meters. Follow these steps to convert between units.

1. Begin by writing down the measurement you want to convert—in this example, 80 centimeters.

2. Write a conversion factor that represents the relationship between the two units you are converting. In this example, the relationship is 1 meter = 100 centimeters. Write this conversion factor as a fraction, making sure to place the units you are converting from (centimeters, in this example) in the denominator.

3. Multiply the measurement you want to convert by the fraction. When you do this, the units in the first measurement will cancel out with the units in the denominator. Your answer will be in the units you are converting to (meters, in this example).

Example

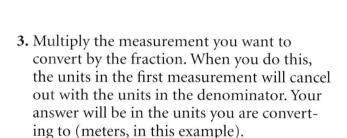

$$80 \text{ centimeters} = \blacksquare \text{ meters}$$

$$80 \text{ centimeters} \times \frac{1 \text{ meter}}{100 \text{ centimeters}} = \frac{80 \text{ meters}}{100}$$

$$= 0.8 \text{ meters}$$

Activity

Convert between the following units.
1. 600 millimeters = ■ meters
2. 0.35 liters = ■ milliliters
3. 1,050 grams = ■ kilograms

Conducting a Scientific Investigation

In some ways, scientists are like detectives, piecing together clues to learn about a process or event. One way that scientists gather clues is by carrying out experiments. An experiment tests an idea in a careful, orderly manner. Although experiments do not all follow the same steps in the same order, many follow a pattern similar to the one described here.

Posing Questions

Experiments begin by asking a scientific question. A scientific question is one that can be answered by gathering evidence. For example, the question "Which freezes faster—fresh water or salt water?" is a scientific question because you can carry out an investigation and gather information to answer the question.

Developing a Hypothesis

The next step is to form a hypothesis. A **hypothesis** is a possible explanation for a set of observations or answer to a scientific question. In science, a hypothesis must be something that can be tested. A hypothesis can be worded as an *If . . . then . . .* statement. For example, a hypothesis might be *"If I add salt to fresh water, then the water will take longer to freeze."* A hypothesis worded this way serves as a rough outline of the experiment you should perform.

Designing an Experiment

Next you need to plan a way to test your hypothesis. Your plan should be written out as a step-by-step procedure and should describe the observations or measurements you will make.

Two important steps involved in designing an experiment are controlling variables and forming operational definitions.

Controlling Variables In a well-designed experiment, you need to keep all variables the same except for one. A **variable** is any factor that can change in an experiment. The factor that you change is called the **manipulated variable**. In this experiment, the manipulated variable is the amount of salt added to the water. Other factors, such as the amount of water or the starting temperature, are kept constant.

The factor that changes as a result of the manipulated variable is called the **responding variable.** The responding variable is what you measure or observe to obtain your results. In this experiment, the responding variable is how long the water takes to freeze.

An experiment in which all factors except one are kept constant is called a **controlled experiment.** Most controlled experiments include a test called the control. In this experiment, Container 3 is the control. Because no salt is added to Container 3, you can compare the results from the other containers to it. Any difference in results must be due to the addition of salt alone.

Forming Operational Definitions Another important aspect of a well-designed experiment is having clear operational definitions. An **operational definition** is a statement that describes how a particular variable is to be measured or how a term is to be defined. For example, in this experiment, how will you determine if the water has frozen? You might decide to insert a stick in each container at the start of the experiment. Your operational definition of "frozen" would be the time at which the stick can no longer move.

Experimental Procedure
1. Fill 3 containers with 300 milliliters of cold tap water.
2. Add 10 grams of salt to Container 1; stir. Add 20 grams of salt to Container 2; stir. Add no salt to Container 3.
3. Place the 3 containers in a freezer.
4. Check the containers every 15 minutes. Record your observations.

Interpreting Data

The observations and measurements you make in an experiment are called **data.** At the end of an experiment, you need to analyze the data to look for any patterns or trends. Patterns often become clear if you organize your data in a data table or graph. Then think through what the data reveal. Do they support your hypothesis? Do they point out a flaw in your experiment? Do you need to collect more data?

Drawing Conclusions

A **conclusion** is a statement that sums up what you have learned from an experiment. When you draw a conclusion, you need to decide whether the data you collected support your hypothesis or not. You may need to repeat an experiment several times before you can draw any conclusions from it. Conclusions often lead you to pose new questions and plan new experiments to answer them.

Activity

Is a ball's bounce affected by the height from which it is dropped? Using the steps just described, plan a controlled experiment to investigate this problem.

Technology Design Skills

Engineers are people who use scientific and technological knowledge to solve practical problems. To design new products, engineers usually follow the process described here, even though they may not follow these steps in the exact order. As you read the steps, think about how you might apply them in technology labs.

Identify a Need

Before engineers begin designing a new product, they must first identify the need they are trying to meet. For example, suppose you are a member of a design team in a company that makes toys. Your team has identified a need: a toy boat that is inexpensive and easy to assemble.

Research the Problem

Engineers often begin by gathering information that will help them with their new design. This research may include finding articles in books, magazines, or on the Internet. It may also include talking to other engineers who have solved similar problems. Engineers often perform experiments related to the product they want to design.

For your toy boat, you could look at toys that are similar to the one you want to design. You might do research on the Internet. You could also test some materials to see whether they will work well in a toy boat.

Drawing for a boat design ▼

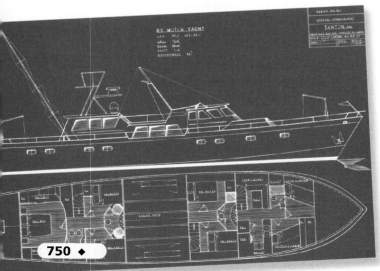

Design a Solution

Research gives engineers information that helps them design a product. When engineers design new products, they usually work in teams.

Generating Ideas Often design teams hold brainstorming meetings in which any team member can contribute ideas. **Brainstorming** is a creative process in which one team member's suggestions often spark ideas in other group members. Brainstorming can lead to new approaches to solving a design problem.

Evaluating Constraints During brainstorming, a design team will often come up with several possible designs. The team must then evaluate each one.

As part of their evaluation, engineers consider constraints. **Constraints** are factors that limit or restrict a product design. Physical characteristics, such as the properties of materials used to make your toy boat, are constraints. Money and time are also constraints. If the materials in a product cost a lot, or if the product takes a long time to make, the design may be impractical.

Making Trade-offs Design teams usually need to make trade-offs. In a **trade-off**, engineers give up one benefit of a proposed design in order to obtain another. In designing your toy boat, you will have to make trade-offs. For example, suppose one material is sturdy but not fully waterproof. Another material is more waterproof, but breakable. You may decide to give up the benefit of sturdiness in order to obtain the benefit of waterproofing.

Build and Evaluate a Prototype

Once the team has chosen a design plan, the engineers build a prototype of the product. A **prototype** is a working model used to test a design. Engineers evaluate the prototype to see whether it works well, is easy to operate, is safe to use, and holds up to repeated use.

Think of your toy boat. What would the prototype be like? Of what materials would it be made? How would you test it?

Troubleshoot and Redesign

Few prototypes work perfectly, which is why they need to be tested. Once a design team has tested a prototype, the members analyze the results and identify any problems. The team then tries to **troubleshoot,** or fix the design problems. For example, if your toy boat leaks or wobbles, the boat should be redesigned to eliminate those problems.

Communicate the Solution

A team needs to communicate the final design to the people who will manufacture and use the product. To do this, teams may use sketches, detailed drawings, computer simulations, and word descriptions.

Activity

You can use the technology design process to design and build a toy boat.

Research and Investigate

1. Visit the library or go online to research toy boats.
2. Investigate how a toy boat can be powered, including wind, rubber bands, or baking soda and vinegar.
3. Brainstorm materials, shapes, and steering for your boat.

Design and Build

4. Based on your research, design a toy boat that
   • is made of readily available materials
   • is no larger than 15 cm long and 10 cm wide

   • includes a power system, a rudder, and an area for cargo
   • travels 2 meters in a straight line carrying a load of 20 pennies
5. Sketch your design and write a step-by-step plan for building your boat. After your teacher approves your plan, build your boat.

Evaluate and Redesign

6. Test your boat, evaluate the results, and troubleshoot any problems.
7. Based on your evaluation, redesign your toy boat so it performs better.

Creating Data Tables and Graphs

**How can you make sense of the data in a science experiment?
The first step is to organize the data to help you understand them.
Data tables and graphs are helpful tools for organizing data.**

Data Tables

You have gathered your materials and set up your experiment. But before you start, you need to plan a way to record what happens during the experiment. By creating a data table, you can record your observations and measurements in an orderly way.

Suppose, for example, that a scientist conducted an experiment to find out how many Calories people of different body masses burn while doing various activities. The data table shows the results.

Notice in this data table that the manipulated variable (body mass) is the heading of one column. The responding variable (for

Calories Burned in 30 Minutes			
Body Mass	Experiment 1: Bicycling	Experiment 2: Playing Basketball	Experiment 3: Watching Television
30 kg	60 Calories	120 Calories	21 Calories
40 kg	77 Calories	164 Calories	27 Calories
50 kg	95 Calories	206 Calories	33 Calories
60 kg	114 Calories	248 Calories	38 Calories

Experiment 1, the number of Calories burned while bicycling) is the heading of the next column. Additional columns were added for related experiments.

Bar Graphs

To compare how many Calories a person burns doing various activities, you could create a bar graph. A bar graph is used to display data in a number of separate, or distinct, categories. In this example, bicycling, playing basketball, and watching television are the three categories.

To create a bar graph, follow these steps.

1. On graph paper, draw a horizontal, or *x*-, axis and a vertical, or *y*-, axis.

2. Write the names of the categories to be graphed along the horizontal axis. Include an overall label for the axis as well.

3. Label the vertical axis with the name of the responding variable. Include units of measurement. Then create a scale along the axis by marking off equally spaced numbers that cover the range of the data collected.

4. For each category, draw a solid bar using the scale on the vertical axis to determine the height. Make all the bars the same width.

5. Add a title that describes the graph.

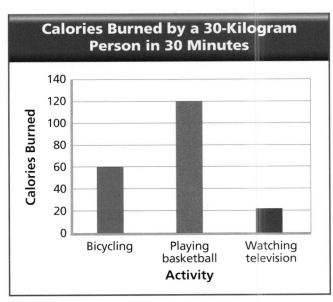

Line Graphs

To see whether a relationship exists between body mass and the number of Calories burned while bicycling, you could create a line graph. A line graph is used to display data that show how one variable (the responding variable) changes in response to another variable (the manipulated variable). You can use a line graph when your manipulated variable is **continuous,** that is, when there are other points between the ones that you tested. In this example, body mass is a continuous variable because there are other body masses between 30 and 40 kilograms (for example, 31 kilograms). Time is another example of a continuous variable.

Line graphs are powerful tools because they allow you to estimate values for conditions that you did not test in the experiment. For example, you can use the line graph to estimate that a 35-kilogram person would burn 68 Calories while bicycling.

To create a line graph, follow these steps.

1. On graph paper, draw a horizontal, or *x*-, axis and a vertical, or *y*-, axis.

2. Label the horizontal axis with the name of the manipulated variable. Label the vertical axis with the name of the responding variable. Include units of measurement.

3. Create a scale on each axis by marking off equally spaced numbers that cover the range of the data collected.

4. Plot a point on the graph for each piece of data. In the line graph above, the dotted lines show how to plot the first data point (30 kilograms and 60 Calories). Follow an imaginary vertical line extending up from the horizontal axis at the 30-kilogram mark. Then follow an imaginary horizontal line extending across from the vertical axis at the 60-Calorie mark. Plot the point where the two lines intersect.

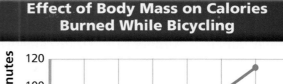

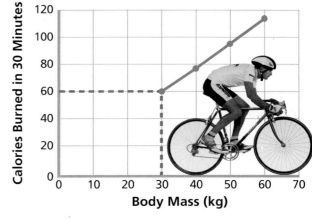

Effect of Body Mass on Calories Burned While Bicycling

5. Connect the plotted points with a solid line. (In some cases, it may be more appropriate to draw a line that shows the general trend of the plotted points. In those cases, some of the points may fall above or below the line. Also, not all graphs are linear. It may be more appropriate to draw a curve to connect the points.)

6. Add a title that identifies the variables or relationship in the graph.

Activity

Create line graphs to display the data from Experiment 2 and Experiment 3 in the data table.

Activity

You read in the newspaper that a total of 4 centimeters of rain fell in your area in June, 2.5 centimeters fell in July, and 1.5 centimeters fell in August. What type of graph would you use to display these data? Use graph paper to create the graph.

Circle Graphs

Like bar graphs, circle graphs can be used to display data in a number of separate categories. Unlike bar graphs, however, circle graphs can only be used when you have data for *all* the categories that make up a given topic. A circle graph is sometimes called a pie chart. The pie represents the entire topic, while the slices represent the individual categories. The size of a slice indicates what percentage of the whole a particular category makes up.

The data table below shows the results of a survey in which 24 teenagers were asked to identify their favorite sport. The data were then used to create the circle graph at the right.

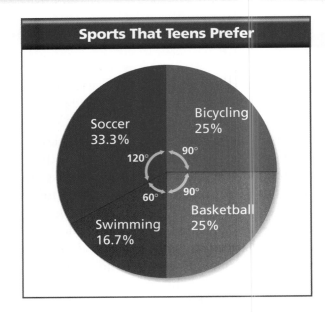

Sports That Teens Prefer

Favorite Sports	
Sport	Students
Soccer	8
Basketball	6
Bicycling	6
Swimming	4

To create a circle graph, follow these steps.

1. Use a compass to draw a circle. Mark the center with a point. Then draw a line from the center point to the top of the circle.

2. Determine the size of each "slice" by setting up a proportion where x equals the number of degrees in a slice. (*Note:* A circle contains 360 degrees.) For example, to find the number of degrees in the "soccer" slice, set up the following proportion:

$$\frac{\text{Students who prefer soccer}}{\text{Total number of students}} = \frac{x}{\text{Total number of degrees in a circle}}$$

$$\frac{8}{24} = \frac{x}{360}$$

Cross-multiply and solve for x.

$$24x = 8 \times 360$$
$$x = 120$$

The "soccer" slice should contain 120 degrees.

3. Use a protractor to measure the angle of the first slice, using the line you drew to the top of the circle as the 0° line. Draw a line from the center of the circle to the edge for the angle you measured.

4. Continue around the circle by measuring the size of each slice with the protractor. Start measuring from the edge of the previous slice so the wedges do not overlap. When you are done, the entire circle should be filled in.

5. Determine the percentage of the whole circle that each slice represents. To do this, divide the number of degrees in a slice by the total number of degrees in a circle (360), and multiply by 100%. For the "soccer" slice, you can find the percentage as follows:

$$\frac{120}{360} \times 100\% = 33.3\%$$

6. Use a different color for each slice. Label each slice with the category and with the percentage of the whole it represents.

7. Add a title to the circle graph.

Activity

In a class of 28 students, 12 students take the bus to school, 10 students walk, and 6 students ride their bicycles. Create a circle graph to display these data.

Math Review

Scientists use math to organize, analyze, and present data. This appendix will help you review some basic math skills.

Mean, Median, and Mode

The **mean** is the average, or the sum of the data divided by the number of data items. The middle number in a set of ordered data is called the **median**. The **mode** is the number that appears most often in a set of data.

Example

A scientist counted the number of distinct songs sung by seven different male birds and collected the data shown below.

Male Bird Songs							
Bird	A	B	C	D	E	F	G
Number of Songs	36	29	40	35	28	36	27

To determine the mean number of songs, add the total number of songs and divide by the number of data items—in this case, the number of male birds.

Mean $= \frac{231}{7} =$ **33 songs**

To find the median number of songs, arrange the data in numerical order and find the number in the middle of the series.

27 28 29 35 36 36 40

The number in the middle is 35, so the median number of songs is 35.

The mode is the value that appears most frequently. In the data, 36 appears twice, while each other item appears only once. Therefore, 36 songs is the mode.

Practice

Find out how many minutes it takes each student in your class to get to school. Then find the mean, median, and mode for the data.

Probability

Probability is the chance that an event will occur. Probability can be expressed as a ratio, a fraction, or a percentage. For example, when you flip a coin, the probability that the coin will land heads up is 1 in 2, or $\frac{1}{2}$, or 50 percent.

The probability that an event will happen can be expressed in the following formula.

$$P(\text{event}) = \frac{\text{Number of times the event can occur}}{\text{Total number of possible events}}$$

Example

A paper bag contains 25 blue marbles, 5 green marbles, 5 orange marbles, and 15 yellow marbles. If you close your eyes and pick a marble from the bag, what is the probability that it will be yellow?

$$P(\text{yellow marbles}) = \frac{15 \text{ yellow marbles}}{50 \text{ marbles total}}$$

$$P = \frac{15}{50}, \text{ or } \frac{3}{10}, \text{ or } 30\%$$

Practice

Each side of a cube has a letter on it. Two sides have *A*, three sides have *B*, and one side has *C*. If you roll the cube, what is the probability that *A* will land on top?

Area

The **area** of a surface is the number of square units that cover it. The front cover of your textbook has an area of about 600 cm^2.

Area of a Rectangle and a Square To find the area of a rectangle, multiply its length times its width. The formula for the area of a rectangle is

$$A = \ell \times w, \text{ or } A = \ell w$$

Since all four sides of a square have the same length, the area of a square is the length of one side multiplied by itself, or squared.

$$A = s \times s, \text{ or } A = s^2$$

Example

A scientist is studying the plants in a field that measures 75 m $\times$ 45 m. What is the area of the field?

$$A = \ell \times w$$
$$A = 75 \text{ m} \times 45 \text{ m}$$
$$A = 3,375 \text{ m}^2$$

Area of a Circle The formula for the area of a circle is

$$A = \pi \times r \times r, \text{ or } A = \pi r^2$$

The length of the radius is represented by r, and the value of π is approximately $\frac{22}{7}$.

Example

Find the area of a circle with a radius of 14 cm.

$$A = \pi r^2$$
$$A = 14 \times 14 \times \frac{22}{7}$$
$$A = 616 \text{ cm}^2$$

Practice

Find the area of a circle that has a radius of 21 m.

Circumference

The distance around a circle is called the circumference. The formula for finding the circumference of a circle is

$$C = 2 \times \pi \times r, \text{ or } C = 2\pi r$$

Example

The radius of a circle is 35 cm. What is its circumference?

$$C = 2\pi r$$
$$C = 2 \times 35 \times \frac{22}{7}$$
$$C = 220 \text{ cm}$$

Practice

What is the circumference of a circle with a radius of 28 m?

Volume

The volume of an object is the number of cubic units it contains. The volume of a wastebasket, for example, might be about 26,000 cm^3.

Volume of a Rectangular Object To find the volume of a rectangular object, multiply the object's length times its width times its height.

$$V = \ell \times w \times h, \text{ or } V = \ell w h$$

Example

Find the volume of a box with length 24 cm, width 12 cm, and height 9 cm.

$$V = \ell w h$$
$$V = 24 \text{ cm} \times 12 \text{ cm} \times 9 \text{ cm}$$
$$V = 2,592 \text{ cm}^3$$

Practice

What is the volume of a rectangular object with length 17 cm, width 11 cm, and height 6 cm?

Fractions

A **fraction** is a way to express a part of a whole. In the fraction $\frac{4}{7}$, 4 is the numerator and 7 is the denominator.

Adding and Subtracting Fractions To add or subtract two or more fractions that have a common denominator, first add or subtract the numerators. Then write the sum or difference over the common denominator.

To find the sum or difference of fractions with different denominators, first find the least common multiple of the denominators. This is known as the least common denominator. Then convert each fraction to equivalent fractions with the least common denominator. Add or subtract the numerators. Then write the sum or difference over the common denominator.

> **Example**
>
> $$\frac{5}{6} - \frac{3}{4} = \frac{10}{12} - \frac{9}{12} = \frac{10-9}{12} = \frac{1}{12}$$

Multiplying Fractions To multiply two fractions, first multiply the two numerators, then multiply the two denominators.

> **Example**
>
> $$\frac{5}{6} \times \frac{2}{3} = \frac{5 \times 2}{6 \times 3} = \frac{10}{18} = \frac{5}{9}$$

Dividing Fractions Dividing by a fraction is the same as multiplying by its reciprocal. Reciprocals are numbers whose numerators and denominators have been switched. To divide one fraction by another, first invert the fraction you are dividing by—in other words, turn it upside down. Then multiply the two fractions.

> **Example**
>
> $$\frac{2}{5} \div \frac{7}{8} = \frac{2}{5} \times \frac{8}{7} = \frac{2 \times 8}{5 \times 7} = \frac{16}{35}$$

> **Practice**
>
> Solve the following: $\frac{3}{7} \div \frac{4}{5}$.

Decimals

Fractions whose denominators are 10, 100, or some other power of 10 are often expressed as decimals. For example, the fraction $\frac{9}{10}$ can be expressed as the decimal 0.9, and the fraction $\frac{7}{100}$ can be written as 0.07.

Adding and Subtracting With Decimals To add or subtract decimals, line up the decimal points before you carry out the operation.

> **Example**
>
> ```
>    27.4          278.635
>  + 6.19        − 191.4
>  -------        ---------
>    33.59          87.235
> ```

Multiplying With Decimals When you multiply two numbers with decimals, the number of decimal places in the product is equal to the total number of decimal places in each number being multiplied.

> **Example**
>
> ```
>      46.2   (one decimal place)
>  ×  2.37   (two decimal places)
>  ---------
>  109.494   (three decimal places)
> ```

Dividing With Decimals To divide a decimal by a whole number, put the decimal point in the quotient above the decimal point in the dividend.

> **Example**
>
> $15.5 \div 5$
>
> $$\begin{array}{r} 3.1 \\ 5\overline{)15.5} \end{array}$$

To divide a decimal by a decimal, you need to rewrite the divisor as a whole number. Do this by multiplying both the divisor and dividend by the same multiple of 10.

> **Example**
>
> $1.68 \div 4.2 = 16.8 \div 42$
>
> $$\begin{array}{r} 0.4 \\ 42\overline{)16.8} \end{array}$$

> **Practice**
>
> Multiply 6.21 by 8.5.

Ratio and Proportion

A **ratio** compares two numbers by division. For example, suppose a scientist counts 800 wolves and 1,200 moose on an island. The ratio of wolves to moose can be written as a fraction, $\frac{800}{1,200}$, which can be reduced to $\frac{2}{3}$. The same ratio can also be expressed as 2 to 3 or 2 : 3.

A **proportion** is a mathematical sentence saying that two ratios are equivalent. For example, a proportion could state that $\frac{800 \text{ wolves}}{1,200 \text{ moose}} = \frac{2 \text{ wolves}}{3 \text{ moose}}$. You can sometimes set up a proportion to determine or estimate an unknown quantity. For example, suppose a scientist counts 25 beetles in an area of 10 square meters. The scientist wants to estimate the number of beetles in 100 square meters.

Example

1. Express the relationship between beetles and area as a ratio: $\frac{25}{10}$, simplified to $\frac{5}{2}$.

2. Set up a proportion, with x representing the number of beetles. The proportion can be stated as $\frac{5}{2} = \frac{x}{100}$.

3. Begin by cross-multiplying. In other words, multiply each fraction's numerator by the other fraction's denominator.

$$5 \times 100 = 2 \times x, \text{ or } 500 = 2x$$

4. To find the value of x, divide both sides by 2. The result is 250, or 250 beetles in 100 square meters.

Practice

Find the value of x in the following proportion: $\frac{6}{7} = \frac{x}{49}$.

Percentage

A **percentage** is a ratio that compares a number to 100. For example, there are 37 granite rocks in a collection that consists of 100 rocks. The ratio $\frac{37}{100}$ can be written as 37%. Granite rocks make up 37% of the rock collection.

You can calculate percentages of numbers other than 100 by setting up a proportion.

Example

Rain falls on 9 days out of 30 in June. What percentage of the days in June were rainy?

$$\frac{9 \text{ days}}{30 \text{ days}} = \frac{d\%}{100\%}$$

To find the value of d, begin by cross-multiplying, as for any proportion:

$$9 \times 100 = 30 \times d \qquad d = \frac{900}{30} \qquad d = 30$$

Practice

There are 300 marbles in a jar, and 42 of those marbles are blue. What percentage of the marbles are blue?

Significant Figures

The **precision** of a measurement depends on the instrument you use to take the measurement. For example, if the smallest unit on the ruler is millimeters, then the most precise measurement you can make will be in millimeters.

The sum or difference of measurements can only be as precise as the least precise measurement being added or subtracted. Round your answer so that it has the same number of digits after the decimal as the least precise measurement. Round up if the last digit is 5 or more, and round down if the last digit is 4 or less.

> **Example**
>
> Subtract a temperature of 5.2°C from the temperature 75.46°C.
>
> **75.46 − 5.2 = 70.26**
>
> 5.2 has the fewest digits after the decimal, so it is the least precise measurement. Since the last digit of the answer is 6, round up to 3. The most precise difference between the measurements is 70.3°C.

> **Practice**
>
> Add 26.4 m to 8.37 m. Round your answer according to the precision of the measurements.

Significant figures are the number of nonzero digits in a measurement. Zeroes between nonzero digits are also significant. For example, the measurements 12,500 L, 0.125 cm, and 2.05 kg all have three significant figures. When you multiply and divide measurements, the one with the fewest significant figures determines the number of significant figures in your answer.

> **Example**
>
> Multiply 110 g by 5.75 g.
>
> **110 × 5.75 = 632.5**
>
> Because 110 has only two significant figures, round the answer to 630 g.

Scientific Notation

A **factor** is a number that divides into another number with no remainder. In the example, the number 3 is used as a factor four times.

An **exponent** tells how many times a number is used as a factor. For example, $3 \times 3 \times 3 \times 3$ can be written as 3^4. The exponent 4 indicates that the number 3 is used as a factor four times. Another way of expressing this is to say that 81 is equal to 3 to the fourth power.

> **Example**
>
> $$3^4 = 3 \times 3 \times 3 \times 3 = 81$$

Scientific notation uses exponents and powers of ten to write very large or very small numbers in shorter form. When you write a number in scientific notation, you write the number as two factors. The first factor is any number between 1 and 10. The second factor is a power of 10, such as 10^3 or 10^6.

> **Example**
>
> The average distance between the planet Mercury and the sun is 58,000,000 km. To write the first factor in scientific notation, insert a decimal point in the original number so that you have a number between 1 and 10. In the case of 58,000,000, the number is 5.8.
>
> To determine the power of 10, count the number of places that the decimal point moved. In this case, it moved 7 places.
>
> **58,000,000 km = 5.8×10^7 km**

> **Practice**
>
> Express 6,590,000 in scientific notation.

Reading Comprehension Skills

Your textbook is an important source of science information. As you read your science textbook, you will find that the book has been written to assist you in understanding the science concepts.

Learning From Science Textbooks

As you study science in school, you will learn science concepts in a variety of ways. Sometimes you will do interesting activities and experiments to explore science ideas. To fully understand what you observe in experiments and activities, you will need to read your science textbook. To help you read, some of the important ideas are highlighted so that you can easily recognize what they are. In addition, a target reading skill in each section will help you understand what you read.

By using the target reading skills, you will improve your reading comprehension—that is, you will improve your ability to understand what you read. As you learn science, you will build knowledge that will help you understand even more of what you read. This knowledge will help you learn about all the topics presented in this textbook.

And—guess what?—these reading skills can be useful whenever you are reading. Reading to learn is important for your entire life. You have an opportunity to begin that process now.

The target reading skills that will improve your reading comprehension are described below.

Building Vocabulary

To understand the science concepts taught in this textbook, you need to remember the meanings of the Key Terms. One strategy consists of writing the definitions of these terms in your own words. You can also practice using the terms in sentences and make lists of words or phrases you associate with each term.

Using Prior Knowledge

Your prior knowledge is what you already know before you begin to read about a topic. Building on what you already know gives you a head start on learning new information. Before you begin a new assignment, think about what you know. You might page through your reading assignment, looking at the headings and the visuals to spark your memory. You can list what you know in the graphic organizer provided in the section opener. Then, as you read, consider questions like the ones below to connect what you learn to what you already know.

• How does what you learn relate to what you know?

• How did something you already know help you learn something new?

• Did your original ideas agree with what you have just learned? If not, how would you revise your original ideas?

Asking Questions

Asking yourself questions is an excellent way to focus on and remember new information in your textbook. You can learn how to ask good questions.

One way is to turn the text headings into questions. Then your questions can guide you to identify and remember the important information as you read. Look at these examples:

Heading: Using Seismographic Data

Question: How are seismographic data used?

Heading: Kinds of Faults

Question: What are the kinds of faults?

You do not have to limit your questions to the text headings. Ask questions about anything that you need to clarify or that will help you understand the content. *What* and *how* are probably the most common question words, but you may also ask *why, who, when,* or *where* questions. Here is an example:

Properties of Waves

Question	Answer
What is amplitude?	Amplitude is . . .

Previewing Visuals

Visuals are photographs, graphs, tables, diagrams, and illustrations. Visuals, such as this diagram of a normal fault, contain important information. Look at visuals and their captions before you read. This will help you prepare for what you will be reading about.

Often you will be asked what you want to learn about a visual. For example, after you look at the normal fault diagram, you might ask: What is the movement along a normal fault? Questions about visuals give you a purpose for reading—to answer your questions. Previewing visuals also helps you see what you already know.

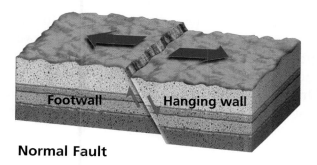

Footwall   **Hanging wall**

Normal Fault

Outlining

An outline shows the relationship between main ideas and supporting ideas. An outline has a formal structure. You write the main ideas, called topics, next to Roman numerals. The supporting ideas, sometimes called subtopics, are written under the main ideas and labeled A, B, C, and so on. An outline looks like this:

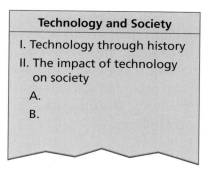

Technology and Society

I. Technology through history

II. The impact of technology on society

   A.

   B.

When you have completed an outline like this, you can see at a glance the structure of the section. You can use this outline as a study tool.

Identifying Main Ideas

When you are reading, it is important to try to understand the ideas and concepts that are in a passage. As you read science material, you will recognize that each paragraph has a lot of information and detail. Good readers try to identify the most important—or biggest—idea in every paragraph or section. That's the main idea. The other information in the paragraph supports or further explains the main idea.

Sometimes main ideas are stated directly. In this book, some main ideas are identified for you as key concepts. These are printed in boldface type. However, you must identify other main ideas yourself. In order to do this, you must identify all the ideas within a paragraph or section. Then ask yourself which idea is big enough to include all the other ideas.

SKILLS
Handbook

Comparing and Contrasting

When you compare and contrast, you examine the similarities and differences between things. You can compare and contrast in a Venn diagram or in a table. Your completed diagram or table shows you how the items are alike and how they are different.

Venn Diagram A Venn diagram consists of two overlapping circles. In the space where the circles overlap, you write the characteristics that the two items have in common. In one of the circles outside the area of overlap, you write the differing features or characteristics of one of the items. In the other circle outside the area of overlap, you write the differing characteristics of the other item.

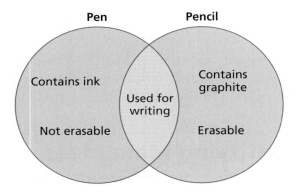

Table In a compare/contrast table, you list the items to be compared across the top of the table. Then list the characteristics or features to be compared in the left column. Complete the table by filling in information about each characteristic or feature.

Blood Vessel	Function	Structure of Wall
Artery	Carries blood away from heart	
Capillary		
Vein		

Sequencing

A sequence is the order in which a series of events occurs. Recognizing and remembering the sequence of events is important to understanding many processes in science. Sometimes the text uses words like *first, next, during,* and *after* to signal a sequence. A flowchart or a cycle diagram can help you visualize a sequence.

Flowchart To make a flowchart, write a brief description of each step or event in a box. Place the boxes in order, with the first event at the top of the page. Then draw an arrow to connect each step or event to the next.

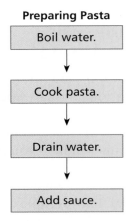

Cycle Diagram A cycle diagram shows a sequence that is continuous, or cyclical. A continuous sequence does not have an end because when the final event is over, the first event begins again. To create a cycle diagram, write the starting event in a box placed at the top of a page in the center. Then, moving in a clockwise direction around an imaginary circle, write each event in a box in its proper sequence. Draw arrows that connect each event to the one that occurs next, forming a continuous circle.

Identifying Supporting Evidence

A hypothesis is a possible explanation for observations made by scientists or an answer to a scientific question. A hypothesis is tested over and over again. The tests may produce evidence that supports the hypothesis. When enough supporting evidence is collected, a hypothesis may become a theory.

Identifying the supporting evidence for a hypothesis or theory can help you understand the hypothesis or theory. Evidence consists of facts—information whose accuracy can be confirmed by testing or observation.

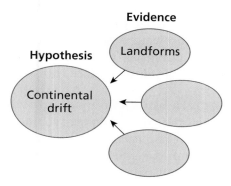

Relating Cause and Effect

Identifying causes and effects helps you understand relationships among events. A cause makes something happen. An effect is what happens. When you recognize that one event causes another, you are relating cause and effect. Words like *cause, because, effect, affect,* and *result* often signal a cause or an effect.

Sometimes an effect can have more than one cause, or a cause can produce several effects. For example, car exhaust and smoke from industrial plants are two causes of air pollution. Some effects of air pollution include breathing difficulties for some people, death of plants along some highways, and damage to some building surfaces.

Science involves many cause-and-effect relationships. Seeing and understanding these relationships helps you understand science processes.

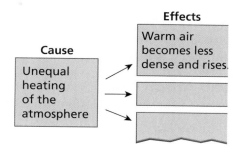

Concept Mapping

Concept maps are useful tools for organizing information on any topic. A concept map begins with a main idea or core concept and shows how the idea can be subdivided into related subconcepts or smaller ideas. In this way, relationships between concepts become clearer and easier to understand.

You construct a concept map by placing concepts (usually nouns) in ovals and connecting them with linking words. The biggest concept or idea is placed in an oval at the top of the map. Related concepts are arranged in ovals below the big idea. The linking words are often verbs and verb phrases and are written on the lines that connect the ovals.

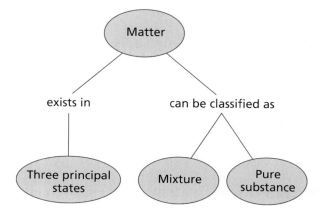

Safety Symbols

These symbols warn of possible dangers in the laboratory and remind you to work carefully.

 Safety Goggles Wear safety goggles to protect your eyes in any activity involving chemicals, flames or heating, or glassware.

 Lab Apron Wear a laboratory apron to protect your skin and clothing from damage.

 Breakage Handle breakable materials, such as glassware, with care. Do not touch broken glassware.

 Heat-Resistant Gloves Use an oven mitt or other hand protection when handling hot materials such as hot plates or hot glassware.

 Plastic Gloves Wear disposable plastic gloves when working with harmful chemicals and organisms. Keep your hands away from your face, and dispose of the gloves according to your teacher's instructions.

 Heating Use a clamp or tongs to pick up hot glassware. Do not touch hot objects with your bare hands.

 Flames Before you work with flames, tie back loose hair and clothing. Follow instructions from your teacher about lighting and extinguishing flames.

 No Flames When using flammable materials, make sure there are no flames, sparks, or other exposed heat sources present.

 Corrosive Chemical Avoid getting acid or other corrosive chemicals on your skin or clothing or in your eyes. Do not inhale the vapors. Wash your hands after the activity.

 Poison Do not let any poisonous chemical come into contact with your skin, and do not inhale its vapors. Wash your hands when you are finished with the activity.

 Fumes Work in a ventilated area when harmful vapors may be involved. Avoid inhaling vapors directly. Only test an odor when directed to do so by your teacher, and use a wafting motion to direct the vapor toward your nose.

 Sharp Object Scissors, scalpels, knives, needles, pins, and tacks can cut your skin. Always direct a sharp edge or point away from yourself and others.

 Animal Safety Treat live or preserved animals or animal parts with care to avoid harming the animals or yourself. Wash your hands when you are finished with the activity.

 Plant Safety Handle plants only as directed by your teacher. If you are allergic to certain plants, tell your teacher; do not do an activity involving those plants. Avoid touching harmful plants such as poison ivy. Wash your hands when you are finished with the activity.

 Electric Shock To avoid electric shock, never use electrical equipment around water, or when the equipment is wet or your hands are wet. Be sure cords are untangled and cannot trip anyone. Unplug equipment not in use.

 Physical Safety When an experiment involves physical activity, avoid injuring yourself or others. Alert your teacher if there is any reason you should not participate.

 Disposal Dispose of chemicals and other laboratory materials safely. Follow the instructions from your teacher.

 Hand Washing Wash your hands thoroughly when finished with the activity. Use antibacterial soap and warm water. Rinse well.

 General Safety Awareness When this symbol appears, follow the instructions provided. When you are asked to develop your own procedure in a lab, have your teacher approve your plan before you go further.

Science Safety Rules

General Precautions

Follow all instructions. Never perform activities without the approval and supervision of your teacher. Do not engage in horseplay. Never eat or drink in the laboratory. Keep work areas clean and uncluttered.

Dress Code

Wear safety goggles whenever you work with chemicals, glassware, heat sources such as burners, or any substance that might get into your eyes. If you wear contact lenses, notify your teacher.

Wear a lab apron or coat whenever you work with corrosive chemicals or substances that can stain. Wear disposable plastic gloves when working with organisms and harmful chemicals. Tie back long hair. Remove or tie back any article of clothing or jewelry that can hang down and touch chemicals, flames, or equipment. Roll up long sleeves. Never wear open shoes or sandals.

First Aid

Report all accidents, injuries, or fires to your teacher, no matter how minor. Be aware of the location of the first-aid kit, emergency equipment such as the fire extinguisher and fire blanket, and the nearest telephone. Know whom to contact in an emergency.

Heating and Fire Safety

Keep all combustible materials away from flames. When heating a substance in a test tube, make sure that the mouth of the tube is not pointed at you or anyone else. Never heat a liquid in a closed container. Use an oven mitt to pick up a container that has been heated.

Using Chemicals Safely

Never put your face near the mouth of a container that holds chemicals. Never touch, taste, or smell a chemical unless your teacher tells you to.

Use only those chemicals needed in the activity. Keep all containers closed when chemicals are not being used. Pour all chemicals over the sink or a container, not over your work surface. Dispose of excess chemicals as instructed by your teacher.

Be extra careful when working with acids or bases. When mixing an acid and water, always pour the water into the container first and then add the acid to the water. Never pour water into an acid. Wash chemical spills and splashes immediately with plenty of water.

Using Glassware Safely

If glassware is broken or chipped, notify your teacher immediately. Never handle broken or chipped glass with your bare hands.

Never force glass tubing or thermometers into a rubber stopper or rubber tubing. Have your teacher insert the glass tubing or thermometer if required for an activity.

Using Sharp Instruments

Handle sharp instruments with extreme care. Never cut material toward you; cut away from you.

Animal and Plant Safety

Never perform experiments that cause pain, discomfort, or harm to animals. Only handle animals if absolutely necessary. If you know that you are allergic to certain plants, molds, or animals, tell your teacher before doing an activity in which these are used. Wash your hands thoroughly after any activity involving animals, animal parts, plants, plant parts, or soil.

During field work, wear long pants, long sleeves, socks, and closed shoes. Avoid poisonous plants and fungi as well as plants with thorns.

End-of-Experiment Rules

Unplug all electrical equipment. Clean up your work area. Dispose of waste materials as instructed by your teacher. Wash your hands after every experiment.

The microscope is an essential tool in the study of life science. It allows you to see things that are too small to be seen with the unaided eye.

You will probably use a compound microscope like the one you see here. The compound microscope has more than one lens that magnifies the object you view.

Typically, a compound microscope has one lens in the eyepiece, the part you look through. The eyepiece lens usually magnifies 10 ×. Any object you view through this lens would appear 10 times larger than it is.

The compound microscope may contain one or two other lenses called objective lenses. If there are two objective lenses, they are called the low-power and high-power objective lenses. The low-power objective lens usually magnifies 10 ×. The high-power objective lens usually magnifies 40 ×.

To calculate the total magnification with which you are viewing an object, multiply the magnification of the eyepiece lens by the magnification of the objective lens you are using. For example, the eyepiece's magnification of 10 × multiplied by the low-power objective's magnification of 10 × equals a total magnification of 100 ×.

Use the photo of the compound microscope to become familiar with the parts of the microscope and their functions.

The Parts of a Compound Microscope

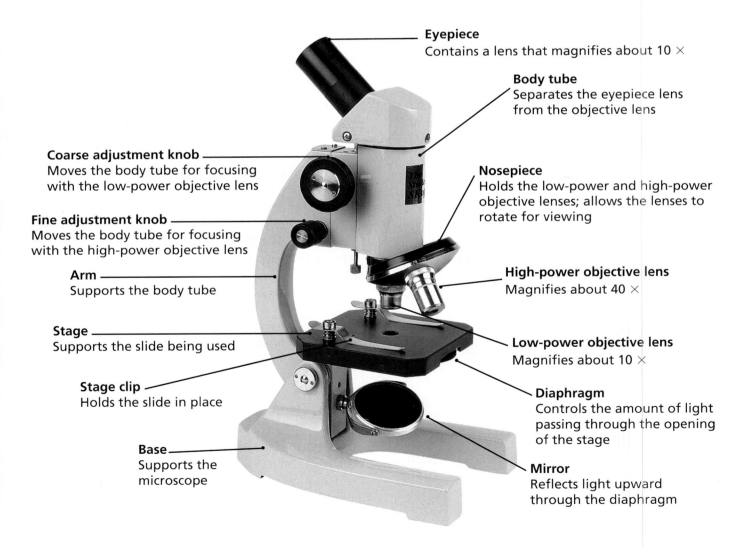

Eyepiece
Contains a lens that magnifies about 10 ×

Body tube
Separates the eyepiece lens from the objective lens

Coarse adjustment knob
Moves the body tube for focusing with the low-power objective lens

Nosepiece
Holds the low-power and high-power objective lenses; allows the lenses to rotate for viewing

Fine adjustment knob
Moves the body tube for focusing with the high-power objective lens

Arm
Supports the body tube

High-power objective lens
Magnifies about 40 ×

Stage
Supports the slide being used

Low-power objective lens
Magnifies about 10 ×

Stage clip
Holds the slide in place

Diaphragm
Controls the amount of light passing through the opening of the stage

Base
Supports the microscope

Mirror
Reflects light upward through the diaphragm

Using the Microscope

Use the following procedures when you are working with a microscope.

1. To carry the microscope, grasp the microscope's arm with one hand. Place your other hand under the base.
2. Place the microscope on a table with the arm toward you.
3. Turn the coarse adjustment knob to raise the body tube.
4. Revolve the nosepiece until the low-power objective lens clicks into place.
5. Adjust the diaphragm. While looking through the eyepiece, also adjust the mirror until you see a bright white circle of light. **CAUTION:** *Never use direct sunlight as a light source.*
6. Place a slide on the stage. Center the specimen over the opening on the stage. Use the stage clips to hold the slide in place. **CAUTION:** *Glass slides are fragile.*
7. Look at the stage from the side. Carefully turn the coarse adjustment knob to lower the body tube until the low-power objective almost touches the slide.
8. Looking through the eyepiece, very slowly turn the coarse adjustment knob until the specimen comes into focus.
9. To switch to the high-power objective lens, look at the microscope from the side. Carefully revolve the nosepiece until the high-power objective lens clicks into place. Make sure the lens does not hit the slide.
10. Looking through the eyepiece, turn the fine adjustment knob until the specimen comes into focus.

Making a Wet-Mount Slide

Use the following procedures to make a wet-mount slide of a specimen.

1. Obtain a clean microscope slide and a coverslip. **CAUTION:** *Glass slides and coverslips are fragile.*
2. Place the specimen on the slide. The specimen must be thin enough for light to pass through it.
3. Using a plastic dropper, place a drop of water on the specimen.
4. Gently place one edge of the coverslip against the slide so that it touches the edge of the water drop at a 45° angle. Slowly lower the coverslip over the specimen. If air bubbles are trapped beneath the coverslip, tap the coverslip gently with the eraser end of a pencil.
5. Remove any excess water at the edge of the coverslip with a paper towel.

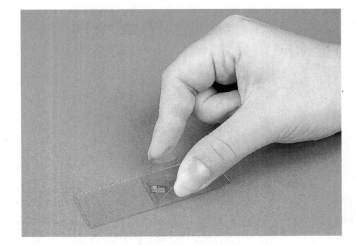

The laboratory balance is an important tool in scientific investigations. You can use a balance to determine the masses of materials that you study or experiment with in the laboratory.

Different kinds of balances are used in the laboratory. One kind of balance is the triple-beam balance. The balance that you may use in your science class is probably similar to the balance illustrated in this Appendix. To use the balance properly, you should learn the name, location, and function of each part of the balance you are using. What kind of balance do you have in your science class?

The Triple-Beam Balance

The triple-beam balance is a single-pan balance with three beams calibrated in grams. The back, or 100-gram, beam is divided into ten units of 10 grams each. The middle, or 500-gram, beam is divided into five units of 100 grams each. The front, or 10-gram, beam is divided into ten major units of 1 gram each. Each of these units is further divided into units of 0.1 gram. What is the largest mass you could find with a triple-beam balance?

The following procedure can be used to find the mass of an object with a triple-beam balance:

1. Place the object on the pan.
2. Move the rider on the middle beam notch by notch until the horizontal pointer drops below zero. Move the rider back one notch.
3. Move the rider on the back beam notch by notch until the pointer again drops below zero. Move the rider back one notch.
4. Slowly slide the rider along the front beam until the pointer stops at the zero point.
5. The mass of the object is equal to the sum of the readings on the three beams.

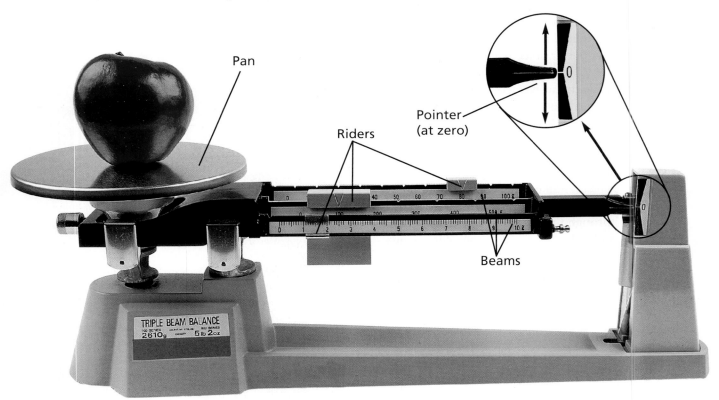

Triple-Beam Balance

English and Spanish Glossary

A

absorption The process by which nutrient molecules pass through the wall of the digestive system into the blood. (p. 359)
absorción Proceso por el cual las moléculas de los nutrientes pasan a través de la pared del sistema digestivo a la sangre.

acceleration The rate at which velocity changes. (p. 614)
acelaración Razón a la que cambia la velocidad.

acid rain Rain that contains more acid than normal. (p. 64)
lluvia ácida Lluvia que contiene más acidez de la normal.

adaptation A characteristic that helps an organism survive or reproduce in its environment. (p. 261)
adaptación Característica que ayuda a un organismo a sobrevivir o a reproducirse en su medio ambiente.

addiction A physical dependence on a substance. (p. 421), (p. 465)
adicción Dependencia física de una sustancia.

adolescence The stage of development between childhood and adulthood when children become adults physically and mentally. (p. 501)
adolescencia Etapa del desarrollo entre la niñez y la adultez cuando los niños empiezan a ser adultos física y mentalmente.

air mass A huge body of air that has similar temperature, humidity, and air pressure throughout. (p. 130)
masa de aire Gran volumen de aire que tiene temperatura, humedad y presión similares en todos sus puntos.

air pressure The pressure caused by the weight of a column of air pushing down on an area. (p. 51)
presión de aire Presión causada por el peso de una columna de aire que empuja hacia abajo en un área.

air resistance The fluid friction experienced by objects falling through the air. (p. 609)
resistencia del aire Fricción de fluido experimentada por los objetos que caen a través del aire.

alcoholism A disease in which a person is both physically addicted to and emotionally dependent on alcohol. (p. 469)
alcoholismo Enfermedad en la que una persona es adicta físicamente y dependiente emocionalmente del alcohol.

alleles The different forms of a gene. (p. 533)
alelos Diferentes formas de un gen.

altitude Elevation above sea level. (p. 53)
altitud Elevación sobre el nivel del mar.

alveoli Tiny sacs of lung tissue specialized for the movement of gases between air and blood. (p. 414)
alveolos Sacos diminutos de tejido pulmonar especializados en el intercambio de gases entre el aire y la sangre.

amino acids Small units that are linked together chemically to form large protein molecules. (p. 347)
aminoácidos Pequeñas unidades que están unidas químicamente entre ellas para formar grandes moléculas de proteínas.

amniotic egg An egg with a shell and internal membranes that keep the embryo moist; a major adaptation to life on land that is characteristic of reptiles, birds, and egg-laying mammals. (p. 286)
huevo amniótico Huevo con cáscara y membranas internas que mantiene al embrión húmedo; adaptación principal a la vida en la tierra característica de los reptiles, las aves y los mamíferos que ponen huevos.

amphibian An ectothermic vertebrate that spends its early life in water and its adult life on land. (p. 284)
anfibio Vertebrado ectotérmico que pasa la primera etapa de su vida en el agua y la madurez en la tierra.

anabolic steroids Synthetic chemicals that are similar to hormones produced in the body. (p. 466)
esteroides anabólicos Sustancias químicas sintéticas que son semejantes a las hormonas producidas por el cuerpo.

anemometer An instrument used to measure wind speed. (p. 99)
anemómetro Instrumento que se usa para medir la velocidad del viento.

aneroid barometer An instrument that measures changes in air pressure without using a liquid. (p. 52)
barómetro aneroide Instrumento que mide los cambios en la presión del aire sin usar líquido.

angiosperm A plant that produces seeds that are enclosed in a protective structure. (p. 239)
angiosperma Planta que produce semillas encerradas en una estructura protectora.

anticyclone A high-pressure center of dry air. (p. 136)
anticiclón Centro de aire seco de alta presión.

English and Spanish Glossary

anus A muscular opening at the end of the rectum through which waste material is eliminated from the body. (p. 369)
ano Abertura muscular al final del recto a través de la cual se elimina el material de desecho digestivo del cuerpo.

aorta The largest artery in the body; receives blood from the left ventricle. (p. 382)
aorta La arteria más grande del cuerpo; recibe la sangre del ventrículo izquierdo.

arachnid An arthropod with two body sections, four pairs of legs, and no antennae. (p. 275)
arácnido Artrópodo con dos secciones corporales, cuatro pares de patas y sin antenas.

Archimedes' principle The rule that the buoyant force on an object is equal to the weight of the fluid the object displaces. (p. 676)
principio de Arquímedes Regla que enuncia que la fuerza de flotación que actúa sobre un objeto es igual al peso del líquido que desaloja.

artery A blood vessel that carries blood away from the heart. (p. 380)
arteria Vaso sanguíneo que transporta la sangre que sale del corazón.

arthritis A disease of the joints that makes movement painful. (p. 321)
artritis Enfermedad de las articulaciones que hace que el movimiento sea doloroso.

arthropod An invertebrate that has an external skeleton, a segmented body, and jointed appendages. (p. 272)
artrópodo Invertebrado que tiene esqueleto externo, cuerpo segmentado y apéndices anexos.

arthroscope A slim, tube-shaped, surgical instrument that doctors use to diagnose a problem in a joint. (p. 321)
artroscopío Instrumento de cirugía con forma de tubo delgado que usan los doctores para diagnosticar un problema en una articulación.

asexual reproduction The process by which a single organism produces a new organism identical to itself. (p. 262)
reproducción asexual Proceso por el cual un solo organismo produce un nuevo organismo idéntico a él.

atherosclerosis A condition in which an artery wall thickens as a result of the buildup of fatty materials. (p. 397)
arteriosclerosis Condición en la que la pared de una arteria se hace más gruesa debido a la acumulación de materiales grasos.

atmosphere The layer of gases that surrounds Earth. (p. 46)
atmósfera Capa de gases que rodea la Tierra.

atrium Each of the two upper chambers of the heart that receives blood that comes into the heart. (p. 379)
aurícula Cada una de las dos cámaras superiores del corazón que reciben la sangre que entra en el corazón.

autonomic nervous system The group of nerves in the peripheral nervous system that controls involuntary actions. (p. 449)
sistema nervioso autónomo Grupo de nervios en el sistema nervioso periférico que controla las acciones involuntarias.

average speed The overall rate of speed at which an object moves; calculated by dividing the total distance an object travels by the total time. (p. 571)
rapidez media Velocidad general a la que se mueve un objeto; se calcula dividiendo la distancia total recorrida por el tiempo total empleado.

axon A threadlike extension of a neuron that carries nerve impulses away from the cell body. (p. 440)
axón Extensión con forma de hilo de una neurona que saca los impulsos nerviosos del cuerpo de la célula.

B

balanced forces Equal forces acting on an object in opposite directions. (p. 630)
fuerzas equilibradas Fuerzas iguales que actúan sobre un objeto en direcciones opuestas.

barometer An instrument used to measure changes in air pressure. (p. 52), (p. 672)
barómetro Instrumento que se usa para medir cambios en la presión del aire.

Bernoulli's principle The rule that a stream of fast-moving fluid exerts less pressure than the surrounding fluid. (p. 656)
principio de Bernoulli Regla que enuncia que la corriente de un fluido de rápido movimiento ejerce menor presión que el fluido del entorno.

bilateral symmetry Line symmetry; the quality of being divisible into two halves that are mirror images. (p. 263)
simetría bilateral Simetría lineal; la cualidad de ser divisible en dos mitades iguales.

bile A substance produced by the liver that breaks up fat particles. (p. 367)
bilis Sustancia producida por el hígado que descompone las partículas de grasa.

bird An endothermic vertebrate that has feathers and a four-chambered heart, and lays eggs. (p. 289)
ave Vertebrado endotérmico que tiene plumas, un corazón de 4 cámaras y pone huevos.

bivalve A mollusk that has two shells held together by hinges and strong muscles. (p. 270)
bivalvo Molusco que tiene dos conchas unidas por charnelas y fuertes músculos.

blood pressure The pressure that is exerted by the blood against the walls of blood vessels. (p. 386)
presión arterial Presión que ejerce la sangre contra las paredes de los vasos sanguíneos.

brain The part of the central nervous system that is located in the skull and controls most functions in the body. (p. 445)
encéfalo Parte del sistema nervioso central que está ubicado en el cráneo y controla la mayoría de las funciones del cuerpo.

brainstem The part of the brain that lies between the cerebellum and spinal cord and controls the body's involuntary actions. (p. 446)
tronco encefálico Parte del encéfalo que se encuentra entre el cerebelo y la médula espinal, y controla las acciones involuntarias del cuerpo.

brainstorming A process in which group members freely suggest any creative solutions that come to mind. (p. 37)
lluvia de ideas Proceso mediante el cual los miembros de un grupo sugieren libremente cualquier solución creativa que se les ocurre.

bronchi The passages that direct air into the lungs. (p. 414)
bronquios Conductos que dirigen el aire hacia los pulmones.

bronchitis An irritation of the breathing passages in which the small passages become narrower than normal and may be clogged with mucus. (p. 422)
bronquitis Irritación de los conductos respiratorios en la que los conductos pequeños se hacen más estrechos de lo normal y se pueden obstruir con mucosidad.

buoyant force The upward force exerted by a fluid on a submerged object. (p. 643)
fuerza de flotación Fuerza ascendente que ejerce un líquido sobre un objeto sumergido.

calorie The amount of energy needed to raise the temperature of one gram of water by one degree Celsius. (p. 343)

caloría Cantidad de energía que se necesita para elevar la temperatura de un gramo de agua un grado Celsius.

cambium The layer of cells in a plant that produces new phloem and xylem cells. (p. 230)
cámbium Capa de células de una planta que produce nuevas células de floema y xilema.

cancer A disease in which some body cells divide uncontrollably. (p. 333)
cáncer Enfermedad en la que algunas células del cuerpo se dividen descontroladamente.

capillary A tiny blood vessel where substances are exchanged between the blood and the body cells. (p. 380)
capilar Vaso sanguíneo minúsculo donde se intercambian las sustancias de la sangre y las células del cuerpo.

carbohydrate Nutrient composed of carbon, oxygen, and hydrogen that is a major source of energy. (p. 344)
carbohidrato Nutriente compuesto de carbono, oxígeno e hidrógeno, que es una importante fuente de energía.

carbon monoxide A colorless, odorless gas produced when substances—including tobacco—are burned. (p. 421)
Monóxido de carbono Gas incoloro e inodoro producido cuando se queman algunas sustancias, incluido el tabaco.

cardiac muscle Muscle tissue found only in the heart. (p. 325)
músculo cardiaco Tejido muscular que sólo se encuentra en el corazón.

cardiovascular system The body system that consists of the heart, blood vessels, and blood; also called the circulatory system. (p. 376)
sistema cardiovascular Sistema corporal que está formado por el corazón, los vasos sanguíneos y la sangre; tambien llamado sistema circulatoria.

carrier A person who has one recessive allele for a trait, but does not have the trait. (p. 569)
portador Persona que tiene un alelo recesivo para un determinado rasgo, pero que no tiene el rasgo.

cartilage A connective tissue that is more flexible than bone and that protects the ends of bones and keeps them from rubbing together. (p. 282), (p. 313)
cartílago Tejido conectivo que es más flexible que el hueso y que protege los extremos de los huesos y evita que se rocen.

cell The basic unit of structure and function in living things. (p. 511)
célula Unidad básica de estructura y función en los seres vivos.

cell membrane A cell structure that controls which substances can enter or leave the cell. (p. 521)
membrana celular Estructura celular que controla qué sustancias pueden entrar y salir de la célula.

cell theory A widely accepted explanation of the relationship between cells and living things. (p. 514)
teoría celular Explicación ampliamente aceptada sobre la relación entre las células y los seres vivos.

cell wall A rigid layer of nonliving material that surrounds the cells of plants and some other organisms. (p. 521)
pared celular Capa rígida de material no vivo que rodea las células vegetales y de algunos organismos.

central nervous system The division of the nervous system consisting of the brain and spinal cord. (p. 444)
sistema nervioso central División del sistema nervioso formado por el encéfalo y en la médula espinal.

centripetal force A force that causes an object to move in a circle. (p. 625)
fuerza centrípeta Fuerza que causa que un objeto se mueva en círculos.

cephalopod An ocean-dwelling mollusk whose foot is adapted as tentacles that surround its mouth. (p. 270)
cefalópodo Molusco que vive en el océano, cuyas extremidades se adaptaron a la forma de tentáculos alrededor de su boca.

cerebellum The part of the brain that coordinates the actions of the muscles and helps maintain balance. (p. 446)
cerebelo Parte del encéfalo que coordina las acciones de los músculos y ayuda a mantener el equilibrio.

cerebrum The part of the brain that interprets input from the senses, controls movement, and carries out complex mental processes. (p. 446)
cerebro Parte del encéfalo que interpreta los estímulos de los sentidos, controla el movimiento y realiza procesos mentales complejos.

chlorofluorocarbons Chlorine compounds that are the main cause of ozone depletion; also called CFCs. (p. 78), (p. 198)

clorofluorocarbonos Compuestos de cloro que son la causa principal de la destrucción del ozono; también se llaman CFC.

chlorophyll A green pigment found in the chloroplasts of plants as well as in algae and some bacteria. (p. 220)
clorofila Pigmento verde que se halla en los cloroplastos de las plantas, así como en las algas y algunas bacterias.

chloroplast A structure in the cells of plants and some other organisms that captures energy from sunlight and uses it to produce food. (p. 526)
cloroplasto Estructura en las células vegetales y algunos otros organismos que captan la energía de la luz solar y la usan para producir alimento.

chordate The phylum whose members have a notochord, a nerve cord, and slits in their throat area at some point in their lives. (p. 279)
cordado Fílum cuyos miembros poseen un notocordio, un cordón nervioso y aberturas en el área de la garganta en alguna

cilia Tiny hairlike extensions that move together in a sweeping motion. (p. 413)
cilios Extensiones minúsculas de las células que tienen forma de pelo y se mueven como un látigo.

cirrus Wispy, feathery clouds made mostly of ice crystals that form at high levels. (p. 110)
cirros Nubes parecidas a plumas o pinceladas blancas formadas principalmente por cristales de hielo que se crean a grandes altitudes.

climate The average, year-after-year conditions of temperature, precipitation, winds, and clouds in an area. (p. 166)
clima Promedio, año a año, de las condiciones de temperatura, precipitación, viento y nubes en un área.

clone An organism that is genetically identical to the organism from which it was produced. (p. 579)
clon Organismo que es genéticamente idéntico al organismo del que proviene.

cnidarians Animals whose stinging cells are used to capture their prey and defend themselves, and who take their food into a hollow central cavity. (p. 267)
cnidarios Animales que usan células punzantes para capturar presas y defenderse, y que

cochlea A snail-shaped tube in the inner ear that is lined with receptor cells that respond to sound. (p. 459)
cóclea Tubo en forma de caracol en el oído interno que está recubierto de células receptoras que responden al sonido.

codominance A condition in which neither of two alleles of a gene is dominant or recessive. (p. 543)
codominancia Condición en la que ninguno de los dos alelos de un gen es dominante ni recesivo.

communicating The process of sharing ideas with others through writing and speaking. (p. 10)
comunicar Proceso de compartir ideas con otras personas a través de la escritura o el lenguage hablado.

compact bone Hard, dense bone tissue that is beneath the outer membrane of a bone. (p. 314)
hueso compacto Tejido de hueso denso y duro que se encuentra debajo de la membrana externa de un hueso.

compound machine A device that combines two or more simple machines. (p. 695)
máquina compuesta Dispositivo que combina dos o más máquinas simples.

concussion A bruiselike injury of the brain that occurs when the soft tissue of the brain collides against the skull. (p. 451)
contusión Magulladura en el encéfalo que ocurre cuando el tejido suave del encéfalo choca contra el cráneo.

condensation The process by which molecules of water vapor in the air become liquid water. (p. 109)
condensación Proceso por el cual las moléculas de vapor de agua en el aire se convierten en agua líquida.

conduction The direct transfer of thermal energy from one substance to another substance that it is touching. (p. 96)
conducción Transferencia directa de energía térmica de una sustancia a otra que la toca.

cone The reproductive structure of a gymnosperm. (p. 236)
cono Estructura reproductora de una gimnosperma.

connective tissue A body tissue that provides support for the body and connects all of its parts. (p. 306)
tejido conectivo Tejido que da soporte al cuerpo y conecta todas sus partes.

constraint Any factor that limits or restricts a design. (p. 37)
restricción Cualquier factor que limita o restringe un diseño.

continental (air mass) A dry air mass that forms over land. (p. 131)
masa de aire continental Masa de aire seco que se forma sobre la tierra.

continental climate The climate of the centers of continents, with cold winters and warm or hot summers. (p. 168)
clima continental Clima del centro de los continentes, con inviernos fríos y veranos templados o calurosos.

contour feather A large feather that helps give shape to a bird's body. (p. 289)
pluma remera Pluma grande que ayuda a dar forma al cuerpo del ave.

controlled experiment An experiment in which only one variable is manipulated at a time. (p. 8)
experimento controlado Experimento en el cual sólo una variable es manipulada a la vez.

convection The transfer of thermal energy by the movement of a fluid. (p. 96)
convección Transferencia de energía térmica por el movimiento de un líquido.

convection currents The circulation of a fluid as it alternately heats up and cools down; in weather, upward movement of warm air and the downward movement of cool air. (p. 96)
corrientes de convección Circulación de un líquido a medida que se calienta y se enfría alternadamente.

coordinate A pair of numbers used to determine the position of a point on a graph. (p. 23)
coordinada Par de números que se usa para determinar la posición de un punto en una gráfica.

Coriolis effect The change that Earth's rotation causes in the motion of objects and that explains how winds curve. (p. 101)
efecto de Coriolis Cambio que causa la rotación de la Tierra en el movimiento de objetos y que explica cómo se curvan los vientos.

cornea The clear tissue that covers the front of the eye. (p. 455)
córnea Tejido transparente que cubre el frente del ojo.

coronary artery An artery that supplies blood to the heart itself. (p. 384)
arteria coronaria Arteria que lleva sangre al corazón en sí.

cotyledon A seed leaf that stores food. (p. 226)
cotiledón Hoja de una semilla, en la que se almacena alimento.

crop A bird's internal storage tank that allows it to store food inside its body after swallowing it. (p. 290)
buche Depósito de almacenamiento interno del ave que permite guardar el alimento dentro del ave después de tragarlo.

English and Spanish Glossary

crustacean An arthropod that has two or three body sections, five or more pairs of legs, and two pairs of antennae. (p. 274)
crustáceo Artrópodo que tiene dos o tres secciones corporales, cinco o más pares de patas y dos pares de antenas.

cumulus Fluffy, white clouds, usually with flat bottoms, that look like rounded piles of cotton. (p. 110)
cúmulos Nubes blancas, que normalmente tienen la parte inferior plana, que parecen grandes masas de algodón esponjosas y redondas.

cuticle The waxy, protective layer that covers the leaves and stems of most plants. (p. 216)
cutícula Capa cerosa e impermeable que cubre las hojas y los tallos de la mayoría de las plantas.

cyclone A swirling center of low air pressure. (p. 136)
ciclón Centro de un remolino de aire de baja presión.

cytoplasm The region between the cell membrane and the nucleus in organisms without a nucleus, the region located inside the cell membrane. (p. 305), (p. 523)
citoplasma Región entre la membrana celular y el núcleo; en los organismos sin núcleo, la región ubicada dentro de la membrana celular.

D

data Facts, figures, and other evidence gathered through observations. (p. 8)
dato Hecho, cifra u otra evidencia reunida por medio de las observaciones.

data point A point on a graph showing the location of a piece of data. (p. 23)
punto de datos Punto en una gráfica que muestra la ubicación de parte de los datos.

dendrite A threadlike extension of a neuron that carries nerve impulses toward the cell body. (p. 440)
dendrita Extensión en forma de hilo de una neurona que lleva los impulsos nerviosos hacia el cuerpo de las células.

density The amount of mass of a substance in a given volume. (p. 17), (p. 51), (p. 677)
densidad Cantidad de masa de una sustancia en un volumen dado.

density The mass of a substance contained in a unit of volume. (p. 645)
densidad Masa de una sustancia contenida en una unidad de volumen.

depressant A drug that slows down the activity of the central nervous system. (p. 466)
sustancia depresora Droga que disminuye la velocidad de la actividad del sistema nervioso central.

dermis The inner layer of the skin. (p. 331)
dermis Capa más interna de la piel.

desert An arid region that on average receives less than 25 centimeters of rain a year. (p. 180)
desierto Región árida que, como promedio, recibe menos de 25 centímetros de lluvia al año.

dew point The temperature at which condensation begins. (p. 109)
punto de rocío Temperatura a la que comienza la condensación

diaphragm A large muscle located at the bottom of a mammal's rib cage that functions in breathing. (p. 293), (p. 416)
diafragma Músculo grande ubicado en la parte inferior de la caja torácica de un mamífero que participa en la respiración.

dicot An angiosperm that has two seed leaves. (p. 244)
dicotiledónea Angiosperma cuyas semillas tienen dos cotiledones.

Dietary Reference Intakes (DRIs) Guidelines that show the amounts of nutrients needed every day. (p. 357)
Dietética ingesta de referencia Pautas que muestran la cantidad de nutrientes que se necesitan diariamente.

diffusion The process by which molecules move from an area of higher concentration to an area of lower concentration. (p. 385)
difusión Proceso por el cual las moléculas se mueven de un área de mayor concentración a un área de menor concentración.

digestion The process by which the body breaks down food into small nutrient molecules. (p. 359)
digestión Proceso por el cual el cuerpo descompone la comida en pequeñas moléculas de nutrientes.

dislocation An injury in which a bone comes out of its joint. (p. 318)
dislocación Lesión en la que un hueso se sale de su articulación.

dominant allele An allele whose trait always shows up in the organism when the allele is present. (p. 533)
alelo dominante Alelo cuyo rasgo siempre se manifesta en el organismo, cuando el alelo está presente.

down feather A short fluffy feather that traps heat and keeps a bird warm. (p. 289)
plumones Plumas cortas y mullidas que atrapan el calor y mantienen al ave abrigada.

drought A long period of scarce rainfall. (p. 118)
sequía Período largo con lluvias escasas.

drug Any chemical taken into the body that causes changes in a person's body or behavior. (p. 463)
droga Cualquier sustancia química que se incorpora al cuerpo, que causa cambios en el cuerpo o comportamiento de una persona.

drug abuse The deliberate misuse of drugs for purposes other than medical. (p. 463)
abuso de drogas Uso indebido deliberado de drogas para fines no médicos.

eardrum The membrane that separates the outer ear from the middle ear, and that vibrates when sound waves strike it. (p. 459)
tímpano Membrana que separa el oído externo del oído medio, y que vibra cuando le llegan ondas sonoras.

echinoderm A radially symmetrical invertebrate that lives on the ocean floor and has an internal skeleton. (p. 277)
equinodermo Invertebrado con simetría radial que vive en el suelo oceánico y tienen esqueleto interno.

ectotherm An animal whose body does not produce much internal heat. (p. 280)
ectotermo Animal cuyo cuerpo no produce mucho calor interno.

efficiency The percentage of the input work that is converted to output work. (p. 679)
eficiencia Porcentaje del trabajo aportado que se convierte en trabajo producido.

El Niño A climate event that occurs every two to seven years in the Pacific Ocean, during which winds shift and push warm water toward the coast of South America; it can cause dramatic climate changes. (p. 194)
El Niño Fenómeno climático en el océano Pacífico durante el cual los vientos se desvían y empujan la superficie más templada del agua hacia la costa de América del Sur.

electromagnetic wave Waves that can transfer electric and magnetic energy through the vacuum of space. (p. 88)
ondas electromagnéticas Ondas que transfieren energía eléctrica y magnética a través del vacío.

embryo The young plant that develops from a zygote. (p. 226)
embrión Planta joven que se desarrolla a partir de un cigoto.

emphysema A serious disease that destroys lung tissue and causes breathing difficulties. (p. 423)
enfisema Enfermedad grave que destruye el tejido pulmonar y causa dificultades respiratorias.

endoplasmic reticulum A cell structure that forms a maze of passageways in which proteins and other materials are carried from one part of the cell to another. (p. 523)
retículo endoplasmático Estructura celular que forma un laberinto de pasajes por los que se transportan las proteínas y otros materiales de una parte de la célula a otra.

endoskeleton An internal skeleton. (p. 277)
endoesqueleto Esqueleto interno.

endotherm An animal whose body controls and regulates its temperature by controlling the internal heat it produces. (p. 280)
endotermo Animal cuyo cuerpo controla y regula su temperatura controlando el calor interno que produce.

engineer A person who is trained to use both technological and scientific knowledge to solve practical problems. (p. 35)
ingeniero Persona capacitada para usar conocimientos tecnológicos y científicos para resolver problemas prácticos.

environmental science The study of the natural processes that occur in the environment and how humans can affect them. (p. 74)
ciencias del medio ambiente Estudio de los procesos naturales que ocurren en el medio ambiente y cómo los seres humanos pueden afectarlos.

enzyme A protein that speeds up chemical reactions in the body. (p. 361)
enzima Proteina que acelera las reacciones químicas en el cuerpo.

epidermis The outer layer of the skin. (p. 330)
epidermis Capa más externa de la piel.

epiglottis A flap of tissue that seals off the windpipe and prevents food from entering. (p. 361)
epiglotis Extensión de tejido que sella la entrada de la tráquea impidiendo la entrada del alimento.

epithelial tissue A body tissue that covers the surfaces of the body, inside and out. (p. 306)
tejido epitelial Tejido corporal que cubre la superficie del cuerpo, por dentro y por fuera.

esophagus A muscular tube that connects the mouth to the stomach. (p. 361)

esófago Tubo muscular que conecta la boca con el estómago.

evaporation The process by which water molecules in liquid water escape into the air as water vapor. (p. 106)
evaporación Proceso por el cual las moléculas de agua líquida son liberadas al aire como vapor de agua.

excretion The process by which wastes are removed from the body. (p. 425)
excreción Proceso por el cual se eliminan los desechos del cuerpo.

exoskeleton A waxy, waterproof outer shell or outer skeleton, protects the animal and helps prevent evaporation of water. (p. 273)
exoesqueleto Concha externa cerosa e impermeable o esqueleto externo

exosphere The outer layer of the thermosphere, extending outward into space. (p. 61)
exosfera Capa externa de la termosfera, que se extiende hacia el espacio.

farsightedness The condition in which a person can see distant objects clearly. (p. 457)
hipermetropía Condición en la que una persona puede ver claramente los objetos distantes.

fat Energy-containing nutrients that are composed of carbon, oxygen. (p. 345)
grasas Nutrientes que contienen energía y están compuestos de carbono, oxígeno e hidrógeno.

feedback The information a technological system uses to monitor the input, process, and output so that the system can adjust itself to meet the goal. (p. 29)
retroalimentación Información que usa un sistema tecnológico para comprobar la entrada, proceso y salida para autoajustarse con el fin de conseguir un objetivo.

fertilization The joining of a sperm cell and an egg cell. (p. 217), (p. 261), (p. 531)
fecundación Unión de un espermatozoide y de un óvulo.

fish An ectothermic vertebrate that lives in the water and has fins. (p. 281)
pez Vertebrado ectotérmico que vive en el agua y tiene branquias.

flash flood A sudden, violent flood that occurs within a few hours, or even minutes, of a storm. (p. 121)

crecida rápida Inundación repentina y violenta que ocurre en unas pocas horas, o incluso minutos, después de iniciada una tormenta.

flower The reproductive structure of an angiosperm. (p. 240)
flor Estructura reproductora de una angiosperma.

fluid A material that can easily flow (p. 636)
fluido Sustancia que puede fluir con facilidad.

fluid friction Friction that occurs as an object moves through a fluid. (p. 604)
fricción de fluido Fricción que ocurre cuando un objeto se mueve a través de un fluido.

follicle Structure in the dermis of the skin from which a strand of hair grows. (p. 331)
folículo Estructura en la dermis de la piel de donde crece un pelo.

Food Guide Pyramid A diagram that classifies foods into six groups to help people plan a healthy diet. (p. 354)
Pirámide guía de los alimentos Diagrama que clasifica los alimentos en seis grupos para ayudar a la gente a planear una dieta sana.

force A push or pull exerted on an object. (p. 596)
fuerza Empuje o atracción que se ejerce sobre un objeto.

fracture A break in a bone. (p. 318)
fractura Rotura de un hueso.

free fall The motion of a falling object when the only force acting on it is gravity. (p. 608)
caída libre Movimiento de un objeto que cae cuando la única fuerza que actúa sobre el mismo es la gravedad.

friction The force that one surface exerts on another when the two surfaces rub against each other. (p. 603)
fricción Fuerza que ejerce una superficie sobre otra cuando se frotan una contra otra.

front The boundary where unlike air masses meet but do not mix. (p. 133)
frente Límite en donde se encuentran masas de aire diferentes, pero no se mezclan.

fruit The ripened ovary and other structures that enclose one or more seeds of an angiosperm. (p. 242)
fruto Ovario que y otras estructuras maduras que encierran una o más semillas de una angiosperma.

fulcrum The fixed point around which a lever pivots. (p. 688)
fulcro Punto fijo en torno al cual gira una palanca.

G

gallbladder The organ that stores bile after it is produced by the liver. (p. 367)
vesícula Órgano que almacena la bilis después de ser producida por el hígado.

gametophyte The stage in the life cycle of a plant in which the plant produces gametes, or sex cells. (p. 220)
gametofito Etapa en el ciclo de vida de una planta en la cual la planta produce gametos, es decir, células sexuales.

gastropod A mollusk with a single shell or no shell. (p. 270)
gasterópodo Molusco con una única concha o sin concha.

gene The set of information that controls a trait; a segment of DNA on a chromosome that codes for a specific trait. (p. 533)
gen Conjunto de información que controla un rasgo; un segmento de ADN en un cromosoma el cual codifica un rasgo determinado.

gene therapy The insertion of working copies of a gene into the cells of a person with a genetic disorder in an attempt to correct the disorder. (p. 581)
terapia génica Inserción de copias activas de un gen en las células de una persona con un trastorno genético para intentar corregir dicho trastorno.

genetic disorder An abnormal condition that a person inherits through genes or chromosomes. (p. 572)
trastorno genético Condición anormal que hereda una persona a través de genes o cromosomas.

genetic engineering The transfer of a gene from the DNA of one organism into another organism, in order to produce an organism with desired traits. (p. 548), (p. 580)
ingeniería genética Transferencia de un gen desde el ADN de un organismo a otro, para producir un organismo con los rasgos deseados.

genetics The scientific study of heredity. (p. 530)
genética Ciencia que estudia la herencia.

genome All of the DNA in one cell of an organism. (p. 582)
genoma Todo el ADN de una célula de un organismo.

genotype An organism's genetic makeup, or allele combinations. (p. 542)
genotipo Composición genética de un organismo, es decir, las combinaciones de los alelos.

germination The early growth stage of the embryo plant in a seed. (p. 228)
germinación La brotadura del embrión de una semilla; ocurre cuando el embrión prosigue su crecimiento.

gizzard A muscular, thick-walled part of a bird's stomach that squeezes and grinds partially digested food. (p. 290)
molleja Parte muscular, de paredes gruesas del estómago del ave que exprime y muele parcialmente el alimento digerido.

global warming The theory that increasing carbon dioxide in the atmosphere will raise Earth's average temperature. (p. 80), (p. 195)
calentamiento global Teoría que dice que al aumentar el dióxido de carbono en la atmósfera, aumentará la temperatura promedio de la Tierra.

global winds Winds that blow steadily from specific directions over long distances. (p. 101)
vientos globales Vientos que soplan constantemente desde direcciones específicas por largas distancias.

glucose A sugar that is the major source of energy for the body's cells. (p. 344)
glucosa Azúcar que es la principal fuente de energía de las células del cuerpo.

goal The overall purpose of a technological system. (p. 29)
objetivo El propósito general de un sistema tecnológico.

Golgi body A structure in a cell that receives proteins and other newly formed materials from the endoplasmic reticulum, packages them, and distributes them to other parts of the cell. (p. 526)
aparato de Golgi Estructura en la célula que recibe del retículo endoplasmático las proteínas y otros materiales recientemente formados, los empaqueta y los distribuye a otras partes de la célula.

graph A picture of information from a data table; shows the relationship between variables. (p. 22)
gráfica Ilustración con información de una tabla de datos; muestra la relación entre las variables.

gravity The force that pulls objects toward each other. (p. 606)
gravedad Fuerza que atrae objetos entre sí.

greenhouse effect The process by which heat is trapped in the atmosphere by water vapor, carbon dioxide, methane, and other gases that form a "blanket" around Earth. (p. 80), (p. 91), (p. 195)

English and Spanish Glossary

efecto invernadero Proceso por el cual el calor queda atrapado en la atmósfera por gases que forman una "manta" alrededor de la Tierra.

gymnosperm A plant that produces seeds that are not enclosed by a protective structure as they develop. (p. 234)
gimnosperma Planta cuyas semillas no están encerradas en una estructura protectora durante su desarrollo.

heart A hollow, muscular organ that pumps blood throughout the body. (p. 378)
corazón Órgano muscular hueco que bombea sangre a todo el cuerpo.

heart attack A condition in which blood flow to part of the heart muscle is blocked, causing heart cells to die. (p. 397)
infarto cardiaco Condición en la que se obstruye el flujo de sangre a una parte del músculo cardiaco, lo que causa la muerte de las células cardiacas.

heat The transfer of thermal energy from one object to another because of a difference in temperature. (p. 96)
calor Transferencia de energía térmica de un objeto a otro debido a una diferencia de temperatura.

hemoglobin An iron-containing protein that binds chemically to oxygen molecules; makes up most of red blood cells. (p. 390)
hemoglobina Proteína que contiene hierro y que se enlaza químicamente a las moléculas de oxígeno; conforma la mayoría de los glóbulos rojos.

heredity The passing of traits from parents to offspring. (p. 530)
herencia Transmisión de rasgos de padres a hijos.

heterozygous Having two different alleles for a trait. (p. 542)
heterocigoto Tener dos alelos diferentes para el mismo rasgo.

homeostasis The process by which an organism's internal environment is kept stable in spite of changes in the external environment. (p. 308)
homeostasis Tendencia del cuerpo a mantener un equilibrio interno, a pesar de los cambios en el ambiente externo.

homozygous Having two identical alleles for a trait. (p. 542)
homocigoto Tener dos alelos idénticos para el mismo rasgo.

horizontal axis (or *x*-axis) A line that runs left to right along the bottom of a graph, on which the manipulated variable (or independent variable) is labeled. (p. 23)
eje horizontal (o eje *x*) Recta que va de izquierda a derecha en la base de una gráfica, en la cual se rotula la variable manipulada (o variable independiente).

host An organism that provides food to a parasite that lives on or inside it. (p. 268)
huésped Organismo que proporciona alimento a un parásito que vive sobre o dentro de él.

humid subtropical A wet and warm climate found on the edges of the tropics. (p. 182)
subtropical húmedo Clima húmedo y templado que se encuentra en los límites de los trópicos.

humidity The amount of water vapor in a given volume of air. (p. 107)
humedad Cantidad de vapor de agua en un volumen de aire definido.

hurricane A tropical storm that has winds of about 119 kilometers per hour or higher. (p. 144)
huracán Tormenta tropical que tiene vientos de cerca de 119 kilómetros por hora o mayores.

hybrid An organism that has two different alleles for a trait; an organism that is heterozygous for a particular trait. (p. 534)
híbrido Organismo que tiene dos alelos diferentes para un rasgo; un organismo que es heterocigoto para un rasgo en particular.

hybridization A selective breeding method in which two genetically different individuals are crossed. (p. 573)
hibridación Método de cruce selectivo en el cual se cruzan dos individuos genéticamente diferentes.

hydraulic system A system that multiplies force by transmitting pressure from a small surface area through a confined fluid to a larger surface area. (p. 685)
sistema hidráulico Sistema que multiplica la fuerza transmitiendo la presión de un área total pequeña a un área total mayor a través de un fluido confinado.

hydroponics A farming method in which plants are grown in solutions of nutrients instead of in soil. (p. 250)
hidroponía Método de cultivo de plantas en el que se usan soluciones de nutrientes en vez de suelos.

hypertension A disorder in which a person's blood pressure is consistently higher than normal; also called high blood pressure. (p. 398)

hipertensión Trastorno en el que la presión arterial de una persona es constantemente más alta de lo normal; tambien se le llama presión alta.

hypothesis A possible explanation for a set of observations or answer to a scientific question; must be testable. (p. 7)
hipótesis Explicación posible a un conjunto de observaciones o respuesta a una pregunta científica

ice ages Cold periods of time in Earth's history, during which glaciers covered large parts of the surface. (p. 190)
glaciacione Períodos fríos en la historia de la Tierra durante los cuales los glaciares cubrieron grandes partes de la superficie.

inbreeding A selective breeding method in which two individuals with identical or similar sets of alleles are crossed. (p. 578)
endogamia Método de cruce selectivo en el que se cruzan dos individuos con pares de alelos idénticos o semejantes.

inclined plane A simple machine that is a flat, sloped surface. (p. 717)
plano inclinado Máquina simple que consiste en una superficie plana con pendiente.

inertia The tendency of an object to resist any change in its motion. (p. 644)
inercia Tendencia de un objeto a resistir cualquier cambio en su movimiento.

infrared radiation Electromagnetic waves with wavelengths that are longer than visible light but shorter than microwaves. (p. 89)
radiación infrarroja Ondas electromagnéticas con longitudes de onda más largas que la luz visible, pero más cortas que las microondas.

input Something that is put into a technological system in order to achieve a goal. (p. 29)
entrada Algo que se agrega a un sistema tecnológico para conseguir un propósito.

input force The force exerted on a machine. (p. 675)
fuerza aplicada Fuerza que se ejerce sobre una máquina.

input work The work done on a machine as the input force acts through the input distance. (p. 675)
trabajo aportado Trabajo realizado sobre una máquina mientras la fuerza aplicada actúa a lo largo de la distancia de aplicación.

insect An arthropod with three body sections, six legs, one pair of antennae, and usually one or two pairs of wings. (p. 274)
insecto Artrópodo con tres secciones corporales, seis patas, un par de antenas y normalmente uno o dos pares de alas.

instantaneous speed The speed of an object at one instant of time. (p. 571)
rapidez instantánea Velocidad de un objeto en un instante de tiempo.

International System of Units (SI) A system of measurement based on multiples of ten and on established measures of mass, length, and time. (p. 569)
Sistema Internacional de Unidades (SI) Sistema de medidas basado en múltiplos de diez y en medidas establecidas de masa, longitud y tiempo.

interneuron A neuron that carries nerve impulses from one neuron to another. (p. 441)
interneurona Neurona que lleva los impulsos nerviosos de una neurona a otra.

invertebrate An animal that does not have a backbone. (p. 262)
invertebrado Animal que no posee columna vertebral.

involuntary muscle A muscle that is not under conscious control. (p. 322)
músculos involuntarios Músculo que no se puede controlar conscientemente.

ionosphere The lower part of the thermosphere, where electrically charged particles called ions are found. (p. 61)
ionosfera Parte inferior de la termosfera, donde se encuentran unas partículas cargadas eléctricamente llamadas iones.

iris The circular structure that surrounds the pupil and regulates the amount of light entering the eye. (p. 455)
iris Estructura circular que rodea la pupila y regula la cantidad de luz que entra en el ojo.

isobar A line on a weather map that joins places that have the same air pressure. (p. 154)
isobara Línea en un mapa del tiempo que une lugares que tienen la misma presión de aire.

isotherm A line on a weather map that joins places that have the same temperature. (p. 154)
isoterma Línea en un mapa del tiempo que une lugares que tienen la misma temperatura.

English and Spanish Glossary

jet streams Bands of high-speed winds about 10 kilometers above Earth's surface. (p. 104)
corriente de chorro Bandas de vientos de alta velocidad a unos 10 kilómetros sobre la superficie de la Tierra.

joint A place in the body where two bones come together. (p. 312)
articulación Lugar en el cuerpo en donde se unen dos huesos.

joule A unit of work equal to one newton-meter. (p. 671)
julio Unidad de trabajo igual a un newton-metro.

karyotype A picture of all the chromosomes in a cell arranged in pairs. (p. 574)
cariotipo Imagen de todos los cromosomas de una célula, organizados en parejas.

kidney A major organ of the excretory system which removes urea and other wastes from the blood. (p. 286), (p. 426)
riñón Órgano principal del sistema excretor que elimina la urea y otros materiales de desecho de la sangre.

La Niña A climate event in the eastern Pacific Ocean in which surface waters are colder than normal; the opposite of an El Niño. (p. 194)
La Niña Fenómeno climático que ocurre en la parte este del océano Pacífico, en el cual las aguas superficiales están más frías que lo normal.

land breeze The flow of air from land to a body of water. (p. 100)
brisa terrestre Flujo de aire desde la tierra a una masa de agua.

large intestine The last section of the digestive system, where water is absorbed into the bloodstream and the remaining material is eliminated from the body. (p. 369)
intestino grueso Última sección del sistema digestivo, donde se absorbe el agua hacia el torrente sanguíneo y los materiales restantes son eliminados del cuerpo.

larva The immature form of an animal that looks very different from the adult. (p. 266)

larva Forma inmadura de un animal que se ve muy diferente al adulto.

larynx The voice box; located in the top part of the trachea, underneath the epiglottis. (p. 418)
laringe Caja de la voz localizada en la parte superior de la tráquea por debajo de la epiglotis.

latitude The distance in degrees north or south of the equator. (p. 102)
latitud Distancia en grados al norte o al sur del ecuador.

law of conservation of momentum The rule that in the absence of outside forces the total momentum of objects that interact does not change. (p. 651)
ley de la conservación del momento Regla según la cual en ausencia de fuerzas externas, el momento total de los objetos no cambia en su interacción.

leeward The side of a mountain range that faces away from the oncoming wind. (p. 170)
sotavento Lado de una cadena montañosa que está resguardado del viento.

lens The flexible structure that focuses light that has entered the eye. (p. 455)
cristalino Estructura flexible que enfoca la luz que entra en el ojo.

levee A long ridge formed by deposits of sediments alongside a river channel. (p. 122)
dique Elevación larga formada por depósitos de sedimentos a lo largo del cauce de un río.

lever A simple machine that consists of a rigid bar that pivots about a fixed point. (p. 688)
palanca Máquina simple que consiste en una barra rígida que gira en torno a un punto fijo.

lift An upward force. (p. 657)
fuerza de elevación Fuerza ascendente.

ligament Strong connective tissue that holds bones together in movable joints. (p. 313)
ligamentos Tejido conectivo resistente que une los huesos en las articulaciones móviles.

lightning A sudden spark, or energy discharge, caused when electrical charges jump between parts of a cloud, between nearby clouds, or between a cloud and the ground. (p. 139)
rayo Chispa repentina o descarga de energía causada por cargas eléctricas que saltan entre partes de una nube, entre nubes cercanas o entre una nube y la tierra.

line of best fit A smooth line that reflects the general pattern in a graph. (p. 24)

recta de mayor aproximación Recta que refleja el patrón general en una gráfica.

linear graph A line graph in which the data points yield a straight line. (p. 24)
gráfica lineal Gráfica en la cual los puntos de los datos forman una línea recta.

liver The largest organ in the body; it plays a role in many body processes. (p. 367)
hígado Órgano más grande del cuerpo; tiene una función en muchos proce sos corporales.

local winds Winds that blow over short distances. (p. 100)
vientos locales Vientos que soplan por distancias cortas.

lung An organ found in air-breathing vertebrates that exchanges oxygen and carbon dioxide with the blood. (p. 284), (p. 414)
pulmón Órgano que se encuentra en los vertebrados que respiran aire con el que intercambian oxígeno y dióxido de carbono con la sangre.

lymph The fluid that the lymphatic system collects and returns to the bloodstream. (p. 395)
linfa Fluido que el sistema linfático recoge y devuelve al torrente sanguíneo.

lymph node A small knob of tissue in the lymphatic system that filters lymph, trapping bacteria and other microorganisms that cause disease. (p. 395)
ganglio linfático Pequeña prominencia de tejido en el sistema linfático que filtra la linfa, atrapando las bacterias y otros microorganismos que causan enfermedades.

lymphatic system A network of veinlike vessels that returns the fluid that leaks out of blood vessels to the bloodstream. (p. 394)
sistema linfático Red de vasos semejantes a venas que devuelve al torrente sanguíneo el fluido que sale de los vasos sanguíneos.

lysosome A small, round cell structure containing chemicals that break down large food particles into smaller ones. (p. 526)
lisosoma Pequeña estructura celular redonda que contiene sustancias químicas que descomponen las partículas de alimento grandes en otras más simples.

machine A device that changes the amount of force exerted, the distance over which a force is exerted, or the direction in which force is exerted. (p. 675)

máquina Dispositivo que altera la cantidad de fuerza ejercida, la distancia sobre la que se ejerce la fuerza o la dirección en la que se ejerce la fuerza.

magnetic resonance imaging A method for taking images of both the bones and soft tissues of the body. (p. 320)
imágenes por resonancia magnética Método que se usa para tomar imágenes claras de los huesos y de los tejidos blandos del cuerpo.

mammal An endothermic vertebrate with a four-chambered heart and skin covered with fur or hair, that feeds its young with milk from the mother's body. (p. 293)
mamífero Vertebrado endotérmico con un corazón de cuatro cámaras y piel cubierta de pelaje o pelo, que alimenta a sus crías con leche materna.

manipulated variable The one factor that a scientist changes during an experiment; also called independent variable. (p. 8)
variable manipulada Único factor que un científico cambia durante un experimento; también llamada variable independiente.

marine climate The climate of some coastal regions, with relatively warm winters and cool summers. (p. 168)
clima marino Clima de algunas regiones costeras, con inviernos relativamente templados y veranos fríos.

maritime (air mass) A humid air mass that forms over oceans. (p. 131)
masa de aire marítima Masa de aire húmedo que se forma sobre los océanos.

marrow The soft connective tissue that fills the internal spaces in bone. (p. 314)
médula ósea Tejido conectivo suave que rellena los espacios internos de un hueso.

marsupial A mammal whose young are born alive at an early stage of development, and which usually continue to develop in a pouch on their mother's body. (p. 295)
marsupial Mamífero cuyas crías nacen vivas en una etapa muy temprana

mass The amount of matter in an object. (p. 16), (p. 638)
masa Cantidad de materia en un objeto.

mechanical advantage The number of times a machine increases a force exerted on it. (p. 678)
ventaja mecánica Número de veces que una máquina amplifica la fuerza que se ejerce sobre ella.

medusa The cnidarian body plan is characterized by a bowl shape and is adapted for a free-swimming life. (p. 267)
medusa Cnidario cuyo cuerpo se caracteriza por tener forma de cuenco, y que está adaptado para nadar libremente en el agua.

meiosis The process that occurs in the formation of sex cells (sperm and egg) by which the number of chromosomes is reduced by half. (p. 548)
meiosis Proceso que ocurre en la formación de las células sexuales (espermatozoide y óvulo) por el cual el número de cromosomas se reduce a la mitad.

melanin A pigment that gives the skin its color. (p. 331)
melanina Pigmento que da color a la piel.

meniscus The curved upper surface of a liquid in a column of liquid. (p. 17)
menisco Superficie superior curvada de un líquido en una columna de líquido.

mercury barometer An instrument that measures changes in air pressure, consisting of a glass tube partially filled with mercury, with its open end resting in a dish of mercury. (p. 52)
barómetro de mercurio Instrumento que mide los cambios en la presión del aire; consiste de un tubo de vidrio parcialmente lleno de mercurio con su extremo abierto posado en un recipiente con mercurio.

mesosphere The layer of Earth's atmosphere immediately above the stratosphere; the layer in which most meteoroids burn up. (p. 60)
mesosfera Capa de la atmósfera de la Tierra inmediatamente sobre la estratosfera.

messenger RNA RNA that copies the coded message from DNA in the nucleus and carries the message into the cytoplasm. (p. 553)
ARN mensajero ARN que copia el mensaje codificado del ADN en el núcleo y lo lleva al citoplasma.

metamorphosis A process in which an animal's body undergoes dramatic changes in form during its life cycle. (p. 274)
metamorfosis Proceso por el cual el cuerpo de un animal cambia de forma de manera drástica durante su ciclo de vida.

meteorologist Scientists who study the causes of weather and try to predict it. (p. 151)
meteorólogos Científicos que estudian las causas del tiempo e intentan predecirlo.

meter The basic SI unit of length. (p. 601)
metro Unidad básica de longitud del SI.

metric system A system of measurement based on the number 10. (p. 14)
sistema métrico Sistema de medida basado en el número 10.

microclimate The climate conditions that exist within a small region; these may be different from the climate of the surrounding area. (p. 166)
microclima Condiciones climáticas en una área pequeña que son diferentes del clima de las áreas de alrededor.

microscope An instrument that makes small objects look larger. (p. 511)
microscopio Instrumento que hace que los objetos pequeños se vean más grandes.

minerals Nutrients that are needed by the body in small amounts and are not made by living things. (p. 350)
minerales Nutrientes que el cuerpo necesita en pequeñas cantidades y que no producen los seres vivos.

mitochondria Rod-shaped cell structures that convert energy in food molecules to energy the cell can use to carry out its functions. (p. 523)
mitocondria Estructura celular con forma de bastón que transforma la energía de las moléculas de alimentos en energía que la célula puede usar para llevar a cabo sus funciones.

mollusk An invertebrate with a soft, unsegmented body most are protected by hard outer shells. (p. 269)
molusco Invertebrado con cuerpo blando y sin segmentos; la mayoría están protegidos por una concha exterior dura.

molting The process of shedding an outgrown exoskeleton. (p. 273)
muda Proceso de cambio de un exoesqueleto a otro.

momentum The product of an object's mass and velocity. (p. 618)
momento Producto de la masa de un objeto por su velocidad.

monocot An angiosperm that has only one seed leaf. (p. 244)
monocotiledónea Angiosperma cuyas semillas tienen un solo cotiledón.

monotreme A mammal that lays eggs. (p. 295)
monotrema Mamífero que pone huevos.

monsoon Sea or land breeze over a large region that changes direction with the seasons. (p. 171)

monzón Vientos marinos o terrestres que soplan sobre una extensa región y cambian de dirección según las estaciones.

motion The state in which one object's distance from another is changing. (p. 597)
movimiento Estado en el que la distancia entre un objeto y otro va cambiando.

motor neuron A neuron that sends an impulse to a muscle or gland, causing the muscle or gland to react. (p. 441)
neurona motora Neurona que envía un impulso a un músculo o glándula, haciendo que el músculo o la glándula reaccione.

mucus A thick, slippery substance produced by the body. (p. 361)
mucosidad Sustancia espesa y lubricante que produce el cuerpo.

multiple alleles Three or more forms of a gene that code for a single trait. (p. 566)
alelo múltiple Tres o más formas de un gen que codifican un solo rasgo.

muscle tissue A body tissue that contracts or shortens, making body parts move. (p. 306)
tejido muscular Tejido corporal que se contrae o acorta, permitiendo así que se muevan las partes del cuerpo.

natural resource Anything in the environment that is used by people. (p. 71)
recurso natural Cualquier cosa del medio ambiente que usa la gente.

nearsightedness The condition in which a person can see nearby objects clearly. (p. 457)
miopía Condición en la que una persona puede ver claramente los objetos cercanos.

nephron Small filtering structure found in the kidneys that removes wastes from blood and produces urine. (p. 426)
nefrón Estructura diminuta de filtración que hay en los riñones, que elimina los desechos de la sangre y que produce la orina.

nerve A bundle of nerve fibers. (p. 440)
nervio Conjunto de fibras nerviosas.

nerve impulse The message carried by a neuron. (p. 440)
impulso nervioso Mensaje que lleva una neurona.

nervous tissue A body tissue that carries electrical messages back and forth between the brain and every other part of the body. (p. 306)
tejido nervioso Tejido corporal que lleva mensajes eléctricos entre el encéfalo y todas las demás partes del cuerpo y viceversa.

net force The overall force on an object when all the individual forces acting on it are added together. (p. 597)
fuerza neta Fuerza total que actúa sobre un objeto cuando se suman las fuerzas individuales que actúan sobre él.

neuron A cell that carries information through the nervous system. (p. 440)
neurona Célula que lleva información a través del sistema nervioso.

newton A unit of measure that equals the force required to accelerate 1 kilogram of mass at 1 meter per second per second. (p. 597)
newton Unidad de medida que es igual a la fuerza necesaria para acelerar 1 kilogramo de masa 1 metro por segundo cada segundo.

nicotine A stimulant drug in tobacco that increases the activities of the nervous system, heart, and other organs. (p. 421)
nicotina Sustancia química en el tabaco que acelera la actividad del sistema nervioso, corazón y otros órganos.

nonlinear graph A line graph in which the data points do not fall along a straight line. (p. 25)
gráfica no lineal Gráfica lineal en la que los puntos de los datos no forman una línea recta.

nonrenewable resource A natural resource that is not replaced in a useful time frame. (p. 71)
recurso no renovable Recurso natural que no se restaura una vez usado, en un período relativamente corto.

nonvascular plant A low-growing plant that lacks vascular tissue. (p. 218)
planta no vascular Planta de crecimiento lento que carece de tejido vascular verdadero.

notochord A flexible rod that supports a chordate's back. (p. 279)
notocordio Bastoncillo flexible que sostiene el lomo de los cordados.

nucleus The control center of a cell that directs the cell's activities and contains the information that determines the cell's form and function. (p. 522)
núcleo Centro de control de la célula que dirige las actividades de la célula y que contiene información que determina la forma y función de la célula.

English and Spanish Glossary

nutrients Substances in food that provide the raw materials and energy the body needs to carry out all its essential processes. (p. 342)
nutrientes Sustancias en los alimentos que proveen la materia prima y la energía que necesita el cuerpo para realizar los procesos elementales.

obsolete No longer in use. (p. 28)
obsoleto Que ya no está en uso.

occluded Cut off, as in a front where warm air mass is caught between two cooler air masses. (p. 135)
ocluido Aislado o cerrado, como cuando la masa de aire cálido queda atrapada entre dos masas de aire más frío.

operational definition A statement that describes how to measure a particular variable or how to define a particular term. (p. 8)
definición operativa Enunciado que describe cómo medir una variable determinada o cómo definir un término determinado..

organ A structure that is composed of different kinds of tissue (p. 260), (p. 306)
órgano Estructura compuesta de diferentes tipos de tejidos.

organ system A group of organs that work together to perform a major function in the body. (p. 306)
sistema de órganos Grupo de órganos que trabajan juntos para realizar una función importante del cuerpo.

organelle A tiny cell structure that carries out a specific function within the cell. (p. 488)
organelo Diminuta estructura celular que realiza una función específica dentro de la célula.

origin The point where the x-axis and y-axis cross on a graph. (p. 23)
origen Punto en donde el eje x y el eje y se cruzan en una gráfica.

osteoporosis A condition in which the body's bones become weak and break easily. (p. 317)
osteoporosis Condición en la cual los huesos del cuerpo se debilitan y se rompen fácilmente.

output The result or product from the operation of a technological system. (p. 29)
salida Resultado o producto de la operación de un sistema tecnológico.

output force The force exerted on an object by a machine. (p. 675)
fuerza desarrollada Fuerza que una máquina ejerce sobre un objeto.

output work The work done by a machine as the output force acts through the output distance. (p. 675)
trabajo producido Trabajo que una máquina efectúa mientras la fuerza desarrollada actúa a lo largo de la distancia desarrollada.

ovary A flower structure that protects seeds as they develop. (p. 241)
ovario Estructura de la flor que protege a las semillas durante su desarrollo.

ovule A plant structure in seed plants that contains an egg cell. (p. 236)
óvulo Estructura de las plantas de semilla que contiene una célula reproductora femenina.

ozone layer The layer of the atmosphere that contains a higher concentration of ozone than the rest of the atmosphere. (p. 77)
capa de ozono Capa atmosférica que contiene una mayor concentración de ozono que el resto de la atmósfera.

pacemaker A group of cells located in the right atrium that sends out signals that make the heart muscle contract and that regulates heartbeat rate. (p. 380)
marcapasos Grupo de células ubicado en la aurícula derecha que envía señales para que el músculo cardiaco se contraiga, y que regula el ritmo cardiaco.

pancreas A triangular organ that lies between the stomach and first part of the small intestine. (p. 368)
páncreas Órgano triangular ubicado entre el estómago y la primera parte del intestino delgado.

parasite An organism that lives inside or on another organism and takes food from the organism in or on which it lives. (p. 268)
parásito Organismo que vive dentro o sobre otro organismo y que se alimenta de él.

pascal A unit of pressure equal to 1 newton per square meter. (p. 635)
pascal Unidad de presión igual a 1 newton por metro cuadrado.

Pascal's principle The rule that when force is applied to a confined fluid, the increase in pressure is transmitted equally to all parts of the fluid. (p. 651)
principio de Pascal Regla que enuncia que cuando se aplica una fuerza a un fluido confinado,

el aumento en la presión es transmitida por igual a todas las partes del fluido.

patent A legal document issued by the government that gives an inventor exclusive rights to make, use, or sell an invention for a limited time. (p. 39)
patente Documento legal emitido por el gobierno que otorga a un inventor los derechos exclusivos de hacer, usar o vender un invento por un tiempo limitado.

pedigree A chart or "family tree" that tracks which members of a family have a particular trait. (p. 573)
genealogía Tabla o "árbol genealógico" que muestra qué miembros de una familia tienen un rasgo en particular.

Percent Daily Value A value that shows how the nutritional content of one serving of food fits into the diet of a person who consumes 2,000 calories a day. (p. 356)
Porcentaje de valor diario Valor que muestra cómo el contenido nutricional de una porción de alimento se corresponde con la dieta de una persona que consume 2,000 Calorías al día.

peripheral nervous system The division of the nervous system consisting of all of the nerves located outside the central nervous system. (p. 444)
sistema nervioso periférico Parte del sistema nervioso formada por todos los nervios ubicados fuera del sistema central nervioso.

peristalsis Involuntary waves of muscle contraction that keep food moving along in one direction through the digestive system. (p. 361)
peristaltismo Ondulaciones involuntarias de contracción muscular que empujan el alimento en una dirección a través del sistema digestivo.

permafrost Permanently frozen soil found in the tundra climate region. (p. 184)
permagélido Suelo permanentemente helado que se encuentra en la región climática de la tundra.

petal The colorful, leaflike structures that some flowers have. (p. 240)
pétalo Estructura de color brillante, en forma de hoja que tienen algunas flores.

pharynx The throat; part of both the respiratory and digestive systems. (p. 413)
faringe Garganta; parte de los sistemas respiratorio y digestivo.

phenotype An organism's physical appearance, or visible traits. (p. 542)
fenotipo Apariencia física de un organismo, es decir, los rasgos visibles.

phloem The vascular tissue through which food moves in some plants. (p. 225)
floema Tejido vascular por el que circula el alimento en algunas plantas.

photochemical smog A brownish haze that is a mixture of ozone and other chemicals, formed when nitrogen oxides, hydrocarbons, and other pollutants react with each other in the presence of sunlight. (p. 64)
neblina tóxica fotoquímica Densa bruma pardusca que es una mezcla de ozono y otras sustancias químicas, que se forma cuando los contaminantes reaccionan entre ellos en presencia de luz solar.

photosynthesis The process by which plants and some other organisms capture light energy and use it to make food from carbon dioxide and water. (p. 214)
fotosíntesis Proceso por el cual las plantas y otros organismos captan la energía de la luz solar y la usan para producir alimento.

phylum One of about 35 major groups into which biologists classify members of the animal kingdom. (p. 262)
fílum Uno de alrededor de 35 grupos principales en los que los biólogos clasifican los miembros del reino animal.

pistil A female reproductive part of a flower. (p. 241)
pistilo Parte reproductora femenina de una flor.

placental mammal A mammal that develops inside its mother's body until its body systems can function independently. (p. 295)
mamífero placentario Mamífero que se desarrolla dentro del cuerpo de la madre hasta que sus sistemas corporales pueden funcionar por sí solos.

plasma The liquid part of blood. (p. 389)
plasma Parte líquida de la sangre.

plate One of the major pieces that make up Earth's upper layer. (p. 579)
placa Una de las partes principales que forman la capa exterior de la Tierra.

platelet A cell fragment that plays an important part in forming blood clots. (p. 392)
plaqueta Fragmento de célula que juega un papel muy importante en la formación de coágulos sanguíneos.

polar (air mass) A cold air mass that forms north of 50° north latitude or south of 50° south latitude and has high air pressure. (p. 131)
masa de aire polar Masa de aire frío que se forma al norte de los 50° de latitud norte o al sur de los 50° de latitud sur y que tiene presión alta.

English and Spanish Glossary

polar zone The areas near both poles, from about 66.5° to 90° north and 66.5° to 90° south latitudes. (p. 167)
zona polar Áreas cercana a los polos, desde unos 66.5° a 90° de latitud norte y 66.5° a 90° de latitud sur.

pollen Tiny particles (male gametophytes) produced by seed plants that contain the cells that later become sperm cells (p. 225)
polen Partículas diminutas (gametofitos masculinos) producidas por las plantas de semillas que contienen las células que posteriormente se convierten en células reproductoras masculinas.

pollination The transfer of pollen from male reproductive structures to female reproductive structures in plants. (p. 236)
polinización Transferencia de polen de las estructuras reproductoras masculinas a las estructuras reproductoras femeninas de las plantas.

pollutants Harmful substances in the air, water, or soil. (p. 62)
contaminantes Sustancias dañinas en el aire, agua o suelo.

pollution The contamination of Earth's land, water, or air. (p. 72)
Contaminación Polución del suelo, agua y aire de la Tierra.

polyp The cnidarian body plan is characterized by a vaselike shape and is usually adapted for a life attached to an underwater surface. (p. 267)
pólipo Cnidario cuyo cuerpo se caracteriza por tener forma cilíndrica, y que generalmente está adaptado para vivir adherido a una superficie submarina.

pore An opening through which sweat reaches the surface of the skin. (p. 331)
poro Abertura a través de la cual el sudor sale a la superficie de la piel.

power The rate at which work is done. (p. 671)
potencia Razon a la que se realiza trabajo.

precipitation Any form of water that falls from clouds and reaches Earth's surface. (p. 113)
precipitación Cualquier forma de agua que cae desde las nubes y llega a la superficie de la Tierra.

precision farming A method of farming in which, aided by technology, farmers fine-tune the amount of water and fertilizer they use to the requirements of a specific field. (p. 250)
agricultura de precisión Método de cultivo en el que los agricultores usan la tecnología para determinar con precisión la cantidad de agua y fertilizante que emplearán, para suplir las necesidades de un terreno específico.

pressure The force exerted on a surface divided by the total area over which the force is exerted. (p. 51), (p. 635)
presión Fuerza ejercida sobre una superficie dividida por el área total sobre la cual se ejerce la fuerza.

probability The likelihood that a particular event will occur. (p. 538)
probabilidad Posibilidad de que ocurra un suceso en particular.

process A sequence of actions that a technological system undergoes to produce an output. (p. 29)
proceso Secuencia de acciones que experimenta un sistema tecnológico para producir un resultado.

projectile An object that is thrown. (p. 642)
proyectil Objeto que es lanzado.

protein Nutrient that contains nitrogen as well as carbon, hydrogen, and oxygen; they are needed for tissue growth and repair and play a part in chemical reactions within cells. (p. 347)
proteínas Nutrientes que contienen nitrógeno, carbono, hidrógeno y oxígeno; son necesarios para el crecimiento y reparación del tejido, y juegan un papel muy importante en las reacciones químicas de las células.

prototype A working model used to test a design. (p. 38)
prototipo Modelo funcional usado para probar un diseño.

psychrometer An instrument used to measure relative humidity, consisting of a wet-bulb thermometer and a dry-bulb thermometer. (p. 108)
psicrómetro Instrumento que se usa para medir la humedad relativa y que consiste de un termómetro, de bulbo húmedo y de un termómetro de bulbo seco.

pulley A simple machine that consists of a grooved wheel with a rope or cable wrapped around it. (p. 692)
polea Máquina simple que consiste en una rueda con un surco en el que entra una cuerda o cable.

pulse The alternating expansion and relaxation of an artery wall as blood travels through an artery. (p. 384)
pulso Expansión y relajación alternada de una pared arterial a medida que la sangre viaja por la arteria.

Punnett square A chart that shows all the possible combinations of alleles that can result from a genetic cross. (p. 540)
cuadrado de Punnett Tabla que muestra todas las combinaciones posibles de los alelos que pueden resultar de una cruza genética.

English and Spanish Glossary

pupil The opening through which light enters the eye. (p. 455)
pupila Abertura por la que entra la luz al ojo.

purebred An organism that always produces offspring with the same form of a trait as the parent. (p. 531)
cepa pura Organismo que siempre produce descendencia con los mismos rasgos que los progenitore.

R

radial symmetry The quality of having many lines of symmetry that all pass through a central point. (p. 263)
simetría radial Cualidad de tener muchos ejes de simetría que pasan por un punto central.

radiation The direct transfer of energy by electromagnetic waves. (p. 88)
radiación Transferencia directa de energía por ondas electromagnéticas.

rain forest A forest in the tropical wet climate zone in which large amounts of rain falls all year-round. (p. 177)
bosque tropical Selva ubicada dentro de la zona de clima tropical húmedo en la cual caen grandes cantidades de lluvia todo el año.

rain gauge An instrument used to measure precipitation. (p. 117)
pluviómetro Instrumento que se usa para medir la precipitación.

recessive allele An allele that is masked when a dominant allele is present. (p. 533)
alelo recesivo Alelo que queda oculto cuando está presente un alelo dominante.

rectum The end of the large intestine where waste material is compressed into a solid form before being eliminated. (p. 369)
recto Final del intestino grueso, donde el material de desecho se comprime a una forma sólida antes de ser eliminado.

red blood cell A cell in the blood that takes up oxygen in the lungs and delivers it to cells elsewhere in the body. (p. 390)
glóbulo rojo Célula de la sangre que capta el oxígeno en los pulmones y lo lleva a las células de todo el cuerpo.

reference point A place or object used for comparison to determine if an object is in motion. (p. 599)
punto de referencia Lugar u objeto usado como punto de comparación para determinar si un objeto está en movimiento.

reflex An automatic response that occurs rapidly and without conscious control. (p. 449)
reflejo Respuesta automática que ocurre muy rápidamente y sin control consciente.

relative humidity The percentage of water vapor in the air compared to the maximum amount of water vapor that air can contain at a particular temperature. (p. 107)
humedad relativa Porcentaje de vapor de agua en el aire comparado con la cantidad máxima de vapor de agua que puede contener el aire a una temperatura particular.

renewable resource A resource that is either always available or is naturally replaced in a relatively short time. (p. 71)
recurso renovable Recurso que está siempre disponible o que es restituido de manera natural en un período relativamente corto.

reptile An ectothermic vertebrate that lays eggs and has lungs and scaly skin. (p. 286)
reptil Vertebrado ectotérmico que pone huevos, y que tiene pulmones y piel con escamas.

respiration The process in which oxygen and glucose undergo a complex series of chemical reactions inside cells; also called cellular respiration. (p. 411)
respiración Proceso en el cual el oxígeno y la glucosa sufren una compleja serie de reacciones químicas en las células; también se llama respiración celular.

responding variable The factor that changes as a result of changes to the manipulated, or independent, variable in an experiment; also called dependent variable. (p. 8)
variable respuesta Factor que cambia como resultado del cambio de la variable manipulada, o independiente, en un experimento; también llamada variable dependiente.

response What the body does in reaction to a stimulus. (p. 439)
respuesta Lo que hace el cuerpo como reacción a un estímulo.

retina The layer of receptor cells at the back of the eye on which an image is focused. (p. 456)
retina Capa de células receptoras en la parte posterior del ojo donde se enfoca una imagen.

ribosome A small grain-like structure in the cytoplasm of a cell where proteins are made. (p. 523)
ribosoma Estructura pequeña parecida a un grano en el citoplasma de una célula donde se fabrican las proteínas.

English and Spanish Glossary

risk-benefit analysis The process of evaluating the possible problems of a technology compared to the expected advantages. (p. 32)
análisis de riesgo y beneficios Proceso por el cual se evalúan los posibles problemas de una tecnología y se compara con las ventajas deseadas.

rolling friction Friction that occurs when an object rolls over a surface. (p. 604)
fricción de rodamiento Fricción que ocurre cuando un objeto rueda sobre una superficie.

root cap A structure that covers the tip of a root, protecting the root from injury. (p. 229)
cofia Estructura que cubre la punta de una raíz y la protege contra daños.

S

saliva The fluid released when the mouth waters that plays an important role in both mechanical and chemical digestion. (p. 360)
saliva Líquido liberado por la boca que juega un papel muy importante en la digestión química y mecánica.

satellite Any object that orbits around another object in space. (p. 625)
satélite Cualquier objeto que orbita alrededor de otro objeto en el espacio.

savanna A tropical grassland with scattered clumps of trees. (p. 177)
sabana Pradera tropical con grupos de árboles.

scattering Reflection of light in all directions. (p. 90)
dispersión Reflexión de la luz en todas las direcciones.

scientific inquiry The ongoing process of discovery in science; the diverse ways in which scientists study the natural world and propose explanations based on evidence they gather. (p. 6)
investigación científica Proceso continuo de descubrimiento en la ciencia; diversidad de métodos con los que los científicos estudian el mundo natural y proponen explicaciones del mismo basadas en la evidencia que reúnen.

scientific law A statement that describes what scientists expect to happen every time under a particular set of conditions. (p. 10)
ley científica Enunciado que describe lo que los científicos esperan que suceda cada vez que se da una serie de condiciones determinadas.

scientific literacy The knowledge and understanding of scientific terms and principles required for evaluating information, making personal decisions, and taking part in public affairs. (p. 11)
alfabetismo científico Conocimiento y comprensión de los términos y principios científicos necesarios para evaluar información, tomar decisiones personales y participar en actividades públicas.

scientific theory A well-tested explanation for a wide range of observations or experimental results. (p. 10)
teoría científica Explicación comprobada de una gran variedad de observaciones o resultados de experimentos.

screw A simple machine that is an inclined plane wrapped around a central cylinder to form a spiral. (p. 687)
tornillo Máquina simple que consiste en un plano inclinado enrollado en un cilindro central para formar una espiral.

sea breeze The flow of cooler air from over an ocean or lake toward land. (p. 100)
brisa marina Flujo de aire más frío desde un océano o lago hacia la costa.

seed The plant structure that contains a young plant inside a protective covering. (p. 225)
semilla Estructura de una planta que contiene una plántula dentro de una cubierta protectora.

selective breeding The process of selecting a few organisms with desired traits to serve as parents of the next generation. (p. 578)
cruce selectivo Proceso de selección de algunos organismos con los rasgos deseados para que sirvan de como progenitores de la siguiente generación.

semicircular canals Structures in the inner ear that are responsible for the sense of balance. (p. 460)
canales semicirculares Estructuras en el oído interno responsables del sentido del equilibrio.

sensory neuron A neuron that picks up stimuli from the internal or external environment and converts each stimulus into a nerve impulse. (p. 440)
neurona sensorial Neurona que recoge los estímulos del medio ambiente interno o externo y convierte cada estímulo en un impulso nervioso.

sepal A leaflike structure that encloses the bud of a flower. (p. 240)
sépalo Estructura, parecida a una hoja, que encierra el botón de una flor.

sex chromosomes a pair of chromosomes carrying genes that determine whether a person is male or female. (p. 561)
cromosomas sexuales Par de cromosomas portadores de genes que determinan si una persona es macho o hembra.

sex-linked gene A gene that is carried on the X or Y chromosome. (p. 568)
gen ligado al sexo Gen portador del cromosoma X o Y.

sexual reproduction The process by which a new organism forms from the joining of two sex cells. (p. 261)
reproducción sexual Proceso por el cual se forma un nuevo organismo a partir de la unión de dos células sexuales.

SI (Système International d'Unités) International System of Units; a version of the metric system used by scientists all over the world. (p. 14)
SI (Sistema Internacional de Unidades) Sistema Internacional de Unidades; version del sistema métrico usado por científicos de todo el mundo.

skeletal muscle A muscle that is attached to the bones of the skeleton and provides the force that moves the bones. (p. 324)
músculos esqueléticos Músculo que está unido a los huesos del esqueleto y que proporciona la fuerza para que los huesos se muevan.

skeleton The inner framework made of all the bones of the body. (p. 310)
esqueleto Estructura formada por todos los huesos del cuerpo.

sliding friction Friction that occurs when one solid surface slides over another. (p. 604)
fricción de deslizamiento Fricción que ocurre cuando una superficie sólida se desliza sobre otra.

slope The steepness of a line on a graph, equal to its vertical change divided by its horizontal change. (p. 24), (p. 606)
pendiente Inclinación de una recta en una gráfica, igual a su cambio vertical dividido por su cambio horizontal.

small intestine The part of the digestive system in which most chemical digestion takes place. (p. 366)
intestino delgado Parte del sistema digestivo en la cual se produce la mayoría de la digestión química.

smooth muscle Involuntary muscle found inside many internal organs of the body. (p. 324)
músculos lisos Músculo involuntario que se encuentra dentro de muchos órganos internos del cuerpo.

somatic nervous system The group of nerves in the peripheral nervous system that controls voluntary actions. (p. 449)
sistema nervioso somático Grupo de nervios en el sistema nervioso periférico que controla las acciones voluntarias.

speed The distance an object travels per unit of time. (p. 570)
rapidez Distancia que viaja un objeto por unidad de tiempo.

spinal cord The thick column of nerve tissue that links the brain to most of the nerves in the peripheral nervous system. (p. 445)
médula espinal Columna gruesa de tejido nervioso que une el encéfalo con la mayoría de los nervios en el sistema nervioso periférico.

spongy bone Layer of bone tissue having many small spaces and found just inside the layer of compact bone. (p. 314)
hueso esponjoso Capa de tejido de un hueso que tiene muchos espacios pequeños y se encuentra justo dentro de la capa del hueso compacto.

sporophyte The stage in the life cycle of a plant in which the plant produces spores for reproduction. (p. 220)
esporofito Etapa en el ciclo de vida de una planta en la que la planta produce esporas para reproducirse.

sprain An injury in which the ligaments holding bones together are stretched too far and tear. (p. 319)
esguince Lesión en la que los ligamentos se estiran demasiado y se rompen.

stamen A male reproductive part of a flower. (p. 241)
estambre Parte reproductora masculina de una flor.

static friction Friction that acts on objects that are not moving. (p. 604)
fricción estática Fricción que actúa sobre los objetos que no se mueven.

steppe A prairie or grassland found in the semiarid climate region. (p. 180)
estepa Pradera o pastizal que se encuentra en las regiones semiáridas.

stimulant A drug that speeds up body processes. (p. 466)
estimulante Droga que acelera los procesos del cuerpo.

English and Spanish Glossary

stimulus Any change or signal in the environment that can make an organism react in some way. (p. 439)
estímulo Cualquier cambio o señal en el medio ambiente que puede hacer que un organismo reaccione de alguna manera.

stomach A J-shaped, muscular pouch located in the abdomen. (p. 362)
estómago Bolsa muscular con forma de J localizada en el abdomen.

stomata The small openings on the undersides of most leaves through which oxygen and carbon dioxide can move. (p. 232)
estomas Pequeñas aberturas en la cara inferior de casi todas las hojas, a través de las cuales pasan los gases.

storm A violent disturbance in the atmosphere. (p. 138)
tormenta Alteración violenta en la atmósfera.

storm surge A "dome" of water that sweeps across the coast where a hurricane lands. (p. 145)
marejadas "Cúpula" de agua que se desplaza a lo largo de la costa donde aterriza un huracán.

stratosphere The second-lowest layer of Earth's atmosphere. (p. 59)
estratosfera Segunda capa inferior de la atmósfera de la Tierra.

stratus Clouds that form in flat layers and often cover much of the sky. (p. 110)
estratos Nubes que forman capas planas y que a menudo cubren gran parte del cielo.

stress The reaction of a person's body to potentially threatening, challenging, or disturbing events. (p. 309)
estrés Reacción del cuerpo de un individuo a amenazas, retos o sucesos molestos potenciales.

striated muscle A muscle that appears banded; also called skeletal muscle. (p. 324)
músculo estriado Músculo con forma de franjas; también se llama músculo esquelético.

subarctic A climate zone that lies north of the humid continental climates. (p. 183)
subártico Zona climática que se encuentra al norte de los climas continentales húmedos.

sunspot A relatively dark, cool region on the surface of the sun. (p. 191)
manchas solares Regiones relativamente frías y oscuras en la superficie del Sol.

swim bladder An internal gas-filled organ that helps a bony fish stabilize its body at different water depths. (p. 283)
vejiga natatoria Órgano interno lleno de gas que ayuda a un pez con esqueleto a estabilizar su cuerpo a diferentes profundidades.

synapse The junction where one neuron can transfer an impulse to the next structure. (p. 442)
sinapsis Unión donde una neurona puede transferir un impulso a la siguiente estructura.

system A group of related parts that work together. (p. 29)
sistema Grupo de partes relacionadas que funcionan en conjunto.

T

tar A dark, sticky substance that forms when tobacco burns. (p. 421)
alquitrán Sustancia oscura y pegajosa producida cuando se quema tabaco.

technology How people modify the world around them to meet their needs or to solve practical problems. (p. 28)
tecnología Cómo la gente modifica el mundo que la rodea para satisfacer sus necesidades o para solucionar problemas prácticos.

temperate zones The areas between the tropical and the polar zones. (p. 167)
áreas templadas Áreas entre las zonas tropical y polar.

temperature A measure of how hot or cold an object is compared to a reference point. (p. 95)
temperatura Medida de lo caliente o frío que está un objeto comparado con un punto de referencia.

tendon Strong connective tissue that attaches muscle to bone. (p. 324)
tendón Tejido conectivo resistente que une un músculo a un hueso.

terminal velocity The greatest velocity a falling object can achieve. (p. 609)
velocidad terminal La máxima velocidad que puede alcanzar un objeto que cae.

theory of plate tectonics The theory that pieces of Earth's outer layer are in constant motion. (p. 579)
teoría de la tectónica de placas Teoría que enuncia que las partes de la capa exterior de la Tierra están en constante movimiento.

thermal energy The total energy of motion in the particles of a substance. (p. 95)
energía térmica Energía de movimiento total en las partículas de una sustancia.

thermometer An instrument used to measure temperature, consisting of a thin glass tube with a bulb on one end that contains a liquid (usually mercury or alcohol). (p. 95)
termómetro Instrumento que se usa para medir la temperatura; consiste en un tubo de fino vidrio con un bulbo en un extremo que contiene un líquido (normalmente mercurio o alcohol).

thermosphere The outermost layer of Earth's atmosphere. (p. 60)
termosfera Capa exterior de la atmósfera de la Tierra.

thunderstorm A small storm often accompanied by heavy precipitation and frequent thunder and lightning. (p. 139)
tronada Pequeña tormenta acompañada de fuerte precipitación y frecuentes rayos y truenos.

tissue A group of similar cells that perform a specific function in an organism. (p. 215), (p. 306)
tejido Grupo de células semejantes que realizan una función específica en un organismo.

tolerance A state in which a drug user needs larger amounts of the drug to produce the same effect on the body. (p. 464)
tolerancia Estado en el que un consumidor de drogas necesita mayores cantidades de la droga para que produzca el mismo efecto en el cuerpo.

tornado A rapidly whirling, funnel-shaped cloud that reaches down from a storm cloud to touch Earth's surface. (p. 140)
tornado Nube con forma de embudo que gira rápidamente y que desciende hasta la superficie terrestre.

trachea The windpipe; a passage through which air moves in the respiratory system. (p. 414)
tráquea Conducto a través del cual se mueve el aire en el sistema respiratorio.

trade-off An exchange in which one benefit is given up in order to obtain another. (p. 37)
trade-off Intercambio en el cual se renuncia a un beneficio para obtener otro.

trait A characteristic that an organism can pass on to its offspring through its genes. (p. 530)
rasgo Característica que un organismo puede transmitir a su descendencia a través de sus genes.

transfer RNA RNA in the cytoplasm that carries an amino acid to the ribosome and adds it to the growing protein chain. (p. 553)
ARN de transferencia ARN en el citoplasma que lleva un aminoácido al ribosoma y lo suma a la cadena proteínica que se está formando.

transpiration The process by which water is lost through a plant's leaves. (p. 233)
transpiración Proceso por el cual las hojas de una planta eliminan agua.

tropical (air mass) A warm air mass that forms in the tropics and has low air pressure. (p. 131)
masa de aire tropical Masa de aire templado que se forma en los trópicos y tiene presión baja.

tropical zone The area near the equator, between about 23.5° north latitude and 23.5° south latitude. (p. 167)
zona tropical Área cercana al ecuador, entre aproximadamente los 23.5° de latitud norte y los 23.5° de latitud sur.

troposphere The lowest layer of Earth's atmosphere, where weather occurs. (p. 58)
troposfera Capa más inferior de la atmósfera de la Tierra, donde ocurre el tiempo meteorológico.

troubleshooting The process of analyzing a design problem and finding a way to fix it. (p. 38)
solución de problemas Proceso por el cual se analiza un problema de diseño y se halla una forma de solucionarlo.

tube feet Extensions of an echinoderm's water vascular system that stick out from the body and function in movement and obtaining food. (p. 277)
pies ambulacrales Extensiones del sistema vascular de agua de un equinodermo que sobresalen del cuerpo y sirven para la locomoción y la obtención de alimento.

tundra A polar climate region, found across northern Alaska, Canada, and Russia, with short, cool summers and bitterly cold winters. (p. 184)
tundra Región climática polar que se encuentra en el norte de Alaska, Canadá y Rusia, que tiene veranos cortos y fríos, e inviernos extremadamente fríos.

ultraviolet radiation Electromagnetic waves with wavelengths that are shorter than visible light but longer than X-rays. (p. 89)
radiación ultravioleta Ondas electromagnéticas con longitudes de onda más cortas que la luz visible, pero más largas que los rayos X.

English and Spanish Glossary

unbalanced forces Forces that produce a nonzero net force, which changes an object's motion. (p. 598)
fuerza desequilibrada Fuerzas que producen una fuerza neta diferente de cero, lo cual cambia el movimiento de un objeto.

urea A chemical that comes from the breakdown of proteins. (p. 426)
urea Sustancia química que viene de la descomposición de proteínas.

ureter A narrow tube that carries urine from one of the kidneys to the urinary bladder. (p. 426)
ureter Conducto estrecho que lleva la orina desde cada uno de los riñones a la vejiga urinaria.

urethra A small tube through which urine flows from the body. (p. 426)
uretra Pequeño conducto a través del cual fluye la orina desde el cuerpo.

urinary bladder A sacklike muscular organ that stores urine until it is eliminated from the body. (p. 426)
vejiga urinaria Órgano muscular con forma de saco que almacena la orina hasta que es eliminada del cuerpo.

urine A watery fluid produced by the kidneys that contains urea and other wastes. (p. 426)
orina Fluido acuoso producido por los riñones que contiene urea y otros materiales de desecho.

vacuole A sac inside a cell that acts as a storage area. (p. 215), (p. 526)
vacuola Saco dentro de la célula que actúa como área de almacenamiento.

valve A flap of tissue in the heart or a vein that prevents blood from flowing backward. (p. 379)
válvula Tapa de tejido en el corazón o en un vena que impide que la sangre fluya hacia atrás.

variable A factor that can change in an experiment. (p. 8)
variable Factor que puede cambiar en un experimento.

vascular plant A plant that has vascular tissue. (p. 218)
planta vascular Planta que tiene tejido vascular verdadero.

vascular tissue The internal transporting tissue in some plants that is made up of tubelike structures. (p. 217)
tejido vascular Tejido de transporte interno en algunas plantas que está formado por estructuras parecidas a tubos.

vein A blood vessel that carries blood back to the heart. (p. 380)
vena Vaso sanguíneo que transporta la sangre de vuelta al corazón.

velocity Speed in a given direction. (p. 572)
velocidad Rapidez en una dirección dada.

ventricle Each of the two lower chambers of the heart that pumps blood out of the heart. (p. 379)
ventrículo Cada una de las dos cámaras inferiores del corazón que bombean la sangre hacia afuera del corazón.

vertebrae The bones that make up the backbone of an animal. (p. 280), (p. 311)
vértebras Huesos que forman la columna vertebral de un animal.

vertebrate An animal that has a backbone. (p. 262)
vertebrado Animal que posee columna vertebral.

vertical axis (or *y*-axis) A line that runs up and down along the side of a graph, on which the responding variable (or dependent variable) is labeled. (p. 23)
eje vertical (o eje *y*) Recta que va de arriba a abajo en el lado vertical de una gráfica, en la cual se rotula la variable respuesta (o variable dependiente).

villi Tiny finger-shaped structures that cover the inner surface of the small intestine and provide a large surface area through which digested food is absorbed. (p. 368)
vellosidades Pequeñas estructuras con forma de dedo que cubren la superficie interna del intestino delgado y proporcionan una amplia superficie a través de la cual se absorbe el alimento digerido.

vitamins Molecules that act as helpers in a variety of chemical reactions within the body. (p. 348)
vitaminas Moléculas que actúan como ayudantes en gran variedad de reacciones químicas que se producen en el cuerpo.

vocal cords Folds of connective tissue that stretch across the opening of the larynx and produce a person's voice. (p. 418)
Cuerdas vocales Pliegues de tejido conectivo que se extienden a lo largo de la abertura de la laringe y producen la voz de la persona.

volume The amount of space an object takes up. (p. 16)
volumen Cantidad de espacio que ocupa un objeto.

voluntary muscle A muscle that is under conscious control. (p. 323)
músculos voluntarios Músculo que se puede controlar conscientemente.

water cycle The continual movement of water among Earth's atmosphere, oceans, and land surface through evaporation, condensation, and precipitation. (p. 106)
ciclo del agua Movimiento continuo de agua entre la atmósfera, los océanos y la superficie de la Tierra mediante la evaporación, condensación y precipitación.

water vapor Water in the form of a gas. (p. 48)
vapor de agua Agua en forma de gas.

water vascular system A system of fluid-filled tubes in an echinoderm's body. (p. 277)
sistema vascular de agua Sistema de vasos llenos de líquidos en el cuerpo de un equinodermo.

weather The condition of Earth's atmosphere at a particular time and place. (p. 46)
tiempo meteorológico Condición de la atmósfera de la Tierra en un tiempo y lugar determinados.

wedge A simple machine that is an inclined plane that moves. (p. 686)
cuña Máquina simple que consiste en un plano inclinado en movimiento.

weight The force of gravity on an object at the surface of a planet. (p. 160), (p. 607)
peso Fuerza de gravedad ejercida sobre un objeto en la superficie de un planeta.

wheel and axle A simple machine that consists of two attached circular or cylindrical objects that rotate about a common axis, each one with a different radius. (p. 690)
rueda y eje Máquina simple que consiste en dos objetos circulares o cilíndricos unidos, de diferente radio, que giran en torno a un eje común.

white blood cell A blood cell that fights disease. (p. 391)
glóbulos blancos Célula de la sangre que protege contra las enfermedades.

wind The horizontal movement of air from an area of high pressure to an area of lower pressure. (p. 99)
viento Movimiento horizontal de aire de un área de alta presión a un área de menor presión.

wind-chill factor A measure of cooling combining temperature and wind speed. (p. 99)
factor de sensación térmica Medida de enfriamiento que combina la temperatura y la velocidad del viento.

windward The side of a mountain range that faces the oncoming wind. (p. 170)
barlovento Lado de una cadena montañosa donde pega el viento de frente.

withdrawal A period of adjustment that occurs when a drug-dependant person stops taking the drug. (p. 465)
síndrome de abstinencia Período de ajuste que ocurre cuando una persona adicta a las drogas deja de consumirlas.

work Force exerted on an object that causes it to move. (p. 668), (p. 700)
trabajo Fuerza ejercida sobre un objeto para moverlo.

X-rays A form of energy that travels in waves. (p. 319)
rayos X Forma de energía que viaja en ondas.

xylem The vascular tissue through which water and nutrients move in some plants. (p. 225)
xilema Tejido vascular por el que circulan agua y nutrientes en algunas plantas.

zygote A fertilized egg. (p. 217)
cigoto Óvulo fecundado.

Index

Page numbers for key terms are printed in **boldface** type.
Page numbers for illustrations, maps, and charts are printed in *italics*.

Index

Page numbers for key terms are printed in **boldface** type.
Page numbers for illustrations, maps, and charts are printed in *italics*.

Index

Page numbers for key terms are printed in **boldface** type.
Page numbers for illustrations, maps, and charts are printed in *italics*.

Index

Page numbers for key terms are printed in **boldface** type.
Page numbers for illustrations, maps, and charts are printed in *italics*.

Index

Page numbers for key terms are printed in **boldface** type.
Page numbers for illustrations, maps, and charts are printed in *italics*.

Index

Page numbers for key terms are printed in **boldface** type.
Page numbers for illustrations, maps, and charts are printed in *italics*.

Index

Page numbers for key terms are printed in **boldface** type.
Page numbers for illustrations, maps, and charts are printed in *italics*.

Index

Page numbers for key terms are printed in **boldface** type.
Page numbers for illustrations, maps, and charts are printed in *italics*.

Index

Page numbers for key terms are printed in **boldface** type.
Page numbers for illustrations, maps, and charts are printed in *italics*.

Index

Page numbers for key terms are printed in **boldface** type.
Page numbers for illustrations, maps, and charts are printed in *italics*.

forces of, *718*
mechanical advantage of, 718
teeth as, 726
workings of, 718
weight, **16**, **639**
of atmosphere, 50, 51
buoyant force and, **675**
of fluid displaced by an object, 676
and mass, 639
of submerged objects, 675
of water, depth and, 672
weight machines, 708, *709*
wells, 118
Welwitschia, 235
whales, 293
wheel and axle, **722**
mechanical advantage of, 724
workings of, 723
white blood cells, **391**
difference between red bloods cells
and, 391
wildlife
effect of pollution on, **72**
habitats in Antarctica, unique, 70
wind, 98, **99**
air pressure and, 99
damage from hurricanes, 145
danger of high, 147
measuring, 99
monsoon, **171**
off ocean, moderating effect of, 168
pollination, 242
seed dispersal by, 227
speeds in intense tornadoes, **141**
strength, in hurricanes, **144**
wind belts
doldrums, 102
global, 102, 104
horse latitudes, 102
polar easterlies, 104
prevailing westerlies, 102
trade winds, 102
wind-chill factor, **99**
wind vanes, 1, 99
windpipe (trachea), **414**, 418
windward, **170**
winter, 172
withdrawal, **465**, 469
woody stems, 230
work, **700**
calculating, 702–703
force, and distance, 702
force, and motion, *701*
force in the same direction, 701
input and output, **707**, *709*, 711, 712
meaning of, 700–701
units of measurement for, 703
worms, 268–269
characteristics of, *268*
flatworms, 268
roundworms, 268
segmented, 269
Wright, Orville, 687, 689
Wright, Wilbur, 687, 689

***x*-axis**, 23, 606
X chromosome, 567, 568, 569
X-rays, **319**
of cancerous brain tumor, *529*
xylem, **225**, 229, 230, 233
annual rings made of, 231

***y*-axis**, 23, 606
Y chromosome, 567, 568, 569
Yelesina, Yelena, 593
Yosemite National Park, establishment of,
72

Zeiss, Carl, 513
zygote, **487**
development of, 494
movement and division of, 495
size of fertilized, 494
zygote (plant), **217**
development into sporophyte of, **220**

Acknowledgments

Acknowledgment for page 210: Excerpt from *Alone* by Richard E. Byrd, reprinted by arrangement with Island Press. Copyright © 1938 by Richard E. Byrd, © renewed 1986.

Staff Credits

Diane Alimena, Michele Angelucci, Scott Andrews, Jennifer Angel, Carolyn Belanger, Barbara A. Bertell, Suzanne Biron, Peggy Bliss, Stephanie Bradley, James Brady, Anne M. Bray, Sarah M. Carroll, Kerry Cashman, Jonathan Cheney, Joshua D. Clapper, Lisa J. Clark, Bob Craton, Patricia Cully, Patricia M. Dambry, Kathy Dempsey, Leanne Esterly, Emily Ellen, Thomas Ferreira, Jonathan Fisher, Patricia Fromkin, Paul Gagnon, Kathy Gavilanes, Joel Gendler, Holly Gordon, Robert Graham, Ellen Granter, Diane Grossman, Barbara Hollingdale, Linda Johnson, Anne Jones, John Judge, Kevin Keane, Kelly Kelliher, Toby Klang, Sue Langan, Russ Lappa, Carolyn Lock, Rebecca Loveys, Constance J. McCarty, Carolyn B. McGuire, Ranida Touranont McKneally, Anne McLaughlin, Eve Melnechuk, Natania Mlawer, Janet Morris, Karyl Murray, Francine Neumann, Baljit Nijjar, Marie Opera, Jill Ort, Kim Ortell, Joan Paley, Dorothy Preston, Maureen Raymond, Laura Ross, Rashid Ross, Siri Schwartzman, Melissa Shustyk, Laurel Smith, Emily Soltanoff, Jennifer A. Teece, Elizabeth Torjussen, Amanda M. Watters, Merce Wilczek, Amy Winchester, Char Lyn Yeakley. **Additional Credits** Allen Gold, Andrea Golden, Etta Jacobs, Meg Montgomery, Kim Schmidt, Adam Teller, Joan Tobin.

Illustration

Morgan Cain & Associates: NC31, NC32, 52, 53t, 55, 77, 94, 97t, 103, 113, 232, 548–549; **Kerry Cashman:** NC28, 150, 192, 257, 311, 312–313, 314–315, 327, 344, 345, 346, 354, 356, 368, 412, 415, 426, 439. 440tl, 445, 449, 450, 452, 463, 464–465, 467, 475r, 479, 490, 493, 497, 506l, 494–495, 550, 560; **David Corrente:** 540–541; **Sandy Durant:** 323; **John Edwards and Associates:** 80, 134, 135, 162l, 172, 173, 200, 226, 324–325, 330–331, 359, 360, 361, 363, 367, 372bl, 377, 380, 384–385, 390–391, 390tl, 395, 406tl, 440–441, 442, 447, 448, 474ml, 488, 491, 505b, 514, 523t, 523b, 526, 541bl; Mark Foerster: 427; **Tom Gagliano:** 475l; **GeoSystems Global Corporation:** 146, 148, 154t, 178, 179, 190r; **Andrea Golden:** 2; **Phil Guzy:** 402–403, 412, 413, 417, 418, 455, 459, 460, 481, 482, 499; **Kevin Jones Associates:** 230–231; **Keith Kasnot:** 522; **Martucci Design:** 154b, 155; **Steve McEntee:** NC24, 57, 85, 89, 90, 91, 109, 110, 111, 131, 136, 158, 170, 171, 195, 553, 554–555; **Richard McMahon:** 105, 117, 256, 398–399, 421tr, 480, 595; **Karen Minot:** 531, 532; **Ortelius Design Inc.:** 162r, 167, 171t; **Pearson Ed:** 305, 307, 342tr, 358, 373, 407, 435, 448, 483, 505tl, 507; **Matthew Pippin:** 51, 81, 126; **Brucie Rosch:** 97b; **Walter Stuart:** 190l; **Cynthia Turner:** 244; J/B **Woolsey Associates:** 229, 240, 247, 543, 580; **XNR Productions:** 74–75, 101, 104, 132, 141b, 144, 169, 198, 199. **All art development for pages** 596–743 **by Morgan Cain and Associates. All charts and graphs by Matt Mayerchak and Joe Paterno.**

Photography

Photo Research John Judge, Sue McDermott, Paula Wehde

Cover Image top, Ernest H. Robi; **bottom,** Peter Barrett/Masterfile. **Page NC34,** Jeremy Horner/Corbis; **vii,** Richard Haynes; **viii,** Steve Vidler/SuperStock; **x** both, NASA; **1,** William Wantland/Tom Stack & Associates; **1** inset, NASA; **2** both, NASA; **3,** NASA.

Chapter 1

Pages 4–5, Flip Nicklin/Minden Pictures; **5** inset, Richard Haynes; **6t,** Richard Haynes; **6b,** M. T. Frazier/Photo Researchers, Inc.; **7,** Richard Haynes; **8,** Richard Haynes; **9** all Richard Haynes; **11,** Fisher/Thatcher/Getty Images, Inc.; **12,** Russ Lappa; **13,** David Young-Wolf//Photo Edit; **14,** Richard Haynes; **15,** Richard Haynes; **16,** Richard Haynes; **17** both, Richard Haynes; **18,** Richard Haynes; **20,** Richard Haynes; **27tl,** Getty Images, Inc.; **27tm,** Casio, Inc.; **27tml,** Corbis; **27tmr,** Corbis; **27tr,** Dolrin; Kindersley; **27ml,** Advertising Archives; **27br,** The Granger Collection; **29,** David Young-Wolf//Photo Edit; **30l,** John Jenkins/AmericanMuseum of Radio & Electricity; **30r,** Science Photo Library; **31l,** AP/Wide World Photos; **31m,** David Ducros/Science Photo Library/Photo Researchers, Inc.; **31r,** Tony Freeman Photographs; **34,** both Russ Lappa; **36l,** Spencer Family Archives; 36r, Grant Heilman Photography; **37,** Tim Flach/Getty Images, Inc.; **38,** Advertising Archive/The Picture Desk, Inc.; **38,** U.S. Patent Office.

Chapter 2

Pages 44–45, Steve Neidorf Photography/Getty Images, Inc.; **45r,** Richard Haynes; **46t,** Russ Lappa; **46b,** NASA/Photo Researchers, Inc.; **47,** Ariel Skelley/Corbis; **48t,** Tom Bean/DRK Photo; **48b,** Karl H. Switak/Photo Researchers, Inc.; **49l,** Michael Fogden/DRK Photo; **49r,** Gail Shumway/Getty Images, Inc.; **50t,** Russ Lappa; **50b,** Eric A. Kessler; **53t,** Ivan Bucher/Photo Researchers, Inc.; **53b,** Zandria Muench Beraldo/Muench Photography; **54,** Zandria Muench Beraldo/Muench Photography; **56t,** Russ Lappa; **56b,** Steve Vidler/SuperStock; **58l,** The Granger Collection, NY; **58m,** The Granger Collection, NY; **58r,** Bettmann/Corbis; **59l,** Corbis; **59m,** NASA; **19r,** NASA; **61,** Photographer's Choice/Getty Images, Inc.; **62t,** Russ Lappa; **62b,** Liba Taylor/Corbis; **63,** Aaron Haupt/Photo Researchers, Inc.; **64,** Will McIntyre/Photo Researchers, Inc.; **65,** AP/Wide World Photos; **66,** Eric Horan/Getty Images, Inc.; **67,** Richard Haynes; **68l,** Ford Motor Co./AP/Wide World Photos; **68–69,** Rob Francis/Robert Harding World Imagery; **70–71,** Key Sanders/Getty Images, Inc.; **72l,** Corbis; **72m,** Corbis; **72r,** UPI/Corbis-Bettmann; **73l,** Erich Hartmann/Magnum Photos; **73m,** Kevin Fleming/Corbis; **73r,** William Campbell/Peter Arnold, Inc.; **74t,** Corbis; **74b,** Warren Morgan/Corbis; **75t,** Ariel Skelley/Corbis; **75b,** Marc Epstein/DRK Photo; **76** both, Richard Haynes; **78,** NASA/Goddard Space Flight Center Scientific Visualization Studio; **79** all, NASA/Goddard Space Flight Center Scientific Visualization Studio.

Chapter 3

Pages 86–87, Roy Morsch/Corbis; **87r,** Richard Haynes; **89,** David Lawrence/Panoramic Images; **93,** Richard Haynes; **94t,** Russ Lappa; **94b,** Yang Liu/Corbis; **95,** Russ Lappa; **98t,** Richard Haynes; **98b,** Anna Zieminski/AFP/Getty Images, Inc.; **99,** SPL/Photo Researchers, Inc.; **100** both, James Schwabel/Panoramic Images; **102,** Corbis; **106t,** Russ Lappa; **106–107b,** Jeremy Horner/Corbis; **108,** Barry Runk/Grant Heilman/Photography; **109,** Bruce Coleman, Inc.; **110t,** Scott Nielsen/Bruce Coleman, Inc.; **110m,** John Shaw/Bruce Coleman, Inc.; **110b,** Claudia Parks/Corbis; **112,** Ed Pritchard/Getty Images, Inc.; **113,** Richard Haynes; **114t,** William Johnson/Stock Boston; **114b,** Bill Marchel; **115t,** Gerben Oppermans/Getty Images, Inc.; **115m,** Nuridsany et Perennou/Photo Researchers, Inc.; **115b,** Phil Degginger/Bruce Coleman, Inc.; **116,** Jim Brandenburg/Minden Pictures; **119,** AP/Wide World Photos; **119** inset, Svenja-Foto/Masterfile; **120,** Comstock; **121** Grant V. Faint/Getty Images, Inc.; **122,** AFP/Corbis.

Chapter 4

Pages 128–129, TSADO/NCDA/NOAA/Tom Stack & Associates; **129r,** Richard Haynes; **130t,** Russ Lappa; **130–131b,** Benjamin Lowy/Corbis; **133,** Gene Rhoden/Peter Arnold, Inc.; **137t,** Accuweather; **137bl,** Mike Chew/Corbis; **137br,** Getty Images Inc.; **138t,** Richard Haynes; **138b,** Peter Menzel; **140,** Warren Faidley/DRK Photo; **141,** Oxford Scientific Films; **142** all, The Granger Collection, NY; **143t,** North Wind Picture Archives; **143bl,** Roger de la Harpe/Dorling Kindersley; **143br,** Corbis; **145t,** NASA; **145b,** AP/Wide World Photos; **146,** Reuters/Corbis; 147, Reuters; **148,** Brownie Harris/Corbis; **150–151b,** Photo Researchers, Inc.; **151t,** Bob Daemmrich/Stock Boston; **152l,** European Space Agency/Science Photo Library/Photo Researchers, Inc.; **152r,** NASA/Goddard Space Flight Center; **158–159** background, A. & J. Verkik/Corbis; **159** both, ©UCAR; **160,** Richard Haynes.

Chapter 5

Pages 164–165, J. Bennett-Peter Arnold, Inc.; **165r,** Richard Haynes; **166t,** Richard Haynes; **166b,** David Muench Photography; **168,** David Madison/Bruce Coleman, Inc.; **171,** Steve McCurry/Magnum Photos; **172** both, Bruce Coleman, Inc.; **174,** Richard Haynes; **176t,** Russ Lappa; **176–177b,** Royalty-Free/Corbis; **177t,** Getty Images, Inc.; **178l,** Bruce Forster/Getty Images Inc.; **178m,** Jess Stock/Getty Images, Inc.; **178r,** David Muench Photography; **179l,** Tom Till/DRK Photo; **179m,** Ragnar Th. Sigurdsson/Artic-Images; **179r,** David Muench Photography; **180l,** J. Cancalosi/DRK Photo; **180r,** Jeff Hunter/Getty Images, Inc.; **181,** Tom Bean/DRK Photo; **182,** Charlie Waite/Getty Images, Inc.; **183l,** Liz Hymans/Corbis; **183r,** DRK Photo; **184,** Bryan & Cherry Alexander/Artic Images; **185,** Adam Jones/Photo Researchers, Inc.; **188,** George H.H. Huey; **189,** Tony Craddock/SPL/Photo Researchers, Inc.; **189** inset, George Godfrey/Animals Animals/Earth Scenes; **193t,** Richard Haynes; **193b,** A. Ramey/PhotoEdit; **194** all, NOAA; **196,** Anne Howard/Artic Images; **197l,** Larry Taylor; **197r,** Kent Syverson; **199** all, TOMS; **200,** J. Cancalosi/DRK Photo; **204–205b,** Jane Faircloth/Transparencies, Inc.; **205** tm, Corbis; **205tr,** Sergio Piumatti; **206,** Bryan & Cherry Alexander/Artic Images; **207t,** The Granger Collection, NY; **207b,** AP/Wide World Photos; **208,** Ragnur Th. Sigurdsson/Artic Images; **209,** Corbis; **210t,** Bettmann/Corbis; **210b,** Dorling Kindersley/New York Museum of Natural History; **210–211** background, Masterfile; **211b,** Alaska Stock.

Chapter 6

Pages 212–213, Norbert Rosing/National Geographic Image Collection; **213** inset, Richard Haynes; **214,** Richard Haynes; **215l,** Ric Ergenbright; **215r,** Runk/Schoenberger/Grant Heilman Photography, Inc.; **216,** Kjell B. Sandved/Photo Researchers, Inc.; **217,** Ludovic Maisant/Corbis; **218l,** Randy M. Ury/Corbis; **218r,** John Shaw/Bruce Coleman; **219bl,** Ron Thomas/Getty Images, Inc.; **219br,** Eastcott Momatiuk/Getty Images, Inc.; **219m,** Barry Runk/Stan/Grant Heilman Photography; **219tl,** R. Van Nostrand/Photo Researchers, Inc.; **219tr,** Brenda Tharp/Photo Researchers, Inc.; **220b,** Frans Lanting/Minden Pictures; **220tl,** Runk/Schoenberger/Grant Heilman Photography, Inc.; **220tr,** Peter Chadwick/Dorling Kindersley; **222,** Royalty Free/Corbis; **223,** Lester Lefkowitz/Corbis; **224,** Russ Lappa; **225** both Phil Schermeister/Corbis; **226l,** Barry Runk/Grant Heilman Photography, Inc.; **226m,** Dave King/Dorling Kindersley; **226r,** Anna W. Schoettle, USDA Forest Service; **227bl,** D. Cavagnaro/Visuals Unlimited; **227br,** Frans Lanting/Minden Pictures; **227m,** Heather Angel/Natural Visions; **227mr,** Color-Pic/Animals Animals/Earth Scenes; **227tl,** John Pontier/Animals Animals/Earth Scenes; **227tr,** J.A.L. Cooke/OSF/Earth Scenes; **228 l** and **r** both, Runk/Schoenberger/Grant Heilman Photography, Inc.; **228–229b,** Color-Pic/Earth Scenes; **229 l** and **r** both, Robert Calentine/Visuals Unlimited; **230b,** Barry Runk/Stan/Grant Heilman; **230t,** Richard Shiell/Animals Animals/Earth Scenes; 231, Darrell Gulin/Getty Images, Inc.; **233** both, Dr.Jeremy Burgess/Photo Researchers, Inc.; **234,** Richard Haynes; **235b,** Ken Brate/Photo Researchers, Inc.; **235l,** Michael

Fogden/Animals Animals/Earth Scenes; **235r,** Breck Kent/Animals Animals/Earth Scenes; **235t,** Jim Strawser/Grant Heilman Photography, Inc.; **236** inset b, Breck P. Kent; 236 inset t, Breck P. Kent/Animals Animals/Earth Scenes; **236l,** Grant Heilman/Grant Heilman Photography, Inc.; **236r,** Patti Murray/Animals Animals/Earth Scenes; **238,** Martin Rogers/Stock Boston; **239b,** Frans Lanting/Minden Pictures; **239t,** Russ Lappa; **241l,** Ian Tait/Natural Visions; **241r,** Merlin D. Tuttle, Bat Conservation International; **241t,** Anthony Bannister/Animals Animals; **242b,** Dwight Kuhn; **242t,** Nancy Rotenberg/Animals Animals/Earth Scenes; **243l,** Perennou et Nuridsany/Photo Researchers, Inc.; **243ml,** Russ Lappa; **243mr,** Philip Dowell /Dorling Kindersley; **243r,** Jules Selmes and Debi Treloar/Dorling Kindersley; **245,** Alan Pitcairn/Grant Heilman Photography, Inc.; **246,** Richard Haynes; **248** both, C-AP/Grant Heilman Photography; **249,** Robert Frerck/Odyssey Productions, Inc.; **250b,** Arthur C. Smith III/Grant Heilman Photography, Inc.; **250t,** Patti McConville/Getty Images, Inc.; **251,** Patti McConville/Getty Images, Inc.; **253,** Richard Haynes.

Chapter 7

Pages 258–259, Deep Sea Photos; **259** inset, Richard Haynes; **260bl,** Heather Angel/Natural Visions; **260br,** Heather Angel/Natural Visions; **261t,** Frank Oberle/Getty Images, Inc.; **261b,** C.C. Lockwood; **262,** Wolfgang Bayer/Bruce Coleman, Inc.; **263,** Stephen Dalton/Animals Animals; **264tl,** Tom and Pat Leeson; **264tm,** Andrew J. Martinez/Photo Researchers, Inc.; **264tr,** James Watt/Visuals Unlimited; **265,** Michael DeFreitas/Bruce Coleman, Inc.; **267** inset, Linda Pitkin/Masterfile Corporation; **272,** Richard Haynes; **275b,** Meckes/Ottawa/Eye of Science/Photo Researchers, Inc.; **275m,** Robert Calentine/Visuals Unlimited; **275t,** Geoff Dann/Dorling Kindersley; **276t,** Tim Flach/Getty Images, Inc.; **276bl,** Marty Cordano/DRK Photo; **276br,** Simon D. Pollard/Photo Researchers, Inc.; **278t,** Kerrick James; **278l** inset, Neil G. McDaniel/Photo Researchers, Inc.; **278m** inset, Brandon D. Cole/Corbis; **278r** inset, Ed Bravendam/Minden Pictures; **279,** Russ Lappa; **280,** Tom Flach/Getty Images, Inc.; **281,** NHPA/Lutra; **282t,** Frank Burek/Animals Animals/Earth Scenes; **282b,** Animals Animals/Earth Scenes; **282b** inset, Herve Berthoule Jacana/Photo Researchers, Inc.; **285,** Kevin & Suzette Hanley/Animals Animals/Earth Scenes; **286,** Jay Ireland & Georgienne Bradley/Bradleyireland.com; **287,** Kim Taylor & Jane Burton/Dorling Kindersley; **288,** Dave B. Fleetham/Visuals Unlimited; **289t,** Richard Haynes; **289b,** Jerome Wexler/Photo Researchers, Inc.; **291t,** Kim Taylor/Dorling Kindersley; **291b,** Richard Wagner; **292t,** NHPA/Manfred Danegger; **292bl,** Dave Watts/Tom Stack & Associates, Inc.; **292br,** Gary Griffen/Animals Animals/Earth Scenes; **293t,** Hilary Pooley/Animals Animals/Earth Scenes; **293t** inset, Phillip Dowell/Dorling Kindersley Media Library; **293b,** Philip Dowell/Dorling Kindersley; **293b** inset, Dave King/Dorling Kindersley Media Library; **294l,** Daryl Balfour/Getty Images, Inc.; **294r,** Art Wolfe; **295,** Dave Watts/Tom Stack & Associates, Inc.; **296t,** Chuck Davis/Getty Images, Inc.; **296m,** Stephen J. Krasemann/DRK Photo; **296b,** M.P. Kahl/DRK Photo.

Chapter 8

Pages 302–303, Matthew Stockman/Getty Images, Inc.; **303** inset, Richard Haynes; **304,** Richard Haynes; **305l,** Richard Haynes; **305r,** K.G. Murti/Visuals Unlimited; **306b,** Biophoto Associates/Photo Researchers, Inc.; **306m,** James Hayden, RBP/Phototake; **306t,** John D. Cunningham/Visuals Unlimited; **306tm,** Fred Hossler/Visuals Unlimited; **307** all, Richard Haynes; **308b,** Myrleen Ferguson Cate/PhotoEdit; **308t,** Jon Feingersh/Corbis; **309,** Mike Powell/Getty Imges, Inc.; **310,** Russ Lappa; **311l,** Richard Haynes; **311r,** Dorling Kindersley; **312l,** David Young-Wolff/PhotoEdit; **312r,** Rudi Von Briel/PhotoEdit; **313l,** Journal-Courier/Steve Warmowski/The Image Works; **313r,** Peter Hvizdak/The Image Works; **314–315t,** Andrew Syred/Photo Researchers, Inc.; **315l, 315tr** Prof. P. Motta/Dept. of Anatomy/University, "La Sapienza", Rome/Science Photo Library; **315br,** David Madison Sports Images, Inc. 2003; **316l,** David Young-Wolff/PhotoEdit; **316r,** Marc Romanelli/Getty Images, Inc.; **317l,** Innerspace Imaging/Photo Researchers, Inc.; **317r,** Zephyr/Photo Researchers, Inc.; **318,** John Meyer/Custom Medical Stock Photo, Inc.; **319b,** Tom McCarthy/PhotoEdit; **319t,** ISM/Phototake; **320l,** Corbis; **320r,** Michael Acliolo/International Stock; **321,** Ted Horowitz/Corbis; **322,** Richard Haynes; **323b,** Eric Grave/Photo Researchers, Inc.; **323l,** Ed Reschke/Peter Arnold, Inc.; **323m, 323tl,** Astrid & Hans-Frieder/Photo Researchers, Inc.; **323bl,** Eric Grave/Photo Researchers, Inc.; **324–325b** all, Jim Cummins/Getty Images, Inc.; **325t,** Richard Haynes; **326,** David Madison Sports Images, Inc. 2003; **327,** Richard Haynes; **328,** Richard Haynes; **329b,** David Madison Sports Images, Inc.; **329t,** Richer Wehr/Custom Medical Stock Photo; **330,** Richard Haynes; **331b,** Russ Lappa; **331t,** Prof. P. Motta/Dept. of Anatomy/University, "La Sapienza", Rome/Photo Researchers, Inc.; **333,** Getty Images, Inc.; **334,** Richard Haynes; **335,** Richard Haynes; **336,** David Young-Wolff/PhotoEdit.

Chapter 9

Pages 340–341, Stephen Simpson/Getty Images, Inc.; **341** inset, Jon Chomitz; **343l,** David Young-Wolf/Getty Images, Inc.; **343m,** Cindy Charles/PhotoEdit, Inc.; **343r,** Jose Lius Pelaez, Inc./Corbis; **344,** Richard Haynes; **345bl,** Royalty-Free/Corbis; **345br,** Davies & Starr/Getty Images, Inc.; **345tl,** Royalty-Free/Corbis; **345tr,** Royalty-Free/Corbis; **346b,** Stephen Oliver/Dorling Kindersley; **346m,** Dorling Kindersley; **346t,** Richard Haynes; **347,** Larry Lefever/Grant Heilman Photography, Inc.; **348,** Jack Montgomery/Bruce Coleman, Inc.; **351,** Joan Baron/Corbis; **353b,** David Young-Wolf/PhotoEdit; **353t,** Richard Haynes; **354,** Michael Malyszko/Getty Images, Inc.; **355,** Richard Haynes; **356,** Richard Haynes; **357,** David Young-Wolf/PhotoEdit; **359,** Richard Haynes; **360l,** Dorling Kindersley; **360r,** Richard Haynes; **363,** Fred E. Hossler/Visuals Unlimited; **365,** Richard Haynes; **366,** Richard Haynes; **368,** Prof. P. Motta/Dept. of Anatomy/University, "La Sapienza", Rome/Photo Researchers, Inc.; **369,** CNRI/Photo Researchers, Inc.

Chapter 10

Pages 374–375, Dennis Kunkel/Phototake; **375** inset, Richard Haynes; **377,** Richard Haynes; **379,** Photo Researchers, Inc.; **380,** Ism/Phototake; **382,** Felix Stensson/Alamy; **383b,** Dorling Kindersley; **383t,** Richard Haynes; **384,** Science Photo Library; **386,** Cabisco/Visuals Unlimited; **387,** Arthur Tilley/Getty Images, Inc.; **388,** Richard Haynes; **389,** Andrew Syred/Photo Researchers, Inc.; **391b,** Bill Longcore/Science Source/Photo Researchers, Inc.; **391m,** National Cancer Institute/Photo Researchers, Inc.; **391t,** Andrew Syred/Photo Researchers, Inc.; **392,** Oliver Meckes/Photo Researchers, Inc.; **395,** Richard Haynes; **396b,** Joel W. Rogers/Corbis; **396t,** Bob Daemmrich/Stock Boston; **397l,** Custom Medical Stock Photo; **397r,** Custom Medical Stock Photo; **398l,** The Granger Collection, NY; **398m,** Courtesy of the Baker Institute; **398r,** Layne Kennedy/Corbis; **399l,** Getty Images; **399m,** Richard T. Nowitz/Corbis; **399r,** Reuters New Media/Corbis; **400,** Nicole Katano/Getty Images, Inc.; **404,** Oliver Meckes/Photo Researchers, Inc.

Chapter 11

Pages 408–409, Mario Corvetto/Evergreen Photo Alliance; **409** inset, Richard Haynes; **410b,** Dennie Cody/Getty Images, Inc.; **410t,** Richard Haynes; **412** all, Richard Haynes; **413,** Richard Haynes; **416,** Mark Gibson/Corbis; **417,** Richard Haynes; **419,** Russ Lappa; **420,** Dorling Kindersley; **422,** Jonathan Nourok/PhotoEdit; **423b,** Photo Researchers, Inc.; **423m,** SIV/Photo Researchers, Inc.; **423tl,** Michal Heron/Prentice Hall; **423tr,** Matt Meadows/Peter Arnold, Inc.; **424,** Sonda Dawes/The Image Works; **425,** Richard Haynes; **426,** Richard Haynes; **428l,** Andy Crawford/Dorling Kindersley; **428r,** Dorling Kindersley; **430,** Ken Karp; **431l,** Andy Crawford/Dorling Kindersley; **431m,** Dorling Kindersley; **431,** Richard Haynes; **432,** Dennie Cody/Getty Images, Inc.; **434,** Ken Karp.

Chapter 12

Pages 436–437, Michael Kevin Daly/Corbis; **437** inset, Richard Haynes; **439,** Micke Blake/Reuters New Media, Inc./Corbis; **443,** Richard Haynes; **444b,** Chet Gordon/The Image Works; **444t,** Richard Haynes; **449,** Tom Stewart/Corbis; **450** all, Richard Haynes; **451,** Barbara Stitzer/PhotoEdit; **452b,** Charlie Borland/Fogstock/Alamy Images; **452** t, Ian Vorster; **454,** Tony Freeman/PhotoEdit; **455b,** Diane Hirsch/Fundamental Photographs; **455t,** Diane Schiumo/Fundamental Photographs; **456,** Omikron/Photo Researchers, Inc.; **460,** Jon Feingersh/Corbis; **461,** Richard Haynes; **462,** Mugshots/Corbis; **463,** Richard Haynes; **464–465,** Digital Vision/Getty Images, Inc.; **466,** David Young-Wolff/PhotoEdit; **468b,** Tom Carter/PhotoEdit; **468t,** Stacy Pick/Stock Boston; **469b,** PhotoEdit; **469t,** CNRI/Photo Researchers, Inc.; **471,** Richard Haynes.

Chapter 13

Pages 476–477, George Shelley/Corbis; **477** inset, Richard Haynes; **479,** PhotoEdit; **481,** Richard Haynes; **482,** Richard Haynes; **483,** David Madison/Getty Images, Inc.; **484,** Richard Haynes; **485** both, Richard Haynes; **486,** Tom Brakefield/Corbis; **487** both, David M. Phillips/Photo Researchers, Inc.; **491,** Professors P.M. Motta & J. Van Blerkom/Science Photo Library; **494bl,** Dr. Yorgos Nikas/Photo Researchers, Inc.; **494br,** CNRI/Photo Researchers, Inc.; **494tl,** Stephen R. Swinburne/Stock Boston; **494tr,** Stephen R. Swinburne/Stock Boston; **495l,** G. Moscoso/Photo Researchers, Inc.; **495r,** Neil Bromhall/Photo Researchers, Inc.; **497,** Petit Format/Photo Researchers, Inc.; **498,** Index Stock Imagery, Inc.; **499l,** Roy Morsch/Corbis; **499r,** Tony Freeman/PhotoEdit; **500l,** Penny Gentieu; 500m, Tony Arruza/Corbis; **500r,** Spencer Grant/PhotoEdit; **501l,** David Grossman/The Image Works; **501r,** Myrleen Ferguson/PhotoEdit; **502,** Michael Newman/PhotoEdit; **504,** Myrleen Ferguson/PhotoEdit.

Chapter 14

Pages 508–509, Ron Kimball Studios; **510t,** Richard Haynes; **510b,** McDonald Wildlife Photo, Inc./DRK Photo; **511t,** Photo Researcher, Inc.; **511b,** Richard Haynes; **512l,** FSU Research Foundation; **512m,** The Granger Collection; **512r,** Bettmann/Corbis; **513l,** Bettmann/Corbis; **513m,** Pascal Goetgheluck/SPL/Photo Researchers, Inc.; **513r,** Lawrence Migdale/Stock Boston; **514,** John Locke/Dembinsky Photo Associates; **515,** Getty Images, Inc.; **516t,** Photo Researchers, Inc.; **516bl,** Sinclair Stammers/SPL/Photo Researchers, Inc.; **516br,** SPL/Photo Researchers, Inc.; **517,** CRNI/SPL/Photo Researchers, Inc.; **518,** Richard Haynes; 519, PhotoDisc/Getty Images, Inc.; **520t,** Doug Wilson/Corbis Westlight; **520b,** Corbis; **521l,** Runk/Schoenberger/Grant Heilman Photography; **521r,** Mike Abbey/Visuals Unlimited; **522,** Alfred Paskieka/SPL/Photo Researchers, Inc.; **523t,** Bill Longcore/Photo Researchers, Inc.; **523b,** SPL/Photo Researchers, Inc.; **526,** Photo Researchers, Inc.; **527t,** Dr. David Scott/CRNI/Phototake; **527b,** Motta & S. Correr/SPL/Photo Researchers, Inc.; **528l,** Dr. Gary Gaugler/Photo Researchers, Inc.; **528m,** SNRI/Phototake; **528r,** Phototake; **529t,** CNRI/Phototake; **529b,** Alfred Pasieka/SPL/Photo Researchers, Inc.; **530t,** Getty Images, Inc.; **530bl,** Hulton Archive/Getty Images, Inc.; **530br,** Jerry Howard/Positive Images; **531,** Jerry

Howard/Positive Images; **533,** Dorling Kindersley; **534l,** Meinrad Faltner/Corbis; **534r,** Meinrad Faltner/Corbis; **535t,** David Young-Wolff/PhotoEdit; **535b,** Villanova University; **536tl,** Michael Newman/PhotoEdit; **536tml,** David Young-Wolff/PhotoEdit; **536tmr,** David Young-Wolff/PhotoEdit; **536tr,** David Young Wolff/PhotoEdit; **536bl,** Mary Kate Denny/PhotoEdit; **536bml,** Nicolas Russell/Getty Images, Inc.; **536bmr,** David Young-Wolff/PhotoEdit; **536br,** Corbis; **538t,** Clive Streeter/Dorling Kindersley; **538b,** Pearson Learning; **539,** Jim Cummins/Getty Images, Inc.; **544,** Dorling Kindersley; **545t,** Dorling Kindersley; **545b,** Richard Haynes; **546l,** Photo Researchers, Inc.; **546r,** University "La Sapienza," Rome/Photo Researchers, Inc.; **547l,** Michael Abbey/Photo Researchers, Inc.; **547r,** E.R. Degginger/Color-Pic, Inc.; **551,** Adrian Warren/Last Refuge Ltd.; **557,** Dorling Kindersley.

Chapter 15

Pages 562–563, Royalty-Free/Corbis; **563** inset, Richard Haynes; **564b,** Michael Newman/PhotoEdit; **564t,** Richard Haynes; **565** grid, all, David Young-Wolff/PhotoEdit; **565l,** Michael Newman/PhotoEdit; **565m,** David Urbina/PhotoEdit; **565r,** Everett Collection; **566,** Camille Tokerud/Getty Images, Inc.; **567l,** Biophoto Associates/Photo Researchers, Inc.; **567r,** Biophoto Associates/Photo Researchers, Inc.; **568l,** Corbis; **568r,** Michael Douma, Institute for Dynamic Educational Advancement; **570,** Amy Etra/PhotoEdit; **571b,** Jonathan Nourok/PhotoEdit; **571t,** CNRI/Photo Researchers, Inc.; **572** both, Stanley Flegler/Visuals Unlimited; **573,** Craig Farraway; **575** both, National Hemophilia Foundation; **577,** South West News Service; **578bl,** Foodpix; **578bm,** Photo Researchers, Inc.; **578br,** Foodpix; **578ml,** Photo Researchers, Inc.; **578tl,** Grant Heilman; **579,** Image Works; **581l,** 5-D and Segrest Farms/AP/Wide World Photos; **581r,** Animals Animals/Earth Scenes; **582,** Photo Researchers, Inc.; **582,** Michael Newman/PhotoEdit; **585,** Andrew Brooks/Corbis; **586b,** Craig Farraway; **586t,** Image Works.

Chapter 16

Pages 596–597, Mark Barrett/Index Stock Imagery/PictureQuest; **597r,** PhotoDisc/Getty Images, Inc.; **598t,** Richard Haynes; **598–599b,** Prisma Dia/Index Stock Imagery, Inc.; **599t,** Sat Yip/SuperStock; **600t,** Chris Sorensen; **600b,** Digital Vision/Getty Images Inc.; **601,** Kim Taylor/Bruce Coleman Inc.; **602–603,** Robert LaBerge/Getty Images, Inc.; **604t,** Topham/The Image Works; **604m,** North Wind Picture Archives; **604b,** NationalMotor Museum, Beaulieu, England; **605l,** Bettmann/Corbis; **605r,** Fritz Hoffmann/documentCHINA; **606,** Bob Daemmrich Photography; **609,** Richard Haynes; **610t,** Russ Lappa; **610b,** Earth Imaging/Getty Images, Inc.; **613,** Richard Haynes; **614t,** Richard Haynes; **614b,** Jamie Squire/Getty Images Inc.; **615l,** Ezra Shaw/Getty Images Inc.; **615m,** Adam Pretty/Getty Images Inc.; **615r,** Nick Wilson/Getty Images Inc.; **617,** Kwame Zikomo/SuperStock; **618,** Eyewire Collection/Getty Images Inc.; **620,** Richard Haynes; **621,** Lou Jones/Image Bank/Getty Images, Inc.; **622,** Robert LaBerge/Getty Images, Inc.

Chapter 17

Pages 626–627, Stephen Munday/Getty Images, Inc.; **627r,** Richard Haynes; **628,** Richard Haynes; **629,** Duomo/Corbis; **630** all, Richard Haynes; **631,** Richard Haynes; **632,** Richard Haynes; **633,** Ken O'Donaghue; **634t,** Richard Haynes; **634b,** Kindra Clineff/Index Stock Imagery, Inc.; **635t,** B & C Alexander/Photo Researchers, Inc.; **635b,** Jan Hinsch/Photo Researchers, Inc.; **636,** Russ Lappa; **637tl,** Michael Newman/PhotoEdit; **637tr,** Michael Newman/PhotoEdit; **637bl,** David Young-Wolff/PhotoEdit; **637br,** Kelly-Mooney Photography/Corbis; **638,** Joe McBride/Corbis; **639,** NASA; **640,** Megna/Peticolas/Fundamental Photographs; **642,** Richard Megna/Fundamental Photographs; **643t,** Russ Lappa; **643b,** Bettmann/Corbis; **655** all, Richard Haynes; **645,** David Madison Sports Photography; **646,** Richard Haynes; **647,** Richard Haynes; **648tl,** David Madison Sports Photography; **648tr,** Omni Photo Communicatons, Inc./Index Stock Imagery, Inc.; **648b,** Lawrence Manning/Corbis; **649l,** Syracuse/Dick Blume/The Image Works; **649r,** Michael Devin Daly/Corbis Stock Market; **650,** Dorling Kindersley; **651tl,** David Davis/Index Stock Imagery, Inc.; **651tr,** Image Source/Alamy Images; **651b,** Russ Lappa; **655,** Richard Haynes; **656t,** Richard Haynes; **656b,** Courtesy of Homer Hickam; **657,** Jeff Hunter/Getty Images, Inc.; **658,** Richard Haynes; **660,** David Young-Wolff/PhotoEdit.

Chapter 18

Pages 664–665, Getty Images, Inc.; **665r,** Richard Haynes; **666t,** Richard Haynes; **666bl,** Milton Feinberg/Stock Boston; **666br,** Chlaus Lotscher/Stock Boston; **667** all, Richard Haynes; **668,** PhotoDisc/Getty Images, Inc.; **669** both, Richard Megna/Fundamental Photographs; **672,** Paul Seheult-Eye Ubiquitous/Corbis; **674t,** Russ Lappa; **674b,** Ken Marshall/Madison Press. Ltd.; **675,** Bill Wood/Bruce Coleman, Inc.; **676** both, Richard Haynes; **677,** Runk/Schoenberger/Grant Heilman Photography, Inc.; **678,** Russ Lappa; **681,** Richard Haynes; **682t,** Richard Haynes; **682b,** Stephen Frink/Corbis; **683,** Richard Haynes; **687t,** Richard Haynes; **687b,** Mercury Archives/Getty Images, Inc.; **688** both, Richard Haynes; **691,** Maxime Laurent/Digital Vision; **694t,** Stephen Frink/Corbis; **694b,** Paul Seheult-Eye Ubiquitous/Corbis; **696,** Russ Lappa.

Chapter 19

Pages 698–699, The G. R. "Dick" Roberts Photo Library; **699r,** Corbis; **700** both, Richard Haynes; **701** all, Richard Haynes; **702** both, Richard Haynes; **703** both, MVR Photo; **704,** Shelley Rotner/Omni-Photo Communications, Inc.; **705,** The Granger Collection, NY; **706t,** Corel Corp.; **706b,** Jim West/The Image Works; **707,** PhotoDisc/Getty Images, Inc.; **708,** Richard Haynes; **709t,** Thinkstock/SuperStock; **709m,** Richard Haynes; **709b,** MVR Photo; **710,** Sergio Piumatti; **711,** Richard Haynes; **712,** Russ Lappa; **713,** "Waterfall" by M.C. Escher, ©1998, Cordon Art-Baarn-Holland, All Rights Reserved; **714,** Richard Haynes; **716t,** Richard Haynes; **716b,** Russ Lappa; **717,** Richard Haynes; **718t,** Tony Freeman/PhotoEdit; **718b,** Russ Lappa; **719l,** Russ Lappa; **719r,** Richard Haynes; **721t,** Richard Haynes; **721m,** David Brownell; **721b,** Karl Weatherly/Corbis; **722l,** Sylvain Grandadam/Getty Images, Inc.; **722r,** Gerard Champion/Getty Images, Inc.; **723l,** Michael S. Yamashita/Corbis; **723m,** Jeffrey Aaronson/Network Aspen; **723r,** Ortelius; **724,** Prentice Hall School Division; **725,** Galen Rowell/Corbis; **726t** all, Richard Haynes; **726b,** David Young-Wolff/PhotoEdit; **727,** Russ Lappa; **728,** Cleo Photography/PhotoEdit; **729,** Richard Haynes; **730t,** Mark Gibson; **730m,** Royalty-Free/Corbis; **730b,** Bettmann/Corbis; **731,** Mark Gibson; **732,** Russ Lappa. **736t,** Martin Puddy/Getty Images, Inc.; **736–737b,** Chris Warren/International Stock; **737t,** PhotoDisc/Getty Images, Inc.; **738–739t,** David Lawrence; **738–739b,** Mitchell Funk/Photographer's Choice/Getty Images, Inc.; **739r,** Richard Haynes; **740l,** Corbis; **740r,** Joseph Pobereskin/Getty Images, Inc.; **741,** Bettmann/Corbis; **742–743,** Richard Weiss/Peter Arnold, Inc.; **744,** Tony Freeman/PhotoEdit; **745t,** Russ Lappa; **745m,** Richard Haynes; **745b,** Russ Lappa; **746,** Richard Haynes; **748,** Richard Haynes; **750,** Morton Beebe/Corbis; **751,** Catherine Karnow/Corbis; **753t,** Dorling Kidersley; **753b,** Richard Haynes; **765,** Richard Haynes; **766,** Paul Seheult-Eye Ubiquitous/Corbis; **767,** David Stoecklein/Corbis; **769,** Richard Haynes; **771l,** Russ Lappa; **770b,** Stephen Frink/Corbis.